The Good Food Guide *1988*

The Good Food Guide *1988*

Edited by Drew Smith

 Published by Consumers' Association
and Hodder & Stoughton

Which? Books are commissioned and researched by
The Association for Consumer Research and published by
Consumers' Association,
14 Buckingham Street, London WC2N 6DS and
Hodder and Stoughton,
47 Bedford Square, London WC1B 3DP

Special thanks for this year's *Guide* to Trevor Melton for
the cover photograph, Mon Mohan for the cover design,
Tim Higgins for the typography. The maps are by
Cartographic Services (Cirencester) Ltd

British Library Cataloguing in Publication Data
Smith, Drew
    The Good food guide
    1988
    I. Restaurants, lunch rooms, etc. –
    Great Britain – Directories
    I. Title   II. Consumers' Association
    647'.9541'05   TX10.G7
ISBN 0 340 41360 3

Photoset in Monophoto Photina
by Vantage Photosetting Co. Ltd
Eastleigh and London
Printed and bound in The Netherlands
by Rotatie Boekendruk B.V., Krommenie

Contents

Standing orders

The first thing to know about this guide is that it is independent. The reviews are the opinions of a great many people from a great many different meals. The second thing to know is that everything recorded here happened in the last year. Restaurants that featured in the last edition have been renominated, reassessed and their entries written afresh. Inspectors, who check nominations from readers, do not announce themselves. They eat as any other paying customer would, and pay their own bill. The *Guide* accepts no free hospitality, no favours and no advertising. It exists purely on the income from sales.

The editor's role is that of chairman, reading everything that comes into the office, arranging for recommendations to be followed up, investigating criticisms, arbitrating between conflicting views and attempting to bring some sense to the debate. The results you hold in your hand provide one consensus as to what good food is and where it may be found. A single overriding thought guides me through the mountains of paper: the *Guide* is a book to be used. Restaurants must, therefore, be open before we go to press, so that they can be assessed. And each one must draw a clear majority of votes in favour from readers and inspectors. Where there is doubt, the restaurant is left out.

Unfortunately, the gastronomic map is not always convenient. For all the publicity cooking now attracts, good food is still only found in isolated pockets. No amount of research alters the fact that Humberside is not the most fruitful area in which to look for places to eat out, nor that the best place to go for Chinese food is Chinatown, for Italian, Chelsea, for British, probably the Lakes. As far as practicable, the coverage aims to be relevant across the country and to every cuisine, but it is wise to travel with an open mind. This is a guide to food that may not always be served on starched linen cloths by waiters in black.

Support the cause

In buying and using the *Guide* you are supporting its aim, to improve standards of food and restauranteuring. But if that is all you do over the coming year, then yours will have been a small contribution. To give substance to your good intentions you should, after next eating out, turn to the back of the *Guide*, take out one of the report forms (or use a clean sheet of writing paper) and write: 'I ate at so-and-so's on such-and-such date and can confirm that it is still worth its place'. You will be helping to compile next year's edition. Old hands use the points system as a shorthand: 10 or more for an interesting place in the neighbourhood, 12 or more for places that stand out in the region, 14 or more for restaurants that excel in one particular department. A rating of 14 or more should not be given lightly. Even better, if you have the time, is to detail the restaurant – its setting, its atmosphere, its food – and give reasons why you thought it good or not. Be critical, if necessary. You have paid the bill and that gives you every right to express your opinion. Equally, if you have been impressed, then you should say why. Faint praise does not forge standards.

Every now and then a reader writes: 'Why did you drop so-and-so? I eat there often and it is fine'. Perhaps so, but any restaurant that is not nominated in the year running up to the *Guide's* publication, is dropped. Our funds are not limitless and it is impractical to send people chasing all over the country checking on restaurants that do not have a single customer who can be bothered to put pen to paper to support it. For the book to rely solely on the judgement of the editor or one of the inspectors, however expert in his or her field, would produce a completely different type of guide, certainly much less reliable. The value of the system as it stands is that, with so many people involved, it can confirm or contradict reputations with impunity. It can deflate the myths created by public relations firms. And it can support talent wherever it may be found.

You, the reader, are our eyes and ears, as well as the final arbiter. However up to date the information, the *Guide* can never be more than a snapshot of what is one of the fastest changing industries. Even as I write this, for sure, a chef somewhere is writing his notice and that restaurant is about to see a decline of standards. If this edition should lead you to two or three good meals then I hope you will feel beholden to your fellow readers to report back to the office. If a restaurant does not live up to its description, then all the more reason to write promptly to save others from a poor meal. All letters to the *Guide* office are acknowledged with a short up-date on this edition.

1987: A bullish year

Catering is on the offensive. At all levels the maxim is: expand. Casualties, of which there are many, are simply picked up and taken on by someone else. The mood is summed up by Trusthouse Forte's move into the country-house hotel market with the acquisition of Leeming Country House Hotel at Watermillock.

At the top end of the industry, this expansion is marked chiefly by a massive hoick in prices. Inflation in London restaurants, particularly those on the international circuit, is rampant. On my desk is a bill for two at a Mayfair restaurant – £167. The Japanese restaurant Suntory, since getting a Michelin rosette in the winter, has put up its prices, which were not cheap to start with, by 21 per cent. Hotels have done the same. Eating at the Savoy is up 20 per cent on last year; at Claridge's, 30 per cent; the Berkeley, 30 per cent; the Mayfair, 30 per cent. In some establishments the increase is even higher.

Dinners of £50 a head are no longer unusual, and that is without any real extravagances – no dessert wines, no extra courses, no cheese as well as sweet, no *digestifs*. Invariably it is the drinks that are the rub: coffee, mineral water, alcohols put up bills sizeably, the more so when 15 per cent VAT and 15 per cent service is added. A teetotaller could eat very well for two thirds or even half the price in most expensive restaurants. Even ethnic restaurants are not exempt. Peking Chinese restaurants now serve such ludicrously small portions that they make the early days of *nouvelle cuisine* seem generous. Three spare ribs for £6? The customer is tricked into ordering many more dishes and all the while the wine glasses are topped up. It is an uncomfortable form of financial torture.

The London effect

Not all the price rises can be laid at the door of greedy restaurateurs. Property prices play their part in London. The capital's centre has long since ceased to be a set of charming, interconnecting villages but instead has become a homogeneous roller-coaster of international tourism. The effect is stultifying. Exceptions are found in the reviving Soho (see Don Philpot's history, on page 530) and Chinatown, but Covent Garden is a gastronomic graveyard and a reminder of how quickly standards change. Last year's optimism over City restaurants was misplaced; increasingly it seems that quality is no longer a concern. Instead, this is the era of the designer – not on the plate, but in the dining-room. Some interiors are breathtakingly inventive. Corney and Barrow's four restaurants, the City Brasserie in Mincing Lane (previously Langan's Bar and Grill), Le Champenois, plus Braganza in Soho and Joe's Café in South Kensington are models of late-twentieth-century design dynamism. Alas the investment in the kitchen does not usually correspond.

It is in the areas around the centre, where most people in the capital actually live, that interesting new restaurants have begun to open. The most opulent Thai restaurant in the country is found in Fulham Broadway, the highest of the hi-tech Chinese in Hampstead. Balham has one of the most interesting new restaurants of the year. Clapham has as much restaurant activity as King's Road, Chelsea ever had. The drift out of town, in a quality sense, is unmistakable.

The ripple effect continues into the Home Counties. Few young chefs can afford to open in London, so places like Stroud, Shinfield, Cricklade, Wymondham, Speen, Canterbury, Sway, Brockenhurst, Roade, Lewes, Cambridge and Oxford take on a gastronomic ring. The rivalry between Glasgow's top restaurants is almost as delineated as between Rangers and Celtic. The irony is that some of these restaurants are empty early in the week but could be triple-booked for 8.15 pm on Saturday. Here the best of the new generation of young chefs are forging their reputations, often for a song. Restaurant 74 at Canterbury does a set lunch for £10; the comparison with London in any terms is vicious. Another remarkable feature of modern cooking is how young many of the chefs are. The average age of the kitchen at Harvey's in Balham is 18, and at Le Manoir aux Quat' Saisons it has been as low as 21. Where will these cooks be in ten years?

Modern British cooking

Within the general resurgence, a definite style is evident. Not everyone follows it, but is is striking how often it appears.

In a week in February, these soufflés were served at different restaurants in Gloucestershire: cinnamon with Drambuie cream (Oakes, Stroud); hot ginger with avocaat sauce (Redmond's, Cheltenham); rhubarb with cream and vanilla (Calcot Manor, Tetbury). Coincidence? Pedants might say that soufflés are French, but the flavourings – the rhubarb, the ginger, the cinnamon – are British.

We see this individualism emerge at at time when traditional French cooking is in decline. Nouvelle cuisine dissolved the pillars of the classic style. The trend towards ever smaller kitchens means that only in the grand kitchens like the Connaught or Le Gavroche are stocks endlessly reduced into sauces. Smaller kitchens usually have little room for a pastry chef and restaurants content themselves with buying in from outside or producing fruits and ices and something with chocolate. The most common new sweet of 1987 was the terrine of fruits – easily prepared in advance, easily garnished, impressive, picturesque, light years away from the dessert trolley sweet.

The single most important change in restaurant menus, however, has been the access in the last few years to much better produce – Real Food. Any chef anxious to express him or herself through cooking is seduced into this array of produce. Now all kitchens might be split between those that follow the market and change their menus and those that are essentially ethnic restaurants, ones that strive to recreate a given cuisine, be it Thai or French. The one is active, the other passive.

Any chef working to the markets produces cooking related to where he or she is. In the country the Britishness of the menu will be more deeply marked. In the cities the cosmopolitan nature of the markets will come out. Either way, chefs have cut away from the notion of cooking as a fixed cuisine and have started to reinterpret for themselves.

It would have been impossible to compile this year's *Guide* without repeated references to the virility of this cooking. Its main aspects are:

- The menu changes with the markets.
- Vegetables are prominent (as they should be, from a nation of gardeners): in combinations in soups; in quantities around centrepieces; as main vegetarian dishes.
- Main dish sauces tend to be offset with relish-style chutneys, stuffings and jellies. Sauces are restrained, often just gravies.
- Flavourings are abundant and vivid – fruits used as seasoning, spices, nuts, herbs.
- Meats and fish tend to be plainly cooked and offset by their accompaniments.
- Traditional sweets – bread and butter pudding, syllabub, treacle tart – are increasingly in evidence.

Where the French chef might be said to take his inspiration from the wine maker, the modern British chef might go to the farmhouse cheesemaker. New and resurrected cheeses, like Swaledale, Beenleigh Blue, Gospel Green and perhaps a hundred others, plus properly matured Cheddars, Cheshires and Stiltons, are lauded wherever they appear.

All these developments can be seen as part of something bigger, part of the great European melt-down of ideas since Larousse and Escoffier were abandoned. But considering that a few years ago British cooking only amounted to roast beef and Yorkshire, there has been a significant step forward.

The pay-off

Each year's mail throws up its own selection of complaints.

Poor service, especially in more expensive restaurants where there is really no excuse, is a perennial problem.

Menus and wine lists that are more concerned with trying to impress than delivering good food are evident everywhere. Overblown, overlong, overpriced are three words that are overused.

The chef's night off is another sore point, which undermines many an otherwise good reputation, most obviously in hotels. If a hotel sells itself on the cooking of the chef, then surely it should not charge the same when he is not there?

But most disturbing of all seems to be an increasingly irresponsible attitude to money . . . in this case the customer's money. Unitemised bills are on the increase. The food is lumped together under one heading saying 'Food £X'. It is impossible to see how much was charged for each item and to check the arithmetic. This is an open invitation to staff dishonesty. The restaurant stands to lose as much as the customer. It should be stamped out. A customer is entitled to a clearly made up record of what he or she has spent. Send examples of bills that have not been properly itemised to the *Guide*, and we will open a dossier.

Alongside the unitemised bill may come the credit card trick, where the bottom line is left blank, inviting a second tip. This evil practice has reached epidemic proportions. The whingeing bleat of restaurateurs who say that some people like to leave an extra tip is sheer foolishness. There may well be some people in the world who like to pay for things twice, but they are quite capable of asking the waiter (who must be an accommodating chap to have earned his extra 15 per cent), to fill out a second slip. Or maybe he might take cash?

When asked if service is or is not included, some waiters lie and if they do not lie, many befuddle the issue. 'Yes it is included, but it doesn't go to the staff'. 'Gratuities are at your discretion', does not answer the question of how much has already been charged. This is a shabby practice touting for extra money.

And finally . . .

To everyone who wrote in last year, most of whom are acknowledged at that back of the *Guide*, and to all the inspectors who gave so generously of their time, their own money and their patience in filling such detailed reports, a very big thank-you. Without your efforts the *Guide* would not be what it is.

In the end a good restaurant is one where you choose to go back a second time; that is the real test. May this edition lead you in the coming months to many such places.

Good eating.

Drew Smith
August 1987

A warning to restaurateurs

Twelve attempts have been made to trade on the name of *The Good Food Guide* in the last six years. The last year has seen no fewer than three major bids by independent operators. In each case money has been requested. Many restaurateurs have been deceived into paying for inclusion in what they thought was *The Good Food Guide* or a related guide but which was nothing of the sort.

Only one of these ventures has so far produced a publication – a slim volume of advertisements for sixty-two restaurants in the West Midlands.

We are aware of two kinds of approach:

1 Salesmen offer paid-for space on Prestel, implying that the advert will go out nationally on a Prestel/Viewdata version of the *Guide*. New variants on this theme are continually cropping up. Since 1982 approaches have been made from salesmen claiming to represent the following:

VISIONVIEW
CONSUMER GOOD FOOD GUIDE
NATIONAL GOOD GOOD GUIDE
COMPUTERTECH INFO SERVICES GOOD FOOD GUIDE
SCREENVIEW
ALPHA TELECOM GOOD RESTAURANT GUIDE
NATIONAL TELEDATA GOOD FOOD GUIDE
GOOD FOOD GUIDE
GOOD FOOD GUIDE NETWORK

In some cases the restaurateurs were also offered certificates to put up in their restaurants.

2 Would-be publishers have written to restaurants proposing to include them in a book they intend to publish with a name similar to *The Good Food Guide*. This has happened three times in the last year. Two have implied that their publications would be based on recommendations from readers. All sent questionnaires similar in design and shape to those used by *The Good Food Guide*. All three asked for money for inclusion. The approaches were made as follows:

(a) In October 1986 Mr Peter Roland wrote to a large number of restaurants on a cream sheet of paper headed THE GOOD FOOD AND RESTAURANT GUIDE to say: '. . . due to my receiving numerous complimentary letters detailing your food quality, presentation and service, you have been elected to be highlighted within THE GOOD FOOD AND RESTAURANT GUIDE. . .' The letter went on to say that because of the rising cost of publishing and carrying out anonymous inspections, a 'small' remittance would be required. The amount asked for was £68.

At the time of going to press, in August 1987, no version of this publication has been seen.

(b) In April 1987 Regional Magazines of Exeter circulated restaurants in the West Country proposing to produce a publication called the GOOD FOOD GUIDE. The cost of inclusion was to be £400. Regional Magazines have since written to all the restaurants they approached pointing out that they are nothing to do with *The Good Food Guide* and that they are abandoning the project.

(c) In 1986 the GOOD FOOD GUIDE (INTERNATIONAL) published a small booklet of restaurants in the West Midlands. It also supplied restaurants with plaques and imposing certificates stating that the restaurant concerned 'has been inspected and approved to be featured in the 1986/ 1987 edition of the GOOD FOOD GUIDE (INTERNATIONAL).' Many of these restaurants believed they had been nominated for *The Good Food Guide*. In 1987 the GOOD FOOD GUIDE (INTERNATIONAL) expanded dramatically into the North-East, South Wales, East Anglia, London and the South-East. Its main target was small, ethnic restaurants. The letter said: 'We have received several complimentary reports regarding the quality of the food and service in your restaurant and as we are currently compiling our 1987/88 issue, I am pleased to inform you that your restaurant has been shortlisted for inclusion.' As a sign of good will restaurants were asked to contribute £53.

The High Court granted Consumers' Association, publishers of *The Good Food Guide*, an injunction against the GOOD FOOD GUIDE (INTERNATIONAL) barring it from trading under that title or any other title confusingly similar to that of *The Good Food Guide*. All the restaurants that were approached have since been written to with an explanation of the position. Many who had already paid the £53 claim to have been deceived and are asking for their money back.

Our advice to restaurants is simple. *The Good Food Guide* never asks restaurants for money. All inspections are anonymous. We never supply plaques or certificates – indeed, we do not allow restaurants to advertise their inclusion in *The Good Food Guide*.

If, as a restaurateur, you are approached by anyone implying he or she is from *The Good Food Guide*, you can be sure that that person is *not* from *The Good Food Guide*. Our advice is not to give that person the time of day – and certainly not to give any money. You may be fairly certain that that person is an impostor. Should you be approached, please let the *Guide* know at once and, if you wish, send on any correspondence you receive.

We will take every step to protect our goodwill and our good name. Any letters that genuinely come out of this office bear my name, as editor, and will carry either our current address, as we go to press, of 14 Buckingham Street, London WC2 6DS or, from the end of 1987, the *Guide's* new address, 2 Marylebone Road, London NW1 4DX.

Drew Smith

How to use this guide

The rating system

All the restaurants in this guide serve good food. If not, they will be excluded from the next edition.

That it is good food implies that it will be fresh, freshly prepared, and served with flair and imagination. It will be Real Food in the sense that the distance between the kitchen and the producer will be as short as is practicable. Not everywhere will necessarily be grand, but it should be clean and reasonably comfortable.

All the restaurants are graded out of a notional 20 points. This indicates the kind of support and estimation accredited, specifically for the food, by readers and inspectors over the last year and before that. The ratings provide a context in which all the multi-faceted and various styles of cooking can be organised into some form of order.

The rating system works like a barometer. Some restaurants have reached a peak, others are moving up, some are moving down because standards are in decline. It is a reflection on improved standards over recent years that there is almost an in-built requirement on restaurants to improve to maintain their rating.

Obviously the system favours long-standing restaurants, but that is not a bad thing. If the only criterion were longevity, as the London list shows at the back of the *Guide*, then the top-rated restaurants would be the Gay Hussar and the Connaught, which nearly corresponds with the current ratings – nearly, but not quite. For popularity or business success is only one aspect, a symptom of quality and not proof positive.

Although it is for the most part true that the more expensive restaurants are found at the top of the ratings and the less expensive at the bottom, money is not a criterion and it is quite possible for an inexpensive restaurant to rate very highly. Lunch at the Yang Sing in Manchester, for instance, rating 15/20, might be £5.

By using the rating system the *Guide* should become more accessible to you as a user. It is also extremely helpful for the office if in reporting you use its codifications.

16 and over denotes rare restaurants of exceptional, international calibre. The chef will be able to express himself through his cooking and have found an appropriate setting that reflects and reinforces his work.

14 and over denotes restaurants that excel in at least one particular aspect. They will be good all-round performers and acquit themselves with merit in most restaurant situations.

12 and over denotes restaurants that stand out in their region as being well organised, consistent and dealing in good-quality produce handled with flair and sensitivity.

10 and over denotes restaurants that provide an invaluable service in their area or good examples of a style of cooking.

9 denotes cafés, fish and chip shops, bars, etc. that serve food of a quality that may be much higher than the rating suggests but do not really fulfil the criteria of being described as a restaurant.

Zero rated denotes a restaurant that is either new to the *Guide* or where there has been an important change in the personnel. Where there is sufficient information to warrant inclusion, the recommendation is a general one and we are anxious to receive reports from readers to build a clearer picture.

How to read a Guide entry

CANTERBURY   Kent ▪1   map 3   ▪2

▲ *Mary's Kitchen* ▪3   [12/20] ▪4

---

16 Elwood Avenue, Canterbury CT41 4RX ▪5
CANTERBURY (0227) 7770666 ▪6
behind Scala Cinema ▪7   ▮ ▪8   £11–£18 ▪9

(main text) ▪10   CELLARMAN'S CHOICE ▪11

CHEF: Mary Smith PROPRIETORS: Mary and David Smith ▪12
OPEN: Mon to Sat ▪13 CLOSED: Aug ▪14 MEALS: 12 to 2, 7 to 9 ▪15
PRICES: £13 (£19), Set D £10.50 (£15), Snacks from £1.50. ▪16 Service, 10% ▪17
CARDS: Access, Amex, Diners, Visa ▪18
SEATS: 72. 4 tables outside. Private parties: 26 main room, 10 private room. ▪19 Car-park,
40 places. Vegetarian meals. ▪20 Children's helpings. No children under 10. ▪21 Jacket and
tie preferred. ▪22 No-smoking area. ▪23 Wheelchair access (2 steps; also w c) ▪24
Music. ▪25 One sitting ▪26
ACCOMMODATION: 14 rooms, all with bath/shower. B&B £20 to £40. ▪27 No
pets ▪28 Afternoon teas. ▪29 Garden. Swimming-pool. Tennis. [GHG] ▪30

▪1 The town and county (in the London section, restaurants are listed
alphabetically by name rather than geographically).

▪2 The map number. The maps are at the end of the *Guide*.

▪3 The name of the restaurant. ▲ by the name denotes that it offers
accommodation too.

▪4 The *Guide* rating out of 20 (see pages 16 and 17).

▪5 The restaurant's address, with post code whenever possible.

▪6 The restaurant's telephone number, including its STD code.

▪7 Any special directions in case the restaurant is difficult to find.

▪8 This symbol is awarded only to restaurants with outstanding wine cellars,
not disproportionately priced.

▪9 This is the price range for three-course meals including half a bottle of house
wine, coffee, service and any hidden extras, such as a cover charge, as
calculated by the *Guide*.

▪10 The text is based on reports sent in by readers during the last *Guide* year,
confirmed by commissioned, anonymous inspections.

▪11 Most entries conclude with a CELLARMAN'S CHOICE. This is a wine, usually more
expensive than the house wine, that the restaurateur assures us will be in
stock during 1988, and that we recommend as suitable for the kind of food
served, if you do not want to order the house wine.

▪12 The names of the chef and the owner, so that any change in management
will be instantly detectable.

13 The days of the week the restaurant is open.

14 Annual closures.

15 The times of first and last orders for meals. It is always advisable to book before going to a restaurant. If you book and then cannot go, please remember to phone the restaurant to cancel.

16 These are typical prices for three-course meals, giving the à la carte price and variations for set lunch (L) and dinner (D) where applicable. The initial price represents the prices on the menu; the second price, in brackets, is the real cost when the extras of wine, coffee and service (at 10% unless otherwise specified) have been added.

17 This indicates that a fixed service charge will be added to the bill. Where service is included in the menu prices this is specified. When service is not mentioned, it is at the discretion of the customer.

18 The credit cards accepted by the restaurant.

19 Not all restaurants will take private parties. The maximum number of people in a party is given.

20 Many restaurants claim to cater for vegetarians but in fact do not. It is always advisable to explain, when booking, if you do not eat meat.

21 Many restaurants and hotels are not keen on children. Where it says children welcome or children's helpings it indicates that they don't mind. Any limitations on age are specified.

22 Jackets and ties are compulsory in very few restaurants and this is specified; otherwise it means the proprietor prefers smart dress.

23 Any no-smoking arrangements as given to us by the restaurants.

24 Wheelchair access means that the entrance is 33 inches wide and the passages four feet across. Where there are steps it will say so. If it says 'also wc', then the toilet facilities are suitable for disabled people.

25 If a restaurant plays music, this is indicated.

26 The restaurant serves a single sitting at a specific time.

27 The price for rooms as given to us by the hotels. The first price is for one person in a single room, the second price is for two people in a double room.

28 Some hotels will not take pets; others prefer to be asked. It is best to check.

29 Teas are served to non-residents.

30 [GHG] denotes that this establishment is also listed in the 1988 edition of our sister guide, *The Good Hotel Guide*.

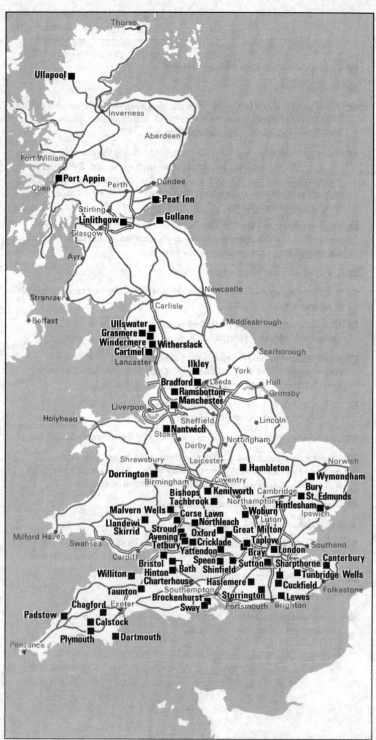

Cartographic Services (Cirencester) Ltd.

The best of the year

18/20

Great Milton, Le Manoir aux
　Quat' Saisons
London, Le Gavroche
　Tante Claire

17/20

London, Connaught Hotel
　Dorchester Hotel

16/20

Canterbury, Restaurant
　Seventy Four
Chagford, Gidleigh Park
Dartmouth, Carved Angel
London, Alastair Little
　L'Arlequin
　Ma Cuisine
　Simply Nico
Malvern Wells, Croque-en-Bouche
Oxford, Le Petit Blanc
Shinfield, L'Ortolan
Stroud, Oakes
Wymondham, Adlard's

15/20

Bath, Clos du Roy
Bray, Waterside Inn
Bristol, Les Semailles
Brockenhurst, Le Poussin
Cricklade, Whites
Gullane, La Potinière
Hambleton, Hambleton Hall
Haslemere, Morels
Ilkley, Box Tree
Llandewi Skirrid, Walnut Tree Inn

London, Gay Hussar
　Inigo Jones
　Le Mazarin
　Rue St Jacques
　Turner's
Manchester, Yang Sing
Peat Inn, Peat Inn
Port Appin, Airds Hotel
Sharpthorne, Gravetye Manor
Storrington, Manleys
Sway, Provence
Taunton, Castle Hotel
Ullapool, Altnaharrie Inn
Windermere, Miller Howe
Yattendon, Royal Oak

14/20

Avening, Gibbons
Bakewell, Fischer's
Bishops Tachbrook, Mallory Court
Bradford, Restaurant Nineteen,
　Belvedere Hotel
Bury St Edmunds, Bradleys
Calstock, Danescombe Valley Hotel
Cartmel, Uplands
Chagford, Teignworthy Hotel
Corse Lawn, Corse Lawn House
Cuckfield, King's Head
Dartmouth, Bistro 33
Dorrington, Country Friends
Grasmere, Michael's Nook
　White Moss House
Hintlesham, Hintlesham Hall
Hinton Charterhouse,
　Homewood Park
Kenilworth, Le Bosquet
Lewes, Kenwards

14/20 (*continued*)

Linlithgow, Champany Inn
London, Al Hamra
   Auberge de Provence
   Bombay Brasserie
   Capital Hotel
   Clarke's
   Harveys
   Langan's Brasserie
   Neal Street Restaurant
   L'Olivier
   Quincy's
   Le Suquet
Nantwich, Rookery Hall

Northleach, Old Woolhouse
Padstow, Seafood Restaurant
Plymouth, Chez Nous
Ramsbottom, Village Restaurant
Speen, Atkins
Sutton, Partners 23
Taplow, Cliveden
Tetbury, Calcot Manor
Tunbridge Wells, Thackeray's
   House
Ullswater, Sharrow Bay
Williton, White House Hotel
Witherslack, Old Vicarage
Woburn, Paris House

Berkshire restaurant of the year L'Ortolan, Shinfield
Bistro of the year Bistro 33, Dartmouth
Buckinghamshire restaurant of the year Atkins, Speen
Cambridge newcomer of the year Midsummer House
Cambridgeshire newcomer of the year Rose and Crown, Wisbech
Cornish newcomer of the year Well House, Liskeard
Derbyshire newcomer of the year Old Vicarage, Ridgeway
Edinburgh restaurant of the year Handsel's
Essex newcomer of the year Langan's, Coggeshall
Gloucestershire restaurant of the year Oakes, Stroud
Merseyside restaurant of the year Far East, Liverpool
South London restaurant of the year Harvey's
Vegetarian menu of the year Inigo Jones, London
Wiltshire restaurant of the year Whites, Cricklade

London

Alastair Little [16/20]

map 14

49 Frith Street, W1V 5TE
01-734 5183   £25

Do not go here on expenses: pay your own bill. There are few of the normal
trappings associated with restaurants of this repute – the napkins are paper, the
service is a direct extension of the kitchen, and the spartan gymnasium style is
relieved only by vivid oils that lighten up a cream room with black tables and
bare floorboards. This is an English cafe that challenges the basically French
ethos of what a restaurant should be. Alastair Little cooks a daily-changing
menu. The cooking lacks some of the polish of a great French restaurant, but the
potency of the best produce of any day is obvious. Witness as a starter in
September a thin slice of tuna char-grilled, covered with pepper, placed across a
salad of young spinach no bigger than mâche, on an oil emulsification with the
flesh of tomatoes, or a main course of onglet steak with kidneys and a meat
reduction sauce that would pass for three stars in Lyons – though who cares,
because this is British food. Vegetables do not come on dainty little side plates but
as great main-course dishes covered with spring greens cooked as tender as
spinach, gratin potatoes, boiled celeriac. And, to finish, a tart of Mascarpone
topped with slices of fig, or maybe a white and dark chocolate truffle cake. There
are ninety-two nominations for dishes as varied as stir-fried turbot in soy sauce,
pastel-coloured fish terrine, and roast veal with rosemary. The cheeses are a new
generation: Bonchester, Benleigh, Castle Ashby, Exmoor. The basement
specialising in fish is expected to open this year. Coffee from the espresso is
predictably fundamental, and the wine list shows an insight into flavours and
tastes. Rothbury Estate Chardonnay '86 and CELLARMAN'S CHOICE: Sancerre,
Domaine Bonnard '85, are both £12·50.

CHEF: Alastair Little
PROPRIETORS: Mercedes Downend, Kirsten Pendersen and Alastair Little
OPEN: Mon to Fri   CLOSED: bank hols, 3 weeks Aug
MEALS: 12.30 to 3, 7 to 11.30
PRICES: £19 (£25)   CARD: Visa
SEATS: 35. Children's helpings

*Restaurants are graded on a scale of 1–20. In the category of 10–11 expect to find the
best food in the locality. Ratings of 12 and more are given to restaurants we regard as
serving the best food in the region.*

Al Hamra [14/20]

map 13

31–33 Shepherd Market, W1Y 7RJ
01-493 1954 and 6934   £19

This, London's foremost Lebanese restaurant, fills up to the seams at times, but at others is quite calm. The major thrust of the cuisine is in the enormous, tantalising variety of the 65 hot and cold starters. The main courses are, in contrast to European cooking, less obviously important, relying heavily on the barbecuing of good meats and on some dishes of the day, of which the vegetarian may be the best. Sweets are honeyed and all baked on the premises, as is the bread. It is a *tour de force*, but although it has the trappings of a French restaurant these are really only a set of clothes provided for London. Service is charming and impeccable – 'even to two women alone'. Tables are set with bowls of fresh salad and olives. Of recommended starters (the recommendations almost follow the sequence of the menu), hummus, moutabel, tabouleh, stuffed vine leaves, pickles, loubieh, even lambs' testicles draw much enthusiasm. But look to the hot section, too. The grills are what you would expect and desserts luscious. See the glossary in Notes on Eating Ethnic for more about Lebanese cooking. Alcohols are expensive in this climate. Arak is what should be drunk but Toama is £2 a glass, Ksara £3.

CHEF: Hassan Mardani PROPRIETOR: Mr Nabulsi
OPEN: all week CLOSED: 25 Dec, 1 Jan MEALS: noon to midnight
PRICES: £9 (£19). Cover £1 CARDS: Access, Amex, Diners, Visa
SEATS: 73. 4 tables outside. Private parties: 80 main room. Vegetarian meals. Children's helpings. Wheelchair access. Music

Anna's Place [12/20]

map 11

90 Mildmay Park, N1 4PR
01-249 9379   £16

The Anna Hegarty floorshow still plays to packed houses, featuring a cast of Swedish dishes and much applause. The gravlax and the pickled herrings are definitive. Robust bakes, such as the lax pudding (salted salmon with potatoes) or pan fries like beef Strindberg (with potatoes), probably service the cafe-style formula best. Ms Hegarty introduces each in turn and is always on hand to welcome and explain. The chocolate fudge cake is singled out for praise. The house wines include Rock's excellent elderflower at £4·95. There are also Swedish beers, Schnapps and mineral water.

CHEFS: Paul Sykes and Elizabeth Kennedy PROPRIETOR: Anna Hegarty
OPEN: Tue to Sat CLOSED: Christmas, Easter, Aug MEALS: 12.30 to 2.30, 7.15 to 10.15
PRICES: £12 (£16). Service 10%
SEATS: 52. 5 tables outside. Private parties: 10 main room. Vegetarian meals. Children's helpings. Wheelchair access. Music

The Ark [9/20]

map 11

122 Palace Gardens Terrace, W8 4RT
01-229 4024   £13

One of the original 1960s bistros. After twenty-five years in the Harris family, it
still picks up votes for inclusion. As one reader puts it: The Ark is somewhere for
'when we tire of taking risks trying new discoveries'. The menu changes with the
market, but its signatures are smoked chicken pancakes, sauté potatoes, endless
coffee. Sometimes there is a surprise: a perfectly cooked sole bonne femme; plump
de-boned pigeon with a sauce sharpened with vinegar. House wine is £4·60.
CELLARMAN'S CHOICE: Côtes du Rhône '83, £6·40.

CHEF: Sarah Harris PROPRIETORS: Colin and Sarah Harris
OPEN: all week, exc Sun L MEALS: 12 to 3, 6.30 to 11.15
PRICES: £8 (£13) CARDS: Access, Amex, Visa
SEATS: 80. 6 tables outside. Private parties: 26 main room. Vegetarian meals. Children's
helpings. Wheelchair access

L'Arlequin [16/20] ✗

map 10

123 Queenstown Road, SW8 3RH
01-622 0555   £22–£36

The Delteils' re-styled, serious modern French restaurant is a grand restaurant in
miniature. Prices reflect the aspirations, but the quality is here without
affectation. The front of house is polished and the cooking accomplished. The
menu deals comfortably in luxuries, such as a salad of foie gras or lobster served
almost plain. The technique shows in persuasive dishes like vegetable tarts with a
carrot sauce or breast of chicken with scallops and fresh noodles. Home-made
chocolate with coffee, or the onion quiches with duck, add to the effect. The wine
list concerns itself mostly in the £10 to £30 region, relieved only by some halves.
It is exclusively French and of good pedigree, though some are flattered by their
mark-ups. House Vacqueyras or Sauvignon are well chosen at £9. The
significant advance all round in recent months leads to the raising of the rating
by two points. CELLARMAN'S CHOICE: St Aubin, Les Frionnes '84, £18, and the
red St Aubin, Les Castets '84, £17, both from Lamy.

CHEFS/PROPRIETORS: Mr and Mrs C. Delteil
OPEN: Mon to Fri CLOSED: 1 week in winter, 3 weeks Aug MEALS: 12.30 to 2, 7.30 to 11
PRICES: £29 (£36), Set L £14·50 (£22). Cover £1. Service inc CARDS: Access, Amex,
Diners, Visa
SEATS: 45. Children welcome. Jacket and tie. Wheelchair access (also WC)

L'Auberge [11/20]

map 10

44 Forest Hill Road, SE22 0RR
01-299 2211   £11–£18

Sami Youssef's pink and green French cafe of a restaurant is in a comfortable
recession. The menu incorporates some French, some *nouvelle* and some Turkish
elements. It is the robust dishes – gratins of shellfish, liver with coriander, lamb
with béarnaise – that are more successful than, for instance, the more delicate
desserts. The thirty wines are well chosen and fit the style. Especially good claret.

CHEF/PROPRIETOR: Sami Youssef
OPEN: Tue to Sat, D only, and Sun L CLOSED: 3 weeks Aug MEALS: 12 to 3, 7 to 10.30
PRICES: Set L £6·95 (£11), Set D £13·95 (£18). Service 10% CARDS: Access, Visa
SEATS: 38. Private parties: 30 main room. Vegetarian meals. Children's helpings.
Wheelchair access. Music

▲ Auberge de Provence, St James Court Hotel [14/20]

map 11

Buckingham Gate, SW1E 6AF
01-834 6655   £22–£30

The small Provence-style restaurant in the front wing of this expanding hotel is
run by a team sent over by André Charial of L'Oustaù de Baumanière. The
cooking is what Roger Vergé describes as 'Provence on a plate'. Some of the
dishes are as powerful and successful as any in London. Fillets of eel provençale
are lightly fried strips of eel radiating from a central mound of chopped onion,
vivid tomato and basil coulis, and superb olive oil. Or look for the duck with
olives, or the charlotte of lamb with aubergines. To finish, tarts, clafoutis, gratins
and intense sorbets all impress. The staff are apprentice but diligent. Alas, all too
often the restaurant is half-empty, killing off the atmosphere, which is ridiculous
for food of this quality at these prices. A trio of good Provençal red wines, and a
brace of rosés, are supported by quality Rhônes, some fine clarets, and house
Ventoux at £8.

CHEF: J. A. Charial PROPRIETORS: Taj International Hotels
OPEN: all week MEALS: 12.30 to 2.30, 7.30 to 11
PRICES: £21 (£30), Set L £15 (£22), Set D from £18 (£26)
CARDS: Access, Amex, Diners, Visa
SEATS: 80. Private parties: 8 main room. Vegetarian meals. Children welcome.
Air-conditioned
ACCOMMODATION: 480 rooms, all with bath/shower. Rooms for disabled. Lift. B&B £95 to
£135. Deposit: 100%. Children welcome. Baby facilities. No pets. Afternoon teas. Garden.
Sauna. Air-conditioning. TV. Phone

Au Bois St Jean

map 11

122 St John's Wood High Street, NW8 7SG
01-722 0400

As the Guide went to press there was a change of chef at this restaurant.

---

*'I mourn the honesty of those old hotels. I am bothered by the pretensions of today's
menus. Modern French cooking requires skills in taste, texture and everything else, of
exceptional calibre. These places don't have it and spend precious time and money on
trying to achieve the impossible when the possible is so achievable, and so much more
appropriate. Spend the money on the flavour to be found in free-range and additive-free
meats, for instance. Sussex must be the most organic-concious county in the whole of
England. There is plenty of excellent produce around which I would prefer to any
amount of appetisers, sorbets or pink peppercorns.'* (On eating in country-house hotels in
the South)

Auntie's [12/20]   map 13

126 Cleveland Street, W1P 5DN
01-387 3226   £20

This small English restaurant's reputation has taken a bit of a bashing from being
in the full glare of revivalist fervour, but Shaun Thomson has tightened up his act
and still deals in The Colonel's curried egg mayonnaise, and cod baked in a paper
parcel opened at the table. Tweed kettle pie of salmon in a thin butter sauce
topped with a pie crust is served in a deep earthenware bowl with a spectacular
puff of pastry. Nanny Campbell's basic lemon fluff has a powerful raspberry
sauce, and there is excellent bread-and-butter pudding. The room is small and
narrow and better suited to the tea-room it used to be, but the intensely green
walls and the black-upholstered sofas lend it some restaurant allure. English
wines feature on the list, but the house is French at £6·50 a bottle.

CHEF: Shaun Thomson PROPRIETORS: Auntie's Brasserie Ltd
OPEN: Mon to Sat, exc Sat L CLOSED: 2 weeks Aug MEALS: 12 to 2.45, 6 to 10.45
PRICES: Set L and D £14 (£20). Service 12.5% CARDS: Access, Amex, Diners, Visa
SEATS: 27. 2 tables outside. Private parties: 30 main room. Children welcome. No smoking.
Wheelchair access. Music

L'Aventure [12/20]   map 11

3 Blenheim Terrace, NW8 4JS
01-624 6232   £16–£25

Catherine Parisot's serious little French restaurant is a blend of cream paintwork,
old prints, tapestries and dark mahogany windowframes. The menu offers a well-
planned choice of modern French dishes with light, interesting flavours: a warm
sweetbread salad on a bed of red and green salad leaves and bright crunchy
broccoli; scallops with spinach sauce; rabbit casserole. Sweets are lifted by good
pastry, and there are French cheeses in fine condition. House burgundy is £6·25.

CHEF: Christian Bretech PROPRIETORS: Catherine Parisot and Chris Mitas
OPEN: all week, exc Sat L MEALS: 12.30 to 2.30, 7 to 11
PRICES: £17 (£25), Set L and D £10·50 (£16). Cover 80p CARDS: Amex, Visa
SEATS: 38. 6 tables outside. Private parties: 40 main room. Children welcome. No cigars/
pipes in dining-room. Wheelchair access. Music

Aziz [10/20]   map 10

116 King Street, W6 0QP
01-748 1826   £13

The Aziz offers reliable, consistent cooking within the confines of a curry-house
menu. Some new dishes have appeared – prawns tandoori and also patia. All the
tandooris, the tikka, the Persian lamb pilau and the butter chicken are worth
looking out. Service matches. A jug of lassi is £4.

CHEF: Mr Aziz PROPRIETORS: Angel Total Ltd
OPEN: Mon to Sat CLOSED: 25 and 26 Dec MEALS: 12 to 3, 6 to 12
PRICES: £7 (£13). Service 10% CARDS: Access, Amex, Diners, Visa
SEATS: 60. Private parties: 24 main room. Vegetarian meals. Children welcome. Wheelchair
access. Music

Bahn Thai [13/20] ✈ map 14

21A Frith Street, W1V 5TS
01-437 8504 and 439 0340 £14–£20

This end of Frith Street, opposite Ronnie Scott's and Alastair Little's, might almost be the epicentre of the Soho renaissance. The second Bahn Thai provides arguably some of the best Thai food in London. Philip Harris presides under a host of coloured umbrellas downstairs (upstairs is more spacious and better for parties) and talks people sensibly across the bridge into what is likely to become the cuisine of the year. Five years ago the first Bahn Thai was the ninth Thai restaurant to open, but last summer the figure was nearly a hundred, many opening in 1987. The menu runs to 130 dishes, most of which are meant to be shared, eaten separately in turn with rice and, properly, with soup. Look among the starters for boned and stuffed chicken wings, dim-sum, spare ribs, satay, and squid in batter; among the soups for hot-and-sour seafood with lemon grass and lemon juice, chicken with coconut, lemon and galangal. Fish dominates the main dishes, and some of it is even imported from Thailand. The heat of some dishes is equally authentic, as is the service – charming but not always efficient. The wine list is a remarkable essay in marrying white wines to this food. Eleven Sauvignons are listed, nine Gewürztraminers. There are also Thai drinks and rice spirits and wines. House French is £5·95. CELLARMAN'S CHOICE: Gewürztraminer, from Kuehn '83, £8·45.

CHEFS: Penn Squires and Nantana Sukmark PROPRIETOR: Philip Harris
OPEN: all week CLOSED: Christmas MEALS: 12 to 2.45, 6 to 11.15 (12.30 to 2.30, 6.30 to 10.30 Sun)
PRICES: £11 (£20), Set L £8·50 (£14). Service 12.5% CARDS: Access, Amex, Carte Blanche, Visa
SEATS: 100. Private parties: 25 main room, 55 private rooms. Vegetarian meals. Children's helpings. Wheelchair access (also WC). Music. Air-conditioned

Bahn Thai [12/20] map 11

35A Marloes Road, W8 6LG
01-937 9960 £20

The original Bahn Thai carries on in its black lacquered basement. Lunches have been abandoned and Philip Harris no longer controls the dining-room, which has not helped the service although otherwise standards are solid. The menu range is similar to that at Frith Street – plenty of wok frying, fine fish dishes, colourful use of some potent spices. The specialities, like the durian and the coconut ice-cream, still stand out. Particular nominations have been received for crab with rice noodles; steamed fish with celery and coriander; satay; nam prik; and grilled chicken wings. The green chillies and the dried prawns provide their own definite flavours. The forty wines include sound choices of white to match the food – three Gewürztraminers at £8·65 and £18·65, for example. House French is £5·95.

CHEF: Penn Squires PROPRIETOR: Philip Harris
OPEN: Mon to Sat, D only CLOSED: Christmas, 2 weeks in summer MEALS: 6 to 11.15
PRICES: £11 (£20). Cover 75p. Service 10% CARDS: Access, Amex, Visa
SEATS: 32. Private parties: 40 main room. Vegetarian meals. Children's helpings. Music. Air-conditioned

La Baita da Piero [10/20]

map 10

98 Station Road, North Chingford, E4 7BA
01-529 8311   £18

The atmosphere is more southern Italy than urban North Chingford. The service is theatrical, the décor is of the Chianti bottle school, and the menu features old favourites honestly prepared: minestrone; cannelloni; calf's liver with onion sauce; good trifle from the trolley. Although the food is not quite of the standard of Umberto's (see Ilford), the difference is marginal and the atmosphere compensates. House Italian is £4·90 a bottle.

CHEF: Apuzzo Martino PROPRIETOR: F. S. Pieropan
OPEN: Tue to Sun, exc Sun L CLOSED: 1 month in summer
MEALS: 12 to 2.30, 6.30 to 11.30
PRICES: £12 (£18). Cover 50p CARDS: Access, Amex, Diners, Visa
SEATS: 48. Private parties: 10 main room. Children welcome. Wheelchair access. Music.
Air-conditioned

Bambaya [12/20]

map 10

1 Park Road, Crouch End, N8 8TE
01-348 5609   £14

Much of the Caribbean cooking in London is under ground in small clubs and cafes, many inaccessible or often unattractively run down. Rosamund Grant's co-operative venture is, by contrast, a restaurant in the European sense – a split-level room filled with tiles and neat Afro prints. The cooking reaches out to either side of the Caribbean, to its roots in West Africa and also its development in southern America. It is hot, but also among the most cultured ethnic food found in London. Typical are a fiery peanut soup; a garlic-aubergine pâté; stuffed Ghanaian fish; or vegetables and ackee served with rice. Coconut or mango ice-cream to finish. For non-alcohol drinkers there is a drink of the day; otherwise cocktails are a speciality.

CHEFS: Rosamund Grant and Jenny Agada PROPRIETORS: Bambaya Restaurant Ltd
OPEN: all week, D only MEALS: 6.30 to 11 (10.30 Sun)
PRICES: £8 (£14). Cover 50p CARDS: Access, Visa
SEATS: 45. Private parties: 45 main room. Vegetarian meals. Children's helpings.
Wheelchair access. Music

Barnaby's [11/20]

map 10

39B High Street, Barnes, SW13 9LN
01-878 4750   £19

The Harrys' small rustic bistro, around the corner from the river, is unusual in its liking for proper, classically cooked bistro dishes. A March meal comprised lentil salad, monkfish kebab with a Nantua butter, and crêpes to finish. There is as much offal as steaks about the menu – sweetbreads with a watercress sauce; lambs' tongues braised with a port and spinach base. Also country dishes like confit of rabbit with ceps. The relaxed, careful service accounts for a high local following. House wine is £6·95 and from the Pyrenees, but there are interesting choices on the 25-strong list spread across France: CELLARMAN'S CHOICE: Mâcon Villages, Les Donzelles '85, £11·95.

CHEF: Claude Harry PROPRIETORS: Mr and Mrs Claude Harry
OPEN: Mon to Sat, exc Mon L and Sat L CLOSED: Christmas, Easter, 3 weeks Sept
MEALS: 12.30 to 1.30, 7 to 10.15
PRICES: £12 (£19). Service inc CARDS: Access, Amex, Diners, Visa
SEATS: 24. Private parties: 24 main room. Children welcome. Wheelchair access

La Bastide [12/20]   map 14

50 Greek Street, WIV 5LQ
01-734 3300   £21–£23

The name derives from Provence and is a country cottage or villa; before that it was used in Gascony to mean a fortified house below the manor. The interior is in peach colours. The cooking is based on France and rolls around the regions in modish essays into different provinces. There is an unchanging nightly *carte*, a regional menu, and a brasserie-style Soho Menu. Some of the cooking demonstrates real guts – the roast hare with red cabbage and cream; or the duck breast with a sauce of walnut and lemon. Hake is accompanied by morels. Venison has been hung properly. Sweets draw great enthusiasm: pancakes with butterscotch sauce, armagnac soufflé, tarte aux pommes. All these dishes, backed up by a cleverly chosen wine list, give an air of authority that suggests as yet unfulfilled potential which might be brought out by more self-confidence. Clarets manage to go back to '59 without breaking the £40 barrier, and mature burgundies include a curiosity from Beaujolais, Chénas '69. The regional approach to the cooking is echoed in wines from the Jura and a spread from the south and south-west. CELLARMAN'S CHOICE: Ch. Bellevue-Puy-Blanquet '75, £11·50.

CHEF: Nicholas Blacklock PROPRIETORS: Nicholas Blacklock and Susan Warwick
OPEN: Mon to Sat, exc Sat L CLOSED: bank hols MEALS: 12.30 to 2.30, 6 to 11.30
PRICES: £14 (£23), Set L and D from £13·90 (£21) CARDS: Access, Amex, Diners, Visa
SEATS: 45. 3 tables outside. Private parties: 60 main room, 75 private room. No children under 11. Air-conditioned

Bayleaf Tandoori [11/20]   map 10

2 North Hill, Highgate, N6 4PU
01-340 1719 and 0245   £11–£14

This is like a country cousin of the Lal Qila (see entry): more space, less frenetic, less crowded. Fish is a particular speciality, including a Bengal-style fish curry, mixing grey and red mullet, eel, trout and pomfret, or king prawns masala, in a creamy, red spicy sauce. Also good is the sizzling murgh chaat masala. Nan is small, white and puffy – a very good example.

CHEF: Hamid Ali PROPRIETORS: A. A. Khan and B. U. Ahmed
OPEN: all week MEALS: 12 to 2.15, 6 to 11.15
PRICES: £8 (£14), Set L £6·95 (£11). Service 10% CARDS: Access, Amex, Diners, Visa
SEATS: 80. 4 tables outside. Private parties: 22 main room, 22 private room. Vegetarian meals. Children's helpings. Wheelchair access. Music

Beau-Rivage [11/20]

map 11

228 Belsize Road, NW6 4BT
01-328 9992 and 624 2333 £15–£22

The fresh fish is displayed in a cold cabinet on the ground floor of this Mauritian restaurant. The dining-room is in the basement, where orange lamps, yellow tablecloths, festoons of velvet curtains, and a stained-glass window of a red-haired woman compete with lively muzak, a birdcage, fans, and textured wallpaper. You are seated on reproduction light wood carvers or at benches decorated with cushions which resemble giant psychedelic fried eggs. The cooking is French with Mauritian accents. The strength is fish, cooked simply or perhaps with a rich but good traditional cream, brandy and ginger sauce. Bouillabaisse has been admired – a generous selection of firm, seasonal fish served in a smallish quantity of rich, aromatic broth. A selection of exotic fruits stands out on the limited sweets menu. Ice-creams and sorbets are bought in. The wine list is not surprisingly mostly whites with a good range in the £10 region. House wine is £6·75. CELLARMAN'S CHOICE: Chablis, *premier cru*, Domaines Servin '85, £14·75.

CHEF/PROPRIETOR: George Ng Yu Tin
OPEN: Mon to Sat, exc Sat L CLOSED: bank hols, 2 weeks Aug
MEALS: 12 to 2.30, 6.30 to 11.30
PRICES: £15 (£22), Set L £9·75 (£15). Cover 75p. Service 10% CARDS: Access, Visa
SEATS: 64. Private parties: 40 main room, 24 private room. Vegetarian meals. Children's helpings. No-smoking area. Wheelchair access. Music. Air-conditioned

The Bengal Lancer [10/20]

map 11

253 Kentish Town Road, NW5 2JT
01-485 6688 £9–£16

This cool, comfortable North Indian restaurant continues to fill a gap in the streets of Kentish Town, and the food is better than average. Potato chaat has clear coriander undertones, onion bhajias are crisp and freshly cooked, and chicken tikka biryani is good too. Lavish prawn bhuna is cooked with peppers and tomatoes. Drink lager or the house wine at around £5 a bottle.

PROPRIETORS: Stanley Krett and Akram Ali
OPEN: all week MEALS: 12 to 3, 6 to 12 (12.30 Thur, Fri and Sat)
PRICES: £9 (£16), Set L £3·50 (£9). Cover £1 CARDS: Access, Amex, Diners, Visa
SEATS: 55. Private parties: 25 main room. Vegetarian meals. Children's helpings. Wheelchair access. Music. Air-conditioned

Bengal Lancer Brasserie [11/20]

map 14

11 Greek Street, WIV 5LE
01-434 4177 £9–£16

The wide glass frontage looks out on to busy Greek Street, but inside the mood is laid-back colonial, with plenty of space, lots of hanging plants, quiet music in the background, and photographs of Queen Victoria on the walls. The shiny, colourful menu has a huge range of Indian dishes with many unusual items, such as cod's roe puri and marinated lambs' brains, as well as a full range of curries and tandooris. Sagwala chicken is cooked with spinach and fresh coriander; balls of minced fish are deep fried with a hot, spicy sauce. Vegetables are good and varied. Sweets include some flamboyant ideas such as hot bananas flambé in rum with cream, raisins and spices. Good-value thalis and set meals.

CHEF: Abdul Monaf PROPRIETORS: Stanley Krett and Akram Ali
OPEN: all week MEALS: 12 to 3, 6 to 12
PRICES: £9 (£16), Set L £3·50 (£9). Cover £1 CARDS: Access, Amex, Diners, Visa
SEATS: 70. Private parties: 8 main room, 40 private room. Vegetarian meals. Children's helpings. No-smoking area. Wheelchair access. Music. Air-conditioned

Beotys [10/20]   map 14

79 St Martin's Lane, WC2N 4AA
01-836 8768   £17–£23

No passing fancy, this one. Beotys is, perhaps surprisingly, one of the longest-serving *Guide* entries. Theodore Frangos has owned it since 1945. It remains, discreetly hidden behind a dull façade, an old-fashioned Greek restaurant, certainly not a taverna. The emphasis is on excellent squid in red wine or stifado or kleftiko, though some Continental-style plates remain. The service is another feature. Very useful for a business lunch or pre-theatre meal. House Kolossi is £6·30, but CELLARMAN'S CHOICE, Naoussa, one of the best Greek red wines, is £7·40.

CHEF: Stelios Sparsi PROPRIETOR: Theodore Frangos
OPEN: Mon to Sat MEALS: 12 to 2.30, 5.30 to 11.30
PRICES: £14 (£23), Set L £10·90 (£17), Set D £11·90 (£18). Cover 90p. Service 10%
CARDS: Access, Amex, Diners, Visa
SEATS: 80. Private parties: 50 main room, 50 private room. Children's helpings. No children under 8. Wheelchair access (also WC). Air-conditioned

Le Bistro [10/20]   map 10

36 High Street, Hornsey, N8 7NX
01-340 2116   £15

Formerly M'sieur Frog's Bistro, but the new husband and wife owners have shortened the name. The plain décor, with its posters and panelling, is in rustic, Gallic style, and the cooking is better than at the average bistro. Portions are generous and prices low for London. Soupe au pistou, sweetbread terrine, and duck breast with raspberry vinegar sauce are supplemented by thick steaks and fish dishes such as turbot with hollandaise. Vegetables are lightly cooked. Cheeses are French, and so are the wines, which include several country wines. CELLARMAN'S CHOICE: Cahors, Carte Noir '83, £7.

CHEF: Alfred Calandra PROPRIETORS: Mr and Mrs Alfred Calandra
OPEN: Tue to Sat, D only MEALS: 6.30 to 11
PRICES: £10 (£15) CARDS: Access, Visa
SEATS: 44. Private parties: 12 main room. Vegetarian meals. Children's helpings. Wheelchair access (also WC)

Reports on shops, cafes and farms are useful, as well as reports on restaurants.

Le Bistroquet [11/20]

map 11

273–275 Camden High Street, NW1 7BX
01-267 4895   £10–£17

The Greek monopoly runs out by Camden Lock, which has become a thriving
area for eating out. Most places aim to be used rather than to win awards. Deep-
fried Camembert with gooseberry sauce abounds. Le Bistroquet is one of the
oldest and more accomplished of the quasi-French. There is a good line in menu
writing. It makes an effort with salmon cooked in paper with fresh coriander and
lime; balsamic vinegar sauce for duck livers. The execution does not always
match, but neither does it pose or posture with any fancy garnishes. Likewise the
good short wine list deals in decent wines at affordable prices. Service is
spasmodic. House wine is £5·25 and served with food throughout the day.

CHEF: Paul Whitaker PROPRIETOR: Russel Joffe
OPEN: all week MEALS: 12 to 3, 7 to 11.30 (11 Sun)
PRICES: £11 (£17), Set L from £6·50 (£10), Set D from £10 (£15). Service 12.5%
CARDS: Access, Amex, Visa
SEATS: 160. Private parties: 120 main room. Vegetarian meals. Children's helpings.
Wheelchair access. Music

▲ *Blakes Hotel* [13/20]

map 12

33 Roland Gardens, SW7 3PF
01-370 6701   £42

London's most exclusive, romantic hotel has a suitably moody, black and
mirrored basement dining-room. Anouska Hempel's eye for design extends to a
menu that might be seen as the forerunner of a number of chic brasserie menus.
Multi-national, eclectic, it does not quite deliver at the top end, which at these
prices it ought to – the foie gras with truffles, although among the most expensive
dishes, is not among the best of its ilk. But through a series of chefs in recent years
standards have stayed broadly on a level, and the service is dutiful to the point of
obeisance. The Szechuan duck is served with breast and thigh on a black plate
and a side order of ground pepper, sea-bass with a horseradish and dill sauce.
Wild rice is offered as an alternative to new or dauphinoise potatoes. Sweets
continue the exotica, with fruits matching some of the Asian framed exotica that
litter the hotel: paw-paw and carambola appear in the fruit salad; avocado ice-
cream is served with honey and almonds. The wine list is exorbitant, though
house Raimat Cabernet-Sauvignon opens at £10. CELLARMAN'S CHOICE is
Moulin-à-Vent at £16. Quality is there at least, but the prices reflect the
internationalism of wine prices.

CHEF: Robert Ridley PROPRIETOR: Anouska Hempel Weinberg
OPEN: all week CLOSED: 24 and 25 Dec MEALS: 12.30 to 2.30, 7.30 to 11.30
PRICES: £27 (£42). Service 15% CARDS: Access, Amex, Diners, Visa
SEATS: 45. Private parties: 10 main room. Vegetarian meals. Children's helpings. Smart
dress preferred. No pipes in dining-room. Music. Air-conditioned
ACCOMMODATION: 55 rooms, all with bath/shower. Lift. B&B £96·90 to £158·80. Children
welcome. Baby facilities. No pets. Afternoon teas. Air-conditioning. TV. Phone [GHG]

The Guide *does not accept free meals.*

Bloom's [9/20]

map 11

90 Whitechapel High Street, E1 7RA
01-247 6001   £15

Were the latkes really this heavy in the olden days? No wonder everyone says
mama's soup is so wonderful. With the closure of Sharon's in Ilford, Morrie's
original place remains one of the last, fading outposts of Ashkenazi cooking as
Jewish families might have eaten in Middle Europe. The smart money is on the
borshchs and broths and the heaped plates of salt beef. The waiters – who own
the tables – have taken to prowling unattractively, which is not good for
business. But there it is. And sometimes the gefilte fish is quite delicately
flavoured. House Israeli is £6·50.

CHEF: Peter Nicholas PROPRIETORS: The Bloom family
OPEN: Sun to Fri, exc Fri D MEALS: 11.30am to 9.30pm (3pm Fri, 2pm Fri in winter)
PRICES: £9 (£15), Snacks from £3·50 CARDS: Access, Visa
SEATS: 160. Private parties: 160 main room. Car-park, 100 places. Vegetarian meals.
Children's helpings. Wheelchair access. Air-conditioned

Blue Elephant [12/20]

map 10

4–5 Fulham Broadway, SW6 1AA
01-385 6595 and 381 2896   £24

This level of Thai restaurant has not been seen before (though there is a sister in
Belgium). The Elephant is a Thai equivalent in décor to the Bombay Brasserie – a
jungle, with the sounds of cooking emanating from behind the bamboo-clad
kitchen: exotic, charming, startling. The menu is a little less so. It concentrates
on fish and salads and there are compensations for a general wetness in
individual dishes with a few that share the same clarity found in the best Thai
food – for instance, a tiny dish of sweetened scallops served on the shell; chicken
and lemon-grass soup served in a beautiful little blue china lidded pot; shellfish
casserole; the carefully composed rice and vegetable dishes. The claim to be Thai
royal cooking ('No imbalance between the quality of the preparation and the
care of presentation') is borne out by top-class service rather than by the intricate
artifice of historic banquets. House wines start at £6·95 and move up into
unsuited elegances.

CHEFS: Thaviseuth Phouthavong and Rungsan Mulijan PROPRIETORS: Blue Elephant Ltd
OPEN: all week, exc Sat L MEALS: 12 to 2.30, 7 to 11.30
PRICES: £12 (£24). Cover £1·50. Service 15% CARDS: Access, Amex, Diners, Visa
SEATS: 150. Private parties: 120 main room. Vegetarian meals. Children welcome.
Wheelchair access. Music

Bombay Bicycle Club [11/20]

map 10

95 Nightingale Lane, SW12 8NX
01-673 6850   £12–£18

This corner building near the Nightingale pub has become one of the most
fashionable restaurants south of the river. The white-walled dining-room has
batik-style prints and the occasional potted palm. The menu mixes Pakistani and
Punjabi dishes, including a dozen or so ways with lamb, plus a few fish

specialities. Unusually good are the sizzling tandoori prawns spiced with fenugreek and ginger, lahore machi (fish in batter), and fragrant lamb biryani. Well-made breads include first-rate keema nan stuffed with mince. The food is wholesome, rather rich, and generously served. Drink Tiger beer.

CHEF: H. Ismail PROPRIETORS: Perry and Amanda de Samarkandi
OPEN: all week, D only, and Sun L CLOSED: Christmas MEALS: 12 to 3, 7 to 12
PRICES: £12 (£18), Set L from £7 (£12), Set D from £12 (£18). Cover £1. Minimum £9
CARD: Visa
SEATS: 60. Vegetarian meals. Children's helpings (Sun L only). Wheelchair access (also WC)

Bombay Brasserie, Bailey's Hotel [14/20] map 12

Courtfield Close, SW7 4QH
01-370 4040   £14–£24

The inside is something of an answer to the Singapore Raffles, and is unlike any other Indian restaurant. The colonial elegance comes from the ornate chandeliers hanging from the enormously high ceiling, sepia photographs and large oils of Old Bombay on the faded rose-coloured walls, and vines in huge copper urns. A lady sits at a white piano. The ceiling fans revolve slowly. The menu is a grand tour, taking in dishes from all regions of the subcontinent: Bombay roadside snacks, tandooris from the Punjab, fish and coconut specialities from Goa, spicy curries from Kashmir, and exotic Parsee dishes. Vegetable dishes can outshine meat and fish: brinjal is grilled until mushy, Punjabi mustard-leaf purée and the special dried fruit curry with beans and peas have also been good. To start, try the elaborately constructed sev puri – a bed of large round crisps topped with green coconut sauce, sweet chutney, red tomato sauce and coriander leaves. In the centre of this mound is a rich yoghurt sauce, soft potato cubes and some mung beans. The lunchtime buffet is renowned for its range and value, while thali dinners are a useful introduction to the menu. Service can be erratic, but reports of dropping standards have been consistently short-lived. A short wine list, plus exotic cocktails, fruit juices and Kingfisher beer.

CHEF: S. Rao PROPRIETORS: Taj International Hotels
OPEN: all week MEALS: 12.30 to 2.30, 7.30 to 12
PRICES: £14 (£24), Set L £8·95 (£14). Minimum £10. Service 12.5% CARDS: Access, Amex, Diners, Visa
SEATS: 175. Vegetarian meals. Children welcome. Smart dress preferred. Wheelchair access (also WC). Music

Boulestin [12/20] map 14

1A Henrietta Street, WC2E 8PS
01-836 7061   £23–£36

Boulestin is an immensely correct restaurant, somewhat dated but imperious in its surroundings, professional to the point of impersonality. There may be better restaurants in London, but there are few better restaurant experiences, something not unnoticed by the waiters. The cheeses are from Androuët in Paris. Order them separately from the sweets as they have an extraordinary intense perfume and arrive in tray-loads. There is foie gras, vintage clarets usually only seen at auction-rooms, and a grill menu to match them. The rest of a copious menu is rooted, commendably, in classical French cooking, is frustratingly erratic for the prices, but can produce impeccable mousse of three fish, can match vegetables to main dishes as disparate as tournedos Rossini and goujons of sole aux girolles à la basilic. Of 280 wines, 30 are between £9·50 and £15, and there is an equivalent reinforcement of digestifs.

CHEF: Kevin Kennedy PROPRIETORS: Grand Metropolitan plc
OPEN: Mon to Sat, exc Sat L CLOSED: 3 weeks Aug, 1 week at Christmas
MEALS: 12.30 to 2.30, 7.30 to 11.15
PRICES: £24 (£36), Set L £15 (£23). Minimum £25 at D. Service 15%
CARDS: Access, Amex, Diners, Visa
SEATS: 70. Private parties: 25 main room. Vegetarian meals. No children under 5.
Jacket and tie

Boyd's Glass Garden [12/20]   map 11

135 Kensington Church Street, W8 7LP
01-727 5452   £15–£23

This is a stylish, modern restaurant squeezed in between the opulent antique shops and under a conservatory dome. The cooking is the antithesis of the excellent Clarke's (see entry) across the road, and it is French, heavily reliant on brilliantly coloured sauces, decorative and feminine. Boyd Gilmour likes puff pastry: it is shaped into a scallop shell with chunky cubes of salmon, scallops and monkfish; it is wrapped around a noisette of lamb and accompanied by a pungent madeira sauce and a garnish of courgettes stuffed with mange-tout; it is part of the pear tart that floats in a syrupy raspberry coulis. Vegetables are outstanding, and to finish there's strong cafetière coffee with a quartet of petits fours. The trappings are all here, and a little more cooking à la minute would make this a very serious restaurant. Front of house is skilfully manipulated. The wine list moves quickly up to expensive vintages, but these are offset by a dozen halves. House Torres Coronas is £6·95. CELLARMAN'S CHOICE: Rully, Château de Monthelie Surmain '84, £16.

CHEF/PROPRIETOR: Boyd Gilmour
OPEN: Mon to Sat, exc Sat L CLOSED: bank hols, 1 week at Christmas
MEALS: 12.30 to 2.30, 7.30 to 10.30
PRICES: Set L from £11 (£15), Set D from £19·50 (£23). Service inc
CARDS: Access, Amex, Visa
SEATS: 40. Private parties: 40 main room. Vegetarian meals. Children welcome

Le Café du Marché [12/20]   map 11

22 Charterhouse Square, Smithfield Market, EC1M 6AH
01-608 1609   £14

Not obviously found: a few doors along from the Fox and Anchor in Charterhouse Street, past some iron gates, and up an alley. The former medical supplies warehouse has been gallified into bare bricks, French cartoons, a piano in the centre, bar top right, kitchen on view bottom left. The menu is French, fish in bias, bourgeois but not without imagination, such as a main course of shredded skate with lemon grass and an oyster sauce. Elsewhere, as in the plate of charcuterie served with a jar of cornichons, or the bourride, or a game ragout, or a fine salad composed of expensive colourful leaves, or the cheeses with bread, the style is distinctly garlicky, and strongly provincial French – quite an oasis amid London's *nouvelle cuisine*. Interesting wines, efficient service, strong coffee complete a solid all-round venture. The house wines are split between table choices at £5 and CELLARMAN'S CHOICE: Vacqueyras from Pascal or Jurançon from the Pyrenees at £8.

CHEFS: Anthony Pitt, Rupert Pitt and Ewan Yapp PROPRIETOR: C. K. Graham-Wood
OPEN: Mon to Sat, exc Sat L MEALS: 12 to 2.30, 6.30 to 10
PRICES: Set L and D from £9 (£14). Service 15% CARDS: Access, Visa
SEATS: 50. Private parties: 50 main room. Vegetarian meals. Children's helpings. No babies.
No pipes in dining-room. Music

Café Flo [10/20]

map 11

205 Haverstock Hill, NW3 4QG
01-435 6744

£9–£17

What was Peachey's, next to the Screen on the Hill, has been transformed into Café Flo, an offshoot of Camden's Bistroquet. The décor has been simplified and the menu enclosed in a corner of France: cassoulet, confit, steak frites, gigot grillé avec flageolets. The set menu at £4·95 is a snip. House wine from the southern Rhône is £5·25, and the rest of the list of twenty wines is not without interest.

CHEF: Dominique Orizet PROPRIETOR: Russel Joffe
OPEN: all week MEALS: 12 to 3 (3.30 Sat, 4 Sun), 6 (6.30 Sat, 7 Sun) to 12 (11 Sun)
PRICES: £11 (£17), Set L and D from £4·95 (£9). Minimum £5. Service 12.5%
CARDS: Access, Visa
SEATS: 38. 6 tables outside. Private parties: 8 main room. Vegetarian meals. Children
welcome. Wheelchair access. Music

Café Rouge [new chef, zero rated]

map 11

2C Cherry Tree Walk,
Whitecross Street, EC1Y 8NX
01-588 0710

£20–£28

Under a gantry less than 150 yards from the Barbican. The rouge is in the décor, which is otherwise deeply Gallic and not unlike the Pompidou Centre, with exposed ducts and pipes inside and out. Bryan Webb has moved to Hilaire and has been replaced by Duncan Hewitson, but the style is still modern French, with some interesting touches: ballotine of foie gras with Gewürztraminer jelly; quail confit; seafood skewered on sticks of lemon grass. The new team seems clearly capable of good things, as in sea-bream with tomato and fennel coulis or red mullet with saffron butter tinged with rosemary. When Hewitson has settled in, the cooking may become more vivid and less cautious. The excellent, well-kept cheeseboard has a wide range from England and France. House Rhône £7·95. More reports, please.

CHEFS: Duncan Hewitson and Paul Baron PROPRIETORS: Danny and Bettie Murphy
OPEN: Mon to Fri CLOSED: 1 week at Christmas, bank hols MEALS: 12 to 2.30, 6 to 11
PRICES: Set L and D from £16·95 (£20) to £25 (£28). Service inc CARDS: Access, Diners, Visa
SEATS: 36. 4 tables outside. Private parties: 20 main room. Vegetarian meals. Wheelchair
access. Music

▲ Capital Hotel [14/20]   map 12

Basil Street, Knightsbridge, SW3 1AT
01-589 5171   £26–£42

The middle-aged, English club-like opulence is enhanced by the extra conceit of
having the menu written entirely in French. The dining-room is done out in
peaches, pinks and rusts, with glass chandeliers and murals of urns overflowing
with flowers, which match the tasteful baskets of real flowers on the tables, and
curtains pulled up over the tall windows like a Victorian lady's hiked-up satin
dress. John Elliot, promoted from number two when Brian Turner left to open his
own restaurant, Turner's (see entry), has carried on in a similar manner, with
grills besides *nouvelle* dishes with good sauces. Specialities include scallop
mousseline with a cream of sea-urchin sauce; fillet of beef with a Roquefort
sauce; and feuilleté of langoustines and scallops. To finish, there is tarte Tatin
and marquise of white chocolate with coffee sauce. Service is formal and mildly
aloof. The set lunch is a bargain next to the *carte*. The wine list has too many
burgundies and clarets to keep the bill within reason.

CHEF: John Elliot PROPRIETOR: David Levin
OPEN: all week MEALS: 12.30 to 2.30, 6.30 to 10.30 (7 to 10 Sun)
PRICES: £30 (£42), Set L £17·50 (£26), Set D £25 (£34). Service inc
CARDS: Access, Amex, Carte Blanche, Diners, Visa
SEATS: 35. Private parties: 10 main room, 24 private room. Car-park, 12 places. Vegetarian
meals. Children's helpings. No children under 4. Jacket and tie preferred. No pipes in dining-
room. Wheelchair access (also WC). Air-conditioned
ACCOMMODATION: 60 rooms, all with bath/shower. Rooms for disabled. Lift. B&B £105 to
£146. Deposit: 1 night's stay. Children welcome. Baby facilities. Afternoon teas.
Air-conditioning. TV. Phone [GHG]

Le Caprice [10/20]   map 13

Arlington House, Arlington Street, SW1A 1RT
01-629 2239   £19

For all its monochromatic superficiality, Le Caprice is a consistently well-run and
well-booked-up restaurant. It might now be seen as the forerunner of the chic
cafe generation of restaurants which has swept London in the last year: Joe's
Cafe, Maxim's Wine Bar, Braganza, Corney & Barrow, Champenois, etc. The
décor is loud and definite, the atmosphere structured and controlled. In most
places the food becomes fairly incidental, but Charles Fontaine for the most part
resists the temptation to fuss and organises his menu in such a way that the
cooking is resilient to the demands of the dining-room – eight grills out of
thirteen main courses, more than half the starters cold. Among these dishes are
fine heart-shaped steak tartare; fish-cakes; calf's liver with shallots; Toulouse
sausages; eggs Benedict; and a surprisingly blue-blooded choice of around sixty
wines including no fewer than nine different rosés. Sunday brunch is booked well
in advance.

CHEF: Charles Fontaine PROPRIETORS: C. J. Corbin and J. R. B. King
OPEN: all week, exc Sat L MEALS: 12 to 2.30 (3 Sun), 6 (7 Sat and Sun) to 12
PRICES: £13 (£19). Cover £1 CARDS: Access, Amex, Diners, Visa
SEATS: 70. Vegetarian meals. No children under 5. Wheelchair access. Music.
Air-conditioned

Champagne Exchange [9/20]

map 13

17C Curzon Street, WIY 7FE
01-493 4490   £23

It could not be more simple: a show of nearly fifty champagnes matched by a
menu of minimum cooking: caviare; smoked fish; salads; cheese. The atmosphere
is clandestine, and few people would eat a full meal. Prices are geared for Mayfair,
and even the service line of the credit card is, arrogantly, left blank. Champagnes
are £2.50 to £5.50 a glass, £5 to £9.50 a tankard.

PROPRIETORS: Champagne Exchange Ltd
OPEN: Mon to Sat, exc Sat L MEALS: 11.30 to 3, 5.30 to 12
PRICES: £16 (£23), Snacks from £3. Service 12.5% CARDS: Access, Amex, Diners, Visa
SEATS: 80. 2 tables outside. Private parties: 100 main room. Vegetarian meals. Children's
helpings. Music. Air-conditioned

Chanterelle [11/20]

map 12

119 Old Brompton Road, SW7 3RN
01-373 5522 and 7390   £11–£16

Fergus Provans's well-established Anglo-French restaurant is reassuringly
reliable. The set menu changes frequently and the lunch particularly is excellent
value and offers a choice of around eighteen dishes. The style is pork fillet with
cream and mustard, or medallions of beef with a green and red pepper sauce,
with occasional flourishes into regional cookery – breast of pigeon with a
tapénade – or more modern, serving lamb with its kidney and crab-apple jelly.
Vegetables are generous. Ices, fruits and farmhouse cheeses to finish. House
French £5·40. CELLARMAN'S CHOICE: Côtes du Ventoux, La Vieille Ferme '82,
£7·30.

CHEF/PROPRIETOR: Fergus Provan
OPEN: all week CLOSED: 4 days at Christmas MEALS: 12 to 2.30, 7 to 11.30
PRICES: Set L £7·50 (£11), Set D £12 (£16). CARDS: Access, Amex, Diners, Visa
SEATS: 45. 3 tables outside. Private parties: 15 main room. Children welcome.
Wheelchair access

Le Chef [10/20]

map 11

41 Connaught Street, W2 2BB
01-262 5945   £15–£20

Twenty years on, Alan King's reliable little bistro still turns out excellent soups,
crêpes au jambon, sweetbreads in port wine sauce, and pork chops stuffed with
Parma ham and cheese. The style does not change, but nor does the quality.
Outstanding French cheeses, with first-rate fruit flans to finish. House French is
£4·75. CELLARMAN'S CHOICE: Ch. Millet '82, £13·65.

'We have eaten in 90 per cent of the places that rate 12 or more in the Guide over the
last two years. Everyone is having to improve to stand still in the ratings.' (Yorkshire
restaurateur)

CHEF/PROPRIETOR: Alan King
OPEN: Mon to Sat, exc Sat L CLOSED: 2 weeks Aug
MEALS: 12.30 to 2.30, 7 to 11.30 (11 Sat)
PRICES: £14 (£18), Set L £14·50 (£15), Set Sat D £17·75 (£20). Cover 50p. Service inc
CARDS: Access, Visa
SEATS: 50. 5 tables outside. Private parties: 20 main room, 20 private room. Vegetarian meals. Children's helpings. Wheelchair access. Music

Chez Biba [new entry, zero rated]   map 10

313 Chiswick High Road, W4 4HH
01-995 3354   £15–£21

In a stretch of Chiswick better known for its cut-price petrol stations and supermarkets than its restaurants. The change of name from Biba's Brasserie has heralded a splash of powder-blue paint on the walls. The menu is quality bistro, with a few tricks up its sleeve: young turbot with a sauce of lavender flowers; fillet of beef with oysters coated in breadcrumbs. In more familiar territory the kitchen can produce croustade of mussels and mushrooms with fine puff pastry, warm salad of chicken livers and spinach, and lamb chops with a fistful of fines herbes. Sweets fade. The wine list shows a fondness for French country wines. CELLARMAN'S CHOICE: Château Bellevue La Forêt, Côtes du Frontonnais '85, £7·50. More reports, please.

CHEF: Philippe Granger PROPRIETOR: M. Sanchez
OPEN: Mon to Sat, exc Sat L CLOSED: Aug, Christmas, bank hols MEALS: 12 to 3, 7 to 11
PRICES: £13 (£21), Set L and D £9·50 (£15). Cover 70p. Service 10%
CARDS: Access, Amex, Carte Blanche, Diners, Visa
SEATS: 55. 8 tables outside. Private parties: 40 main room. Vegetarian meals. Children's helpings. Smart dress preferred. Wheelchair access (also WC). Music

Chez Liline [10/20]   map 10

101 Stroud Green Road, Finsbury Park, N4 3PX
01-263 6550   £10–£16

The tropical fish from next door supplies much of a thirty-dish menu at this eccentric cafe. The front is takeaway and the back is a Formica-style room almost devoid of any décor, but everything is cooked to order, flavours are intense, portions large, and prices low. The Mauritian bouillabaisse is very rich; prawns chow-chow are cooked with tropical fruit. Lobster, squid, salmon, and mussels have all been skilfully handled as well as the more exotics. The platter Sétoise has been comprised of half a lobster, scallops, king prawns, and salmon in a cream sauce. Salads and vegetables are crisp. The thirty-five wines are carefully selected and are priced from £4·25.

CHEF: Sylvain Ho Wing Cheong PROPRIETOR: Liline Ng Yu Tin
OPEN: all week, exc Mon L and Sun L MEALS: 12 to 2.30, 6 to 11
PRICES: £10 (£16), Set L from £6 (£10), Set D from £8 (£12)
SEATS: 40. 2 tables outside. Private parties: 50 main room. Children welcome. Wheelchair access. Music

It is helpful if restaurateurs keep the office up to date with any changes.

Chez Moi [13/20]   map 10

1 Addison Avenue, W11 4QS
01-603 8267   £21–£26

Red walls and ceiling relieved only by a bit of greenery and some mirror give a
sense of warmth rather than elegance. Richard Walton's team is French and is
one of the most reliable in London. The set menu provides for some
experimentation, but for the most part the *carte* sets out to deal with its much-
loved, well-supported repertoire. Lamb – diable, stuffed with garlic and mint, or
with apricots – is reputedly the best in London. But it is in the less obvious
touches that the skill shows – a first-class tomato soup; calves' kidneys with
mashed potatoes and, instead of the usual cloying mustard and cream, a beurre
rouge, nicely sharp. 'Somebody had poked their finger into this and tasted it until
they got it right.' Service is good, and the forty wines have been selected with the
same eye for classical integrity. House wine is £6. CELLARMAN'S CHOICE: Ch. de
Pez '79, £15·75.

CHEF: Richard Walton PROPRIETORS: Richard Walton and Colin Smith
OPEN: Mon to Sat, D only CLOSED: 2 weeks Aug, 2 weeks at Christmas, bank hols
MEALS: 7 to 11.30
PRICES: £18 (£26), Set D £16·50 (£21) CARDS: Access, Amex, Diners, Visa
SEATS: 45. Children's helpings. No pipes. Wheelchair access. Air-conditioned

Chiang Mai [11/20]   map 14

48 Frith Street, W1V 5TE
01-437 7444   £12–£17

The smartness of the entrance is matched by the calm of the interior. Wooden
pillars and floors and white walls give almost a temple-like feeling, though the
atmosphere is far from reverential. The Thai cooking has quite an edge to it –
chicken, coconut and galingale soup; beef in basil; vegetable curry; chicken with
garlic. House Blanc de Blancs at £5·55 helps to cool the heat.

CHEF/PROPRIETOR: Vatcharin Bhumichitr
OPEN: Mon to Sat MEALS: 12 to 3, 6 to 11.30
PRICES: £9 (£17), Set L and D from £14 (£24) for two. Service 10%
CARDS: Access, Amex, Visa
SEATS: 60. Private parties: 12 main room, 20 and 25 private rooms. Vegetarian meals.
Children welcome. Music

Chinon [new entry, zero rated]   map 10

25 Richmond Way, W14 0AS
01-602 5968 and 4082   £15–£26

An unrelieved urban density of tightly packed flats in a tall, austere converted
Victorian block surrounds this restaurant, which opened in the summer of 1987.
It is small, elegantly pink, drag-painted room with a gilt-framed mirror across
one wall giving an illusion of space (but with Filofax-sized tables). The bright
modern lighting makes the customers part of the décor. The vivid, modern British
carte is varied with some seasonal and daily choices, and pointed up at first meals
by some fine pastrywork. Good dishes have been cold melon soup on a hot night;

breast of pigeon in a pastry case with green noodles and a cream sauce flavoured with cardamom or perhaps vanilla; best end of lamb with ratatouille; salmon, steamed and served with a tarragon sauce to one side and a herb butter to the other. Minor elements like good bread and butter impress. Sweets favour complex mousses, such as butterscotch slice on hazelnut meringue; light and dark chocolate mousse, with a spun sugar basket of raspberries and cherries stealing the attention, and another sauce flavoured with cardamom. There are the makings here of a very serious restaurant, though first meals have been slow, stretching into two and a half hours, and the service could sharpen up. Fifty wines show an enlightened attitude similar to the cooking, from house wine from Duboeuf at £6·95 upwards. More reports, please.

CHEFS/PROPRIETORS: Barbara Deane and Jonathon Hayes
OPEN: Tue to Sat, exc Sat L MEALS: 12 to 2.30, 7 to 10.30 (11 Fri and Sat)
PRICES: L £12 (£20), Set L £8·50 (£15), Set D £17·50 (£26). Service 15%
CARDS: Access, Amex
SEATS: 30. Private parties: 35 main room. Vegetarian meals. Children welcome. Smart dress preferred

Christian's [12/20]   map 10

1 Station Parade, Burlington Lane, W4 3HD
01-995 0382 and 0208   £18

On warm nights, when the door is left open, this converted corner shop, in the heart of urban Chiswick, feels like a rural backwater. Christian Gustin is the guiding spirit, although he now has some assistance in the kitchen. His cooking has evolved from a version of dinner party food into an eclectic modern style with its roots in the French tradition. Meat and fish are lightly cooked, salads are pretty. His hugely risen soufflé made with English cheese is outstanding, and other good dishes have included warm salad of scallops on lightly cooked samphire and colourful leaves, poached haddock with beurre blanc, and a big hunk of chicken with mushrooms and wine sauce. Dishes are cooked to order, so the pace is leisurely. Sweets might include a clafouti-style greengage tart. Short list of well-chosen wines. House French £5·45.

CHEF/PROPRIETOR: Christian Gustin
OPEN: Tue to Sat, D only MEALS: 7.30 to 10.15
PRICES: £11 (£18). Service 10%
SEATS: 32. Private parties: 8 main room. Vegetarian meals. Children's helpings. Music

Chuen Cheng Ku [11/20]   map 14

17 Wardour Street, W1 3HD
01-437 1398   £8 – £20

Going up in the world under its new management, with a red carpet, giant chandeliers like upside-down jelly-fish, and walls papered and painted white. The waitresses have uncommonly fluent English. Dim-sum remain a major attraction. Look for inexpensive meals of roast duck noodle soup; more luxurious plates of cold roast suckling pig complete with crackling; excellent dry fried dishes like spring rolls or, wetter, wrapped in bean-curd skin, the warm chicken morsels flavoured by a slice of wind-dried sausage. The main menu is also showing signs of recuperation with such dishes as aubergine and bean curd or fried scallops. Tea is free.

CHEF: Yat Au PROPRIETORS: Choi and Kam Au
OPEN: all week MEALS: 11am to 11.45pm (11.30pm Sun)
PRICES: £13 (£20), Set L from £4 (£8), Set D from £7 (£11). Service 10%
CARDS: Access, Amex, Diners, Visa
SEATS: 400. Private parties: 150 main room, 50 and 80 private rooms. Vegetarian meals. Children welcome. Wheelchair access. Music

Ciboure [13/20]
map 11

21 Eccleston Street, SW1 9LX
01-730 2505
£16–£26

This small, neat, cream, white and black French restaurant has held its place when others have gone by the wayside. The set lunch at £12·50 (served also after 10pm) is a good £5 less than at most other French heavyweights. The cooking is varied, careful and picturesque. Fashions, such as sashimi, or caul for wrapping a veal kidney, or chicken with a saffron and mussel sauce – a speciality is the potato charlotte with a leek sauce – are taken in its stride. Enjoyed dishes include lightly curried courgette and carrot soup; plaice with an asparagus coulis; duck with limes; fillet of beef with a beetroot sauce. It is almost a surprise to find bread-and-butter pudding among the artifice of mille–feuilles and chocolate quenelles of the sweets. Service is swift and pleasant. 'We never use frozen foods.' Thirty wines favour small French properties and range upwards from £7. CELLARMAN'S CHOICE: Ch. Bechereau '81, £13·80.

CHEF: Richard Price PROPRIETOR: Jean-Louis Journade
OPEN: Mon to Sat, exc Sat L MEALS: 12 to 2.30, 7 to 11.15
PRICES: £19 (£26), Set L and D £12·50 (£16) CARDS: Access, Amex, Diners, Visa
SEATS: 36. Children welcome. No cigars/pipes. Wheelchair access. Air-conditioned

Clarke's [14/20]
map 11

124 Kensington Church Street, W8 4BH
01-221 9225
£16–£26

The elegant dining-room needs to sharpen up if it is to handle the kind of customers Sally Clarke's reputation is starting to attract, but for the moment it is a calm alternative to the hurly-burly of other London restaurants. At dinner there is no choice. It is modern British cooking: dishes are put together thoughtfully but with a free hand. The emphasis is on the market, with plenty of fresh fish, seasonal game and salad ingredients handled very simply. Char-grilling and marinating set the style, there are few sauces and there's not much fat. The results can be brilliant, full-blooded and sensual. Salads are highlights from the starters: firm, fleshy tomatoes with fresh basil and raw spinach leaves; warm Parma ham with lettuces; spinach salad with a mousse of duck livers – all pointed up with subtle dressings made from fine oils and vinegars. Main courses are presented using crisp vegetables as a nest for, say, marinated pigeon breast, or char-grilled chicken with lime topped with a blob of avocado purée. Cheeses show faith in the younger generation; slices of Beenleigh Blue and Timsbury with warm toasted onion bread and soft, crumbly oatmeal and sesame seed biscuits.

Lunch draws more praise than dinner. The wine list is still developing, and there are some useful bottles from the New World which suit the food admirably.

CHEF/PROPRIETOR: Sally Clarke
OPEN: Mon to Fri CLOSED: Christmas, Easter, 2 weeks in summer
MEALS: 12.30 to 2, 7.30 to 11
PRICES: Set L from £12·50 (£16), Set D £22 (£26). Service inc CARDS: Access, Visa
SEATS: 60. Children welcome. Wheelchair access

▲ Connaught Hotel [17/20]   map 13

Carlos Place, W1Y 6AZ
01-499 7070   £25–£50

Fashionable it is not, but the Connaught alone now offers the kind of grand hotel gastronomy which sustained British catering for the last 150 years. Michel Bourdin has devoted his career to keeping the old motor up and running. The atmosphere is heavily Edwardian – waiters in formal black, gleaming panels, the glittering chandelier, the glass partitions – as is the menu. But do not be deceived. There is cooking here of the finest quality – intense crab soup, careful pastry on the fruit tarts, Devon lamb noisettes with a tarragon sauce. The sauces are old school, not striving desperately for the intensity of modern cooking, rather the gentle letting down of flavours with a little cream. Luxuries abound, but they are understood. The foie gras prepared in the chef's *façon* has a trolley to itself – an oblong loaf, a single truffle through the centre, served in slices with warm brioche and fragrant port jelly diced into tiny cubes; such is cuisine. The faults are of all hotel dining-rooms – the famous croustade d'oeufs de caille Maintenon left as two little canoes to swim naked on a great white plate because no one finished it – but the atmosphere has the ignition of all great restaurants. The number of American customers tends to make it a dining-room that peaks early, and by 10.30 it may be nearly empty. In continuing his dynasty Bourdin has become a great trainer of other chefs. Among those with a Connaught upbringing are: John Dickens, ex-Longueville Manor, Jersey; Christian Delteil, L'Arlequin; Martyn Pearn, ex-Buckland Manor; Mario Lesnick, Claridges; François Huguet, ex-Inverlochy Castle; Robert Mabey at Hintlesham Hall; John Elliot at the Capital Hotel; David Adlard at Adlard's, Wymondham; Richard Sparrow at the Swan, Streatley. Most are or have been in the *Guide*. The wine list has clarets for tourists but also good drinking around £12 in Gigondas from Jaboulet and Riesling from Beyer.

CHEF: Michel Bourdin PROPRIETORS: Savoy Hotel plc
OPEN: all week CLOSED: weekends and bank hols (Grill Room)
PRICES: £33 (£50), Set D from £15·35 (£25). Service 15% CARD: Access
SEATS: 80 (Restaurant), 35 (Grill Room). Private parties: 20 main room, 20 private room. No
children under 6. Jacket and tie. No pipes. Wheelchair access. Air-conditioned
ACCOMMODATION: 90 rooms, all with bath/shower. Rooms for disabled. Lift. Rates on
application only. Afternoon teas. TV. Phone [GHG]

CELLARMAN'S CHOICE: *This is a wine recommended by the restaurateur which is more expensive than the house wine but is good value and fitting for the kind of food served.*

F. Cooke   [9/20]   map 11

41 Kingsland High Street, E8 2JS
01-254 2878   £3

The sign dates the East End's most famous pie and eel shop to 1862, but it has
been here only since the turn of the century. The sawdust and the mirrors are
still the genuine articles. The menu has not changed; eel pie was chopped after
the First World War because of lack of demand. Fred and Chris Cooke, grandsons
of the first owners, are craftsmen and proud of it. They deal in eels, procuring
tanker-loads direct from fishermen in undisclosed parts of southern England, as
well as buying from Billingsgate. Their mash is made from real potatoes and they
always use fresh parsley for their liquor. Jellied eels make a fine alternative to the
stewed kind, and meat pies are made from scratch in the bakery at the back of the
shop. The late Victorian tiles depict early Dutch eel barges. The Cockney
atmosphere survives. Takeaways. Tea 23p; no licence.

PROPRIETORS: F. S. and C. R. Cooke
OPEN: Mon to Sat CLOSED: bank hols
MEALS: 10am to 8pm (6pm Tue and Wed, 10pm Fri and Sat)
PRICES: £3. Unlicensed, but bring your own: no corkage
SEATS: 70. Private parties: 28 main room, 40 private room. Children welcome. Wheelchair
access (also WC). Music. Self-service

La Corée   [10/20]   map 13

56 St Giles High Street, WC2H 8LH
01-836 7235   £12–£17

Some of the most genuine Korean food in London is served at this modest
restaurant in a curving back street behind Centre Point. There's not much décor
– a few paintings on the walls, ginseng roots in tall jars – but the waitresses
charm and the kitchen has no expense-account aspirations. The short menu
never strays far from the classic beef, fish and vegetable specialities, and the
results are forthright. Amso kalbi gooi – a variation of bulgogi – is short beef ribs
marinated in sesame oil, sugar, and pear juice, then grilled on a shield-like
apparatus at the table. Otherwise there are fried dumplings, bean-cakes, boiled
octopus, and jellyfish with vegetables in mustard sauce. Good-value composite
meals include a dish of ox-tail with rice that might raise a few staunchly English
eyebrows. Kim-chee (preserved Chinese cabbage) is pungent, but mints help to
dispel any after-effects. Drink barley tea, Korean saké or dried persimmon punch.

CHEF: Mr Nho PROPRIETOR: Mr Park
OPEN: Mon to Sat MEALS: 12 to 3, 6 to 11
PRICES: £9 (£17), Set L £8 (£12), Set D from £8 (£12). Service 10%
CARDS: Access, Amex, Diners, Visa
SEATS: 61. Private parties: 45 main room. Vegetarian meals. Children welcome. Wheelchair
access. Music

*Please keep the Guide informed of any changes to the restaurants listed. Report forms
are at the back of the book.*

Cork & Bottle [9/20]

map 14

44–46 Cranbourn Street, WC2H 7AN
01-734 7807

 £12

Handily placed for Leicester Square, this well-discovered wine bar features an unusually intelligent selection of wines with strong sections from the New World. The food is cosmopolitan and unfussy, but it can be a squeeze finding somewhere to put the plate.

CHEF: Dympna Carey PROPRIETOR: Don Hewitson
OPEN: all week MEALS: 11.30 to 2.45, 5.30 to 10 (12 to 2, 7 to 10.30 Sun)
PRICES: £8 (£12) CARDS: Access, Amex, Diners, Visa
SEATS: 100. Vegetarian meals. Music. Air-conditioned. Self-service

Corney & Barrow [12/20]

map 11

118 Moorgate, EC2M 6UR
01-628 2898

£32

One of the City's new breed of high-powered dining-rooms, a mirrored and designed basement. The food matches the paintings – loud, clear, modern, masculine, extravagant and sometimes intriguing, as in a calf's foot mayonnaise decorated with strips of red peppers and a salad of expensive leaves dressed in expensive oils. Fish features strongly, often as not in cheaper items like mussels surrounding an oblong mousse on a powerful sauce. Occasional flamboyances are pulled off with gusto – ox-tail off the bone, placed in a pastry case with citrus fruits. Rice pudding served warm and topped with cinnamon sticks and half a strawberry is the main gesture to modern British cooking among fashionable ice-creams and mousses. All this complexity does not necessarily suit the extensive merchant's wine list, which earns the bottle symbol for its breadth, but it is the drinks – with coffee at £1·95, Perrier at £1 a glass – that lift the bill out of the ordinary.

CHEF: Robin Stewart PROPRIETORS: Corney & Barrow Restaurants Ltd
OPEN: Mon to Fri, L only MEALS: 11.30 to 3
PRICES: £21 (£32), Snacks from £3·25. Minimum £20 in rest. Service 12.5%
CARDS: Access, Amex, Diners, Visa
SEATS: 100. Private parties: 250 main room. Vegetarian meals. No children under 6.
Air-conditioned

Corney & Barrow [12/20]

map 11

109 Old Broad Street, EC2N 1AP
01-638 9308

£43–£46

Before the Big Bang there was hope that the City would at last become somewhere in which to eat out, and many restaurants opened in anticipation. This elegant British racing-green basement was one of four from Corney & Barrow, wine merchants. These phenomenal prices are not really matched by great leaps ahead in cooking or restaurateuring. Gross touches include making a self-congratulatory mousse of turbot and caviare. Can it really be that such indulgent menus are now the language of the executive from Hong Kong to Dallas? The ostentatious flourishes seem to come from a kitchen almost in paranoia that it cannot keep up. The gravlax comes with an oyster garnish; the soft-shelled crabs with scallops and with a whole plate of vegetables, identical to a first-course starter. All told, the effect is of a superior dinner party, though much of the gastronomy found last year when this was our City newcomer of the year has left along with the chef, M. François Schmitt. In its place there is a fine cheeseboard and more examples of enormous mark-ups on the wine list. The food is not bad, but if all the money being generated in the City is spent like this, expect the crash soon.

CHEFS: David Rayner and Matthew Bunn PROPRIETORS: Corney & Barrow Restaurants Ltd
OPEN: Mon to Fri, L only MEALS: 12 to 2.30
PRICES: £29 (£43), Set L £33·95 (£46). Service15% CARDS: Access, Amex, Diners, Visa
SEATS: 30. Private parties: 60 main room. Smart dress preferred. No pipes. Music.
Air-conditioned

La Coupée [new entry, zero rated]   map 10

17 Half Moon Lane, Herne Hill, SE24 9JU
01-737 1556   £11–£18

The décor is Paris bistro, with big gilt-framed mirrors, half-curtains at the windows, and a varnished wood bar for drinks and coffee. The kitchen performs well in the main events, such as hot chicken liver mousse, young rabbit in a very un-peasantish provençale sauce, and chunks of steamed monkfish with tomatoes and a creamy stock-based sauce. To go with this, salad and cheese may be a better choice than vegetables and dessert. House wine is £4·95; otherwise there is a list of around twenty mainly French vintages. More reports, please.

CHEF: Dermot Jones PROPRIETORS: Dermot Jones and Cyril McCandless
OPEN: Tue to Sat, exc Sat L CLOSED: 2 weeks at Easter, 2 weeks Sept
MEALS: 12 to 2.30, 6.30 to 9.30
PRICES: £14 (£18), Set L £6·95 (£11), Set D £11·95 (£17) CARDS: Access, Visa
SEATS: 40. 2 tables outside. Private parties: 40 main room. Vegetarian meals. Children
welcome. No pipes. Wheelchair access

La Croisette [12/20]   map 11

168 Ifield Road, SW10 9AF
01-373 3694   £27

The original of Pierre Martin's stable of five restaurants is unostentatiously hidden in a side street and, as at L'Olivier (see entry), a spiral staircase leads to a Cannes-style basement, cramped but efficient and distinctly French. The set price includes a Kir before a procession of shellfish. The platter is legendary in its generosity, and the tureen of rich fish soup is left on the table for second helpings. Main-course fish are presented lightly but effectively sauced. 'The high standard of food and service is astonishing.' Other trimmings – such as salad as a course on its own, and cafetière coffee – match. House wine from Provence is £7·50.

CHEF: Robert Lanoé PROPRIETOR: Pierre Martin
OPEN: Tue to Sun, exc Tue L CLOSED: 2 weeks at Christmas
MEALS: 12.30 to 2.30, 7.30 to 11.30
PRICES: Set L and D £20 (£27). Service 15% CARDS: Access, Amex, Diners, Visa
SEATS: 55. 5 tables outside. Children welcome. Music

Crowthers [13/20]   map 10

481 Upper Richmond Road West, East Sheen, SW14 7PU
01-876 6372   £18–£24

The Crowthers share nearly all the duties in their small, Laura Ashley-style restaurant which has been consistently good for the last three years. Philip cooks, Shirley serves. The menu is carefully composed to give texture and a choice between sauce and dry, oil and butter, alcohol and purées. It fits squarely between modern French and British. Monkfish with samphire and saffron sauce, and loin of pork marinated with currants and coriander, show the seasoning of Britain, but the texture of the sauces, as in, say, lambs' kidneys with Meaux mustard, is French. The choice of perhaps fifteen dishes in an evening encompasses most of the soigné touches of the moment: sweetbreads in a brioche, wild rice with roast quail, a parfait of three chocolates – white, milk, and dark. Biscuits with cheese are home made. Fifty wines are chosen with acumen and cover a wide area of France. House claret opens at £8·50. CELLARMAN'S CHOICE: Australian Bin 389, Cabernet Shiraz '82 from Penfolds, £14·50.

CHEF: P. A. Crowther PROPRIETORS: P. A. and S. A. Crowther
OPEN: Mon to Sat, exc Mon L and Sat L MEALS: 12 to 2, 7 to 11
PRICES: Set L £12 (£18), Set D £18 (£24) CARDS: Access, Amex
SEATS: 30. Private parties: 12 main room. Vegetarian meals. Children welcome. Wheelchair access. Music. Air-conditioned

Daphne [10/20]   map 11

83 Bayham Street, NW1 0AG
01-267 7322   £14

Daphne, 'as chaste as she was beautiful', was turned into a laurel tree to escape being raped by Apollo. Her incarnation in whitewash and elegant prints, a cut above the average taverna, is on the fringes of an increasingly fragmented Greek area of Camden Town. The meze is exceptional value. A blackboard menu has daily specials which break away from the usual predictable formula and provide dishes such as squid – stuffed, or in ink and wine – stuffed artichokes; slow casseroles of lamb with spinach and beans. There are mentions also for the fixtures: avgolemono soup; hot pitta bread; swordfish kebabs; stifado; afelia and home-made baklava. Service is unobtrusive and courteous. House wine is, unusually, a Beaujolais at £6·10 a litre.

CHEFS: S. Christodoulou and L. Georgiou PROPRIETORS: Anthony Evangelou and
A. Lymbouri
OPEN: Mon to Sat MEALS: 12 to 3, 6 to 12
PRICES: £8 (£14) CARD: Access
SEATS: 85. 10 tables outside. Private parties: 30 main room. Vegetarian meals. Children welcome. Wheelchair access (also WC). Music

'My wife's grilled goats' cheese starter was OK, except that you can buy crottins for £1 in Sainsbury's and grill them yourself and you don't have to put them on a sheet of Wonderloaf like this was.' (On eating in London)

Desaru [10/20]

map 14

60–62 Old Compton Street, W1V 5PA
01-734 4379   £15–£21

Sleeker, with its turquoise cloths and mirrored walls, and more fashionable than
its near neighbour, the Equatorial, which also serves Indonesian/Malay food.
The menu is marginally more interesting. Cooks can be seen tossing the rice in
big woks at the far end. Sauces are thick and spicy, beef rendang has a well-
reduced, pungent coconut sauce, and there are big bowls of laksa too.
Vegetarians fare well with French beans with salted yellow beans, stuffed
aubergine, crisp noodles, and garlic-flavoured sauces. Alas, it is not Indonesia,
but it is a compromise. Service has returned to its flashy best. House wine
is £5·40.

CHEF: Yurnas Zainvdin PROPRIETOR: Michael Gan
OPEN: all week MEALS: noon to 11.45pm (1pm to 10pm Sun)
PRICES: £8 (£15), Set L and D £30·50 (£42) for two. Cover 50p. Minimum £5. Service 10%
CARDS: Access, Amex, Diners, Visa
SEATS: 60. Private parties: 50 main room. Vegetarian meals. No children under 10. Music.
Air-conditioned

Dining Room [9/20]

map 11

1 Cathedral Street, SE1 9DE
01-407 0337   £13

Unlikely corners are taken over and forced into service for the cause of
vegetarianism. Here in the shadow of Southwark Cathedral, and virtually under
Borough wholesale fruit and vegetable market, is a basement reached via a long
corridor. It is almost a dungeon, and the sun is blocked out as anyone walks past
on the pavement. The half a dozen large tables are for sharing. Some off-the-shelf
ornaments like a typewriter pass for decoration. A mandatory blackboard has the
menus: three starters, two main dishes, and three sweets. It is always on the
move: imaginative, freshly prepared and devoid of pretensions – either brown-
sandaled or otherwise. The mushroom bake with a tomato sauce is served with a
side salad of grains melded with an avocado mousse. Wholemeal bread is
excellent. Produce is all organic, the influences global. The result in March was a
far from cranky cream of almond soup; seaweed and chestnut fritters with dill
mayonnaise; courgette and tomato casserole; and fried Jerusalem artichokes. To
finish, there are Milleens and Waun Gron cheeses with oatcakes. House wine is
£5·50, and beyond the fruit juices is CELLARMAN'S CHOICE: Puligny-Montrachet
'85, £18.

CHEF: Sandra Cross PROPRIETORS: William English and Sandra Cross
OPEN: Tue to Fri MEALS: 12.30 to 2.30, 7 to 10
PRICES: £9 (£13). Service 10%
SEATS: 32. Private parties: 35 main room. Vegetarian meals. Children's helpings. Music

*'Fillets of turbot and salmon in a champagne and prawn sauce: the dish was 100 per
cent but suffered from the often-mentioned complaint – the plate was so hot that the
delicate sauce evaporated before my eyes.'* (On eating in Buckinghamshire)

▲ *Dorchester Hotel* [17/20] map 13

(1) Grill Room,
(2) Terrace Restaurant
Park Lane, W1A 2JH
01-629 8888 £19–£43

A phenomenal amount of creative cooking is going on at the Dorchester. Menus at both the Terrace and the Grill overflow with ideas. Anton Mosimann's creative canvas has never been wider. At last *cuisine naturelle* is starting to take form and substance and become a style in its own regard irrespective of its healthiness. Witness steamed brill on a bed of mussels and carrots or terrine of orange and mint with raspberry sauce. But dishes fight to get on the menu – there is competition from the market, from Mosimann's own style of exact *nouvelle cuisine* and the resurrection and development of traditional British dishes such as Wiltshire onion soup and bread-and-butter pudding. What is remarkable in recent months has been the way that all the promise that was prematurely lauded and never really borne out night after night has started to jell. The kitchens are producing food that rivals small chef/patron restaurants. Innovation walks side by side with tradition – a consommé of rabbit flavoured with ginger; chicken breast stuffed with sweetbreads in a clear meat *jus* with diamonds of colourful peppers. These are both *cuisine naturelle* dishes that demonstrate the full consummation of the style. The Grill Room, with its old-fashioned, Spanish gold-and-red décor and its fleet of beige-tunicked waiters armed with a triumphant trolley of breads, is the lunch-room, the Terrace, with its faintly harem-like décor and Vince Prince and his Band, is open only in the evenings. Alas, the wine list is atrociously expensive. Mineral water at £3·15 a bottle is no solace, though with Graves starting at £23, Meursault at £46, and even an ordinary Brouilly from a bad year at £18, invoking the spirit of *cuisine naturelle* and staying with the water may be a good idea.

CHEF: Anton Mosimann PROPRIETORS: Dorchester Hotel Ltd
OPEN: (1) all week. (2) Mon to Sat, D only MEALS: (1) 12.30 to 3 (2.30 Sun), 6.30 to 11 (7 to 10.30 Sun). (2) 6.30 to 11.30
PRICES: (1) £23 (£32), Set L and D £17·50 (£19 and £24). Service inc. (2) £35 (£43), Set D £31 (£37). Service inc CARDS: Access, Amex, Diners, Visa
SEATS: (1) 85. (2) 100. Car-park, 40 places. Vegetarian meals. No children under 9. Jacket and tie. No pipes in dining-room. Wheelchair access (also WC). Music. Air-conditioned
ACCOMMODATION: 275 rooms, all with bath/shower. Rooms for disabled. Lift. B&B £105·65 to £190. Deposit: 1 night's stay. No children under 9. Afternoon teas. Air-conditioning. TV. Phone. Confirm by 6

La Dordogne [12/20] map 10

5 Devonshire Road, Chiswick, W4 2EU
01-747 1836 £23

This restaurant says more about London restaurants than it does about Dordogne. Behind roll-over timber shutters is a heavy helping of décor – dark greens, lots of mahogany-stained wood and brass. The staff are almost begrudging in the manner of Chinese restaurants – waitresses dart frantically around like birds in a cage under the watchful eye of Mlle Bitton. Due to its popularity it has expanded next door and a wine bar is expected to open for

Christmas 1987. Since opening, the cooking has been bourgeois, then there was an errant flirtation into luxuries and *nouvelle* – now thankfully checked. It is a remarkably good bistro, and this is what it ought to stay as. Erratic it is, especially in the sweets, but there is mitigation here in lamb with a mint and honey sauce; feuilleté of asparagus with a beurre blanc; goats' cheese salad; and as good a chicken liver pâté as is found in London. The kitchen is under pressure. Thirty dishes a night plus a regional menu from France are too much to guarantee consistency with more modern dishes, which all require cooking à la minute. That said, it is a gem in the area and it is possible to eat as easily for around £16 as £25 a head. The wine list has a good showing of French country wines which keeps the prices under control.

CHEF: Vincent Adam PROPRIETOR: Miss Bitton
OPEN: Mon to Sat, exc Sat L MEALS: 12 to 2.30, 7 to 11
PRICES: £15 (£23). Cover 90p. Service 10% CARDS: Access, Amex, Diners, Visa
SEATS: 64. 6 tables outside. Private parties: 64 main room. 38 private room. Smart dress preferred. Wheelchair access. Music

Drakes [new entry, zero rated]   map 12

2A Pond Place, SW3 6QJ
01-584 4555   £30

This subterranean, somewhat international basement virtually beneath the Meridiana and next to one of Anouska Hempel's clothes shops has begun to do under new chef David Bickford what it always set out to do – namely, to serve proper English food. The exposed brickwork and oils of ducks are reminiscent of that era of restaurant design which took in the Grange in Covent Garden, verging uncomfortably on the impersonality of the hotel. A glass screen divides it from the kitchen, with its large range of charcoal grills. The menu has been sensibly reworked into a traditional British style – more in keeping with the old battleaxes like Wiltons and Rules than modern British – and offers perhaps the best food of its ilk outside the Dorchester. It is un-mucked about, with roasts and grills showing off the produce to effect. Alas, the bargain lunches that drew many reports have been dispensed with – more's the pity, because dinner is priced along with the cream of London. But dishes are properly done – scallops wrapped in individual pieces of bacon, char-grilled, dusted with fresh breadcrumbs and served with a little pot of béarnaise; a fine Dorset soup of spinach and almonds and Jersey cream; top-quality liver grilled just right; Cornvale duck off the bone with the breast and the thigh and wing on a deep gravy with a tart purée of Victoria plums. The traditional tone of the sweets is offset by some modern artifice: summer pudding is conical, its strawberry coulis feathered with cream; apple and ginger crumble is an individual shaped saucer. Fine bread, salty butter, soft chocolate truffles with the coffee, enthusiastic service – all encourage. The wine list opens at £7 and moves swiftly upwards with the emphasis towards vintage clarets. More reports, please.

CHEF: David Bickford PROPRIETORS: Stephen Moss and Partners
OPEN: all week, D only, and Sun L MEALS: 12.30 to 3, 7 to 11 (10.30 Sun)
PRICES: £19 (£30). Service 12.5% CARDS: Access, Amex, Diners, Visa
SEATS: 70. Private parties: 100 main room. Vegetarian meals. Children welcome. Smart dress preferred. No-smoking area. Music. Air-conditioned.

▲ *Dukes Hotel* [12/20]   map 13

St James's Place, SW1A 1NY
01-491 4840   £25–£43

Dukes is an antidote to other London hotels; quiet, secluded, old school, it takes its cue from its address, which also makes it popular with American visitors. The dining-room is small, calm, and run with thought, and the menu, without obviously cutting a dash, is reliably built around first-class ingredients and executed carefully. Fish is notably good: turbot, sole, brill, offered grilled or poached. Saucing is restrained but not shy – horseradish for brill, Stilton for chicken. Sweets are of the bread-and-butter pudding type. The prices have leaped up since a year ago, when the wine list was not cheap either. The concentration is on '79, '78, '76 claret and £20 burgundy. House claret £8·50. CELLARMAN'S CHOICE: St Emilion, Ch. Destieux, £19·50.

CHEF: Tony Marshall PROPRIETORS: Dukes Hotel Ltd
OPEN: all week MEALS: 12.30 to 2.30, 6 (7 Sun) to 10
PRICES: £30 (£43), Set L from £16 (£25) CARDS: Access, Amex, Carte Blanche, Diners, Visa
SEATS: 50. Private parties: 45 main room, 12 private room. Vegetarian meals. Children welcome. Jacket and tie. Wheelchair access (also WC)
ACCOMMODATION: 57 rooms, all with bath/shower. Rooms for disabled. Lift. B&B £115 to £180. Baby facilities. TV. Phone [GHG]

Eatons [11/20]   map 12

49 Elizabeth Street, SW1W 9PP
01-730 0074   £19

Eaton's is a dependable neighbourhood restaurant. There are prints and modern paintings on the hessian-covered walls of the long narrow room. Off a limited menu, familiar French-style dishes are executed with care: pancakes stuffed with fresh salmon; veal lightly fried and served in a cream, white wine and mushroom sauce. The sweets trolley is furnished with strawberry Romanoff, chocolate cake and cream. The wines match the food, and the CELLARMAN'S CHOICE is Ch. Millet '78 at £13·50 (or £7·20 for a half-bottle of '82).

CHEF: Santosh Bakshi PROPRIETORS: Shayne Pope and Dieter Vagts
OPEN: Mon to Fri CLOSED: bank hols MEALS: 12 to 2, 7 to 11.15
PRICES: £12 (£19). Service inc CARDS: Access, Amex, Diners, Visa
SEATS: 40. Private parties: 14 main room. Children welcome. Wheelchair access. Music

Efes Kebab House [11/20]   map 13

80 Great Titchfield Street, W1P 7AF
01-636 1953   £13

Widely held to be among the best Turkish restaurants in London; the atmosphere bustles and the value is good. The menu has enormous variety both in its starters and also in its kebabs – no fewer than nineteen, including liver with aubergine. The platter of fruit can come adorned with a sparkler. Coffee is strong, and there's an interesting choice of Turkish wines or raki to drink. It was at Efes (Ephesus) that the Virgin Mary is said to have spent the last years of her life.

CHEFS/PROPRIETORS: K. Akkus and I. Akbas
OPEN: Mon to Sat MEALS: noon to 11.30pm
PRICES: £8 (£13). Minimum £4 CARDS: Access, Amex, Visa
SEATS: 100. Private parties: 50 main room. Vegetarian meals. Children welcome. Music.
Air-conditioned

Fleet Tandoori [10/20]   map 11

104 Fleet Road, NW3 2QX
01-485 6402   £11–£12

The most consistent and unpretentious curry-house in the area. The décor may
be spartan, but the service is courteous and the food good value. Regulars praise
the vegetarian dishes, especially creamy mattar paneer and spicy chana
masaladar. Other good dishes have included a starter of prawn purée, and lamb
pasanda and chicken tikka masala. Nan are fresh, poppadums are free. Thalis are
less than £8. Drink lassi or lager.

CHEF: Amzad Ali PROPRIETOR: Abdur Rahman Khan
OPEN: all week MEALS: 12 to 2.30, 6 to 11.30 (noon to 11.30pm Sun)
PRICES: £8 (£12), Set L and D from £7·20 (£11). Service 10%
CARDS: Access, Amex, Diners, Visa
SEATS: 52. Private parties: 52 main room. Vegetarian meals. Children's helpings.
Wheelchair access

Forum Court [10/20]   map 10

7A – 8 High Street, South Norwood, SE25 6EP
01-653 0295 and 771 7965   £13–£15

A sound, suburban Peking restaurant marked by shiny blue canopies and
bamboo blinds. The décor and the menu have been tailored to Western tastes,
but the cooking has been reliable and dishes well presented. The menu is in the
mould of bang-bang chicken, prawn toasts, fried seaweed, Peking duck, and dry
shredded chilli beef with carrots. Oysters come sizzling with big slices of fresh
ginger and spring onions. Set meals show off the range. Jasmine tea is 50p.

PROPRIETOR: Kwok Ying Loh
OPEN: all week CLOSED: 25 and 26 Dec MEALS: 12 to 2.15, 6 to 11.15 (11.45 Fri and Sat)
PRICES: £8 (£15), Set D from £8·90 (£13). Service 10% CARDS: Access, Amex, Diners, Visa
SEATS: 80. Private parties: 80 main room. Vegetarian meals. Children's helpings (Sun L
only). Music

Fung Shing [13/20]   map 14

15 Lisle Street, WC2H 7BE
01-437 1539   £12–£22

Of all the yoyos in Chinatown, Fung Shing is the most likely to provide genuine
Cantonese cuisine of a level usually reserved for special occasions by the Chinese.
The décor fits neatly between original cafe-style and modern neon, but the menu
is long and is of the old school. Listed specialities are shredded boneless salt-baked
chicken; crispy fried pigeon; and carp with ginger and spring onion. The range
encompasses popular westernised dishes such as quail wrapped in lettuce, which

are done competently, but it is really the mainline Cantonese dishes that excel: wun-tun soup; deep-fried pig's intestines; duck and plum hot-pot; winter melon soup. House French is £6·50.

CHEF: Fu Kwun PROPRIETORS: Traceflow Ltd
OPEN: all week MEALS: noon to 11.45pm
PRICES: £14 (£22). Set L and D from £7·50 (£12). Minimum £6·50. Service 10%
CARDS: Access, Amex, Diners, Visa
SEATS: 85. Private parties: 50 main room, 30 private room. Vegetarian meals. Children welcome. Music. Air-conditioned

Ganpath [9/20]

map 11

372 Grays Inn Road, WC1 8BB
01-278 1938

£10

Just down the road from Kings Cross Station: the sign says South Indian brasserie – in fact it is a no-frills curry-house with a vegetarian slant. Despite a revamp, the décor is still bare and the tube trains still shake the dining-room as they rumble under ground. The cooking is earthy and excellent value, with many dishes under £2. From the south come bhajias, iddly, and samosas. Freshly made masala dosai is served with coconut relish and thick sambar for dipping. Interesting vegetables and first-rate breads. Drink lassi or lager.

CHEF: Mr Ramalingam PROPRIETORS: Mr Ramalingam and Mr Sivamatham
OPEN: all week CLOSED: 25 and 26 Dec MEALS: 12 to 3, 6 to 11
PRICES: £5 (£10). Minimum £2·50. Service 10% CARD: Access
SEATS: 42. Private parties: 25 main room. Vegetarian meals. Children's helpings. Wheelchair access

Garbo's [11/20]

map 11

42 Crawford Street, W1H 1HA
01-262 6582

£18

The only Swedish restaurant in central London is well placed between the Swedish Embassy and the Swedish Church. Pictures of Carl Gustav and Queen Silvia hang from the walls in the small dining-room. The style is Swedish home-cooking at its best. Janson's Temptation is a fine version of the classic, julienne potatoes with plenty of anchovies and a restrained amount of cream. Cabbage is stuffed with minced pork and beef, braised until brown, then served with rice and cranberry sauce. Other good dishes have included smoked eel cooked in beer and served with scrambled eggs, and fine-cut fillet of beef with mustard and a helping of tiny sauté potato cubes. Vegetables are plain and virtuous. Disappointing sweets. Skane Schnapps and Pripps Export beer go well through the meal. House wine is £5·45 a bottle.

CHEF: Clive Barrett PROPRIETOR: Ake Lindholm
OPEN: all week, exc Sat L and Sun L MEALS: 12 to 3, 6 to 12
PRICES: £11 (£18). Cover £1 CARDS: Access, Amex, Diners, Visa
SEATS: 48. Private parties: 50 main room, 45 private room. Children's helpings. Wheelchair access. Music. Air-conditioned

Le Gastronome [13/20]

map 10

309 New King's Road, SW6 4RS
01-731 6993   £18–£22

Moved a few doors down the road (the old premises are now a Chinese Chin's)
and dropped the One from its name, but owner Matthew Wallis and chef Thierry
Aubugeau continue to offer a fine version of modern French cooking in the style
of terrine of duck confit; home-made ravioli with snails or wild mushrooms; and
fillet of John Dory with citrus fruits. The fresh vegetable soup is well liked, and
M. Aubugeau is also a fine charcutier. Fillet of lamb with mushroom sauce,
pheasant with pears, and salmon with lime have all shown the skill of the
kitchen. Dishes receive a lot of embellishment, which reaches its peak in the
desserts, ranging from home-made sorbets to a selection of light mousses. The
wine list shows its pedigree in the vintage clarets, and there's a choice of house
wines at £7 a bottle. CELLARMAN'S CHOICE: Morgon, Domaine de la Chanaise '84,
£10·50.

CHEF: Thierry Aubugeau PROPRIETOR: Matthew Wallis
OPEN: Mon to Sat, exc Sat L MEALS: 12 to 2, 7 to 11
PRICES: £17 (£22), Set L £12·50 (£18), Set D £14·50 (£20). Service inc
CARDS: Access, Amex, Visa
SEATS: 50. Private parties: 35 main room. Vegetarian meals. Children's helpings. No
children under 6. Smart dress preferred. No-smoking area. Wheelchair access. Music

Le Gavroche [18/20]

map 13

43 Upper Brook Street, W1Y 1PF
01-408 0881   £26–£51

Le Gavroche has that supreme restaurant virtue of consistency. The style is
classical. The mood is formal, but the dining-room, under the watchful eyes of
Silvano Geraldin and sommelier Peter Davies, is a model of its kind. Some might
object to the style, but that is not the point. Nowhere else is it possible to find a
well-defined cuisine being practised in such breadth and range. The dark green
basement is hung with oils. The menu is loyal to the dishes that earned its
reputation – soufflé suissesse, sole mazarin, pot au feu. The pike mousse, sauce
Chloe, is a reinforcement of the mastery of those pillars of French cuisine, the egg
and pastry. But on the daily set menus there is infinite texture, variety and
development in line with the markets – foie gras on slices of crunchy Jerusalem
artichokes; roast sea-bass with a meat-juice sauce. Some of the sauces are
elastically deep. The details can be star attractions in their own right – the
breads, the salads, the extraordinary array of cheeses, the rows of petits fours
with coffee. Lunch remains a relative bargain. It has become fashionable to say
that it is past its peak, but that is in complete contradiction to all the reports we
have received. House wines are Brouilly and Mâcon-Prissé at £12. The range of
the list is reminiscent of a quartermaster setting up for a long campaign, but
before the big vintages can be found wines at under £20 – Lirac at £12·50, Ch.
Monlot-Capet '83 at £17·50 – and there are halves. CELLARMAN'S CHOICE: Pinot
Auxerrois, Les Lutins '81, £10·50.

An index of restaurants by name appears at the back of the Guide.

CHEF: A. H. Roux PROPRIETORS: Le Gavroche Ltd
OPEN: Mon to Fri CLOSED: 23 Dec to 2 Jan MEALS: 12 to 2, 7 to 11
PRICES: £42 (£51), Set L £19·50 (£26), Set D £40 (£49). Minimum £35 at D. Service inc
CARDS: Access, Amex, Carte Blanche, Diners, Visa
SEATS: 60. Private parties: 10 main room. No children under 8. Jacket and tie. No pipes.
Air-conditioned

Gavvers [11/20]

map 12

61–63 Lower Sloane Street, SW1W 8DH
01-730 5983

£19·75

Not a place at which to try to buck the system. Arrive on time, order according to
the daily menu and you will eat well, at a reasonable price, food that feels as if it
should be more expensive. The young staff are barely out of the Lycée before
signing up at the Roux académie. Among the immaculate linen and cutlery they
learn to manoeuvre between the tightly packed tables and to advance to higher
English, as in, 'Yes, monsieur'. The foie gras salad, the pastry case of fresh
asparagus, the chocolate truffle cake continue to impress on either side of
signature early Roux brothers' main courses such as blanquette de poisson. A
glass of Kir, Evian water and a half-bottle of one of half a dozen bottles of wine are
included.

CHEF: Denis Lobry PROPRIETORS: Roux Restaurants Ltd
OPEN: Mon to Sat, D only MEALS: 7 to 11
PRICES: Set D £19·75. Service inc CARDS: Access, Amex, Diners, Visa
SEATS: 80. Children welcome. Wheelchair access. Air-conditioned

Gay Hussar [15/20]

map 14

2 Greek Street, W1V 6NB
01-437 0973

£16–£24

The Gay Hussar remains one of Soho's most enduring institutions. It is a
restaurant for regulars, but everyone is a regular after five minutes. The caring
attitude is old-fashioned in the nicest way, as is the cooking itself, which is
wholesome, comforting and evocative of Eastern Europe, pre-war. Hangover
Soup – actually sauerkraut with Wurst – is first class, and there are consistent
reports of the jellied carp and fish salad. Roast goose comes with Hungarian
potatoes and cranberry sauce, while baked minced veal is offset by spicy cabbage.
Both the dobas torte and a winter version of summer pudding have been
excellent sweets. It is still exceptional value for money. Rumours of Mr Sassie's
retirement still seem premature. Bookings are not accepted too far in advance.
There are some good clarets, but Hungarian wines draw the interest: old sweet
Tokays for three-figure sums, younger ones including a dry Szamorodni '78 for
£7 and an Essencia '57 for ten times that. More modestly, CELLARMAN'S
CHOICE: Hungarian Merlot and Morí Ezerjó at £6·50 each.

---

*All details are as accurate as possible at the time of going to press. Please notify the
Guide office of any changes.*

CHEF: Leslie Holecz PROPRIETOR: Victor Sassie
OPEN: Mon to Sat MEALS: 12.30 to 2, 5.30 to 10.30
PRICES: £16 (£24), Set L £10·50 (£16). Cover 50p
SEATS: 35. Children's helpings (L only). Wheelchair access. Air-conditioned

Ginnan [11/20]

5 Cathedral Place, EC4M 7EA
01-236 4120 and 5150   £11–£32

Some of the fastest – and cheapest – Japanese lunches in London are served in
this busy restaurant in a dark shopping arcade under St Paul's Cathedral. It feels
like a cafe, and it is possible to be in and out within fifteen minutes. The good-
value set meals for £6 centre on tempura, sashimi, grilled fish and pork cutlets,
with appetisers, soup and rice. The pace is fast and service is ruthlessly efficient
without ever seeming rude. In the evening the restaurant calms down and
reverts to the classic style, with high-class classical cooking to match. Set meals
are backed up by dishes of the day on a Japanese menu. The class shows in the eel
sushi, the impeccable tempura, and the grilled salmon brushed with a sweet
brown glaze. The dish of simmered buckwheat noodles rolled in a piece of thick
white fish highlight the flair and eye for presentation. To drink, there are
Japanese wines, Kirin beer and Suntory whisky.

CHEF: Mr Goto PROPRIETORS: Ninjin Ltd
OPEN: Mon to Sat, exc Sat D CLOSED: bank hols MEALS: 12 to 2.30, 6 to 10
PRICES: £11 (£16), Set L £6 (£11), Set D £25 (£32) CARDS: Access, Amex, Diners, Visa
SEATS: 45. Private parties: 10 main room. Children welcome. Music. Air-conditioned

Golden Chopsticks [12/20]   map 12

1 Harrington Road, SW7 3ES
01-584 0855   £22–£23

A few more customers and this elegant Chinese restaurant, behind its smoked-
glass frontage, would likely be recognised as one of the better of the new wave of
Chinese restaurants in the country. Some nights it has been so becalmed that
Prince Charles and Princess Diana are said to take advantage of the exclusivity
by eating upstairs. Unusual care is taken in the cooking of dishes such as deep-
fried crispy chicken, steamed sea-bass, and squid in black-bean sauce, and in the
picturesque array of starters around a sculptured carrot. The special rice is
excellent. Alas, it lacks the consistency its prices demand, especially to non-
Chinese. House French is £7.

CHEF: Mr Wong PROPRIETORS: Blakeleigh Ltd
OPEN: all week MEALS: 12 to 2.15, 6 to 11.30 (11 Sun)
PRICES: £14 (£22), Set D £15 (£23). Cover 50p. Minimum £10. Service 12%
CARDS: Access, Amex, Diners, Visa
SEATS: 75. Private parties: 40 main room. Vegetarian meals. Children's helpings. Music.
Air-conditioned

*Many of the more expensive restaurants offer bargain lunches for half the price of a
meal in the evening. Details are given in the text.*

Good Food [new entry, zero rated] map 14

8 Little Newport Street, WC2H 7JJ
01-734 2130 £5–£14

With the burning of the Diamond, this represents an interesting alternative
further down the road. On three cramped floors filled with mirrors, it is smart in
the modern moneyed style. The menu is Cantonese and includes, unusually,
crocodile – flown in dried from Singapore and reconstituted with chicken stock in
the same way as dried abalone (it is reputed to be good for children's asthma). It
appears with shark's fin in a soup, or with scallops as a broth. The rest of the
menu is one of those wonderful collections of 250 dishes that straddle the
inexpensive – one-plate meals, soups, good noodles – and the seductive – not just
fine crab with spring onions and ginger or paper-wrapped spare ribs with star
anise, but squid seven ways, eel four ways, lobster and duck. House wine is
£4·80. More reports, please.

CHEFS: C. K. Yip and S. Y. Wong PROPRIETORS: Haylin Ltd
OPEN: all week, D only MEALS: 4.30pm to 4.30am
PRICES: £8 (£14), Set D from £1·80 (£5). Service 10% CARDS: Access, Amex, Visa
SEATS: 70. Private parties: 30 main room, 30 private room. Vegetarian meals. Music.
Air-conditioned

Good Friends [10/20] map 10

139–141 Salmon Lane, E14 7PG
01-987 5541 and 5498 £18

The Good, the New, and the Old Friends were the first restaurants to develop
authentic Cantonese cooking in London's East End after the War. The Good
Friends is now the best, a good box-like period-piece of a restaurant. There are
delicious soups and steamed and stuffed dishes, but the strength, with
Billingsgate just up the road, is in the fish: whole sea-bass with ginger, huge king
prawns, and scallops all feature. Best to book at peak times.

CHEFS: Wah Moon Cheung and Wah Tong Cheung PROPRIETORS: Cheung Brothers Co. Ltd
OPEN: all week MEALS: 12 to 3, 5 to 11.30
PRICES: £11 (£18). Service 10% CARDS: Access, Amex, Diners, Visa
SEATS: 100. Private parties: 80 main room. Vegetarian meals. Children welcome.
Wheelchair access. Music. Air-conditioned

Gordon's Wine Bar map 13

47 Villiers Street, WC2N 6NE
01-930 1408

As the Guide *went to press there was a change of chef at this restaurant.*

Grahame's Seafare [10/20]

map 13

38 Poland Street, W1V 3DA
01-437 3788 and 0975   £19

The talk in this marvellous anachronistic dining-room is often about the old
days: how the original Mr Grahame used to run the place almost single-handed,
grabbing a couple of hours' sleep then getting up at four every morning to buy
the day's fish from Billingsgate. Not much has changed. A team of cooks and
kindly waitresses now keeps the Jewish flag flying. The fish is still market-fresh –
and some of the finest to be had anywhere in the orbit of Oxford Circus. It is fried
in light matzo flour, as well as grilled or cooked in milk and butter. Haddock is
served as steaks or as massive fillets cut from the meaty head end, plaice comes
three ways (whole, middle or fillet) and the range takes in lemon sole, halibut
and salmon. Shot-put sized balls of gefilte fish are a favourite, and there are
cheese blintzes to finish. The smoked salmon is good, too. To drink, try a tumbler
of cold borshch as an alternative to wine or tea.

CHEF/PROPRIETOR: Robert Dehaan
OPEN: Mon to Sat, exc Mon D MEALS: 12 to 2.45, 5.30 to 8.45 (7.45 Fri)
PRICES: £13 (£19). Cover 50p at D. Minimum £5 CARDS: Amex, Visa
SEATS: 90. Children's helpings. Wheelchair access. Air-conditioned

Great Nepalese [9/20]

map 11

48 Eversholt Street, NW1 1DA
01-388 6737   £7–£11

Within earshot of the train announcements at Euston Station, this is again one of
the most genuine Nepalese restaurants in London. The décor has been spruced
up. The cooking is gutsy, with the emphasis on fresh herbs, vegetables, and
pulses. The spicing is restrained and gives the food a lighter touch than
comparable Indian places. Look for the interesting Nepalese starters: mamoch
(steamed pastries), bhutuwa chicken livers, and masco bara (fresh deep-fried
black lentil cakes). Otherwise there are pork curries as well as chicken and
mutton, some of the best boiled Basmati rice in town, brilliant green coriander
pickle, and unusual accompaniments such as kerauko achar (a cold dish of
potatoes with sesame seeds). Finish with a shot of devastating Nepalese
Coronation Rum served from a bottle shaped like a ghurka knife. House wine is
£3·95 a litre.

CHEF: Mr Masuk PROPRIETOR: Gopal Manandhar
OPEN: all week CLOSED: 24 and 25 Dec MEALS: 12 to 2.45, 6 to 11.45
PRICES: £7 (£11), Set L £3·75 (£7), Set D £6·25 (£10). Minimum £4. Service 10%
CARDS: Access, Amex, Carte Blanche, Diners, Visa
SEATS: 48. Private parties: 34 main room. Vegetarian meals. Children's helpings.
Music

Reports on shops, cafes and farms are useful, as well as reports on restaurants.

*Files are kept on every restaurant, so reports of poor meals are just as valuable as
reports of good meals because they save unnecessary inspections.*

The Greenhouse [12/20]

map 13

27A Hay's Mews, W1X 7RJ
01-499 3331

£22

Essentially a modern English restaurant that aspires to be old-fashioned. There
are elements of both qualities: venison sausage with braised red cabbage versus
roulade of halibut and pink mousse with courgette coulis, for instance.
Centrepieces such as roast lamb with rosemary and the rösti potatoes (order
separately) lead up to excellent bread-and-butter pudding. Service can creak
under the strain of a full dining-room and detract from the food, but the club-like
atmosphere compensates. The wine list is youthful, moderately priced and
accomplished. CELLARMAN'S CHOICE: Len Evans's Hunter Valley Chardonnay
'85, £11·75.

CHEF: Julian Jeffrey PROPRIETOR: David Levin
OPEN: Mon to Sat, exc Sat L MEALS: 12 to 2.30, 7 to 11
PRICES: £14 (£22) CARDS: Access, Amex, Carte Blanche, Diners, Visa
SEATS: 85. Private parties: 12 main room. Children welcome. Air-conditioned

Green's [12/20]

map 13

36 Duke Street, St James's, SW1Y 6BR
01-930 4566 and 1376

£27

Green's is not quite as old as it feels (circa 1982, in fact) but it fits neatly on to the
Mayfair map alongside Fortnums, Paxtons, Christies, etc. Behind the smoked-
glass windows are clubby, varnished dark wood panels and Spy-style prints. The
champagne and oyster bar dispenses the highest calibre of both. To the other
side, the dining-room specialises in the simple – smoked meats and fish, plain
crustaceans – and the traditional – kedgeree, bangers and mash, nursery
puddings. As wine merchants the company has operated since 1787.
Champagne rises from £15 to magnums of Dom Pérignon '78 at £100.

CHEFS: Beth Coventry and Heather Angeard PROPRIETOR: Simon Parker Bowles
OPEN: all week, exc Sun D MEALS: 11.30 to 3, 5.30 to 10.45
PRICES: £17 (£27). Cover £1 CARDS: Access, Amex, Diners, Visa
SEATS: 110. Private parties: 8, 18 and 26 private rooms. Children's helpings. No children
under 5. Wheelchair access. Air-conditioned

Hard Rock Cafe [9/20]

map 13

150 Old Park Lane, W1Y 3LN
01-629 0382

£14

The Deep South roadside cafe is reincarnated on Hyde Park Corner as 'the
world's only rock 'n' roll museum'. The collection of memorabilia, which rotates
between the branches in different cities, features, among other things, the
Allman brothers' guitar; George Harrison's Fender Stratocaster; David Bailey's
Olympus OM-2. A framed poster proclaims Elvis Presley's favourite
meal: vegetable soup, pork chop with brown gravy, and apple pie. Even the
queue, which seems to have been ever-present since 1971, has become a cult.
The turnover on tables runs at around half an hour, so it is rarely a longer wait.
Drinkers at the bar get preference. The music is dated but loud. The cooking is

indubitably still the best of its kind in London – the ribs are over a foot long and covered with meat; the burgers are made with meat; the chips are slim; salads crisp; the blue-cheese dressing as elegant as any French sauce. Sundaes and banana splits with real American ice-cream are here for the self-indulgent. Drink beer, coke and cocktails. Many of the staff have now been here since the mid-1970s, another testimony to the good sense of Isaac Tigrett's business acumen.

PROPRIETORS: Hard Rock Cafe plc
OPEN: all week MEALS: noon to 12.30am (1am Fri and Sat)
PRICES: £10 (£14). Minimum £4. Service 10%
SEATS: 100. Vegetarian meals. Children welcome. Smart dress preferred. Wheelchair access. Music. Air-conditioned

Harvey's [14/20]

2 Bellevue Road, Wandsworth, SW17 7EG
01-672 0114 and 0115

map 10

£17–£23

The hottest restaurant in South London by quite a long street. Marco Pierre White, having done stints at Le Gavroche, Chez Nico, Box Tree, Tante Claire and Le Manoir aux Quat' Saisons, opens as chef/patron facing the Common. The short menu is written in English and has assimilated much from all the great kitchens. The smart bourgeois décor is in the manner of the old Chez Nico, staff are young and professional and add to the impression that this is very much a restaurant in the round. A trademark is vegetables cut into pasta-like lengths – green beans sliced to decorate the show-stopping leek terrine stuffed with scallops and langoustines and dressed in a virgin olive oil, a pile of shredded carrots around the tortelloni of langoustines (a slightly heavy, herbed mousse filling), or the cucumber with a speciality of a tagliatelle of oysters. Sauces are immaculate – a deep stock, not over-reduced but diluted with Sauternes for braised calves' sweetbreads. This is not delicate cookery, but expressive and confident: a guinea-fowl breast and duck meat piled high in the centre of a plate garnished with baby leeks, dried morels and trompettes de mort, and a cream sauce, this time cut with the taste of morels; or baked pigs' trotters stuffed with morels and sweetbreads; or baby pigeon with fresh truffles. Cheeses from Olivier favour goats' and are ripe to the point that a thumbnail-sized piece is sufficient. Desserts have a supplement and include terrine of fresh fruits with sorbet – lemon, lime, and fresh cubes of mangoes and pineapple or pavé of dark chocolate in a caramel sauce. Good strong cafetière coffee comes with enough petits fours to feed a table. Lunch is a bargain and does not need booking far in advance. Everything is cooked to order. This is serious stuff. The wine list is emerging. House wines are from Languedoc and Gascogne at £7·50. CELLARMAN'S CHOICE: Châteauneuf-du-Pape '83, Domaine Font de Michelle, £16·50.

CHEF/PROPRIETOR: Marco Pierre White
OPEN: Mon to Sat, exc Sat L CLOSED: bank hols MEALS: 12.30 to 2.30, 7.30 to 11.30
PRICES: Set L from £9·95 (£17), Set D from £15·50 (£23) CARDS: Access, Amex, Visa
SEATS: 45. Private parties: 8 main room, 20 private room. No children under 10. No cigars/pipes. Air-conditioned

'Perhaps someone will tell me why my bowl of excellent soup near the River Cam was 70p but £2.50 near the Thames (Henley)?' (On eating in Cambridgeshire)

L'Herisson [12/20]

map 10

8 High Street, Wimbledon, SW19 5DX
01-947 6477   £15–£20

Formerly the Village Restaurant, from which it inherited the fine spacious dining-room. The clutter of paintings must make chef David Healey feel at home, as previously he was at Langan's Bistro. The menu evolves day to day but offers as many as a dozen dishes, written in English, and shows a liking for pairing fruit with meats. Soups such as broccoli or leek and almond have had a depth of flavour; terrines have tasted freshly made; dishes such as grilled salmon with a lemon, sorrel and tomato sauce or best end of veal with a Pommery sauce have been exactly timed. The French cheeses have been impeccably ripe, or else there are mousses and cheesecakes. Downstairs is a wine bar with the same menu. Wines are well spread, with the emphasis on the £7 to £9 range. House Vin de Pays de l'Aude is £5·50. CELLARMAN'S CHOICE: Sancerre, Clos du Chêne Marchand '86, £10·20.

CHEF: David Healey PROPRIETORS: G. Thomson, I. Thomson and A. Wood
OPEN: all week, exc Mon L, Sat L and Sun D MEALS: 12 to 3, 7 to 11
PRICES: £13 (£20), Set L £9·50 (£15) CARDS: Access, Amex, Visa
SEATS: 50. Private parties: 12 main room. Children's helpings (Sun L only). No pipes.
Wheelchair access (also WC). Air-conditioned

Hiders [12/20]

map 10

755 Fulham Road, SW6 5UU
01-736 2331   £18

An air of comfort and good living pervades here: the basement dining-room is reminiscent of an expensive yacht, and the atmosphere is as informal as the service is professional. While restaurants in the centre of town fall over themselves to flirt with fashion, the kitchen here gets quietly on with the job of cooking a modern menu: pigeon breast on salad leaves; ravioli with crab and ginger; monkfish and scallop with leeks and celeriac in beurre blanc. Although dishes sound fussy they work out simpler on the plate and the flavours are well judged: a Pernod and tarragon sauce with breast of chicken builds up gradually to a peak. Vegetables demonstrate how precise the cooking can be, and the service matches the assurance and confidence of the kitchen. Two dozen French wines are spread across vintages and prices, with house red and white at £5·95.

CHEFS: Paul Duvall and Andrew George PROPRIETORS: Richard and Hilary Griggs
OPEN: Mon to Sat, exc Sat L CLOSED: bank hols MEALS: 12.30 to 2.30, 7.30 to 11.30
PRICES: Set L and D from £13 (£18). Service 12.5%
CARDS: Access, Amex, Visa
SEATS: 70. Private parties: 40 main room. Children welcome. Wheelchair access

Hilaire [13/20]

map 12

68 Old Brompton Road, SW7 3LQ
01-584 8993   £19–£27

Simon Hopkinson, who made this pistachio-green French restaurant one of the most popular of the London listings, has gone to launch Terence Conran's new flagship in Sloane Avenue, but his replacement, Bryan Webb, earned his own rating at the becalmed Café Rouge. It is the most individualistic of all the Kennedy Brooks restaurants. The menu style retains its key points, such as good marinated herring and gravlax, and always a fish of the day, but Webb's instincts tend to be more modern than Hopkinson's, who in many ways is a traditionalist. Of early dishes under the new regime, there has been zippy gazpacho; excellent steak au poivre with chips; salmon neatly seared on one side and served with a tomato sauce laced with samphire. As before, meals are well balanced all the way through, and might end with the fashionable fruit terrine or the less fashionable crêpe with brandied apricots. The wine list is well chosen, but reflects South Kensington prices and tastes, which are not cheap.

CHEF: Bryan Webb PROPRIETORS: Kennedy Brooks plc
OPEN: Mon to Sat, exc Sat L MEALS: 12.30 to 2.30, 7.30 to 11
PRICES: Set L £13·50 (£19), Set D £21 (£27). Minimum £13·50 CARDS: Access, Amex, Carte Blanche, Diners, Visa
SEATS: 50. Private parties: 8 main room. Children's helpings. Air-conditioned

L'Hippocampe [11/20]

map 10

231A Munster Road, SW6 6DD
01-736 5588 and 4711

£10–£26

The violet-blue lighting glows in the night, giving the impression of an aquarium. This small modern fish restaurant is dominated by its bar. The menu is a well-thought-out formula of mostly pre-prepared starters and sweets which leaves the kitchen free to concentrate on its sauces and the timing of the fish: for instance, scallops in pastry with a beurre blanc; a range of cod, monkfish, sea-bass, red mullet, poached and sauced with saffron; sea-bass with a red wine sauce. Twenty-five wines fit the pattern, with only three reds, but a good choice around £10. House Muscadet is £5·50.

CHEF: Laurent Santerre PROPRIETORS: Pierre and Cathy Condou
OPEN: Mon to Sat, exc Sat L MEALS: 12.30 to 2.30, 7.30 to 11
PRICES: £16 (£23), Set L from £4·50 (£10), Set D from £18 (£26). Cover £1. Service 15%
CARDS: Access, Amex, Visa
SEATS: 25. 3 tables outside. Private parties: 12 main room. Children's helpings. Wheelchair access. Music

Ho-Ho [10/20]

map 10

20 High Road, South Woodford, E18 2QL
01-989 8021 and 1041

£9–£18

Some better-than-usual Peking/Szechuan food on the fringes of London is served at this one-time trattoria, now dominated by Samurai prints and photographs of old colonial China. The menu has its share of ginger and spring onions, and black-bean sauce, but there are less predictable items, such as lamb and cucumber broth, not often found in run-of-the-mill places. The freshness of the fish shows in the steamed scallops. Other good dishes have included crab and sweetcorn soup; garlicky egg-dipped fish; Manchurian lamb served with pickled vegetables; and bean curd with beef and chilli. The crispy duck comes with half a dozen pancakes. Griddle dishes are a feature. The wine list has a solid Alsace section to complement the spiciness. CELLARMAN'S CHOICE: Gewürztraminer '83 from Gisselbrecht, £8·25.

CHEF: Yuk Chu PROPRIETOR: Steve Man
OPEN: all week MEALS: 12 to 2.30, 6 to 11
PRICES: £10 (£18), Set L from £5 (£9), Set D from £11 (£16). Cover 50p. Service 12.5%
CARDS: Access, Amex, Diners, Visa
SEATS: 80. 2 tables outside. Private parties: 60 main room. Vegetarian meals. Children welcome. Wheelchair access (also WC). Music. Air-conditioned

Hoizin [10/20]   map 11

72–73 Wilton Road, SW1V 1DE
01-630 5107   £11–£17

The pastel, almost suburban décor evokes another second-generation Peking/Szechuan restaurant of the kind that now proliferates – indeed, there is one next door. But the Hoizin is unusual in that the menu stays in Canton and, uniquely, specialises in fish. Mr Tsang also owns a fishmonger's in Chinatown and a farm supplying Chinese-style vegetables. The 155-strong menu concentrates on fine prawn dishes; exotics like razor-fish; squid and chilli salad; steamed red snapper; spicy scallops. Other items like lotus-leaf rice and the stir-fried broccoli with ginger juice suggest the kitchen is more interested in cooking than is usually the case. Italian Chardonnay is £5·50.

CHEF: Mr Chan PROPRIETOR: Mr Tsang
OPEN: Mon to Sat MEALS: 12 to 2.30, 6 to 11.30
PRICES: £11 (£17), Set L £6·50 (£11), Set D £10 (£15). Service 12%
CARDS: Access, Amex, Visa
SEATS: 90. Private parties: 60 main room. Vegetarian meals. Children welcome. Wheelchair access. Music. Air-conditioned

Hollywood's [new entry, zero rated]   map 12

2 Hollywood Road, SW10 9HY
01-352 6884

This restaurant was sold as the Guide *went to press.*

Hung Toa [9/20] map 11

54 Queensway, W2 3RY
01-727 6017   £11–£18

This old-style Cantonese restaurant is singularly notable for the quality of its
roast meats – crispy roast pork, duck, chicken – available through the day only.
Combined with rice or noodles, they comprise perhaps the best cheap meal in
West London. The rest of the menu is less special. Tea.

CHEFS: Mr Wong and Mr Kiw Lun PROPRIETORS: Jeromglen Ltd
OPEN: all week MEALS: noon to 11pm
PRICES: £11 (£18), Set D £6·50 (£11). Service 10%
SEATS: 70. Private parties: 30 main room, 30 private room. Vegetarian meals. Children
welcome. Air-conditioned

Ikeda [10/20] map 13

30 Brook Street, W1Y 1AG
01-499 7145   £19–£40

The fifteen or so specials are thoughtfully written in Japanese characters to shield
innocent Western eyes from the horror of Tokyo prices. Set meals are less
rapacious. Two kitchen bars fill nearly half the space at this small restaurant and
provide demonstrations in the art of Japanese cooking. In essence this is Japanese
country cooking, less formalised than other London Japanese restaurants and
with some scope for innovation. Stir-fried asparagus, king prawns tempura,
grilled aubergine, and chicken yakitori, grilled in a silver foil oven and served
with a slurp of the soy sauce kept in a washing-up basin, all take shape in front of
diners. At the far end, the knife of the sushi chef wields elegant patterns for the
raw fish and vinegared rice. There are a few tables away from the action. Service
has become increasingly acclimatised to non-Japanese. Extras put up the
bill: house wine, for instance, is £9 a bottle.

CHEF/PROPRIETOR: S. Ikeda
OPEN: Mon to Fri MEALS: 12.30 to 2.30, 6.30 to 10.30
PRICES: £22 (£40), Set L from £9·50 (£19), Set D from £23 (£34). Cover 50p at L, £1 at D.
Service 15% CARDS: Access, Amex, Diners, Visa
SEATS: 25. Private parties: 30 main room. Vegetarian meals. No children under 10.
Wheelchair access. Music. Air-conditioned

Ikkyu [10/20] map 13

Basement, 67 Tottenham Court Road, W1P 9PA
01-636 9280   £8–£16

The sign and the entrance close to Goodge Street Tube Station hardly suggest a
restaurant at all, but go down the steep stairs into the basement and here is one

It is helpful if restaurateurs keep the office up to date with any changes.

Please keep the Guide *informed of any changes to the restaurants listed. Report forms
are at the back of the book.*

of the least expensive, most relaxed Japanese eating-places in the West End.
There are cheap set meals featuring fish with miso soup, rice and pickles, and the
scrawled, handwritten menu has a good range of sushi, sashimi and yakitori –
including chicken hearts, skin, asparagus with bacon, okura and squid.
Otherwise the range takes in rolled conger in seaweed, stewed potato with meat,
cucumber with moromi miso; grilled dry cuttlefish. Tofu is boiled with oyster
mushrooms in a pot, fried with ginger sauce or served cold. Whisky is sold by the
bottle, saké is £2·50 a small bottle, and green tea is free.

CHEF: M. Suzuki PROPRIETOR: M. Kawaguchi
OPEN: Mon to Fri, and Sun D MEALS: 12.30 to 2.30, 6 to 10.30
PRICES: £9 (£16), Set L and D from £4·20 (£8). Service 10%
CARDS: Access, Amex, Diners, Visa
SEATS: 65. Private parties: 70 main room. Vegetarian meals. Children welcome. Music.
Air-conditioned

Inigo Jones [15/20]

map 14

14 Garrick Street, WC2E 9BJ
01-836 6456 and 3223

£27–£48

Very expensive, but often very good: Inigo Jones has always been among
London's most affluent restaurants – even lunch can creep uncomfortably near
to £100 for two. But Paul Gayler's colourful dishes look the part. He is a master of
the visual. Some of the tastes dim in this striving for artistry, but Inigo borders
tantalisingly close to a rating of 16/20. A little more consistency of flavours
would tip the balance. At his best all the aspects of gastronomy come together, as
in a main dish in April – pigeon suprêmes, their juices mixed with cream and
sorrel for a sauce, a log pile of beetroot, another of French beans, a perfect circle
of dauphinoise potatoes, a scoop of carrot purée, all perfectly spaced on the plate.
The Shevelove Menu for lunch and pre-theatre dinner is excellent value for such
artistry compared to the prices of a *carte* that roams about from one fashion to
another (though there is a commendable vegetarian menu too) and might
profitably settle on one theme. But look at these: a terrine of artichoke, carrot and
foie gras with a sauce of red peppers; grey mullet with beurre blanc; a plate of
lamb's offals in a sticky (over-) reduced sauce; beef fillet with a red wine and
marrow sauce; duck thigh with onion marmalade. A sweet might be a small taste
of all the many fruit mousses that populate the menu, cheeses are from Androuët
in Paris. The wines are very expensive, upwards from £10·55 for the house
burgundy, but at last there are wines of quality in the £10 to £20 bracket.
CELLARMAN'S CHOICE: Ch. la Louvière '75, £23·15, and Chinon '78, £19·50.

CHEF: Paul Gayler
PROPRIETORS: Peter Ward, Jean Kaeser, William Chalmers and Paul Gayler
OPEN: Mon to Sat, exc Sat L MEALS: 12 to 2.30, 5.30 to 11.30
PRICES: £33 (£48), Set L and D £16·25 (£27). Cover £2 after 7pm. Service 15%
CARDS: Access, Amex, Diners, Visa
SEATS: 70. Private parties: 35 main room. Vegetarian meals. Children welcome. Smart dress
preferred. Air-conditioned

---

*'A very fragile and buttery square of flaky pastry, topped with an onion mixture with a
sliver of anchovy seems to be all the rage.'* (On eating in Gloucestershire)

Interlude [new entry, zero rated] map 14

7/8 Bow Street, WC2E 7AH
01-379 6859 and 6473   £14·95–£37

Taking over an established restaurant from as great a chef as Jean-Louis Taillebaud (last heard of in America) and running it along the same lines is a fraught business. The décor of the blinds and the wooden tables remains the same, as does the set-menu formula, though now there are four – the cheapest, the pre-theatre, is £14·95 including wine, the most expensive, the gastronomique, is £32. The lunch starts with a complimentary Pineau des Charentes. The menu is stylistically similar, too, with the emphasis on many sauces and quenelles, but the taste is markedly different and individual. The cooking of David Lawrence (who took over only at the start of 1987) has its own voice – witness a light pastry case of mussels, or an inventive salad of warm kidneys on frisée and dressed with orange, before fine main courses of panaché of shellfish or hare with spinach. Desserts are picturesque – strawberries arranged around the Villeroy and Boch floral plates with a coulis to one side, a sorbet to another, and a tuile of strawberries in the centre. The service is better than before. The wine list is a grand tour of major areas with some fairly grand prices, too – upwards from £9·50.

CHEF: David Lawrence PROPRIETORS: Interlude Restaurants Ltd
OPEN: Mon to Sat, exc Sat L CLOSED: Aug MEALS: 12.15 to 2.15, 6 to 11.30
PRICES: Set L £19·50 (£19·50), Set D £14·95 (£14·95) to £32 (£37). Service inc
CARDS: Access, Amex, Diners, Visa
SEATS: 50. Private parties: 24 main room. Vegetarian meals. Children welcome.
Air-conditioned

Jacques [12/20] map 11

130 Blackstock Road, Highbury Vale, N4 2DX
01-359 3410   £18–£24

Jacques Herbert dominates this wine bar and runs the show at his own pace. There's not much space, but the kitchen delivers. This is old-style French cooking that has no truck with new-fangled ideas about vegetarianism or healthy eating: magret of duck gets a hefty sauce of French cream and brandy; wild salmon is served in a pool of pink sauce made with Pineau des Charentes. And to finish there's rich chocolate charlotte with home-made custard. Sunday brunch with champagne is worth the £9·50. Around fifty Gallic wines; there's also a special list of twenty-year-old vintages. CELLARMAN'S CHOICE: Chinon, Les Gravières d'Amador, Couly-Dutheil '85, £9·25.

CHEF/PROPRIETOR: J. R. Herbert
OPEN: Tue to Sun, D only, and Sat L and Sun L CLOSED: 1 week at Christmas, 1 week Aug
MEALS: 12 to 2.30 (2 Sun), 6 to 10.45 (10 Sun)
PRICES: £18 (£24), Set D (served 6 to 7.30) £12·50 (£18) CARD: Access
SEATS: 35. 4 tables outside. Private parties: 8 main room. Children welcome. Wheelchair access (also WC). Music

Restaurants are checked every year and their entries rewritten. The restaurant scene changes very rapidly. Don't trust an out-of-date Guide.

Jams [13/20] map 13

42 Albemarle Street, W1X 3FE
01-499 8293 £27

Jonathan Waxman commutes between here and the parent restaurant in New York. He lays down the formula: charcoal-grilled (not mesquite, as in the US) centrepieces with light sauces and crowds of baby vegetables: grilled salmon with celery root and Pommery mustard; sea-bass with avocado, red onion and lime butter sauce; Barbary duck with hash browns, chillies and a duck stock sauce. The split-level dining-room is clean and modern – upstairs is an open window on the street at one end and an open-plan kitchen at the other, while the downstairs reminds one of a trattoria. Standards yoyo according to who's cooking. Starters are vivid, too, such as fine red pepper pancakes with crème fraîche and salmon caviare or deep-fried squid with chilli mayonnaise. The seasoning – as in a steak au poivre with zest of orange – is parallel to modern British cooking (evoking John Tovey more than anyone). Sweets are in the cake mould and can be superlative, especially pecan pie and lemon meringue. Good Californian wines, too, at a price. House California is £7. CELLARMAN'S CHOICE: Fetzer Chardonnay '85, £14·50.

CHEFS: Jonathan Waxman and Willis Baye PROPRIETOR: Jonathan Waxman
OPEN: Mon to Sat, exc Sat L MEALS: 12 to 2.30, 6.30 to 11
PRICES: £19 (£27). Service 15% CARDS: Access, Amex, Visa
SEATS: 90. Private parties: 75 main room. Vegetarian meals. Children welcome. Wheelchair access. Music. Air-conditioned

Jensen's [new entry, zero rated] map 14

6 Greek Street, W1V 5LA
01-437 2006 £23–£31

Jensen's is a deliberate attempt to set up a high-class European restaurant in the middle of Soho. The early days have been punctuated by some rather gauche touches, but the main thrust is that of a quality restaurant. Formerly the Old Budapest, the dining-room has been magically transformed into a grey elegance, almost a smoother version of La Bastide opposite (see entry). Menus abound: of the day, specialities of the day and a rambling French *carte* complete with long English explanations. There have been some good dishes beneath the show – a salmon fillet, cut across the bone and surrounded by diced green and yellow courgettes; calf's liver smothered in green peppercorns. The quality of the canapés and petits fours almost preclude a starter or sweet. Sorbets and ice-creams are excellent. The service is anxious and the wine list of a pedigree, though lacking the invention and calibre of some of Greek Street's other venues. More reports, please.

CHEF: Luc Ferrand PROPRIETORS: Mint Vale Ltd
OPEN: Mon to Sat, exc Sat L MEALS: 12 to 2.30, 6 to 11.30
PRICES: £22 (£31), Set L and D £16·95 (£23) CARDS: Access, Amex, Visa
SEATS: 33. Private parties: 10 main room. Vegetarian meals. Children's helpings. No children under 5. Smart dress preferred. No cigars/pipes. Wheelchair access. Music. Air-conditioned

Justin de Blank [10/20] map 13

54 Duke Street, W1M 5DS
01-629 3174   £12

Justin de Blank is to cheap eating out what the Roux brothers are to high-class
French cooking. This is perhaps his most accomplished outlet – high-quality food
served self-service. The secret is the use of proper ingredients: bread and
croissants from his own bakery; home-made sausages flavoured with sage and
parsley; Ayrshire bacon. The range of the cooking stretches beyond fine salads
into roulades and terrines. Typical of recommendations are pork casserole, red
pepper and watercress quiche, celery tart, and fruit brûlée. The main drawback is
the pressure on space at peak times. House Merlot and Chardonnay from
Bulgaria, £4·30.

CHEF: Robert Selick PROPRIETOR: Justin de Blank
OPEN: Mon to Sat, exc Sat D CLOSED: bank hols MEALS: 8.30 (9 Sat) to 3.30, 4.30 to 9
PRICES: £8 (£12)
SEATS: 60. Private parties: 14 main room, 8 and 14 private rooms. Vegetarian meals.
Children's helpings. Air-conditioned. Self-service

Kalamaras [11/20] map 11

76–78 Inverness Mews, W2 3JQ
01-727 9122   £19

Cheerful polyglot waitresses, seemingly in their dozens, inhabit the dimly lit
basements of both the restaurant – licensed – and, a few doors down the alley,
the smaller dining-room – unlicensed. Stelios Platonos has since the 1960s
(when he was in Queensway) provided some of the more ambitious Greek food in
London. The waitresses reel off the list of specials at an incomprehensible speed.
Listen for the suckling pig, grilled lamb, red mullet, and moussaka as centrepieces, with the more familiar lukanika sausages, filo pastries filled with spinach
and baklava. The twenty Greek wines can surprise, notably those from Boutari.
House Greek is £5·80.

CHEF/PROPRIETOR: Stelios Platonos
OPEN: Mon to Sat, D only CLOSED: bank hols MEALS: 7 to 12
PRICES: £10 (£19). Cover £1 CARDS: Access, Amex, Diners, Visa
SEATS: 96. Private parties: 12 main room, 16 and 28 private rooms. Vegetarian meals.
Children's helpings. Wheelchair access. Music. Air-conditioned

Kettners [10/20] map 14

29 Romilly Street, W1V 5TQ
01-437 6437   £15

The most elegant of pizza houses, housed in a historic, thirty-year-old Soho
dining-room, with an added champagne bar, and more modern monochromatic
dining at the back. The pizzas are by Pizza Express, of which this is the flagship –
Italian, freshly baked, generously covered. The Venice in Peril fund still receives
20p for each Veneziana sold – onions, capers, olives, pine-kernels, sultanas,
Mozzarella, tomato. There are fifteen other variations, and good reports also of

the hamburgers. Like much of Soho these days it can get crowded and noisy at theatre times. House Italian is £6·50.

PROPRIETOR: Mr Peter Boizot
OPEN: all week CLOSED: 25 Dec MEALS: 11am to midnight
PRICES: £10 (£15) CARDS: Access, Amex, Diners, Visa
SEATS: 200. Private parties: 50 private room. Vegetarian meals. Children welcome.
Wheelchair access. Music

▲ *Kingfisher, Halcyon Hotel* [new entry, zero rated] map 11

81–82 Holland Park, W11 3RZ
01-221 5411 £20–£28

A sumptuously cosmopolitan conversion has turned these two late-Victorian houses into a lavish new hotel of similar style to, say, Blakes or the Capital (see entries). Visual impact is all. The menu is in the same vein: a star-shaped salad of langoustines with slices of artichoke, bacon shavings and a sprinkling of dill comes with a separate jug of hollandaise. It doesn't all taste dramatic, but the open-mindedness is admirable – black (grey, in fact) tagliatelle with scallops; spinach and Parmesan soup; venison with salsify and parsley purée; espresso coffee ice-cream with chocolate sauce and caramelised almonds. Service is well trained and polite. There are some fine Italian wines on the reasonably priced list. CELLARMAN'S CHOICE: Dolcetto del Piemonte, Ascheri '85, £8·75. More reports, please.

CHEF: James Robins PROPRIETORS: Halcyon Hotel Corp.
OPEN: all week MEALS: 12.30 to 2.30, 7.30 to 11.30
PRICES: £19 (£28), Set L from £13·50 (£20), Snacks from £8. Service 15%
CARDS: Access, Amex, Carte Blanche, Diners, Visa
SEATS: 66. 6 tables outside. Private parties: 60 main room. Children's helpings. Jacket and tie. Music. Air-conditioned
ACCOMMODATION: 44 rooms, all with bath/shower. Rooms for disabled. Lift. B&B £103 to £158. Deposit: 1 night's stay. Children welcome. Baby facilities. Afternoon teas. Sauna. Air-conditioning. TV. Phone. Scenic. Confirm by 6

Korea House [10/20] map 13

10 Lancashire Court, New Bond Street, W1Y 9AD
01-493 1340 £11–£20

The great advantage of this Korean restaurant in an alley off New Bond Street is the ground-floor patio garden. Plants creep and climb everywhere, there's lots of light, and it suits perfectly the al fresco, barbecue style of bulgogi. Downstairs is a dark, pink dining-room with lots of Korean artefacts but also a massive open fireplace, big solid doors and heavy wooden panelling. It's a curious collision of cultures. The menu is long and adventurous and the Chinese influence shows in deep-fried oysters, the hot-pot dishes, the beef dumplings in soup, the steamed scallops with ginger and spring onion, and the boiled belly-pork. Bulgogi is chicken, pork and sometimes venison, as well as beef, and is cooked in a heavy ribbed pan; the quality of the meat is excellent. Also worth trying are bin dae gok (bean-flour pancakes filled with pork and vegetables) and yuk kwe – strips of raw marinated beef on a bed of grated pears. Kimchee is potent, rice is sticky. Set lunches are good value; other meals can be expensive. Barley tea is free. Ginseng brandy or ginseng vodka are offered as liqueurs.

CHEF: Mr Hur PROPRIETOR: Y. S. Rhee
OPEN: Mon to Sat MEALS: 12 to 3, 6 to 11
PRICES: £9 (£17), Set L from £6 (£11), Set D from £14·50 (£20). Service 12.5%
CARDS: Access, Amex, Diners, Visa
SEATS: 100. Private parties: 72 main room, 30 private room. Vegetarian meals. Children's helpings. Smart dress preferred. Music. Air-conditioned

Lakorn Thai [10/20] map 11

197–199 Rosebery Avenue, EC1R 4TJ
01-837 5048 £12–£15

Perfectly placed for a meal before or after Sadlers Wells. Its popularity has resulted in the opening of a new first-floor dining-room. The menu, more than a hundred items strong, has a whole page of vegetarian dishes, from hot-and-sour bamboo shoot salad to fried noodles with soya sauce and vegetables. Soups are a highlight; otherwise the range includes good poo pahd curry with crab claws; beef with Kaffir lime leaves and chillies; chicken with red wine sauce; and peanut cake. Drink Singha Thai beer.

CHEF: N. Bhumitchitr PROPRIETOR: Stephen Binns
OPEN: Mon to Sat, exc Sat L MEALS: 12.30 to 3, 6 to 11.30
PRICES: £8 (£15), Set L £7·50 (£12). Service 10% CARDS: Access, Amex, Visa
SEATS: 77. Private parties: 30 main room, 40 private room. Vegetarian meals. Children's helpings. Wheelchair access. Music

Lal Qila [12/20] map 13

117 Tottenham Court Road, W1P 9HL
01-387 4570 £16

Low-key surroundings of smoky glass mirrors and moghul miniatures are a deliberate antithesis of the old-style British curry house. This is still the most consistent food to be found in London's new-wave Indian restaurants. Service is unpredictable but seems to have picked up a faster pace. The kitchen cooks a manageable menu of classy North Indian dishes. Tandooris and tikkas are excellent, subtly marinated, tender and crisp on the outside. Curries, such as kahrai murgh and rogan josh, are subtly spiced, and vegetables show the capabilities of the kitchen: spinach comes as a rich but light firm purée, little potatoes are cooked in their skins with fenugreek and ginger, firm pieces of smoky, pulpy aubergine are served in a strong sauce. Basmati rice is delicately handled, and the best of the breads is the puffy peshwari nan stuffed with raisins and almonds. Good kulfi and rasmalai. Flashy cocktails and Kingfisher beer to drink.

CHEF: Ayub Ali PROPRIETORS: Lal Qila Ltd
OPEN: all week CLOSED: 25 and 26 Dec MEALS: 12 to 3, 6 to 11.30
PRICES: £9 (£16). Service 15% CARDS: Access, Amex, Diners, Visa
SEATS: 68. Private parties: 68 main room. Vegetarian meals. Children's helpings. Jacket and tie. Music. Air-conditioned

Langan's Bistro [12/20]

map 13

26 Devonshire Street, W1N 1RJ
01-935 4531   £18

Peter Langan's bistro is almost the blueprint for the franchised Bar and Grill format spreading nationwide (those still in his control, such as the one at Coggeshall (see entry), being perceptibly better than those out of it). The décor here has been smartened up, with linen replacing the brown paper cloths. The Langan fascination with art looms large on the walls. The menu is a sensible well-handled rendition of modern dishes: smoked mackerel pâté; gratin of mussels; goats' cheese salad; veal with Pommery mustard and tarragon. Of couse, the lauded chocolate pudding earmarks the desserts. It is good value for the neighbourhood, and, that rare restaurant virtue, consistent. House French is £7·35.

CHEF: Mark Sage PROPRIETOR: Peter Langan
OPEN: Mon to Sat, exc Sat L MEALS: 12.30 to 2.30, 7 to 11.30
PRICES: £12 (£18). Cover 75p. Service 10% CARD: Amex
SEATS: 40. Private parties: 8 main room. Vegetarian meals. Children welcome. Wheelchair access. Air-conditioned

Langan's Brasserie [14/20] ✗

map 13

Stratton Street, W1X 5SD
01-493 6437   £21

The menu moves from day to day. It takes its inspiration from the same kind of classical hotel cooking that is found at the Connaught, which at its worst – and Langan's is not beyond passing out a dud dish or two – is the ubiquitous brown sauce, but at its best means fragile croustade d'oeufs de caille (indeed better than at the Connaught, for here it is one large pastry sealed with hollandaise) or the soufflé of spinach with anchovy sauce or a turbot à l'anglaise. The English roasts are unadorned – duck and chicken are comfortably reliable. Vegetables are abundant and al dente and the sweets have more than their taste of the tradition . . . rice pudding, treacle tart. Look also for the splendid Gospel Green, a new English cheese from Sussex. The customers are as distracting as the paintings, and except for the glacial moments when the entire dining-room starts to check to see who else is there, the place reverberates. Richard Shepherd has been a regular force in the dining-room but is moving into other areas – he has a restaurant in the Quinta de Lago in the Algarve and is looking to develop Odins too. A new generation is asserting itself in the kitchen. Vin de la maison is £5·50, champagnes from £25 to £42 for Krug Grande Cuvée. Reports on progress on all fronts, please.

CHEF: Richard Shepherd
PROPRIETORS: Peter Langan, Michael Caine and Richard Shepherd
OPEN: Mon to Sat, exc Sat L MEALS: 12.30 to 2.45, 7 to 11.45 (8 to 12.45 Sat)
PRICES: £14 (£21). Service 12.5% CARDS: Access, Amex, Diners, Visa
SEATS: 200. Private parties: 12 main room. Children's helpings. Wheelchair access. Music. Air-conditioned

It is always advisable to book a restaurant in advance.

The Lantern [9/20]

map 11

23 Malvern Road, NW6 5PS
01-624 1796   £11

The light that launched a chain of now six inexpensive restaurants. This was the first and it established the formula: a cramped, atmospheric, 1960s bistro with 1970s dishes like crab profiteroles, poussin dijonnaise, breast of duck with yoghurt, and excellent prices. Pigeon at 606 Fulham Road SW6 (736 4618) and La Cloche at 304 Kilburn High Road NW6 (328 0302) are almost identical, newer branches more gimmicky: at Just Around the Corner, 446 Finchley Road NW3 (431 3300), you pay as much as you think the meal is worth; Casino, 77 Lower Sloane Street SW1 (730 3313), is open twenty-four hours a day; the newest, Mercury, 140 Upper Street N1 (354 4088), has a 'nutritionally' balanced menu upstairs.

CHEF/PROPRIETOR: Peter Ilic
OPEN: all week MEALS: 12 to 3, 7 to 11
PRICES: £7 (£11). Service 10%
SEATS: 75. Private parties: 20 main room, 35 private room. Vegetarian meals. Children's helpings. Music

Last Days of the Raj [11/20]

map 14

42 Dean Street, W1V 5AP
01-439 0972 and 734 3339   £16

All the opulent trappings of the Indian new wave are here: smoked-glass windows, a mirrored cocktail bar, and more mirrors at the far end of the dining-room to make it look bigger than it is. The cooking is creditable North Indian, although it lacks the fine touch and subtlety of comparable places such as Lal Qila (see entry). The menu has one or two unusual dishes such as aushak (leeks in pastry with minced meat), but mostly it stays with the likes of murgh makhani, rogan josh and chingri bhuna. Tandooris and tikkas sizzle on their serving-dishes, and fried Basmati rice is heavily spiked with cloves and cumin seeds. Waiters dressed in the regimental green tunics of Amin Ali's army patrol the restaurant slowly, trying to be helpful. Cocktails, Kingfisher beer and house wine at £1·50 a glass.

CHEF: Mashur Miah PROPRIETORS: Last Day of the Empire Ltd
OPEN: all week MEALS: 12 to 3, 6 to 11.30
PRICES: £10 (£16). Service inc CARDS: Access, Amex, Carte Blanche, Diners, Visa
SEATS: 120. Private parties: 120 main room. Vegetarian meals. Children's helpings.
Wheelchair access (also WC). Music. Air-conditioned

Launceston Place [13/20]

map 12

1A Launceston Place, W8 5RL
01-937 6912   £14–£21

Launceston has the elegance other brasseries lack. The style is of a restaurant. The very shape of the rooms in this old house lends a sense of importance. They are instantly familiar from TV period dramas. The tables are small and crammed in, but neatly laid with elegant cutlery and glasses. The prices reflect this lack of space. The menu is a persuasive explanation of modern British cooking – not always carried off with the same élan because the energy here comes from the front of house in the form of owners Nick Smallwood and Simon Slater. The menu's inspiration is with the markets: scallop and artichoke soup; freshly made cannelloni filled with crab; ceviche in the starters in June. Main courses are generous: duck, both leg and breast, in a little honey stock reduction; beef in a sticky shallot reduction with caramelised onions; dainty roundels of pink pigeon in a tayberry sauce. A speciality sums it up: grilled calf's liver with bubble and squeak and red onion marmalade. Sweets bring back such traditions as stewed rhubarb with clotted cream as well as elegantly presented praline ices. The bill is helped on its journey upwards by extra charges for vegetables and for potatoes. Before eight o'clock the good-value lunch menu operates, which is a bargain. The wines are intriguing – Côtes du Rhône '74, from Jaboulet, at £12.50, or Californian and Australian to contrast with the classic French regions. The house claret is excellent at £6·95.

CHEF: Philip McMullen PROPRIETORS: Nick Smallwood and Simon Slater
OPEN: all week, exc Sat L and Sun D MEALS: 12.30 to 2.30, 7 to 11.30
PRICES: £14 (£21), Set L and D from £8·50 (£14) CARDS: Access, Visa
SEATS: 55. Private parties: 25 main room, 12 private room. Vegetarian meals. Children's helpings (L only). No pipes in dining-room. Wheelchair access. Air-conditioned

Laurent [9/20]   map 11

428 Finchley Road, NW2 2HY
01-794 3603   £14

Laurent Farrugia's couscous has earned itself such a reputation that it is now the only main course on offer. There are three versions: vegetarian, complet, and royal, which includes a mixed grill. On either side there is brique à l'oeuf (a crisp deep-fried pancake filled with egg) and ices or crêpe suzette. The décor is similarly unabashed, with only candles on the tables for decoration. M. Farrugia recommends the Moroccan red Chantebled or Algerian Coteaux de Mascara at £6 to accompany.

CHEF/PROPRIETOR: Laurent Farrugia
OPEN: all week, exc Sun D CLOSED: 1 week July, 2 weeks Aug MEALS: 12 to 2, 6 to 11
PRICES: £9 (£14) CARDS: Access, Visa
SEATS: 38. Private parties: 50 main room. Vegetarian meals. Children's helpings

Leek's Fish Bar [9/20]   map 10

23 Lavender Hill, SW11 5QW
01-228 9460   £13

This up-market chippy – a sign of Clapham's new-found wealth – is equipped with bistro-style check cloths. Deep-fried cod and haddock are supplemented by a steamed fish of the day and traditional puddings. There are good soup and fishcakes, too. House French is £5·25.

Reports on good shops, hotels and cafes in your area are welcome.

CHEF: H. Reyes PROPRIETOR: Rita Leek
OPEN: Mon to Sat, D only MEALS: 5.30 to 10.45
PRICES: £8 (£13)
SEATS: 70. Private parties: 20 main room. Children's helpings. Wheelchair access

Lemonia [10/20]   map 11

154 Regent's Park Road, NW1 8XN
01-586 7454   £13

Although it gets classified among the Greek-Cypriot restaurants of Camden
Town, George Ioannou's taverna is in the more gentrified Primrose Hill and is
almost smart enough to be called a restaurant. The meze offers the same kind of
value as the run-down, shabbier kebab houses to the south, and the quality of
the cooking has perked up after a poor patch which led to its omission last year.
Chicken shashlik and kleftiko are recommended, and there are interesting daily
dishes such as skate or lamb with beans. The meze comes in erratic waves: fine
dips with hot pitta bread; then sausages and grilled halloumi cheese; then deep-
fried fresh squid rings, mushrooms à la grecque and spana kopita; finally kebabs,
cutlets, more sausages and Feta cheese salad. Good coffee. Service is leisurely.
House French is £6 a litre, retsina £5 a bottle.

CHEF: George Ioannou PROPRIETOR: Anthony Evangelou
OPEN: Mon to Sat, D only CLOSED: 2 weeks Aug MEALS: 6 to 11.30
PRICES: £7 (£13)
SEATS: 85. Private parties: 12 main room. Vegetarian meals. Children welcome. Wheelchair
access (also WC). Music. Air-conditioned

Lena's [10/20]   map 10

196 Lavender Hill, SW11 1JA
01-228 3735   £11–£22

There has been a profusion of Thai restaurants in the suburbs in the last two
years. This is a neat, box-shaped teak and tiled dining-room run with charm. The
menu is concise, specialising in fine steamboat dishes and a relative imbalance
towards meat. The cooking is accurate – spring rolls, rice and satay are well
done, but the small portions push up the bill rapidly. House wine is £5·85.

CHEF: B. Limnamkam PROPRIETORS: K. Limnamkam and M. Pearson
OPEN: all week, exc Sun L and Mon L MEALS: 12 to 2.45, 6.30 to 11.30
PRICES: £13 (£22), Set L from £5·50 (£11). Cover 75p at D. Service 12%
CARDS: Access, Amex, Diners, Visa
SEATS: 50. Private parties: 45 main room. Vegetarian meals. Children's helpings. Music.
Air-conditioned

Lilly's [new entry, zero rated]   map 11

6 Clarendon Road, Holland Park, W11 3AA
01-727 9359   £25

The stated aim of this cream and yellow wine bar/restaurant is to serve dishes
using little cream, butter and alcohol. The puritanism can run through the
courses with a vengeance, and some dishes cry out for a little seasoning. The

difficulty with this kind of cooking is that it requires not just technical excellence but also a deep understanding of how flavours work. When it comes off, it can be striking: venison fillet, roasted, cut in four, arranged lazily on a pastry tart base with a smear of game pâté and a tablespoon of good stock for sauce. Some exotic ingredients and eclectic ideas fill out the menu – dishes like smoked sturgeon, and lobster satay. Fine roast woodcock and game pie reassure where some of the newer ideas do not. Summer pudding in February seems a step in the wrong direction. The wine list has been put together with much imagination. House wine is £4·95. CELLARMAN'S CHOICE: Australian Chardonnay, Rosemount '86, £9·40. More reports, please.

CHEF: J. Roger Jones PROPRIETORS: Dr Peter and Mrs C. Lillywhite
OPEN: all week CLOSED: Aug MEALS: 12 to 2.45, 7 to 11.15
PRICES: £18 (£25) CARDS: Access, Amex, Diners, Visa
SEATS: 32. Private parties: 40 main room. Children welcome. Music

Lindsay House [new entry, zero rated] map 14

21 Romilly Street, W1V 5TG
01-439 0450 £16–£28

Lindsay House is an almost identical twin to the English House and the English Garden in Chelsea. Reacting against the monopoly of blasé French cooking, their restaurants are conceived as forays into the virtues of traditional English cooking which predates much of the French School. They unashamedly promote plain roasts and hearty puddings. Instead of contemporary fashions, they prefer seventeenth-century obscure methods and recipes. The irony is that much of the early good impression here has been from the quality of the French-style saucing. The competition in this part of Soho, under the shadow of St Anne's Church and a hundred Chinese restaurants, may have given the restaurant an edge on its established forerunners, which rely heavily on tourists. Lindsay's décor is oppressively like the first day of the Liberty sale, a baroque symphony of reds and greens, full of flowing curtains and wall drapery. Rich oil paintings affirm the Englishness of the occasion by depicting hunting scenes and portraits of fat horses with their owners. The frilliness is so much that one almost expects Elizabethan wenches to come and serve tankards of ale followed by lusty renditions of *Greensleeves*. Instead, there are Chopin waltzes in the background. The ladies' lavatory features two Venus shell handbasins and glorious red and orange wallpaper showing an army of parrots in a jungle. Wrought-iron bars surround the room, all painted in gold; they rise to curve and meet at the top, serving to entrap the onlooker in a gilded cage. The parrots stare demurely while noses are powdered. The menu has eight starters, ten main courses and eight puddings. Hannah Glasse's stewed scollops with oranges arrive in a superb cream and onion sauce sharpened with the zest and whole segments; Brie (why Brie?) Favors are wrapped in crisp flaking pastry on a tomato coulis. Main courses can be Southdown rack of lamb sealed in the same type of pastry as the Brie, or else a straight fish pie. Sweets like syllabub and summer pudding have not shown the same class. Service is courteous, English and charming. The wine list is long, but shows little of interest under £15 except for a few token bottles of Montagny, Sancerre and lesser-known *petits chateaux*. House French is £7·50. More reports, please.

CHEF: Paul Hodgson PROPRIETORS: Roger Wren and Malcolm Livingston
OPEN: all week MEALS: 12.30 to 2.30, 6 to 12.30 (12 to 2, 7 to 10 Sun)
PRICES: £21 (£28), Set L £12·50 (£16). Service inc CARDS: Access, Amex, Diners, Visa
SEATS: 35. Private parties: 40 main room, 6 and 14 private rooms. Vegetarian meals.
Children welcome. Music. Air-conditioned

London Chinatown [10/20]

map 14

27 Gerrard Street, W1V 7LP
01-437 3186 £10·50 – £20

One of what seems like a pair but are in fact rival restaurants side by side on
Gerrard Street, one called Chinatown and this one, London Chinatown. The
décor in both might be identical – westernised, pastels and light, and very much
second-generation Chinese. Dim-sum are served throughout the day and have
been freshly made. The roast lacquered duck served hot or cold is exemplary and
as good as anywhere. The more Eastern-favoured dishes, such as chicken and
salted fish casserole, belly-pork with yams, or sizzling beef with preserved, salted
and sour vegetables, have lacked precision if not guts. But the sea-bass with
ginger and spring onions has been excellent. It appears to be on the up in an area
not short of Chinese eating – fifty-five alternatives in a hundred yards or so.
House wine is £5.

PROPRIETOR: L. S. Man
OPEN: all week MEALS: noon to 11.30pm (11am to 11pm Sun)
PRICES: £14 (£20), Set D from £13 (£21) for two. Service 10% CARDS: Access, Amex, Visa
SEATS: 200. Private parties: 200 main room, 40 private room. Vegetarian meals. Children
welcome. Air-conditioned

Lou Pescadou [10/20]

map 11

241 Old Brompton Road, SW5 9HP
01-370 1057 £19

Out of the same aquarium as La Croisette, Le Suquet and Le Quai St Pierre (see
entries), but less expensive, more relaxed and no booking. It serves fast food,
South-of-France-style: pasta, pizzas, and pissaladière as well as fresh fish,
delivered regularly from Brittany. As a rule stay with the simplest items – the
platters of fresh shellfish, and main dishes without a sauce. House wine is £6·90
per bottle.

CHEF: Laurent David PROPRIETORS: Oakhelm Ltd
OPEN: all week MEALS: 12 to 3, 7 to 12
PRICES: £13 (£19). Cover 90p CARDS: Access, Amex, Diners, Visa
SEATS: 50. 7 tables outside. Children welcome. Wheelchair access. Music

Lowiczanka [10/20]

map 10

238 – 264 King Street, W6 0RS
01-741 3225 £15

On the first floor of the Polish Social and Cultural Centre, the largest in the UK, a
modern, rather ugly building, the restaurant is decorated in blacks and salmon
pinks and is probably the best place to eat Polish cooking. It compares well with

the competition – Daquise at South Kensington is under new owners, the Ognisko Polski in Exhibition Road tends to the relatively expensive and stodgy, although the new Gentry at 253 High Street, Acton, attached to a baker's, has been good when not doing Continental dishes. Not all the Polish on the menu here represents Polish dishes, but beyond the prawn cocktails are to be found bigos, tripe, stuffed cabbage, wild mushrooms in season, and fine gateaux. Some of the luke-warm boiled potatoes are probably authentic too. On Fridays and Saturdays a trio of drums, piano and guitar plays melodies of Old Poland, and, when the lights dim, the vodka flows, the tango starts up, and it at last becomes, for a few moments, another world.

CHEF: Mrs Mifniark PROPRIETOR: Mr Mifniark
OPEN: all week, exc Tue D
MEALS: 12.30 to 3, 6 to 10 (9.30 Mon and Sun, 10.30 Fri, 11 Sat)
PRICES: £10 (£15). Minimum £6 Fri D and Sat D CARDS: Amex, Diners, Visa
SEATS: 80. 2 tables outside. Private parties: 100 main room, 50 private room. Vegetarian meals. Children welcome. Wheelchair access (also WC). Music

Ma Cuisine [16/20]

map 12

113 Walton Street, SW3 2JY
01-584 7585

£25

There are two things to know about this restaurant. The first is that Guy Mouilleron has been cooking again. He is undoubtedly one of the best French chefs in London, able to express himself though a *carte* that mixes bourgeois and modern with equal verve. The second is that by current standards it is excellent value. It is, of course, one of London's smallest dining-rooms. The terrines and pâtés still festoon the table by the bow window. The menu is still French to the hilt, designed for all seasons not just in the choice of the main ingredients but also in the spikes of seasoning thrown in – anis, juniper, Drambuie. Each day also brings the specials of the market, usually extremely good fish. The combinations lend the menu an identity – both duck breast and liver together on a salad as a starter or else gelatinous pig's trotter stuffing a breast of chicken with a grain mustard sauce. The seven fish dishes can be starters or main courses. Rumours of sales have consistently led to nothing, and the break while M. Aubertin took over for a short time seems to have served only to invigorate M. Mouilleron. The wine list is fittingly strong in clarets and burgundies. House French is £9·95.

CHEF/PROPRIETOR: Guy Mouilleron
OPEN: Mon to Fri MEALS: 12.30 to 2.30, 7.30 to 11
PRICES: £15 (£25) CARDS: Amex, Diners
SEATS: 32. Children's helpings. No pipes in dining-room. Wheelchair access (also WC)

Magno's [12/20]

map 14

65A Long Acre, WC2E 9JH
01-836 6077

 £12–£24

No longer a brasserie but a full-blown restaurant. But at least the rise in prices has been matched by an improvement in the quality of the ingredients. The greens and creams of the décor have barely changed, but the staff are organised. Some dishes still straddle the divide – smoked pork with green lentils, pike sausage – but recently the cooking has swayed into a more modern style, with good breast of duck with its own stock in a pancake, or a gratin of shrimps and scallops. The pre-theatre menu is especially good value. The wine policy has similarly gone up a notch, with fine Burgundy, impressive claret, an Australian Chardonnay from Wynns, and CELLARMAN'S CHOICE: Mâcon-Loché, Domaine Mathias '84, £9·75, and Crozes-Hermitage, Jaboulet '82, £9·65.

CHEF: Gilles Feougier   PROPRIETORS: E. Coliadis and A. Wastell
OPEN: Mon to Sat, exc Sat L   CLOSED: 24 Dec to 2 Jan   MEALS: 12 to 2.30, 6 to 11.30
PRICES: £16 (£24), Set D £8·45 (£12). Cover 75p. Service 12.5% alc
CARDS: Access, Amex, Diners, Visa
SEATS: 50. Private parties: 60 main room. Vegetarian meals. Children welcome. Wheelchair access. Music

Malabar   [10/20]

map 11

27 Uxbridge Street, W8 7TQ
01-727 8800

£14–£17

The atmosphere is that of a bazaar, and the style is Indian home cooking, with some dishes not normally found in run-of-the-mill Indian restaurants. Charcoal-grilled chicken livers and deep-fried prawns in lentil batter appear among the starters; green bananas and pumpkin feature as vegetables. Otherwise the menu takes in lamb korma, chicken dhansak, and prawns masala. On Fridays there's a fish curry – such as grey mullet, eel or pomfret – and Sunday lunch is a buffet for £5 a head. Drink lassi or Kingfisher beer.

PROPRIETORS: Jo Chalmers and Anil Bist
OPEN: all week   CLOSED: 1 week Aug, 4 days at Christmas
MEALS: 12 to 3, 6 to 11.30
PRICES: £10 (£17), Set L and D £19 (£28) for two. Cover 50p. Service 12.5%
CARDS: Access, Visa
SEATS: 56. Private parties: 12 main room. Vegetarian meals. Children welcome

Mandeer   [10/20]

map 13

21 Hanway Place, W1P 9DG
01-323 0660

£10–£11

Uncompromising Indian vegetarian food is served in this dark basement dining-room not far from Tottenham Court Road. That means no fish, no eggs, lots of tofu, unpolished brown rice, even some dishes made without spices, garlic or onions. The owners say that vegetables are cooked according to the principles of Ayurveda – the ancient Indian science of life. The menu takes in bhajias, pani puri, dosai, puffed lotus savoury, and all kinds of curried vegetables and pulses from bhindis and aubergines to chunks of sun-dried lentils with onions or sev usher – dried yellow peas with vermicelli and green chutney topped with yoghurt. Five thalis. Bargain self-service lunches in the Ravi Shankar Hall. Licensed.

'Our Christmas treat this year would be to sample the menu gastronomique instead of taking ourselves to the opera.'   (On eating in London)

CHEF: Mr Daudbhai PROPRIETORS: Mr and Mrs Patel
OPEN: Mon to Sat CLOSED: bank hols MEALS: 12 to 2.30, 6 to 10.15 (10.30 Fri and Sat)
PRICES: £7 (£11), Set L and D from £5·75 (£10). Minimum £5. Service 10%
CARDS: Access, Amex, Diners, Visa
SEATS: 75. Private parties: 100 main room. Vegetarian meals. Children's helpings.
No-smoking area. Music. Self-service at L

---

(1) Maroush [10/20]   map 11

21 Edgware Road, W2 2JH
01-723 0773   £18–£21

(2) Maroush II [10/20]   map 12

38 Beauchamp Place, SW3 1NV
01-581 5434   £22–£27

This pair of Lebanese restaurants provides fine meze throughout the day and into
the small hours. Marble Arch is the more souk-like and marginally cheaper,
while Beauchamp Place is glitzy, with mirrors and a fountain. Starters and
sweets provide the major interest. Main dishes of kebabs or grilled fish are of good
quality, but the dish of the day is likely to hold more culinary interest. The cellar
has vintage Lebanese wines from '64, '68 and '71, but alcohols boost the bill
substantially. Used, as the Lebanese do, as a cafe rather than a restaurant in the
European sense, there is no reason to spend overly despite minimum charges of
£7 at Edgware Road and £10 at Beauchamp Place.

PROPRIETOR: Mr M. C. Abouzaki
OPEN: all week MEALS: (1) noon to 2am; (2) noon to 5am
PRICES: (1) £11 (£19), Set L from £10 (£18), Set D from £12 (£21). Cover £1. Minimum £7;
(2) £11 (£22), Set L from £12 (£23), Set D from £15 (£27). Cover £1·50. Service 15%
CARDS: Access, Amex, Diners, Visa
SEATS: (1) 80. Private parties: 60 main room, 60 private room; (2) 80. Private parties: 50
main room, 30 private room. Vegetarian meals. Children's helpings. Smart dress preferred.
Music. Air-conditioned

Martin's [13/20]   map 11

239 Baker Street, NW1 6XE
01-935 3130 and 0997   £21–£23

Transplanted from Ifield Road, where it was becalmed without a lunch trade,
Martin Caldicott, furnished with money from customers under the Business
Expansion Scheme, reopened in reasonably spectacular aplomb in the old Bill
Bentley's premises at the Regent's Park end of Baker Street. The same peach pink
dominates but is eased by a domed conservatory-style ceiling and vivid Ting
prints. The menus have their own original paintings, too. In terms of décor it is in
the top league, elegant without going over the top. The menu is held on a
sensibly tight financial rein, which makes it one of the better-value restaurants of
its ilk. There is a sensible show of grills as well as sauces. Notable dishes have
been the warm mousse of mushrooms redolent of morels, and excellent venison
noisettes with poached bone-marrow, roast garlic and a profound stock juice.
Touches like cabbage diced and wrapped in cabbage leaf impress, gratin of warm
fruits would impress more if there were less citrus and apple. Fine cheeses.

Interesting wines, with house selections sensibly split with offers at £6, £9 and £12 before a more complete assemblage of well-chosen but expensive clarets and half a dozen dessert wines in halves from £6 to £18.

CHEF: Robert Hendry PROPRIETORS: Scott Salisbury Ltd
OPEN: Mon to Sat, exc Sat L MEALS: 12 to 2.30, 6 to 11
PRICES: £17 (£23), Set L £15·50 (£21), Set D £16·50 (£22). Service 15%
CARDS: Access, Amex, Diners, Visa
SEATS: 60. Private parties: 16 private room. Children welcome. Wheelchair access. Music. Air-conditioned

La Mascotte [10/20]   map 10

54 Cricklewood Lane, NW2 1HG
01-452 1299   £13–£16

This oblong little French restaurant run by two brothers is notable for its friendliness and good value. The menu is short, comforting and deals in the kind of dishes we knew before *nouvelle cuisine* with varying amounts of skill. Good soups; marmite of fish; cheeses. Some of the main dishes, such as chicken in wine, cream and thyme, or mignon de boeuf, could use a little more resolution, but there is no arguing with the set-price menu. Twenty French wines from £5·75. CELLARMAN'S CHOICE: Roc de Cailloux, Buzet '82, £7·25.

CHEF: Phillip Kanoun PROPRIETORS: Rachish and Phillip Kanoun
OPEN: Tue to Sun, D only, and Sun L MEALS: 12 to 2.30, 7 to 11
PRICES: £10 (£16), Set L and D £8·50 (£13). Cover 80p CARDS: Access, Amex, Visa
SEATS: 40. Private parties: 40 main room. Vegetarian meals. No children under 5. Music

Mayflower [11/20]   map 14

68–70 Shaftesbury Avenue, W1V 7DF
01-734 9207   £13–£17

The two best Chinese restaurants on Shaftesbury Avenue (see also Mr Tang) stand directly opposite one another. The Mayflower is moody, dark and like a secret world. The long Cantonese menu has inexpensive soups, bean-curd dishes and congees; there are also unusual hot-pots; stewed yam with coconut chicken; belly-pork with plums; fish lips; and ox-mallow. Fish is a strong point: seafood and bean-curd soup is generously filled with sole, while crisply battered squid is served, for contrast, with scallops. One-plate rice and noodle dishes are not available between 5 and 11 in the evening, when it gets very busy and the set meals come into their own. Service can be brusque.

CHEF: F. Chung PROPRIETOR: Patrick Tsang
OPEN: all week CLOSED: 25 and 26 Dec MEALS: noon to 3.30am
PRICES: £12 (£17), Set D from £8·50 (£13). Service 10%
CARDS: Access, Amex, Diners, Visa
SEATS: 140. Private parties: 40 main room, 20, 30 and 40 private rooms. Vegetarian meals. Children welcome. Music. Air-conditioned

'The hostess dressed like a female lion-tamer to charm the business tycoons.' (On eating in Hampshire)

Le Mazarin [15/20]

map 11

30 Winchester Street, SW1V 4NZ
01-828 3366   £22

A gaudy and untypical Mexican-style bandana announces the presence of René
Bajard in a basement catacomb in the outlying regions of Sloane-Land. The
dining-area is a cavernous set of interconnecting rooms in a confused muddle off
a small corridor into which tables have had to be put to meet the demand. These
are ones to avoid. Mirrors give some sense of style and space, reflecting the
Scarfean prints along the off-pink walls. For this quality of French cooking the set
meals represent remarkable value. Bajard, formerly head chef at Le Gavroche, is
a skilled saucier – champagne with prawns and mussels; madeira with pheasant;
green peppercorns with beef and noodles. Nor are they tiny intense puddles;
rather like Albert Roux's, they are gravies spreading around the plate. The menu
is rich in luxuries sensibly used – sole fillets with a parsley and thyme sauce or,
on another night, with mussels and a foie gras salad. Plates are symmetrical and
picturesque. The French cheeses have been in superb condition and rival the
desserts' twin themes of pastry and/or sorbets. Wines are French and on the
young side. The cheapest is £11·50, apart from house wine at £7·50.

CHEF/PROPRIETOR: René Bajard
OPEN: Mon to Sat, D only CLOSED: bank hols, 1 week at Christmas MEALS: 7 to 11.30
PRICES: Set D from £17·50 (£22). Service inc CARDS: Access, Amex, Diners
SEATS: 55. Private parties: 10 main room, 6 and 12 private rooms. Vegetarian meals.
Children's helpings. Wheelchair access (also WC). Music. Air-conditioned

Melati [10/20]

map 14

21 Great Windmill Street, WIV 7PH
01-437 2745   £15–£17

When the formidable Mrs Ong is on the premises, the pace and the cooking in
this buzzy South-East Asian cafe move up a gear. The menu has a full range of
Malaysian and Indonesian specialities – satays, huge bowls of laksa soup, fish
dishes, noodles, and a good showing of vegetarian specialities such as sambal
tauco (French beans in brown-bean sauce) and tumis terong (aubergines in
tamarind gravy with bilis). Look out for specialities like the fish head curry, achar
(sweet pickled vegetables), lurid sweets and weird ice-creams. Drink Tiger beer or
fruit juice.

CHEFS: S. Alamsjah and H. Hasyem PROPRIETORS: Mrs M. C. W. Ong and S. Alamsjah
OPEN: all week MEALS: noon to 11.30pm (12.30am Fri and Sat)
PRICES: £8 (£17), Set L and D £27 (£30) for two. Service 10% Set
CARDS: Access, Amex, Diners, Visa
SEATS: 70. Private parties: 30 main room. Children welcome. Wheelchair access. Music

Meridiana [new entry, zero rated]

map 12

169 Fulham Road, SW3 6SP
01-589 8815   £20–£37

This old landmark among the Chelsea trattorias – no longer with the al fresco
balcony, but now a conservatory – is in new ownership. Chef Alberico Penati has

made a wholly commendable and long overdue attempt to revitalise the notion of Italian cooking in London. Here is an Italian menu with only one veal dish; instead there have been some fine examples of risotto – with quails or with asparagus and dill – of ravioli with a subtle, excellent lettuce sauce, and of matured Parma ham. Fish features strongly but has lacked the kind of execution that the prices demand. The dining-room is elegant, service rather overbearingly of the peppermill school. House wine is £7·50. The rest of the Italian list concentrates on the £12 to £15 range. More reports, please.

CHEF: Alberico Penati PROPRIETOR: John Leyton
OPEN: all week MEALS: 12.30 to 2.30, 7.30 to 11.30
PRICES: £22 (£37), Set L £12·50 (£20). Cover £1·50. Service 12.5%
CARDS: Access, Amex, Diners, Visa
SEATS: 120. Private parties: 60 main room, 60 private room. Children's helpings. Wheelchair access. Music

▲ Le Metro Wine Bar [9/20]   map 12

28 Basil Street, SW3 1AS
01-589 6286   £16

The Metro tends to live up to its name – overcrowded at peak times. It is streets ahead of the average wine bar and has two overriding advantages: it shares its kitchen with the Capital Hotel (see entry) and the quality of, say, the pea soup or the saucing of the shellfish with young vegetables may not be that different. Other touches, like the fish pâtés, warm salads, fresh bread, and fine cheeses, are also of a high-class restaurant. A Cruover machine enables ten fine wines to be offered by the glass off a commendable list.

CHEF: John Elliot PROPRIETOR: David Levin
OPEN: Mon to Sat, exc Sat D CLOSED: bank hols MEALS: noon to 10pm
PRICES: £11 (£16) CARDS: Amex, Visa
SEATS: 60. Private parties: 15 main room. Vegetarian meals. Children's helpings (L only). Wheelchair access. Air-conditioned
ACCOMMODATION: 12 rooms, all with bath/shower. Rooms for disabled. Lift. B&B £90. Children welcome. Baby facilities. No pets. TV. Phone. Doors close at 11

Michel [12/20]   map 11

343 Kensington High Street, W8 6NW
01-603 3613   £16–£22

From the same mould of those London French restaurants called the Toulouse or the Caen or wherever it is the owner or financial backer comes; in this case the restaurant is named after the owner himself, Michel Ferret. It is a corridor with washed walls, chicken prints, smart and noticeably French waiters, and well used by local French. The printed and unchanging menu seems at first glance duller than it is – snails, of course, but also halibut with coriander, beef with five peppercorns – black, white, yellow, pink, green – and pheasant with pine kernels. The wine list is similarly short but has a good choice of less expensive wines like Chinon, Crozes-Hermitage and Sauvignon de St Bris.

▲ *This restaurant has rooms.*

CHEF/PROPRIETOR: Michel Ferret
OPEN: all week   CLOSED: Sun in July and Aug   MEALS: 12 to 2.30, 7 to 11
PRICES: £14 (£22), Set L £8·90 (£16). Service 15%
CARDS: Access, Amex, Carte Blanche, Diners, Visa
SEATS: 50. 2 tables outside. Private parties: 55 main room. Vegetarian meals. Children
welcome. Wheelchair access. Music. Air-conditioned

Mijanou [13/20]   map 12

143 Ebury Street, SW1W 9QN
01-730 4099   £16–£25

The Blechs' small, well-decorated restaurant is notable for the complex cooking
and a serious collection of wines. Upstairs is for smokers, and the garden on a
summer night is idyllic: phone to get in. Sauces figure prominently on the menu
and are subtle and textural – lemon butter with a warm salad of scallops and
prawns or, from the same meal in May, mushroom with chicken and pasta. Some
combinations are startling – grapefruit and offal, for instance – but the zest for
adventure is tempered also by bourgeois points like chocolate mousse. The wine
list challenges the house claret at £7·50 with many other good-value bottles.
CELLARMAN'S CHOICE: Vosne Romanée, Clos Parantoux '81, £34·50.

CHEF: Sonia Blech   PROPRIETORS: Neville and Sonia Blech
OPEN: Mon to Fri   MEALS: 12.30 to 2, 7.30 to 11
PRICES: Set L from £10·95 (£16), Set D from £19 (£25)
SEATS: 30. 4 tables outside. Private parties: 24 main room. Children welcome.
No-smoking area

Ming [10/20]   map 14

35– 36 Greek Street, W1V 5LN
01-734 2721   £11–£18

On the wrong side of the tracks from Chinatown for a Chinese restaurant: oddly,
those that stray to the other side of Shaftesbury Avenue are not usually
Cantonese but are Szechuan or, as in this case, one of the few Pekingese
restaurants in the area. The corner building has windows on to the distractions
of the Soho streets. The inclination is to think of this as a smart new-wave style of
Chinese restaurant, but it eschews fancy fire symbols in favour of hot-pot dishes
of eel, or smoked skate so rinsed in aniseed it resembles duck. Its heart is with the
tradition of Chinatown – namely, that it should also please the waiters in the
other Chinese restaurants nearby. Of particular interest are the fine dim-sum and
the hand-made noodles, fat as a worm, served with the three delicacies – carved
squid, pork, and prawns. Staples like aromatic duck, the prawn toasts, the spare
ribs and crispy beef are accomplished foils to the more exotic uses found for
aubergines. Service is jovial and concerned and for the most part excellent.
Details like the jasmine tea and the orange segments with the bill are not
overlooked.

*'"Is the roast beef rolled or from a joint?" "Rolled." "Is the roast beef reheated?"
"Reheated." "Can I have some lemon and plain olive oil?" "No, we have no olive oil."
"Is the haddock fresh?" "Frozen." Enough said.'* (On eating in Lothian)

CHEFS: H. C. Ha and Mr Wong PROPRIETORS: Frank Liu, C. Yau and H. C. Ha
OPEN: all week MEALS: noon to midnight
PRICES: £10 (£18), Set L £7·50 (£11), Set D from £7·50 (£12). Minimum £5. Service 10%
CARDS: Access, Amex, Diners, Visa
SEATS: 80. Private parties: 56 main room, 24 private room. Vegetarian meals. Children
welcome. Wheelchair access. Music. Air-conditioned

Miyama [13/20]   map 13

38 Clarges Street, W1Y 7PJ
01-499 2443   £15–£32

Lacking some of the showy mannerisms of the more expensive, kudos-seeking
Japanese restaurants, this, the first Miyama, is more attuned to London. The
cooking is also more ambitious, interesting and successful. The dining-room is
airy and spacious and decorated with artistic origami in modern Tokyo style.
Service has a smidgen of English and is immaculately proper. Diners are greeted,
shown to a table and requests dealt with in a trice. There is no gimmickry, just a
long menu that has exceptional-value set lunches from £5·60. The set dinners at
almost four times that amount, plus fifteen per cent service, centre round
tempura, teriyaki, and yakitori, and a long list of daily specialities for initiates.
The variety of pickles, the depths of the soup, the fragility of the rice (all of which
accompany the set meals) are of a sophistication that does rather more than rival
French restaurants. Centrepieces of perhaps a piece of plain salt grilled salmon, or
maybe tofu with miso, or aubergine deep fried or as a ragout are magisterial. The
set meals require only the choice of main course to keep the bill in check. The
teppan-yaki bar is a feature, with five courses cooked in front of you. Mark-ups
on the wines should point you to Kirin beer (£1·80), sweet plum wine (£1·80)
and the whiskies.

CHEF/PROPRIETOR: Mr Miyama
OPEN: Mon to Sat, exc Sat L MEALS: 12.30 to 2.30, 6.30 to 10.30
PRICES: £19 (£32), Set L from £5·60 (£15), Set D from £19 (£32). Cover £1·50. Service 15%
CARDS: Access, Amex, Diners, Visa
SEATS: 70. Private parties: 18 main room. Vegetarian meals. Children welcome. Smart dress
preferred. Wheelchair access. Music. Air-conditioned

Miyama [new entry, zero rated]   map 11

17 Godliman Street, EC4V 4PN
01-489 1937   £18–£38

Tables are highly coveted for the basement, but upstairs is given over to sushi
and teppan-yaki bars, both of which seem bookable a day ahead. Both are of the
finest quality. Given the price of eating in the City now, £40 a head does not seem
so expensive for rare quality. If money is no object, then there are good reasons to
eat Japanese, and this must rank currently among the very best in London. Fillet
steaks are cooked along the hot steel teppan-yaki bar in front of patrons, who are
given clean white aprons: garlic is diced and laid out on the stainless-steel pan
while delicate appetisers like vinegared salmon, and seafood soup served in a
little enamel kettle are served, and finally the whole main course is brought
together in a more than generous dish. Fish or shellfish is the other option.
Around the corner at the sushi bar, the choice is varied and includes choices of

eel. Look also for the aubergine with miso and the aduki bean ice-cream. As in the similar (but less expensive) Clarges Street branch, the specials of the day are written in Japanese, but the staff, in impeccable, classical kimonos, have passable English. Saké, beer or whisky fit better than wine. More reports, please.

CHEFS: Y. Ishibashi and T. Miura PROPRIETORS: F. Miyama, T. Miura and Y. Ishibashi
OPEN: Mon to Fri MEALS: 12 to 3, 6 to 10
PRICES: £16 (£31), Set L from £7·50 (£18), Set D from £25 (£38). Cover £1·50. Service 15%
CARDS: Access, Amex, Diners, Visa
SEATS: 80. Private parties: 30 main room. Vegetarian meals. Children's helpings (L only). Music. Air-conditioned

Molnars [10/20]   map 11

144 Finchley Road, NW3 5HS
01-794 9942   £12–£18

The feel is very much like a little brother to the Gay Hussar (see entry): the décor is Hungarian rustic, and the cooking is sound and patriotic. Recommended dishes include bean soup with Czarda salad; garlicky pak with tiny dumplings the size of plump rice grains; duck in red wine; and goose with scholet (brown beans, barley and spices baked for twenty-four hours). Beef goulash with egg dumplings and red cabbage is good too. Excellent pancakes to finish. House Hungarian is £6·50 a bottle.

CHEF: Stephen Banar PROPRIETORS: Mrs Molnar and Stephen Banar
OPEN: Tue to Sat, D only, and Sun L MEALS: 12.30 to 2.30, 6.30 to 11
PRICES: £11 (£18), Set L from £7·50 (£12). Cover 50p. Service 10% CARDS: Access, Visa
SEATS: 46. Private parties: 46 main room. Children welcome. Wheelchair access. Music

Monkeys [11/20]   map 12

1 Cale Street, Chelsea Green, SW3 3QT
01-352 4711   £19–£23

Monkeys is more a good neighbourhood restaurant than a bistro and in season has fine game. Inside it feels French, with mirrors, round tables covered with blue clothes and assorted prints of monkeys on the walls. The strengths are its eclectic approach and its regularly changing menu. Steaks and grills are a permanent feature, and in season there is fine game, but the interesting dishes are the likes of ragout of monkfish provençale, warm salad of turbot, or mignons of veal with oyster mushrooms. Vegetables – including marsh samphire – are more generous than *nouvelle*, but less abundant than in modern British cooking. To finish, there's English treacle tart with custard, or a board of good-looking French cheeses. Coffee is strong cafetière. The handwritten list of 175 wines makes for some interesting drinking. House wine is £7.

CHEF: T. Benham PROPRIETORS: T. and B. Benham
OPEN: all week CLOSED: 24 and 25 Dec, 1 week Feb, 3 weeks Aug
MEALS: 12.30 to 2.30 (1.15 to 3 Sun), 7.30 to 11.30 (10.30 Sun)
PRICES: L £12 (£19), Set Sun L £13·50 (£19), Set D £17·50 (£23)
SEATS: 50. Private parties: 20 main room, 12 private room. Children's helpings (Sun L only). No pipes in dining-room. Wheelchair access. Air-conditioned

Mon Plaisir [10/20]   map 14

21 Monmouth Street, WC2H 9DD
01-836 7243   £15–£20

Not much has changed in twenty-five years at this bustling restaurant. The décor
has been spruced up, but the tables are still cramped and there's plenty of noise.
Watercress soup, mushrooms à la grecque, coq au vin, and raspberry tart are
typical of a menu that is stoically patriotic. The wine list is strong on burgundies,
and there's a mini-list of *cru classé* vintage clarets from £30 upwards. House
French is £5·50 a bottle.

CHEF: Michel Dubarbier PROPRIETOR: A. Lhermitte
OPEN: Mon to Sat, exc Sat L MEALS: 12 to 2.30, 6 to 11.15
PRICES: £14 (£20), Set L £9·50 (£15). Service 12.5%
SEATS: 75. 7 tables outside. Private parties: 26 main room, 30 private room. Vegetarian
meals. Children's helpings. Wheelchair access. Music

Mr Ke [10/20]   map 11

7 New College Parade, Finchley Road, NW3 5EP
01-722 8474   £15–£17

The stretch of Finchley Road between Swiss Cottage and Finchley Road Tube
Station is dotted with Chinese restaurants of various persuasions. Mr Ke is,
unusually, a chef-proprietor and, also unusually, from Peking. The décor is sparse
modern: ceramic tiled floors and slatted wooden ceilings. Peking dumplings with
red chilli oil are the genuine article; king prawns are correctly sauté in a light egg
batter; Peking duck has been good, too. When the cooking moves into Szechuan
the results can be less appetising. The short wine list suits the food.

CHEF: Zhu Gi Ke PROPRIETORS: Mr and Mrs Zhu Gi Ke
OPEN: all week CLOSED: 24 and 25 Dec MEALS: 12 to 2.30, 6 to 11
PRICES: £11 (£17), Set L and D from £10 (£15). Service 10%
CARDS: Access, Amex, Diners, Visa
SEATS: 60. Private parties: 30 main room. Vegetarian meals. Children welcome.
Air-conditioned

Mr Tang [11/20]   map 14

61–63 Shaftesbury Avenue, W1V 7AA
01-734 4488 and 5001   £13–£19

The Chinese Embassy favours this sprawling first-floor restaurant in Shaftesbury
Avenue, and so do passing tourists. The menu accommodates allcomers, but
shows its authentic Cantonese origins in specials, such as suckling pig, braised
pigeon and stuffed quail. The rare beef with pungent Chinese mushrooms and
crunchy lily flowers in a hot-pot illustrates the kitchen's strength. Dim-sum are
served throughout the day.

CHEF: W. Cheung PROPRIETOR: Bill Tang
OPEN: all week MEALS: noon to midnight
PRICES: £13 (£19), Set D from £16 (£26) for two, Dim-sum from £1. Service 10%
CARDS: Access, Amex, Diners, Visa
SEATS: 200. Private parties: 100 main room, 25 private room. Vegetarian meals. Children's
helpings. Music. Air-conditioned

M'sieur Frog [12/20]   map 11

31A Essex Road, N1 2SE
01-226 3495   £21

The cramped room in a cramped corner of London is part bistro and part
brasserie. The fine welcome, intelligent service and excellent fresh food put it on
the level of a serious restaurant. It is now open for lunch as well as dinner.
Robust French provincial dishes are the key points: leek and potato soup, onion
tart (served with *nouvelle* leaves), mignons of beef with mustard, and fillet of lamb
in pastry with basil have all drawn good reports. Sweets are skilfully done: apple
tartlet comes topped with slices of sugared oranges, meringue Chantilly with
fresh raspberries is served with a raspberry coulis. Beyond the house pichet from
Cahors at £5·35 is a surprisingly safe choice of claret and burgundy. M'sieur
Frog's Bistro at Hornsey has been sold.

CHEF: Jean Luc Guiral PROPRIETORS: Howard and Tina Rawlinson
OPEN: Mon to Sat, exc Sat L CLOSED: 1 week at Christmas, 1 week Aug
MEALS: 12 to 2.30, 7 to 11.30
PRICES: £15 (£21). Service 10% CARDS: Access, Visa
SEATS: 63. Private parties: 12 main room. Vegetarian meals. Children's helpings.
Wheelchair access

Nanten Yakitori Bar [9/20]   map 13

6 Blandford Street, W1H 3HA
01-935 6319   £10–£18

The tiny bar and basement turn out inexpensive set lunches incorporating main
courses of sashimi and tempura. Dinner is more elaborate. The range of yakitori
(grilled foods) stretches from two skewers of chicken hearts, gizzard, wing tip,
skin or liver. There are steamed dumplings, noodle dishes, rice soaked in tea, and
saké or Japanese vodka to drink.

CHEF: K. Deguchi PROPRIETORS: Ninjim Ltd
OPEN: Mon to Sat, exc Sat L MEALS: 12 to 2, 6 to 10
PRICES: £13 (£18), Set L from £5·20 (£10) CARDS: Access, Amex, Diners, Visa
SEATS: 31. Private parties: 4 and 25 private rooms. Children welcome. Wheelchair access.
Music

Neal Street Restaurant [14/20]   map 14

26 Neal Street, WC2H 9PH
01-836 8368   £30

Given the great rise in prices last year, restaurateur Antonio Carluccio's neat
restaurant comparatively may not seem quite so expensive – a point usually used
against it, though the quality is not stinted. It has many of the great virtures – a
proprietor who understands food, and who is nearly always present, décor that
impresses with its original Hockneys, staff who know what they are about, and a
menu and a wine list that challenge. It is somewhere particularly to eat in
autumn, when the white truffles are in from Alba and are grated on scrambled
eggs or over carpaccio; when the wild mushrooms are fresh and there is game to
accompany them. Venison is properly hung and given a dark sauce of ceps.

Classic dishes like liver à la Venezia are properly executed, while the cosmopolitan flavour of what is a long menu, at forty-plus dishes, is heady with modern ideas – foie gras on radicchio; parmigiana of courgette; veal with a walnut sauce. Puddings are for non-pudding people – tiramisu ice-cream with Mascarpone or almond biscuits to dip into a glass of vin santo. Four house wines at £7 open a sophisticated list. CELLARMAN'S CHOICE: Gavi Pio Cesare '86, £11·80.

CHEF: M. Santiago Gonzalez PROPRIETOR: Sir Terence Conran
OPEN: Mon to Fri CLOSED: Christmas to New Year MEALS: 12.30 to 2.30, 7.30 to 11
PRICES: £18 (£30). Cover £1·10. Service 15% CARDS: Access, Amex, Diners, Visa
SEATS: 65. Private parties: 65 main room, 20 private room. Vegetarian meals. Children's helpings. Wheelchair access. Air-conditioned

New World [11/20]   map 14

Gerrard Place, W1V 7LL
01-734 0677   £6–£16

The cavernous rooms that hold 250-plus each are used for afternoon wedding banquets so the guests can get back to their restaurants in time for their evening shift. It is the dim-sum at which the New World excel. They come round on a procession of trolleys – cold roast duck, suckling pig with crackling, and chicken are all inexpensive and succulent. Dumplings of all sorts – from pasta to bread dough-style coverings – cover a myriad of fillings, from intensely flavoured stewed chicken to variations on pork and prawns. In the evening only the main menu operates. It has interesting shellfish, such as inexpensive lobster, and other novelty shellfish, such as soft-shelled crabs or the current Chinese fad for geoduck (razor fish). On occasions there are unusual daily dishes rarely found on menus where Westerners eat. Tea is free.

CHEFS: K. Tang and C. Poon PROPRIETORS: Honsway Ltd
OPEN: all week MEALS: 11am to 11.45pm (11pm Sun)
PRICES: £13 (£16), Set L from £3 (£6), Set D from £5 (£8). Service inc
CARDS: Access, Amex, Diners, Visa
SEATS: 550. Private parties: 200 main room, 20, 80 and 100 private rooms. Vegetarian meals. Children welcome. Wheelchair access (also WC). Music. Air-conditioned

▲ Ninety Park Lane, Grosvenor House [13/20]   map 13

90 Park Lane, W1A 3AA
01-499 6363   £30–£54

In his autobiography Charles Forte writes: 'To be really outstanding, a luxury restaurant must be individualistic. It must reflect the personality of le patron, the man who is always there, who knows and greets his customers.' Quite who is le patron here these days is in some doubt. Consultant Louis Outhier flies in to make occasional dazzling visits, but vanishes again to leave behind him a vacuum. The Guide was the first to recognise the emergence of Ninety Park Lane four years ago. Since then, on its day, it has served dishes as good as anywhere, which makes its slide-over into anonymity the sadder. The prices have become an affront: £7 for a taste of (inferior) Cheddar; mineral water £2·20; a glass of Muscat de Beaumes de Venise £5; coffee £3·50. The cheapest set dinner menu at

£32·50 has amounted to salad, chicken, cheese, sweet and coffee. The *carte* feels more derivative than it should at this level – salmon with cream and mushrooms; duck with orange zest; and also Outhier's questionable follies with oriental flavours. Diced lobster with mints and pink grapefruit is dull and contrary. Does sweet-and-sour sauce really match turbot? Of course, much of this is an argument as to what a diner can expect for upwards of £50 a head. The ingredients are impeccable, so too the details, such as the breads. Service is by terribly well-schooled young men who smile a lot and negotiate a tricky kick-and-push double door from the kitchen without falling over the tables with the silver domes. The sweets stand is stupendous; identical to the one at L'Oasis, five feet tall with swivelling wooden circular shelves, each covered with raspberry tarts; frothy vanilla cheesecake with a hint of strawberry jam on the base; bombe-shaped chocolate sponge dusted with cocoa with, inside, a light banana cake. It is a wonderful sight. Not many people see it, though. On a Thursday in July when London bulged with visitors, only two other tables were taken, which underlines the point that great restaurants grow because they have customers; most of this restaurant's customers must have been in the South of France. And that explains why the house wine has to be £15. The cellar is extensive, with 350-plus bottles, but is too snooty to stock much under £25, and the service does not match the quality anyway.

CHEF: Stephen Goodlad PROPRIETORS: Trusthouse Forte Ltd
OPEN: Mon to Sat, exc Sat L MEALS: 12.30 to 2.30, 7.30 to 10.45
PRICES: £42 (£54), Set L £22·50 (£30), Set D from £32·50 (£40). Service inc Set
CARDS: Access, Amex, Carte Blanche, Diners, Visa
SEATS: 85. Private parties: 100 main room. Vegetarian meals. Children welcome. Jacket and tie. Music. Air-conditioned
ACCOMMODATION: 468 rooms, all with bath/shower. Rooms for disabled. Lift. B&B £165 to £185. Children welcome. Pets welcome. Afternoon teas. Swimming-pool. Sauna. Air-conditioning. TV. Phone

Nontas [10/20] ✗   map 11

16 Camden High Street, NW1 0JH
01-387 4579   £10

This Greek/Cypriot taverna is judged by its meze, which is excellent value at £5·95 a head for dips, squid, salad, red mullet, pork afelia, pourgouri, stuffed vine leaves and much more. The dish of the day might be baked cod or chicken cooked with Jerusalem artichokes in red wine sauce. Drinkable Demestica or Ulysses retsina at £5·30 a bottle.

CHEF: Nontas Vassilakas PROPRIETORS: Nontas and Helen Vassilakas
OPEN: Mon to Sat MEALS: 12 to 2.45, 6 to 11.30
PRICES: £6 (£10) CARDS: Access, Amex, Diners
SEATS: 50. Private parties: 25 main room. Children welcome. Wheelchair access. Music

Good vintages for drinking in 1988: Alsace '85, Beaujolais '86, Germany '85, petits chateaux clarets '81, lesser clarets '83.

If you suspect that a restaurant is using processed food, always ask. It would be a contravention of the Trade Descriptions Act for the restaurant to lie.

Odette's [13/20]

map 11

130 Regent's Park Road, NW1 8XL
01-586 5486   £24

The arrival of John Armstrong at Simone Green's intimate, sexy restaurant has put the kitchen up another gear, moving out of France into the richer pastures of modern British cooking. Front of house is skilfully run by waiters in black with white aprons tied at the waist, as if out of a Beardsley print. It is divided into an elegant front room, where the walls are jam-packed with gold-framed mirrors, and a more brasserie-like conservatory to the back covered with old and new photographs. Real plants hang from baskets. A dozen modern dishes on the *carte* are supplemented by as many specials. There is a sense of fashion about the fruit soup as a starter in May, or the skate, sauté and spiced with saké and ginger as a main dish. But there is also a thoroughness to the thinking which makes for fine dishes, like the ragout of artichokes; lightly poached scallops and salmon with a sauce of dill and ginger; goose with a perfumed chestnut honey sauce and a potato-cake filled with rhubarb. The use of seasoning is very modern British, but there is also a parallel Frenchness, as in the hot gratin of fruits as one sweet, rice pudding with mango, and a strawberry coulis as others. Cheeses are also farmhouse English. The wine list offers a good range of prices from £6·50 upwards, but with a bias towards claret.

CHEF: John Armstrong PROPRIETOR: Simone Green
OPEN: Mon to Sat, exc Mon D and Sat L MEALS: 12.30 to 2, 7.30 to 10.45
PRICES: £17 (£24). Service 12.5%
SEATS: 55. Private parties: 28 private room. Children welcome

Oh Boy [10/20]

map 10

843 Garratt Lane, SW17 0PG
01-947 9760   £16

One of the first Thai restaurants in London. The French accent is stronger than in the new wave of Thai restaurants, but a new gold-lettered sign, dark glass and blue Venetian blinds testify not only to this run-down part of London being on the up, but also to the cuisine being in the ascendant. Photographs of the King and Queen of Thailand and two gold buddhas look down on a small, comfortable, well-run dining-room. The long menu is an eclectic mix, rather what might be expected at a well-attended beach restaurant. Prawn cocktail, steak Diane and Siam flambés (prawns and chicken in Pernod) mingle with more main-stream Thai flavours. Soups are well seasoned with lemon grass; the curries spicy; and the Thai custard is not too different from English, only it is green. Suprême de volaille volcano – charcoal grilled baby chicken with garlic – arrives on a round metal platter and is flambé at the table. House wine is £4·40.

CHEF/PROPRIETOR: Paranee Pokavanit
OPEN: Mon to Sat, D only CLOSED: 2 weeks Aug MEALS: 7 to 10.30 (10.45 Fri and Sat)
PRICES: £11 (£16). Service 12.5% CARDS: Access, Amex, Diners, Visa
SEATS: 55. Private parties: 40 main room, 15 private room. Vegetarian meals. Children welcome. Music. Air-conditioned

It is always advisable to book a restaurant in advance.

L'Olivier [14/20]

map 11

116 Finborough Road, SW10 9ED
01-370 4183   £23–£27

The entrance is club-like: ring the bell to get in. The basement has been
transformed into a predominantly French dining-room. The main thrust is meat
(in contrast to its sisters in the Croisette chain who specialise in fish). The formula
is simple – choose a set meal from £15 to £23 or a combination from an almost
redundant *carte* which takes in a few token shellfish and also foie gras at £9. The
cheapest meal brings fresh bread, a wide choice of hors d'oeuvre and saucisson
displayed on a vast lazy Susan on the table, followed by a little dish of ravioli,
then excellent soup de pistou. The choice is of roast poultry or a quartet of dishes
of the day; then salad and a vast selection of cheeses. Kirs are included in the
price. Service is very French and fifteen per cent extra. Wines start at £7·50 for
the house wine from Provence, and a Brazilian combo appears for the late-night
sitting until 2am.

CHEF: Philippe Moron PROPRIETOR: Pierre Martin
OPEN: Mon to Sat, D only CLOSED: 2 weeks at Christmas
MEALS: 7.30 to 1.30 (last orders 11.30 Set)
PRICES: £19 (£27), Set D from £15 (£25). Cover £1 CARDS: Access, Amex, Diners, Visa
SEATS: 50. Children welcome. Music

One Two Three [12/20]

map 13

27 Davies Street, W1Y 1LN
01-409 0750   £17–£37

In the rarefied atmosphere of Mayfair, the set meals in this long Japanese
basement favoured by embassy staff offer good value. Wooden partitions separate
the tables, and the staff, as is noticeable in many of London's Japanese
restaurants in the last year, have become more relaxed and deal easily with
Western customers. Set meals centre around one of the classic dishes – tempura,
sashimi, yakitori – but either side of it is a consistent meal of pickles, picturesque
soups, rice, and cherries and green tea. The belly-pork simmered in saké is one of
the signature dishes of Japanese cooking: two fatty nuggets coated with mustard
in a soy-based sauce with green stems. Extras, like beers, put up the bill, as might
be expected, as this is more formal than its sister, Ikeda.

CHEF: K. Soda PROPRIETOR: S. Ikeda
OPEN: Mon to Fri MEALS: 12 to 2.30, 6.30 to 10.30
PRICES: £22 (£37), Set L from £9·50 (£17), Set D from £23 (£33). Cover 50p at L, £1 at D.
Service 15% CARDS: Access, Amex, Diners, Visa
SEATS: 50. Private parties: 50 main room. Vegetarian meals. No children under 10. Music.
Air-conditioned

Orso [13/20]

map 14

27 Wellington Street, WC2E 7DA
01-240 5269   £22

Around the corner from its elder sister, Joe Allen's, this smart Italian restaurant
has the elegant frontage of an architect's or a design centre. The wash of the
orange walls, the open-plan kitchen, the vividly colourful thick Mediterranean

country crockery reinforce a sense of style. The cooking is not to be dismissed.
The thin-cut pizzas are lavishly filled with Gorgonzola and Parma ham, or
tomato, Mozzarella, basil and Parmesan. The pastas, too, mark the place out as
somewhere interested in breaking the mould, which for the best part of three
decades has been set by Italian cafe-style bars: sauced with roast duck and leeks;
lamb, white beans, Swiss chard and onions. Warm salads of wild mushrooms,
thinly sliced veal tonnato, venison with green peppercorns and polenta are more
its cut. Staff, unusually, are not Italian, which means their pace is a little less
allegro than usual. Wines are from impeccable sources: Lungarotti, Antinori,
Tedeschi, Frescobaldi . . . The house white wine in a fat glass carafe tastes of
Tuscany and the coffee of the Gaggia.

CHEF: Martin Wilson PROPRIETORS: Orso Restaurants Ltd
OPEN: all week CLOSED: 25 and 26 Dec MEALS: noon to midnight
PRICES: £15 (£22)
SEATS: 110. Vegetarian meals. Children welcome

Il Passetto [10/20]   map 13

230 Shaftesbury Avenue, WC2H 8EG
01-836 9391   £16

This is a useful, archetypal corridor of a ristorante. The cold trolley is notable,
pasta is reliable, and the tomato sauce ubiquitous. There is the usual selection of
veal dishes, but good fish too. Our comment last year that it was one of the best
West End trattorias perhaps raised expectations too much, although there are
few suggestions for anywhere better in the area. Skip the vegetables. There is
white Vernaccia di San Gimignano and red Campo Fiorin, or house wine at
£4·95.

CHEF: Jesus Sanchez PROPRIETOR: Lindown Ltd
OPEN: Mon to Sat, exc Sat L MEALS: 12 to 3, 6 to 11.30
PRICES: £10 (£16). Cover 95p CARDS: Access, Amex, Diners, Visa
SEATS: 42. Private parties: 20 main room. Vegetarian meals. Children welcome. Wheelchair
access. Air-conditioned

Phoenicia [10/20]   map 11

11–13 Abingdon Road, W8 6AH
01-937 0120   £10–£16

Some of the best Lebanese food in London is served at this brown and green
family-run restaurant. The meze is outstanding: chicken livers and wings, spicy
sausages, hummus, falafel and kibbeh (raw lamb with olive oil, mint and onion);
tabouleh is good too. Main courses centre on grills and kebabs. A new
conservatory is being built for families with children, and £6 buffet lunches are
now available. Drink mint tea, Turkish coffee, or arak. Three dozen wines include
Château Musar '79 and '80 at £9·90 a bottle.

CHEF: Chaoki Serhal PROPRIETOR: Hani Khalife
OPEN: all week MEALS: noon to midnight
PRICES: £10 (£16), Set L from £6 (£10), Set D from £9·50 (£15). Cover £1·25. Minimum
£9·50. Service inc CARDS: Access, Amex, Diners, Visa
SEATS: 80. Private parties: 80 main room, 15, 25 and 40 private rooms. Vegetarian meals.
Children's helpings. Wheelchair access. Music. Air-conditioned

Pollo [9/20]

map 14

20 Old Compton Street, W1V 5PE
01-734 5917 £9

The cheapest and best fresh pasta in the West End is served at this modest, but lately very fashionable, Old Compton Street cafe. From the outside it looks like a faded coffee bar, but the queues on the stairs, the friendliness and the no-fuss efficiency of the staff tell a different story. The menu is heavy with pasta (courtesy of I. Camisa) – tagliatelle, tortellini, spaghetti – served with fresh regional sauces such as pesto genovese, arrabiata and napoli. The timing is spot on and platefuls are huge. Other dishes such as chicken Kiev also have their supporters. House wine £3·95.

CHEF: Zazi Adermo   PROPRIETOR: M. Mansini
OPEN: Mon to Sat   CLOSED: bank hols   MEALS: 12 to 3, 6 to 11
PRICES: £5 (£9)
SEATS: 80. Vegetarian meals. Children's helpings. Wheelchair access

Pollyanna's [11/20]

map 10

2 Battersea Rise, SW11 1ED
01-228 0316 £15–£22

Pollyanna is like a debutante who has not yet come out. She has her dowry – a splendid run of clarets and burgundies from good domaines – but her décor is still a rather make-do plywood affair. The menu too is caught in an adolescent mid-stage between desperately wanting to offer good value and also grown-up sort of things like salmon stuffed with lobster and monk-fish and served with a red pepper sauce. The blackboard menu has the market choices, the long typed *carte* has a fondness for mousses and seems to whizz things up a lot. The good ingredients for the most part get through an inclination to fuss: Cantal cheese soufflé is the size of a scone, veal is served with mushroom and beetroot mousses and champagne and chive sauce. Portions are *nouvelle* and small, but the treacle tart is suitably sticky. House wine is £5.95. CELLARMAN'S CHOICE: St Romain '85, £14·50.

CHEF: Eamonn Connolly   PROPRIETOR: Norman Price
OPEN: Mon to Sat, D only, and Sun L   CLOSED: 4 days at Christmas, 1 Jan
MEALS: 1 to 3, 7 to 12
PRICES: £15 (£22), Set L £9·95 (£15). Service 10%   CARDS: Access, Amex, Visa
SEATS: 90. 4 tables outside. Private parties: 12 main room, 30 private room. Vegetarian meals. Children's helpings (Sun L only). Music

Ponte Nuovo [12/20]

map 12

126 Fulham Road, SW3 6HU
01-370 6656 £18–£25

A better-than-average Italian restaurant, albeit at better-than-average prices. The familiar array of pasta and veal dishes is given new variations – for instance,

This symbol is awarded only to restaurants with outstanding wine cellars.

veal with a brandy and coffee sauce. Pasta is freshly made. Much use is made of paper bags – for noodles with seafood, and again for salmon. Chicken with rosemary and chilli is a good dish. Service is professional. Extras put the bill up. House Chianti is £7.

CHEF: Luigi Penna PROPRIETOR: Walter Mariti
OPEN: all week MEALS: 12.30 to 3, 7 to 12
PRICES: £16 (£25), Set L and D from £12 (£18). Cover £1
CARDS: Access, Amex, Diners, Visa
SEATS: 78. 10 tables outside. Vegetarian meals. Children's helpings. Wheelchair access. Air-conditioned

Poons [11/20] ✗

map 14

4 Leicester Street, WC2H 7BL
01-437 1528

£8–£18

Poons is supreme at wind-dried foods, a Chinese method of preserving foodstuffs to make them last through the winter. Sausages, whole ducks, and liver are unmatched. Other dishes range from excellent, as in the hot-pot of eel, belly-pork, and garlic, to less so, depending on the evening. The décor is monochromatic, cafe-like but clean, and the queues, even for people who have booked, frequent. Tea to drink.

CHEF/PROPRIETOR: W. N. Poon
OPEN: Mon to Sat CLOSED: 25 Dec MEALS: noon to 11.30pm
PRICES: £10 (£18), Set L and D £8·50 (£16) for two
SEATS: 100. Private parties: 30 main room. Children welcome. Air-conditioned

Ports [11/20]

map 12

11 Beauchamp Place, SW3 1NQ
01-581 3837

£14–£22

In a pretty cellar in the sprawling underworld of Beauchamp Place is this smart Portuguese restaurant with decorative tiles, and sweets laid out by the bar. Fish dominates the long menu. Charcoal-grilled squid comes with a cream and lemon sauce and plenty of crusty bread; bacalhau (dried cod) is grilled black on the outside and swims in a pool of olive oil and garlic. Balancing this, there is cataplana of diced pork with Venus clams, or rack of lamb in red wine sauce. The deliberate *nouvelle*-style presentation of some dishes seems to go against the spirit of the food. Sweets are Portuguese classics: cold rice pudding dusted with cinnamon, cheese tartlet with raspberry sauce, warm custard tarts. The wine list draws on the whole of Portugal, with house wine, Serradayres from the Ribatejo region, at £6·20; there's also Portuguese Sagres lager.

CHEF: Elio de Andrade PROPRIETORS: Luis Pimentel and A. Valerio
OPEN: Mon to Sat CLOSED: bank hols MEALS: 12 to 3, 6.30 to 12
PRICES: £14 (£22), Set L £8·75 (£14). Service 12.5% CARDS: Access, Amex, Diners, Visa
SEATS: 45. Private parties: 45 main room. Children welcome. Music. Air-conditioned

'There is always the hint of rushing the service, but to be brought one's coat with the bill is going too far.' (On eating in Leicestershire)

Le Poulbot [13/20]   map 11

45 Cheapside, EC2V 6AR
01-236 4379   £30

This, the Roux brothers' second restaurant, remains one of the more civilised
places for a business lunch, the more so given the kind of bullish pretentions the
City has seen in the last two years. The basement is secluded from the bustle of
the excellent-value but tiny brasserie upstairs. Tables are sectioned off from each
other by red banquettes. The menu is selective, modern French in tone, taking its
cue from Le Gavroche or, in one meal, from the recipes of Joël Robuchon in such
as the sea-bass topped with diced vegetables and truffle or the bolero of
langoustines. It is artistic, consistent, classically inclined and professional.
Excellent fish is used in scallop, leek and cream soup, or red mullet worked in a
number of ways. Rowley Leigh is an accomplished butcher and a meticulous
cook. As in other Roux restaurants, the system, which includes the serving of kir,
canapés, petits fours and coffee, does not take much broaching, but is usually
swift enough for a 2.45 meeting. Interesting to note that lunch here is virtually
the same price as at Le Gavroche – and is relatively cheap for the area. Wines can
push the bill up substantially, opening at £11.

CHEFS: R. R. Leigh and Mr Cottard PROPRIETORS: Roux Restaurants Ltd
OPEN: Mon to Fri, L only CLOSED: bank hols, 2 weeks at Christmas MEALS: 12 to 3
PRICES: Set L £24·50 (£30). Service inc CARDS: Access, Amex, Carte Blanche, Diners, Visa
SEATS: 55. Private parties: 55 main room. Vegetarian meals. Children welcome. Jacket and
tie. Air-conditioned

Le Quai St Pierre [11/20]   map 11

7 Stratford Road, W8 6RF
01-937 6388   £26

The atmosphere upstairs, which is more of a dining-room, is very different from
the atmosphere downstairs, where the long bar gives it more of a cafe feeling.
Either way it is French. The style is identical to its related establishments
stemming from La Croisette (see entry): fish is served plain, as with seven sizes of
oysters, or in variations – five ways with mussels (raw, marinière, Madras,
farcies, rochelaises), three with langoustines, four with scallops. The whole, often
magnificent platter of shellfish is £12. Main-course white fish are mostly grilled
and served with fashionable sauces. House wine is £7·50.

CHEF: Alain Patrat PROPRIETORS: La Francine Ltd
OPEN: Mon to Sat, exc Mon L CLOSED: 2 weeks at Christmas
MEALS: 12.30 to 2.30, 7 to 11.30
PRICES: £18 (£26). Cover £1. Service 15% CARDS: Access, Amex, Diners, Visa
SEATS: 55. 3 tables outside. Children welcome. Wheelchair access. Music

Quincy's [14/20]   map 11

675 Finchley Road, NW2 2JP
01-794 8499   £17–£20

The older wicker chairs have been replaced by more comfortable ones, but at
heart Quincy's is a sophisticated bistro. The cooking is modern British: potted

crab with toasted brioche; brill with rhubarb in a vanilla sauce; veal fillets with a sweetbread custard. Plainer dishes (steak béarnaise and rhubarb crumble) are not excluded. Standards have been commendably consistent over the last few years and prices kept in check. One of the few serious restaurants to be open seven days a week. House Gamay is £6·50.

CHEF: Sandy Anderson PROPRIETORS: D. J. C. Wardle and D. A. Anderson
OPEN: all week, D only, and Sun L MEALS: 12 to 2, 7.30 to 10.30 (9.30 Sun)
PRICES: Set L £12 (£17), Set D £14·75 (£20) CARDS: Access, Visa
SEATS: 30. Private parties: 30 main room. Vegetarian meals. Children's helpings.
Wheelchair access. Music. Air-conditioned

Ragam [10/20]

map 13

57 Cleveland Street, W1P 5PQ
01-636 9098

£7–£11

Dishes from the Kerala coast are the main point of interest at this modest South Indian restaurant. Classics such as kaallan (a curry made with yoghurt, sweet mangoes, coconut and spices) and avial (mixed vegetables with coconut and curry leaves) are supplemented by more familiar vegetarian items such as masala dosai, vadai and uppuma. Oothappam is a pizza-style pancake made of rice, lentil flour, onions, green chillies and tomatoes. Like the Ganpath (see entry), this restaurant also has a full menu of meat, poultry and seafood dishes from lamb korma to prawns malabar. To drink, there's sweet, salt or fruit-flavoured lassi.

CHEFS: J. Dharmaseelan and Mojid Ullah
PROPRIETORS: J. Dharmaseelan, T. Haridas and S. Pillai
OPEN: all week MEALS: 12 to 3, 6 to 12
PRICES: £5 (£11), Set L and D £3 (£7). Service 10%. Licensed, plus bring your own: corkage £1 CARDS: Access, Amex, Diners, Visa
SEATS: 34. Private parties: 34 main room, 25 private room. Vegetarian meals. Children's helpings. Wheelchair access (also WC). Music

Rani [12/20]

map 10

35 Long Lane, Finchley, N3 2PR
01-349 4386 and 2636

£10–£14

Surrounded by restaurants of all nations on a corner parade near Barnado's; inside is whites and reds, small, ex-teashop. On the walls are stylised prints of Indian scenes from an age of elegance. These, the sitar and drums perched precariously high up in a corner, and the unwesternised Indian music set the tone. The cooking is home-style Indian vegetarian with the emphasis on spicing that complements and does not overwhelm. Highlights are tamarind-flavoured samosas; cool, yoghurty aloo dhai puhri; pilau rice packed with nuts, sultanas and fresh vegetables; and banana methi with tomato. Ordinary-sounding vegetable curry may turn out to be a delectable mixture of aubergine and potato, and the stuffed parathas are unbeatable. Service would not be out of place in a

If, in your opinion, a restaurant is not maintaining the standard of its rating, please inform the Guide *office. Report forms are at the back of the book.*

restaurant of the highest calibre, the food is cheap, and the myriad of flavours make Rani one of the best-value places to eat in the capital.

CHEFS: Kundan and Sheila Pattni PROPRIETOR: Jyotindra Pattni
OPEN: Tue to Sun, exc Tue L CLOSED: 25 Dec MEALS: 12.30 to 2, 6 to 10.30
PRICES: £8 (£14), Set L from £5 (£10), Set D from £7 (£12). Minimum £4. Service 10%
CARDS: Access, Visa
SEATS: 34. Vegetarian meals. Children's helpings. No children under 6. No cigars in dining-room. Music

Rebato's [11/20]   map 10

169 South Lambeth Road, SW8 1XW
01-735 6388   £14

The frontage on to the upwardly mobile part of Stockwell is deceptively low-key, but, inside, this Spanish restaurant has some of the glamour of a ballroom dance – all golds and glints and lights. The front bar features some of the best tapas in the country: trays of sardines, octopus, spicy sausage, baby eels, anchovies and excellent tripe. At the back is the restaurant, serving good-value set meals with gazpacho or plump grilled sardines to start, then paella, or lamb cutlets or grilled fish. A guitarist plays most nights. Good Spanish wines and sherries. House wine is £4·95.

CHEF: Manuel Perez PROPRIETORS: Tino and Sheila Rebato
OPEN: Mon to Sat, exc Sat L MEALS: 12 to 2.30, 7 to 11.15
PRICES: Set L and D £9·75 (£14), Snacks from £1·25 CARDS: Access, Amex, Diners, Visa
SEATS: 60. Private parties: 60 main room. Children welcome. Wheelchair access. Music.
Air-conditioned

Red Fort [13/20]   map 14

77 Dean Street, W1V 5HA
01-437 2525 and 2410   £15–£21

The Red Fort has a classy, dignified air. Women in saris wait at the door, the waiters are dressed in dark pink jackets to match the décor, and it feels very spacious, very cool. The kitchen can produce some of the most subtle North Indian food in the West End, although some still find it less consistent than its rival, Lal Qila (see entry). The spicing shows in quails in a rich, mild sauce garnished with fresh coriander. Vegetables and accompaniments are notably good: brown, grainy dhal tarka, baingan bartha with a real taste of grilled aubergine, and chunky home-made paneer cooked with spices and tomatoes. Rice is impeccable Basmati. Breads have improved noticeably, and the peshwari nan stuffed with ground almonds and raisins has been outstanding. Vegetarians do well. The choice of drinks extends to masala tea and non-alcoholic cocktails.

CHEF: N. P. Pittal PROPRIETOR: Amin Ali
OPEN: all week CLOSED: 25 and 26 Dec MEALS: 12 to 2.30, 6 to 11.30
PRICES: £10 (£17), Set L from £10 (£15), Set D from £15 (£21). Service 15%
CARDS: Access, Amex, Diners, Visa
SEATS: 160. Private parties: 60 main room, 100 private room. Vegetarian meals. Children's helpings (weekends only). Jacket and tie. Wheelchair access (also WC). Music.
Air-conditioned

Red Sea [10/20]   map 11

51 Kilburn High Road, NW6 5SB
01-624 5289   £10–£12

Ethiopian cuisine may not rank among the finest Africa can provide, but within a
short spectrum it provides plenty of fire and drama. It is peculiarly sociable food,
and set menus here are designed for no fewer than ten people. The engera
pancakes are excellent and, along with yoghurt, counteract the heat of the stews
and casseroles. House wine £4.

CHEF: Tse Hay Taye PROPRIETOR: Mr Maalo
OPEN: all week, D only MEALS: 6 to 11 (6.30 to 11.30 Fri and Sat)
PRICES: £8 (£12), Set D from £7·50 (£10). Service inc CARDS: Access, Amex, Diners, Visa
SEATS: 42. Private parties: 42 main room. Vegetarian meals. Children welcome. Wheelchair
access. Music

La Rive Gauche [new entry, zero rated]   map 11

61 The Cut, SE1 8LL
01-928 8645   £16–£25

Formerly Mabileau, and conveniently situated for the South Bank arts and
theatre complex. The classy room is long, thin and cream, filled with scalloped
lights and natural wood chairs. The menu is French but has some different ideas
from the normal London run of the mill, which give it character: eel in red wine;
scallops in red pepper sauce; chicken mousse with its livers in a port sauce as a
main course. Service is French and willing. House wine is from Duboeuf at
£6·50. More reports, please.

CHEF: Alain Cahour PROPRIETORS: G. Jarvis and Alain Cahour
OPEN: Mon to Sat, exc Sat L MEALS: 12 to 2.30, 6 to 11
PRICES: £20 (£25), Set L and D from £12·50 (£16). Service inc
CARDS: Access, Amex, Diners, Visa
SEATS: 35. Private parties: 35 main room. Vegetarian meals. Children's helpings.
Wheelchair access (also WC). Music. Air-conditioned

Royal Thai Orchids [10/20]   map 10

141 Upper Richmond Road, SW15 2TX
01-789 4304   £20

The old part of Putney has a wealth of restaurants. This one, despite its name, is
one of the less pretentious of the Thai restaurants encircling London. The dining-
room is plain; waiters have good English. The menu does not seem to promise a
great deal but delivers good satay, dim-sum, and crisp fried fish.

CHEFS: Mrs Suwankumpoo and Mr Panrod PROPRIETORS: The Suwankumpoo family
OPEN: Mon to Sat CLOSED: 2 weeks Aug
MEALS: 12 to 2.30, 6.30 to 11 (11.30 Fri and Sat)
PRICES: £14 (£20)
SEATS: 110. Private parties: 80 main room, 50 private room. Vegetarian meals. Children's
helpings. Music

Restaurants rating 12 or more serve the best food in the region.

RSJ [12/20]

map 11

13A Coin Street, SE1 8YQ
01-928 4554   £18–£21

The reinforced steel joist after which it is named is almost as legendary a fixture of the South Bank as any of its great cultural neighbours whose visitors the restaurant has serviced so ably for the last decade. The menu is modern, dishes decorative without being too fussy: salad of citrus fruits, monkfish and scallops; pigeon breast with chocolate and raisin sauce; biting Stilton tart; chicken with noodles, walnuts and redcurrant sauce. Set meals can offer better value than the *carte*. To finish, there's good crème caramel with almonds, and fruit crumble with clotted cream. The décor is in keeping, and the service is unfussy. The selection of Loire wines is unparalleled; the region is good value compared to other parts of France, and here are most of its aristocrats starting around £7.

CHEF: Ian Stable PROPRIETOR: Nigel Wilkinson
OPEN: Mon to Sat, exc Sat L CLOSED: 3 days at Christmas MEALS: 12 to 2, 6 to 11
PRICES: £15 (£21), Set L and D £12·75 (£18). Service 10% CARDS: Access, Amex, Visa
SEATS: 30. Private parties: 30 main room, 20 private room. Children welcome. Jacket and tie. Wheelchair access. Air-conditioned

Rue St Jacques [15/20]

map 13

5 Charlotte Street, W1P 1HD
01-637 0222   £23–£43

Günther Schlender's mirrored and ruched restaurant, now redecorated, has become a junction box on the international circuit – a place where Americans eat what is perceived to be French but is really the *cuisine* of big hotels. Schlender's cooking saves this from the anonymity that usually descends on such places. The artifice is now so elaborate that the execution verges on the mechanical. Dishes are refined to a point: artichoke hearts come with two mousses; scallop timbale with a prawn sauce; sweetbreads with a sorrel and mushroom sauce. If all food is, in the last resort, regional, then this region is of banks, airport lounges and duty-free jewellery shops. The ingredients are impeccable, and so are the wines, though the prices are astronomical.

CHEF: Günther Schlender PROPRIETOR: Vincent Calcerano
OPEN: Mon to Sat, exc Sat L CLOSED: Christmas, Easter, bank hols
MEALS: 12.30 to 2.30, 7.30 to 11.15
PRICES: £31 (£43), Set L from £15 (£23). Minimum £25 at D. Service 15%
CARDS: Access, Amex, Diners, Visa
SEATS: 70. Private parties: 25 main room, 12, 25 and 30 private rooms. Children's helpings. Jacket and tie. No pipes. Wheelchair access. Music. Air-conditioned

Sabras [12/20]

map 10

263 Willesden High Road, NW10 2RX
01-459 0340   £8–£11

Sabras still has the edge on its nearest rival, Rani (see entry), and continues to serve the most authentic and wide-ranging Indian vegetarian food in the capital. It has had a major facelift to the frontage, the furniture and décor. The menu retains all its classics: the farshan snacks, the cold puris, the Gujerati specialities including ragada patish (grilled potato-cake topped with yellow peas, tamarind chutney and onions), as well as the superb vegetables: palak, chana aloo, undhiu (a curry of aubergines, sweet potatoes, bananas and garlic, served only in winter). New additions are likely to include baked millet parathas and special 'fasting' dishes made purely with root vegetables and nuts. Home-make kulfi and shrikhand as well as Loseley ice-creams to finish. Buffet-style lunches. The owners have applied for a licence to sell Indian beers and wines.

CHEFS/PROPRIETORS: Hemant and Nalinee Desai
OPEN: Tue to Sun MEALS: 12.30 to 3, 6 to 9.30 (12.30pm to 9.30pm Sat and Sun)
PRICES: £6 (£11), Set L and D from £5 (£8), Snacks from £1·50. Service 10%. Unlicensed, but bring your own: 75p corkage. CARDS: Access, Visa
SEATS: 24. Private parties: 28 main room. Vegetarian meals. Children's helpings. Wheelchair access. Music

Saga [12/20]

map 13

43 South Molton Street, W1V 1HB
01-629 3931
£13–£30

The Saga has been discovered but remains a good all-round, very accessible Japanese restaurant. The menu encompasses most of the important styles of cooking – tempura, sashimi, sukiyaki, teppan-yaki. The atmosphere is relaxed in the basement among the paper screens. The rice for the sushi is well flavoured, and on some evenings the fish are as exotic as octopus. Vegetarians do well in a diet where meat was virtually unknown before the second half of this century. Lunch is conspicuously cheaper than dinner. Drink green tea, whisky or saké.

OPEN: Mon to Sat CLOSED: bank hols MEALS: 12.30 to 2.30, 6.30 to 10.30
PRICES: £14 (£26), Set L from £7 (£13), Set D from £20 (£30). Cover £1 at D. Service 15%
CARDS: Access, Amex, Diners, Visa
SEATS: 120. Children welcome. Wheelchair access. Music. Air-conditioned

Saigon [11/20]

map 14

45 Frith Street, W1V 5TE
01-437 7109
£15–£18

Generally accepted currently as the best of the Vietnamese restaurants. The atmosphere is almost night club like, on the little-hut-in-the-middle-of-the-jungle theme. The cooking is clear, illuminated with herbs like peppermint, lemon grass, chilli, lemon, and garlic. Some of it is tactile: Vietnamese duck uses rice paper, cucumber, mint and coriander for rolling together at the table, while deep-fried squid cakes come with a spicy dip and lettuces to wrap them in. The barbecued beef and the crab make fine centrepieces. House wine is £4·90.

CHEF: C. H. Lin PROPRIETOR: E. C. L. Man
OPEN: Mon to Sat CLOSED: bank hols MEALS: noon to 11.30pm
PRICES: £11 (£18), Set L and D from £10 (£15). Service 10%
CARDS: Access, Amex, Diners, Visa
SEATS: 80. Private parties: 40 main room, 50 private room. Children welcome. Music

All letters to the Guide *are acknowledged.*

St Quentin [11/20]   map 12

243 Brompton Road, SW3 2EP
01-589 8005 and 581 5131   £15–£27

A hard core of local Chelsea and exiled French keep this little corner of Paris in
London on its toes. The prices reflect Knightsbridge, but the cooking and décor
are St Germain. The kitchen has developed from the popular, reliable dishes like
côte de boeuf or kidneys in mustard sauce to complexities like a sausage of
scallops with lemon butter. Sweets and cheeses from the brilliant specialist St
Quentin around the corner. The wine list has also matured and is now a serious
collection. CELLARMAN'S CHOICE: Pouilly Fumé '85 from Dagueneau at
£11·80 (£6·85 for a half).

CHEF: Christian Autier PROPRIETOR: Hugh O'Neill
OPEN: all week MEALS: 12 to 3 (4 Sat), 7 to 12 (11.30 Sun)
PRICES: £18 (£27), Set L £9·50 (£15), Set D £12·90 (£19). Cover £1·20. Service 12.5%
CARDS: Access, Amex, Diners, Visa
SEATS: 85. Private parties: 30 private room. Children's helpings. Wheelchair access.
Air-conditioned

Salloos [11/20]   map 12

62 Kinnerton Street, SW1X 8ER
01-235 4444   £14·50–£27

Mr Salahuddin's restaurant lives up to its Knightsbridge address. The décor is
elegant, prices are high, and in the evening it caters very much for the
international set. The cooking is Pakistani. Many of the dishes are based on
family recipes, prepared by a team of cooks who have been with the restaurant
for more than twenty years. Tandooris are freshly cooked to order – says the
menu – and no colouring is added. High points are the almond soup, chicken
taimuri (marinated and deep fried in a batter of flour, milk, eggs, onions and
tomatoes), allo zeera, and haleen akbari (shredded lamb cooked with whole
wheatgerm, lentils and spices). There is also a curious-sounding dish of chicken
pieces baked with cheese, milk and eggs like a soufflé. Basmati rice is simmered in
mildly spiced lamb stock. The better-than-average wine list has special selections
from Corney & Barrow.

PROPRIETOR: M. Salahuddin
OPEN: Mon to Sat CLOSED: bank hols MEALS: 12 to 2.30, 7 to 11.30
PRICES: £15 (£27), Set L £11·50 (£14·50). Cover £1. Service inc set, 15% alc
CARDS: Access, Amex, Carte Blanche, Diners, Visa
SEATS: 70. Children welcome

San Frediano [12/20]   map 12

62 Fulham Road, SW3 6HH
01-584 8375   £19

San Frediano is the natural successor to the cafes and coffee bars with which
Italian immigrants first established themselves. The formula is more
sophisticated – more of a restaurant in the round – but the ground rules are
unalterable – the daily produce on display in the centre of the right-hand room to

arrange as you choose, the *carte* of standard dishes, the same number of dishes of the day, sometimes scrawled in pencil at the last minute across the top – 'lobster £8'. The basis is good pasta (tortellini stuffed with radicchio), gratins, cold dishes, fine fish on occasion. Among specialities are scallops, monkfish, scampi and mussels on black noodles or fried fresh anchovies. The main dishes have a cafe-like *esprit* to cover all angles – lamb chops, steak au poivre, a dull vitello tonnato. The waiters weave through the tables to ensure two sittings. Usually a table can be had after ten without booking the day ahead. It earns its popularity and its relatively high rating because at its heart it is about food and eating, and quite regularly it can produce strikingly fine dishes. The wines are inexpensive Italians – sixty in total, mostly around £6.

CHEF: Bruno Lambi   PROPRIETOR: Mr Robertilli
OPEN: Mon to Sat   MEALS: 12.30 to 2.30, 7.15 to 11.15
PRICES: £11 (£19). Cover 80p. Minimum £5. Service 12.5%   CARDS: Access, Carte Blanche, Diners, Visa
SEATS: 85. Private parties: 12 main room. Vegetarian meals. Children's helpings. No pipes in dining-room. Wheelchair access. Air-conditioned

Santini   [12/20]   map 11

29 Ebury Street, SW1W 0NX
01-730 4094 and 8275   £20–£30

Italian regional dishes – the kind most high-street trattorias avoid these days – are served with gusto in this fresh, airy restaurant. The loyalty is to Venice, but it looks further afield for specialities such as stuffed courgette flowers, scallops grilled in their shells, and lightly cooked marinated Scotch salmon. Pasta is made on the premises and might be served with artichoke sauce. The staples of the menu, such as hot carpaccio topped with sharp-tasting ruccola leaf, roast quails with polenta, and fillets of sole cooked in butter with courgettes, are supplemented by the likes of osso buco, bagna cauda and bollito misto. Prices are not cheap, nor are the wines from the Santini Private Cellar: Barolo Pio Cesare Riserva '81 at £19·50 is one of the cheapest offerings. House wine is £8·80 a bottle.

CHEFS: Mr Santin and G. Rosselli   PROPRIETOR: Mr Santin
OPEN: all week, exc Sat L and Sun L   CLOSED: bank hols   MEALS: 12.30 to 2.30, 7 to 11.30
PRICES: £19 (£30), Set L £12·50 (£20). Cover £1. Service 12%
CARDS: Access, Amex, Diners, Visa
SEATS: 65. Private parties: 25 main room. Vegetarian meals. Children's helpings. Wheelchair access. Air-conditioned

Seashell   [9/20]   map 11

424 – 426 Kingsland Road, E8 4AT
01-254 6152   £10

The famous Lisson Grove branch has been sold, though many of the staff remain, but we have not been able to inspect. The driving force, John Faulkner, has moved to the East End branch and, as we went to press, renamed the restaurant Faulkner's. There is no stinting on the quality. The fish are prime cuts and fresh, the batter is crisp and the chips thickly cut and fried in hot oil.

Alternatives to cod or skate may be poached salmon. Children are half-price. Russian tea at 35p is another historical pointer. The waitresses wear the familiar Seashell green and white pinnies. Unlicensed.

CHEF: Michael Webber PROPRIETOR: John Faulkner
OPEN: Tue to Sat CLOSED: 1 week at Christmas
MEALS: 12 to 2, 5 (4.30 Fri) to 10 (11.30am to 10pm Sat)
PRICES: £8 (£10). Minimum £2·50. Unlicensed, but bring your own: no corkage
SEATS: 45. Children welcome. Music. Air-conditioned

Shanghai [10/20]   map 11

38C/D Kensington Church Street, W8 4BX
01-938 2413 and 2501   £16-£22

Discreetly hidden behind wooden slats on the bend of the road. Upstairs is the size of a hairdresser's, but a long mural across a partition gives the dining-room a level of sophistication a cut above the usual Peking restaurant. The menu also has a special interest in noodles and dumplings. Shanghai and Peking dumplings, like plump ravioli, are griddle-fried, boiled or steamed. Noodles are worm-fat and served with char siu. Other items on the fashionably westernised menu, drawing on all provinces and centring on Peking duck, suggest that this kitchen is less inclined to compromise than most. Eel dishes feature strongly, and the cheung-du chicken is regaled by its chillies. Spare ribs are better than usual, but mixed rice is not. The fifteen per cent service charge and jasmine tea at 90p per person are reminders that this is a long way from Chinatown.

CHEF: Mr Yee PROPRIETORS: S. K. Lai, K. H. Ching and H. Lok
OPEN: all week MEALS: 12 to 2.30, 6.30 to 11.30
PRICES: £12 (£22), Set L £10 (£16), Set D £12·50 (£20). Cover 80p at D. Service 15%
CARDS: Access, Amex, Diners, Visa
SEATS: 90. Private parties: 70 main room. Vegetarian meals. Children welcome. Music. Air-conditioned

Shapla [10/20]   map 10

380 Brixton Road, SW9 7AW
01-733 7053   £12

Once a shoe shop, now an up-market Indian restaurant with white Doric columns and tubs of flowers on the pavement. Tandoori and Kahrai dishes are good, and there's a range of familiar curries such as rogan josh. Not the cheapest curry in the neighbourhood, but still good value. House wine is £4·50 a bottle.

CHEF: M. Miah PROPRIETOR: Ranu Miah
OPEN: all week MEALS: 12 to 3, 6 to 12
PRICES: £8 (£12) CARDS: Access, Amex, Visa
SEATS: 80. Private parties: 80 main room. Vegetarian meals. Children's helpings. Wheelchair access (also WC). Music

It is helpful if restaurateurs keep the office up to date with any changes.

Restaurants are not expected to solicit customers to send in reports. Please let us know if this happens to you.

Shireen Tandoori [11/20]

map 10

270 Uxbridge Road, W12 7JA
01-743 6857 and 749 5927

£12–£14

The neon lights suggest a night-club, but this is a smart North Indian restaurant with a distinctive menu. Interest centres on the less familiar items, such as masala aubergine with spiced yoghurt, marinated lamb's liver cooked in a kahrai, and chicken Hyderabadi – simmered with yoghurt, tamarind, browned onions and saffron. Otherwise there are votes for the onion bhajias, chicken tikka and rogan josh. To finish, there's hot carrot halva, or cold sheer khurma – a dessert made from milk, vermicelli, dates, nuts and saffron. House French at £4·70 a bottle is an alternative to lager.

CHEF/PROPRIETOR: R. Choudhury
OPEN: all week CLOSED: 25 and 26 Dec MEALS: 12 to 3, 6 to 11.30
PRICES: £8 (£14), Set L and D from £7·50 (£12). Service 10%
CARDS: Access, Amex, Diners, Visa
SEATS: 35. Private parties: 40 main room. Vegetarian meals. Children's helpings.
Wheelchair access (also WC). Music. Air-conditioned

Si Chuen [12/20]

map 14

56 Old Compton Street, W1V 5PN
01-437 2069

£12–£18

Full of light and style, and more like an up-market bistro than a refugee from Chinatown, this is the new incarnation of what was the Dragon Gate, London's seminal and arguably only Szechuan restaurant. Ex-Dragon Gate waitresses are sharp, quick and efficient. Mr Tsoe-Bing who, unusually for Chinese chefs, was born in Zhongqing in Szechuan province and has since worked in both Japan and Hong Kong, stands at the open hatch scrutinising the kitchen and checking each dish before it is sent out. Somehow this brings together cook and eater. Meticulous and colourful dishes emanate, in the form of bang-bang chicken; sliced pork in bruised garlic chilli soy sauce; tea-smoked duck; dai-chin chicken with chilli; and definitive shredded beef with celery, carrot and chilli. As always with Chinese cooking, pork figures enterprisingly: twice-cooked in hot soya paste, or shredded with aubergine in fish-flavoured spicy sauce. It is the heat of the spicing that gives the cooking its impact, from the opening, innocent-looking pickled cabbage that comes with the menu. House wine is £5·80.

CHEF: Tsoe-Bing PROPRIETORS: K. C. Chew and C. L. Man
OPEN: all week MEALS: 12 to 2.30, 5.30 to 11.30
PRICES: £11 (£18), Set L and D from £7·50 (£12). Service 12.5%
CARDS: Amex, Diners, Visa
SEATS: 65. Private parties: 36 main room. Vegetarian meals. Children welcome. Music.
Air-conditioned

Simply Nico [16/20]

map 11

48A Rochester Row, SW1P 1JU
01-630 8061

£28–£45

Safely back in their beloved London following the aborted move to Berkshire, the Ladenis phenomenon gathers pace. A press officer is now employed. For all the obvious Frenchness this is really more of a taverna than a restaurant. The brooding proprietorial presence is a constant factor in the stark, masculine, cramped dining-room, and even in the cooking there are Greek touches, as in a slow roasting of veal studded with pistachios. You eat chez Nico. Simple it is not. Working in the Ladenis kitchens is like getting a bit part in a Fritz Lang movie – endless hours of sieving and re-sieving and endlessly adding ingredients one on top of another to produce a weight of flavour. What Nico is good at is *cooking*, plain and simple – the actual transformation of ingredients from their raw state into deep, sculpted, deliberate tastes. His inspiration is Provence. It's those loud, almost brass-band flavours that speak in all his dishes. His potions are red mullet soup with a rouille; sole with a beurre blanc on a bed of shredded cabbage. Often, so many ingredients are used that dishes have an indeterminate taste. Increasingly, the menu of around twenty dishes has become more abrasive – chicken with Gruyère; Cumberland sauce with a veal and bacon terrine. Sweets are downright provocative: marquises reading almost like an index to a box of Cadbury's Milk Tray – chocolate with orange, with raspberry, with pineapple sorbet, and one day in April a fine crème anglaise laden with vanilla. He too seems to have caught the general mood of dissatisfaction with the constrictions of late *nouvelle cuisine* and, like the modern British chefs, has developed the menu and turned to more powerfully contasting flavours. There is an element too of the mocking, most obviously in the £25 gastronomic menu of foie gras, steak, and chocolate to finish. And there are mistakes – incredible mistakes: overcooked salmon (not that fresh salmon either), the glorious foie gras terrine reduced to a greasy ball in a pink, plastic, sweet-and-sour sauce. Can this be? Such are the perils of delegation. There have been more reports of sous chefs being abused than of customers, for a change, after the events in Shinfield. With three restaurants opened in just over a year – the original Chez Nico, now sold to the couple who had Pebbles at Aylesbury; Shinfield, sold on as the Ortolan to John and Christine Burton-Race; here; and talk of a fourth imminent – it is obviously in the opening of restaurants where the obsessive concentration is now more usually focused. The set lunch is good value but extras like Perrier at £1·50 a small bottle, or coffee at £2·50, each bring the bill closer to the *carte*; so do the quality wines.

CHEF/PROPRIETOR: Nico Ladenis
OPEN: Mon to Fri CLOSED: 1 week at Christmas, 3 weeks Aug MEALS: 12 to 2, 7.30 to 11
PRICES: £24 (£28) to £35 (£45)
SEATS: 35.

Soho Brasserie [11/20]   map 14

23–25 Old Compton Street, W1V 5PJ
01-439 9301   £20

The cream and blue facia might suggest another West End clip joint, but in fact Ind Coope's flagship has been one of the stars of the Soho renaissance. The mood is not overly French, and the menu is so cosmopolitan it might qualify as modern British. Typical successes are fish soup with croûtons, aoïli and Gruyère; bean and walnut salad with Roquefort dressing; sausage and mash; and steak tartare. Light meals are served in front of the bar, where happy hour coincides with the pre-theatre menu. French cider and beers fill out a workable list of forty wines.
CELLARMAN'S CHOICE: Sauvignon du Haut-Poitou '85, £7·45.

CHEF: David Schwartz PROPRIETORS: Ind Coope Ltd
OPEN: Mon to Sat MEALS: 10am to 11.30pm
PRICES: £12 (£20), Snacks from £1·95. Cover 75p CARDS: Access, Amex, Diners, Visa
SEATS: 75. 5 tables outside. Private parties: 20 main room. Vegetarian meals. Children
welcome. Wheelchair access. Music. Air-conditioned

Sonny's [11/20] ✝

map 10

94 Church Road, SW13 0DQ
01-748 0393   £13–£17

The long room's starkness is emphasised by bare, dyed floorboards, and even the
flowers reflect this minimalist approach – white tulips on white linen in
February. The menu by contrast is rich in different influences and complexities.
Eclectically cosmopolitan: excellent fish soup with rouille; spicy flavours of chilli
and ginger prominent in the sliced, pink beef with yam; merguez with a tabouleh
redolent of mint and chilli. It is all summed up in tutti frutti steamed pudding
with orange sauce – not a sticky and heavy sweet stodge, but healthy boiled
sponge with a sharp sauce that whips across the textures. The menu changes
weekly. House wine is £5, but look also to the Italian Chardonnay on an
inventive short list.

CHEF: Kath Lynch PROPRIETOR: Rebecca Mascarenhas
OPEN: all week, exc Sat L and Sun D MEALS: 12.30 to 2.30 (3 Sun), 7.30 to 11
PRICES: £11 (£17), Set L and D £8·95 (£13) CARDS: Access, Visa
SEATS: 70. Private parties: 50 main room. Vegetarian meals. Children welcome. Wheelchair
access. Music. Air-conditioned

▲ Le Soufflé
Inter-continental Hotel [13/20]

map 12

1 Hamilton Place, W1V 0QY
01-409 3131   £26–£41

Peter Kromberg enjoys the envied reputation for running the most proficient
banqueting kitchen in London. The Soufflé restaurant on the ground floor has
been frustratingly erratic but is capable of producing individual dishes of
immense flair. Like the hotel itself, the dining-room is modern and international.
The décor has about as much elegance as a packet of flip-top (duty-free)
cigarettes, and the service can be as anonymous as it is with airline stewards, but
the kitchen is seriously staffed. Two chefs are deputed to soufflés alone – but they
are, after all, the restaurant's stated aim, and they are executed with elan in
many varieties, both to start and to finish. A main dish in January was smoked
haddock soufflé with a Dijon mustard sauce. Pasta is another element in an
enterprising modern menu. Other successes have been sweetbreads on a potato
pancake; wild mushroom soup; steamed langoustines and turbot in a tarragon
sauce. Desserts can be stylish. House wine is from Bordeaux and is £10.
CELLARMAN'S CHOICE: Santenay '79, £21·50.

*Places rating 9 may not be restaurants at all, but still serve good food: expect to find
pubs, cafes, small hotels and wine bars.*

CHEF: Peter Kromberg PROPRIETORS: Inter-continental Hotels Corp.
OPEN: all week, exc Sat L MEALS: 12.30 to 3, 7 to 11.30
PRICES: £26 (£37), Set L £19 (£26), Set D £32 (£41) CARDS: Access, Amex, Diners, Visa
SEATS: 76. Private parties: 15 main room, 700 private room. Car-park, 100 places.
Vegetarian meals. Children's helpings. Jacket and tie. No-smoking area. Wheelchair access
(also WC). Air-conditioned
ACCOMMODATION: 500 rooms, all with bath/shower. Rooms for disabled. Lift. B&B £163 to
£190. Afternoon teas. Sauna. Air-conditioning. TV. Phone

Sree Krishna [10/20]   map 10

194 Tooting High Street, SW17 0SF
01-672 4250   £9

The main interest is in the South Indian vegetarian dishes, which some say are
the best in any comparable restaurant south of the river. Dosais, dahi vada (lentil
'donuts' marinated in yoghurt) and uppuma (fried semolina with onions) all
come with coconut chutney. The South Indian influence extends to the green
banana bhajia and the lemon rice. Standard curry-house meat and fish dishes
are in the mould of sag josh and prawn bhuna. Long queues, low prices. Drink
lassi or lager.

CHEF/PROPRIETOR: R. Ramanarayanan
OPEN: all week MEALS: 12 to 2·45, 6 to 10·45 (11·45 Fri and Sat)
PRICES: £4 (£9). Minimum £2·50. Service 10%
SEATS: 120. Vegetarian meals. Children welcome. Wheelchair access (also WC). Music.
Air-conditioned

Suntory [12/20]   map 13

72 St James's Street, SW1A 1PH
01-409 0201   £20–£47

Revered for its status among the Japanese community, the Suntory is good as it
should be at nearly £50 a head. The black lacquered tables open up to take the
electrical fittings for the shabu-shabu or the sukiyaki, the two most modern and
dullest forms of the cuisine. The *carte* holds more interest than the mechanical
kaiseki menu at £30 a head. Sushi has been properly fired with enough wasabi to
bring tears to the eyes; the Suntory salad is generously arranged with lobster,
clams and octopus, and slightly sharpened with citrus juices. At these prices it is
possible to eat better elsewhere, including Japanese, though the coveted
downstairs rooms are booked well in advance, even for Japanese customers. The
tappan-yaki rooms are fun to start, but the novelty soon wears thin.

CHEF: K. Miura PROPRIETORS: Suntory Limited
OPEN: Mon to Sat MEALS: 12.30 to 1.30, 7 to 9.30
PRICES: £28 (£47), Set L £12 (£20), Set D from £20 (£29). Cover £1·60. Minimum £25
at D. Service 15% CARDS: Access, Amex, Diners, Visa
SEATS: 130. Children welcome

*'I have enjoyed a few good risottos (risotti?), but this was not one of them. It did not
seem to have been slaved over and stewed from beginning to end, as it should have been.
It was more like cooked rice. It was tedious and mediocre.'* (On eating in London)

Le Suquet [14/20]

map 12

104 Draycott Avenue, SW3 3AE
01-581 1785 £28

A miracle with space means that fifty people can actually be seated in supposed comfort in Pierre Martin's excellent little French fish restaurant. It is noisy, cramped and crowded. The main fish dishes, such as grilled bream, sea-bass in a beurre blanc, or monkfish in a lobster sauce, have all the virtues of simplicity and freshness. The cork platter of shellfish is as fresh as when the van arrived from Brittany. The waiters are ebullient and work at an amazing speed considering the lack of space. This and the meat restaurant L'Olivier (see entry) are the pick of M. Martin's restaurants and a persuasive defence of the first principles of restaurateuring – the finest ingredients simply presented. House wine is £7·50.

CHEF: Jean Yves Darcel PROPRIETOR: Pierre Martin
OPEN: all week CLOSED: 1 week at Christmas MEALS: 12.30 to 2.30, 7 to 11.30
PRICES: £20 (£28). Cover £1 CARDS: Access, Amex, Diners, Visa
SEATS: 50. 8 tables outside. Private parties: 16 main room. Children welcome. Wheelchair access. Air-conditioned

Suruchi [10/20]

map 11

18 Theberton Street, Islington, N1 0QX
01-359 8033 £2–£8

One of the smartest and most sophisticated bhel puri houses in London. The pale green décor, bamboo blinds and subdued classical music are a world away from the dim, red flock of most curry houses and very different to the stripped pine image of vegetarian cafes. The menu has the full range of South Indian vegetarian snacks and specialities. The bhel puris are crisp, crunchy puris with puffed rice, potatoes and onions, garnished with garlic and chilli chutneys and tamarind sauce. Other dishes worth trying are khati (vegetable kebabs), pani puri (crisp wheatballs with tamarind and date sauce) and masala dosai (rice pancakes served with coconut chutney and sambar). Good rasmalai to finish. Drink lassi or passion-fruit juice; otherwise bring your own wine – there's a branch of Oddbins only fifty yards away.

PROPRIETORS: Suruchi Partnership
OPEN: all week MEALS: 12.15 to 2.30, 6.15 to 10.45
PRICES: £5 (£8), Set L from £1·50 (£2), Set D from £4 (£5). Unlicensed, but bring your own: no corkage CARDS: Amex, Visa
SEATS: 40. Vegetarian meals. Children welcome. Music

Tante Claire [18/20]

map 12

68 – 69 Royal Hospital Road, SW3 4HP
01-352 6045 £22–£41

The pleasure of Pierre Koffmann's restaurant is in the understated professionalism. No fawning personal appearances, no over-elaboration, just a beautiful modern summer's room now filled with vibrant paintings and cooking of rare excellence. Here the full subtlety of the cook's armoury comes to the fore. This is modern French cooking on a level with the best in France. Sauces are used to perfume or stimulate the real flavours. They uplift. Whole langoustines wrapped in ravioli are served with a consommé flavoured with truffles and asparagus; venison with a sauce of raspberry and chocolate. The technique is admirable and brings on to the menu such dishes as a duck leg stuffed with its liver; rabbit with langoustine, pigs' trotters with morels. The infectious mood of modern British cookery (after all, this is cooking in Britain) is found in some individual pairing of flavours: lobster with Madiran; turbot on lentils; pistachio soufflé with a tea sauce. All of this comes at a price – cheeses are £6·90 – but it is cheaper than going to France, and there would be no guarantee of finding anything comparable. The wine list is predictably weighted to expensive classic French regions at high prices, but it is not rapacious and with good intent a way can be found – house Provence is commendably pegged at £7·75, there are fine Alsace wines around £12, equally from the Loire, and a spattering of halves before the precipice of the classed growths and burgundies. Some New World wines would help, but that would be to miss the point.

CHEF: Pierre Koffmann PROPRIETORS: Mr and Mrs Pierre Koffmann
OPEN: Mon to Fri MEALS: 12.30 to 2, 7 to 11
PRICES: £34 (£41), Set L £18 (£22). Minimum £25 at D. Service inc
CARDS: Access, Amex, Diners, Visa
SEATS: 38. Children welcome. Jacket and tie. Wheelchair access

Tate Gallery [9/20]

map 11

Millbank, SW1P 4RG
01-834 6754

 £19

The romance of the Whistler mural that surrounds this basement is slightly off key to the deep institutional structure of the restaurant. The heroically inexpensive wine list of many, many bargains, although thinner than previously, is an easy match for the red meats, Stiltons and Cheddars on the menu. The cooking of other dishes is erratic and not always in sympathy with the quality of the wines, despite commendable efforts at patriotism.

CHEF: Michael Driver PROPRIETORS: Trustees of the Tate Gallery
OPEN: Mon to Sat, L only CLOSED: most bank hols MEALS: 12 to 3
PRICES: £13 (£19). Minimum £4
SEATS: 130. Private parties: 15 main room. Vegetarian meals. Children's helpings.
No-smoking area. Wheelchair access (also WC). Air-conditioned

Tiger Lee [12/20]

map 11

251 Old Brompton Road, SW5 9HP
01-370 2323 and 5970

£29–£31

When Chinese restaurants were cheap, Tiger Lee was expensive. Now it does not seem that astronomic by comparison. It is meant for business accounts and is strong on service and pretension. But there are a number of dishes here not usually found elsewhere: lacquered pigeon (not on the menu, but ask), and deep-fried crispy chicken. Fish is the main business, and there is a range of it: eel, abalone, prawn, and lobster dishes. Warm-water fish like tilapia are bred in Surrey. Wines are expensive and start at £8·80.

CHEF: Cheong Hong PROPRIETOR: C. Cassuto
OPEN: all week, D only CLOSED: Christmas MEALS: 6 to 11.15
PRICES: £18 (£31), Set D from £20 (£29). Service 15% CARDS: Amex, Diners, Visa
SEATS: 56. Private parties: 36 main room. Vegetarian meals. Children welcome. Smart dress
preferred. No-smoking area. Wheelchair access. Air-conditioned

Topkapi [12/20]   map 13

25 Marylebone High Street, W1A,3PE
01-486 1872   £13–£14

The kitchen in the window suggests that this has the confidence of much of
London's Turkish community. The Eastern promise of the décor in glittering
hanging lamps, brass plates on the walls and authentic music is repeated in the
menu. Each visit can be a new experience. The meze range from filo pastry
triangles filled with soft cheese to stuffed aubergines; from goat's milk cheese
whipped up with sweet red pepper and mint to haricot beans with oil, carrots and
tomatoes. Minced lamb with vine leaves, peppers and rice is a speciality, and
some of the best doner kebabs in central London are found here. Service is
courteous. The Turkish wines include Villa Doluca red at £7·50 and white at £7.

CHEF: R. Kalayci PROPRIETOR: U. Fahri
OPEN: all week MEALS: noon to midnight
PRICES: £8 (£14), Set L and D £9 (£13). Service 10% CARDS: Access, Amex, Diners, Visa
SEATS: 50. Private parties: 20 main room. Vegetarian meals. Children's helpings.
Wheelchair access (also WC). Music

Tui [11/20]   map 12

19 Exhibition Road, SW7 2HE
01-584 8359   £22

A small Thai restaurant decorated in Western designer style with Conran blinds,
and a long Buddhist scroll on gold-painted palm leaves, but otherwise all black
and white, with high ceilings and spotlights. The food is genuine enough, with
plenty of chilli in the garnishing. Spicy soups, such as coconut milk, lemon grass,
galingale and chicken, are consistently popular, pomfret comes crispy with red
peppers and chillies, and prawns are fried in oil with spices. The three Thai
sweets may be an acquired taste, but the fresh fruits and vegetables are not.
Expensive Thai beer, as well as a short list of good wines.

CHEFS: Mr and Mrs Kongsvivilai PROPRIETOR: Ekachai Thapthimthong
OPEN: all week MEALS: 12 to 2.30, 6.30 to 11 (12.30 to 3, 7 to 10.30 Sun)
PRICES: £12 (£22). Cover 75p. Service 12.5% CARDS: Access, Amex, Diners, Visa
SEATS: 50. Private parties: 20 main room. Children welcome. No cigars. Wheelchair access.
Music

Turner's [15/20]   map 12

87–89 Walton Street, SW3 2HP
01-584 6711   £19–£30

Brian Turner, formerly at the Capital Hotel, reappears in his own restaurant, an
elegant, L-shaped, pastel-coloured room with sunken sofas, respectable prints

and a view through blinds on to the riches of Walton Street, itself preoccupied with art galleries and fashion. The deeply French menu is tailored in the same mood, a set meal for midday, a *carte* of safe, expensive choices, each carefully sauced and seasoned – a tartare of scallops with thinly sliced gherkins on a spread of winter salads with a grind of pepper; a golden clear chicken consommé with herbs; very good lamb in a salt and herb crust with a creamy, deep reduction of stock; a main course of quenelles of pike in a saffron sauce with side plates of mixed vegetables. The repertoire does not vary much, but Mr Turner is usually in the dining-room to help things along. The touches, like jewellery – canapés of escargots vol-au-vent and the acute wine list that has picked what it wants – reinforce the sense of style, as do the female staff. House Côtes du Rhône or Muscadet are £10·50 and £11·50 respectively. A trio of Sancerre from Dezat – red, rosé and white – provides interest, though the Alsace section is probably better value at £3 less. CELLARMAN'S CHOICE: Domaine de Fontarney '79, £19·50.

CHEFS: Brian J. Turner and Mark Clayton PROPRIETOR: Brian J. Turner
OPEN: Sun to Fri MEALS: 12.30 to 2.45, 7.30 to 11
PRICES: £23 (£30), Set L from £13·50 (£19), Set D from £19·50 (£25). Service inc
CARDS: Access, Amex, Diners, Visa
SEATS: 52. Private parties: 16 main room. Wheelchair access. Music. Air-conditioned

Twenty Trinity Gardens [11/20] ✔   map 10

20 Trinity Gardens, SW9 8DP
01-733 8838   £7 – £18

The cooking offers plenty of choice and also value at this elegant brasserie-cum-restaurant. The style is one of cosmopolitan modern British as cooked by a Frenchman under the organising eye of an Englishwoman using, in the case of the bouillabaisse, West Indian fish stalls at the market to supply the ingredients for this Mediterranean dish (shark, snapper, tuna, mussels, fennel, garlic and chilli make up the broth). Recommended starters include eggs Arnold Bennett, vegetable soup, and aubergine charlotte. Reports mention beef in all manner of ways, from rib eyes with red wine and onions; with parsley and horseradish; with sour cream and paprika. Among meringues and gateaux there is also spotted dick to finish. The related Brixton Brasserie nearby in Acre Lane does not really compete. House French is £5·75. CELLARMAN'S CHOICE: Ch. La Gaffelière, St Emilion '70, £12·95.

CHEFS: Jacques Bergougnoux and Kim Welch PROPRIETORS: Jane Mann and David Spence
OPEN: Mon to Sat, exc Sat L MEALS: 12.30 to 2.30, 7 to 10.30
PRICES: Set L £2·50 (£7) to £12·75 (£18), Set D £8·50 (£13) to £12·75 (£18) CARD: Visa
SEATS: 50. 3 tables outside. Private parties: 8 main room, 20 private room. Vegetarian meals. No children under 8. No-smoking area. Music

Upper Street Fish Shop [9/20]   map 11

324 Upper Street, N1 2XQ
01-359 1401   £8

There is always a great deal of bustle about the Conways' fish cafe. The walls are covered with posters advertising forthcoming events in Islington. Although the main menu deals with standard chippie fare like cod, plaice, skate (wing and middle), scampi (which is monk) the daily specials tip their hat to fashions such as salads for the weight-conscious and tend to make use of the more expensive fish like salmon, sea-bass, and halibut. In season there are oysters. The fish soup is excellent, halibut fried in egg is as 'greaseless as fried food could be'. Chips are old English – some soggy, some crisp – and always plentiful. The sweets are from the nursery and include one of the best treacle tarts in London; other dishes like jam roly-poly are reassuringly good too. Unlicensed.

CHEF: Alan Conway PROPRIETORS: Alan and Olga Conway
OPEN: Mon to Sat, exc Mon L CLOSED: bank hols MEALS: 11.30 to 2, 5.30 to 10
PRICES: £7 (£8). Unlicensed, but bring your own: no corkage
SEATS: 48. Children's helpings. Wheelchair access. Air-conditioned

Wakaba [11/20]   map 11

122A Finchley Road, NW3 5HT
01-586 7960   £22 – £25

Wakaba has moved to what was London's only Chinese vegetarian restaurant, Green Cottage II. It sports a pure white hi-tech interior. The use of panels, lighting, interesting shapes and pillars makes this dramatic and in co-ordination with the food. Service is friendly, and regulars especially are warmly welcomed. It is one of the more accessible of London's Japanese restaurants. The array of fresh fish and prawns is impressive at the sushi bar. They serve on immaculate light wood blocks. Other dishes to look for are: salmon grilled with salt; four pads of fried bean curd with soy sauce and ginger; mixed tempura. Beef teriyaki comes as a row of thick slices of steak surrounded by vegetables. Sukiyaki cooked at the table and served DIY into bowls with raw egg is a good version. Desserts are fresh fruits carved into exotic shapes. Drink tea, saké or whisky.

CHEF/PROPRIETOR: Minoru Yoshihara
OPEN: Tue to Sun CLOSED: 5 days at Christmas, 4 days at Easter MEALS: 12 to 2.30, 6 to 11
PRICES: £19 (£25), Set D from £16·80 (£22). Cover 50p. Service 12.5%
CARDS: Access, Amex, Diners, Visa
SEATS: 60. Private parties: 40 main room, 20 private room. Children welcome. Wheelchair access (also WC). Air-conditioned

Waltons [12/20]   map 12

121 Walton Street, SW3 2HP
01-584 0204   £18 – £41

Waltons is an anachronism: neither properly French nor English; giving a nod to *nouvelle cuisine* while serving scrambled eggs to conservative businessmen for lunch; having tired and over-the-top décor combining several styles at once; with very high prices; where women are given unpriced menus; with service of the gracious undertaker school; without the confidence in the basic integrity of its cooking not to serve a sauce with almost every dish to make it appear special. It seems to serve no clear purpose in the scheme of restaurant life in today's London and to be totally oblivious of the fact that it is on one of the most competitive up-market restaurant streets in Britain. On the credit side, the set menus do provide a stark financial contrast to the *carte*, and lunch in particular is a snip. The wine list is classically French and superlative in the £30 to £70 range of vintage clarets. The Rhône and Alsace ease the financial leash somewhat. Some New World wines would add some humanity. As it is, Waltons represents a serious risk of pecuniary embarrassment for relatively inconsequential, international hotel food to anyone who cannot easily put up the ante.

CHEF: Gary Jones PROPRIETORS: Waltons Restaurants Ltd
OPEN: all week CLOSED: bank hols
MEALS: 12.30 to 2.30 (2 Sun), 7.30 to 11.30 (10.30 Sun)
PRICES: £27 (£41), Set L from £12 (£18), Set D (after 10pm) £19·50 (£27). Service 15%
CARDS: Access, Amex, Diners, Visa
SEATS: 65. Private parties: 65 main room. Children welcome. Smart dress preferred.
Wheelchair access. Air-conditioned

White Tower [12/20]   map 13

1 Percy Street, W1P OET
01-636 8141   £24

The White Tower is an old-fashioned treat, that rarity of a restaurant whose reputation has not crushed its kitchen. It is a tribute to the elegantly written literary menu, now in its fourth decade, that it can stand the passage of time and remain, even today, the most persuasive defender of Greek-style cooking. Some of the dishes are definitive: taramosalata; fish salad; aubergine Imam Bayeldi; duck stuffed with bougourie, almonds, and its liver. The run of grills provides a safe alternative, and a pair of daily specials the spice. The whole atmosphere, even some of the resorting to processed vegetables, smacks of the 1950s, as does the solicitous, intrusive service. The wine list even carries the legend PRICES INCLUDE V A T, as if this were a new thing. Alas, the prices are rather more than up to date. House Othello is £6·50.

CHEF: Luigi Contini PROPRIETOR: E. Stais
OPEN: Mon to Fri CLOSED: 1 week at Christmas, 3 weeks Aug
MEALS: 12.30 to 2.30, 6.30 to 10.30
PRICES: £17 (£24). Cover £1. Minimum £12·50 CARDS: Access, Amex, Diners, Visa
SEATS: 80. Private parties: 10 main room, 16 private room. Children welcome.
Air-conditioned

Wiltons [12/20]   map 13

55 Jermyn Street, SW1Y 6LX
01-629 9955   £33

The taste is of that peculiarly English era on either side of the war. The premises may have changed, but little else, least of all the atmosphere. Wiltons remains somewhere to find unmucked-around food of good quality in a dining-room of memories. Shellfish is reliable in the form of langoustines, crabs or lobsters, sole or plaice, as are other punctuation marks of English cooking such as grouse or bread-and-butter pudding. All of this comes at a handsome price, not least the wines, and with a conspiratorial sniff from the staff. House claret £9.

'As a pipe-smoker who refrains in a restaurant with a cigarette substitute, I was appalled by the perfume of another diner.' (On eating in London)

CHEF: Ross Hayden PROPRIETORS: Wiltons Ltd
OPEN: Mon to Sat, exc Sat L CLOSED: 3 weeks in summer
MEALS: 12.30 to 2.30, 6.30 to 10.30
PRICES: £23 (£33). Cover £1. Minimum £12·50 CARDS: Access, Amex, Diners, Visa
SEATS: 90. Private parties: 20 main room, 18 private room. Children welcome. Jacket and
tie. Wheelchair access. Air-conditioned

Wong Kei [9/20]   map 14

41–43 Wardour Street, W1V 3HA
01-437 3071 and 6833   £4–£9

An old clock high above the entrance spells out that this was once a wig-maker's.
Now it is one of the cheapest eating-places in Chinatown (or London), where the
waiters work like policemen on point duty, directing customers to the four floors
of the emporium. The menu revolves around one-plate dishes, a bowl or a
plateful of food that can provide a quick, cheap meal. This is Cantonese fast food
at its speediest and most efficient. The quickest meal of all is a dish of soup and
noodles; otherwise there are massive platefuls of noodles with all kinds of meat,
offal, seafood, and vegetables. The full menu – for those who have time to spare –
includes superb steamed chicken, which is virtually half a bird cleaved into
pieces, cooked pink and served with heaps of pak-choi as succulent as asparagus.
Tea is free and a pot comes with the menu. Cash only.

CHEF: T. F. Tang PROPRIETORS: E. Liu and M. H. Lo
OPEN: all week MEALS: noon to 11.30pm
PRICES: £7 (£9), Set L and D £1·80 (£4). Service inc
SEATS: 435. Private parties: 80 main room, 80 private room. Vegetarian meals. Children
welcome. Wheelchair access (also WC)

Yerakina [11/20] 🥢   map 11

10 Kentish Town Road, NW1 9NX
01-485 5743   £8–£15

The meze raises this Cypriot taverna above the local average – thirty snack-sized
dishes served in three great waves. First might come squid salad with coriander;
pickled octopus; cold quail in vinegar; then char-grilled haloumi cheese; half a
dozen fish dishes including kalamari and mussels; and then meaty stews and
casseroles served with pourgouri (cracked wheat cooked with onions); and
finally a Greek salad to refresh the palate. Centrepieces on the full menu are grills,
kebabs and hearty dishes such as pork afelia with coriander seeds, moussaka and
lucanika. Coffee comes with grapes and sweetmeats. House wine is Greek
Rotonda at £4·50 a bottle.

CHEFS: Andreas Gregoriades, E. Ramudo and C. Lambrou
PROPRIETOR: Andreas Gregoriades
OPEN: all week MEALS: 12 to 3, 6 to 12
PRICES: £9 (£15), Set L from £4 (£8). Service 10% CARDS: Access, Diners, Visa
SEATS: 90. Private parties: 90 main room. Vegetarian meals. Children welcome. Wheelchair
access (also WC). Music. Air-conditioned

All inspections are carried out anonymously.

Yung's [11/20]

map 14

23 Wardour Street, W1V 3HD
01-734 4566

£11–£19

On three pistachio-coloured levels: in the basement sit the Chinese, the ground floor the Europeans, and upstairs the English. Yung's has a number of advantages over the competition – it is open very late, and the menu encompasses Canton, Peking and Szechuan apparently with equal verve. Spare ribs are meaty and falling off the bone; hot-and-sour soup has amazing bite; chicken with three kinds of mushrooms including wild as well as cultivated; crispy beef fried with carrots is exemplary. The food is slow to come out of the dumb-waiters. There are always queues at peak hours, and extra tables are bustled out when necessary. Once the oranges arrive your time is limited. Well favoured by waiters from other Chinese restaurants.

CHEF/PROPRIETOR: N. G. Ming
OPEN: all week MEALS: 4pm to 4am
PRICES: £11 (£19), Set D from £6·50 (£11). Minimum £5·50. Service 10% CARDS: Access, Amex, Diners, Visa
SEATS: 95. Private parties: 30 main room. Children welcome. Air-conditioned

Zen [12/20]

map 12

Chelsea Cloisters, Sloane Avenue, SW3 3DN
01-589 1781

£10–£29

Imitations spawn faster than microchips, but the original Zen thrives beneath Chelsea Cloisters in the same arena that saw the death of many a European venture before. It is imperiously opulent, one of the more successful marriages of Asian street food to the Western concept of the restaurant, more conservative and middle-aged even compared to its vibrant younger brother in Hampstead. The menu is long but pivots on a few central expensive dishes – steamed sea-bass; lobster with spring onions; crab with black beans; Peking duck; suckling pig (twenty-four hours' notice needed for this). Nam King duck arrives whole at the table before being carved – first the reddened crisp skin laid on prawn toasts with the mandatory pancakes, hoisin and spring onions, and then the legs and parson's nose, crisped, surrounding a mix of the trimmings with vegetables. The array of nearly sixty starters from all the provinces of China are more than competently executed. There are vegetarian dishes including good bean curd, which testifies to the fact that Zen has not been completely deserted by Chinese. The wine list is an intelligent attempt to marry the cultures of two countries a world apart.

CHEF: K. S. Leung PROPRIETOR: Lawrence Leung
OPEN: all week CLOSED: 25 to 27 Dec MEALS: 12 to 2.30, 6 to 11.30 (noon to 11.30pm Sat and Sun)
PRICES: £17 (£29), Set L £4·50 (£10). Minimum £8. Service 15% CARDS: Access, Amex, Diners, Visa
SEATS: 120. Private parties: 100 main room, 20 private room. Vegetarian meals. Children welcome. Wheelchair access. Music. Air-conditioned

If you cannot honour a restaurant booking, always phone to cancel.

Zen Central [new entry, zero rated]

map 13

20–22 Queen Street, W1X 7PJ
01-629 8103   £27

The newest Zen opened as the *Guide* was going to press. But first meals confirmed
the thought that the partnership of Lawrence Leung on the money and Michael
Leung overseeing the kitchen is one of the most dynamic of the 1980s. The
bubbling waters and rectangular glass are a far cry from the off-street Soho days
of Shu Shan or the Earls Court hinterland of I Ching – and that was only six years
ago. What the Leungs perceived and fulfil is the demand for a high-quality
alternative to French cooking. They are also quick enough to pick up on the new-
wave design in restaurants. The menu runs to 86 items, strongly biased towards
Canton, but plundering the usual provinces for Peking duck. Sole or sea-bass
come five ways: steamed with ginger and spring onions; with black-bean sauce;
with tangerine peel (excellent); deep fried and braised with fresh coriander and
chilli; and sweet and sour. Sauces are based on a stock-pot in the kitchen. No MSG
is used. Unusually for a Chinese (indeed Oriental) restaurant there is innovation
here, signs of a cook responding to circumstances – for instance, the excellent
smoked chicken, which is first cooked in soy combined with spices before being
smoked. Of dishes tasted, the dumplings are good without really being better
than anywhere in Chinatown; but there is a variation of the famous Cantonese
sliced cold trotter and chicken marinated in rice wine; or again prawns and sole
fillets wrapped and steamed in lotus leaves served without sauce to allow the
freshness to show. Portions are small, which adds to the bill, but the true
comparison is not really with Chinatown, where the food is cheaper but less
polished, but with other Central London restaurants. In that light it becomes
better value, and service and surroundings and wine list demand a fair price. A
hundred wines are well spread and make a reasonable attempt to bring cultures
together. There's even Vendange Tardive.

CHEF: Michael Leung PROPRIETOR: Lawrence Leung
OPEN: all week CLOSED: 25 Dec MEALS: 12 to 3, 6 to11.45 (11.15 Sun)
PRICES: £14 (£27). Cover £1. Service 15% CARDS: Access, Amex, Diners, Visa
SEATS: 110. Private parties: 80 main room, 20 private room. Vegetarian meals. Children
welcome. Jacket and tie. Music. Air-conditioned

Zen W3 [11/20]

map 11

83 Hampstead High Street, NW3 1RE
01-794 7863 and 7864   £12–£17

The fashionable place to eat in North London for the last year has been this glitzy,
new-wave Chinese restaurant. The menu is an intelligent selection from different
regions with a few innovations, such as boiled medallions of veal with black
pepper. Standards fluctuate, but the bean curd dishes, such as spinach sauté with
chilli, or steamed and stuffed with prawn paste, suggest the kitchen has not

All inspections are carried out anonymously.

The Guide *is independent, accepts no advertising and survives solely on the number of
copies sold.*

abandoned all its ethics for a few gimmicks. The generous use of chilli through prawns and ravioli hides the faults. In essence it is modern cooking – charcoal grilled meats, 'lightning' fried meats and seafoods, spicy salads. No MSG is used. The wine list has some Californians and is unusually strong in good Chardonnay and champagne.

CHEF: K. S. Leung PROPRIETOR: Lawrence Leung
OPEN: all week CLOSED: 25 to 27 Dec MEALS: noon to 11.30pm
PRICES: £10 (£17), Set L £6·80 (£12). Service 12.5% CARDS: Access, Amex, Diners, Visa
SEATS: 155. Private parties: 135 main room, 20 private room. Vegetarian meals. Children welcome. Music. Air-conditioned

England

AISLABY North Yorkshire   map 6A

▲ *Blacksmith's Arms* [11/20]

Aislaby YO18 8PE
PICKERING (0751) 72182
1½m W of Pickering, on A170   £16

The trappings of the smithy's old forge – anvil, bellows, tools and harness – have
been retained and in the dining-room the original oven is now a log fire. The
menu is short, with fish among the starters, from a light terrine of sole or smoked
haddock with white wine and chive sauce, to a neatly garnished parcel of trout
mousse wrapped in smoked salmon. The Englishness of the cooking shows in the
use of local game, for instance pheasant with a sage and port sauce, or there is
pork with delicate orange and lime sauce. Local Beamerdale, a soft goats' cheese,
makes an appearance, along with Wensleydale and unpasteurised Colston
Bassett Stilton; the walnut bread is home made. Brandy-snap basket filled with
exotic fruits, in a pool of mango sauce, makes a dramatic finish. House wine is £5
a carafe.

CHEF: Linda Stevenson PROPRIETORS: Mr and Mrs G. Webster
OPEN: Wed to Sat D, and Sun L CLOSED: Jan MEALS: 12 to 2, 7 to 9.15
PRICES: £12 (£16) CARD: Access
SEATS: 40. Private parties: 40 main room. Car-park, 20 places. Vegetarian meals. Children's
helpings. Wheelchair access
ACCOMMODATION: 5 rooms, 3 with bath/shower. B&B £15 to £30. Afternoon teas

---

ALDBOROUGH Norfolk   map 6

Old Red Lion [10/20]

The Village Green, Aldborough, NR11 7AA
CROMER (0263) 761451   £12–£19

An old pub on the village green has been turned into a useful local restaurant
serving familiar Continental dishes. Italian-born Bruno Diluzio cooks and runs
the place with his wife and relatives. The food is unpretentious, and ingredients
are of good quality: fish salad has plenty of seafood in a piquant sauce; veal
marsala is a fine piece of meat. French bistro dishes include moules marinière and
coquilles St Jacques parisienne. Vegetables might feature petits pois cooked with
lettuce and onions, and there's excellent caramel fluff to finish.

CHEF: Mr Diluzio PROPRIETORS: Mr and Mrs Eyles and Mr and Mrs Diluzio
OPEN: Tue to Sun, exc Sun D MEALS: 12 to12.30, 7 to 10.30
PRICES: £12 (£19), Set L £8·45 (£12), Set D £9·25 (£13), Snacks £1·15
CARDS: Access, Visa
SEATS: 40. Private parties: 60 main room. Car-park, 12 places. Children's helpings. Music

---

ALDBOURNE Wiltshire   map 2

Raffles [10/20]

1 The Green, Aldbourne SN8 2BW
MARLBOROUGH (0672) 40700   £19

The best-kept bistro in the best-kept village in the county; highly varnished
tables, wall-mounted globe lamps and prints of Victorian fashions help to make it
look neat and up-market, and the menu follows suit. The Hannans are working
to improve the quality of their ingredients, and the menu has some interesting
ideas – medallions of veal with ceps and home-made noodles; fresh scallops with
Ricard – as well as bistro staples: French onion soup, calf's liver cooked in butter,
fillet of pork in pastry with mustard sauce. Good, plainly cooked vegetables are
served on to the plate. Sweets are plain and down-market. Fifty French wines
start at £5·25. CELLARMAN'S CHOICE: Ch. La Tour de By '83, £10·60.

CHEF: James Hannan PROPRIETORS: James and Mary Hannan
OPEN: Mon to Sat D, and Tue to Fri L CLOSED: 2 weeks Aug, 25 to 30 Dec MEALS: 12.30 to
2.15, 7 to 11
PRICES: £14 (£19) CARDS: Access, Amex, Diners, Visa
SEATS: 36. 3 tables outside. Private parties: 36 main room. Children's helpings (L only).
Smart dress preferred. Wheelchair access. Music

ALFRISTON East Sussex   map 3

Moonrakers [10/20]

High Street, Alfriston BN26 5TD
ALFRISTON (0323) 870472   £18

The wines and some old-fashioned French cooking are the main attractions at
the Wilkinsons' sixteenth-century cottage, which has lots of beams, leaded
window panes and bare varnished tables. The short menu seldom changes:
coarse chicken-liver terrine, Burgundy pie, and hot Sussex smokie still feature,
with a few nods to 1988, such as crispy duck with kumquats, or sole with lime
and ginger. Sauces are flour-based and sweets are sweet, but the wine list is as
kind under £10 as it is to mature claret and burgundy. There are gems among
the few bottles from Spain and Italy.

CHEF: Elaine Wilkinson PROPRIETORS: Elaine and Barry Wilkinson
OPEN: Tue to Sat, D only MEALS: 7 to 9.15 (6.45 to 9.45 Sat)
PRICES: Set D £13·90 (£18)
SEATS: 32. 2 tables outside. Private parties: 32 main room. Vegetarian meals.
Children's helpings

Reports on shops, cafes and farms are useful, as well as reports on restaurants.

ALRESFORD Hampshire   map 2

Old School House [new entry, zero rated]

60 West Street, Alresford SO24 9AN ✗
ALRESFORD (096 273) 2134   £12–£19

Probably the headmaster's house; the school itself is further up the road. It has
been enlarged inside, with two dining-rooms in rust red, fresh flowers, and white
china. Sara McTurk cooks a modern, Anglo-French menu based on reduced
stocks. A timbale of smoked haddock in a lightly curried sauce is sliced open to
reveal a filling of prawns; other good dishes have been cauliflower and bacon
soup, stuffed duck, chicken with walnuts, hazelnut roulade. Service from Terry
McTurk is accomplished. The young wine list centres on France, but there are
mature Portuguese wines, including a Garrafeira Particular '74 at £9·75. House
wine is £5·50 a bottle. More reports, please.

CHEFS/PROPRIETORS: Sara and Terry McTurk
OPEN: Tue to Sat D, and Sat and Sun L MEALS: 12.30 to 2, 7 to 10
PRICES: £13 (£19), Set L £7·50 (£12), Set D £8·50 (£13). Minimum £7·50
SEATS: 76. Private parties: 24 main room. Children welcome. Wheelchair access (1 step).
Music. Air-conditioned

ALSTON Cumbria   map 7

▲ *High Fell* [11/20]

Alston CA9 3BP
ALSTON (0498) 81597
1½ m S of Alston, on A686   £23

The approach to this upland farmhouse is unimpressive, but once inside things
are quite different: rooms are warm and pleasant, the dining-room in particular
being welcoming and restful. What impresses most of all is the quality of Patricia
Chipman's classic bourgeois French cooking. Boeuf royale and salmon in
tarragon and tomato sauce have both been first class. Vegetables are outstanding
– baby turnips baked in butter, parsnips with a hint of apricot, carrots with
lemon. The Chipmans have been threatening to retire, but were still in charge as
we went to press. The wine list is in a perpetual state of evolution.

CHEF: Patricia Chipman PROPRIETORS: John and Patricia Chipman
OPEN: all week MEALS: 12.30 to 2, 7.30 to 9
PRICES: £18 (£23). Licensed, but bring your own: corkage £2
SEATS: 16. 1 table outside. Private parties: 16 main room. Car-park, 12 places. No children
under 5. No-smoking area
ACCOMMODATION: 5 rooms, 3 with bath/shower. B&B £23·50 to £46. Deposit: £20.
No children under 12. Garden. Fishing. Golf. Scenic

▲ *This restaurant has rooms.*

*The entries are compiled from the views of readers who have eaten at the restaurants in
the last year, backed up by anonymous inspections and by information supplied and
facts verified by the restaurants.*

ALTRINCHAM Greater Manchester   map 5

French [new entry, zero rated]

25 The Downs, Altrincham WA14 2QD
061 – 941 3355   £10 – £15

The mirrored glass with blinds, the reproduction, varnished tables, a fake tree in the middle of the room and Ella Fitzgerald on tape, give an incredibly French impression. There are two menus: one of regional dishes from Burgundy, such as coq au Chambertin, the other of fashionable bistro specialities. Fish soup has a hint of fennel and saffron and pieces of strawberry added; wild mushrooms are served with a lozenge of puff pastry and winter salad dressed with an impressive mustardy vinaigrette. Boned, stuffed poussin comes with three sauces, and there is plenty of duck, goose and pork in the cassoulet. There are many good touches: abundant well-cooked vegetables, interesting salads, decent home-made pastry and no irrelevant little garnishes. All in all, good value for money. The mainly French wine list has many bottles under £10. More reports, please.

CHEF: Dave Johnson-Cree PROPRIETOR: Chris Hume
OPEN: all week, exc Sat L MEALS: 12 to 2.30, 6 to 11.30
PRICES: £10 (£15), Set L and early D £5·50 (£10) CARDS: Access, Visa
SEATS: 85. Private parties: 80 main room, 25 private room. Vegetarian meals. Children's helpings. Wheelchair access (2 steps). Music

---

AMBLESIDE Cumbria   map 7

▲ *Kirkstone Foot Country House Hotel* [10/20]

Kirkstone Pass Road, Ambleside LA22 9EH
AMBLESIDE (0966) 32232   £17

The lawned garden looks up to Wansfell and down to the beck; after a hard day's walking there is a simple, regimented formula at the Batemans' – dinner at eight, and ties preferred. The centrepiece roast meat with vegetables and gravy is homely, as are the soups which precede it. The chief area of excellence, though, is the sweets trolley: nutty meringues with raspberries and cream; blackberry soufflé; pears in cinnamon pastry. Second and third helpings are encouraged, and this can be followed by a very good selection of English cheeses. The sixty wines are varied, with gratifyingly low mark-ups. CELLARMAN'S CHOICE: Australian Chardonnay, Hill-Smith '85, at £8·25.

CHEF: Jane Bateman PROPRIETORS: Jane and Simon Bateman
OPEN: all week, D only CLOSED: mid-Dec to mid-Feb MEALS: 8
PRICES: Set D £12·50 (£17) CARDS: Access, Amex, Diners, Visa
SEATS: 65. 8 tables outside. Private parties: 70 main room, 12 and 25 private rooms. Carpark, 40 places. Vegetarian meals. Children's helpings. No children under 8. Jacket and tie. No smoking during meals. Wheelchair access (also WC). Air-conditioned. One sitting
ACCOMMODATION: 14 rooms, all with bath/shower. B&B £22; D, B&B £35. Pets welcome. Afternoon teas. Garden. TV. Phone. Scenic. Doors close at 12. Confirm by 6

Many of the more expensive restaurants offer bargain lunches for half the price of a meal in the evening. Details are given in the text.

▲ *Rothay Manor* [12/20] ✗

Rothay Bridge, Ambleside LA22 0EH
AMBLESIDE (053 94) 33605   £10–£23

The reception rooms at the Nixons' Lakeland country house are honest-to-goodness old fashioned, though the dining-room overlooking the lawned gardens is more elegant, with deep-pile carpets and velvet curtains. Ancient, polished, candlelit tables, heavy cutlery, and serving girls with mob caps and pinnies complete the scene. Set five-course dinners are rooted in the English tradition of fine centrepieces, such as roast loin of pork with savoury bacon and onion stuffing, poached salmon, or pheasant cooked in wine. To start there are pâtés, terrines, and soups, from consommé to cream of courgette. The Englishness of the cooking shows in the wide range of pickles, chutneys and relishes, and again in the puddings. Good buffet lunches and afternoon teas. The wines straddle the classic and the commonplace, reaching from Chile through Bulgaria to Lebanon. Southern France – Ardèche, Dordogne, Gascony, Haut-Poitou, Languedoc, Provence and Corsica – provides in miniature what all wine lists should, namely variety and character at sensible prices. Whole bottles can be served as halves at three-fifths of their full price.

CHEF: Jane Binns PROPRIETORS: Nigel Nixon and Stephen Nixon
OPEN: all week CLOSED: 4 weeks, Jan to Feb MEALS: 12.30 to 2 (12.45 to 1.30 Sun), 8 to 9
PRICES: Set weekday L from £6 (£10), Set Sun L £9·50 (£14), Set D £17·50 (£23)
CARDS: Access, Amex, Diners, Visa
SEATS: 70. Private parties: 12 main room, 30 private room. Car-park, 30 places. Vegetarian meals. Children's helpings. Smart dress preferred. No smoking in dining-room. Wheelchair access (also WC). Air-conditioned. Self-service weekday L
ACCOMMODATION: 18 rooms, all with bath/shower. Rooms for disabled. B&B £49 to £70. Deposit: £50. Children welcome. Baby facilities. Afternoon teas. Garden. TV. Phone. Scenic. Doors close at 12. Confirm by 12 [GHG]

Sheila's Cottage [10/20]

The Slack, Ambleside LA22 9DQ
AMBLESIDE (0966) 33079   £13

In an alley of the old town. After twenty-three years, Stewart and Janice Greaves' daytime eaterie gets frantically busy in the high season. The mood is English, and local produce features strongly – including air-dried hams from Waberthwaite – though there are Alpine overtones in the Gruyère vegetable tart and the ham in mushrooms and sour cream topped with Raclette. Sweets star: rhubarb with Grasmere gingerbread; brown sugar meringues with elderflower curd; Lakeland lemon bread with lemon cheese; the renowned sticky toffee pudding. Afternoon teas are equally popular.

CHEFS: Janice Greaves and Jane Sutherland PROPRIETOR: Stewart Greaves
OPEN: all week CLOSED: Jan MEALS: 12 to 5.30 (L to 2.30)
PRICES: £9 (£13). Minimum £2·50 at L
SEATS: 38. Private parties: 38 main room. Children's helpings (L only). Wheelchair access. Music. Air-conditioned

If, in your opinion, a restaurant is not maintaining the standard of its ratings please inform the Guide *office. Report forms are at the back of the book.*

ASCOT Berkshire	map 2

▲ Stateroom Restaurant, Royal Berkshire Hotel [new entry, zero rated]

London Road, Sunninghill, Ascot SL5 0PP
ASCOT (0990) 23322   £22–£43

This sumptuous Queen Anne mansion, built in 1705, has been the home of the Churchill family for more than a hundred years. Ladbrokes has managed to anaesthetise it quite successfully into a conference orientated hotel. The surprise is Jonathan Fraser's excellent cooking. The set meals offer good value and include some remarkable dishes: suprême of brill wrapped in a spinach leaf, stuffed with oysters, leeks and tomatoes and served with tarragon sauce; lamb with lavender; saddle of venison garnished with russet apples. All power to him to have achieved this in an unlikely hotel environment. Make no mistake, this is classy cuisine – red mullet mousse lifted by a vinaigrette loaded with salmon roe; sorbet of Earl Grey and calvados; smoked foie gras with monkfish; rhubarb-based summer pudding flavoured with Pastis. Fine crockery is used and the dining-room looks out on to a trimmed lawn. The wine list is very long, very varied (it even includes a Russian bottle) and disgracefully marked up: Mâcon-Lugny is a horrifying £20·60. This is nothing short of exploiting people who know nothing about current wine prices. With house wine at £8·85 there is little relief. The list even has the local Ascot, a commendable wine, but priced at £10·90. More reports, please.

CHEF: Jonathan Fraser PROPRIETORS: Ladbroke Hotels
OPEN: all week MEALS: 12.30 to 2 (2.30 Sun), 7.30 to 9.30 (10.30 Fri and Sat)
PRICES: £31 (£43), Set L £15 (£22), Set D £22·50 (£30). Service 12.5% CARDS: Access, Amex, Diners, Visa
SEATS: 46. 5 tables outside. Parties: 16 main room, 10, 25 and 80 private rooms. Car-park, 150 places. Vegetarian meals. Children's helpings. Jacket and tie. No smoking in dining-room. Wheelchair access (also WC). Music
ACCOMMODATION: 65 rooms, all with bath/shower. Rooms for disabled. B&B £55 to £80. Children welcome. Baby facilities. Pets welcome. Afternoon teas. Garden. Swimming-pool. Sauna. Tennis. TV. Phone. Scenic. Confirm by 6

ASHBOURNE Derbyshire	map 5

▲ Callow Hall [11/20]

Mappleton Road, Ashbourne DE6 2AA
ASHBOURNE (0335) 43403   £13–£22

This is Izaak Walton country and fishing is still one of the main attractions. The hotel stands at the end of a tree-lined drive overlooking Bentley Brook and the River Dove. The menu has some fashionable touches – a sorbet between courses, lots of greens in the salads, crisp vegetables served on a crescent-shaped plate. Creamy leek soup is based on duck stock; salmon and monkfish come in a beurre

Restaurants are not expected to solicit customers to send in reports. Please let us know if this happens to you.

blanc with chives; pork cutlets are in a creamy red-pepper sauce. To finish there is Callow Hall tart with almond paste, apples and mincemeat. The cheeseboard has half a dozen English varieties, including a local goats'. The Spencer family has had a business in Ashbourne for five generations, bakery being one of their specialities. The reasonably priced list of some seventy-five wines has house wine at £3·50 per half-litre.

CHEF: David Spencer PROPRIETORS: David and Dorothy Spencer
OPEN: Tue to Sat D and Sun L MEALS: 12.30 to 2.30, 7.30 to 9.30
PRICES: £15·60 (£22), Set L from £8·50 (£13), Set D £15·50 (£21)
CARDS: Access, Amex, Diners, Visa
SEATS: 80. Private parties: 50 main room, 50 private room. Car-park, 70 places. Vegetarian meals. Children's helpings (Sun L only). Wheelchair access (also WC)
ACCOMMODATION: 9 rooms, 3 with bath/shower. B&B £35 to £50. Deposit: 10%. Children welcome. Baby facilities. Pets by arrangement. Garden. Fishing. Golf. TV. Phone. Scenic. Doors close at 11.30

ASTON CLINTON Buckinghamshire   map 3

▲ *Bell Inn* [13/20]

Aston Clinton HP22 5HP
AYLESBURY (0296) 630252   £15–£32

The enduring quality of the Bell was momentarily threatened by chef Jack Dick's retirement. Kevin Cape trained with Michel Bourdin – he was at the Connaught for eight years. The transition appears to have been smooth. The style remains entrenched in classical French cooking, but there are some more modern touches. Terrines, for instance, come as a trio to start – meat, fish and pâté – and solo to finish – fruit surrounded by its coulis. Also good from the new team have been smoked salmon soup with two caviares, and salmon in champagne sauce (the sauces, in particular, have gained in potency). Roasts for two remain a big feature. The dining-room staff are young, European trainees, and dinners can amble on beyond three hours, which reinforces the grand, old-fashioned feel of the dining-room with its railway-style seating, face to face. The wine list is a compendium: two pages of hock; four of claret with plenty of choice in '78, '71 and '70; three of red burgundy. But it doesn't spurn the better-value areas either, and includes half a dozen from Australia; house wine is commendably pegged at £5·45. CELLARMAN'S CHOICE: Ch. Lanessan '75, £17·50.

CHEF: Kevin Cape PROPRIETORS: The Harris family
OPEN: all week MEALS: 12.30 to 2, 7.30 to 10
PRICES: £27 (£32), Set L £12·50 (£15). Service inc CARDS: Access, Visa
SEATS: 100. Private parties: 20 and 200 private rooms. Car-park, 250 places. Children welcome. Wheelchair access (also WC)
ACCOMMODATION: 21 rooms, all with bath/shower. Rooms for disabled. B&B £55 to £77. Children welcome. Baby facilities. Garden. TV. Phone

---

'*As on the rest of the island, the butter is a soft standard yellow – presumably Jersey. A pity this is so, because there's certainly nothing outstanding about it. As with the farmed Jersey cream, I could find nothing out of usual. The cows themselves are absolute darlings.*' (On eating in Jersey)

Gibbons [14/20]

Avening GL8 8NF
NAILSWORTH (045 383) 3070   £11–£32

Clearly the most French of all the restaurants in this less touristic part of the
Cotswolds. Not just in the posters and the *chansons*, but also in Philip Gibbons'
unashamedly Gallic menu, which makes, 'considerable use of the superb local
cream'. The food is top-class modern French in style: sauces laced with alcohol;
fish *à point*; meat rare; superb plain green salads ('a match for the Croque-en-
Bouche'); simple vegetables and sweets. His queues de langoustines et leur beurre
rose is excellent – sixteen Dublin Bay prawns, peeled, arranged in twos crossed
like an X, on a pool of pink sauce garnished with mange-tout for contrast. The
sauce was butter, good rosé wine and pale, lilac-coloured, finely chopped
shallots. Other shellfish dishes have been nearly as good. It is the sense of timing
in the cooking that impresses, along with the quality of the ingredients. A little
more variety would avoid the problem of running one sauce into the next – a
typically Gallic failing anyway – but the quality of, say, gratin dauphinois, or the
St Emilion au chocolat – a whole wedge from a large cake – stand out. Cafetière
coffee and a fitting selection of French regional wines, intelligently assembled,
described in detail and well spread. House French £4·75.

CHEF: Philip Gibbons PROPRIETORS: The Gibbons family
OPEN: Mon to Sat, exc Mon and Sat L MEALS: 12.30 to 3.30, 7 to 10
PRICES: Set L from £8 (£11), Set D £14 (£18) to £27 (£32). Minimum £10 CARDS: Access,
Amex, Diners, Visa
SEATS: 24. Private parties: 28 main room. Car-park, 8 places. Vegetarian meals. Children's
helpings. No pipes in dining-room. Music

Fischer's [14/20]

Bath Street, Bakewell DE4 1BX
BAKEWELL (062 981) 2687   £13–£27

The ugly exterior conceals a charming inside, filled with beams, flowers, pine
furniture and whitewashed walls. The Fischers are established as running the
most accomplished restaurant in the region. Bookings are phased so that the
kitchen can cook to order. The attention to detail impresses: the calvados in the
French apple tart; the home-baked brown bread; the decorative terrine – salmon
sandwiched between two layers of white fish on a salad of expensive leaves and a
garnish of a green herb sauce. Sunday lunch is not beyond roast beef and
Yorkshire pudding. Successes from the short menu have included asparagus
soup; excellent hot cream-cheese and onion pastries; roast monkfish with orange
and ginger sauce; saddle of veal with onion sauce; and sweets, such as lemon
soufflé. Vegetables come in profusion on a side plate. House burgundy is £6·60.
CELLARMAN'S CHOICE: Comte de Sansac, red and white, £6·90.

The Guide does not accept free meals.

CHEF: Max Fischer PROPRIETORS: Max and Susan Fischer
OPEN: Tue to Sun, exc Sat L and Sun D CLOSED: 2 weeks at Christmas, 2 weeks July to Aug
MEALS: 12 to 2, 7 to 9.30 (10 Sat)
PRICES: £19 (£27), Set Sun L £8·25 (£13), Set L £9·50 (£14) CARDS: Access, Amex,
Diners, Visa
SEATS: 35. Private parties: 40 main room, 12 private room. Children's helpings (L only).
No children under 10. No cigars/pipes in dining-room. Wheelchair access (also WC).
Air-conditioned

BARNARD CASTLE Durham map 7

Market Place Teashop [9/20]

29 Market Place, Barnard Castle DL12 8NE
TEESDALE (0833) 690110 £9

In the centre of the market place, this venerable all-day tea-shop provides some
excellent traditional cooking – the Yorkshire cheesecake is made to a recipe from
the Middle Ages. Pies, pot-roasts and bakery are the mainstays, though a
vegetarian accent is becoming more noticeable. Specials of the day are worth
attention. House French is £4·90 a litre.

CHEF: J. Moffat PROPRIETOR: R. A. Hilton
OPEN: all week CLOSED: 1 week at Christmas, Sun Dec to Mar MEALS: 10 to 5.30
PRICES: £5 (£9)
SEATS: 46. Private parties: 46 main room. Vegetarian meals. Children's helpings.
Wheelchair access

BARNSTAPLE Devon map 1

Lynwood House [12/20]

Bishops Tawton Road, Barnstaple EX32 9DZ
BARNSTAPLE (0271) 43695
on A377, between Barnstaple and Exeter £17

The Roberts's distinguished house stands on a hill overlooking the River Torridge
and the rooftops of Barnstaple. This is a family business. Ruth Roberts cooks, her
husband runs the front of house, the sons are waiters. Downstairs is cheaper and
more of a bistro, but fish dominates both menus, in soup, huge pots of mussels in
wine, prawn pancakes with tomato and basil sauce, mousse of lemon sole, and
fricassee of turbot in brown-butter sauce. The galleypan features whatever fish
are available, which often means scallops and lobster. Fresh bread is brought in
each day from Combe Martin and sliced at the table, from a trolley. Desserts
range from fresh pineapple with honey and almond paste to chocolate pot. Coffee
is served in the lounge with chocolate mints and truffles coated in crushed
hazelnuts. The wine list is safe and mostly sound, with the bulk of it under £10.

---

*If you suspect that a restaurant is using processed food, always ask. It would be a
contravention of the Trade Descriptions Act for the restaurant to lie.*

*Good vintages for drinking in 1988: Alsace '85, Beaujolais '86, Germany '85, petits
chateaux clarets '81, lesser clarets '83.*

CHEF: Ruth Roberts PROPRIETORS: John and Ruth Roberts
OPEN: Mon to Sat, exc Sat L MEALS: 12 to 2, 7 to 10
PRICES: £13 (£17), Snacks from £1·05. Service inc CARDS: Access, Visa
SEATS: 70. Private parties: 70 main room, 24 and 80 private rooms. Car-park, 25 places.
Vegetarian meals. Children's helpings. Wheelchair access (also WC)

BARWICK Somerset   map 2

▲ *Little Barwick House* [13/20]

Barwick BA22 9TD
YEOVIL (0935) 23902
leave Yeovil by A37, take 2nd left opposite
Red House pub, ¼ mile on left   £18

Christopher and Veronica Colley's converted Georgian dower house is a good
example of a restaurant with rooms, typical of many to be found in France. The
dining-room is done out in red, with magnificent curtains and a fine marble
fireplace. Veronica cooks a sensibly short menu, using fresh ingredients: local
lamb appears with cucumber and mint in a thick cream sauce, or with garlic and
rosemary; wild duck is served with orange sauce and there are plenty of well-
cooked local and home-grown vegetables. Pancakes filled with spinach and
cream cheese or leeks and mushrooms are favourite starters, otherwise there
might be fish and fennel soup, grilled mussels, or mushrooms stuffed with celery,
garlic, nuts and tomato. There is wild salmon in season, and big portions of
English cheeses include a fine Blue Shropshire. Sweets feature a good chocolate
pot or orange caramel with brandy-snaps. House claret is £6·80.
CELLARMAN'S CHOICE: St Emilion, Ch. Rozier '78, at £14·50.

CHEF: Veronica Colley PROPRIETORS: Mr and Mrs C. Colley
OPEN: Mon to Sat, D only MEALS: 7 to 9.30
PRICES: Set D from £14.90 (£18). Service inc CARDS: Access, Amex, Diners, Visa
SEATS: 30. Private parties: 50 main room. Car-park. Children's helpings. Music
ACCOMMODATION: 6 rooms, all with bath/shower. B&B £55 for 2. Pets welcome. Garden. TV.
Scenic. Doors close at 11 [GHG]

BATH Avon   map 2

Clos du Roy [15/20]

7 Edgar Buildings, George Street, Bath BA1 2EH
BATH (0225) 64356   £15 – £29

'Customers were finding the explanations of dishes too elaborate . . . so we
reduced the number of dishes.' Philippe Roy is a flamboyant experimenter. Ideas
come in threes: pieces of grilled venison on three croûtons with different
accompaniments; three profiteroles, each filled with a different ice-cream; three
pieces of different gateaux on a strawberry and apricot sauce. The breadth of his
style shows in the many recommended dishes, which range from ballotine of
pheasant with foie gras to sea bass with cream and tomato sauce. Soups taste of

---

This symbol is awarded only to restaurants with outstanding wine cellars.

their main ingredient, be it wild mushroom or fish, and there are pretty touches in the crescent-shaped dishes of vegetables. Unsalted Normandy butter and calvados sorbet bring the menu back to its Gallic roots, though it is the French sense of fantasy that is most characteristic – courgette and aubergine soup with squid, and guinea-fowl and lobster with a vanilla sauce have both appeared. Mr Roy is a sufficiently good chef not to lose sight of the simple and to offer less dramatic dishes as well. Nevertheless, he reports the finding in Avon of summer truffles and wild asparagus, both of which have been on the menu. The wine list has a similar taste for variety but is built around good Bordeaux, albeit at a price. House burgundy is £8·50; nearly everything else is in double figures.

CHEF: Philippe Roy PROPRIETORS: Philippe and Emma Roy
OPEN: Tue to Sat CLOSED: 1 week Aug, 2 weeks Jan to Feb MEALS: 12 to 2, 7 to 10.15
PRICES: £20 (£29), Set L from £8·95 (£15), Set D from £18·50 (£27). Service 12%
CARDS: Access, Amex, Diners, Visa
SEATS: 30. Private parties: 30 main room. Vegetarian meals. Children's helpings. Music

Flowers [10/20]

27 Monmouth Street, Bath BA1 2AP
BATH (0225) 313774   £14–£20

Usefully sited within striking distance of the Theatre Royal – it caters both for pre- and post-theatre meals. The décor is a hotch-potch of prints and pictures. The short menu offers a good variety of country cooking: leek and watercress soup; tomato and Stilton tart; cassoulet; beautiful savoury soufflés. Puddings come on a separate menu and provide persuasive ends to meals in the form of chocolate pot with Tia Maria, brown-bread ice-cream, or hazelnut meringue. Cafetière coffee. Four house wines lead a well-spread list specialising in claret.

CHEF/PROPRIETOR: Teresa Lipin
OPEN: Tue to Sat CLOSED: Feb MEALS: 12 to 2, 7 to 10.30
PRICES: Set L £8·50 (£14), Set D from £14 (£20)
CARDS: Access, Amex, Carte Blanche, Diners, Visa
SEATS: 24. Private parties: 30 main room. Children's helpings. Smart dress preferred

Moon and Sixpence [9/20]

6A Broad Street, Bath BA1 5LJ
BATH (0225) 60962   £14–£20

This converted post office wears two sets of clothes. At lunchtime it is a bustling, crowded bistro serving cold meats, quiches, salads and hot dishes such as stuffed aubergines. In the evening it becomes a formal restaurant with a rather long menu taking in salmon with scallops, partridge with juniper berries, and lamb cooked the French way. Coffee is recommended, as are the modestly priced wines, which ...clude a French regional selection. CELLARMAN'S CHOICE: Sauvignon du Haut Poitou '85, at £6·75.

CHEF: Kevin King PROPRIETOR: Keith Waving
OPEN: all week MEALS: 12 to 12.30, 5.30 (7 Sun) to 10.30
PRICES: £14 (£20), Set L £9·50 (£14) CARDS: Access, Amex, Visa
SEATS: 70. 15 tables outside. Private parties: 25 main room, 25 private room. Vegetarian meals. Children's helpings. Music.

▲ *Priory Hotel* [13/20]

Weston Road, Bath BA1 2XT
BATH (0225) 331922   🍾 £20–£34

The *entente cordiale* seems to know no bounds where chefs are concerned. Michael Collom, like many others, has been spending time at the Côtes St Jacques at Joigny and the resulting lurch in the menu is towards mousselines, poaching in champagne, and pastry work. The Priory is the more conventional option if you want modern cooking in Bath, the other being the radical inventiveness of Clos du Roy (see entry). A skilful combination of antiques and modern furniture lends some character to a hotel that might otherwise have become impersonalised by its international and business through-put. Service is formal and impeccable, from being met at the door. The dinner menu – there is a lighter lunch – offers eight starters, eight main dishes and perhaps ten sweets. Typical might be a fluffy crab omelette, generously filled and served with a cream leek sauce; sweetbreads on a bed of spinach and endive with a lemon sauce; artistically presented and lushly sauced venison with pears and cranberries. Vegetables are *nouvelle* in style. The croûte épicure is a savoury variation – Stilton, egg and brandy on toast. Prices are not low but the restaurant does deliver what it promises and has consistently impressed professionals, often more so than readers. The strength of the wine list comes from an enviable collection of mature clarets and red burgundies (the whites are more recent but still impressive), with realistic mark-ups and many half-bottles. House Ch. de Pitray '81 is £11·20. CELLARMAN'S CHOICE: Venegazzù '79, £11·50.

CHEF: Michael Collom PROPRIETOR: John Donnithorne
OPEN: all week MEALS: 12.30 to 2, 7 to 9.15
PRICES: £25 (£32), Set L from £12·50 (£20), Set D from £27 (£34). Service inc
CARDS: Access, Amex, Carte Blanche, Diners, Visa
SEATS: 64. Private parties: 40 main room, 22 and 40 private rooms. Car-park, 25 places.
No children under 10. Smart dress preferred. No smoking. Wheelchair access
ACCOMMODATION: 21 rooms, all with bath/shower. Rooms for disabled. B&B £54 to £92.
No children under 10. Afternoon teas. Garden. Swimming-pool. TV. Phone. Scenic.
Doors close at 12 [GHG]

Supannahong [9/20]

3 John Street, Bath BA1 2JL
BATH (0225) 28889   £15

Over the crowded Salamander pub, with an emblem that looks more Viking than Thai, Suraphon Klinpikuln and sister Pasana cook a short Thai menu. The décor is an uncomfortable mix of bar room and oriental café, with tinkling music, Thai mobiles and posters, but the food is single-minded enough. Chilli is used to effect in dishes such as beef with French beans. Also potent are the spring rolls and the casserole of chicken with chickpeas and coconut. Jasmine-scented rice can be ordered as white or brown. Licensed.

The Guide recruits new inspectors from readers who write in regularly. If you would like to apply, write to the editor with (a) a detailed report on a restaurant where you have eaten and (b) a comparative study of restaurants known to you.

CHEF/PROPRIETOR: Suraphon Klinpikuln
OPEN: Mon to Sat, exc Mon D and Sat L CLOSED: bank hols MEALS: 12 to 2.30, 7 to 10.30
PRICES: £10 (£15) CARD: Visa
SEATS: 28. Private parties: 28 main room. Vegetarian meals. Children's helpings. Music

Tarts [new entry, zero rated]

8 Pierrepoint Place, Bath BA1 1JX
BATH (0225) 330280   £17

This unpretentious cellar is filled with posters for Bath Festival – appropriately, as
it is opposite the festival office. The interconnecting rooms create an intimate
atmosphere and the menu is resolutely bistro in style, with large portions, good-
quality meats and a daily blackboard. Recommended dishes are spinach and
Stilton pancakes; peppered steak flamed in whisky with wholegrain mustard;
pecan chicken with more mustard; copious vegetables; lemon cheesecake. Garlic
bread comes as a third of a loaf; coffee is unlimited. Fifty wines. House wine
£5·60. More reports, please.

CHEF: Tom Bridgeman PROPRIETORS: Tom Bridgeman and John Edwards
OPEN: Mon to Sat CLOSED: 25 and 26 Dec, 1 Jan MEALS: 12 to 2.30, 7 to 10.30
PRICES: £12 (£17) CARDS: Access, Visa
SEATS: 50. Private parties: 80 main room. Vegetarian meals. Children welcome. Music

Woods [10/20]

9–13 Alfred Street, Bath BA1 2QX
BATH (0225) 314812 and 22493   £7–£16

The Prices' good-value brasserie is enhanced now by Wedgwood plates and an
increasingly cosmopolitan menu. The standard Frenchness of garlic mushrooms
is offset by stir-frying; vivid combinations of ingredients and spices; and some
sophisticated modern dishes, like veal with madeira and rhubarb; lamb with its
sweetbreads, and a compote of onion. Good reports encompass praline chocolate
meringue, and brown-bread ice-cream. The wine list is short, and mostly French.
CELLARMAN'S CHOICE: Muscadet '85, £7·95.

CHEF: Mary Alley PROPRIETORS: David and Claude Price
OPEN: Mon to Sat CLOSED: 8 days at Christmas MEALS: 12 to 2.15, 6.45 to 10.15
PRICES: £12 (£16), Set L from £3·45 (£7), Set D from £10·50 (£15)
CARDS: Access, Visa
SEATS: 100. Private parties: 70 main room, 36 private room. Vegetarian meals. Children's
helpings. No cigars/pipes in dining-room. Wheelchair access (also WC). Music

BAWTRY South Yorkshire   map 5

China Rose [10/20]

27 Market Place, Bawtry DN10 6IL
DONCASTER (0302) 710461   £13–£14

The display of artificial flowers in the Georgian bow window suggests a funeral
parlour, but inside there are mirrored walls, Buddhas and plates in little niches.
This Cantonese restaurant is useful in the area, unpretentious and well

patronised. Sizzling dishes are predictably spectacular; also good are the wun-tun soup, sea bass, king prawns in rice paper, and Cantonese roast duck. The Alaska surprise is indeed a surprise – spring roll filled with ice-cream and fruit. The list of dishes is longer than average, but, alas, tea is charged at 40p, suggesting an overt consciousness of western restaurant practices.

CHEF/PROPRIETOR: Wai Leung Wan
OPEN: all week, D only MEALS: 5.30 to 10.30
PRICES: £8 (£14), Set D from £8 (£13) CARDS: Access, Amex, Diners, Visa
SEATS: 85. Private parties: 60 main room. Vegetarian meals. Wheelchair acesss (also WC).
Music. Air-conditioned

BEACONSFIELD Buckinghamshire   map 3

Leigh House [10/20]

Wycombe End, Beaconsfield HP9 1XL
BEACONSFIELD (049 46) 6348   £14–£16

The atmosphere is peculiarly English in this Peking restaurant set in an ivy-clad house. The dining-room is filled with candles, starched linen and wood panels, and only the pictures are Chinese. The menu, though, offers 76 dishes, mostly from the popular northern Chinese repertoire, for instance bang-bang chicken, steamed dumplings with red wine vinegar, a colourful dish of prawns with Chinese mushrooms, and four vegetables – baby sweetcorn, green pepper, button mushrooms and bamboo shoots – in a chilli-laced sauce. Accomplished service.

CHEF/PROPRIETOR: S. W. Tang
OPEN: all week MEALS: 12 to 2, 6 to 11
PRICES: £10 (£16), Set L and D from £9·50 (£14). Service 10% CARDS: Access, Amex,
Diners, Visa
SEATS: 100. Private parties: 25 main room. Car-park, 8 places. Vegetarian meals. Children
welcome. Wheelchair access. Music. Air-conditioned

BECKINGHAM Lincolnshire   map 6

Black Swan [12/20] ✦

Hillside, Beckingham LN5 0RF
FENTONCLAYPOLE (063 684) 474   £11–£18

Anton Indans worked with Peter Kromberg at Le Soufflé in London, before setting up this serious restaurant in an eighteenth-century building by the River Witham, on the Lincolnshire/Nottinghamshire border. He cooks a fashionable set menu of elaborately conceived dishes served in small portions, and the results can be very successful. Typically good are the cold ham mousseline studded with vegetables on a light, sharp tomato coulis; fricassee of guinea-fowl and oyster mushrooms with an excellent potato pancake; and marinated salmon with aniseed cream sauce. Pigeon is stuffed with walnut mousse; lamb is served on a pea purée with tomato sauce. There are good sweets, ranging from hot chocolate

---

▲ *This restaurant has rooms.*

---

and orange soufflé (echoes of The Intercontinental) to yoghurt orange cream with raspberries, as well as unexpected fresh fruit. The wine list is good value, starting at £5·10. CELLARMAN'S CHOICE: Australian Cabernet Sauvignon, McWilliam's '84, £8·60

CHEF: Anton Indans PROPRIETORS: Anton and Alison Indans
OPEN: Tue to Sun, exc Sun D MEALS: 12 to 2, 7 to 10
PRICES: Set L from £6·50 (£11), Set D £13·80 (£18) CARDS: Access, Visa
SEATS: 30. Private parties: 24 main room, 12 and 24 private rooms. Car-park, 9 places. Children's helpings (L only). Wheelchair access (also WC). Music

---

BELPER Derbyshire map 5
Remy's [10/20]

84 Bridge Street, Belper DE5 1AZ
BELPER (077 382) 2246 £16–£20

Martin Smee has kept Remy Bopp's first-floor French restaurant going with a mix of enthusiasm and ambitious cooking. A few plainer dishes might help the accounts, but there is no shortage of adventure: brioches filled with avocado and served with a hot mint vinaigrette; quails with fig coulis. Good French cheeses and good puddings – for instance poppyseed parfait with a ragout of apricots flavoured with rum – wind up meals. There is a short but balanced French wine list. CELLARMAN'S CHOICE: Cahors, Château de St Didier '85, £8·90. The Bopps are in Torquay.

CHEF/PROPRIETOR: Martin Smee
OPEN: Tue to Sat D (L by arrangement) MEALS: 7.30 to 9.30
PRICES: Set L and D £10·95 (£16) to £15·45 (£20) CARDS: Amex, Diners, Visa
SEATS: 26. Private parties: 26 main room. Vegetarian meals. Children's helpings. Smart dress preferred. No-smoking area. Music. Air-conditioned

---

BERKHAMSTED Hertfordshire map 3
La Fiorentina [10/20]

21–23 Lower Kings Road, Berkhamsted HP4 2AE
BERKHAMSTED (044 27) 3003 £12–£19

Still the most agreeable and authentic trattoria in the neighbourhood. Vincenzo Iannone has moved back into the kitchen and his style has given the food a more gutsy, genuine edge. Good pasta includes excellent al dente spaghetti tossed with roughly chopped garlic, olive oil and parsley. Veal is well handled, and other dishes of interest include minestrone, mussels, and involtini di pollo. Desserts are rich; coffee is espresso. The wine list has a good selection from Piedmont, but CELLARMAN'S CHOICE is Chianti Classico, Riserva Ducale '82, from Ruffino, at £9·80.

CHEF/PROPRIETOR: Vincenzo Iannone
OPEN: Mon to Sat MEALS: 12 to 2, 7 to 10
PRICES: £13 (£19), Set L £8·25 (£12). Service 10%, D only CARDS: Access, Amex, Diners, Visa
SEATS: 90. Private parties: 40 main room, 40 private room. Car-park. Vegetarian meals. Children's helpings. Wheelchair access. Music. Air-conditioned

BERKSWELL West Midlands   map 5

▲ *Nailcote Hall* [10/20]

Nailcote Lane, Berkswell CV7 7DE
COVENTRY (0203) 466174   £22

This small fifteenth-century manor-house, with a Georgian wing added in 1780,
is set in wooded country typical of old Warwickshire, five miles from Coventry
and the NEC. It is the home of Tony and German-born Hedy Katharina Barnes, as
well as a restaurant with rooms, and the proprietors have made it warm and cosy
rather than grand. The style is of home cooking, with more than a few German
links: celery soup, sauté chicken livers in garlic and red wine sauce, locally shot
pheasant, and rolled fillets of pork stuffed with apricots and almonds. House
Duboeuf red and white are £6·75.

CHEF: Hedy Katharina Barnes PROPRIETORS: Tony and Hedy Katharina Barnes
OPEN: Mon to Sat CLOSED: bank hols MEALS: 12 to 2, 7 to 9.30 (10 Sat)
PRICES: £13 (£22). Service 10% CARDS: Access, Amex, Diners
SEATS: 50. Private parties: 30 main room, 20 and 30 private rooms. Car-park, 28 places.
Vegetarian meals. No children under 10. Jacket and tie. Wheelchair access (also WC)
ACCOMMODATION: 4 rooms, all with bath/shower. B&B £50 to £90. No children under 10.
No pets. Garden. TV. Scenic. Doors close at 12. Confirm by 6

BERWICK-UPON-TWEED Northumberland   map 8

Funnywayt'mekalivin [new entry, zero rated]

53 West Street, Berwick-upon-Tweed TD15 1AS
BERWICK-UPON-TWEED (0289) 308827   £5–£9

The name says it: Elizabeth Middlemiss's uncommercial cottage restaurant is a
private house full of unmatching furniture, offers no choice, is unlicensed, and
smoking is banned. But the cheap lunches and more formal dinners on Fridays
and Saturdays are fresh in every sense of the word. Mushroom and sherry soup,
courgette soufflé, turkey hollandaise, and arrays of Tovey-like vegetables are all
typical. Cheeses are excellent Cotherstone or Bonchester. This is modern British
cooking asserting itself again, although here at the level of an everyday café.
Perrier is put on the tables; alternatively, Victoria Wine is 200 yards away. More
reports, please.

CHEF: Elizabeth Middlemiss PROPRIETORS: Mr and Mrs Middlemiss
OPEN: all week L, exc Thur and Sat; Fri and Sat D MEALS: 12 to 2, 8
PRICES: £4 (£5), Set Sun L and Set D £8·95 (£8·95). Service inc. Unlicensed, but bring your
own: corkage 80p
SEATS: 25. Private parties: 25 main room. Vegetarian meals. No children under 8. No
smoking in dining-room. Wheelchair access (1 step). Music. One sitting at D

*'The host paraded around one black and one white truffle in the lounge to give everybody
a smell while informing us all: "There's about £300-worth there".'* (On eating in
Lancashire)

*The entries are compiled from the views of readers who have eaten at the restaurants in
the last year, backed up by anonymous inspections and by information supplied and
facts verified by the restaurants.*

BIDDENDEN Kent   map 3

Three Chimneys [9/20]

Biddenden TN27 8HA
BIDDENDEN (0580) 291472   £10

A classic Kentish pub: dried hops hanging from the dark beams, simple wooden
furniture and stone floors. The menu, chalked on a blackboard, is short and
seasonal. Everything is home made: leek and potato soup, beef pie, pork terrine
ribboned with spinach. Traditional English puddings include upside-down
marmalade cake served with a bowl of unsweetened farmhouse Jersey cream. Six
real ales and local Biddenden cider, plus house wines by the glass.

CHEFS: Audrey Morris and Janet Croucher PROPRIETORS: Christopher and Pippa Sayers
OPEN: all week CLOSED: 25 and 26 Dec MEALS: 11.30 to 2 (12 to 1.30 Sun), 6.30 to 10
PRICES: £7 (£10), Snacks from £1·50
SEATS: 100. 40 tables outside. Private parties: 40 main room. Car-park, 50 places.
Vegetarian meals

BILBROUGH North Yorkshire   map 5

▲ *Bilbrough Manor* [new entry, zero rated]

Bilbrough YO2 3PH
TADCASTER (0937) 834002   £15–£34

The manor, four miles south-west of York, has been sympathetically and
expensively restored, and charges for it. The kitchen has been given over to Idris
Caldora, whose presence is electric – so much so, his absences in early months
have been marked. An historical panelled dining-room complements a menu of
modern French cooking: ornate, classical, and with plenty of verve, but rather
long. Caldora can cook: brill with pink grapefruit and vermouth, baked sea bass,
wrapped in lettuce, covered in filo pastry and served with a tomato vinaigrette,
are fine examples. A breast of chicken marinated in lemon and thyme, grilled,
and served with a rich sauce of the marinade, is testimony to both kitchen and
shopping. The technique is such that a dessert of almond biscuits, layered with
glazed pears, and served hot, with a heavily liqueured William pear sabayon, is
achieved as effortlessly as if it were a crème brûlée. It is all served on fine
Wedgwood, and the service, at least when the restaurant has been quiet, early in
the week, is professional. The wine list runs to just sixty bottles, which in the
context seems small. The house Coteaux du Tricastin is a good robust red for
£6·50. CELLARMAN'S CHOICE: Ch. Millet '78, £15·75.

CHEF: Idris Caldora PROPRIETORS: Mr and Mrs C. C. Bell
OPEN: all week MEALS: 12 to 2, 7 to 9.30
PRICES: £26 (£34), Set L £10 (£15), Set D £17·50 (£23). Minimum £14 CARDS: Access,
Amex, Diners, Visa
SEATS: 45. Private parties: 14 private room. Car-park, 30 places. Vegetarian meals.
No children under 12. Jacket and tie. Music
ACCOMMODATION: 12 rooms, all with bath/shower. B&B £75 to £120. Deposit: £30.
No children under 12. Afternoon teas. Garden. TV. Phone. Scenic

All inspections are carried out anonymously.

BIRDLIP Gloucestershire

map 2

▲ *Kingshead House* [new entry, zero rated]

Birdlip GL4 8JH
GLOUCESTER (0452) 862299   £13–£20

Birdlip is one of the highest villages in Gloucestershire and lies on the Cotswold
Way. The Knocks (ex-Gentle Gardener, Tetbury) are well-meaning, charming
hosts who make this eighteenth-century coaching-inn feel like home. An
extended menu mixes French and English; it is possible to eat a complete
vegetarian meal. Not all the romance of the menu comes across on the plate, but
all the dishes are resolutely home made, even pastry. Typical might be a goats'
cheese brioche, or baked fillet of pork with apple, onion and horseradish. The
excellence of, say, the white rolls, has not extended to all parts of the meal, and
complex dishes, for instance a sandwich of salmon with salmon mousse and
asparagus with an (excellent) hollandaise, may not always be a wise choice. A
heavily annotated list of sixty wines incorporates some gems, such as Marqués de
Murrieta white Rioja, Cru du Coudoulet Côtes du Rhône, and Château Carras
from Greece, all under £10, plus a Chardonnay from northern Italy and one from
California. CELLARMAN'S CHOICE: Domaine de Beaucastel '83, £10·50.

CHEF: Judy Knock PROPRIETORS: Warren and Judy Knock
OPEN: Tue to Sun, exc Sat L and Sun D MEALS: 12.15 to 2.15 (1.45 Sun), 7.15 to 10
PRICES: £14 (£20), Set L from £7·50 (£13), Set D £12·75 (£17), Snacks from £2·20.
Licensed, also bring your own: corkage £1 CARDS: Access, Amex, Diners, Visa
SEATS: 32. 2 tables outside. Private parties: 36 main room. Car-park, 12 places. Vegetarian
meals. Children's helpings. Wheelchair access (also WC). Music
ACCOMMODATION: 1 room, with bath/shower. B&B £24 to £35. Garden. Scenic. Doors close
at 12. Confirm by 6

BIRKENHEAD Merseyside

map 5

Beadles [10/20]

15 Rosemount, Oxton, Birkenhead L43 58G
051-653 9010   £17

The décor is matter-of-fact, but Bea Gott cooks a well above average bistro menu.
The accent is French, taking in anything from pheasant with white wine and
cream sauce to veal with mangoes, or blackcurrant and almond tartlets. House
wine is £4·50 a bottle.

CHEF: Bea Gott PROPRIETORS: Roy and Bea Gott
OPEN: Tue to Sat, D only CLOSED: Aug MEALS: 7.30 to 9
PRICES: £11 (£17)
SEATS: 34. Private parties: 30 main room. Vegetarian meals. Children welcome. Wheelchair
access (1 step). Music

If you cannot honour a restaurant booking, always phone to cancel.

*Files are kept on every restaurant, so reports of poor meals are just as valuable as
reports of good meals because they save unnecessary inspections.*

Adil   [9/20]

148–150 Stoney Lane, Sparkbrook, B11 8AJ
021-449 0335   £7

The décor is spartan, menus are tucked under the transparent table-tops and there's no cutlery, but this neighbourhood restaurant serves some of the most uncompromising Indian food in Birmingham. Highlights are the superb balti dishes, cooked and served in blackened iron pans, the fresh spinach, and the unusual vegetables from shops in the area: mustard leaf, tinda, valor (Kashmiri green beans). Breads are outstanding: tandoori chapatis are actually steaming hot roti, the size of dinner plates, while a single 'large' nan is enough bread for four people. Unlicensed, but there's an off-licence next door.

CHEF: Mr Ashraf   PROPRIETOR: Mr Arif
OPEN: all week   MEALS: noon to midnight
PRICES: £5 (£7). Unlicensed, but bring your own: no corkage   CARDS: Access, Visa
SEATS: 70. Private parties: 50 private room. Vegetarian meals. Children welcome

Los Andes   [10/20]

806 Bristol Road, Selly Oak, B29 6NA
021–471 3577   £10

After four years in their tiny cramped restaurant opposite the monumental Old Varsity Tavern, the four Chilean owners have moved down the road to more roomy and comfortable premises in a converted curry-house overlooking the new Sainsbury. This is still one of the most genuine and likeable eating-places in Birmingham, proving that there's more to authentic South American cooking than Tex-Mex tacos and chilli. The food is gutsy and full-blooded, but with some delicate touches: a tinge of fresh coriander in the ceviche, a scattering of cumin seeds in the Brazilian feijoada (a stew of pork, smoked ham, chorizo and red beans). Empanadas de horno are like big Cornish pasties filled with minced meat, sultanas, and olives, and for vegetarians there is chipahauzu – a baked vegetable and cheese dish topped with sweetcorn purée. Excellent value for money.

CHEFS: Roque Milla, Fredy Aburto and Amando Pardo   PROPRIETORS: Roque Milla, Fredy Aburto, Amando Pardo and Gregorio Grandon
OPEN: Mon to Sat   MEALS: 12 to 2, 7 to 11.30
PRICES: £9 (£10). Unlicensed but bring your own: corkage 50p   CARDS: Access, Amex, Diners
SEATS: 66. Private parties: 80 main room. Vegetarian meals. Children's helpings. No smoking. Music

The average price quoted in brackets is for an average three-course meal including service, VAT, coffee and half a bottle of house wine or the equivalent in an ethnic restaurant.

'Am I very old-fashioned or wrong to long for the good old days when one was served tureens full of vegetables to help yourself from. Perhaps with the new move towards English old-fashioned cooking, people will start to serve vegetables in large portions.'
(On eating in Devon)

Le Biarritz [11/20]

148–149 Bromsgrove Street, B5 6RG
021-622 1989   £12–£25

The wholesale market is just down the road from this provincial-looking French restaurant on a corner in Birmingham's Chinatown. Carl Timms is one of the few chefs in the city – apart from his Cantonese neighbours – who take fish seriously. Handling and timing are spot-on, although many dishes rely on the formula of herbs and cream sauces: escalope of salmon with sorrel; monkfish with basil; brill on a bed of leeks with chives. Away from fish, the menu fashionably takes in hot goats' cheese in flaky pastry, roast rack of lamb, and fillet steak with thyme sauce. Sweets always include an impressively risen hot soufflé, such as honey and lemon. The home-made petits fours are better than the coffee. More than sixty exclusively French wines, including a strong showing of clarets and good-value whites from the Loire. CELLARMÁN'S CHOICE: Vouvray '83, from Marc Brédif, £11·60.

CHEF: Carl Timms PROPRIETOR: Andrea Lo Coco
OPEN: Mon to Sat, exc Sat L CLOSED: 25 Dec to 9 Jan MEALS: 12 to 2, 7 to 10.30
PRICES: £17 (£25), Set L £7·50 (£12), Set D £18 (£24). Service 10% CARDS: Access, Amex, Diners, Visa
SEATS: 40. Private parties: 50 main room. Car-park, 10 places. Vegetarian meals. Children's helpings. Smart dress preferred. Wheelchair access. Music. Air-conditioned

Chung Ying [12/20]

16–18 Wrottesley Street, B5 6RT
021-622 5669 and 1793   £9–£16

On the corner of Wrottesley Street, a cul-de-sac with the vast Day In supermarket and the back entrance to Forbidden City. What lifts Chung Ying above the competition is the quality of ingredients: fish, liver, greens, even bean curd. The menu is an unashamedly Cantonese monster, with over three hundred dishes, ranging from the familiar to steamed pork pie with squid, or grilled eel balls. The cooking captures the bold, full-blooded character of Cantonese food, then adds finer touches to make it fresh and unexpected. Fried noodles with assorted meat is a real buzz for the palate with fragrant barbecued pork, tender fresh pork, duck, thin, pink-tinged liver, fish balls, curled king prawn and dazzlingly fresh squid, lifted by vivid green, crunchy French beans. The mini-menu of about 30 dim-sum runs to steamed ox tripe with ginger and spring onion, sausage buns, and excellent glutinous rice and minced chicken steamed in lotus leaves. Tea is free.

CHEF/PROPRIETOR: Siu Chung Wong
OPEN: all week MEALS: noon to midnight
PRICES: £10 (£16), Set D from £6 (£9). Service 10% CARDS: Access, Amex, Diners, Visa
SEATS: 200. Private parties: 200 main room, 100 private room. Car-park, 10 places. Vegetarian meals. Children welcome. Smart dress preferred. Music. Air-conditioned

Restaurants rating 12 or more serve the best food in the region.

Places rating 9 may not be restaurants at all, but still serve good food: expect to find pubs, cafes, small hotels and wine bars.

Days of the Raj [new entry, zero rated]

51 Dale End, B4 7LN
021-236 0445 £9-£16

A plain white canopy and wooden window shutters mark out this restaurant
beneath the back of Tesco, in a street of multi-storey car parks. The trappings are
those of new-wave Indian and nothing could be further from red flock and brutal
chicken Madras. The place adds another, welcome dimension to Indian food in
the city. At lunch there's an excellent-value hot buffet; at night you can linger
amid the rattan and bamboo furniture and faded photos. There is a theatrical
view, through a glass panel, of the tandoor chef at work; a fountain bubbles. The
cooking is refined, sophisticated North Indian and Punjabi. Moghlai kebab is
delicately marinated chicken breast fillets grilled in the tandoor; rogan josh is
garnished with pine kernels; bara masala is barbecued lamb chops tinged with
lemon and garlic, in a vivid orange sauce enriched with yoghurt and bristling
with chopped coriander. Otherwise the menu ranges from Himalayan chat
(chicken and potato salad with tamarind dressing), to Kashmiri navrattan pilau.
Fragrant Basmati rice comes perfumed with saffron; breads are taken seriously;
and the all-Indian sweets trolley has pretty arrangements of multi-coloured barfi,
rasgulla and gulab jamun. Service knocks spots off comparable London
restaurants for politeness and efficiency. The short wine list has been compiled by
someone who knows their way round the lesser French and German vineyards.
House wine is £5·45. More reports, please.

CHEFS: Ramesh Chander and Rashpal Sunner PROPRIETORS: Balbir Singh, P. S. Kulaiv and
B. S. Chuhan
MEALS: 12 to 2.30, 7 (6 Fri and Sat) to 11.30
PRICES: £11 (£16), Set L £5·50 (£9), Set D from £7 (£11). Minimum £6·50 CARDS: Access,
Amex, Diners, Visa
SEATS: 120. Private parties: 100 main room, 25 and 30 private rooms. Vegetarian
meals. Children's helpings. Smart dress preferred. Wheelchair access (also WC). Music.
Air-conditioned

Forbidden City [11/20]

36 Hurst Street, B5 4BN
021-622 2454 £14

This is a huge Chinese restaurant beneath the China Palace casino. The front
entrance is in Hurst Street, the back is at the top of the Wrottesley Street cul-de-
sac, next to the huge Day In supermarket. Between the two is one sprawling
dining-room, designed for all events. The décor is a bright, flamboyant collage of
red paintwork, elaborately designed grey ceiling, gold dragons, lanterns, ornate
black screens and plants. At peak times it is a riot of colour, sound and activity.
Chef Cheung Tin cooks a wide-ranging menu that includes Pekinese and
Szechuan dishes, but its heart is in the Cantonese tradition of barbecued meats,
including squab (young pigeon), dim-sum (there are 40, served until 6pm), and
fish. There's also a strong showing of casseroles and hot-pots, such as steamed
abalone with duck web, and braised chicken with taro. Hot-and-sour soup has
just the right balance of chilli heat and vinegar acidity, barbecued pork with
honey is a pile of glistening lean meat on a bed of crispy pickled vegetables, and

deep-fried squid comes with a warm, red, sweet-and-sour dip. Delicate steamed scallops topped with shreds of fresh ginger show the quality of the fish. Chef's specialities (not listed on the main menu) inhabit the world of boiled geoduck, deep-fried pig's bowel and stewed sea moss with dried oysters. Affable service.

CHEF: Cheung Tin PROPRIETORS: K. W. Cheung, F. Y. T. Liu, K. M. Yip and M. Y. Tsang
OPEN: all week MEALS: noon to 11.45
PRICES: £8 (£14), Set L and D from £9 (£14). Service 10% CARDS: Access, Amex, Diners, Visa
SEATS: 450. Private parties: 400 main room, 40 four private room. Vegetarian meals. Children welcome. No-smoking area. Music. Air-conditioned

Henry's [10/20]

27 St Paul's Square, B3 1RB
021-200 1136   £9–£15

Henry Wong's latest venture is close to the city centre in an area with reminders of the Industrial Revolution: the square is dominated by a blackened church dedicated to James Watt, and the canal and viaducts are close by, as is the Museum of Science and Industry. An odd location for a relatively expensive Chinese, but it's also near enough to the cultural centres, the college and the Holiday Inn to draw in trade. The creamy-white building looks like a ranch-house bungalow, and it has all the trappings of its brother Henry Wong in Harbourne (see below): napkins sculpted into wine glasses, lots of light and space, soothing décor and extremely friendly service. The menu is fashionable, taking in satays, fried scallops with cashews nuts and shredded fillet steak in crispy birds' nests. But the underlying conservativeness of the food is exposed in the versions of old-style Cantonese dishes, such as stuffed aubergines with black-bean sauce, which would not pass muster in Chinatown. In its favour, the cooking is reliable; it has few peaks, but few troughs, either.

CHEF: C. W. Choi PROPRIETORS: H. Y. Wong and C. W. Choi
OPEN: Mon to Sat CLOSED: one week Aug MEALS: 12 to 2, 6 to 11 (11.30 Sat)
PRICES: £8 (£15), Set L from £5 (£9), Set D from £8 (£13). Service 10% CARDS: Access, Amex, Diners, Visa
SEATS: 95. Private parties: 80 main room. Vegetarian meals. Children welcome

Henry Wong [10/20]

283 High Street, Harborne, B17 9QH
021-427 9799   £13–£17

The Chinese restaurant scene has splintered into deep schizophrenia. Here is the archetypal example of the modern, westernised restaurant. The menu is a mixed bag, tailored to Western palates with sizzling dishes, king prawns with black-bean sauce, sesame prawn toasts and dramatic horticultural sculptures as garnishes, designed to impress. Crispy duck is the centrepiece and pretty overcooked, though it is a robust dish. Tables are set with beige napkins concertina'd like fans into the wine glasses, which end up being filled with some rather dull wines. It is cheap by the standards of French restaurants – Michelin even award this place a red 'M' – but expensive compared with the Chinatown Cantonese places like Forbidden City and Chung Ying.

CHEF: Steven Yeung PROPRIETORS: Henry Wong and Steven Yeung
OPEN: Mon to Sat MEALS: 12 to 2, 6 to 11 (11.30 Fri and Sat)
PRICES: £9 (£17), Set L and D from £8 (£13). Service 10% CARDS: Access, Amex,
Diners, Visa
SEATS: 120. Private parties: 100 main room, 20 private room. Vegetarian meals. Wheelchair
access (also WC). Music

Ho Tung [10/20]

308 Bull Ring Centre, B5 4PY
021-643 0033 and 0183   £7-£16

Flashy fairy lights give this Cantonese restaurant the mood of a night-club – in
fact there is live entertainment every Saturday. The first-floor dining-room is vast
and sleek, with black and chrome chairs, lacquered screens and wooden
latticework cages around the spherical white lampshades. The kitchen works
best when it is cooking for its Chinese customers; Westerners can fare less well.
Best bets are the authentic hot-pots and the open-plate rice and noodle dishes,
which show off the quality of the roast meats, offal and seafood. Other items can
be overpriced and disappointing. At lunchtime choose excellent dim-sum rather
than the anglicised set meal.

CHEF: Winston Cheng PROPRIETOR: Tony Ho
OPEN: all week, exc Sat L and Sun L MEALS: noon to midnight
PRICES: £8 (£16), Set L from £3 (£7), Set D from £3·50 (£8). Service 10%. Licensed, also
bring your own: no corkage CARDS: Access, Amex, Diners, Visa
SEATS: 160. Private parties: 250 main room, 90 private room. Car-park, 100 places.
Vegetarian meals. Children welcome. Wheelchair access (also WC). Music. Air-conditioned

Loon Fung [10/20]

37-41 Pershore Street, B5 4BS
021-622 7395 and 5056   £12

One of the new arrivals in Birmingham's growing Chinatown. It stands a
hundred yards from the Chung Ying (see entry), the two restaurants facing each
other across the junction of Pershore Street and Ladywell Walk. The pink and
grey dining-room is elegant, the service tries very hard to please, and the music
strikes an occidental note. But the menu – 235 dishes – makes few compromises
to western tastes and is firmly in the Cantonese mould of sizzling eel balls, stuffed
crispy duck, and authentic one-plate rice and noodle dishes. There are votes for
the sweet-tasting steamed scallops with black-bean sauce, and roasted spare ribs
with salt and chilli. The thirty-strong dim-sum menu has its own chef, and
there's roast suckling pig on Sundays.

CHEFS: P. Li and S. Law PROPRIETOR: Y. C. Cheung
OPEN: all week MEALS: noon to 11.45
PRICES: £8 (£12). Service 10% CARDS: Access, Amex, Diners, Visa
SEATS: 250. Private parties: 100 main room, 100 private room. Car-park, 15 places.
Vegetarian meals. Children welcome. Wheelchair access (1 step; also WC). Music.
Air-conditioned

An index of restaurants by name appears at the back of the Guide.

Maharaja [10/20]

23–25 Hurst Street, B5 4AS
021-622 2641   £11–£14

In the evening, when the drapes are drawn, this small North Indian restaurant
feels as calm as an English hotel dining-room. It is a world away from the Indian
cafés in the Sparkhill district of the city. The menu features curries and tandoori
dishes, but is pared down and avoids clichés and bogus ideas. The cooking is
authentic, with particularly good curries; chicken bhuna masala is skilfully
spiced, tinged with lemon and given a sprinkling of fresh coriander. There are
lotus roots among the vegetables, and the channa masaladar is decorated
with raw onion and whole green chillies. Good rice and breads. Extremely
courteous service.

CHEF: Bhupinder Waraich PROPRIETOR: N. S. Batt
OPEN: Mon to Sat MEALS: 12 to 2.30, 6 to 11.30
PRICES: £7 (£14), Set L from £6·50 (£11), Set D from £8·50 (£13). Service 10%
CARDS: Access, Amex, Diners, Visa
SEATS: 65. Private parties: 30 main room. Vegetarian meals. Wheelchair access. Music.
Air-conditioned

Rajdoot [10/20]

12–22 Albert Street, B4 7UD
021-643 8805 and 8749   £10–£22

Inside the plain black and white stone frontage is an extraordinary museum of
Indian culture: sculpted figurines of dancers and deities stand in little alcoves,
wood carvings and ornate brasses are arranged on the walls like works of art,
and cordons of tiny bells and finger-cymbals hang from the ceiling. The waiters
wear full headgear; almondy lamb pasanda is garnished with edible silver leaf.
Next to all this, the cooking might seem overshadowed but it is competent
Punjabi, taking in birianis, curries and tandooris, including fish and kidneys.
Basmati rice is fragrant and aromatic, paneer is home made. The 50p cover
charge includes a poppadum and very good pickles.

CHEF: B. Mali PROPRIETOR: D. R. Sarda
OPEN: all week, exc Sun L MEALS: 12 to 2.30, 6.30 to 11.30
PRICES: £13 (£22), Set L £5·50 (£10), Set D from £9·50 (£15). Cover 50p. Minimum £6.50.
Service 12.5% CARDS: Access, Amex, Diners, Visa
SEATS: 80. Private parties: 40 main room. Vegetarian meals. Children welcome. Wheelchair
access (also WC). Music. Air-conditioned

Satay House [9/20]

92 Hurst Street, B5 4TE
021-622 1313   £12

An idiosyncratic South-East Asian café with a pink awning outside and a
rambling, low-ceilinged dining-room with rough-plastered white walls, grey
beams and pink tablecloths. The cooking centres on the charcoal grill and the
wok. Excellent smoky-flavoured satays can be served with a dish of hot or cold
noodles and vegetables, and there are stir-fried dishes, one-plate meals and crispy

duck. The short menu also has spring rolls, deep-fried seaweed with dried meat, and shredded chilli beef, as well as a couple of steaks and sizzling dishes. A trio of dips is left on the table: peanut sauce, fish sauce and a powerful sambal. Drink Chinese tea or bring your own wine.

CHEF: Danny Ngo PROPRIETORS: Winston Louey and Morry Chan
OPEN: Mon to Sat, exc Sat L MEALS: 12 to 2.15, 6 to 11.45
PRICES: £8 (£12). Service 10%. Unlicensed, but bring your own: no corkage
SEATS: 42. Private parties: 50 main room. Vegetarian meals. Music

Sloans [12/20]

27–29 Chad Square, Hawthorne Road, Edgbaston, B15 3TQ
021-455 6697   £16–£27

The Narbetts moved here from the Bell Inn at Belbroughton. The restaurant is fashionably surburban, with soft pink lighting, glittering silver and glass, and beige palm-feather wallpaper. Classical music plays quietly in the background. Roger Narbett has steered the cooking away from fish into a more balanced mixture of modern French dishes. The style is of poached seafood sausage with champagne sauce; grilled fillet of rabbit with port and thyme sauce; strawberry mousse with strawberry coulis and crème anglaise. The kitchen also proves its skill with pheasant consommé, and fillet of sole filled with salmon mousse and lobster. Vegetables come as a side plate of nouvelle miniatures. Lunches may not show the restaurant in its best light. Seventy wines are strongest on French reds. House wine is from Duboeuf at £7·50. CELLARMAN'S CHOICE: Ch. Gruaud-Larose '74, at £22·75.

CHEF: Roger Narbett PROPRIETORS: W. J. Narbett and Roger Narbett
OPEN: Mon to Sat, exc Sat L CLOSED: bank hols, 2 weeks July to Aug MEALS: 12 to 2, 7 to 10
PRICES: £19 (£27), Set L £11 (£16), Set D £16·50 (£22). Minimum £10·50 CARDS: Access, Amex, Diners, Visa
SEATS: 60. Private parties: 30 main room. Car-park, 60 places. Children welcome. Smart dress preferred. Wheelchair access (1 step; also WC). Music. Air-conditioned

Thai Paradise [10/20]

31 Paradise Circus, B1 2BJ
021-643 5523   £8–£16

Easily missed, as it is tucked away in a parade of shops and offices, not far from the town hall. Ingredients are genuine and the menu shows off Thai food at its most accessible: soups, salads (including an interesting version with boiled squid, chillies and coriander), stir-fried dishes, eight ways with crab, as well as powerful curries made with coconut milk and 'red' or 'green' curry paste. Flavours are sometimes cautious, but there is real ferocity about the sharp, spicy chicken soup with kaffir lime leaves and lemon grass, and the potent peanut sauce with the

The average price quoted in brackets is for an average three-course meal including service, VAT, coffee and half a bottle of house wine or the equivalent in an ethnic restaurant.

excellent pork satay. There are cooling rambutans, jack fruit and Thai mangoes to finish. Drink Singha Thai beer or Chinese tea.

CHEF: Surachet Lathe PROPRIETORS: Preecha and Robert Lathe
OPEN: Mon to Sat, exc Sat L MEALS: 12 to 3, 6 to 12 (1am Fri and Sat)
PRICES: £9 (£16), Set L £4·95 (£8), Set D from £7·50 (£11). Service 10% CARDS: Access, Amex, Diners, Visa
SEATS: 60. Private parties: 25 main room. Vegetarian meals. Children's helpings. Smart dress preferred. Wheelchair access. Music. Air-conditioned

---

BISHOP'S CLEEVE Gloucestershire   map 2

▲ *Cleeveway House* [11/20]

Bishop's Cleeve GL52 4SA
BISHOP'S CLEEVE (024 267) 2585
3m N of Cheltenham on A435   £20

This civilised country house has an air of quiet perfection, although it stands in grounds right by the main Cheltenham to Evesham road. Chef/proprietor John Marfell continues to provide a very extensive menu of sound cooking, along the lines of spiced sardines, correctly made beef Stroganoff, and chocolate gateau. Poultry and game (some shot by Mr Marfell), show up well in a soup of pheasant and chicken, duck livers with capers, and breast of duck with walnuts and Grand Marnier sauce. There is enough variety on the French and German wine list to suit most pockets and tastes. CELLARMAN'S CHOICE: Mâcon-Clessé '83, from Thévenin, £9 (£4·50 for a half-bottle).

CHEF/PROPRIETOR: John Marfell
OPEN: Mon to Sat, exc Mon L CLOSED: 1 week after Christmas, Good Fri and all bank hols
MEALS: 12 to 1.45, 7 to 9.45
PRICES: £14 (£20)
SEATS: 38. Private parties: 10 main room. Car-park, 50 places. Vegetarian meals. Children's helpings. No cigars/pipes in dining-room. Wheelchair access (also WC). Air-conditioned
ACCOMMODATION: 3 rooms, all with bath/shower. B&B £25 to £40. Children welcome. Pets welcome. Garden. TV. Phone. Doors close at 1

BISHOPS TACHBROOK Warwickshire   map 2

▲ *Mallory Court* [14/20]

Harbury Lane, Bishops Tachbrook CV33 9QB
LEAMINGTON SPA (0926) 30214
off A452, 2m S of Leamington Spa   £22–£37

The polish extends beyond the mahogany in this luxurious hotel: there are fresh flowers, leather chesterfields, log fires, panelled rooms, mullioned windows looking out on to manicured grounds. Allan Holland's cooking is modern French: salmon and smoked salmon sausage; lobster and sweetbread terrine; grilled fillet of rabbit on a chestnut purée with button onions and bacon lardons in a sherry vinegar and wine sauce. Sauces are sparse, rich and intense, with cream and butter making a comeback, along with ample portions, in a medley of poached sea bass, monkfish, red mullet and lobster with lobster sauce; breast of chicken with wild mushrooms and madeira; roast pigeon with raspberry vinegar sauce enriched with bitter chocolate. Razzamatazz puddings include a hot coconut soufflé flavoured with Malibu, accompanied by a pineapple sorbet, and passion-fruit ice-cream with shortbread and strawberry sauce. Lunch, being half the price of dinner, is more of a bargain. On the blue-chip wine list, affordable bourgeois clarets rub shoulders with first growths; burgundy keeps its feet on the ground thanks to Mâconnais and Chalonnais; and there are a few bottles from the New World, including Mondavi and Rothbury Chardonnays. House wines start at £6·95.

CHEFS: Allan J. G. Holland and A. Wright PROPRIETORS: Allan J. G. Holland and J. R. Mort
OPEN: all week MEALS: 12.30 to 1.30, 7.30 to 9.30 (10 Sat)
PRICES: Set L £16·50 (£22), Set D £32 (£37). Service inc CARDS: Access, Amex, Visa
SEATS: 50. Private parties: 50 main room. Car-park, 50 places. No children under 12. Jacket and tie. No cigars/pipes in dining-room
ACCOMMODATION: 10 rooms, all with bath/shower. D, B&B £70 to £184. No children under 12. Afternoon teas. Garden. Swimming-pool. Tennis. TV. Phone. Doors close at 12 [GHG]

BLACKPOOL Lancashire map 5

Danish Kitchen [9/20]

95 Church Street, Blackpool FY1 1HU
BLACKPOOL (0253) 24291 £6

Blackpool bursts with places to eat, many of them remarkable only for their mediocrity. The Danish Kitchen, taking its name from the open sandwiches served, has earned inclusion in the *Guide* for nine years, partly for the contrast it creates. All the food is freshly made and the pine and white cafeteria is kept scrupulously clean. There's a good showing of quiches, omelettes and pizzas for vegetarians. House wine by the carafe.

CHEFS: Nadine Simister and Samantha Carter PROPRIETOR: A. Barker
OPEN: all day, Mon to Sat MEALS: 9.15 to 5
PRICES: £3 (£6), Snacks from 39p
SEATS: 110. 4 tables outside. Vegetarian meals. Children welcome. Air-conditioned. Self-service

---

BLANDFORD FORUM Dorset map 2

▲ *La Belle Alliance* [11/20] ✈

White Cliff Mill Street, Blandford Forum DT11 7BP
BLANDFORD FORUM (0258) 52842 £11–£18

The Davisons' restaurant with rooms occupies one wing of a large Victorian mansion on a street leading out of town. The décor harks back to Jane Austen's time, with frilly pink and green curtains and lots of feminine touches, such as yellow carnations on the tables. Philip Davison cooks a short menu of seasonal dishes. His style is still evolving, but most of the ingredients are seasonal and local, in the manner of the best modern cooking. Properly hung steak from a nearby butcher is served with Stilton and hollandaise sauce; noisettes of lamb come with a mushroom and rosemary sauce; venison is from the New Forest; a friend grows the herbs for the restaurant. Fruit appears in many dishes, from smoked quail with orange segments and kiwi-fruit, to pigeon casseroled with red wine and grapes. Bread is home made, as are the ice-creams. The short wine list is reasonably priced. CELLARMAN'S CHOICE: Chablis, *premier cru* Montmains, Domaine J. P. Droin '85, £13·25.

CHEF: P. Davison PROPRIETORS: Mr and Mrs P. Davison
OPEN: Mon to Sat, and Sun L MEALS: 12.30 to 1.30, 7 to 9.30 (10 Sat)
PRICES: Set L £7·50 (£11), Set D from £13·75 (£18) CARDS: Access, Amex, Diners, Visa
SEATS: 28. Private parties: 36 main room. Car-park, 9 places. No children under 7. Smart dress preferred. No smoking in dining-room. Wheelchair access. Music
ACCOMMODATION: 5 rooms, all with bath/shower. B&B £28 to £38. No children under 7. Pets welcome. TV. Phone. Confirm by 6 [GHG]

BOLLINGTON Cheshire   map 5

Mauro's [new entry, zero rated]

88 Palmerston Street, Bollington SK10 5PW
BOLLINGTON (0625) 73898   £16

The Mauros moved from Penzance and run this former Indian restaurant along the same lines as their former trattoria, Enzo's. The strong points are home-made pasta and fresh fish of the day, which might be halibut in butter and lemon sauce. There are two trolleys, one for antipasti and one for puddings: cold zabaglione, chocolate and almond slice, and Tira-mi-su, made from cream cheese. Thirty well-chosen Italian wines stay mostly under £10. CELLARMAN'S CHOICE: Frascati Superiore, Gotto d'Oro '85, £6·90. More reports, please.

CHEF/PROPRIETOR: V. Mauro
OPEN: Tue to Sat MEALS: 12 to 2.30, 7 to 10
PRICES: £11 (£16)
SEATS: 50. Private parties: 70 main room. Vegetarian meals. Children's helpings. Wheelchair access (also WC). Music

---

BOTLEY Hampshire   map 2

Cobbett's [11/20]

15 The Square, Botley, SO3 2EA
BOTLEY (048 92) 2068   £17–£29

Named after William Cobbett – Botley's famous son – this village restaurant feels English, with dark beams and windows looking on to the street, but Lucie Skipwith is French and cooks that way. Excellent soups might include creamy watercress or pumpkin, before pepper stuffed with fish mousseline or crab, or rolled shoulder of lamb with capers. The pheasant, as ever these days, would benefit from being hung for longer. Sweets, such as jalousie de pommes or tarte au citron, rival the selection of more than a dozen French cheeses. The bar area is cramped for drinks, but the dining-room is spacious. The wine list runs to fifty bottles, mostly between £7 and £15, including good house Sauvignon and Rhônes and Loires.

Anyone claiming to be from The Good Food Guide *is an impostor. Restaurateurs are advised to contact the office immediately if any fraudulent claims are made.*

CHEFS: Lucie Skipwith and Peter Hayes PROPRIETORS: Charles and Lucie Skipwith
OPEN: Mon to Sat, exc Mon and Sat L CLOSED: 2 weeks in summer, 2 weeks winter
MEALS: 12 to 2, 7.30 (7 Sat) to 10
PRICES: Set L £9·50 (£17), Set D £20·50 (£29) CARDS: Access, Amex, Visa
SEATS: 40. Private parties: 35 main room, 14 private room. Car-park, 15 places. Vegetarian
meals. Children's helpings. No cigars/pipes in dining-room. Wheelchair access (also WC)

BOURNEMOUTH Dorset   map 2

Crust [10/20]

Hampshire House, Bourne Avenue,
The Square, Bournemouth BH2 6EA
BOURNEMOUTH (0202) 21430   £11–£17

A reliable bistro serving home-made soup, salads, steaks, and some rich
puddings. Fish is fresh – halibut in prawn and white wine sauce; monkfish in
orange sauce – and vegetables are a strength. A blackboard list of specials
supplements the regular dishes, and puddings include lemon and treacle tart,
and banana and pineapple fool with Canary Island liqueurs. Wines are
reasonably priced with good Rhônes to support the burgundies and clarets, and
particularly inexpensive bottles from Italy. Five Australian wines from
Lindemans have been added. CELLARMAN'S CHOICE: Mâcon-Viré, Domaine de
Roally '84, £10·50.

CHEFS: Paul Harper and Alan Cutler PROPRIETORS: Tricia and Paul Harper
OPEN: all week MEALS: 12 to 2.30, 6.30 to 11 (11.30 Sat)
PRICES: £11 (£17), Set L £5·95 (£11) CARDS: Access, Diners, Visa
SEATS: 50. Vegetarian meals. Children's helpings. Smart dress preferred. Wheelchair
access. Music

Sophisticats [10/20]

43 Charminster Road, Bournemouth BH8 8UE
BOURNEMOUTH (0202) 291019   £18

Bernard Calligan's small converted shop is predictably, given the name, filled
with cat ornaments. The menu is eclectic and on the long side, with two dozen
dishes, but is based on fresh produce and makes good use of local fish. Typical
might be lettuce and almond soup; roast duck with port and cherries; entrecôte
marchand de vin; veal with a tarragon sauce. Service is cheerful, if a bit off-hand.
The wine list is also eclectic, dealing superficially in many regions. House French
£5·40.

CHEF: Bernard Calligan PROPRIETORS: John Knight and Bernard Calligan
OPEN: Tue to Sat, D only CLOSED: one week June and Oct, 2 weeks Jan MEALS: 7 to 10
PRICES: £12 (£18)
SEATS: 32. Private parties: 20 main room. Vegetarian meals. Children welcome. Wheelchair
access (also WC). Music

The Guide *recruits new inspectors from readers who write in regularly. If you would
like to apply, write to the editor with (a) a detailed report on a restaurant where you
have eaten and (b) a comparative study of restaurants known to you.*

BOURTON-ON-THE-WATER Gloucestershire — map 2

Rose Tree [12/20]

Riverside, Bourton-on-the-Water GL54 2BX
COTSWOLD (0451) 20635

 £14–£22

This cottage, by the stream that runs through the village green, has an exceptional wine cellar and an imaginative menu. Some of the combinations clash with the bright pink hues of the décor – pheasant with orange; goujons of halibut with mangoes; grapefruit cheesecake – and you may flinch at some of the lurid descriptions on the menu – 'oozing', 'morsels', 'succulent' – but Val Grundy is another who is moving into modern British cooking. A platter of smoked poultry with smoked quails' eggs and orange segments, a Stilton and leek tart, a soup of courgette, basil and tomato, or of turnip and dill, may figure alongside more prosaic dishes, on the lines of duck breast with armagnac or fillet of beef with cream and mustard sauce. The kitchen moves with the times by using wholemeal flour, semi-skimmed milk and low-fat cheeses in some dishes. The seventy or so wines are well spread, mostly from Europe, and wisely chosen; house Côtes du Ventoux '85 is £5·95. CELLARMAN'S CHOICE: Chardonnay del Friuli '85, £7·25.

CHEF: Val Grundy PROPRIETORS: Chris and Val Grundy
OPEN: Tue to Sat D, and Sun L CLOSED: 12 Jan for 5 weeks MEALS: 12.30 to 2, 7.30 to 10
PRICES: Set L £8·95 (£14), Set D £9·50 (£15) to £15·95 (£22) CARDS: Access, Amex, Diners, Visa
SEATS: 28. 6 tables outside. Private parties: 30 main room. Children's helpings. Wheelchair access. Music

BOWNESS-ON-WINDERMERE Cumbria — map 7

Porthole Eating House [13/20]

3 Ash Street, Bowness-on-Windermere LA23 3EB
WINDERMERE (096 62) 2793

£21

Close to Bowness waterfront, the modest exterior has a solid, portholed door and tiny blackboard showing some of the specialities in multi-coloured chalks. Inside, the nautical, rag-bag décor is at odds with the quality of the daily cooking, and indeed the wine list. The Bertons have been here since 1972 and it is still the most unusual eating-house in the Lake District. The *carte* is modest compared to the seasonal weekly menu, which changes on Friday. Fish is the trump suit, notably grilled Windermere char, and fresh pasta is good, too. But there may also be more complex dishes, such as poached pears served with Roquefort mousse and a sauce of watercress and cream. The wine list towers: prices for the '61 classed growths are available on request, though there is plenty of cheap drinking from all over the world – Spain, California and Australia have invigorating sections. Côte de Nuits take up a whole page; there are eight

The average price quoted in brackets is for an average three-course meal including service, VAT, coffee and half a bottle of house wine or the equivalent in an ethnic restaurant.

Gewürztraminers. House Merlot is £6·60 a litre, though Mr Berton points to his Australian Semillons (four) and Chardonnays for value.

CHEF: Michael Metcalfe PROPRIETORS: Judy and Gianni Berton
OPEN: all week, exc Tue, D only CLOSED: mid-Dec to mid-Feb MEALS: 6.30 to 11
PRICES: £13 (£21) CARDS: Access, Amex, Diners, Visa
SEATS: 40. Private parties: 36 main room, 22 private room. Vegetarian meals. Children's helpings. Music

BRADFIELD COMBUST Suffolk   map 3

Bradfield House [12/20]

Sudbury Road, Bradfield Combust IP30 0LR
SICKLESMERE (028 486) 301   £15–£27

The mood of the Stephensons' seventeenth-century house changes with the seasons: in summer the garden is in full bloom, there are tables on the lawn and the vegetable plot is at its peak; in winter the feeling of bleakness that descends is dispelled by a huge log fire. Victoria Stephenson's cooking is a full-blooded, generous mixture of past and present, with the emphasis on home-grown and local ingredients: bread is made with flour from a nearby mill; all kinds of old-fashioned fruit and vegetables are cultivated in the garden; there are free-range eggs. This translates into a four-course menu that can run from broad bean, courgette flower and lovage soup, through rabbit with lavender flowers, cider and local mustard, to apricot and saffron ice-cream served with crystallised yellow rose petals. House wine is £6·90 a bottle.

CHEF: Victoria Stephenson PROPRIETORS: R. M. and Victoria Stephenson
OPEN: Wed to Sat D, and Sun L MEALS: 12.30 to 2, 7.30 to 10
PRICES: £15 (£21), Set L £8·95 (£15), Set D £14 (£20) and £20 (£27). Service 10%
CARDS: Access, Diners, Visa
SEATS: 24. Private parties: 24 main room. Children's helpings (Sun L only). Wheelchair access (2 steps; also WC)

BRADFORD West Yorkshire   map 5

Kashmir [9/20]

27 Morley Street, Bradford BD7 1AG
BRADFORD (0274) 726513   £6

There's no décor to speak of and knives and forks are a rare sight, but this place sets the standard for Indian cafés in Bradford and beyond. The spotlessly clean basement dining-room has Formica tables and an unpriced menu board, but £2 will buy a bowl of curry with three perfectly made, steaming hot chapatis, and there will still be change. What stands out is the freshness and quality of the ingredients, which knocks spots off most high-street Indian restaurants: keema dhal is heavy with cumin; vindaloo is laced with seeded, chopped chillies; and

Restaurants are checked every year and their entries rewritten. The restaurant scene changes very rapidly. Don't trust an out-of-date Guide.

meat with spinach has a potent, aromatic sauce. Unlicensed, 'but even the water tastes good here'.

CHEF: F. Hussaien   PROPRIETORS: M. Latif and M. Bafhir
OPEN: all week   MEALS: 11am to 3.30am
PRICES: £4 (£6). Minimum £1·30. Unlicensed, but bring your own: no corkage
SEATS: 80. Private parties: 60 main room, 14 private room. Vegetarian meals. Music

▲ *Restaurant Nineteen, Belvedere Hotel*   [14/20]

North Park Road, Bradford BD9 4NT
BRADFORD (0274) 492559   £18–£25

The high-ceilinged, pink and green dining-room feels like a Victorian front room, but Stephen Smith's cooking is modern and has come on apace since the *Guide* discovered him three years ago. Menus change according to produce, and France has given way as the main inspiration; some of the best dishes have been modern British. Stephen Smith cites as examples of the transition sliced fillet of hare with beetroot and apple relish, squab with a purée of lentils and smoked bacon, warm walnut tart. Excellent soups rely heavily on vegetables, such as lettuce and cress. And how about this for a statement on the new cooking – duck leg casseroled in red wine and orange, with the breast roasted and served with a compote of rhubarb and ginger. The wines are utterly respectable and mostly French, though there are not many in single figures. Californian and Australian Chardonnays weigh in at just under £12 and CELLARMAN'S CHOICE is St Emilion, Ch. Berliquet '80, at £15·85.

CHEF: Stephen Smith   PROPRIETORS: Stephen Smith and Robert Barbour
OPEN: Tue to Sat, D only   MEALS: 7 to 9.30 (10 Sat)
PRICES: Set D from £11·50 (£18) to £17 (£25)   CARDS: Amex, Diners, Visa
SEATS: 40. Private parties: 10 main room. Car-park, 16 places. No children under 14. Smart dress preferred. Music.
ACCOMMODATION: 13 rooms, 3 with bath/shower. B&B £21·50 to £30. TV. Doors close at 11.30. Confirm by 6

BRAMPTON Cumbria   map 7

▲ *Farlam Hall*   [10/20]

Brampton CA8 2NG
HALLBANKGATE (069 76) 234
on A689, 2½ m from Brampton (not at Farlam village)   £19

The Quinion family's dark, warm, country-house hotel is set in four acres of mature grounds. The set dinner menu of perhaps ten dishes, followed by a sideboard of sweets, is a mix of country cooking and Cordon Bleu. Good-quality meats stand out: beef with pink peppercorns is a regular main course. Someone also has a skilled eye for vegetarian dishes. Service is accomplished. Thirty wines, from the English Lamberhurst, as a house wine, at £5·50.

'Maybe I am naive, but I fail to understand how anyone with a love of cooking real food cannot also be interested in books, the garden and buying Stilton that doesn't come in a plastic seal.'   (On eating in Yorkshire)

CHEF: Barry Quinion PROPRIETORS: The Quinion family
OPEN: all week, D only CLOSED: Nov and Feb MEALS: 8
PRICES: Set D from £15 (£19). Minimum £15 CARDS: Access, Amex, Visa
SEATS: 40. Private parties: 30 main room. Car-park, 30 places. No children under 4. Smart
dress preferred. Wheelchair access. One sitting
ACCOMMODATION: 13 rooms, all with bath/shower, D, B&B £55 to £110. Afternoon teas.
Garden. TV. Scenic. Doors close at 12. Confirm by 2 [GHG]

BRANSCOMBE Devon   map 2

▲ *Masons Arms* [9/20]

Branscombe EX12 3DJ
BRANSCOMBE (029 780) 300   £11–£15

A fourteenth-century inn at the foot of the valley, a short walk from the pebbled
cove. Rooms are clean, the bar is ample and the building full of history. The
kitchen does not take many short cuts and produces dishes such as steak and
kidney pie, sweetbreads with lemon sauce, and lemon meringue pie, for a dining-
room that has a few more airs than the rest of the house. Good beers, and an even
better wine list. CELLARMAN'S CHOICE: Gigondas, Domaine des Bosquets '83,
from G. Meffre, £9·70.

CHEF: J. Kickinger PROPRIETORS: Mrs J. and Mr M. Inglis
OPEN: all week D, and Sun L MEALS: 12.30 to 1, 7.15 to 8.30
PRICES: Set L £7·50 (£11), Set D from £11 (£15), Snacks from 90p CARDS: Access, Visa
SEATS: 46. 11 tables outside. Private parties: 30 main room, 14 and 30 private rooms.
Car-park, 45 places. Vegetarian meals. Children's helpings. Wheelchair access (also WC)
ACCOMMODATION: 20 rooms, 16 with bath/shower. Rooms for disabled. B&B £19 to £38.
Children welcome. Baby facilities. Pets welcome. Fishing. TV. Phone. Scenic. Doors
close at 12 [GHG]

BRAY Berkshire   map 2

Waterside Inn [15/20]

Ferry Road, Bray SN6 2AT
MAIDENHEAD (0628) 20691 and 22941   £45

An old Thames-side house with a modern extension giving views through sliding
windows to the river, with its willow trees, boats, swans and ducks. The décor
stands the test of time, unashamedly designed to create a feeling of well-being;
there are glitzy touches, for instance the artificial fruit and mirrors adorning the
alcoves, and fresh, light colours in the carpets, blinds and table napery. The *carte*
seems to be fixed in stone; there is only a fixed-price lunch as innovation. The
details of the accompaniments – bread, pastry, petits fours, vegetables, salad
dressings, cheeses – show the class, rather than the main dishes. The text of the
Roux brothers' book, *New Classic Cuisine*, is followed precisely by a young team
who produce the extraordinarily rich mix of three types of egg in oeufs brouillés

---

*Restaurants that we have not been able to assess as fully as we would like are given a
zero rating this year. We are particularly keen to have reports on these places.*

aux oeufs; a gamey partridge with young cabbage; lamb with garlic and wild mushrooms. Michel Roux's flair as a pâtissier shows in the brilliant desserts, for example a sablé of pears on a raspberry coulis. Michel is now more the soloist to his brother's conductor, content, for the most part, to let others take the limelight, though when he plays, the vibrancy returns. Wines are what to expect in a three-star Michelin restaurant – good quality, carrying high mark-ups.

CHEF/PROPRIETOR: Michel Roux
OPEN: Tue to Sun CLOSED: 25 Dec to 25 Jan MEALS: 12.30 to 2, 7.30 to 10
PRICES: £35 (£45)
SEATS: 80. Car-park, 50 places. Children welcome. Smart dress preferred. Wheelchair access (also WC). Air-conditioned

---

BRIDGNORTH Shropshire   map 5

Old Colonial [10/20]

3 Bridge Street, Low Town, Bridgnorth WV15 6AF
BRIDGNORTH (074 62) 66510   £9–£13

The 350-year-old, half-timbered building looks like an old pub, and inside it is more Laura Ashley than red flock, but it is a smart Indian restaurant, with cane furniture and fresh flowers on the tables. The menu stays with the North Indian stalwarts. There are recommendations for the aloo bhartha (mashed potatoes with coriander and chilli), the tandoori specialities, and the creamy, scented kormas. Vegetable bhaji dishes are good, too, and there is now rasmalai and kulfi. Speedy, courteous service. Kingfisher beer to drink, as well as Assam and Darjeeling tea.

CHEF: Gulam Hussain and Ali Ahmad PROPRIETORS: M. E. H. Chowdhury and A. Ahmad
OPEN: all week, D only MEALS: 5.30 to 11.45 (1 Fri and Sat)
PRICES: £8 (£13), Set D from £6 (£9) CARDS: Access, Amex, Diners, Visa
SEATS: 28. Private parties: 32 main room. Vegetarian meals. Children's helpings. Music

---

BRIGHTON East Sussex   map 3

Chilka [11/20]

58 Preston Street, Brighton BN1 2HE
BRIGHTON (0273) 27343   £15

This is a rare find: a genuine Bengali eating place, set in a street full of restaurants. Mr Ghoshal is both cook and owner and takes the trouble to talk knowledgeably about the food and its origins. Everything is cooked to order, so this is not the place for a 'quick curry'. Local fish is a feature: halibut is lightly cooked with fresh coconut and lemon, or in a spicy sweet-and-sour sauce with honey; salmon and hake also appear in different guises. Duck vindaloo is the real thing, made with red wine, potatoes and lots of lemon grass, while the house speciality, dhokar dalna, is cubes of chickpea paste in a mild sauce. Mr Ghoshal's skill shows in the spicy kotfas, the subtle kormas, and the chicken tikka marinated in lemon juice, garlic, chilli and coriander. Breads are light and fresh and to finish there's home-made kulfi or superb fresh mangoes. The dining-room is quite small, dimly lit and romantic. Service is extremely friendly.

CHEF/PROPRIETOR: A. K. Ghoshal
OPEN: Wed to Sun, D only CLOSED: 1 week Feb, March, May, June, Oct, Nov and
22 Dec to 1 Jan MEALS: 6.30 to 11.15
PRICES: £8 (£15). Minimum £5 CARDS: Access, Amex, Diners, Visa
SEATS: 32. Private parties: 36 main room. Vegetarian meals. Children welcome. Smart dress
preferred. Wheelchair access (also WC). Music

Food for Friends [10/20]

17A–18 Prince Albert Street, The Lanes, Brighton BN1 1HF
BRIGHTON (0273) 202310   £4–£7

The position on The Lanes, the touristic Brands Hatch of Brighton, means that
Simon Hope's vegetarian restaurant is usually full. In a town where good food is
hard to find, it is a joy – a genuine vegetarian restaurant able to convince, not
just because of its cheapness, but because of its value, too. Details, like the brown
bread and the soups, are excellent, and then there is falafel with fresh coriander
and yoghurt sauce; Ukrainian Kasha layer bake; and fresh fruit pizza. House
wine is £4 a bottle and there are Continental lagers.

CHEF: Philip Taylor PROPRIETOR: Simon F. Hope
OPEN: all week MEALS: 9am (10am Sun) to 10pm (11pm Fri and Sat)
PRICES: £4 (£7), Set L and D from £1·95 (£4)
SEATS: 55. Vegetarian meals. Children's helpings. Wheelchair access. Music. Self-service

French Cellar [12/20]

37 New England Road, Brighton BN1 4GG
BRIGHTON (0273) 603643   £22

The restaurant is tucked against a hill, with a railway viaduct up the road. It
brightens up a dreary neighbourhood and gives a boost to the Brighton eating-
out scene. The casual, ground-floor brasserie has been turned into a formal
lounge with heavy armchairs. Downstairs is the dining-room. Jean-Claude
Rozard offers unselfconscious French bourgeois cooking with strong, direct
flavours and generous helpings. Starters of tomato and onion salad, mussels or
Jesus sausage can be followed by New Forest venison with port wine sauce, or
grilled sea bass with herbs and Pernod. There are also votes for the rack of lamb
crusted with garlic and breadcrumbs. Vegetables are unfussy. Light crêpes or
meringues filled with raspberry sorbet to finish. The restaurant offers five per cent
discount for cash payments. A score of wines offer some decent drinking for
around £10. CELLARMAN'S CHOICE: Pinot Blanc '83, at £9.

CHEFS/PROPRIETORS: Mr and Mrs Jean-Claude Rozard
OPEN: Tue to Sat D, and Sun L in winter CLOSED: 1 to 15 Sept MEALS: 1.30 to 7.30, 7 to 10
PRICES: £14 (£22). Service 12.5% CARDS: Access, Visa
SEATS: 38. Private parties: 26 main room. Children welcome. Smart dress preferred.
No cigars/pipes in dining-room

*The 1989 Guide will appear before Christmas 1988. Reports are particularly helpful
in the spring. Report forms are at the back of this book, but just write a letter if you
prefer. Address it to* The Good Food Guide, FREEPOST, *14 Buckingham Street, London
WC2N 6BR. No stamp is necessary if you post it in the UK.*

Swans [new entry, zero rated]

21 Norfolk Square, Brighton BN1 2PD
BRIGHTON (0273) 721211   £15

Off the tourist track, Swans is set to appeal to its neighbourhood more than to
visitors. Service is conspicuously thoughtful, yet informal; the menu, though
with a strong 1950s-style taste for English fruit with everything, offers excellent
value and the care in the cooking is genuine. Dishes arrive piping hot from the
kitchen. Little touches here and there stand out: an almond and apricot stuffing
for best end of lamb; beautifully crisp skin on a duck with cider and apples; perfect
Stilton; excellent treacle tart. The table settings are of a standard you might
expect in a more expensive restaurant. A sensible, conservative list of wines
covers most of the French regions. House wine £5·50. More reports, please.

CHEF: Donald Jackson PROPRIETORS: Graham Swan and Ronald Ulyatt
OPEN: Tue to Sun, D only MEALS: 7.30 to 10
PRICES: Set D from £10·95 (£15). Minimum £10·95 CARDS: Access, Amex, Diners, Visa
SEATS: 30. Private parties: 30 main room. Children welcome. Wheelchair access (also WC).
Music

▲ The Twenty One [11/20]

21 Charlotte Street, Brighton BN2 1AG
BRIGHTON (0273) 686450 and 695560   £24

'Although I speak French in the kitchen and write my menus in French, my style
is definitely British.' There is no choice on the menu at the residents-only
restaurant of this personalised hotel, but the place offers some of the best cooking
in town. A typical five-course menu runs from watercress and sorrel soup, to
monkfish terrine with tomato and Pernod sauce, guinea-fowl wrapped in smoked
bacon with a port and thyme sauce, goats' cheese with fresh figs, and hot
raspberry soufflé. Warm oysters, quail egg salad, and mussel soup, give the
flavour of other evenings. The wines permit both modest drinking and
indulgence. House Duboeuf is £5·80 a bottle.

CHEF: Simon Ward PROPRIETORS: Simon Ward and Stuart Farquharson
OPEN: Mon to Sat, D only CLOSED: Christmas and Jan MEALS: 7 to 8.30
PRICES: Set D £18 (£24). Service 12.5% CARDS: Access, Amex, Diners, Visa
SEATS: 14. Private parties: 12 main room. No children under 12. No cigars/pipes in dining-
room. Music
ACCOMMODATION: 7 rooms, 5 with bath/shower. B&B £29 to £48. Deposit £25. No children
under 12. Pets by arrangement. TV. Phone. Confirm by 5.30   [GHG]

BRIMFIELD Hereford & Worcester   map 2

Poppies, The Roebuck [12/20]

Brimfield SY8 4WE
BRIMFIELD (058 472) 230   £20

The Evans' restaurant within a pub has a menu that changes from day to day,
and is not afraid to take on new tastes. Roast lobster with hazelnut and garlic
figures on the same night as duck with port and cherries. Orders are taken at the

rather dowdy bar, but the extended modern dining-room and trappings, for instance the bread, or the glass of dessert wine, are those of a serious restaurant. Good dishes range from spinach soufflé to crab pot, and pork fillet in filo. Imagination runs throughout the meal, to the port-wine jelly with fresh figs and Guernsey cream, or poppyseed parfait with date ragout, to finish. The fifty wines are well spread, but it is a dull selection as a whole.

CHEF: Carole Evans PROPRIETORS: John and Carole Evans
OPEN: Mon to Sat, exc Mon L CLOSED: 2 weeks Feb and Oct, 25 and 26 Dec MEALS: 12 to 2 (1.45 Sun), 7 to 10 (9.30 Sun)
PRICES: £14 (£20), Snacks from £2·20
SEATS: 32. Private parties: 32 main room. Vegetarian meals. Children welcome. No-smoking area. Wheelchair access (also WC)

BRISTOL Avon   map 2

Bistro Twenty One [new owners, zero rated]

21 Cotham Road South, Kingsdown, Bristol BS6 5TZ
BRISTOL (0272) 421744   £20

Alan Dubois has moved to this legendary restaurant from the Lygon Arms, Broadway; the Markwicks have gone into temporary retirement. It is still an archetypal bistro, with linoleum floors and red oilcloths on the tables. The menu is part-bistro, part-Elizabeth David, with a lot of cream, by today's standards. The stalwarts still dominate: onion soup; pork with cider and apples; chocolate mousse. Good ingredients can be enhanced by some decent sauces: scallops with mushrooms and cheese; roast best end of lamb with ginger and honey. A quartet of fish dishes includes monkfish in red wine sauce. Sweets are mostly cream. Sixty wines include some petit château clarets and one or two decent burgundies. More reports, please.

CHEF/PROPRIETOR: Alan Dubois
OPEN: Mon to Sat, exc Sat L CLOSED: 1 week at Christmas, 1 week at Easter
MEALS: 12 to 2.30, 6.30 to 11.30
PRICES: £14 (£20) CARD: Visa
SEATS: 26. Private parties: 8 main room. Vegetarian meals. Children's helpings. Wheelchair access. Music

---

Edwards [11/20]

24 Alma Vale Road, Clifton, Bristol BS8 2HY
BRISTOL (0272) 741533   £15

Tucked away in a narrow street, the oak-panelled dining-room has a friendly atmosphere and service to match. The short menu is bolstered by a blackboard. Almost everything fishy is good: seafood chowder; smoked salmon pâté; sole on the bone; or there are kidneys in Meaux mustard. Vegetables are plentiful, and to

---

The average price quoted in brackets is for an average three-course meal including service, VAT, coffee and half a bottle of house wine or the equivalent in an ethnic restaurant.

---

finish there's home-made ice-cream, or cherry tart with custard. The wine list is short and unimaginative, with vin de table at £4·95. CELLARMAN'S CHOICE: Chardonnay d'Oc, £7·45.

CHEFS: John Pitchford and Gerard Perry PROPRIETORS: John and Margot Pitchford
OPEN: Tue to Sat, exc Sat L MEALS: 12 to 2, 7 to 10.30
PRICES: £10 (£15) CARDS: Access, Visa
SEATS: 30. Private parties: 24 main room, 10 private room. Vegetarian meals. Children's helpings. Smart dress preferred. Wheelchair access

Ganges [10/20]

368 Gloucester Road, Horfield, Bristol BS7 8TP
BRISTOL (0272) 45234 and 428505 £11–£15

An efficient Indian restaurant with bright green, red and gold decoration and a degree of comfortable luxury. Dishes range from mild lamb pasanda and Afghan chicken to hot vindaloo and chicken jhal noorpuri. Sauces are not too oily and both nan and rice are good. Barfi and mint water-ice with pistachios are among the less westernised sweets.

CHEFS: B. Bista and H. Ali PROPRIETOR: Ahmed Chowdhury
OPEN: all week MEALS: 12 to 2.15, 6 to 11.30
PRICES: £9 (£15), Set L and D from £7·95 (£11). Service 10% CARDS: Access, Amex, Diners, Visa
SEATS: 54. Private parties: 30 main room, 24 private room. Vegetarian meals. Children's helpings. Smart dress preferred. Wheelchair access. Music. Air-conditioned

Harveys [10/20]

12A Denmark Street, Bristol BS1 5DQ
BRISTOL (0272) 277665 and 273768 £17–£24

Harveys has completely taken over the catering in its former wine cellar, and is clearly trying to emulate the length of the wine list by featuring no fewer than sixty-eight starters and main courses, many of them pretty vintage in concept. Choose the grills, or maybe game in season. Claret is probably what to drink, from one of the finest selections in the world. Ch. Latour goes back to 1917. Other regions are well represented, but overshadowed in this context. Service is quick and attentive.

CHEF: Thierry Rouvrais PROPRIETORS: John Harvey & Sons Ltd
OPEN: Mon to Sat, exc Sat L CLOSED: bank hols MEALS: 12 to 2.15, 7 (6.30 Sat) to 11.15
PRICES: £16 (£24), Set L £11·50 (£17). Cover £1 CARDS: Access, Amex, Diners, Visa
SEATS: 120. Private parties: 60 main room. Children's helpings. Jacket and tie. No-smoking area. Wheelchair access (also WC). Music. Air-conditioned

Jameson's [10/20]

30 Upper Maudlin Street, Bristol BS2 8DJ
BRISTOL (0272) 276565 £17

Bristol's great tradition of French restaurants is backed up by this red Victorian building. Inside is pure bistro: plants, plain crockery, and a long blackboard menu of what is really mid-Channel cooking, taking in tuna, chicken and avocado salad; beef Wellington; shark steak with Tabasco butter; and lamb with blackcurrant, but the fish soup, crab served with pincers and mayonnaise, and the generosity of portions are evocative of the bistro genre. Window seats can make you self-conscious. Forty wines start at £6, for the house Côtes du Frontonnais. CELLARMAN'S CHOICE: Ch. Coufran '79, £10·95.

CHEFS: Filali, and Carole Jameson PROPRIETORS: Carole Jameson and John Holmes
OPEN: Tue to Sat, D only MEALS: 7 to 11 (11.30 Fri and Sat)
PRICES: £12 (£17) CARDS: Access, Amex, Diners, Visa
SEATS: 70. Private parties: 30 main room. Vegetarian meals. Children's helpings.
Wheelchair access. Music

Muset [10/20]

12 Clifton Road, Bristol BS8 1AF
BRISTOL (0272) 732920   £15

A converted dress shop on two floors. Already under its second management, but the pattern remains consistent: French food and some good Australian wines. Onion soup, sirloin steak with sweet-pepper butter, and fresh fish – all with garlic bread – are the style. Vegetables are steamed; sweets are more showy. Interesting, unvintaged, short list of wines, from house French at £3·95 to CELLARMAN'S CHOICE: Coonawarra Cabernet Sauvignon, McWilliam's '81, £9·95.

CHEFS: A. Portlock, Peter Bates and C. Portlock PROPRIETORS: B. Y. O. Holdings
OPEN: Tue to Sat, D only MEALS: 7 to 10.30
PRICES: £11 (£15). Minimum £7. Licensed, also bring your own: no corkage
CARDS: Access, Amex, Visa
SEATS: 70. Private parties: 30 main room. Children's helpings. No children after 9pm. Music

Rajdoot [10/20]

83 Park Street, Bristol BS1 5PJ
BRISTOL (0272) 268033 and 291242   £10–£20

Some new Indian reliefs, huge prints, and green plants picked out by spotlights, have been added, and the smell of incense wafts around the entrance. The kitchen delivers good North Indian and Punjabi dishes with well-chosen ingredients and careful spicing; shish kebabs, chicken tikka and king prawn bhuna are all competently done. There is little grease or oil in the dishes, and pilau rice is well cooked, with a few raisins for contrast. Sweets disappoint, however. Turbanned waiters serve efficiently and deliver rather more in atmosphere than do comparable places. House French is £5·90.

CHEFS: C. and S. Mali PROPRIETOR: D. R. Sarda
OPEN: all week, exc Sun L MEALS: 12 to 2.30, 6.30 to 11.30
PRICES: £11 (£20). Set L from £5·50 (£10), Set D from £6·50 (£11). Cover 50p. Minimum
£6·50. Service 12.5% CARDS: Access, Amex, Diners, Visa
SEATS: 60. Private parties: 30 main room. Vegetarian meals. Children's helpings.
Wheelchair access. Music

Please keep the Guide informed of any changes to the restaurants listed. Report forms are at the back of the book.

Les Semailles [15/20]

9 Druid Hill, Stoke Bishop, Bristol BS9 1EW
BRISTOL (0272) 686456   £12–£24

René Gaté's cooking stays with the principle that food should taste of its main ingredients. The results can be brilliantly imaginative: broccoli mousse in a leek mould; squab cooked with candied lemon; wild duck breast on a bed of Chinese leaves; passion-fruit mousse with tiny marbles of sweet carrot. Dishes are like exquisite miniatures in the modern French style; they are preceded by canapés – a tiny pizza, a single mussel on a spinach leaf – and followed by coffee with petits fours. Presentation matches the best, and the keynote simplicity ensures that flavours are not wasted: a sweet tomato sauce is paired with young pigeon; an orange and carrot sauce sharpened with sherry vinegar partners milk-fed calf's liver. The sound French wine list bubbles with interest, and although there are expensive burgundies, mark-ups are generally no more than par for the course. CELLARMAN'S CHOICE: Ch. Haut Sociondo '82, £9·90, and Muscat d'Alsace, Schleret '85, £10·90.

CHEF: René Gaté PROPRIETORS: René and Jillian Gaté
OPEN: Tue to Sat CLOSED: some bank hols, 10 days in winter, 2 weeks in summer
MEALS: 12 to 2, 7 to 10.30
PRICES: £17 (£24), Set L from £7·80 (£12). Cover 50p. Minimum £7·80. Service inc
CARDS: Access, Visa
SEATS: 26. Private parties: 20 main room. Children welcome

Vintner Wine Bar [9/20]

Crusader House, St Stephen's Street, Bristol BS1 1EL
BRISTOL (0272) 291222   £12

This is *the* wine bar in the city centre, with flagstone floors and long polished tables. It is light, despite being underground, and there are tables outside on the patio. The blackboard lists egg mousse with prawns and celery, salmon pie, beef in red wine, and apricot crumble, and there are a dozen wines by the glass, plus three dozen assorted bottles. Breakfast is £2·90.

CHEF: B. Giardina PROPRIETOR: Colin Flint
OPEN: Mon to Fri, exc Mon D MEALS: 7.45 to 10.30, 12 to 2.30, 6 to 8.30
PRICES: £8 (£12). Snacks from £1·50
SEATS: 80. 10 tables outside. Private parties: 80 main room; 10 private room. Vegetarian meals. No children under 18. Music. Self-service

---

BROADWAY Hereford & Worcester   map 2

▲ Collin House [10/20]

Collin Lane, Broadway WR12 7PB
BROADWAY (0386) 858354
on A44, 1m NW of Broadway   £13–£16

A beautiful, if rather severe Cotswold-stone building dating from the sixteenth century, with mullioned windows, ancient beams and great stone slabs on some of the floors. The kitchen turns out traditional British dishes, from jugged hare to beef with Guinness and dumplings, and some modern ones, too, such as

Gloucester cheese and almond croquettes with green noodles and basil-flavoured tomato sauce. Old fashioned home-made sweets include damson ice-cream and meringues. Generally, look for the daily dishes. During the week light lunches are served in the bar and lounge. There is no shortage of attractive wines on the list – Alsace Riesling, Domaine d'Engelgarten '83 is £8·66, and Rosemount Estate Chardonnay '85 is £9·30 – and the bin-ends can be interesting.

CELLARMAN'S CHOICE: Australian Cabernet Sauvignon '82, from Taltarni, at £10·10.

CHEF: Judith Mills   PROPRIETORS: John and Judith Mills
OPEN: all week, exc Sun D   MEALS: 12 to 1.30, 7 to 9
PRICES: Set Sun L £9.50 (£13), Set D from £11 (£16), Bar L £8 (£13)   CARDS: Access, Visa
SEATS: 35. 5 tables outside. Private parties: 30 main room. Car-park, 30 places. Children's helpings. No children under 8 at D. Wheelchair access (also WC)
ACCOMMODATION: 7 rooms, all with bath/shower. B&B £29·50 to £54. Deposit: £25. Garden. Swimming-pool. Scenic. Doors close at 12   [GHG]

Hunters Lodge   [10/20]

High Street, Broadway WR12 7DT
BROADWAY   (0386) 853247   £12–£24

Although Broadway is hostage to coach-loads of visitors in summer, the Friedlis' comfortable, well-established restaurant is supported mostly by locals. The front of this handsome, creeper-covered stone house is spoilt by car parking, but at the back are lawns and an orchard. The menu combines traditional French and English stalwarts: roast duck with honey and almonds, grilled Dover sole with prawn butter, oxtail, and lamb cutlets. Quaintly, lunch is written in English, dinner in French. Vegetables are excellent, as can be the sweets, notably almond meringue with apricot sauce. Fifty wines are supplemented by some Grand Vins at grand prices, otherwise there are a lot of split vintages. The Friedlis' own-label house wine, at £5·50, provides sound drinking.

CHEF: Kurt Friedli   PROPRIETORS: Kurt and Dottie Friedli
OPEN: Tue to Sun, exc Sun D   CLOSED: 2 weeks Feb, 2 weeks Aug   MEALS: 12.30 to 2, 7.30 to 9.45
PRICES: L £11 (£17), Set L £8 (£12), D £16 (£24)   CARDS: Access, Amex, Diners, Visa
SEATS: 55. 6 tables outside. Private parties: 35 main room, 22 private room. Car-park, 20 places. Vegetarian meals. Children's helpings. No children under 8. No cigars/pipes in dining-room. Wheelchair access (also WC)

▲ Lygon Arms   [new owners, zero rated]

Broadway WR12 7DU
BROADWAY   (0386) 852255   🍾 £30

The village of Broadway owes its name to its main street being wide enough to take the floods of Cotswold sheep that brought it prosperity in the sixteenth century. The Lygon Arms has been here for a long time, earliest evidence being from the fourteenth century; the gabled front and carved doorways date from 1620, but the two bedroom wings at the back are twentieth century. Now it is owned by the Savoy Group, and Michael Quinn has moved from the increasingly commerical, conference-inclined Ettington Park to head the kitchen. It is a seductive proposition. Quinn's cooking is superlatively simple and was invariably

159

let down at Ettington by poor service and, perhaps, lack of customers, which should not be a problem here. Of all the many irregular-shaped rooms, the barrel-shaped, brightly coloured, almost theatrical dining-room is the finest. Service is formal yet relaxed, quicker to top up wine than water. The menu is extravagant and notable for the quality of its ingredients. The rather reserved French flavours of Alain Dubois' cooking (he has gone to Bistro Twenty One, Bristol) have been replaced by a strident confidence. Grills appear on the menu, as well as more elaborate dishes. The wines are professionally put together, with a range of vintages and prices to suit allcomers. Claret and burgundy hold most of the aces but there are good bottles from Spain and the New World, including Chardonnay from Australia and New Zealand. And there is choice under £10. More reports, please.

CHEF: Michael Quinn PROPRIETORS: The Savoy Group
OPEN: all week MEALS: 12.30 to 2.30, 7.15 to 9.30
PRICES: £22 (£30) CARDS: Access, Amex, Diners, Visa
SEATS: 120. Private parties: 90 main room, 90 private room. Car-park, 150 places. Vegetarian meals. Children's helpings. Jacket and tie. No cigars/pipes in dining-room. Wheelchair access (also WC)
ACCOMMODATION: 64 rooms, all with bath/shower. Rooms for disabled. B&B £70 to £195. Children welcome. Baby facilities. Pets welcome. Garden. Tennis. TV. Phone. Scenic. Confirm by 6 [GHG]

BROCKDISH Norfolk map 6

▲ *Sheriff House* [11/20]

Brockdish IP21 4JY
HOXNE (037 975) 316 £19

What the Pichel-Juans do, which is unusual, is faithfully to produce some very rare classical French dishes. These are invariably best ordered in advance, when booking, to give the kitchen time to shop and prepare. A scaled-down selection is, reluctantly, produced as a menu from day to day, but is rarely as successful. Be warned – this old-style cooking can be rich and creamy. A typical meal might consist of mousse d'écrevisse sauce Nantua; les escargots à la chablisienne; le râble de lièvre à la Piron; cheeses from Burgundy, and les tartes aux poires Williams. For a Russian dinner, duck stuffed with salt mushrooms and served with fried cucumber and baked aubergine, has been a major triumph. The wine list is too aristocratic to be affordable, but there is an everyday drinking section that tries to stay in sight of £10.

CHEFS: E. and J. Pichel-Juan PROPRIETORS: F., E. and A. Pichel-Juan
OPEN: all week, exc Wed MEALS: 12 to 2, 7 to 9
PRICES: £13 (£19) CARDS: Access, Visa
SEATS: 32. Private parties: 6 main room, 16 private room. Car-park. No children under 14. Jacket and tie. No pipes in dining-room
ACCOMMODATION: 2 rooms, 1 with shower. B&B £7 to £14. No children under 14. Doors close at 12

The Guide is independent, accepts no advertising and survives solely on the number of copies sold.

BROCKENHURST Hampshire   map 2

▲ *Le Poussin* [15/20]

57–59 Brookley Road, Brockenhurst SO42 7RB
LYMINGTON (0590) 23063 £17–£27

The Aitkens' neat little restaurant by the station is developing fast: the
hairdresser's next door has been bought and turned into a delicatessen; the
expanded front of house has been sharpened up. Alexander Aitken is serious
about what he does and was among the first chefs to start matching wines to
dishes – a Rioja with an aromatic casserole of veal offal and wild mushroom; a
Côtes du Rhône with a pastry case filled with guinea-fowl pâté and spinach.
Flavours are distinct, from a well-judged dressing for pigeon and mango salad, to
three cuts of duck: the leg crisp on a salad; the breast with a port sauce; the foie
gras with orange. Sweets make use of exotic fruits. The leisurely pace and the
attention to detail help to give this place stature; there are good canapés, using
ingredients from the delicatessen, excellent bread, unsalted butter, and classy
petits fours. The wine list has depth and breadth, with an eye for small vineyards
as well as claret. House Rhône or Gros Plant is £6·95. CELLARMAN'S CHOICE:
St Joseph '78, from Berry Bros, £9·95, or follow the nightly suggestions by
the glass.

CHEF: Alexander Aitken PROPRIETORS: Mr and Mrs Aitken
OPEN: Mon to Sat, exc Mon L MEALS: 12.30 to 2, 7 to 10
PRICES: £19 (£27), Set L £9·95 (£17), Set D from £15·95 (£19) CARDS: Access, Visa
SEATS: 35. Private parties: 35 main room, 10 private room. Vegetarian meals. Children's
helpings (L only). No children under 6. Jacket and tie. No smoking in dining-room.
Wheelchair access (also WC)
ACCOMMODATION: 4 rooms, all with bath/shower. B&B £20. Deposit £10. Children welcome.
Baby facilities. Doors close at 12. Confirm by 4

BROMSGROVE Hereford & Worcester   map 5

▲ *Grafton Manor* [12/20]

Grafton Lane, Bromsgrove BG1 7HA
BROMSGROVE (0527) 31525 and 37247
1½m SW of Bromsgrove, on B4091 £19–£28

Five of the Morris family help run this sedate, beautifully restored sixteenth-
century manor. The restaurant is getting more stable, perhaps because of custom
from the new motorway nearby. Dinners run to four courses and the fixed-price
menu changes almost every day. Gravlax is a permanent feature; otherwise the
style follows the spirit of modern British cooking. Tureens of soup, such as turnip
and dill, are left on tables and come with good home-made bread. Flavours are
vivid and seasonal: grilled fillets of grey mullet with lemon butter; Evesham
asparagus in a herb pancake; lemon sole with prawn and lovage sauce and okra;
roast lambs' hearts stuffed with leeks and cheese. Vegetables are excellent. Fine

*Files are kept on every restaurant, so reports of poor meals are just as valuable as
reports of good meals because they save unnecessary inspections.*

English cheeses are well worth the extra charge of £2·50, and sweets range from lemon tart to whisky steamed pudding with whisky cream. A vegetarian menu is also available. The largely French wine list explores southern burgundy in search of value, but also keeps up with the classic regions. CELLARMAN'S CHOICE: Ch. La Tour Haut Vignoble '78, £16·90.

CHEFS: Nicola, John and Simon Morris PROPRIETORS: John and June Morris
OPEN: all week D, and Sun L MEALS: 12.30 to 1.30, 7.30 to 9
PRICES: Set L £12·75 (£19), Set D £21 (£28) CARDS: Access, Amex, Diners, Visa
SEATS: 50. 2 tables outside. Private parties: 14 main room. Car-park, 55 places. Vegetarian meals. No children under 12. Wheelchair access
ACCOMMODATION: 8 rooms, all with bath/shower. B&B £49 to £70. No children under 7. Garden. Tennis. Fishing. Air-conditioning. TV. Phone. Doors close at 12. Confirm by 6 [GHG]

BROUGHTON Lancashire map 5

▲ Courtyard,
Broughton Park Hotel [new entry, zero rated]

Garstang Road, Broughton PR3 5JB
BROUGHTON (0772) 864087 £27

One of the few restaurants in the area attempting serious cuisine within the confines of a hotel. The details are impressive: meals begin with fresh Stilton cheese balls, anchovy sticks and a slice of smoked salmon stuffed with cream cheese, as appetisers; coffee comes with very good home-made petits fours. A meal in May consisted of terrine of Scottish lobster with young leeks and sour cream, and roasted veal kidney in a star anise sauce with whole shallots in their skins, accompanied by a spinach mould filled with oyster mushrooms. To finish, a puff pastry case filled with poached pear and a caramel and ginger sauce. Other good dishes have included lamb terrine with cherry and tomato coulis, and monkfish with scallops in white wine sauce. House claret is £9.
CELLARMAN'S CHOICE: Mâcon-Lugny '84, £13·50. More reports, please.

CHEF: Paul Heathcote PROPRIETORS: Kevinsfort Ltd
OPEN: Mon to Sat, D only MEALS: 7 to 10.30
PRICES: £19 (£27) CARDS: Access, Amex, Diners, Visa
SEATS: 30. Private parties: 30 main room. Car-park, 65 places. Vegetarian meals. Children welcome. Jacket and tie. No smoking during meals. Wheelchair access (also WC). Music
ACCOMMODATION: 98 rooms, all with bath/shower. Rooms for disabled. Lift. B&B £45 to £53. Children welcome. Baby facilities. Afternoon teas. Garden. Swimming-pool. Sauna. TV. Phone. Scenic. Confirm by 6

BROXTED Essex map 3

▲ Whitehall [12/20]

Church End, Broxted CM6 2BZ
BISHOP'S STORTFORD (0279) 850603 £18–£30

This fine period house, once the home of Rab Butler, has a handsome dining-room with a vaulted ceiling, exposed beams and a brick chimney breast as the focal point. Paula Keane's cooking is highlighted by the use of vivid accompaniments: garlic purée with best end of lamb; avocado purée with home-cured salmon; a heavily dosed saffron sauce for grilled monkfish. Vegetables are stir fried and salads are first rate. There is a six-course surprise menu at £47 for two, as well as a twenty-dish set dinner. The modern style also shows in the sweets, such as white and dark versions of a chocolate cake with an unsweetened raspberry purée. Portions have become more substantial of late, especially in the three-course set menu. The sixty wines have good range but with house claret at £8, like the rest of the operation, aspirations are rising.

CHEF: P. Keane PROPRIETORS: Mr and Mrs G. M. Keane
OPEN: Tue to Sun, exc Sun D CLOSED: 3 weeks Jan MEALS: 12 to 1.30, 7 to 9.30
PRICES: Set L from £12·50 (£18), Set D £23·50 (£30) CARDS: Access, Amex, Visa
SEATS: 40. 4 tables outside. Private parties: 20 main room, 10 private room. Car-park, 20 places. Vegetarian meals. Children's helpings (Sun L only). No children under 5
ACCOMMODATION: 12 rooms, all with bath/shower. Rooms for disabled. B&B £45 to £55. No children under 5. Garden. Swimming-pool. Tennis. Golf. TV. Phone. Scenic. Doors close at 11 [GHG]

BUCKDEN North Yorkshire map 7

▲ *Low Greenfield* [11/20]

Langstrothdale Chase, Buckden BD23 5JN
KETTLEWELL (075 676) 858 £13

'We discovered Low Greenfield walking the Dales Way on a day when we had paddled a soggy sixteen miles in drenching rain. We arrived sodden, cold, fed up and hungry, wondering what on earth had possessed us to spend our summer holiday in such a way, and tentatively opened the door. Perhaps our prospects were not as dismal as our day had been? Somewhere we could hear a Beethoven symphony and there were wonderful smells emanating from the kitchen.' The Sedgleys' four-course, no-choice dinner is served to residents only – understandably, as the seventeenth-century farmhouse is among the most secluded in England. Soups and pâtés precede roasts from the Aga, then there are cheeses, huffs and crêpes. 'When we came down for breakfast (equally excellent) the coal fire was already blazing.' The area is known for its dry-stone walls, flora, fauna and solitude. House Nicolas £5·50 a litre.

CHEF: Lindsay Sedgley PROPRIETORS: Austin and Lindsay Sedgley
OPEN: Mon to Sat D CLOSED: Nov to Easter, and Aug MEALS: 8
PRICES: Set D £9·50 (£13). Service inc
SEATS: 8. Car-park, 6 places. Children welcome. No smoking. Music. One sitting
ACCOMMODATION: 3 rooms. B&B £15. Deposit: £10. Children welcome. Baby facilities. Garden. Sauna. Fishing. Scenic. Confirm by 10 [GHG]

BURNHAM MARKET Norfolk map 6

Fishes' [10/20]

Market Place, Burnham Market PE31 8HE
FAKENHAM (0328) 738588 £11–£19

An uncomplicated restaurant on the village green. Fish is the main attraction and salmon fish-cakes with crab sauce are a speciality. Seafood gratin, crab soup, and sea trout with hollandaise have all been good. Oysters come from Fishes' own beds; the rest is from the local boats. Meat, poultry and seafood are still smoked on the premises. Lately, standards have been rather erratic; it is to be hoped this is only a temporary set-back. The wine list has some well-chosen whites, including house Chenin at £5·25. CELLARMAN'S CHOICE: Rully Blanc, Domaine du Prieuré '84, at £12·50.

CHEFS: Carole Bird and Gillian Cape PROPRIETOR: Gillian Cape
OPEN: Tue to Sun CLOSED: Sun D Oct to June, 24 to 28 Dec, 2 weeks end Jan
MEALS: 12 to 2, 7 to 9.30
PRICES: £12 (£19), Set L from £6·75 (£11) CARDS: Access, Amex, Diners, Visa
SEATS: 48. Private parties: 12 main room, 24 private room. Children's helpings.
Wheelchair access

BURNHAM-ON-CROUCH Essex
map 3

Contented Sole [10/20]

80 High Street, Burnham-on-Crouch CM0 8AA
MALDON (0621) 782139
£12–£19

The Walton family's smart, yellow-painted restaurant specialises in fish. The menu takes in halibut with lemon and tarragon, poached turbot with lobster sauce, and grilled Dover sole; seafood pancakes are a speciality . Meat eaters can go for steaks. The cheeseboard is a good buy at £1·70, or there are home-made sorbets to finish. The wine list has about eighty bottles, with plenty of choice around £10. House wine from Paul Bocuse is £6.

CHEF: Roy Walton PROPRIETORS: Roy Walton, Elaine Walton and Simon Walton
OPEN: Tue to Sat CLOSED: last 2 weeks July, 4 weeks at Christmas MEALS: 12 to 2,
7 to 9.30
PRICES: £14 (£19), Set L £6·50 (£12). Minimum £6·50. Service inc
SEATS: 65. Private parties: 40 main room, 28 private room. Vegetarian meals. Children's
helpings. Wheelchair access (also WC)

Polash [9/20]

169 Station Road, Burnham-on-Crouch CM0 8JH
MALDON (0621) 782233
£12–£14

A consistent Indian restaurant with a long menu of tandooris, birianis and bhunas. Chicken, meat, prawn and lobster are wrapped up in varying degrees of heat, from korma through Madras and vindaloo to pall. Set menus for up to eight people bring variety.

CHEFS: Kacha Miah and Abdul Shofique PROPRIETORS: Faruque Ahmed, Kacha Miah and
Abdul Shofique
OPEN: all week MEALS: 12 to 2.45, 6 to 11.45
PRICES: £8 (£14), Set D from £8·95 (£12) CARDS: Access, Amex, Diners, Visa
SEATS: 52. Private parties: 40 main room. Vegetarian meals. Children's helpings.
Wheelchair access (also WC). Music. Air-conditioned

Restaurants change owners and chefs constantly. Please help keep the Guide *informed of any changes you find.*

▲ *Angel Hotel* [11/20]

Angel Hill, Bury St Edmunds IP33 1LT
BURY ST EDMUNDS (0284) 3926   £22

The Angel is at the heart of Bury town life. The ivy-clad building faces the ruins
of the old abbey across the square. Freshly baked cakes are set out in the lounge
for afternoon tea; the bar is well used for just drinking. Of the two dining-rooms,
one, downstairs in the vaults, is more modern, serving lighter meals. The other is
more formal, more in keeping with the grandeur of the house, a pristine red room
with red candles a foot high, long draped curtains, crystal glasses, a gleaming,
silver-domed roasts trolley. The menu is accomplished, old school but not
atrophied, with touches of innovation, such as fillet of beef stuffed with a sweet
purée of onion and potato and served with a madeira sauce. Other adventurous
dishes may be less successful than the tried and tested rack of lamb or the familiar
sights on the sweets trolley. The wine list is adequate, with one or two pleasant
surprises under £10, for instance St Joseph, Le Grand Pompée '83, from Jaboulet,
at £9·95.

CHEFS: B. Harrison, B. MacCallum, J. Fulcher PROPRIETOR: M. F. Gough
OPEN: all week MEALS: 12.30 to 2, 7 to 9 (10 Sat)
PRICES: £15 (£22), Snacks from £1·80 CARDS: Access, Amex, Diners, Visa
SEATS: 80. Private parties: 12 main room, 14, 60 and 120 private rooms. Car-park, 45
places. Vegetarian meals. Children's helpings. Jacket and tie. No smoking in dining-room.
ACCOMMODATION: 37 rooms, all with bath/shower. B&B £26 to £61. Afternoon teas. TV.
Phone. Scenic. Doors close at 12. Confirm by 6 [GHG]

Bradleys [14/20]

St Andrews Street South, Bury St Edmunds IP33 1SD
BURY ST EDMUNDS (0284) 703825   £26

It is not immediately obvious why this part of Bury, with its builders' merchants
and lock-up garages, should be a conservation area. In a converted chip-shop,
David and Mina Weston run a *nouvelle* menu with as many dishes as there are
seats. He cooks, behind a tall counter, with great attention to detail, as in
mousseline of crawfish in a pool of creamy smoked salmon sauce; chicken stuffed
with ham mousseline and served with watercress sauce; feuilleté of lambs'
kidneys. The pace is slow and prices high for the area (VAT and service are not
included), but the quality is evident both in ingredients and cuisine, witness the
poached pear with an intense chocolate and port sauce. The short wine list
concentrates on the lighter-weight French regions to keep prices under £10.

CHEF: David Weston PROPRIETORS: David and Mina Weston
OPEN: Tue to Sat, D only; L by arrangement CLOSED: 26 Dec for 2 weeks MEALS: 7 to 11
PRICES: £17 (£26) CARD: Visa
SEATS: 18. Private parties: 18 main room. Children's helpings

*'Lunches were increasingly difficult, so we finally reduced the price to what looked like
an uneconomic level but found that we generated such a volume of trade it made
financial sense again.'* (Midlands restaurateur)

CALSTOCK Cornwall	map 1

▲ *Danescombe Valley Hotel* [14/20]

Lower Kelly, Calstock PL18 9RY
TAVISTOCK (0822) 832414   £18

The hotel is a Georgian building, with Cothele woods to the right, Calstock railway viaduct to the left, cows in the middle, and the tidal River Tamar, with pleasure boats up from Plymouth, flowing past. The Smiths' tiny dining-room only seats eighteen (if all the bedrooms are full, they do not take dinner bookings). Anna Smith's cooking shows the hallmarks of revivalist West Country cooking: a no-choice set menu, changing from day to day, and a firm commitment to local supplies and ingredients. Flavours are spot-on and there is a confidence about the cooking that bypasses pretension: twice-baked soufflé; feuilleté of prawns with asparagus; baked trout with tarragon butter; Tamar salmon en papillote on a bed of root vegetables. The admirable cheeseboard now features six from the south-west, including Danescombe goats' (made for the restaurant) and mid-Devon Wheatland, which can put most imported Camembert to shame. To finish, the French apple tart with plenty of Cornish cream is a model of its kind. Mark-ups are commendably low on the forty-strong, mainly European wine list, which makes nearly everything a good buy.
CELLARMAN'S CHOICE: Gran Coronas '79, from Torres, £6·85.

CHEF: Anna Smith PROPRIETORS: Martin and Anna Smith
OPEN: all week, D only CLOSED: Jan and Feb MEALS: 7 to 8
PRICES: Set D £15 (£18). Service inc
SEATS: 12. 2 tables outside. Private parties: 12 main room. No children under 12
ACCOMMODATION: 7 rooms, 2 with bath/shower. B&B £25 to £36. Deposit: 30%. No children under 12. Garden. Scenic. Doors close at 12 [GHG]

CAMBRIDGE Cambridgeshire	map 3

Browns [10/20]

23 Trumpington Street, Cambridge CB2 1QA
CAMBRIDGE (0223) 461655   £14

The city's food renaissance – prompted by the arrival of the hi-tech industries, rather than the influence of the university – suggests that anything Oxford can do, Cambridge can do better (or at least the same). It has now spawned a sister to Oxford's favourite American-style hangout. The solid brick building was, until recently, a hospital, but sports a huge dining-room with plants in hanging-baskets, large ceiling fans, polished wooden floors, dark wood circular tables, bentwood chairs, creamy yellow walls and energetic young waitresses in white aprons and black trousers or short skirts who compete for the longest pony tail. Large blackboards high up on the wall announce the daily specials, but the standbys are spaghettis, huge salads, hamburgers, hot sandwiches and various

The entries are compiled from the views of readers who have eaten at the restaurants in the last year, backed up by anonymous inspections and by information supplied and facts verified by the restaurants.

char-grilled dishes. Desserts are largely American, but a daily special might include a freshly made strawberry tart. Milk shakes are suitably thick with ice-cream; alternatively, try one of the numerous cocktails. The wines are modest by comparison. No booking permitted.

CHEFS: Stephen Shepherd and Stephen Farrant PROPRIETORS: Jeremy Mogford and John Mayhew
OPEN: all week CLOSED: 24 to 28 Dec MEALS: 11am (12 Sun) to 11.30pm
PRICES: £9 (£14)
SEATS: 325. 10 tables outside. Private parties: 12 main room. Vegetarian meals. Children's helpings. Wheelchair access (also WC). Music. Air-conditioned

Free Press [9/20] ✕

7 Prospect Row, Cambridge CB1 1OU
CAMBRIDGE (0223) 68337 £6

Through the dark years of Cambridge's gastronomic depression, this back-street pub was one of the few places in the city where you could find good food. The overall picture may be brighter now, but the Free Press still earns its place, serving some of the best pub food in East Anglia at lunchtime only. The style is macaroni cheese; thick soups with good bread; salads; apple pie; summer pudding. The varied choice includes vegetarian dishes. Beers are Greene King and IPA.

CHEF: Debbie Lloyd PROPRIETORS: Chris and Debbie Lloyd
OPEN: all week, L only MEALS: 12 to 2
PRICES: £3 (£6)
SEATS: 45. 2 tables outside. Private parties: 12 main room, 6 private room. Vegetarian meals. Children welcome. No-smoking area. Wheelchair access. Self-service

Midsummer House [12/20]

Midsummer Common, Cambridge CB4 1HA
CAMBRIDGE (0223) 69299 £18-£29

The former common-keeper's cottage was one of the most prominent council houses in the city, but now spearheads the revival of eating out. It is reached on foot; park on the far side of the common or on the other side of the River Cam and walk across the footbridge. The house has been adapted to include kitchens and conservatory, but the old atmosphere survives. The menu is modern British, multi-coloured, with choices at each stage of meals that can run from three to seven courses. Soup of red pepper, of celeriac and orange, of Stilton, or a consommé, may precede warm salads or pastries with offal. Main dishes include imaginative vegetarian choices, such as steamed cabbage filled with mushrooms and chestnuts, as well as roast sirloin with horseradish sabayon, or stuffed chicken. Cheeses, salads, ice-creams and breads are all excellent. Service,

If you cannot honour a restaurant booking, always phone to cancel.

Restaurants are graded on a scale of 1–20. In the category of 10–11 expect to find the best food in the locality. Ratings of 12 and more are given to restaurants we regard as serving the best food in the region.

like the rest of the operation, is developing. The wines, mostly French, include '83 Alsace, decent claret, and house wine at £7·50. CELLARMAN'S CHOICE: Cabernet Franc, Château du Petit Thomas '85, £6·75.

CHEFS: Jacky Rae and Louise Harrington PROPRIETORS: Jack Lang and Diana Lloyd
OPEN: Tue to Sun MEALS: 12 to 2, 7 to 10
PRICES: Set L £12·50 (£18), Set D £16·50 (£22) to £22·50 (£29). Licensed, also bring your own: corkage £3 CARDS: Access, Amex, Diners, Visa
SEATS: 60. 5 tables outside. Private parties: 40 main room, 10 and 20 private rooms. Vegetarian meals. Children's helpings. Smart dress preferred. No-smoking area. Music

Shao Tao [10/20]

72 Regent Street, Cambridge CB2 1DF
CAMBRIDGE (0223) 353942   £14–£17

Smarter than the average provincial Chinese restaurant, Shao Tao is unashamedly westernised, but nevertheless offers an interesting range of Peking/ Szechuan dishes, for instance three meats soup, Peking duck, scallops with ginger. Sauces are hot and spicy, portions small. House wine is £5.

CHEF/PROPRIETOR: Mr Tao
OPEN: all week MEALS: 12 to 2.30, 6 to 11 (11.30 Fri and Sat)
PRICES: £9 (£17), Set L and D from £9·50 (£14). Cover 25p. Service 10% CARDS: Access, Amex, Diners, Visa
SEATS: 100. Private parties: 100 main room, 30 private room. Vegetarian meals. Children's helpings. Wheelchair access (also WC). Music. Air-conditioned

Twenty Two [13/20]

22 Chesterton Road, Cambridge CB4 3AX
CAMBRIDGE (0223) 351880   £19

Possibly the best food in Cambridge is served behind the colourful stained-glass window of this terraced house. It is an idiosyncratic, informal restaurant with a pretty pink dining-room, thoroughly good-humoured service and a menu that moves with the seasons. There is no standing on ceremony, yet the food can dazzle. The style is unmistakably modern British: fresh soups, such as cold mange-tout and mint, or tomato and sorrel; buttery home-made pasta with Brie, pine nuts, tomatoes and pesto; duck sausages wrapped in vine leaves with a lime sauce. Vegetables and salads emphasise the theme, although there's a bourgeois French flavour to some dishes, such as boudin noir with sour cream and horseradish, venison bourguignonne, and leg of lamb with aubergine purée and mint. Fish is cooked *à point*: sea trout with a faultless dill hollandaise; fricassee of monkfish; fillet of plaice with mango sauce. Sweets pile one flavour on top of another, and might include orange, pineapple and passion-fruit ice-cream cake, and apricot, gooseberry and elderflower compote with smetana and shortbread. The intelligent wine list favours good-value regions such as Rioja, and has some ungreedy mark-ups. House French is £5·95 a bottle.

[GHG] *after the details of an entry means that the establishment is also included in* The Good Hotel Guide.

CHEF/PROPRIETOR: H. A. S. Brown
OPEN: Tue to Sat, D only CLOSED: Christmas to New Year, 3 weeks Sept, 1 week Mar
MEALS: 7.30 to 10
PRICES: Set D £13·50 (£19)
SEATS: 32. 4 tables outside. Private parties: 28 main room. Vegetarian meals. Children
welcome. Music

Upstairs [11/20]

71 Castle Street, Cambridge CB2 3AH
CAMBRIDGE (0223) 312569   £13

An eccentric, cramped Middle Eastern/North African restaurant in a room above
Waffles. Persian carpets, Islamic screened windows and black-painted tables set
the mood. Hywel Evans lived in Morocco for seven years and produces authentic
dishes with good ingredients. Filfil – sweet peppers dressed with lemon, olive oil,
honey and mint – is a good starter, or there is filling spicy harira – Moroccan beef
soup with lentils and chickpeas. Lamb couscous is an impressively large portion
served in an Arabic domed dish, otherwise the menu takes in trout with a sauce
of limes, pistachios and pine kernels, and vegetarian options, such as tajine
naboul – peppers and courgettes baked with eggs and Parmesan cheese. Sweet
crêpes or refreshing haytaliah to finish. Good Turkish coffee. The wine list roams
from Moroccan Tarik M'tir at £5·25 to Ch. du Tertre '70, at £20.

CHEF: Hywel Evans PROPRIETORS: Virginia and Pat La Charité
OPEN: Tue to Sun D MEALS: 6.30 to 10.30 (9.30 Sun)
PRICES: £8 (£13) CARDS: Access, Visa
SEATS: 36. Vegetarian meals. Children's helpings. Smart dress preferred. Music

---

CAMPSEA ASH Suffolk   map 3

▲ *Old Rectory* [12/20]

Campsea Ash IP13 0PU
WICKHAM MARKET (0728) 746524
1½m from A12, going E   £18

A gravel drive leads up to this seventeenth-century house outside the village of
Campsea Ash, on the B1078 near Wickham Market station. Chef/patron Stewart
Bassett usually selects from a magnificent list a suitable wine to accompany each
course. Reports run hot and cold, ranging from, 'guaranteed to kill any romance'
to, 'one of the most interesting meals in a long time', or, 'the koulibiac with
beurre blanc was a masterpiece'. The organisation has not matched the
gastronomy, but Mr Bassett assures us help is to hand. It had better be, before the
new conservatory adds another twenty seats. The style is not fashionable: hot
pike terrine; baked eels with leeks and white wine; lamb with a sauce edged with

---

*The 1989 Guide will appear before Christmas 1988. Reports are particularly helpful
in the spring. Report forms are at the back of this book, but just write a letter if you
prefer. Address it to* The Good Food Guide, FREEPOST, 14 Buckingham Street, London
WC2N 6BR. No stamp is necessary if you post it in the UK.

garam masala. Sirloin of beef is marinated for three days in burgundy with root vegetables and herbs, then roasted and cut thick, while still pink. Cheeses are another highlight; sweets have suffered most from the pressure on a one-man operation. The wine list is aristocratic and remarkable in the classic regions – claret spans four decades. Unusually, there are petit château wines from '70 for between £12 and £13, and some '61 under £20. Prices are inviting, right across the board, and the choice is impressive, from Drouhin burgundy to Jaboulet Rhônes. CELLARMAN'S CHOICE: Ch. Méaume '82, £8.

CHEF/PROPRIETOR: Stewart Bassett
OPEN: all week, D only MEALS: 7 to 10
PRICES: Set D from £13·50 (£18) CARDS: Access, Amex, Diners, Visa
SEATS: 48. Private parties: 18 main room, 8 and 24 private rooms. Car-park, 20 places.
Vegetarian meals. Children's helpings. No children under 10. Wheelchair access
ACCOMMODATION: 8 rooms, all with bath/shower. B&B £24 to £42. Deposit: 10%.
No children under 8. Garden. TV. Phone. Doors close at 1

CANTERBURY Kent
map 3

Restaurant Seventy Four [16/20] ✗

74 Wincheap, Canterbury CT1 3RX
CANTERBURY (0227) 67411 and 67412
£14–£31

Wincheap meant Wine Street, and this double-fronted sixteenth-century house belonged to a wine merchant and then a saddler; although it is away from the centre of town, it is within walking distance of East Street station. Its history is obvious in the dark panels and spacious inglenook fireplaces; there is also a priest's hole and a secret passage to the cathedral. Ian McAndrew's cooking is modern, with brave, striking combinations of ingredients, profound sauces and colourful arrangements: duck-liver tart with leeks; a warm salad of smoked salmon, foie gras and mango; breast of pheasant fanned out beside a pheasant rillette. Magret of duck comes on a marmalade of shallots with a rich armagnac sauce and a side dish of crisply cooked buttery vegetables. Fish supplies are excellent. Mr McAndrew has published a book of recipes for fish, and among his signature dishes are lamb with scallops, and beef consommé with crayfish. As a starter in April came five mounds of marinated fish surrounding a central salad dressed in mild aïoli: a pair of thick slices of gravlax, plus oak-leaf lettuce; sea bass in walnut oil and roughly chopped herbs; monkfish with tomatoes and tarragon; salmon tartare with a tiny cucumber and dill salad; scallops with pink grapefruit. As the inspector commented, 'The style seems pure modern British – there was little sign of anything classic or French'. The visual artistry comes again at the end of meals, for instance three little apples stuffed with apple purée, cinnamon ice-cream, and apple and calvados sorbet: or fig sorbet in a brandy-snap with slices of fresh fig to one side and a fig sauce streaked with cream to the other. Only a true chocaholic could have created the dessert of three chocolates, a masterpiece of dark chocolate marquise, white chocolate mousse and milk chocolate ice-cream, tiered on top of flower petals outlined on the plate in cream and dark chocolate. The strength of the well-spread wine list is in the £10 to £15 bracket. House wine is £6·20 – the white selected by Troisgros – but there is also a quartet from Provence, selected by Vergé. CELLARMAN'S CHOICE: Rully, Clos St Jacques, Domaine de la Folie '84, £16·80.

CHEF/PROPRIETOR: Ian McAndrew
OPEN: Mon to Sat, exc Sat L CLOSED: bank hols, 1 week at Easter, 3 weeks in autumn
MEALS: 12.30 to 2, 7.30 to 9.30
PRICES: £23 (£31), Set L from £10 (£14), Set D from £22 (£30) CARDS: Access, Amex, Diners, Visa
SEATS: 34. Private parties: 34 main room. Car-park, 12 places. No children under 5. Smart dress preferred. No smoking in dining-room. Wheelchair access (also WC)

Tuo e Mio [10/20]

16 The Borough, Canterbury CT1 2DR
CANTERBURY (0227) 61471   £13–£17

A small period-house near the cathedral, with a changing display of pictures on its white walls. Pasta is freshly made, and herbs from the garden pep up dishes such as lobster stew with a strong taste of the Mediterranean, and calf's liver with onions. Veal dishes are supplemented by the likes of partridge in a clove-flavoured wine sauce. Good pasta and fish combine in fettuccine with crab. House Sicilian is £5 a bottle.

CHEFS: Bernardino Lambardo and Tino Guzman PROPRIETORS: Mr and Mrs Greggio
OPEN: Tue to Sun, exc Tue L CLOSED: 18 Aug to 6 Sept MEALS: 12 to 2.30, 7 to 10
PRICES: £11 (£17), Set L £8·50 (£13). Cover 50p. Service 10% CARDS: Access, Amex, Diners, Visa
SEATS: 40. Private parties: 20 main room. Vegetarian meals. Children welcome. No pipes in dining-room. Wheelchair access (also WC). Music

Waterfields [13/20]

5A Best Lane, Canterbury CT1 2JB
CANTERBURY (0227) 450276   £18

Michael Waterfield's converted forge in the centre of town still has its share of heavy beams and bare brickwork, but the pastel colour schemes, the flower paintings and the glass roof give it the light feel of a conservatory. In its search for unusual and inventive dishes, the menu rambles, taking in classic French dishes, specialities from the eastern Mediterranean, and a few original creations. This translates into a vivid assortment that can lose its focus: avocado with pistachio dressing; Tunisian-style roast rack of lamb with courgette purée; marinated lemon sole; bourride. Some dishes, though, work brilliantly: fennel, aubergine and pepper fritters fried crisply and served on a rough, herby tomato purée; veal sweetbreads with mushroom, tarragon and sherry sauce. The modern British style reappears in pears and rhubarb in elderflower wine, served with almond cake. The high quality of the ingredients extends to the excellent hot rolls and unsalted butter. The wine list is decidedly French and mostly under £10. Three Kentish wines, at £6 each.

Report forms are at the back of the book.

The Guide *recruits new inspectors from readers who write in regularly. If you would like to apply, write to the editor with (a) a detailed report on a restaurant where you have eaten and (b) a comparative study of restaurants known to you.*

CHEF/PROPRIETOR: Michael Waterfield
OPEN: Mon to Sat CLOSED: Feb MEALS: 12 to 12.30, 7 to 10.45
PRICES: £13 (£18). Service 10% CARDS: Access, Amex, Visa
SEATS: 60. Private parties: 12 main room, 24 private room. Vegetarian meals. Children's
helpings. Wheelchair access (also WC).

CARTMEL Cumbria   map 7

▲ *Aynsome Manor* [12/20]

Cartmel LA11 6HH
CARTMEL (044 854) 653   £11–£17

Cartmel is isolated from much of Windermere's tourism. Here, the hills start to
roll. The Varleys' Georgian manor, which they run with obvious affection, is on
the edge of the village, and there are fine, open views from the elegant, panelled
dining-room with its soft colours, well-lit paintings and polished, candle-lit
tables. The setting is matched by the cooking. Traditional English dishes with a
few Continental touches are in evidence, but in essence, like other places in the
Lakes, this is modern British cooking of high quality. Soups, such as
mulligatawny, leek and almond, or courgette and fennel are served as a second
course, from a tureen left on the table, after ham and cheese aigrettes, or avocado
with crab and lime mayonnaise. Good sauces are a feature of main courses
parsley and white wine with halibut; redcurrant and mulled wine with roast
rack of lamb. Vegetables are handled with care. The sweets trolley has five or
six high-cholesterol offerings doused in cream. Irish tipsy cake is generously
alcoholic and there's a light touch to the pastry for the fresh apple pie. Service is
attentive. The wine list takes in examples from many regions and countries.
House Merlot is £5·60 a litre. CELLARMAN'S CHOICE: Gigondas '82, from
Bouchard, at £7·30.

CHEFS: Ernest Scott, Tony Varley and Christopher Varley PROPRIETORS: Tony and
Margaret Varley
OPEN: Mon to Sat D, and Sun L CLOSED: 2 to 23 Jan MEALS: 1, 7 to 8.15
PRICES: Set L £6·75 (£11), Set D £12·30 (£17) CARDS: Access, Amex, Visa
SEATS: 35. Private parties: 35 main room. Car-park, 20 places. Children's helpings.
No children under 5 at D. Smart dress preferred. No smoking in dining-room.
Wheelchair access
ACCOMMODATION: 13 rooms, 12 with bath/shower. B&B £31·50 to £63.
No children under 5. Pets welcome. Garden. Fishing. Golf. TV. Scenic. Doors close at 11.30

▲ *Uplands* [14/20]

Haggs Lane, Cartmel LA11 6HD
CARTMEL (044 854) 248 and 249   £15–£23

Tom Peter has cooked some vivid four-course dinners in the scaled-down, less
flamboyant, less expensive first cousin to the illustrious Miller Howe. It is also a
house with a view, this time not over Windermere, but, being perched almost on
the ridge of the hill dividing Cartmel and Grange-over-Sands, across Morecambe
Bay. The house is old in its structure but modern in its pinks, greys, art posters,
glossy magazines, loud classical music, and also in its cooking, which is modern
British par excellence. The Peters were both key figures in the success of Miller

Howe. Their workmanship is solid. He excels at pastry, at matching different flavours – often in profusion for dramatic effect – and at many of the classic Tovey dishes, such as quail eggs with a mushroom duxelles. Subtle it is not: the flavours are as solid as a brass band, with everyone playing at once. Five vegetables surround the main course of sliced fillet of beef already in its madeira sauce with mushrooms: mange-tout dressed in nut oil; carrots in Pernod; creamed parsnips with horseradish; sliced courgettes and peppers. Tarts, savoury and sweet, are good. Sometimes sheer bravado makes the cooking topple over, as in a parsnip soup flavoured with too much stem ginger, but the main theme is to keep with the seasons and involve the diner, for instance by leaving the whole hot malt/treacle loaf on the table for cutting, also the soups, for self-service. Service is fluent. The wine list is concise, with interesting New Worlds, notably from Australia and New Zealand. CELLARMAN'S CHOICE: Ch. Dillon '82, £8·50.

CHEF: Tom Peter PROPRIETORS: John J. Tovey, Tom and Diana Peter
OPEN: Tue to Sun, and Mon bank hols CLOSED: 4 Jan to 12 Feb MEALS: 12.30 to 1, 7.30 to 8
PRICES: Set L £9 (£15), Set D £15 (£23). Service 10% CARDS: Access, Amex
SEATS: 34. Private parties: 34 main room. Car-park, 18 places. Vegetarian meals. No children under 12. No smoking in dining-room. Wheelchair access. Music
ACCOMMODATION: 4 rooms, all with bath/shower. B&B £35 to £54. No children under 12. Pets welcome. Garden. TV. Phone. Scenic. Doors close at 11. Confirm by 3 [GHG]

CHADDESLEY CORBETT Hereford & Worcester map 5

▲ *Brockencote Hall* [new entry, zero rated]

Chaddesley Corbett DY10 4PY
CHADDESLEY CORBETT (056 283) 876 £15–£24

The hall is a magnificent eighteenth-century building in seventy acres of landscaped grounds with a two-acre lake and superb trees from Europe and North America. The style is pure classical elegance, with crystal chandeliers in the dining-room and fresh flowers everywhere. Serge Demollière's cooking matches this and is in the mould of modern French hotel food: dishes are served under huge silver domes that are lifted with a flourish. Fish dishes are well reported: fillets of sole with fish mousse and chive sauce; scallops arranged as a rose around a plate, surrounded by a langoustine sauce; baked monkfish in red-wine sauce. Other successes have included creamy scrambled eggs with Parma ham; sweetbread and lobster with home-made noodles; and simple grilled fillet of Scotch beef. Sweets are the showy kind: a biscuit basket of fresh fruits and cream; an exotic fruit filled pancake 'tied' with a glazed strip of orange peel. There are around seventy wines, including two dozen champagnes, among them a 1900 Dom Perignon for £62. House wine is somewhat cheaper, at £9·70 a bottle. More reports, please.

Restaurants rating 12 or more serve the best food in the region.

The entries are compiled from the views of readers who have eaten at the restaurants in the last year, backed up by anonymous inspections and by information supplied and facts verified by the restaurants.

CHEF: Serge Demollière PROPRIETORS: Mr and Mrs J. Petitjean
OPEN: all week, exc Sat L MEALS: 12.30 to 2, 7.30 to 9.30
PRICES: £19 (£24), Set L £10·50 (£15). Service inc CARDS: Access, Amex, Diners, Visa
SEATS: 38. 5 tables outside. Private parties: 40 main room, 25 private room. Car-park,
45 places. Vegetarian meals. Children welcome. Smart dress preferred. Wheelchair access
(also WC). Music
ACCOMMODATION: 9 rooms, all with bath/shower. B&B £50 to £58. Afternoon teas. Garden.
TV. Phone. Scenic. Doors close at 12

CHAGFORD Devon   map 1

▲ *Gidleigh Park* [16/20]

Chagford TQ13 8HH
CHAGFORD (064 73) 2367 and 2225
from Chagford Square turn R at Lloyds,
then R at first fork for 2 miles   £25 – £39

After ten years the Hendersons are still developing – revamped rooms, water
garden, regenerated breakfasts – and at each stage, quality has been paramount.
Shaun Hill has established his kitchen style, which is more robust than the
modern classical style of his predecessor, John Webber, now at Cliveden. For
example, he uses intensely reduced pure stocks for sauces, avoiding reduced
wines and brandies, except at the last minute, for extra flavour. He also likes to
work with apples, pears, mulberries, quinces and tangerines as well as the
sophisticated imported fruits that have become obligatory. The menu has almost
moved out of its indeterminate, quasi-French phase into the kind of cosmopolitan
variation on modern British cooking that is usually found only in cities. Among
the starters, a Thai soup vies with bresaola and foie gras sauté with a sauce of
Sauternes. There are some explosive concoctions when Hill brings together all
these ideas – saffron soup; herb ravioli filled with white truffles and Parmesan;
Challans duck with roast shallots and red wine. Coriander is used to spice sauté
scallops with lime or steamed red mullet on its bed or frisée. Scallops, another
night, come with fettuccine, basil and pepper, the fish slightly crunchy from
being sauté in walnut oil, with a few pine kernels scattered over for extra texture.
Sauces have been excellent. At the same time, there is no fear of the plain: roast
rib of beef is served in its juices with tiny, light Yorkshire puddings. Cheeses,
trimmings and service all betray the thoroughness of American planning, as does
the cellar. With over four hundred wines on the list, and a futher two hundred
and fifty bin-ends, it is small wonder Paul Henderson asks for special orders to be
placed before 5pm, 'so that we can try to find them'. That there is precious little
under £10 is due to the high quality of the wines, rather than excessive mark-
ups. American wines include vintages of Martha's Vineyard Cabernet
Sauvignon, from Heitz, back to 1973, and there are two dozen California
Chardonnays to play off against splendid but increasingly expensive white

---

All inspections are carried out anonymously.

The Guide *is independent, accepts no advertising and survives solely on the number of
copies sold.*

---

burgundies. House burgundy is £9. CELLARMAN'S CHOICE: Gewürztraminer, Seigneurs de Ribeaupierre '83, from Trimbach, £13.

CHEF: Shaun Hill PROPRIETORS: Kay and Paul Henderson
OPEN: all week MEALS: 12.30 to 2, 7 to 9
PRICES: Set L £17·50 (£25) to £25 (£33), Set D £25 (£33) to £30 (£39). Service inc
CARDS: Access, Amex, Diners, Visa
SEATS: 35. Private parties: 18 main room. Car-park, 25 places. Children welcome. Smart dress preferred. No cigars/pipes in dining-room. Wheelchair access
ACCOMMODATION: 14 rooms, all with bath/shower. B&B £55 to £125. Children by arrangement. Pets welcome. Afternoon teas. Garden. Tennis. Fishing. TV. Phone. Scenic. Doors close at 12 [GHG]

▲ Teignworthy Hotel [14/20]

Frenchbeer, Chagford TQ13 8EX
CHAGFORD (064 73) 3355
3m SW of Chagford: from Chagford Square follow signs to
Fernworthy, then Kestor and Thornworthy   £30

The house is virtually a carbon copy of the Lutyens-designed Castle Drogo. Inside it is orderly, uncluttered, almost austere – a country house in the old style, with superb panoramic views as the main distraction for the eye. David Woolfall dazzles with the simplicity of his dishes and the perfect quality of his raw materials. The short menu is plainly written and to the point. Sauté of Cornish scallops on a bed of rocket is exactly what it says: a classic warm salad with sliced scallops in walnut oil and a little vinegar, piled on leaves of rocket and radicchio. Spot-on timing shows in the medallions of Devon beef in a burgundy and shallot sauce, which comes unadorned and ungarnished. This is modern cooking pared down to its essentials, a philosophy that extends to the excellent plain vegetables. The menu takes in fillets of Dover sole stuffed with pike mousse, corn-fed guinea-fowl studded with oregano and garlic, and vegetarian options, such as a ragout of vegetables in puff pastry with saffron sauce. A note of sophistication and complexity appears in the sweets: chocolate and pear truffle cake is actually a creamy mousse embedding half a pear and bits of fresh orange rind, all on a liqueur-soaked sponge base and served in a pool of cream dragged with raspberry coulis. Appetisers, unpasteurised butter, coffee and petits fours are all top-drawer. Wines include good claret from the 1970s, some pedigree burgundy, and bottles under £10 from around the regions. Prices are generally sympathetic. CELLARMAN'S CHOICE: Beaujolais blanc, Château des Tours '85, £9.90.

CHEF: David Woolfall PROPRIETORS: John and Gillian Newell
OPEN: all week MEALS: 12 to 2, 7.30 to 9
PRICES: Set L and D £24·50 (£30), Snacks from £7
SEATS: 30. 3 tables outside. Private parties: 30 main room. Car-park. Vegetarian meals. No children under 12. No smoking in dining-room. Wheelchair access (also WC)
ACCOMMODATION: 9 rooms, all with bath/shower. B&B £45 to £78. No children under 12. Afternoon teas. Garden. Sauna. Tennis. Fishing. TV. Phone. Scenic [GHG]

The average price quoted in brackets is for an average three-course meal including service, VAT, coffee and half a bottle of house wine or the equivalent in an ethnic restaurant.

CHEAM Surrey	map 3

Al San Vincenzo [11/20]

52 Upper Mulgrave Road, Cheam SM2 7AJ
01-661 9763   £18 – £21

Vincenzo Borgonzolo cooks robust, strongly flavoured dishes in his friendly
Italian restaurant near the station. One secret is the ingredients: organic
vegetables, hormone-free meat and fresh fish from local shops and suppliers, plus
Italian oils and vinegar. The menu features al dente fusilli; red mullet baked with
herbs; medallions of veal stuffed with Mozzarella and Parma ham; and there are
Pecorino Romana, Provolone, Taleggio and Mascarpone on the cheeseboard. As
an alternative to imported gateaux there are seasonal fruit specialities, such as
papaya with raspberries and grappa, or prickly pear with amaretto. House wines
– Rosso Conero and Bianco D'Ischia – are £7·60 a bottle.

CHEF: Vincenzo Borgonzolo PROPRIETORS: Vincenzo and Elaine Borgonzolo
OPEN: Mon to Sat MEALS: 12 to 2.30, 6.30 to 10.30
PRICES: Set L £12·50 (£18), Set D £15·50 (£21) CARDS: Access, Amex, Diners, Visa
SEATS: 20. Private parties: 22 main room. Children's helpings. No cigars/pipes. Wheelchair
access. Music

CHEDINGTON Dorset	map 2

▲ *Chedington Court* [11/20]

Chedington DT8 3HY
CORSCOMBE (093 589) 265
off A356 4½m SE of Crewkerne   £22

Tranquillity pervades this beautiful, yellow-stone house looking out over its
grounds (with yews and lake) and beyond, across the border into Somerset.
Inside is panelled, filled with books and flowers. Hilary Chapman cooks a no-
choice, English menu that is alert to new styles: baby vegetables tossed in a
saffron vinaigrette as a starter; tomato and orange soup spiced with coriander.
Her roast beef and Yorkshire pudding remain exemplary. The wine list is
extensive, running to a thousand bottles, including some early claret, interesting
sections from Spain and Portugal and no fewer than seventeen rosés. There is a
page of CELLARMAN'S CHOICES on the wine list.

CHEF: Hilary Chapman PROPRIETORS: Philip and Hilary Chapman
OPEN: all week, D only MEALS: 7 to 9
PRICES: Set D £18·50 (£22). Service inc
SEATS: 30. 1 table outside. Private parties. 40 main room, 50 private room. Car-park,
20 places. Vegetarian meals. Children's helpings. Smart dress preferred. No cigars/pipes in
dining-room. Wheelchair access (also WC). Music
ACCOMMODATION: 10 rooms, all with bath/shower. D, B&B £53 to £106. Deposit £30. Baby
facilities. Garden. Snooker. TV. Phone. Scenic. Doors close at 12. Confirm by 9 [GHG]

*'The total bill was around £55, to which to my annoyance they added an "optional
service charge of 15 per cent for your convenience". I am quite able to add service at my
own convenience.'* (On eating in London)

CHELMSFORD Essex   map 3

Melissa [9/20] ✈

21 Broomfield Road, Chelmsford CM1 1SY
CHELMSFORD (0245) 353009   £8–£12

The best value in the area for daytime eating is this vegetarian sister of
Farmhouse Feast at Roxwell (see entry). Blackboards list the set lunch of the
day: lentil and vegetable soup, nut cottage pie, mocha ice-cream or carob and
strawberry gateau. Otherwise there are filled baps, jacket potatoes, and upwards
of a dozen salads. The restaurant is spotless. On the first Friday of each month
there is a more formal dinner, celebrating cuisines from around the world; dinner
parties for other evenings can be arranged. House Italian is £4·50.

CHEFS/PROPRIETORS: Rosemary and Melanie Upson
OPEN: Mon to Sat L only, and D first Fri each month MEALS: 9 to 4
PRICES: £4 (£9), Set L £4·60 (£8), Set D £7·95 (£12), Snacks from 80p
SEATS: 24. Private parties: 28 main room. Vegetarian meals. Children's helpings. No
smoking in dining-room. Wheelchair access. Self-service (waitress service at D)

CHELTENHAM Gloucestershire   map 2

Le Beaujolais [new entry, zero rated]

15 Rotunda Terrace, Cheltenham GL50 1SW
CHELTENHAM (0242) 525230   £14–£21

The Rotunda purveys a great variety of commodities. Bakers, estate agents and
Ladbrokes share the street with this down-market, rather than up-market, bistro
that has been improving steadily. The menu has elements of many different
styles: modern British, in cauliflower mousse with a Stilton sauce; *nouvelle*, in the
emphasis on herbs and good sauces; fashionable salmon tartare; fairly classic
French sweets – petit pot au chocolat crème – and cheeses. Dishes are all given on
the menu in French, at least at night, and served with enthusiasm in the tiny
dining-room beneath a huge propeller fan. The cooking is honest and makes up
in gusto what it lacks in technique. Ad lib coffee with home-made petits fours.
Three dozen exclusively French wines (barring two Germans) start at £5·55 and
are mostly under £10. CELLARMAN'S CHOICE: white Côtes du Rhône, £9·95. More
reports, please.

CHEFS: Colin Sparks and R. Speaks PROPRIETOR: A. M. Amos
OPEN: Mon to Sat MEALS: 12.30 to 2, 7.30 to 10.30 (11.30 Sat)
PRICES: £13 (£21), Set L from £8·65 (£14). Licensed, also bring your own: corkage £5
CARDS: Access, Amex, Diners, Visa
SEATS: 40. Private parties: 26 main room. Vegetarian meals. Children's helpings.
Wheelchair access (1 step). Music. Air-conditioned

*The 1989 Guide will appear before Christmas 1988. Reports are particularly helpful
in the spring. Report forms are at the back of this book, but just write a letter if you
prefer. Address it to* The Good Food Guide, FREEPOST, 14 Buckingham Street, London
WC2N 6BR. No stamp is necessary if you post it in the UK.

La Ciboulette

24 – 26 Suffolk Road, Cheltenham GL50 9QT

As the Guide went to press, Kevin and Blandine Jenkins sold this restaurant, which the new owners have renamed.

Number Twelve [10/20]

12 Suffolk Parade, Cheltenham GL50 2AB
CHELTENHAM (0242) 584544   £13 – £20

In the heart of Cheltenham's food quarter – now a rich hunting ground for eating out – which is bounded by Suffolk Parade and Suffolk Road. The shop frontage has darkened glass windows, although inside is a civilised town-house conservatory with a pink colour scheme, ruched floral curtains and lots of greenery. The cooking is French and notable for its good, clear, strong taste combinations. Ideas are often new versions of classics, as in smoked rack of lamb with cream and mint sauce; mushrooms in flaky pastry with a sweet garlic sauce; chocolate pot filled with ginger mousse in a pool of raspberry coulis. Vegetables are fresh and plainly cooked, allowing the main courses to stand out. Small details, for instance the butter and coffee, could profitably be improved. Mature, loyal, involved service. The wine list is intelligently described, and takes in England and the New World. CELLARMAN'S CHOICE: Moulin à Vent '83, at £11·95.

CHEFS: Norman Young and David Harker PROPRIETOR: Norman Young
OPEN: Tue to Sun, exc Sat L and Sun D MEALS: 12 to 2, 7.30 to 10 (10.30 Fri and Sat)
PRICES: £14 (£20), Set L £7·25 (£13) CARDS: Access, Amex, Diners, Visa
SEATS: 40. Private parties: 48 main room. Children's helpings. Music

Redmond's [13/20]

12 Suffolk Road, Cheltenham GL50 2AQ
CHELTENHAM (0242) 580323   £14 – £21

Redmond Hayward, formerly of Anna's Place, when it rated 15/20, and ex-Calcot Manor, Tetbury, re-emerges with his vivacious wife Pippa in their own small converted shop. Only the tomato purée and the anchovies are tinned, otherwise everything is home made. Bookings are staggered, so the Haywards can cope. The yellow dining-room has deep blue curtains that match the marbled octagonal under-plates. The menu is short, innovative and a prime example of modern British cooking: red mullet with an orange and Pernod sauce; roast pigeon with apples and a game sauce seasoned with cinnamon. On a good night, Hayward competes with the best. Soufflés, such as hot ginger with advocaat sauce, are his forte, or else there are good sorbets, but the menu moves along with the seasons. The wine list is short, French, mostly from the classic regions, and well chosen, especially under £10. House wine is £5·95.
CELLARMAN'S CHOICE: Madiran, Domaine Bouschasse '85, £8·30.

It is helpful if restaurateurs keep the office up to date with any changes.

CHEF: Redmond Hayward PROPRIETORS: Redmond and Pippa Hayward
OPEN: Tue to Sun, exc Tue L and Sun D CLOSED: first week Jan, 2 weeks Aug to Sept,
1 week May MEALS: 12.30 to 2, 7.15 to 10
PRICES: £17 (£21), Set L £9·75 (£14). Service inc CARDS: Access, Amex, Diners, Visa
SEATS: 22. 4 tables outside. Private parties: 22 main room. Children's helpings.
No children under 5. No cigars/pipes in dining-room. Wheelchair access (1 step).
Air-conditioned

CHESTER Cheshire map 5

Abbey Green [10/20] ✈

2 Abbey Green, Northgate Street, Chester CH1 2JH
CHESTER (0244) 313251 £5–£14

This accomplished vegetarian restaurant, down a narrow cobbled passage
leading to the green, is well supported by meat eaters too, and tables for
Saturdays have to be booked well in advance. There is a bright Victorian/
Regency dining-room with fresh carnations on the tables, a blazing fire and
classical music, which makes an unlikely setting for Julia Lochhead's vegetarian
food. Lunch is simple and cheap, with vegetable lasagne, pies and salads with
natural dressings. Dinners offer a more imaginative choice: baked avocado with
tangerine and sour-cream filling; stuffed globe artichokes with a sauce of lemon
and grapes. The wine list of twenty bottles shows the same imagination –
Bulgarian Chardonnay, New Zealand Chenin Blanc, Australian Shiraz. House
French is £5·20 a litre.

CHEFS: Julia Lochhead and Colin Gillies PROPRIETORS: Julia and Duncan Lochhead
OPEN: L all week, D Tue to Sat MEALS: 11.30 to 3, 6.30 to 10.15
PRICES: £9 (£14), Set L from £2 (£5) CARD: Visa
SEATS: 48. 6 tables outside. Private parties: 8 main room, 24 private room. Car-park, 20
places. Vegetarian meals. Children's helpings. No-smoking area. Wheelchair access. Music

---

▲ Grosvenor [10/20]

Eastgate Street, Chester CH1 1LT
CHESTER (0244) 24024 £16–£45

The seven million pounds spent on this hotel is recouped via some hefty bills, but
the facelift has not been skimped. Paul Reed cooks a pretentiously worded French
menu in the modern style: guinea-fowl minestrone flavoured with orange; veal
kidneys with green noodles; chocolate marquise. The set menus are excellent
value in the area. The *esprit*, though, is perhaps at its height with traditional
afternoon tea: scones, clotted cream, pastries, slices of Bakewell tart, as well as
beef and salmon sandwiches, all served in traditional fashion on a tea-stand. The

---

The Guide *recruits new inspectors from readers who write in regularly. If you would
like to apply, write to the editor with (a) a detailed report on a restaurant where you
have eaten and (b) a comparative study of restaurants known to you.*

Anyone claiming to be from The Good Food Guide *is an impostor. Restaurateurs are
advised to contact the office immediately if any fraudulent claims are made.*

wine list is a book of exorbitantly priced, but well-known, names. There is little of elegance at the affordable end, bar house French, commendably reduced in price by £1·95 since last year, but £8. CELLARMAN'S CHOICE: Ch. Latour '73, £40.

CHEF: Paul Reed PROPRIETORS: Grosvenor Estate Holdings
OPEN: all week MEALS: 12 to 2, 7 to 10
PRICES: £32 (£45), Set L from £10·50 (£16), Set D from £17 (£23) CARDS: Access, Amex, Carte Blanche, Diners, Visa
SEATS: 100. Private parties: 12 main room, 18, 60 and 350 private rooms. Vegetarian meals. Children's helpings. Jacket and tie. Wheelchair access (also WC). Air-conditioned
ACCOMMODATION: 85 rooms, all with bath/shower. Rooms for disabled. Lift. B&B £77.50 to £120. Deposit: one night's stay. Children welcome. Baby facilities. Afternoon teas. Air-conditioning. TV. Phone. Confirm by 4

CHILGROVE West Sussex

map 3

White Horse Inn [10/20]

Chilgrove PO18 9HX
EAST MARDEN (024 359) 219

 £20–£23

The reputation of this eighteenth-century country pub is based on its spectacular wine cellar, but chef Neal Findley offers an enjoyable fixed-priced menu with a complimentary course, such as a pâté, after the starter. One typical meal in August featured light crab mousse and new season's grouse with thyme. Sauces are first rate and the cheeseboard includes well-matured English varieties. The wine list is a bottle by bottle guide to some of the world's best drinking, across countries, continents, styles and decades. Instead of ploughing through the list, just think of a wine and order it. The chances are it will be there somewhere, and if not, there will be one very like it. If claret dating from the First World War or forty vintages of Ch. Latour make it difficult to choose, take the CELLARMAN'S CHOICE: St Emilion, Ch. Haut Veyrac '82, at £8·45. Some wonderful wines are available by the glass, too.

CHEF: Neal Findley PROPRIETORS: Dorothea and Barry Phillips
OPEN: Tue to Sat CLOSED: 3 weeks Feb, 1 week Oct MEALS: 12 to 1.45, 7 to 9.30
PRICES: Set L £12·95 (£20), Set D £15·95 (£23). Service 12.5%
CARDS: Access, Amex, Diners, Visa
SEATS: 65. 12 tables outside. Private parties: 65 main room. Car-park, 50 places. Vegetarian meals. Children's helpings. Wheelchair access (also WC). Music

---

CHINNOR Oxfordshire

map 2

Sir Charles Napier Inn [11/20]

Sprigg's Alley, nr Chinnor, OX9 4BX
RADNAGE (024 026) 3011
M40 exit 6. In Chinnor turn R at crossroads, continue 2 miles

£14–£22

The road gets increasingly narrow on the way to this isolated old English pub, two miles outside Chinnor. The Griffiths have set up a small-holding to supply turkeys for Christmas and suckling lamb for Easter, among other things. The menu looks to France for fish soup, duck and port rillettes, and salmon en croûte with hollandaise, but returns home for roast beef and lamb. The cheeseboard is first rate, and home-made mousses are stars among the sweets. In summer the terrace provides a magical open air dining-area. Service is personal and unobtrusive. A hundred wines are augmented by two dozen half-bottles, with plenty of interest from around France and a good selection from the New World. Chardonnays come from Petaluma, the Napa Valley, Oregon and Chile. CELLARMAN'S CHOICE: Ch. Caronne Ste-Gemme '79, £10·75.

CHEF: Batiste Tollu PROPRIETORS: The Griffiths family
OPEN: all week MEALS: 12 to 2 (3 Sun), 7.30 to 10 (10.30 Fri and Sat)
PRICES: £14 (£22), Set L from £9 (£14). Service 12.5% CARDS: Amex, Diners
SEATS: 65. 10 tables outside. Private parties: 45 main room, 25 and 45 private rooms.
Car-park, 60 places. Vegetarian meals. Children's helpings (L only). No children under 7.
No cigars/pipes in dining-room. Wheelchair access. Music. Air-conditioned

---

CHIPPING NORTON Oxfordshire

map 2

La Madonette [13/20]

7 Horsefair, Chipping Norton OX7 5AL
CHIPPING NORTON (0608) 2320

£25

Alain Ritter's low-ceilinged dining-room has all the atmosphere of a family restaurant in a French provincial town. The cooking may verge on the theatrical, but has produced impressive results. Meals begin with smoked salmon canapés and quail eggs; local sorrel is turned into a soup. The menu stays in France – moving slowly with the seasons – for warm salad of pigeon breasts and fillet of beef in a brandy and green peppercorn sauce. Despite the distance from the sea, fish is a speciality: warm salmon mousse with prawns and champagne sauce; salmon and brill plaited and poached; a fricassee of langoustines, scallops and prawns. Half a dozen vegetables come in a big lidded dish, and sweets rely heavily on exquisite presentation. Cheeses come from Philippe Olivier in Boulogne, and Alain Ritter takes the trouble to explain them in detail, as he does with the seventy French wines, well chosen from around the provinces.

CHEF/PROPRIETOR: Alain Ritter
OPEN: Tue to Sat, D only MEALS: 7.30 to 10
PRICES: £18 (£25) CARDS: Access, Visa
SEATS: 32. Private parties: 10 main room. Children's helpings. No cigars in dining-room

---

CHITTLEHAMHOLT Devon

map 1

▲ Highbullen Hotel [11/20]

Chittlehamholt EX37 9HD
CHITTLEHAMHOLT (076 94) 561

£11–£15

The Victorian Gothic mansion stands on high ground between the Mole and Taw valleys. As a hotel it has more than its share of amenities, from a croquet lawn and squash court to a spa bath and helipad, for which its many faithful regulars return. There is even a deer park. The cooking can be reminiscent of that of a

---

Files are kept on every restaurant, so reports of poor meals are just as valuable as reports of good meals because they save unnecessary inspections.

good English hostess, with dishes on the lines of stuffed tomatoes provençale, calf's liver bordelaise, and loin of pork cooked with apple juice and brandy. The set menu is rounded off with frosted almond creams, lemon soufflé and apple crumble, or cheeses. The wine list has some bargains among the clarets, which hark back to 1961, and would be difficult to replace at these prices. A short, catholic collection of bottles under £8 is very reliable, and there are seven vintages of Lebanon's Château Musar, and a California Chardonnay '83 from Mondavi. CELLARMAN'S CHOICE: White St Pourçain '85, at £6·95, and red Brouilly, Château des Tours '85, at £9·50 (£4·80 a half-bottle).

CHEF: Pam Neil PROPRIETORS: Hugh and Pam Neil
OPEN: all week D, and Sun L MEALS: 1 to 2, 7.30 to 9
PRICES: Set Sun L £8·50 (£11), Set D £12·50 (£15), Snacks from £1. Service inc
SEATS: 60. 5 tables outside. Private parties: 10 main room. Car-park, 50 places. Vegetarian
meals. No children under 10. Smart dress preferred. No smoking in dining-room
ACCOMMODATION: 35 rooms, all with bath/shower. Rooms for disabled. B&B £30 to £60. No
children under 10. Garden. Swimming-pool. Sauna. Tennis. Fishing. Golf. Snooker. TV.
Phone. Scenic. Doors close at 11 [GHG]

CHRISTCHURCH Dorset map 2

Splinters [10/20]

12 Church Street, Christchurch BH23 1BW
CHRISTCHURCH (0202) 483454 £19

Some reliable, old-fashioned, French bistro cooking of the cream and butter school provides a backdrop to one of the great cellars of the South of England. This is a place to start with the wine list. Clarets run back to '61, and burgundy goes almost as far, at prices probably below current auction-room knock-down rates: Ch. Millet '78, for instance, is £12. The menu of the day is not without a sense of adventure – monkfish with black butter, pheasant eggs with two sauces, Dover sole roe deep fried with a sauce tartare. Local salmon with hollandaise is a feature.

CHEFS: Jua Franke and Shelia Scott PROPRIETORS: John Carter and Jua Franke
OPEN: Mon to Sat, D only MEALS: 6.30 to 10.30
PRICES: £12 (£19). Cover 50p CARDS: Amex, Diners, Visa
SEATS: 40. Private parties: 20 main room, 8 and 12 private rooms. Vegetarian meals.
Children's helpings. No children under 3. Wheelchair access (also WC)

CLANFIELD Oxfordshire map 2

▲ *Plough* [11/20]

Clanfield OX8 2RB
CLANFIELD (036 781) 222 and 494 £15–£23

Refurbishment has given the restaurant a mood of English gentility – there are copies of Old Masters on the walls, beams, mullioned windows and a pink flowery dining-room. The menu is all things to all men, an unrestrained mixture of French provincial, traditional British, nouvelle and innovative, bolstered by savouries as well as sweets to finish, and platefuls of home-made petits fours. The concern for good ingredients extends to cheeses from Paxton and Whitfield and fish delivered by Vin Sullivan's van from Abergavenny. Dishes range from a version of brandade de morue to steamed sponge pudding or apple and rhubarb crumble with custard. Lightly cooked veal kidney comes with an elaborate sauce of tomatoes, tarragon, white wine and mushrooms, while breast of chicken gets a lobster, saffron and watercress sauce. The extensive, 150-strong wine list is mostly between £10 and £20.

CHEF: Paul Barnard PROPRIETORS: Hatton Hotels Ltd
OPEN: all week MEALS: 12 to 1.45, 7 to 9.45
PRICES: Set L from £9·95 (£15), Set D from £16·95 (£23) CARDS: Access, Amex, Diners, Visa
SEATS: 45. 6 tables outside. Private parties: 30 main room, 16 and 30 private rooms. Car-park, 40 places. Children's helpings. No smoking in dining-room. Wheelchair access (also WC). Music
ACCOMMODATION: 7 rooms, all with bath/shower. B&B £50 to £65. Deposit: £40. Baby facilities. Afternoon teas. Garden. TV. Phone. Scenic. Confirm by 6 [GHG]

CLUN Shropshire map 5

▲ *Old Post Office* [11/20] ✗

9 The Square, Clun SY7 0HG
CLUN (058 84) 687 £13–£18

In the heart of Houseman country, this restaurant with rooms faces a pub and looks like three shops knocked together; it is more solid than picturesque. The emphasis is on local produce: damson jam and marmalade à la Post Office, honey from up the road, Welsh lamb. Martin Pool also intends to go after the crayfish in the Clun, which apparently are unable to resist chunks of dog-food. The style is French provincial; the set meal takes in four courses. Highlights have been ramekins of smoked haddock; watercress soup; marinated pigeon stuffed with pigeon pâté and cooked in red wine. A cheeseboard of local goats' and perhaps Shropshire Blue breaks the meal before trifle, profiteroles, meringues and gateaux. The wine list does its best for all pockets, with good Rhônes to the fore. CELLARMAN'S CHOICE: Cahors, Château St Didier-Parmac '83, £8·50. There is good walking nearby.

CHEFS: Martin Pool and Pam Linnett PROPRIETOR: Martin Pool
OPEN: Tue to Sat CLOSED: Feb MEALS: 12.30 to 2, 7.30 to 9.30
PRICES: L £8 (£13), Set D £13·50 (£18).
SEATS: 20. 1 table outside. Private parties: 20 main room. Vegetarian meals. Children's helpings (L only). Music
ACCOMMODATION: 3 rooms. B&B £14 to 29. Deposit: £10. Baby facilities. Afternoon teas. Scenic. Doors close at 11.30. Confirm by 4.30

COGGESHALL Essex map 3

Langan's [13/20] ✗

4–6 Stoneham Street, Coggeshall CO6 1TT
COGGESHALL (0376) 61453 £10–£16

The former Musketeers wine bar is now decked out as a low-ceilinged, mini-Langan's Brasserie with good, eclectic paintings, polished wood floors and buttermilk interior. The short, sensible, daily changing menu offers four choices at each course. Cream of cauliflower soup with very garlicky croûtons, marinated fillet of beef with a good mustard dressing, and grilled herrings with Meaux mustard, have all been well-received starters. There are good sauces for fish, and spring chicken with bread sauce and Langan's moussaka have been attractive main courses. Every day there is a hot soufflé for pudding; lemon cheese flan with fruit coulis has been a light alternative. Service is from the Nortons, who ran the wine bar before going into partnership with Peter Langan, helped by young girls. Value is remarkable: four can dine out for virtually the same sum as two could pay for a mediocre meal in this part of Essex. The wine list is short and mostly under £10. House Provence £5·20. CELLARMAN'S CHOICE: Ch. Laroze '83, £7·95.

CHEFS: Mark Baumann and Mark Muncey PROPRIETORS: Peter Langan and Bruce Norton
OPEN: Tue to Sun, exc Sat L and Sun D CLOSED: 3 weeks Jan MEALS: 12.30 to 2, 7 to 9.45
PRICES: £11 (£16), Set L from £6·50 (£10) CARDS: Access, Amex, Diners, Visa
SEATS: 60. Private parties: 40 main room. Children's helpings. Wheelchair access (2 steps)

▲ White Hart [10/20]

Market End, Coggeshall CO6 1NH
COGGESHALL (0376) 61654   🍾 £19–£31

There are two notions of the function of a restaurant. Coggeshall has them both. Above is the young contender. This fifteenth-century inn, on the other hand, is the incumbent champion of a style that has survived since the war. The differences are stark: here there is enormous choice, designed to cater for anyone, at any time, taking a fancy to, say, steak au poivre or lobster bisque or even caviare. The pride is in meeting the demand. This choice comes at a high price, but with plenty of service. The same goes for the wine front: this is a phenomenal, comprehensive wine list, and any page taken at random illustrates the point: there is an old-style Doudet-Naudin Chambolle-Musigny '66; Bollinger champagne of the same vintage; an Oestricher Lenchen Trockenbeerenauslese '71 from Deinhard; Trefethen Chardonnay '79. There are bottles under £10, too, and pages of half-bottles. But, and it is a very big but, the customer can only drink one, or at a pinch two, bottles and there are one or two good bottles across the road, in a relatively tiny selection. In terms of value as cooking, Langan's rates higher, but there is good food and wine to be found here, even if the Hart has to leap a bit to keep up. Comparisons would be welcome.

CHEF: John Grimsey PROPRIETORS: Mr and Mrs Raymond Pluck
OPEN: Mon to Thur, exc Mon L; plus Sat D and Sun L CLOSED: Aug, last week Dec, first week Jan MEALS: 12.30 to 2, 7.30 to 9
PRICES: £22 (£31), Set Sun L £11·75 (£19). Minimum £12·95 CARDS: Access, Amex, Diners, Visa
SEATS: 50. 5 tables outside. Private parties: 50 main room, 20 private room. Car-park, 20 places. Vegetarian meals. Children's helpings. Wheelchair access (also WC). Music
ACCOMMODATION: 18 rooms, all with bath/shower. B&B £35 to £60. TV. Phone. Doors close at 12. Confirm by 6

Restaurants are checked every year and their entries rewritten. The restaurant scene changes very rapidly. Don't trust an out-of-date Guide.

COLLINGBOURNE KINGSTON Wiltshire

map 2

Old School House [10/20]

Collingbourne Kingston SN8 3SD
COLLINGBOURNE DUCIS (026 485) 799 £16

The owners moved from Livio's in Andover to this village school-house, which has been completely renovated and given a new lease of life as an Italian restaurant. The dining-room is elegant in pink offset by touches of blue in the carpets and the tablecloths. It also boasts a high vaulted ceiling and a stairway in one corner leading to a gallery. Old school photos are a reminder of the building's younger days. The cooking homes in on Italian stalwarts, supplemented by a few vaguely international dishes. Spaghetti bolognese comes with a separate bowl of sauce for topping up, and pollo sorpresa is a crisp, deep-fried breast bursting with butter and fresh herbs. Fresh spinach is cooked to softness with olive oil and garlic, and there is zabaglione from a copper bowl to finish. Good selection of well-known Italian wines.

OPEN: Tue to Sat MEALS: 12 to 1.30, 7 to 9.30
PRICES: £12 (£16)
SEATS: 60. Private parties: 60 main room. Children welcome

COOKHAM Berkshire

map 2

Alfonso's [10/20]

19 – 21 Station Hill Parade, Cookham SL6 9BR
BOURNE END (062 85) 25775 £22

A small, family-run restaurant in a row of modern shops, with a strong line in fish and shellfish: thick, fish-soup-like bouillabaisse; grilled lobster tails with a mustard dressing. The style is Continental but reaches to dishes from Bocuse, Point, and so on, and can feature unusual items, for instance kid with morels. Presentation is nouvelle, service warmly professional, and the décor spotless. The simple dishes work best. Spanish wines stand out on the forty-strong list, and include half a dozen from Torres.

CHEFS: Manuel Manzano and Richard Manzano PROPRIETORS: Alfonso Baena and Manuel Manzano
OPEN: Mon to Sat, exc Sat L MEALS: 12.30 to 2, 7 to 10 (11 Fri and Sat)
PRICES: £16 (£22) CARDS: Access, Amex, Diners, Visa
SEATS: 36. Private parties: 36 main room. Car-park, 50 places. Children's helpings. No pipes in dining-room. Wheelchair access (also WC)

CORBRIDGE Northumberland

map 7

Ramblers Country House [10/20]

Farnley, nr Corbridge, NE5 5RN
CORBRIDGE (043 471) 2424
1m S of Corbridge on Riding Mill road £15–£18

The Herrmann family's Victorian house high above the Tyne has a formal, Germanic restaurant, which stands out in the area. The cooking is vivid –

smoked mussels spicing a soufflé; a batter of sour cream, herbs and cheese for lamb chops – and consistent. The wine list represents France and Germany and starts at £4·95. CELLARMAN'S CHOICE: Hochheimer Stein '85, £10·45.

CHEF: Heinrich Herrmann PROPRIETORS: Heinrich and Jennifer Herrmann
OPEN: Tue to Sat, D only CLOSED: 1 week Feb, 2 weeks Sept MEALS: 7 to 10
PRICES: £13 (£18), Set D £9·85 (£15) CARDS: Acess, Amex, Diners, Visa
SEATS: 80. Private parties: 80 main room, 40 private room. Car-park, 30 places. Children's helpings. Smart dress preferred. Wheelchair access (1 step; also WC)

CORFE CASTLE Dorset   map 2

▲ *Mortons House Hotel*   [new entry, zero rated]

East Street, Corfe Castle BH20 5EE
CORFE CASTLE (0929) 480988   £11–£17

The village is in grey Purbeck stone, dominated by the gaunt pile of the castle on a conical hill. Mortons is a beautiful E-shaped Elizabethan manor, and is even more impressive inside. The entrance hall has a bare, stone-tiled floor and huge stone fireplace. The room for pre-dinner drinks is also breathtaking, but in a different way, with marvellous carved and decorated wall panelling in oak, with an elm frieze. The dining-room is tame by comparison. In this imposing setting is a menu of modern British style, not technically over-complicated in the first months since opening. Ideas are good: warm quiche on a bed of leeks with a port sauce; asparagus with salmon and lemon butter; scallops with sesame. Timing has been askew, and service pleasant but inexperienced. The wine list has been carefully composed of fifty bottles, more than half of which are under £10, ranging from the local village wine to good New Zealand bottles. House Fitou is £6·35, Hawkes Bay Sauvignon Blanc, £8·50. More reports, please.

CHEFS: Janice Timothy and Simon Wright PROPRIETORS: Janice Hughes, Gerhard Bockau and Janice Timothy
OPEN: all week MEALS: 12.30 to 2, 7.30 to 10
PRICES: Set L from £7·50 (£11), Set D from £12·75 (£17), Snacks from £2·50. Service inc
CARDS: Access, Visa
SEATS: 40. 6 tables outside. Private parties: 200 main room, 30 private room. Car-park, 30 places. Vegetarian meals. Children's helpings. Wheelchair access
ACCOMMODATION: 7 rooms, all with bath/shower. B&B £40 to £60. Deposit: 20%. Children welcome. Baby facilities. Afternoon teas. Garden. Fishing. Golf. Scenic. Doors close at 12. Confirm by 11

CORSE LAWN Gloucestershire   map 2

▲ *Corse Lawn House*   [14/20]

Corse Lawn GL19 4LZ   ✚
TIRLEY (045 278) 479
on B4211, 5m SW of Tewkesbury   £15–£26

The Hines' tall, red-brick house with a man-made pond outside, where the horse-drawn coaches would drive to be washed, works to a big canvas. It succeeds because it is run on sensible principles. The high rooms are handsomely set with large tables; candles are lit. On the walls, watercolours of wild mushrooms –

Boletus edulis, morels, chanterelles – interrupt hunting scenes. The menu offers a good choice of modern British cooking with French accents, served by a young, black-suited brigade, and takes in moules marinière and duck ballotine with orange chutney. Fine game has impressed, likewise the kitchen's skills with fish soup, guinea-fowl, tarte Tatin, and picturesque arrangements of fruit. The wine list concentrates on claret and quality; local wines include Three Choirs. CELLARMAN'S CHOICE: Savennières, La Roche aux Moines '84, from Brincard, at £13·50.

CHEF: Baba Hine PROPRIETORS: Denis and Baba Hine
OPEN: all week, exc Sun D CLOSED: 1 week mid-Jan MEALS: 12.30 to 2, 7 to 10
PRICES: £19 (£26), Set L £11·50 (£15), Set D £15·75 (£19). Service inc CARDS: Access, Amex, Diners, Visa
SEATS: 45. 8 tables outside. Private parties: 55 main room, 24 private room. Car-park, 50 places. Vegetarian meals. Children's helpings. Wheelchair access (also WC)
ACCOMMODATION: 10 rooms, all with bath/shower. Rooms for disabled. B&B £35 to £45. Baby facilities. Pets welcome. Garden. TV. Phone. Scenic. Doors close at 12. Confirm by 6 [GHG]

COUNTESTHORPE Leicestershire

map 5

Old Bakery [new entry, zero rated] ✗

Main Street, Countesthorpe LE8 3QX
LEICESTER (0533) 778777 £12–£17

The conversion is so thorough that there is barely a clue that this was a Victorian bakery. It has been transformed into a modern, pink and grey room filled with watercolours by local artists. Menus offer a wide choice, plenty of colourful flavours, and are good value, especially lunch. The style is of home-made leek soup, roast spring chicken, steak and kidney pudding and rhubarb crumble with custard. Most main dishes come with both fruit and alcohol, for instance venison braised with cherries and port. Seventy wines offer similarly good value, starting at £5·50. CELLARMAN'S CHOICE: St Véran, Les Monts, Cave de Prisse '84, £11·50. More reports, please.

CHEF: R. Gilbertson PROPRIETORS: R. Gilbertson, P. Chivers and G. Turner
OPEN: Tue to Sun, exc Sat L and Sun D MEALS: 12.15 to 1.45 (2 Sun), 7 to 9 (9.45 Sat)
PRICES: Set L from £7.75 (£12), Set D from £12·50 (£17) CARDS: Access, Visa
SEATS: 50. Private parties: 50 main room. Car-park, 20 places. Vegetarian meals. Children welcome. Jacket and tie. Wheelchair access (also WC). Music

---

COVENTRY West Midlands

map 5

▲ *Herbs, Trinity House Hotel* [10/20]

28 Lower Holyhead Road, Coventry CV1 3AU
COVENTRY (0203) 555654 £11

The thin green line of vegetarian restaurants narrows even more in the West Midlands. In fact, this thriving restaurant in a privately run hotel is virtually out

---

Reports on shops, cafes and farms are useful, as well as reports on restaurants.

on its own. Robert Jackson has succeeded by putting his faith in fresh, natural ingredients, offering exceptional value for money, and steering away from stodgy wholefoods into more imaginative, eclectic vegetarian cooking. Having proved the point, he has expanded the menu (as well as the dining-room) and now includes fish and poultry dishes, such as seafood crumble or chicken and spinach lasagne. But the vegetarian specialities are the most interesting: parsnip timbale is topped with a dribble of creamy Dijon vinaigrette; pine-nut and asparagus loaf comes on a purée of mangoes and apricots; vegetables in coconut sauce are served with different-coloured wholewheat pastas. Salads are well dressed and sweets are rich, although soya ice-cream appears alongside cholesterol-laden whipped cream. To drink there's Hugh Rock's elderflower wine and a modest list, with most bottles around £6.

CHEF: Robert Jackson PROPRIETORS: Robert Jackson, Lesley Jackson and Charles Davis
OPEN: Mon to Sat, D only MEALS: 6.30 to 9.30
PRICES: £7 (£11). Service inc
SEATS: 42. 3 tables outside. Private parties: 42 main room. Vegetarian meals. No children under 5. Wheelchair access. Music
ACCOMMODATION: 7 rooms. B&B £15 to £25. Doors close at 11. Confirm by 6

Quo Vadis [10/20]

72 Barker Butts Lane, Coventry CU6 1DY
COVENTRY (0203) 594124   £9–£19

Coventry's best Italian restaurant is of the old school. The menu is conservative in the best sense: brodo is full-bodied and nourishing, saltimbocca is topped with wafer-thin slices of ham in a potent garlic and wine sauce, and there are good-looking fish dishes, including lobster and Dover sole at the market price. Flavours are fresh, and so are the vegetables – baked fennel has been first rate. Sweets are creamy and flamboyant. Service is as frothy as the cappuccino. Modest, reasonably priced wines, including drinkable Montepulciano at £5·75 a carafe, and a few special bottles, including Tignanello '79 and Masi's Recioto Amarone '79.

CHEF/PROPRIETOR: Carmine Chiccarella
OPEN: Mon to Sat, exc Sat L MEALS: 12 to 2, 7 to 11.30
PRICES: £15 (£19). Set L £6·65 (£9). Minimum £7·50. Service inc Set L only
CARDS: Access, Carte Blanche, Diners, Visa
SEATS: 75. Private parties: 85 main room. Vegetarian meals. Children's helpings. Smart dress preferred. Music. Air-conditioned

CRICKLADE Wiltshire   map 2

Whites [15/20]

WILTSHIRE
OF THE
YEAR
RESTAURANT

93 High Street, Cricklade SN6 6DF
SWINDON (0793) 751110   £18–£26

Colin and Gwen White moved here from the Jews House in Lincoln, previously rated 14/20. They have re-vamped the six-bedroomed house into two stylish dining-rooms, with wines in the fireplaces and tall, thin lamps on the varnished wooden tables. The break, plus new customers, has given the cooking a new dynamism. The Whites have always supported local producers, and the quality shows in dishes such as succulent fillet of free-range pork with quinces and apples, or the harlequin omelette with a central strand of spinach, in a tomato sauce. The menu brings together French and English influences, and there are plenty of good bourgeois ideas: fleshy salmis of pigeon, for instance, is in a very rich juice, with a side plate of potato pancake and a bowl of red cabbage. Other brilliant successes have included Dartmouth pie, of mutton and dried fruits, a warm salad of leeks, mussel and chervil, and a brioche, hollowed out and filled with white crab-meat, the last two both served with a saffron butter sauce. To finish there are calvados pancakes served with bowls of cream and ice-cream, or oeufs à la neige in a chocolate sauce. The wine list has very good house Sauvignon from the Loire, and follows the same policy of seeking out excellence without lavishly involving itself in expensive fashions. There are Chardonnays from Australia and California, but CELLARMAN'S CHOICE is Soave, Costalta '85, £8·50, and Rubesco di Torgiano '80, from Lungarotti, £9.

CHEF: Colin White PROPRIETORS: Colin and Gwen White
OPEN: Mon to Sat, exc Mon L MEALS: 12.30 to 2, 7.30 to 9.30
PRICES: £18 (£26), Set L £10·50 (£18), Set D £15 (£23). Licensed, also bring your own: corkage £2 CARDS: Access, Amex, Visa
SEATS: 32. Private parties: 20 main room, 16 and 20 private rooms. Vegetarian meals. Children's helpings. No cigars/pipes in dining-room. Wheelchair access. Air-conditioned

---

CROYDE Devon   map 1

▲ *Whiteleaf* [new entry, zero rated]

Croyde EX33 1PN
CROYDE (0271) 890266   £10

David and Flo Wallington, formerly of the Rhydspence Inn, took over this guest-house last year and serve dinner, but only to residents. The five courses have a strong British feel: English asparagus with baked egg, ballotine of goose with red-bean chutney, rack of lamb on a bed of potatoes and leeks, culminating in beef Wellington. This cube of hung steak cooked in the centre of a Yorkshire pudding endorses the house penchant for, 'robust roasts and casseroles and a right good bellyful'. Locally grown vegetables are enterprisingly served – beetroot crumble, hops with a cheese and spinach sauce, parsnip purée – and there are English cheeses. Fifty wines are very reasonably priced and Italy is a speciality. CELLARMAN'S CHOICE: Chardonnay, Rosemount Estate '85, £7·80. More reports, please.

CHEF: David Wallington PROPRIETORS: David and Florence Wallington
OPEN: all week, D only MEALS: 7.30 to 8.30
PRICES: Set D from £7·50 (£10). Minimum £7·50. Service inc CARDS: Access, Visa
SEATS: 16. Private parties: 24 main room. Car-park, 10 places. Children's helpings. Smart dress preferred
ACCOMMODATION: 5 rooms, all with bath/shower. B&B £26 to £32. Deposit: £20. Children welcome. Baby facilities. Pets welcome. Garden. TV. Phone. Scenic. Doors close at 12. Confirm by 7

Restaurants that we have not been able to assess as fully as we would like are given a zero rating this year. We are particularly keen to have reports on these places.

CROYDON Surrey   map 3

Dijonnais [11/20] ✗

299 High Street, Croydon CRO 1QL
01-686 5624   £9 – £17

The Jolivet family's converted terraced house between a hairdresser's and a
courier car service feels like a French country café with rough-plastered walls,
red and white check tablecloths and the kitchen at one end. Lionel Jolivet cooks a
traditional French menu based on strong sauces from a glace de viande base and
plenty of cream and butter. Fish is well handled: monk with raspberry vinegar;
salmon in a lattice of pastry; sole with a fennel sauce. Other good dishes have
been the kidneys dijonnais (Dijon is the Jolivets' home town), the weekly
changing dish of mussels through the winter, and a poussin, boned and served
with a creamy cheese sauce. Portions are generous, vegetables crisp, the
atmosphere relaxed and the value good. The wide-ranging list of wines opens
with Petit Chaumont at £4·95.

CHEF: Lionel Jolivet PROPRIETORS: Mr and Mrs Lionel Jolivet
OPEN: Mon to Sat, exc Mon D and Sat L CLOSED: 2 weeks Aug, 1 week Feb MEALS: 12 to 2,
7.30 to 9.30 (10 Sat)
PRICES: £12 (£17), Set L from £5·50 (£9), Set D £12 (£16) CARDS: Access, Amex,
Diners, Visa
SEATS: 28. Private parties: 28 main room. Children welcome. Wheelchair access. Music

Hockneys [10/20]

98 High Street, Croydon CRO 1ND
01-688 2899   £11

Hockneys was a respectable vegetarian restaurant before vegetarian restaurants
were respectable. It is clean, calm and spacious, and run increasingly with the
kind of professionalism usually associated with French restaurants. Simon
Beckett has moved the menu into interesting pastures – saffron risotto; a tofu and
vegetable casserole; tagliatelle Stroganoff. The gazpacho is always written about,
as is the Mine of Serpents, made up of fruit salad, rum and raisin ice-cream,
strawberry syrup, brandy-snaps and a sparkler. Daytime meals are cheaper by a
third than at night. Unlicensed; corkage £1·35.

CHEF: Simon Beckett PROPRIETORS: Rainbow (Croydon) Ltd
OPEN: Tue to Sat CLOSED: 2 weeks Christmas, 1 week Easter, 2 weeks Aug
MEALS: noon to 10.30
PRICES: £8 (£11), Snacks from 95p. Unlicensed, but bring your own: corkage £1·35
CARDS: Access, Amex, Diners, Visa
SEATS: 80. Private parties: 25 main room. Vegetarian meals. Children's helpings.
No smoking. Music

All inspections are carried out anonymously.

*'We assumed that a mistake had been made, but the waiter, after enquiries, assured us
that this main course known as "selection of fish" was the same as the "panache de
poissons" but the portions were slightly larger.'* (On eating in Derbyshire)

Kelong [10/20]

1B Selsdon Road, Croydon CR2 6PU
01-688 0726   £12–£22

This south-east Asian restaurant, with its neatly set tables and a wide-ranging
menu dealing strongly in fish, is well adopted in the area. The tastes make a
pleasant change from more familiar cuisines, though the heat level is lower than
at similar restaurants in central London. Much of the cooking is formularised –
wok frying with garlic; battering and deep frying for chicken; shredding and
spicing for vegetables – but there are subtleties too, for instance whole squid
stuffed with pork and vegetables. Attractive meals can be made up of popular
dishes, like spring rolls and satays. The monosodium glutamate level is low.
House beer is Tiger.

CHEF: Tom S. L. Ho PROPRIETORS: Tarngrove Ltd
OPEN: Mon to Sat MEALS: 12 to 2.30, 6 to 10.45
PRICES: £10 (£18), Set L and D £8·50 (£12) to £17·50 (£22). Service 10%
CARDS: Access, Amex, Diners, Visa
SEATS: 70. Private parties: 60 main room. Children welcome. Music

Munbhave [11/20]

305 London Road, Croydon CR0 3BA
01-689 6331   £11–£13

Outside it is marked by a neon sign, inside it is warmed by paraffin heaters, but
this tiny restaurant serves some of the best Gujerati vegetarian cooking south of
the Thames. Kesh Tank gives a new meaning to lightness and subtlety in this
style of cooking: onion bhajias are crisp; bhel poori are full of soft chickpeas and a
yoghurt sauce laced with chillies; rolls of green patra come topped with sesame
seeds. Curries can disappoint, but there is always good masala dosa – a feather-
light pancake full of onions, peas and swede served on a mint, chilli and yoghurt
sauce. Sturdy, palate-cleansing lassi to drink, alternatively wine, at £6·95 a
bottle. The pace is admirably leisurely.

CHEF/PROPRIETOR: Kesh Tank
OPEN: Tue to Sun, D only CLOSED: 3 weeks Aug MEALS: 6 to 11 (12 Sat)
PRICES: £6 (£11), Set D £7·65 (£13). Service 10% CARDS: Access, Visa
SEATS: 40. Vegetarian meals. Children's helpings. Wheelchair access. Music

Tung Kum [11/20]

205–207 High Street, Croydon CR0 1QR
01-688 0748   £12–£15

Since 1978 this has been one of the most reliable Cantonese restaurants south of
the Thames. The menu isn't long or taxing by Soho standards, but it is rooted in
the mainstream of authentic cooking: there are good roast meats and one-plate

*Files are kept on every restaurant, so reports of poor meals are just as valuable as
reports of good meals because they save unnecessary inspections.*

rice and noodle dishes, as well as specialities, for instance cuttlefish in black-bean sauce, stewed pork ribs with salty plum sauce, roast chicken in salt. Set lunches are amazing value at under £3 for beef and green peppers on crispy noodles or chicken and vegetables on rice. Wan Fu house white is £5·60 a bottle.

CHEF: Hung Chiu PROPRIETOR: Tony Lam
OPEN: all week MEALS: 12 to 2.30, 5 to 11.30 (all day Sat and Sun)
PRICES: £9 (£15), Set L £2·50 (£6), Set D from £7 (£12). Minimum £6 at D. Service 10%
CARDS: Access, Amex, Diners, Visa
SEATS: 95. Children welcome. Wheelchair access (also WC). Music

---

CUCKFIELD Sussex   map 3

▲ *King's Head* [14/20] ✗

South Street, Cuckfield RH17 5VY
HAYWARDS HEATH (0444) 454006   £11–£18

The small franchise that Jeremy Ashpool has on this pub dining-room is a bit too close to the bare boards for comfort, but nevertheless he produces meals in the modern British style that have a vigour and directness to rival anything in plusher surroundings. A simple lunch in May produced crab ravioli, chicken with spinach and lime, and a slice from a large crème brûlée served with strawberry purée and vanilla feathering. There is nothing fussy or disguised. The quality of the lamb, tasting almost wild, shines through in a grilled leg steak, sauced with just a small amount of pan juices, wine and garlic. To one side is a charlotte of aubergine, courgette and tomato in good oil; to the other a shortcrust tart filled with minced lamb, herbs and more garlic, the whole served with virtually raw carrots and a turnip mousse. Classic dishes, like Sussex Pond, are raised out of their stodgy retirement to explosive new realms. The wine list makes up, in comments, for what it lacks in bottles. Expect a move in 1988 to a more appropriate building, where Ashpool will really be able to shine. In the words of a top inspector who has been abroad for a couple of years, 'If this is modern British cooking lead me to more, although I presume there isn't much of it about?'

CHEF: Jeremy Ashpool PROPRIETORS: J. Lindley and P. Tolhurst
OPEN: Mon to Fri, exc Mon D CLOSED: bank hols MEALS: 12.30 to 2, 7.30 to 10
PRICES: Set L from £5·75 (£11), Set D from £11·95 (£18) CARDS: Access, Visa
SEATS: 33. 3 tables outside. Private parties: 20 main room. Children welcome.
Wheelchair access
ACCOMMODATION: 9 rooms, 8 with bath/shower. B&B £25 to £36. Baby facilities. Pets welcome. Snooker. TV

DARLINGTON Durham   map 7

Boobi's [11/20]

16–18 Coniscliffe Road, Darlington DL3 7RG
DARLINGTON (0325) 482529   £18

The chairs might not look out of place in a Salvation Army hall and the tables are really for the pantry rather than the best, but the cooking eclipses both and compensates for a most spartan setting. The blackboard adds to a *carte* that has a safe vein of chicken-liver pâté and steaks, but also a taste for innovations, such as a black pudding and apple with mustard sauce, jumbo prawns in garlic butter, and pan-fried veal kidneys. The char-grilled steaks and beef Wellington are good-quality meat. Fresh fruit is an alternative to otherwise calorific sweets. House claret £6·95.

CHEFS: Kenneth Marley and Elizabeth Parker PROPRIETOR: Colin Easby
OPEN: Mon to Sat, exc Sat L MEALS: 12 to 2, 7.30 to 11
PRICES: £12 (£18), Snacks from £1·50
SEATS: 50. Private parties: 30 main room. No children under 8. Wheelchair access. Music

Victor's [12/20]

84 Victoria Road, Darlington DL1 5JW
DARLINGTON (0325) 480818   £9–£17

Near the station. The Robinsons visit the markets daily and produce an English/French menu that manages to mix old and new. Everything that can be prepared on the premises, is, and the enthusiasm is infectious. Set-price dinners are taken from a repertory of a dozen dishes and conclude with fine unpasteurised English cheeses. Some of the combinations are striking, for instance sole with a Barsac and pistachio sauce. The cream sauces, such as Noilly Prat for scallops and for beef, draw praise, as do tomato and sweet-pepper soup, sweetbreads in pastry, meringues with mango. Service is attentive. Coffee comes with petits fours, and wines have a flat-rate mark-up of £2·50, which makes the quality wines attractive. Côtes du Rhône and Muscadet open at £6 on a list of twenty.
CELLARMAN'S CHOICE: Ch. du Lyonnat '81, £8·95.

CHEFS/PROPRIETORS: Peter and Jayne Robinson
OPEN: Tue to Sat MEALS: 12 to 2.30, 7 to 10.30
PRICES: Set L £4·25 (£9), Set D £12 (£17) CARDS: Access, Amex, Diners, Visa
SEATS: 26. Private parties: 26 main room. Vegetarian meals. Children's helpings. Wheelchair access. Music

DARTMOUTH Devon   map 1

Bistro 33 [14/20]

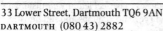

33 Lower Street, Dartmouth TQ6 9AN
DARTMOUTH (080 43) 2882   £16–£19

Perhaps it is the street that gives the frontage the air of a sandwich bar, but inside is pure café – red and green décor, checked cloths, hanging plants, pictures of cooking and rural scenes. Richard Cranfield trained up the road with Joyce Molyneux and comparisons are inevitable, but the lack of pretence here, the cheery, cheap decoration and the motherly service are more in keeping with the legendary Walnut Tree at Llandewi Skirrid, or Alastair Little in Soho. As with other young, modern British chefs, the cooking has shot ahead of the surroundings. You may eat a terrine of sole, salmon and sorrel with a prawn mayonnaise, followed by an immaculate variation of beef Wellington, but the place is still a café. Cranfield is a talent in his own right, and despite the restaurant's popularity, there seems rarely to be any sense of panic. Fish is a highlight: massive portions of poached salmon with hollandaise; timbale of smoked haddock with prawns, dill and a bright, colourful saffron sauce; marinated fillets of sole coiled on to thin slices of mango. Menus follow the season and there is a daily blackboard menu offsetting the dynamic, twelve-dish *carte*. Main dishes have at least three components: noisettes of lamb are with onion sauce and pommes dauphinoise; fillet of pork baked with rosemary in a salt crust is served with red cabbage and apple; roast fillet of beef arrives with horseradish butter and leek and tomato charlotte. Vegetables taste very fresh, and the crème brûlée is memorably good. Sauces tend to the old fashioned, being egg- and cream-based. The well-chosen French list of forty wines opens at £5·75, and offers better value all round than at the illustrious neighbour, but the solitary Australian is perhaps the best value. It is also the CELLARMAN'S CHOICE: Chardonnay, Rosemount Estate '85, £9·75.

CHEF: R. J. Cranfield PROPRIETORS: R. J. Cranfield, G. M. Cranfield and J. R. Gillo
OPEN: Tue to Sun, D only MEALS: 7 to 10
PRICES: Set D £11·75 (£16) to £14·75 (£19). Service inc
SEATS: 30. Private parties: 30 main room. Vegetarian meals. Children's helpings.
No cigars/pipes in dining-room. Wheelchair access (also WC)

Carved Angel [16/20]

2 South Embankment, Dartmouth TQ6 9BH
DARTMOUTH (080 43) 2465   £17–£27

Joyce Molyneux possibly out-cooks Elizabeth David – she has, at any rate, become the foremost proponent of the David style. She has re-worked a Mediterranean-inspired repertoire into what is now arguably provincial Devon cooking. The familiar wooden angel presides. Inside is warm, fragrant and full of light and sounds of cooking. Textures and contrasts are subtle yet exciting: puff pastry, for instance, is filled with sweet scallops, mussels and leek in a smooth, velouté-based sauce, then crusted with sesame seeds; a fine peasant dish of delicately flavoured boudin blanc is grilled crisply and served with earthy, al dente lentils and thin slices of sweet apple. The smell of Provençal fish soup heralds its arrival – in a small tureen, so that you can help yourself. Ingredients include leek, onion, tomato, good olive oil, saffron, flecks of parsley and pasta; garlicky croûtons, Parmesan and fearsomely spiced rouille, accompany. Cheese soufflé with pepperonata is highly praised, and dishes generally transcend the mundane descriptions on the menu: hollandaise is a perfect lemony emulsion; a fish hors d'oeuvre brings smoked salmon, brill ceviche, scallops and salt herring with a sweet-and-sour pickle. A speciality in summer is Dart salmon with samphire and champagne; in winter, Dartmouth mutton pie. Puddings take in all things chocolatey – a ginger-flavoured roulade, a marquise, mocha parfait and an ice-cream all appear on the same plate – but there are also Slapton strawberries with clotted cream, a hot Grand Marnier soufflé with orange and cardamom ice-cream, and a selection of English cheeses. The wine list is still long (almost two hundred labels), with a wide selection of burgundies and clarets, and many half-bottles. There is a good selection from the Loire, plus whites from England, the Rhône and New Zealand. CELLARMAN'S CHOICE: Savennières, Clos du Papillon '85, from Baumard, £9·50.

CELLARMAN'S CHOICE: *This is a wine recommended by the restaurateur which is more expensive than the house wine but is good value and fitting for the kind of food served.*

CHEF: Joyce Molyneux PROPRIETORS: George Perry-Smith, Heather Crosbie, Joyce
Molyneux and Meriel Boydon
OPEN: Tue to Sun, exc Sun D MEALS: 12.30 to 1.45, 7.30 to 9.30
PRICES: £22 (£27), Set L from £12·50 (£17), Set D from £22 (£27). Service inc
SEATS: 30. Private parties: 30 main room, 15 private room. Children's helpings

---

DEDHAM Essex   map 3

▲ *Terrace Restaurant, Dedham Vale Hotel* [11/20]

Stratford Road, Dedham CO7 6HW
COLCHESTER (0206) 322273   £24

The inside presents a bewildering jumble of lamps and cones of light; it is an
architectural pot-pourri, mixing up Gothic, Georgian, Arab awnings, Botticelli
wallpaper, and the Hanging Gardens of Babylon. The menu centres on grilled
and spit-roasted meats and poultry: leg of English lamb with rosemary and garlic;
T-bone steak. Sweets are from a trolley, and Indian food is now added to the
repertoire, with curries and a vegetarian thali, although the prices would shock
the average take-away. The youthful wine list runs from Lay & Wheeler claret to
Australian Chardonnay, with house Duboeuf at £6·40.

CHEF: Terry Barber PROPRIETOR: Gerald M. W. Milsom
OPEN: all week, exc Sat L and Sun D MEALS: 12.30 to 2, 7 to 10
PRICES: £17 (£24). Service 10% CARDS: Access, Amex, Diners, Visa
SEATS: 110. Private parties: 100 main room. Car-park, 80 places. Vegetarian meals.
Children's helpings. Smart dress preferred. Music
ACCOMMODATION: 6 rooms, all with bath/shower. B&B £50 to £80. Baby facilities. No pets.
Garden. Tennis. Golf. TV. Phone. Scenic. Confirm by 6 [GHG]

DORRINGTON Shropshire   map 4

Country Friends [14/20]

Dorrington SY5 7JD
DORRINGTON (074 373) 707
A49, 5m S of Shrewsbury   £13–£18

The Whittakers' black and white timbered building on the main road from
Ludlow to Shrewsbury is supplied with vegetables from the walled garden of a
nearby manor and takes its butter and Cheshire cheese from the Applebys at
Hawkstone Abbey. The menu robustly adopts the best of modern British cooking,
for example in ravioli stuffed with broccoli in a blue-cheese sauce, guinea-fowl
with a green grape and armagnac sauce, and superb venison. Main courses come
with satellite plates of vegetables. The pastry work is unusually good. Puddings
are on the lines of banoffi pie and chocolate pot. The wine list is conventional but

---

*'I phoned up to say we would be flying in for Sunday lunch. The airstrip is a field and the
farmer had to clear the sheep out. On the way back, the yearly cricket match between
the Island and the rest of the world (i.e. visitors) had to stop to allow the plane to take
off. I was not told on the phone that only bar snacks were available on Sunday . . .'*
(On eating on the Isle of Colonsay)

sound. Snack lunches and dinners on quiet nights (only during the week) are cheaper, and bargains.

CHEFS/PROPRIETORS: Charles and Pauline Whittaker
OPEN: Mon to Sat, exc Mon L MEALS: 12 to 2, 7 to 9.30
PRICES: £13 (£18), Set L and D £9·50 (£13), Snacks £1·50 CARDS: Amex, Diners, Visa
SEATS: 40. Private parties: 45 main room, 10 private room. Car-park, 40 places. Children welcome. Wheelchair access

---

DREWSTEIGNTON Devon   map 1

▲ *Old Inn* [10/20]

The Square, Drewsteignton EX6 6QR
DREWSTEIGNTON (0647) 21276   £11–£17

Seventeen years ago this was a farm and pub; since then it has dealt in B&B and was, for a while, a Yugoslav restaurant, but it is now owned and run by Rose Chapman, sculptress among other trades. The village is like a picture-book illustration and the inn is below Castle Drogo, the Lutyens masterpiece. Inside, the Laura Ashley wallpaper is one gesture to the 1980s – unlike the surface wiring. The cooking is English country style, influenced by modern journalism and cook-books. The treacle tart, which is not inconsequential, is a speciality; so are some vivid main-course saucings – venison comes with rhubarb and Glenfiddich, veal with apples and walnuts. The wine list extends to sixteen bottles, which is to scale.

CHEF: Rose Chapman PROPRIETORS: V. L. and R. Chapman
OPEN: Tue to Sun, D only; residents only Sat and Sun CLOSED: weekdays in Feb
MEALS: 7.30 to 9
PRICES: Set D £8 (£11) to £13 (£17)
SEATS: 20. Private parties: 20 main room. Vegetarian meals. Children restricted.
No cigars/pipes in dining-room
ACCOMMODATION: 5 rooms. B&B £12

DULVERTON Somerset   map 1

▲ *Ashwick House* [new entry, zero rated]

Dulverton TA22 9QD
DULVERTON (0398) 23868
Signposted from B3223 N of Dulverton   £12–£17

This Edwardian house is set in six acres of grounds on the edge of Exmoor, well off the beaten track. Outside there are sweeping lawns and lily ponds, inside are fireside chairs and displays of fresh and dried flowers. The emphasis is on simple home cooking, using local lamb, venison, pheasant, partridge, trout and salmon. Sunday lunch at £7·25 is good value for smoked haddock and tomato pancakes, or deep-fried Camembert with apple and gooseberry preserve, before roast beef or lambs' kidneys with mustard sauce. Vegetables are good and fresh, and there's bread pudding with local clotted cream to finish. The modest wine list includes Hugh Rock's elderflower wine, or there is Yearlstone vintage cider. The Sherwoods have been here since October 1983 and have picked up occasional nominations since. More reports, please.

CHEF: C. T. Bramble PROPRIETORS: R. D. and P. E. Sherwood
OPEN: Tue to Sat D, and Sun L MEALS: 12.15 to 1.15, 7.15 to 8.45
PRICES: Set Sun L £6·75 (£12), Set D £11·75 (£17)
SEATS: 30. 3 tables outside. Private parties: 30 main room. Car-park, 30 places. No children
under 8. Jacket and tie. No smoking in dining-room
ACCOMMODATION: 6 rooms, all with bath/shower. D, B&B £39 to £66. Deposit: £25.
No children under 8. Afternoon teas. Garden. TV. Scenic. Doors close at 11. Confirm
by 6 [GHG]

EAST BERGHOLT Essex

map 3

Fountain House [10/20]

The Street, East Bergholt CO7 6TB
COLCHESTER (0206) 298232 £13–£15

A fifteenth-century cottage in the centre of the village, with beams, flag floors
and impeccable linen, china and cutlery. The menu reads modestly – smoked
mackerel, navarin of lamb, chocolate mousse – but so do the prices. There have
been endorsements for poached chicken breast in tarragon sauce, fresh crab
salad, and lemon mousse. Low prices extend to the wines, for this is an
enthusiast's list. Four of the sparklers are under £10, and there is a trio of still
wines from Coteaux Champenois. Guigal Rhônes and Hugel Alsaces provide the
class, Italy and Spain the bargains. CELLARMAN'S CHOICE: Mâcon-Villages,
Domaine de la Bon Gran '84, £8·50.

CHEF: Wendy Anne Sarton PROPRIETOR: James F. Sarton
OPEN: Tue to Sun, exc Sun D CLOSED: 2 weeks Jan MEALS: 12.30 to 2, 7.30 to 10
PRICES: Set L £8·95 (£13), Set D £10·95 (£15) CARDS: Access, Visa
SEATS: 32. 3 tables outside. Private parties: 30 main room. Car-park, 12 places. Vegetarian
meals. Children's helpings. No cigars/pipes in dining-room. Wheelchair access. Music

---

EASTBOURNE East Sussex

map 3

Byrons [12/20]

6 Crown Street, Old Town, Eastbourne BN21 1NX
EASTBOURNE (0323) 20171 £17

The Scruttons' tiny bistro has developed into the main place to eat in the town.
Marian is a gifted hostess and Simon's cooking has gone from bistro to mid-
Channel combinations with more than a few flourishes of modern British
cooking – the attention to vegetables, the use of unpasteurised cheeses, the
traditional Bakewell tart among the sweets. Fish, naturally, is prominent:
scallops with gin; halibut with sorrel and a cream sauce; crab gratin. Some of the
pre-prepared dishes, for instance duck terrine with onion marmalade, and the
sweets, for instance chocolate mousse with coffee sauce, or prime ice-cream with

---

*The 1989 Guide will appear before Christmas 1988. Reports are particularly helpful
in the spring. Report forms are at the back of this book, but just write a letter if you
prefer. Address it to* The Good Food Guide, FREEPOST, *14 Buckingham Street, London
WC2N 6BR. No stamp is necessary if you post it in the UK.*

Pineau des Charentes, have been excellent. The wine list remains short, but is not short on interest under £10.

CHEF: Simon Scrutton PROPRIETORS: Simon and Marian Scrutton
OPEN: Mon to Sat, exc Fri L CLOSED: 1 week at Christmas MEALS: 12.30 to 1.30, 7.30 to 10.30
PRICES: £11 (£17) CARDS: Amex, Diners, Visa
SEATS: 22. Private parties: 10 main room, 10 private room. Vegetarian meals. Children welcome. No smoking during meals. Music

---

EAST BUCKLAND Devon   map 1

▲ *Lower Pitt* [10/20]

East Buckland EX32 0TD
FILLEIGH (059 86) 243
3m NW of South Molton   £15

The road ends at this still-working agricultural hamlet. The long, low, whitewashed building was built when everyone was two feet shorter than today; the inglenook and the hand-painted china add to the genuine, warm cottage atmosphere. Suzanne Lyons' honest home cooking is in the same style. Local ingredients feature strongly, and fish is well reported: grilled mussels with garlic and cheese; scallops served on reduced mushrooms; turbot with shrimps. Good meat and game dishes have included loin of pork with cider (both local), game casserole, and lamb steak with hot redcurrant sauce. Vegetables are mostly from the garden behind the house, and come in abundance. Gâteau lyonnais is the pick of the sweets. Fifty wines feature, with short sections on most popular areas.
CELLARMAN'S CHOICE: Brouilly, Château des Tours '86, £7·90.

CHEF: Suzanne Lyons PROPRIETORS: Jerome and Suzanne Lyons
OPEN: Tue to Sat, D only MEALS: 7 to 9
PRICES: £11 (£15). Service inc CARDS: Access, Amex, Visa
SEATS: 28. Private parties: 28 main room. Car-park, 25 places. Children's helpings. Music
ACCOMMODATION: 3 rooms, all with bath/shower. B&B £20 to £35. Deposit: £10.
No children under 11. Garden. Scenic. Doors close at 10.30. Confirm by 6 [GHG]

EAST HORSLEY Surrey   map 3

▲ *Thatchers* [10/20]

Epsom Road, East Horsley KT24 6TB
EAST HORSLEY (048 65) 4291   £17–£25

A mock-Tudor house renovated in 1930s style, with blue and pink rooms, brick walls and lattice windows. The menu has come down fairly decisively on the English side, with boned quail stuffed with quail egg and pistachios; veal kidney baked in its suet; best end of English lamb. Desserts are artistic, for instance light, crisp lemon tart with strawberry sauce, though the award for glorious

---

If you suspect that a restaurant is using processed food, always ask. It would be a contravention of the Trade Descriptions Act for the restaurant to lie.

---

technicolour goes to the meringue swan swimming in bright blue sauce (colour courtesy of curaçao). The proprietors are rightly proud of their cheeseboard. The wine list is wide ranging in price, quality and geography, with a few New World wines and a good showing of half-bottles. CELLARMAN'S CHOICE: Provençal white Bandol, Mas de la Rouvière '84, at £10·95.

CHEF: Jeffrey Concliffe PROPRIETORS: Fine Inns plc
OPEN: all week   MEALS: 12.30 to 2, 7.30 to 9.30
PRICES: £15 (£25), Set L £9·50 (£17), Set D £10·50 (£18) CARDS: Access, Amex,
Diners, Visa
SEATS: 50. Private parties: 60 main room, 12 private room. Car-park, 60 places. Vegetarian
meals. Children's helpings. Wheelchair access (also WC)
ACCOMMODATION: 29 rooms, all with bath/shower. Rooms for disabled. B&B £53 to £67.
Baby facilities. Afternoon teas. Garden. Swimming-pool. TV. Phone. Scenic. Doors close
at 12. Confirm by 6

EAST MOLESEY Surrey   map 3

Lantern [11/20]

20 Bridge Road, East Molesey KT8 9AH
01-979 1531   £22

The glass conservatory adds some glamour, beyond the Lautrec posters, to the Morphews' French restaurant near the bridge. The menu is bravely provincial French of the kind that is found less and less – soupe à l'oignon, filets de sole Dugléré. The fish and also the pastry work, as in the Apfelstrudel, draw specific praise. Service is attentive. The wine list is not over-priced, and represents most of the regions from which the dishes come. House wine is £6·45.

CHEF: P. Morphew PROPRIETORS: Mr and Mrs P. Morphew
OPEN: Mon to Sat D, Tue to Fri L CLOSED: Aug MEALS: 12.15 to 2.15, 7 to 10.30 (11 Sat)
PRICES: £13 (£22), Set D from £14·25 (£22). Cover 85p. Service 12.5% CARDS: Access,
Amex, Diners, Visa
SEATS: 50. Private parties: 25 main room. Children's helpings. Smart dress preferred. Music

---

EGHAM Surrey   map 3

La Bonne Franquette [13/20]

5 High Street, Egham TW20 9EA
EGHAM (0784) 39494   £16–£28

The set dinner is quite remarkable value – a four-course meal with aperitif and three wines served by the glass, plus coffee, for £20 inclusive. It is all the more so, compared with the prices of the showy French *carte*. David Smart aspires to cook in a style to equal the top French chefs in this country. Rich, reduced sauces offset generous main dishes: duck is basted with honey and sesame seeds and given a cider vinegar sauce; pork is with calvados and grated horseradish. Duck and

---

The entries are compiled from the views of readers who have eaten at the restaurants in the last year, backed up by anonymous inspections and by information supplied and facts verified by the restaurants.

---

goose foie gras are made into a terrine and served with smoked duck and a glass of Château Coutet '79 Portions are uncharacteristically generous. The pace is slow, and the resolve to make this a major restaurant is let down only by some overgilding of the lily. The 150 wines are too aristocratic to be cheap (though there are half-bottles), which may be another reason for following the set menu. House French is £6·50. CELLARMAN'S CHOICE: Caillou Blanc du Ch. Talbot '85, £17·45.

CHEF: David Smart PROPRIETORS: David Turvey and David Smart
OPEN: all week, exc Sat L CLOSED: bank hols MEALS: 12 to 2, 7 to 9.30
PRICES: £20 (£28), Set L £12·50 (£16), Set D £20 (£20). Service inc CARDS: Access, Amex, Diners, Visa
SEATS: 46. 3 tables outside. Private parties: 20 main room, 8 private room. Car-park, 14 places. Children welcome. Smart dress preferred. Wheelchair access. Music

---

ELLAND West Yorkshire

map 5

Berties Bistro [11/20] ✗

7–10 Town Hall Buildings, Elland HD1 2TA
ELLAND (0422) 71724

£13

There is no booking, which leads to crushes and waits, but also makes for a bustling yet relaxed atmosphere on busy evenings towards the end of the week. Sandwiched between Job Centre and Town Hall, the décor mixes Edwardian (Edward VII, hence Bertie) and bistro. The cooking is fond of French, though there are exceptions, like tandoori chicken suprême. Puddings – toffee and apple, or Stilton and Guinness cake – are certainly British. The value is good, the staff work to a common cause, and portions are substantial. Good examples have been chicken livers Véronique; moussaka; lemon tart. The less delicate dishes survive best. Berties Bombe is a triangular wedge of meringue filled with ice-cream, sitting on a typically sweet sauce of chocolate and toffee. Wines, like the menu, are written on the blackboard in the bar and on a card at the table. House wine is £5·50 a litre.

CHEF: Michael Swallow PROPRIETOR: Brett Woodward
OPEN: Tue to Sun, D only MEALS: 7 to 11 (11.30 Fri and Sat, 5 to 9.30 Sun)
PRICES: £9 (£13)
SEATS: 110. Private parties: 40 private room. Car-park, 60 places. Vegetarian meals. Children's helpings. Smart dress preferred. No-smoking area. Wheelchair access. Music. Air-conditioned

---

ELSWORTH Cambridgeshire

map 3

▲ *Meadow Farm* [12/20]

Broad End, Elsworth CB3 8JD
ELSWORTH (095 47) 413
3m off A604, Cambridge to Huntingdon

£21

The farm is not easily found: when heading from the A604, go through Elsworth and turn right at the village playing-field. The restaurant is the family home, and drinks are served in the sitting-room, which has an eccentric assortment of furniture and antiques. By contrast, the dining-room is in the modern style, with cane chairs. The menu is French, but depends on home-grown or British ingredients. Scottish langoustines are turned into a spicy bisque; salmon comes with an old-fashioned, Mrs Beeton-style relish of hard-boiled egg white, herring, tarragon and butter. Chicken is cooked with calvados; slices of lamb come with freshly picked broad beans and an intense sauce of cream and meat juices. Vegetables are harvested fresh from the garden. Sweets rely heavily on ice-cream and sorbet concoctions. Any lack of polish in the cooking is offset by the seriousness of purpose, the effort and the freshness of ingredients. The solid, dependable wine list is strong on clarets, and includes half a dozen Chablis and four Muscadets. CELLARMAN'S CHOICE: Côtes de Duras, Château La Grave Béchade '82, £8·45.

CHEFS/PROPRIETORS: Leonora Cooke and Nicolas Toke-Nicols
OPEN: Tue to Sat, D only
CLOSED: 2 weeks Jan, 2 weeks Aug MEALS: 7.30
PRICES: Set D £15 (£21) CARDS: Access, Amex, Visa
SEATS: 20. Private parties: 20 main room. Car-park, 16 places. Vegetarian meals. Children welcome. Wheelchair access (also WC). One sitting
ACCOMMODATION: 1 room, with bath/shower. B&B £18 for 2. Garden

---

ELY Cambridgeshire   map 6

Old Fire Engine House [13/20]

25 St Mary's Street, Ely CB7 4ER
ELY (0353) 2582   £16

Ann Ford and Michael Jarman have championed English cooking in their converted Fenland fire station since 1968. The restaurant is like a farmhouse kitchen, with quarry tiles and bare wooden tables. Old-fashioned generosity and second helpings are a matter of course. Beef is cooked in beer or red wine, pigeon is casseroled or roasted. The menu changes in some way every day, and features dishes such as turkey soup, a Northumbrian dish of mitton of pork, and steak-and-kidney pie, as well as stuffed leg of lamb in pastry, and veal in lemon and thyme sauce. Chicken and ham pie is notably good, and vegetarians also fare well, for a change, particularly if they give advance notice. Sweets, such as plum pie, syllabub and summer pudding, are served with extra cream. Wines do a commendable job of combining low prices with interest and variety.

CHEFS/PROPRIETORS: Ann Ford and Michael Jarman
OPEN: all week, exc Sun D
CLOSED: 24 Dec for 2 weeks MEALS: 12.30 to 2, 7.30 to 9
PRICES: £12 (£16)
SEATS: 36. 8 tables outside. Private parties: 36 main room, 22 private room. Car-park, 8 places. Vegetarian meals by arrangement. Children's helpings

---

'The coffee was a thin beige liquid served in half-pint mugs in which there was about enough flavour for a small espresso. One of the waitresses, changing the filter, was earnestly warned by another, looking obviously over at the proprietor, not to put too many spoonfuls in. He may think he's got the margins sorted out, but the same amount of coffee and a quarter as much hot water would give three times the pleasure.'
(On eating in London)

EMSWORTH Hampshire   map 2

36 North Street [new entry, zero rated]

36 North Street, Emsworth PO10 7DG
EMSWORTH (0243) 375592   £22–£29

Quite how this small, formal restaurant picked up a Taste of Britain award is
something of a mystery: Vivian Abady is a New Zealander who cooks in the
classic old-fashioned French style of lobster bisque, cornets of gravlax filled with
mustardy sour cream, quail stuffed with pistachio and game pâté, and noisettes
of pork with prunes. There is at least local game, Scottish salmon and excellent
boned rack of lamb with masses of black mushrooms, but the tone of the menu is
pitched firmly at the gourmet. She is, as an inspection meal showed, a good
technician, but inclined to elaborate showily, as in 'birds of a feather': breast of
duckling, pigeon and quail, each in a pastry case, each sitting on a different
vegetable, with different sauces in between. Vegetables are tiny, but green salad
is generous. The whole outfit is professionally run by Tim Abady, who is also
responsible for the wines. The claret section is strongest, closely followed by
sherries. House wine, from Bocuse's selection, is £5·95. More reports, please.

CHEF: Vivian Abady PROPRIETORS: Tim and Vivian Abady
OPEN: Tue to Sat, D only CLOSED: 23 Dec to mid-Jan MEALS: 7.30 (7 Sun) to 11
PRICES: £20 (£29). Set D from £14·95 (£22). Minimum £14·95 CARDS: Access, Amex,
Diners, Visa
SEATS: 38. Private parties: 22 main room, 8 private room. Vegetarian meals. No children
under 5. Smart dress preferred. No cigars/pipes in dining-room. Music. Air-conditioned

EPWORTH Humberside   map 5

Epworth Tap [9/20]

9–11 Market Place, Epworth DN9 1EU
EPWORTH (0427) 873333   £13

A wine buff's wine bar with an extraordinary selection of well-chosen bottles at
bargain prices. The setting downstairs is of flagstone floors and church pews;
upstairs is a candlelit dining area. Food is casual, but fresh and well prepared: a
tiny ramekin of ratatouille; Provençal fish soup; spare ribs; rich beef in red wine.
There are home-made sweets and well-kept French cheeses. The wine list shines
like a beacon, and includes, for example, six different *premiers crus* Chablis and six
California Chardonnays. Prices are reasonable: most of the burgundy is under
£20, and much of southern Rhône, the Midi, Italy and Spain stays well under
£10. CELLARMAN'S CHOICE: Chablis, *premier cru* Fourchaume '84, from Laroche
£10·99; Crozes-Hermitage, Thalabert '82, from Jaboulet, £8·95.

CHEF: Helen Wynne PROPRIETORS: Helen and John Wynne
OPEN: Tue to Sat, D only MEALS: 7.30 to 10 (10.30 Sat)
PRICES: £8 (£13) CARD: Access
SEATS: 74. Private parties: 50 main room, 24 private room. Vegetarian meals. Children
welcome. No-smoking area. Wheelchair access (3 steps). Music

All inspections are carried out anonymously.

ESHER Surrey   map 3

Les Alouettes [12/20]

7 High Street, Claygate, Esher KT10 0JW
ESHER (0372) 64882   £18–£24

A corner house, smartly adorned in pale beige with long drapes and cut-glass
chandeliers. Thomas Stewart's fixed-price menu is long and classically French:
calf's liver with blackcurrant and cassis; wild salmon with beurre blanc; lamb
cutlets with an alcoholic madeira sauce. Of the many, many highly priced
restaurants in Surrey now, this seems to be one where the outlay is spent to good
effect. Presentation is attractive but not fussy: warm salad of duck breast, for
instance, comes with orange, strawberries, avocado and salad leaves dressed in
walnut oil. Good sweets include cold lime soufflé, and lemon meringue tart. The
cellar is well managed, with an eye for both price and quality, and there is
something for everybody, from top claret to house wine at £6·95, bottled for the
restaurant.

CHEF: Thomas Stewart PROPRIETOR: Steve Christou
OPEN: Mon to Sat, exc Sat L MEALS: 12 to 2.15, 7 to 10
PRICES: Set L £12·75 (£18), Set D £18·50 (£24). Service 10% CARDS: Access, Amex,
Diners, Visa
SEATS: 65. Private parties: 65 main room. Vegetarian meals. Children welcome. Music

Read's [12/20] ✗

4 The Parade, Claygate, Esher KT10 0NU
ESHER (0372) 65105   £13–£21

This family business is a convincingly transformed converted shop, with the
trappings of a well-heeled eating place: immaculate linen, large octagonal plates,
big glasses. The mood is friendly and prices are not unreasonable for these parts –
especially at lunch time. Fish is the main line: crab terrine; sauté of scallops and
Jerusalem artichokes with chervil; turbot with fresh morels; three char-grilled
fishes with lime sauce. Otherwise the menu steers its way confidently through
steak and kidney pie and roast loin of new season's lamb, to sauté calf's liver with
ginger, sage and garlic butter sauce and warm mango. Sweets feature hot treacle
sponge pudding as well as marquises and mille-feuilles. Cheeses are new British
names, such as Castle Hill and Lanarkshire Blue. The wine list has been increased
to seventy, and is well annotated. CELLARMAN'S CHOICE: Caillou Blanc du
Ch. Talbot '85, £12·95.

CHEF: Stephen Read PROPRIETORS: The Read family
OPEN: Tue to Sat MEALS: 12 to 2, 7 to 10 (10.30 Sat)
PRICES: £15 (£21), Set L £7·95 (£13) CARDS: Access, Amex, Diners, Visa
SEATS: 28. Children's helpings (L only). Smart dress preferred. Wheelchair access. Music.
Air-conditioned

*The average price quoted in brackets is for an average three-course meal including
service, VAT, coffee and half a bottle of house wine or the equivalent in an ethnic
restaurant.*

ETON Berkshire

map 3

Eton Wine Bar [9/20]

82–83 High Street, Eton SL4 6AF
ETON (0753) 854921 and 855182   £15

The seats are church pews and there are hanging-baskets of flowers in this
informal wine bar close to Windsor Bridge. The menu has some adventurous
choices, from courgette, green pepper and Cheddar soup to carrot, date and
walnut cake with a lemon cream sauce. In between there might be chicken,
tarragon and almond roulade, or spinach pancake filled with prawns, ham and
leek in a Gruyère sauce. Wines are now divided up by price rather than region,
with a good selection under £10, thanks largely to the south of France and
Beaujolais. CELLARMAN'S CHOICE: Chardonnay, vin de pays de L'Ardèche,
Domaine de Bournet '86, at £6·85.

CHEFS: Mrs Caroline Gilbey, Mrs Linda Gilbey, the Hon. William Gilbey and Deborah Wicks
PROPRIETORS: The Hon. William Gilbey, Mrs Caroline Gilbey, the Hon. Michael Gilbey and
Mrs Linda Gilbey
OPEN: all week CLOSED: 3 days at Christmas MEALS: 12 to 2.30, 6 to 10.30 (7 Sun)
PRICES: £9 (£15) CARDS: Access, Visa
SEATS: 75. 5 tables outside. Private parties: 34 main room. Vegetarian meals. Children
welcome. Wheelchair access (also WC). Music

EVERSHOT Dorset

map 2

▲ Summer Lodge [12/20]

Evershot DT2 0JR
EVERSHOT (093 583) 424   £12–£19

A good place to stay; nothing is too much trouble. The Corbetts' flair as hoteliers
extends to the kitchen, which deals mostly in simple English food done
properly: in June there was half a pound of asparagus a head (from East Coker,
also with literary associations), followed by Somerset lamb roasted with
rosemary and garlic. A parade of dishes is brought by streams of young
waitresses, and great ceremony is made of pouring the iced water. The menu has
three courses and no choice: hot gammon; beef Wellington; excellent cheeses.
Breakfasts and afternoon teas are high points. The wine list shows the same
careful understanding of its opportunities, with bottles from Dorset and Somerset
as well as a long suit in mature claret, modest mark-ups, and a page of half-
bottles. CELLARMAN'S CHOICE: St Emilion, Ch. Franc-Grace-Dieu '82, £11·90.

*Restaurants are graded on a scale of 1–20. In the category of 10–11 expect to find the
best food in the locality. Ratings of 12 and more are given to restaurants we regard as
serving the best food in the region.*

The Guide *recruits new inspectors from readers who write in regularly. If you would
like to apply, write to the editor with (a) a detailed report on a restaurant where you
have eaten and (b) a comparative study of restaurants known to you.*

CHEFS: Margaret Corbett and Anne Knebel PROPRIETORS: Nigel and Margaret Corbett
OPEN: all week CLOSED: 20 Dec to 15 Jan MEALS: 12.30 to 1.30, 8
PRICES: Set L £8·50 (£12), Set D £15 (£19), Snacks from £2·50 CARDS: Access, Visa
SEATS: 28. Private parties: 28 main room. Car-park, 30 places. Vegetarian meals.
No children under 8. Wheelchair access (also WC). One sitting
ACCOMMODATION: 12 rooms, all with bath/shower. B&B £43 to £65. No children under 8.
Pets welcome. Afternoon teas. Garden. Swimming-pool. Tennis. Snooker. Phone. Scenic.
Doors close at 12   [GHG]

EVESHAM Hereford & Worcester map 2

▲ *Cedar Restaurant, The Evesham Hotel* [10/20]

Cooper's Lane, Evesham WR11 6DA
EVESHAM (0386) 49111 £16

For all their good humour, the Jenkinson family run a thoroughly professional
hotel, with a dining-room that takes its name from the immense tree outside. A
bottle symbol is awarded for sheer cheek: the wine list seemingly has wines from
every producing country in the world, bar France and Germany (Champagne is
the exception). The menu has similarly gypsy tastes, but there are grills to match
the wines and the kitchen can handle dishes as disparate as lamb in pastry and
Dutch-style fish stew. The buffet is excellent value. Coffee is endless and comes
with bowls of fruit. In the bar, the cocktail compendium is as wide ranging as the
wines, and includes bottles with pickled snakes and chameleons in them. On the
list, Australasia and North America hog most of the limelight as far as quality is
concerned, with a dozen and a half Chardonnays, including Roxburgh '84,
Tyrell's Vat 47 '82, and Wynn's '82, all around £16. CELLARMAN'S CHOICE
includes New Zealand Sauvignon, Matua Valley '85 at £11·50 and Brown Bros
Orange Muscat dessert wine at £8 per half-bottle.

CHEF: Brian Simmonds PROPRIETORS: The Jenkinson family
OPEN: all week CLOSED: 25 and 26 Dec MEALS: 12.30 to 2, 7 to 9.30
PRICES: £12 (£16). Service inc CARDS: Access, Amex, Diners, Visa
SEATS: 55. Private parties: 12 main room, 15 private room. Car-park, 50 places. Vegetarian
meals. Children's helpings. Wheelchair access (also WC)
ACCOMMODATION: 34 rooms, all with bath/shower. B&B £39 to £54. Baby facilites. Pets
welcome. Afternoon teas. Garden. TV. Phone. Doors close at 12. Confirm by 6

FARNHAM Surrey map 3

Tirolerhof [10/20]

84 West Street, Farnham GU9 7EN
FARNHAM (0252) 723277 £21

Well hidden in a row of shops at the top of Farnham, past the one-way system,
this remains one of the better Austrian restaurants in the country. Herring with
schnapps, Schnitzels, Sauerkraut, coleslaw, pastries, and on Saturday night,

---

*All details are as accurate as possible at the time of going to press. Please notify the
Guide office of any changes.*

predictably, an accordion. Portions are large. House Grüner Veltliner is £5·80, and there are sixty different schnapps.

CHEF: Gerhard Krug PROPRIETORS: Helmuth Staffler and Gerhard Krug
OPEN: Mon to Sat, D only CLOSED: 2 weeks July MEALS: 7 to 10.30 (1am Fri and Sat)
PRICES: £14 (£21). Service 10% CARDS: Access, Amex, Visa
SEATS: 100. Private parties: 60 main room, 60 private room. Vegetarian meals. Children's
helpings. Smart dress preferred. Music

FARNLEY TYAS West Yorkshire   map 5

Golden Cock [10/20]

Farnley Tyas HD4 6UD
HUDDERSFIELD (0484) 661979 and 663563   £11–£21

The old stone village pub on the edge of the Pennines has open fireplaces,
flagstoned floors and a dining-room in shades of blue. The style is French with a
few English dishes, 'for our clients who prefer traditional cooking'. Meat and
poultry stand out, vegetables are nicely timed, and portions are generous. Quails
are boned, stuffed and served with a raspberry sauce; venison comes in thick
slices with a cream and chestnut sauce. Caramelised kumquat ice-cream and
Swiss truffle tart are good sweets. Service is neat and correct. The cheaper
Charcuterie restaurant upstairs takes no bookings. House wine is £3·95 a bottle.

CHEFS: Peter John Midwood and David Midwood PROPRIETOR: Peter John Midwood
OPEN: all week, exc Sat L and Sun D MEALS: 12.15 to 2, 7.15 (6.30 Sat) to 9.45
PRICES: £14 (£21), Set L from £8·25 (£11), Snacks from £1 CARDS: Access, Amex,
Diners, Visa
SEATS: 125. 11 tables outside. Private parties: 48 main room. Car-park, 75 places.
Vegetarian meals. Children's helpings. Wheelchair access (also WC). Music

---

FARRINGTON GURNEY Avon   map 2

▲ *Old Parsonage* [11/20]

Main Street, Farrington Gurney, BS18 5UB
TEMPLE CLOUD (0761) 52211   £13–£18

The Victorian solidity and standards of housekeeping that characterise the
dining-room of the Old Parsonage earn inclusion yet again, after thirteen
successive years in the *Guide*. Meals are leisurely. The tables are set with white
linen and gleaming glass. Soup is out of the pot and seconds are offered. But it is
the Frenchness of the noisettes of lamb with herb butter, or the pommes
dauphinoise, that stamps the menu. Other dishes, such as whole duck with sage
and onion stuffing and apple sauce, can be ordered by arrangement. Sunday
lunch of roast beef is good value. Mr Watson usually does most of the serving

---

*'Last year I travelled widely in Burgundy, the Upper Loire, Provence and the South-
west on two long trips. I ate in many noted places. It is no exaggeration to say that our
new restaurant here now equals or surpasses the performance of any of the one-star
Michelin establishments.'* (On eating in Kent)

himself, with help from just one waitress. The wine list includes a dozen useful half-bottles. House Côtes du Ventoux is £5·50.

CHEF: H. M. Gofton-Watson PROPRIETORS: W. E. and H. M. Gofton-Watson
OPEN: all week, exc Mon L and Sun D CLOSED: 25 to 28 Dec, Good Friday
MEALS: 12.30 to 1.30, 7 to 10
PRICES: £13 (£18), Set Sun L £8·50 (£13). Service 10% CARD: Visa
SEATS: 26. Private parties: 14 main room, 14 private room. Car-park, 100 places. Children's helpings. Wheelchair access (also WC)
ACCOMMODATION: 3 rooms, all with bath/shower. B&B £25 to £40. Baby facilities. Garden

---

FAVERSHAM Kent — map 3

Read's [12/20] 𝒴

Painter's Forstal, Faversham ME13 0EE
FAVERSHAM (0795) 535344 £13–£27

At the end of a narrow, winding road stands this red-brick, one-storey building, the ugly exterior in marked contrast to the ambience and professionalism inside. David Pitchford cooks a complex French menu owing more to classical cooking than nouvelle. Seafood sausage, for instance, is sauced with cream and Sauternes. The use of expensive wines or digestifs is common: champagne for poaching salmon; a measure of armagnac in the bisque de homard. Sauces are excellent. The elaboration is quite remarkable. Take gâteau filet de boeuf, l'oignon lyonnaise, sauce poivre: the fillet, sliced and interleaved with onion, is reshaped and surrounded by a velvet beef-stock reduction seasoned with peppercorns. Chocaholics Anonymous is a similar artifice of no fewer than six confections. Wine is a passion. The list is a treasure of vintages – Ch. de Sales '79, £18; Ch. Durfort-Vivens '70, £25 – from more than fifteen merchants. In this context it can be wise to stay with the plainer dishes, in order to find good marriages. House French is £6·40. CELLARMAN'S CHOICE: Gigondas '82, £10·50.

CHEF: David Pitchford PROPRIETORS: David and Rona Pitchford
OPEN: Mon to Sat MEALS: 12 to 2, 7 to 10
PRICES: £17 (£27), Set L from £8·50 (£13) CARDS: Amex, Diners, Visa
SEATS: 72. 3 tables outside. Private parties: 72 main room. Car-park, 30 places. Children's helpings. Wheelchair access (1 step; also WC). Music

---

FELSTED Essex — map 3

Rumbles Cottage [10/20]

Braintree Road, Felsted CM6 3DJ
GREAT DUNMOW (0371) 820996 £12–£16

Joy Hadley's good-value menus set out to offer what diners might not have at home. Some of the results in this basement sixteenth-century beamed cottage are quite striking: avocado ice-cream, and tomato sorbet with tomatoes and kiwi fruit, appear alongside familiar cottage dishes, such as pigeon pâté, casseroled partridge, and pork coated in sage and onion breadcrumbs. Vegetables are fresh.

This symbol is awarded only to restaurants with outstanding wine cellars.

Thirty wines are nearly all under £10. CELLARMAN'S CHOICE: Rioja Reserva, Don Jacobo '79, £8·25

CHEF: E. Joy Hadley PROPRIETORS: E. Joy Hadley and M. Donovan
OPEN: L Wed to Sun, exc Sat; D Tue to Sat CLOSED: 3 weeks Feb, 1 week Aug
MEALS: 12 to 2, 7 to 9
PRICES: £10 (£16), Set Sun L £8 (£12) CARDS: Access, Visa
SEATS: 46. Private parties: 24 main room, 8 and 10 private rooms. Vegetarian meals.
Children's helpings. Wheelchair access

FELTHAM Greater London   map 3

W. R. Grant [9/20]

499 Staines Road, Bedfont, Feltham TW14 8BN
01-890 3845   £1.60+

Mr Grant's wet-fish shop sells prime cuts at half the price of some supermarkets. The take-away eschews anything frozen and the quality shows in the Peterhead cod and the Blonde Wing of skate. Fish from £1·25; chips 35p.

PROPRIETOR: W. R. Grant
OPEN: Mon to Sat MEALS: 10 to 2, 4 to 10.30 (8.30 Mon)
PRICES: from £1·60. Unlicensed

FLITWICK Bedfordshire   map 3

▲ Flitwick Manor [13/20]

Church Road, Flitwick MK45 1AE
FLITWICK (0525) 712242
off A5120, S of Flitwick   £21–£36

For twenty years, Somerset Moore has been associated with a succession of restaurants in the *Guide*: the Lygon Arms, Broadway; the Pheasant, Keyston; the White Hart, Flitton. Since 1984 he has been transforming this Georgian manor into one of the most civilised and unfettered country-house hotels in the Home Counties, giving it the trappings of gentrified English elegance, from the croquet lawn and secluded grotto to the Union Jack, permanently at full mast. A new mood of smoothness and confidence coincides with the arrival of chef Geoffrey Welch. The menu reflects Somerset Moore's talent for spotting and moving with the trends: fish still dominates a very long menu, but there's a good showing of vegetarian specialities: cous-cous tartare; oriental vegetable terrine; hazelnut, water-chestnut and potato fritters. The move towards 'healthy eating' has spawned such dishes as roulade of Scotch salmon and turbot with tomato vinaigrette. The cooking moves comfortably between classic French and modern British, taking in baby scallops with tomato and chive sauce, and sea bass wrapped in spinach with red burgundy butter sauce, as well as rabbit pâté with apricot and ginger sauce, and stir-fried mange-tout and sweetbreads with toasted

---

Files are kept on every restaurant, so reports of poor meals are just as valuable as reports of good meals because they save unnecessary inspections.

sesame seeds. Shellfish are kept in seawater tanks outside the kitchen; many vegetables are home grown; venison is from nearby Woburn Park. A local provisions merchant smokes bacon and blends coffee for the restaurant. The wines major in pedigree burgundy and reliable claret, but there are also respectable Rhônes, Alsaces and Loires. CELLARMAN'S CHOICE: Ch. La Tour St-Bonnet '79, £15·70.

CHEFS: Somerset Moore and Geoffrey Welch PROPRIETORS: Somerset and Hélène Moore
OPEN: all week, exc Sun D MEALS: 12 to 2, 7 to 9.30
PRICES: £25 (£36), Set L and D from £15·50 (£21), Snacks from £3·40 CARDS: Access, Amex, Diners, Visa
SEATS: 90. 6 tables outside. Private parties: 65 main room, 10 and 50 private rooms. Car-park, 70 places. Vegetarian meals. Children's helpings. No pipes in dining-room. Wheelchair access (also WC)
ACCOMMODATION: 15 rooms, all with bath/shower. Rooms for disabled. B&B £58 to £90. Deposit: 50%. Children welcome. Garden. Tennis. Fishing. Golf. Air-conditioning. TV. Phone. Scenic [GHG]

FOLKESTONE Kent   map 3

India [12/20]

1 Old High Street, Folkestone CT20 1RJ
FOLKESTONE (0303) 59155   £8–£15

In the evening, curtains are drawn across the converted shop front, shutting out the amusement arcades and the nearby cinema. The feel is of a private house, apart from the artificial bouquets, the incense, the muzak, and the dim lights: Ali Ashraf calls his style 'nouvelle Indienne'. It is an unexpected fusion of Bengali and French, with the emphasis on the former. The freshness of the ingredients, the subtle flavours and fragrance of the dishes put this place in a different league to most Indian restaurants. Lamb tikka is excellent-quality meat with a fine charcoal flavour, while the Gallic influence shows in the prawn bhajias – crisp, deep-fried pastries with prawns, cumin and coriander. The menu runs comprehensively through curries and tandooris taking in sita's dosha – pancake with meat, crab, prawns and mushrooms; Shahi korma – lamb with cashew-nuts and poppy seeds; and specialities based on duck and lobster. A handful of flag-waving French dishes, such as poulet provençale and salad niçoise, also feature. Very good breads and pickles. The waiters smile and charm. The modest, plain wine list includes Indian Beena at £6·25 a bottle.

CHEF/PROPRIETOR: Ali Ashraf
OPEN: all week MEALS: 12 to 3, 6 to 11.30
PRICES: £8 (£15), Set L from £3·95 (£8). Cover 50p. Minimum £5 CARDS: Access, Amex, Diners, Visa
SEATS: 52. Private parties: 56 main room. Vegetarian meals. Children's helpings. Wheelchair access. Music

---

'We make all stocks from leftover carcasses and bones and vegetable peelings, which then form the base for soups, poaching liquids, sauces, reductions. No cooking liquids are thrown out; those left in the roasting and sauté pans are scraped up and put to another use.' (East Anglian restaurateur)

Paul's [10/20]

2A Bouverie Road West, Folkestone CT20 2RX
FOLKESTONE (0303) 59697   £14

The Haggers run a good-value bourgeois menu in a spacious, cool dining-room.
Many of the dishes are bakes – pigeon pie; mussels and prawns – augmented with
cream and herbs. The ingredients are fresh and the quantities generous. Sixty
wines are mostly under £10.

CHEFS/PROPRIETORS: Paul and Penny Hagger
OPEN: Mon to Sat CLOSED: 1 week in winter, 1 week in summer MEALS: 12 to 2,
7.30 to 9.30
PRICES: £10 (£14). Service 10% CARDS: Access, Visa
SEATS: 44. 3 tables outside. Private parties; 50 main room. Car-park, 20 places (D only).
Vegetarian meals. Children's helpings by arrangement

 FOTHERINGHAY Northamptonshire   map 6

Falcon Inn [10/20]

Main Street, Fotheringhay PE8 5HZ
COTTERSTOCK (083 26) 254   £11

Order anything from a bowl of soup to a three-course meal at this village pub by
the church. Sausages are made locally, and the menu also has good moussaka,
steak and kidney pie, grills, and blackcurrant cheesecake. A dinner for two can
cost as little as £10. Book well in advance for weekend meals. Drink Greene King
ales or house wine at £4 a bottle.

CHEF: Alan Stewart PROPRIETORS: Alan and Jill Stewart
OPEN: Tue to Sun MEALS: 12.30 to 2, 6.45 to 9.45 (7 to 9 Sun)
PRICES: £8 (£11), Snacks from £1
SEATS: 50. 10 tables outside. Private parties: 60 main room, 12 and 36 private rooms.
Car-park, 30 places. Vegetarian meals. Children's helpings. Wheelchair access (also WC).
Air-conditioned

FRESSINGFIELD Suffolk   map 6

Fox and Goose [11/20]

Fressingfield IP21 5PB
FRESSINGFIELD (037 986) 247   £19–£29

The Clarkes have been in residence at this early sixteenth-century building next
to the church, since 1967. Son Adam keeps on the family tradition, following his
father's death last spring. The formula is this: book ahead, have a menu sent on,
and order in advance. Old-style classical specialities, for instance calf's
sweetbreads in puff pastry, Dover sole cooked in butter and prawns, peppered
steak with horseradish and brandy cream sauce, are done properly. Set meals of

---

*Good vintages for drinking in 1988: Alsace '85, Beaujolais '86, Germany '85, petits
chateaux clarets '81, lesser clarets '83.*

---

the day are available, but that is not the way to extract the best. The formidable wine list is not sent on ahead, unfortunately – the clarets are an education, and too good to be under £20, for the most part.

CHEF: A. P. Clarke PROPRIETORS: Mr and Mrs A. P. Clarke
OPEN: all week, exc Tue CLOSED: 1 week at Christmas MEALS: 12 to 1.30, 7 to 9
PRICES: £22 (£29), Set L and D from £14 (£19), Snacks from £2·25 CARDS: Access, Amex, Diners, Visa
SEATS: 24. Private parties: 32 main room. Car-park, 30 places. No children under 10

FROGHALL Staffordshire   map 5

Wharf [new entry, zero rated]

Foxt Road, Froghall ST10 2HJ
IPSTONES (053 871) 486   £19

Bill and Peggy Young spent years on canal boats before setting up boat-trips with Badger, the horse, pulling the butty. They have converted a derelict, waterside warehouse into a rustic, brick-walled restaurant with flowering vines and picnic tables outside. During the day the place functions as a café, turning into a more formal restaurant in the evening. The cooking is a good mix of straightforward ideas and invention, from chicken and red peppers in pistachio butter, or tartlet of sweetbreads and mushrooms with mango coulis, to French onion soup, surf and turf, or boned poussin with sherry and honey sauce. Mrs Young is a vegetarian, and the menu reflects this, offering rice and vegetable bake or a trio of mousses (aubergine, celeriac and carrot) with a citrus sauce. Vegetables get more than their share of attention, and sweets have included cheesecake roulade filled with home-made plum jam. A basic list of about twenty wines includes house wine at £4·55. More reports, please.

CHEF: Julia Hartley PROPRIETORS: R. and J. Young
OPEN: Tue to Sat, and Sun L CLOSED: daytime Oct to Easter MEALS: 11 to 5, 7.30 to 9.15
PRICES: D £16 (£19), Snacks from £1·95. Service inc CARD: Access
SEATS: 40. Private parties: 40 main room. Car-park, 60 places. Vegetarian meals. Children's helpings. Wheelchair access (1 step)

GATWICK West Sussex   map 3

▲ *Garden Restaurant, Gatwick Hilton* [10/20]

Gatwick Airport, Gatwick RH6 0LL
CRAWLEY (0293) 518080   £21–£27

The Hilton, an oasis for travellers from the airport, has been adopted by locals, who visit at Sunday lunchtime to use the swimming-pool. The Garden Restaurant is big, modern and aspires to much; it is helped by the use of vacuum-packing in the preparation. The repertoire loves rack of lamb with celery sauce, scallops with Sauternes, and pigeon consommé; the grill produces good steaks. Between 6 and 7.30pm there's a Happy Hour Menu with similar food at reduced prices. Complex dishes, and the more twisted combinations, are not the most successful, but even so, the place is worth knowing about. The well-spread list of about a hundred wines has a reasonable showing of half-bottles.
CELLARMAN'S CHOICE: Savennières, Clos du Papillon '85, £12·75.

CHEF: Patrick John PROPRIETORS: Hilton International
OPEN: all week, exc Sat L MEALS: 12 to 2.30, 6 to 11
PRICES: £18 (£27), Set L from £12·50 (£21), Set D (6 to 7.30pm) £13·25 (£22)
CARDS: Access, Amex, Carte Blanche, Diners, Visa
SEATS: 180. Private parties: 20 main room, 350 private room. Car-park, 90 places.
Vegetarian meals. Children's helpings. Smart dress preferred. No-smoking area. Wheelchair
access (also WC). Music. Air-conditioned
ACCOMMODATION: 550 rooms, all with bath/shower. Rooms for disabled. Lift. B&B £82 to
£100. Deposit: one night's stay. Children welcome. Baby facilities. Pets welcome. Afternoon
teas. Swimming-pool. Sauna. Air-conditioning. TV. Phone. Confirm by 6

GILLINGHAM Dorset   map 2

▲ *Stock Hill House* [12/20]

Wyke, Gillingham SP8 5NR
GILLINGHAM (074 76) 3626   £16–£23

The welcome, amid log fires in winter, is spontaneous. The cooking is robust,
with seconds offered of the Provençal fish soup. The style is warm poacher's salad
with hot venison and quail eggs, or pork with sweetbreads, in a sauce coloured
with Pernod. The cheese is a flamboyant display, with brioche, dates, walnuts,
grapes and celery. A short, well-chosen wine list has strength in the Rhône.
House red is Gamay de L'Ardèche at £6·50. CELLARMAN'S CHOICE: Coteaux des
Baux-en-Provence, Domaine de Trévallon '84, at £10·60.

CHEF: Peter Hauser PROPRIETORS: Peter and Nita Hauser
OPEN: Tue to Sun, exc Sun D MEALS: 12.30 to 2, 7.30 to 9
PRICES: Set L £11 (£16), Set D £18 (£23) CARDS: Access, Visa
SEATS: 26. Private parties: 12 main room, 12 private room. Car-park, 25 places. Children's
helpings (L only). No children under 7. Jacket and tie. No smoking in dining-room
ACCOMMODATION: 7 rooms, all with bath/shower. B&B £45 to £90. No children under 7.
No pets. Garden. Swimming-pool. Sauna. TV. Phone. Scenic. Doors close at 12. Confirm
by 8 [GHG]

GLEMSFORD Suffolk   map 3

Barretts [new entry, zero rated]

31 Egremont Street, Glemsford CO10 7SA
GLEMSFORD (0787) 281573   £15–£21

Barretts used to be Weeks, which rated 15/20 but struggled to stay commercial
in this straggly, out of the way village. The basic décor remains the same, but a
few changes have made the atmosphere less stark – the dining-tables are set at
angles rather than on the square; one is round; the removal of an enormous pot
plant makes the reception area feel larger. The etchings have been replaced by
pictures in the genre of chubby children in period clothes. The menu has been
expanded to offer a generous choice and repeats the mid-Channel style of the
Pink Geranium at Melbourn, where Nicholas Barrett cooked for the last four
years until it was sold last winter. Ingredients are good and the cooking sound,
though some dishes seem to fall between an aspiration for out-and-out excellence
and a desire to offer value. Pastry has overstretched the kitchen. The cliché of
deep-fried Brie has been cleverly re-worked with blue Brie and a strawberry and

black pepper coulis. Main dishes, such as beef fillet with rosemary, or a fine glace de viande, home-made ice-creams and good home-made bread, all indicate that this could be a very serious kitchen, once the priorities are sorted out, and if it can keep the custom. A hundred and twenty wines favour the classic regions. Dessert wines are sold by the glass. House claret is £6·95. More reports, please.

CHEF/PROPRIETOR: Nicholas Barrett
OPEN: Tue to Sat D, and Sun L CLOSED: 2 weeks Jan MEALS: 12 to 2, 7 to 9.30
PRICES: £15 (£21), Set L £9·95 (£15) CARDS: Access, Visa
SEATS: 18. Private parties: 12 main room. Car-park, 10 places. Children's helpings
(Sun L only). Wheelchair access

GLOUCESTER Gloucestershire   map 2

College Green [10/20] ✗

9 College Street, Gloucester GL1 2NE
GLOUCESTER (0452) 20739   £9–£19

A reliable bistro in a quiet area near the cathedral, with black and white timbered rooms, elegant pink tablecloths and candles. Lunches are English – braised ox-tail, steak and kidney pudding, steamed puddings and crumbles – but dinner moves into another gear. Red wine, madeira and thyme flavour the sauce for beef, and lemon sole is served with a scallop mousse and star anise sauce. Plentiful coffee. House wine, from a short list, is £5·50 a bottle.

CHEF: David Spencer PROPRIETORS: David and Francis Spencer
OPEN: Mon to Sat, exc Mon and Tue D CLOSED: bank hols MEALS: 12 to 2, 6.30 to 9.30
PRICES: £14 (£19), Set L from £5·75 (£9) CARDS: Access, Amex, Visa
SEATS: 30. Private parties: 44 main room, 30 private room. Children's helpings. Music

---

GOLCAR West Yorkshire   map 5

Weavers Shed [12/20] ✗

Knowl Road, Golcar HD7 4AN
HUDDERSFIELD (0484) 654284   £13–£20

Almost at the top of the hill is this eighteenth-century cloth-finishing mill, looking like a couple of converted cottages, with a cobbled yard and an old-fashioned gas-lamp. Inside are spinning-wheel stands and bare stone walls hung with bobbins and shuttles. Appropriately, the cooking is part of the British revival, with an occasional glance across the Channel. To start there might be gamey terrine of pheasant with kumquats, or Arbroath smokies with cream and cheese, then a soup, such as parsnip and ginger, or a sorbet, before the main course. Sauces figure strongly: medallions of venison with port; breast of chicken with vinegar

---

'I am all for creative cuisine, but we are now getting to the stage where it is all being rather overdone. Each chef seems to be trying to outdo the other in the way they carve a beetroot, polish a pea-pod, stretch each leaf. As a result, the food is beginning to take second place and is coming up to the table just a little tired.' (On eating in Buckinghamshire)

---

and butter; slices of fillet steak with green peppercorns, brandy and cream. Vegetables are served in abundance. To finish, the banana toffee tart has been better than the Old English trifle. Sunday lunch is a splendid buffet for the whole family. The sound, predominantly French wine list is reasonably priced, with house wine at £5·50. CELLARMAN'S CHOICE: Rioja Gran Reserva, Imperial '75, at £12.

CHEFS/PROPRIETORS: Betty and Peter Saville
OPEN: Tue to Sun, exc Sat L and Sun D CLOSED: 2 weeks Jan, 2 weeks July MEALS: 12 to 2, 7.30 to 9 (9.30 Sat)
PRICES: £14 (£20), Set Sun L £5·75 (£13)
SEATS: 70. Private parties: 30 main room, 30 private room. Car-park, 40 places. Vegetarian meals. Children welcome. Smart dress preferred. Wheelchair access (also WC)

GRASMERE Cumbria   map 7

▲ *Michael's Nook* [14/20]

Grasmere LA22 9RP
GRASMERE (096 65) 496   £23–£32

Reg Gifford's stoically English Lakeland hotel, high above Grasmere, has an imposing, antiquated, flowery entrance; a rickety antique lounge bar, complete with ancient Chinese porcelain, old photographs and prints, an Adam fireplace and 1973 wine magazines; and an equally antiquated dining-room with ancient polished tables and painted anaglypta walls. The cooking, though, is modern. Of all the Lakeland restaurateurs, Mr Gifford, working over recent years with a number of young chefs, has developed a style that might be called nouvelle and modern British at the same time. Leek and foie gras terrine is served with a sauce of honey, avocado, dill and vinegar; light textured sole mousse is wrapped in a spinach leaf and accompanied by a saffron and tomato sauce. Main courses move up a gear for pink, sauté duck breast with a powerfully reduced syrupy stock pointed up with lime and ginger. Equally impressive is a veal sweetbread, braised, coated with a port and truffle glaze and served on a delicate carrot and Sauternes sauce. Vegetables come as tiny, delicate arrangements, almost in the Mosimann style. To finish, apple tartlets are served with calvados sabayon and cinnamon ice-cream. Bread could improve. The wine list runs to 120 bottles and is classically inclined, but has an exceptional showing of half-bottles, superb value in the Loire, and is strong in '78 and '75 claret. House Gamay is £5·40.
CELLARMAN'S CHOICE: Ch. La Garde '78, £13·95.

CHEF: Andrew Eastick PROPRIETOR: R. S. E. Gifford
OPEN: all week, exc Sat L MEALS: 12.30, 7.30 (7 and 9, Sat in summer)
PRICES: Set L £18·50 (£23), Set D £26 (£32) CARD: Amex
SEATS: 26. Private parties: 28 main room. Car-park, 20 places. Children welcome. Smart dress preferred. No smoking in dining-room. Wheelchair access
ACCOMMODATION: 11 rooms, all with bath/shower. B&B £78 to £159. Deposit: £30. Garden. Swimming-pool. Sauna. Golf. TV. Phone. Scenic

---

'The Italian waiter, after 45 years, still spoke very limited English. He was very confused by my request for Tisane or herb tea. He thought I wanted grass tea. "We have Ole Grey or Chelon [Ceylon]."' (On eating in the Midlands)

▲ *White Moss House* [14/20]

Rydal Water, Grasmere LA22 9SE ✈
GRASMERE (096 65) 295   🍾 £22

'The more extreme practitioners of *nouvelle cuisine* have tended to forget about
texture. Different game and meat dishes lose a lot when turned into boudins and
mousses,' argue Susan and Peter Dixon. His cooking is modern British – and
elicited from German gourmet magazine *Feinschmecker* the comment, 'I felt, for
the first time in my life, the urge to give three cheers for English cooking'. Maybe
so, but our high rating for such a rigid, almost boarding-house style, is not to
everyone's taste. The dining-room is in the old part of the house and is small
enough to feel communal. The menu has no choice, but the meal is virile and
persuasive, with excellent wines to match. Soups are complex: mushroom,
marjoram and marsala; fennel and apple; lovage and leek. Then follows perhaps
a fish soufflé or a terrine, before a main-course roast. The habit is to combine
three offsetting flavours: claret, port and damson with duck; oloroso, dry madeira
and sour cream for pork; orange, redcurrant and mint for lamb. Guinea-fowl has
been dry, but four vegetables enliven the plate. There is a choice of three
traditional and alcoholic sweets – Gewürztraminer sorbet, bread-and-butter-
pudding with calvados – and then perhaps fifteen unpasteurised British cheeses,
at their best when taken out of the fridge in advance. Runs of good vintages and
affordable bottles – with plenty under £10 – betray an enthusiasm for good
drinking. Beaujolais starts at £6·90, Bordeaux and burgundy at £6·20, but there
is enough interest at the top end to satisfy anybody, from '61 claret and '69
burgundy to Jaboulet Rhônes and Hugel Alsace. New Zealand Chardonnay,
Delegat's '85, is £11·50; half-bottles of Gigondas '67, from Jaboulet, are
£9·90; and CELLARMAN'S CHOICE is Ch. la Gurgue '82 at £10 (half-bottles of
'83 at £5·25).

CHEF: Peter Dixon PROPRIETORS: Susan and Peter Dixon
OPEN: Mon to Sat, D only CLOSED: mid-Nov to mid-Mar MEALS: 8
PRICES: Set D £16·95 (£22)
SEATS: 18. Private parties: 18 main room. Car-park, 10 places. No children under 10. Smart
dress preferred. No smoking in dining-room. Wheelchair access. Music. One sitting
ACCOMMODATION: 7 rooms, all with bath/shower. B&B £25 to £55. No children under 10.
Garden. Fishing. TV. Phone. Scenic. Doors close at 11. Confirm by 4 [GHG]

GRAYSHOTT Hampshire   map 2

Woods [12/20]

Headley Road, Grayshott GU26 6LB
HINDHEAD (042 873) 5555   £24

The Norrgrens' converted shop is in a satellite of Hindhead, right on the Surrey/
Hampshire border. The eating area is three rooms, their connecting doors
removed. The mood is quiet and intimate. This is a restaurant of quality, solid but
static, not aspiring to the zip of Morels, its nearest rival, in Haslemere (see entry).
Little changes. Gravlax is still a favourite, as is its meat equivalent of superb raw
fillet of beef marinated in madeira and black pepper. Fish continues to be a strong
point, from sea-bass to brill with yellow-pepper sauce, and smoked eel poached in
beer and served with scrambled eggs. Meals begin with good caraway-seed bread

and end on a high note, with sweets such as a pastry bowl filled with fruit salad and chocolate mousse. The token Australian Chardonnay is Bortoli's '85 at £10·10, but the bulk of the short list is French, with house Chantovent at £5·20. CELLARMAN'S CHOICE: Beaujolais, Les Grandes Coasses '85, from Durdilly, at £8·40.

CHEF: Eric Norrgren PROPRIETORS: Eric and Dana Norrgren
OPEN: Tue to Sat, D only MEALS: 7 to 12
PRICES: £16 (£24). Cover 45p CARDS: Access, Amex, Diners, Visa
SEATS: 35. Private parties: 12 main room. Children's helpings. Wheelchair access (also WC)

GREAT DUNMOW Essex   map 3

Starr [11/20]

Market Place, Great Dunmow CM6 1AX
GREAT DUNMOW (0371) 4321   £18–£28

Large slate menus are carried around this fine, partly fifteenth-century town-centre house, along with a ceramic basket of polished fruit and vegetables to show off the quality of the house produce. The strengths are simple marriages of good ingredients: smoked chicken with mango; melon with pastrami; scallops and langoustines in a salad dressed with walnut oil. Creamy mushroom terrine comes with a rather sweet apple and mint jelly. Steamed pudding with custard is a favourite sweet. Main courses are mostly sauced, though it may be wiser to follow the menu suggestion and order dishes plain, to offset the excellent wines. Claret is dominated by 'second' wines from great estates, which offer relatively inexpensive, though still two-figure, drinking. Beaujolais hangs its hat on the good '85 vintage, and there is burgundy from good shippers. House French is Cabernet '82 from the Haut Poitou Co-operative, at £7·20.
CELLARMAN'S CHOICE: Australian Chardonnay, Mount St Helen '82, at £16·65.

PROPRIETORS: Mr and Mrs B. Jones
OPEN: all week, exc Sat L and Sun D CLOSED: 3 weeks Aug, 2 weeks at Christmas
MEALS: 12 to 1.30, 7 to 10
PRICES: Set L from £12·50 (£18), Set D from £22 (£28). Licensed, also bring your own: corkage £5 CARDS: Access, Diners, Visa
SEATS: 60. Private parties: 8 main room. Car-park, 15 places. Vegetarian meals. Children's helpings. Wheelchair access (also WC). Music

---

GREAT HARWOOD Lancashire   map 5

Tiffany [12/20]

79 Church Street, Great Harwood BB6 7QB
GREAT HARWOOD (0254) 889528   £22

Dark and noisy, from both the open-plan kitchen and the music. Daily specials are reeled off by waitresses and augment a menu that is already varied and often quite adventurous. Fish is Neil Wigglesworth's most accomplished area: sashimi; grilled tuna steaks; sea trout with a vermouth cream sauce. Herbs abound, as do vegetables – no fewer than eight on the platter. The sweets trolley is a mountain of fresh fruit, boosted by strawberry bavarois, caramelised apple flan and poached pears in champagne and brandy. The handwritten list of two dozen wines starts at £6·25.

CHEF: Neil Wigglesworth PROPRIETORS: Brian and Neil Wigglesworth
OPEN: Tue to Sun, exc Sat L and Sun L MEALS: 11.30 to 2.30, 7 to 10
PRICES: £14 (£22). Service 10% CARD: Access
SEATS: 32. Private parties: 16 main room. Vegetarian meals. Children's helpings.
No children under 6. Smart dress preferred. Wheelchair access (also wc). Music.
Air-conditioned

GREAT MILTON Oxfordshire   map 2

▲ Le Manoir aux Quat' Saisons [18/20]

Church Road, Great Milton OX9 7PD
GREAT MILTON (084 46) 8881/2/3   £30–£53

Raymond Blanc's cooking is personal, original, technically impressive. He specialises in clear, intense flavours, is increasingly moving away from oils and creams to vegetable stock, and is passionate about the quality of his ingredients. He demonstrates, above all, the French genius for fantasy. Some nights not all the dishes are of equal standard and the service is not as polished as at, say, Le Gavroche, and yet . . . here there might be a Norfolk squab in a salt pastry case the size of a small football, or lobster served plainly with young vegetables and juices heightened with aniseed. Look at this *menu gourmand* from February: charlotte of aubergines and red peppers; gateau of Jerusalem artichoke; ballotine of salmon with cabbage; mint sorbet; slices of suckling pig with crisp crackling, its juices flavoured with marjoram; and finally, the consistent brilliance of the trois petits bonheurs du Manoir – a purée of apples between toffee lozenges in a light vanilla custard; a caramel soufflé with a creamy prune and armagnac ice-cream; and an intense grapefruit and orange jelly, garnished with segments of orange and grapefruit and a minted syrup of the fruits. On other menus look for warm duck in fried apples and celeriac; beef fillet, lightly smoked before pan frying; calvados soufflé in an apple, baked and served with a sabayon and a sorbet. The fantasy extends to the economics, which are probably as frightening for the Blancs as for the customers. Breakfasts are in the same league: a large glass of freshly squeezed orange juice, stewed pears with cinnamon, impeccable rolls, croissants and brioches, home-made conserves and excellent tea or coffee. Bedrooms are booked months ahead in summer, though there have been bargain breaks in winter. The wine list opens at £9·50, deals creditably in the teens with the lesser-known regions of France, and then takes off into the classic claret and burgundy stratosphere of high finance. The list is worthy of a bottle symbol, but for its having so little inexpensive drinking (though there are many half-bottles). Another niggle is that service can be disjointed. CELLARMAN'S CHOICE: Domaine de La Bernarde '83 from Madame Meulnart (Provence), at £16·30, and Fixin, Clos Napoleon '82, at £26.

▲ *This restaurant has rooms.*

Many of the more expensive restaurants offer bargain lunches for half the price of a meal in the evening. Details are given in the text.

CHEF: Raymond Blanc PROPRIETORS: Raymond and Jenny Blanc
OPEN: Tue to Sun, exc Tue L and Sun D CLOSED: 4 weeks from 24 Dec MEALS: 12.15 to
2.30, 7.15 to 10.30
PRICES: £40 (£53), Set L from £18·50 (£30), Set D £35 (£46). Service inc. Licensed, also
bring your own: corkage £5 CARDS: Access, Amex, Diners, Visa
SEATS: 70. 4 tables outside. Private parties: 10 main room, 45 private room. Car-park,
45 places. Vegetarian meals. Children's helpings. Smart dress preferred. No smoking in
dining-room. Wheelchair access (also WC)
ACCOMMODATION: 10 rooms, all with bath/shower. B&B to £220. Deposit: £50. No children
under 7. Baby facilities. Pets welcome. Afternoon teas. Garden. Swimming-pool. Tennis. TV.
Phone. Scenic [GHG]

GREAT YARMOUTH Norfolk map 6

Seafood Restaurant [11/20]

85 North Quay, Great Yarmouth NR30 1JF
GREAT YARMOUTH (0493) 856009 £26

Local fish is now hard to come by, even in a place like Great Yarmouth, because
fish has become fashionable and the pick of the catch goes to London. This is
what happened to south-coast ports a hundred years ago; history is virtually
repeating itself. Nonetheless, the finest fresh fish from Lowestoft is served in this
small restaurant down by the docks. The long menu depends for its main interest
on the catch, and the cooking is to trusted recipes – lightly fried whitebait,
excellent poached turbot served neatly with mange-tout and new potatoes. There
is a range of sauces but simple and unadorned seems the best option. Home-made
sorbets to finish. Burgundy dominates a good spread of mostly white wines;
house wine is £6. CELLARMAN'S CHOICE: Pouilly-Fumé, Domaine de Berthiers
'85, £11·75.

CHEF: Mathew Chrisostomou PROPRIETORS: Christopher and Miriam Kikis
OPEN: Mon to Sat, exc Sat L MEALS: 12 to 2, 7 to 10.45
PRICES: £18 (£26) CARDS: Access, Amex, Diners, Visa
SEATS: 40. Private parties: 40 main room. Children's helpings. Smart dress preferred. Music

---

GRIMSTON Norfolk map 6

▲ *Congham Hall* [12/20] ✈

Lynn Road, Grimston PE32 1AH
HILLINGTON (0485) 600250 £13–£25

This small, Georgian, country-house hotel set in its own lawns lacks some
personality, but Robert Harrison, formerly at Woods at Chesterton, cooks a
modern, classically inclined menu of some twenty dishes, not short on contrasts
or luxuries – lamb fillets with sweetbreads; fillet of beef in a rich red-wine sauce;
veal pan fried in a lime-scented sauce, served with herb butter. As so often
happens in this complex cookery, especially in hotels, all the handling dims the

---

Restaurants are not expected to solicit customers to send in reports. Please let us know
if this happens to you.

---

flavours. Sweets, though, are vivid: lemon cheesecake; ginger ice-cream with mango sauce. There is a random element to the selection of a hundred wines, but the list takes in affordable bottles and quality. House Rhône is £7.

CHEF: Robert Harrison PROPRIETORS: T. C. and C. K. Forecast
OPEN: all week, exc Sat L MEALS: 12.30 to 2, 7.30 to 9.30
PRICES: Set L from £8·50 (£13), Set D from £19·50 (£25), Snacks from £1·50
CARDS: Access, Amex, Diners, Visa
SEATS: 34. Private parties: 8 main room, 12 private room. Car-park, 50 places. No children under 12. Jacket and tie. No smoking in dining-room. Wheelchair access (also WC)
ACCOMMODATION: 11 rooms, all with bath/shower. B&B £50 to £64. No children under 12. Garden. Swimming-pool. Tennis. TV. Phone. Scenic. Doors close at 11.30. Confirm by 6

GUILDFORD Surrey   map 3

▲ *Manor*   [new entry, zero rated]

Newlands Corner, Guildford GU4 8SE
GUILDFORD (0483) 222624
3 miles E of Guildford on A25   £13–£15

The prices at some Surrey restaurants are now higher than in London and very few places can justify them, but this manor, set in its own grounds and being extensively upgraded by its new owners, has, certainly in the first months, offered good value for fairly lavish and complex cooking. Chef David Ostle takes on some vivid ideas – monkfish cooked with honey and tarragon on a spinach and mussel purée; duck leg boned and filled with the bird's liver; large crisp tuiles filled with paw-paw fool and surrounded by raspberry coulis. Service is canny and conscientious. The wine list opens at £5·90 but is being developed beyond its hundred French bottles. Champagnes are extensive. More reports, please.

CHEF: David Ostle PROPRIETORS: Gillian and Michael Hill
OPEN: all week CLOSED: 25 Dec D, 31 Dec D MEALS: 12 to 2, 7 to 9.30 (8.30 Sun)
PRICES: Set L £8·75 (£13), Set D from £11 (£15), Snacks from £1·25 CARDS: Access, Amex, Diners, Visa
SEATS: 76. Private parties: 80 main room, 24 and 150 private rooms. Car-park, 100 places. Vegetarian meals. Children's helpings. No cigars/pipes in dining-room. Wheelchair access. Music
ACCOMMODATION: 20 rooms, all with bath/shower. B&B £48 to £68. No children under 7. Afternoon teas. Garden. Golf. TV. Phone. Scenic. Doors close at 11.30

Rumwong   [12/20]

16–18 London Road, Guildford GU1 2AF
GUILDFORD (0483) 36092   £16–£17

The pine furniture, lace curtains and PVC table-mats give this the air of a comfortable suburban dining-room, but the dark wooden carvings and Thai staff indicate authenticity. And indeed here is some of the best Thai cooking. Poh-taek is a clear seafood soup with squid, prawn, crab and mushroom flavoured with lemon grass, lime leaves and lemon juice. Spiced beef satay and salad of boiled eggs and green vegetables both come with first-class peanut sauce. Spicing is vivid: curry paste with coconut milk for big juicy prawns; pickled plum, ginger and cucumber; honey, soy, brandy and spices with barbecued beef. In the smaller, Khan Tok dining-room you sit on cushions on the floor. House Nicolas is £5·80 on a basic wine list.

CHEF: Keow Sae Lao PROPRIETOR: Wanjai Poonum
OPEN: Tue to Sun CLOSED: 2 to 15 Aug MEALS: 12 to 2.30, 6 to 10.45 (10.30 Sun)
PRICES: £9 (£16), Set D £12 (£17). Service 10% alc, 12.5% set CARDS: Access, Visa
SEATS: 100. Private parties: 70 main room, 30 private room. Vegetarian meals. Children's helpings. Smart dress preferred. Wheelchair access. Music. Air-conditioned

---

GUISELEY West Yorkshire   map 5

Harry Ramsden's [9/20]

White Cross, Guiseley LS20 8L7
GUISELEY (0943) 74641   £4

Alec Outing has steered Britain's largest and most famous fish and chip shop back to the listings with a diligent enforcement of quality control. Specials are nearly always fresh and freshly cooked; skinned haddock in beef dripping is the main line. Waitresses in tight-fitting brown tunics are trained in the kitchen and progress to the dining-room, and they have a veto on fish and chips coming through. The unlikely dining-room – a huge, institutional room like some post-revolution proletarian chandeliered entertainment centre, with a Blackpool sonata coming out of the speakers – serves a staggering one and a half million customers a year. Souvenirs range from Harry Ramsden rock to Harry Ramsden mugs and teatowel. This is its sixtieth year of trading.

CHEF: Alec Outing PROPRIETORS: Associated Fisheries Ltd
OPEN: all week CLOSED: 25 and 26 Dec MEALS: 11.20am to 11.30pm
PRICES: £3 (£4) CARDS: Access, Visa
SEATS: 180. Car-park, 300 places. Children's helpings. Wheelchair access (also wc). Music

---

GUIST Norfolk   map 6

Tollbridge [12/20]

Dereham Road, Guist NR20 5NU
FOULSHAM (036 284) 359
on B1110, 10m SW of Holt   £11–£16

The Starks' modest, secluded mill is by the old bridge. The beamed, brick dining-room overlooks the River Wensum which, in effect, is floodlit at night. William and Glynis Stark have been here since 1977 and the menu treads a familiar path that does not seem to waver, being either French with a Norfolk accent, or Norfolk with a French accent: pike mousseline, chicken with plum sauce, rendezvous of halibut and salmon in a white wine and butter sauce, and of course, home-made ice-creams with fresh fruits. The style and finish of dishes is a bit ragged, in the old manner, but when the ingredients are fresh, the cooking

---

If, in your opinion, a restaurant is not maintaining the standard of its ratings please inform the Guide office. Report forms are at the back of the book.

---

can have real zip. The hundred wines, many of them under £15, hold plenty of interest, and represent most major regions. House claret and burgundy open at £4·95.

CHEF: William Stark PROPRIETORS: William and Glynis Stark
OPEN: Tue to Sat CLOSED: 3 weeks Jan, 1 week Oct MEALS: 12 to 1.45, 7 to 9.30
PRICES: £11 (£16), Set L £7.50 (£11). Minimum £10 at D CARD: Visa
SEATS: 40. 6 tables outside. Private parties: 44 main room. Car-park, 25 places. Children's helpings. No cigars in dining-room. Wheelchair access (also WC)

GULWORTHY Devon   map 1

▲ *Horn of Plenty* [11/20] ✗

Gulworthy PL19 8JD
TAVISTOCK (0822) 832528
3m W of Tavistock, off A390   £14–£31

Out of vogue perhaps, but Sonia Stevenson, one of the first women chefs to assert herself in a male-dominated bastion, can still compete at the highest level when she chooses. The subtleness of her skills is seen in her use of the classical sauces, in her use of the forgotten art of seasoning. A Savoy dinner last autumn, for example, yielded a small river-trout tart with cream, wine, herbs and nutmeg. The menu has celebrated its coming of age, and twenty dishes are marked as being either 'recent' or 'of earlier years': terrine of ham with nutmeg and green peppercorns, and sweetbreads in brown sauce with spinach, from the former; Peruvian duck and lamb en croûte from the latter. The style may lack fantasy, but in catering the real triumph is longevity. The wine list has many classed growths, but at least has financial breadth. House wine is from Cahors, at £10·90, but CELLARMAN'S CHOICE is Frascati at £4·85.

CHEF: S. Stevenson PROPRIETORS: S. and P. R. N. Stevenson
OPEN: all week, exc Thur and Fri L MEALS: 12 to 2, 7 to 9.30
PRICES: £22 (£31), Set L £12·50 (£14), Set D from £25 (£29) CARDS: Access, Amex, Visa
SEATS: 60. 6 tables outside. Private parties: 25 main room, 10 private room. Car-park, 30 places. Vegetarian meals. Children's helpings (L only). No children under 10 at D. Wheelchair access (4 steps; also WC)
ACCOMMODATION: 6 rooms, all with bath/shower. Rooms for disabled. B&B £47 to £62. Garden. TV. Phone. Scenic. Doors close at 12 [GHG]

HADLOW Kent   map 3

La Crémaillère [10/20]

The Square, Hadlow TN11 0DD
HADLOW (0732) 851489   £18

Michel Maillard cooks dependable French provincial dishes for a two hundred-year-old dining-room (plus a conservatory in summer). The menu takes in confit of duck, grilled lobster with fennel, and filet d'agneau dijonnaise. Vegetables are

---

The Guide *is independent, accepts no advertising and survives solely on the number of copies sold.*

---

served very hot in copper saucepans. Service is knowledgeable and pleasant. House red wine from the Ardèche is £5·80; alternatively, go for good value in the better Rhônes and Loires, for instance Lirac and Quincy.

CHEF/PROPRIETOR: M. Maillard
OPEN: Mon to Sat, exc Sat L MEALS: 12.30 to 1.30, 8 to 9
PRICES: Set L and D £12·80 (£18). Service 10%. Licensed, also bring your own: corkage £2
CARDS: Access, Amex, Visa
SEATS: 31. Private parties: 19 main room. Children welcome

HALIFAX West Yorkshire   map 5

▲ Holdsworth House [12/20]

Holdsworth, Halifax HX2 9TG
HALIFAX (0422) 240024   £16–£23

Holdsworth House, three miles north of Halifax, dates from 1435. It boasts a Grade I listed gazebo, a Grade II listed barn, heavy wood panelling, sumptuous rooms, open fires and antique furniture. The feel is of comfort, nostalgia and elegance. The menu is a French/English mix of diverse dishes, ranging from wild rabbit and pistachio pâté, with chunks of rabbit fillet surrounded by softer pâté and pistachios, to magret of duck with Marsala sauce with pleurottes and turned swede. Fish is a strength too: meaty poached brill fillet is served with a pistou sauce and garnished with green beans; envelope of salmon is filled with scallop mousse and served on braised lettuce with a dill sauce. Desserts are also elaborate, from marquise au chocolat with coffee-bean sauce to iced nougat in a brandy-snap basket. The wine list does more than justice to the classic French regions, and there are some gems among the mature clarets. The list would be worth a bottle award were it not for some of the mark-ups. House French is £6·95.

CHEF: Eric Claveau PROPRIETORS: The Pearson family
OPEN: all week, exc Sat L and Sun L CLOSED: Christmas and New Year MEALS: 12.30 to 1.30, 7.30 to 9.30
PRICES: £18 (£23), Set L from £12 (£16), Set D from £14 (£18). Service inc CARDS: Access, Amex, Diners, Visa
SEATS: 45. Private parties: 100 main room, 8, 10 and 14 private rooms. Car-park, 40 places. Children's helpings. No pipes in dining-room. Wheelchair acess (also WC)
ACCOMMODATION: 40 rooms, all with bath/shower. Rooms for disabled. B&B £43 to £63. Baby facilities. Pets welcome. Afternoon teas. Garden. Snooker. TV. Phone. Scenic. Doors close at 1. Confirm by 6 [GHG]

HAMBLETON Leicestershire   map 6

▲ Hambleton Hall [15/20]

Hambleton LE15 8TH
OAKHAM (0572) 56991
off A606, 3m SE of Oakham   ▮ £21–£34

Nicholas Gill has gone, and his former number two, Brian Baker, runs the kitchen and the seductive, wide-ranging, English-inspired menu. Amid the calm of an aristocratic household dressed in ruched curtains and gold-embossed frames, the pace and the style of meals have not changed. Extravagance takes the form of shellfish and unusual game in season. Dishes charm – melon is sliced thinly, like an orange, and arranged round a plate scattered with fruits – and sometimes vibrate with invention, as in the gravy for a roast woodcock that is spiked with the liver. Others, though, court affectation – Dublin Bay prawns served standing on their heads, or rice pudding done, unnecessarily, in nouvelle cuisine style. Dishes always look a treat even if the balancing of flavours is out of line. Recent additions have improved the choice of wines under £20, which leads to our restoration of the bottle symbol. The house claret is exemplary, and Graves, Ch. Rahoul '80, Jaboulet's Côtes du Rhône '82 and '83, and an '83 Hugel Alsace from the Sporen vineyard, are among the other less expensive delights. There is impeccable mature claret and burgundy for those who can afford it: Ch. Pichon-Longueville-Baron '61 at £75, Morey-St-Denis '78, from Dujac, at £33, and so on. The token Californian Chardonnay is a Clos du Val '83 at £15. CELLARMAN'S CHOICE: Haut-Médoc, Ch. Maucamps '81, at £14·50.

CHEF: Brian Baker PROPRIETORS: Timothy and Stefa Hart
OPEN: all week MEALS: 12 to 1.45, 7 to 9.30
PRICES: £28 (£34), Set L from £14·75 (£21), Set D from £24 (£30). Service inc   *XMAS BREAK*
CARDS: Access, Amex, Diners, Visa
SEATS: 60. Private parties: 45 main room, 20 private room. Car-park, 40 places. Vegetarian meals. Children's helpings. Smart dress preferred. Wheelchair access (also WC)
ACCOMMODATION: 15 rooms, all with bath/shower. Rooms for disabled. Lift B&B £60 to £120. Children welcome. Baby facilities. Afternoon teas. Garden. Tennis. Fishing. Golf. TV. Phone. Scenic. Doors close at 12.30 [GHG]

HARROGATE North Yorkshire   map 5

Drum and Monkey [12/20]

5 Montpellier Gardens, Harrogate HG1 2TF
HARROGATE (0423) 502650   £11–£19

'Freshness of product and simplicity of preparation', is the maxim of this well-established restaurant, long regarded as offering the best value in this conference town. There are two floors; downstairs is more casual, with marble-topped tables; upstairs has linen napery. As, seemingly, with all fish restaurants, it draws a number of complaints each year, but this may say more about national attitudes to fish (never popular) than the skills of the kitchen. The 'dry halibut' of one report contrasts with accounts of 'the best fish in Yorkshire'. Sole and lobster are mainstays, but all manner of fish appear, mostly sauced in traditional ways – with lemon and parsley butter, as a gratin, or florentine. Sweets are limited. Service copes admirably. The thirty wines are mostly white, starting at £4·95. CELLARMAN'S CHOICE: Muscadet, Coupe d'Or, from Louis Métaireau, £9·25.

CHEF: Patrick Laverack PROPRIETOR: William Fuller
OPEN: Mon to Sat CLOSED: Christmas to New Year MEALS: 12 to 2.30, 7 to 10.15
PRICES: L £7 (£11), D £12 (£19) CARDS: Access, Visa
SEATS: 48. Private parties: 8 main room. Children's helpings

Reports on good shops, hotels and cafes in your area are welcome.

▲ *Hodgson's, Russell Hotel* [12/20]

Valley Drive, Harrogate (0423) 509866
HARROGATE (0423) 509866   £16–£23

Valley Drive is a great, tree-lined sweep up one side of the Valley Gardens.
Hodgson's is one of the most professionally run hotels in the north of England,
though from the street little distinguishes it from anywhere else offering rooms.
The dining-room is panelled and dressed in rich red velvets, giving it the air of a
1930s provincial male club. The cooking is modern: up-to-date French plus the
vivid and detailed flavour contrasts typical of today's English cooking. A small,
home-baked loaf waits on each table. Pastry work is accomplished in such dishes
as asparagus parcels in hollandaise. Turbot is served as a whole young fish with a
beurre blanc; veal in breadcrumbs has a port and mushroom sauce. For garnish,
whole onions are baked, hollowed out, and filled with celeriac and diced French
beans. Amazing-sounding dishes, or elements of dishes, work surprisingly well,
for instance deep-fried orange rice balls served with a vanilla sauce, and the
elderflower and fennel sauce for the sea bass wrapped round a scallop. Staff know
what they are serving. The wine list finds plenty of interesting bottles, many of
them inexpensive: Dão from Portugal, Torres from Spain, and half a dozen
English wines. Burgundy and Bordeaux are well served, and Australia, New
Zealand and California bring flavours of late-picked Muscat, Shiraz and Zinfandel
to match the food. CELLARMAN'S CHOICE from New Zealand is Cook's Cabernet
Sauvignon '83 at £7·25.

CHEF: Richard Hodgson PROPRIETORS: Martin and Richard Hodgson
OPEN: Tue to Sat D MEALS: 7.30 to 10.30
PRICES: £17 (£23), Set D £11·50 (£16). Minimum £8·95 CARDS: Access, Amex, Carte
Blanche, Diners, Visa
SEATS: 75. Private parties: 30 main room, 12 private room. Vegetarian meals. No children
under 8. Jacket and tie preferred. No cigars/pipes in dining-room
ACCOMMODATION: 34 rooms, all with bath/shower. B&B £23·75 to £53·50. Baby facilities.
Pets welcome. Lift. TV. Phone. Confirm by 6 [GHG]

HARWICH Essex ✈   map 3

The Pier at Harwich [10/20]

The Quay, Harwich CO12 3HH
HARWICH (0255) 503363   £10–£24

Here are two restaurants: downstairs is fish and chips; upstairs, overlooking the
harbour, is a twenty-dish menu featuring Native oysters; hot-pot of smoked
haddock; and gateau of cod fillet sandwiched with crab-meat. The value is good,
service can be slow, but the thematic décor lends some atmosphere. The wines
complement the food: a good selection of whites includes inexpensive French

---

All letters to the Guide *are acknowledged.*

*'Reports that I have stopped cooking and have employed a new chef can safely be
discounted. I have merely lost 60 pounds in weight and this can lead to people thinking
the place has changed hands.'* (Welsh restaurateur)

---

country wines, and Chardonnays from California, Italy and Australia.
Chardonnay, Mildara, Merbein Church Hill '86, is £11·70 (£5·90 a half-bottle).
CELLARMAN'S CHOICE: Chardonnay di Appiano '85, from Alto-Adige, at £9·20.

CHEF: Chris Oakley PROPRIETOR: G. M. W. Milsom
OPEN: all week MEALS: 12 to 2, 6 to 9.30
PRICES: £16 (£24), Set L from £6·25 (£10). Service 10% CARDS: Access, Amex, Diners, Visa
SEATS: 80. Private parties: 85 main room, 50 private room. Car-park, 10 places. Children's
helpings. Wheelchair access (2 steps). Music

HASLEMERE Surrey map 3

Morels [15/20] ✕

25–27 Lower Street, Haslemere GU27 2NY
HASLEMERE (0428) 51462 £17–£27

Haslemere is an old-fashioned village. Even the banks are in eighteenth-century
houses. Morels has a bow-windowed frontage with hanging-baskets of flowers,
set on a raised pavement ten feet above the road. Jean-Yves Morel's menu is
modern French at its most classy. Classical ideas, such as blinis with smoked
salmon and caviare, mingle with more modern items: cheese and garlic soufflé in
a puddle of parsley sauce; warm salad of confit of duck with croûtons and
beetroot; duck cooked with honey and kumquats. The miniature selection of
desserts appears as a plate divided into four by lines of piped cream, with delicate
heaps of sliced strawberries and blackberries in the middle. In each quarter is a
different sweet: two strawberries dipped in caramel with a net of caramel
enclosing them; a pastry bowl of ice-cream and blackcurrants; hazelnut ice-
cream in apricot and raspberry sauce; a slice of chocolate marquise. The wine list
is exclusively French, apart from Spanish house red, Torres Coronas, at £7, and
there are plenty of half-bottles.

CHEF: Jean-Yves Morel PROPRIETORS: Jean-Yves and Mary Anne Morel
OPEN: Tue to Sun, exc Sat L and Sun D CLOSED: 3 weeks Feb, 2 weeks Sept MEALS: 12.30
to 1.45, 7 to 10
PRICES: £20 (£27), Set L £11 (£17), Set D £14 (£21) CARDS: Access, Amex, Diners, Visa
SEATS: 45. Private parties: 12 main room. Children's helpings. No pipes in dining-room.
Wheelchair access (1 step; also WC). Music

HASTINGLEIGH Kent map 3

▲ Woodmans Arms Auberge [12/20]

Hassell Street, Hastingleigh TN25 5JE
ELMSTED (023 375) 250 £20

This used to be a very weird pub in the middle of nowhere on top of the Wye
Downs. You walked in and felt that you had turned up as an uninvited guest at a
wedding. There was a large table in the middle of the room with hard chairs
arounds the walls, and beer by the glass was brought up from the cellars. Things

---

All inspections are carried out anonymously.

have changed since the Campions took over, and now on entering you are greeted with an exquisite smell of hyacinths. They have turned it into one of the most charming, secret, eccentric bed-and-breakfast places in the country. Susan cooks a no-choice, six-course dinner of enormous breadth. A January meal encompassed curried parsnip soup and pheasant en croûte with port and cream sauce, while in March there was a real French fish soup and a marmalade sorbet. Indeed, sweets stand out: lemon meringue pie, chocolate fondant with mocha sauce, hazelnut meringue with raspberry purée. The cooking justifies wines that are above the base line. CELLARMAN'S CHOICE: Ch. Paveil de Luze '82 at £14·50.

CHEF: Susan Campion PROPRIETORS: Susan and Gerald Campion
OPEN: all week, D only. L by arrangement CLOSED: 1 week before Easter, 2 weeks Sept
MEALS: 8
PRICES: Set D £15·50 (£20). Service inc
SEATS: 10. 3 tables outside. Private parties: 10 main room. Car-park, 6 places. No children under 12. No smoking in dining-room. One sitting
ACCOMMODATION: 3 rooms, all with bath/shower. Rooms for disabled. B&B £28·50 to £40. Deposit: 25%. No children under 12. No pets. Afternoon teas. Garden. TV. Scenic. Doors close at 12 [GHG]

HATFIELD Hertfordshire   map 3

The Salisbury [12/20]

15 The Broadway, Hatfield AL9 5JB
HATFIELD (070 72) 62220
in the Old Town   £15–£26

The Salisbury is a restaurant with aspirations – tables well spaced, fine china, impeccable presentation. The cooking makes its impact with complex combinations: duck with apple and cucumber; leek and avocado soup; monk and brill with rhubarb in pastry, with noodles on the side. The colours are of modern British cooking but the packaging is more French. Lunch is a relative bargain, at half the price of dinner. Campari sorbet features as both starter and dessert. The house claret opens an expensive list, at £8·20. An unusual section of Gascony wines offers some financial relief on an imbalanced list. CELLARMAN'S CHOICE: Madiran, Domaine de Pierron '83, £12·75.

CHEF/PROPRIETOR: Julian Waterer
OPEN: Tue to Sun, exc Sat L and Sun D MEALS: 12.30 to 2, 7.30 to 9.30
PRICES: £20 (£25), Set L from £9·75 (£15), Set D £21 (£26). Service inc CARDS: Access, Amex, Diners, Visa
SEATS: 55. Private parties: 50 main room, 28 private room. Car-park, 20 places. Vegetarian meals. Children's helpings (L only). Wheelchair access. Air-conditioned

The average price quoted in brackets is for an average three-course meal including service, VAT, coffee and half a bottle of house wine or the equivalent in an ethnic restaurant.

Anyone claiming to be from The Good Food Guide *is an impostor. Restaurateurs are advised to contact the office immediately if any fraudulent claims are made.*

HAWES North Yorkshire   map 7

▲ *Cockett's* [12/20] ⟨

Market Place, Hawes DL8 3RD
HAWES (096 97) 312   £16

Cherry Guest's cooking lights up this hotel high up in Wensleydale. She works
hard at dishes. A meal in March began with pasta stuffed with smoked haddock
and served with fennel sauce, then chicken breasts marinated in yoghurt and
ginger, served with brown, sugared parsnips; grilled aubergines topped with
cheese, and duchesse potatoes; and finally, home-made pear ice-cream with
kirsch. The extravagant scrawl of the menu contains much in the way of
adventure – Spanish pigeon with chocolate; sweetbreads with walnut and
chicory – as well as perennial favourites, like duck casserole. Many dishes are
priced as extra, above the set-meal cost. Breakfasts are plainer. The wine list is
similarly intriguing, and mostly anchored under £10. Hugel's trio of Alsace
wines is attractive. House claret is £6. CELLARMAN'S CHOICE: Ch. Latour
Seguy '82, £7·90.

CHEF: Cherry Guest PROPRIETORS: Mr and Mrs B. Guest
OPEN: all week, D only MEALS: 7.30 to 9.30
PRICES: Set D from £11·95 (£16) CARDS: Access, Visa
SEATS: 30. 4 tables outside. Private parties: 20 main room. Vegetarian meals. Children's
helpings. No children under 10. No pipes in dining-room. Music
ACCOMMODATION: 5 rooms, all with bath/shower. B&B £26 to £39·50. Baby facilities. Pets
by arrangement. Afternoon teas. Fishing. TV. Scenic. Doors close at 11.30. Confirm by 5

HAWORTH West Yorkshire   map 5

Weavers [10/20] ⟨

15 West Lane, Haworth BD22 8DU
HAWORTH (0535) 43822   £12–£19

A pair of converted weavers' cottages with appropriate memorabilia, an informal
style, and dishes such as Yorkshire pudding with gravy, cow pie, sticky toffee
pudding, and jam sponge with custard. The blackboard lists special dishes
midweek, but spinach and Feta cheese pastry, loin of pork with Wensleydale
cheese, and rabbit and pigeon pie, are regular features. The short wine list
concentrates on sound, inexpensive bottles. CELLARMAN'S CHOICE: Mâcon-
Villages, Château de Mirande '85, £8·50.

CHEFS/PROPRIETORS: Colin and Jane Rushworth
OPEN: Tue to Sat D, and Sun L CLOSED: 19 June for 3 weeks, 1 week at Christmas, and Sun
July, Aug, Sept, Jan and Feb MEALS: 12.30 to 1.30, 7 to 9.30
PRICES: £13 (£19), Set L £7·95 (£12), Set D from £7·95 (£13) CARDS: Access, Amex,
Diners, Visa
SEATS: 60. Private parties: 14 main room, 14 private room. Vegetarian meals. Children's
helpings. Smart dress preferred. Music. Air-conditioned

*Restaurants that we have not been able to assess as fully as we would like are given a
zero rating this year. We are particularly keen to have reports on these places.*

HAYDON BRIDGE Northumberland   map 7

General Havelock Inn [10/20]

Radcliffe Road, Haydon Bridge NE47 6ER
HAYDON BRIDGE (043 484) 376   £9–£18

The merits of the old inn by the Tyne are the unpretentious atmosphere and the
reliable, plain English cooking with some embellishments. Good fish, bread, pies
and roasts feature strongly. The sweets are for lovers of cream and richness.
Angela Clyde does all the cooking and keeps standards consistent – at lunch-time
even doing the serving as well. The beer is Tetleys, and the house wine £2·95 for
a half-litre.

CHEF: Angela Clyde PROPRIETORS: Ian and Angela Clyde
OPEN: Wed to Sun, exc Sun D CLOSED: first 2 weeks Jan, last week Aug, first week Sept
MEALS: 12 to 1.30, 7.30 to 9
PRICES: Set L from £5 (£9), Set D from £12·50 (£18)
SEATS: 28. 4 tables outside. Private parties: 30 main room. Car-park, 12 places. Vegetarian
meals. Children's helpings. Wheelchair access (1 step; also WC)

HELFORD Cornwall   map 1

▲ *Riverside* [new owners, zero rated]

Helford TR12 6JU
MANACCAN (032 623) 443   £29

Once great, under George Perry-Smith and Heather Crosbie, this restaurant has
been sold, but the new owners have made a creditable attempt at carrying on.
The setting overlooking the creek remains, of course, the same, so too does the
style of cooking – still very much in the Elizabeth David mould: excellent
Provençal fish soup, guinea-fowl with rosemary, even St Emilion au chocolat.
Peter Todd and Sandro Malnati both worked with Perry-Smith the summer
before the handover and every effort seems to have been made to preserve a
successful format. Fish has been particularly well chosen and can veer towards
nouvelle, as in monkfish with lobster sauce. The wine list is long, with little under
£10, but strong on half-bottles. More reports, please.

CHEFS: Sandro Malnati and Peter Todd PROPRIETOR: Susan Darrell
OPEN: all week, D only CLOSED: Nov to early Mar MEALS: 7.30 to 9.30
PRICES: Set D £24 (£29). Service inc
SEATS: 36. Private parties: 20 main room. Vegetarian meals. No children under 10.
Wheelchair access (also WC)
ACCOMMODATION: 7 rooms, all with bath/shower. Rooms for disabled. B&B £69 to £75.
Garden. TV. Scenic

*Files are kept on every restaurant, so reports of poor meals are just as valuable as
reports of good meals because they save unnecessary inspections.*

The Guide *recruits new inspectors from readers who write in regularly. If you would
like to apply, write to the editor with (a) a detailed report on a restaurant where you
have eaten and (b) a comparative study of restaurants known to you.*

HERSTMONCEUX East Sussex   map 3

Sundial   [11/20]

Gardner Street, Herstmonceux BN27 4LA
HERSTMONCEUX (0323) 832217   £19–£29

For twenty years the Bertolis' smart French/Italian restaurant has held its own in
the district. The menu is a long tour de force, augmented by a handsome display
of produce and sweets on a central table. Some of the cooking is needlessly
ornate. It is at its best when simple – most obviously, the excellent fish – or when
it is rendering some classical, rarely found dish, such as roast partridge, sauce
smitane. The wine list is an aristocrat, having been built up over many years –
there is superb claret and burgundy – but alas, very highly priced, with few
concessions under £10. House Bergerac £7·95.

CHEF: Guiseppe Bertoli PROPRIETORS: Laurette and Guiseppe Bertoli
OPEN: Tue to Sun, exc Sun D CLOSED: mid-Aug to Sept, 25 Dec to 20 Jan MEALS: 12.30 to
2.30, 7.30 to 9.30 (10 Sat)
PRICES: £19 (£29). Set L from £12·50 (£19), Set D £17·50 (£24). Service 10%
CARDS: Amex, Diners, Visa
SEATS: 70. 8 tables outside. Private parties: 50 main room, 22 private room. Car-park,
25 places. Vegetarian meals. Children's helpings. No smoking in dining-room. Wheelchair
access (also WC). Music

HETTON North Yorkshire   map 5

Angel Inn   [11/20] ✈

Hetton BD23 6LT
CRACOE (075 673) 263   £12–£16

The Angel is part of North Yorkshire mythology, keeping up standards of real
ales and real foods. The extended building reflects the extension of the menu
beyond good-value bar meals. Notable are the massive display of cold hors
d'oeuvre, served with home-made mayonnaise, and the unusually good supplies
of fish. Otherwise, Denis Watkins balances the style of the menu between sausage
and chips and langoustines. Both avenues lead to sticky-toffee pudding. The
cooking has, however, become increasingly elaborate: breast of guinea-fowl, for
example, has been placed on a mousseline of crab, folded over in foil (slashed to
reveal the skin), then roasted for twelve minutes and sliced on to a lobster sauce.
Fish and meat combinations are common, as are other, equally provocative,
pairings. A hotch-potch of wines, plus Younger's and Theakston's beers.
CELLARMAN'S CHOICE: Blauburgunder, Schloss Gobelsburg '79, £6·95.

CHEF: Denis Watkins PROPRIETORS: Denis and Juliet Watkins
OPEN: Mon to Sat D, and Sun L CLOSED: 1 Jan MEALS: 12.15 to 2, 7 to 9.30
PRICES: Set L £7·75 (£12), Set D £11·95 (£16), Snacks from £1·35 CARD: Access
SEATS: 36. Private parties: 40 main room. Car-park, 17 places. Children's helpings (L only).
Smart dress preferred. No pipes in dining-room. Wheelchair access (also WC). Music

Restaurants change owners and chefs constantly. Please help keep the Guide *informed
of any changes you find.*

HILDENBOROUGH Kent
map 3

Gate Inn [10/20]

Rings Hill, Hildenborough TN11 8LX
HILDENBOROUGH (0732) 832103   £18

This old pub operates as a fish restaurant, serving 'very simple cooking, to stress
the "fresh" aspect,' as Mr Sankey explains. Hence: langoustines with
mayonnaise or garlic butter; soft shell crabs; good Dover sole; smoked salmon.
Fish soup includes mullet, conger and John Dory and is served with Gruyère and
a rouille. All dishes arrive with bread and butter. House Blanc de Blancs £4·75.
CELLARMAN'S CHOICE: Chardonnay, Monterey County '85, from Masson, £7.

CHEF: Alerterio Lizzi PROPRIETOR: Guy Sankey
OPEN: Mon to Sat CLOSED: bank hols MEALS: 12 to 1.30, 7 to 10
PRICES: £14 (£18) CARDS: Amex, Visa
SEATS: 40. 6 tables outside. Private parties: 8 main room, 14 private room. Car-park,
40 places. Vegetarian meals. Children's helpings. Wheelchair access

HINTLESHAM Suffolk
map 3

▲ Hintlesham Hall [14/20] ❧

Hintlesham IP8 3NS
HINTLESHAM (047 387) 268
on A1071 W of Ipswich   £17–£30

In August the pale lemon of the building matches the surrounding dirty cream of
the corn fields. Catering's most dangerous bend leads into the grounds of an
impressive double-winged Tudor house. Although the bones of the hall are clad
in Georgian finery, lift the petticoats and the Tudor oak framework stands
revealed. All Robert Carrier's theatrical decorations have been replaced by gentle
pastels and great slashes of Liberty-style prints. The menu reads well and
fashionably: grilled turbot with chive-butter sauce; fillet of lamb on spinach with
saffron sauce. Dishes are pretty and correct – courgette flower is stuffed with
chicken mousse and served with a cream sauce; chicken breast sits on home-
made noodles with a crayfish-flavoured sauce – but are sometimes short on
power. Sweets draw the most praise – tart summer pudding soufflé: banana in a
paper packet. Details, for instance the breads, the choice of coffees, the breakfasts,
are all of a high standard, as is the service from a young, dedicated crew, though
it can be badly stretched on Saturdays. An impressive wine list comes with good
annotation and recommendations, although mark-ups can be high.
CELLARMAN'S CHOICE: Mâcon-Villages, Domaine de la Bon Gran '83, £15·20.

*'We still find it difficult to recruit good waiting staff. There just doesn't seem to be the
same enthusiasm for waiting as there is for the kitchen.'* (West Country restaurateur)

*'We sat in the windowed lean-to extension where it was icy. The fan heater helped until
the waiter tripped over it and it blew up. Then the manager went outside with a roll of
Sellotape and stuck up all the joins and cracks except the floor join through which the
icy blast was mainly blowing.'* (On eating in London)

CHEF: Robert Mabey PROPRIETORS: Ruth and David Watson
OPEN: all week, exc Sat L MEALS: 12 to 1.45, 7 to 9.15
PRICES: £25 (£30), Set L £13.95 (£17), Set D £23 (£26), Snacks from £1·70. Service inc
CARDS: Access, Amex, Diners, Visa
SEATS: 75. 10 tables outside. Private parties: 40 main room, 100 private room.Car-park, 50
places. Vegetarian meals. Children by arrangement. Smart dress preferred. No cigars/pipes
in dining-room. Wheelchair access
ACCOMMODATION: 17 rooms, all with bath/shower. B&B £50 to £130. Deposit: one night's
stay. Children by arrangement. Pets by arrangement. Garden. Tennis. Golf. Snooker. TV.
Phone. Scenic. Doors close at 1 [GHG]

HINTON CHARTERHOUSE Avon   map 2

▲ *Homewood Park* [14/20]

Hinton Charterhouse, BA3 6BB
LIMPLEY STOKE (022 122) 3731
off A36, 5½m S of Bath   £20–£24

The setting is utterly English: this is the abbot's house of the ruined thirteenth-
century Hinton Priory, surrounded by ten acres of grounds, complete with
croquet hoops on the lawn. Inside there are real fires and fresh flowers
everywhere, and the rooms have been redecorated in shades of apricot and blue.
Stephen Ross's cooking succeeds by using top-quality ingredients in ways that
are true to the spirit of modern British cooking. Minced venison comes with a
sweet-and-sour leek sauce; warm spiced sweetbreads are served on a salad of
lettuces with pine-kernel dressing; roast duckling with lentils and smoked bacon
is a refined British cousin of cassoulet. Fish is well reported, from hot crab in
pastry to Cornish plaice with tomatoes and mussels. Otherwise the menu steers
its way from hot tart of quails' eggs with leeks and saffron, through stuffed loin of
veal in pastry, to warm winter fruit salad. A good French list is helped along with
a spread from California, including Phelps' Rieslings and a short but to-the-point
Spanish section.

CHEF: Stephen Ross PROPRIETORS: Penny and Stephen Ross
OPEN: all week CLOSED: 2 weeks from 23 Dec MEALS: 12 to 1.30 (2 Sun), 7 to 9.30
(8.30 Sun)
PRICES: Set L £14·50 (£20), Set D from £18·50 (£24). Service inc CARDS: Access, Amex,
Diners, Visa
SEATS: 50. 3 tables outside. Private parties: 36 main room, 12 and 25 private rooms.
Car-park, 30 places. Children's helpings by arrangement. No smoking in dining-room.
Wheelchair access (also WC)
ACCOMMODATION: 15 rooms, all with bath/shower. Rooms for disabled. B&B £40 to £100.
Afternoon teas. Garden. Tennis. TV. Phone. Scenic. Doors close at 12 [GHG]

HOCKLEY HEATH West Midlands   map 5

▲ *Nuthurst Grange Hotel* [new entry, zero rated]

Nuthurst Grange Lane, Hockley Heath B94 5NL
LAPWORTH (056 43) 3972   £17–£26

The Randolphs moved here from their *Guide* restaurant, Randolph's, in Warwick,
and have spent months turning this private residence into a country-house hotel.

There are marvellous views from the patio over the seven and a half acres of grounds, complete with croquet lawn. The restaurant is the hub. A fixed-price menu moves through feuilleté of asparagus with chervil sauce, fillet of lamb on a croûton with garlic and redcurrant glaze, and white and dark chocolate mousse in a cage of spun sugar. Baby vegetables are outstanding. David Randolph still hangs his Herefordshire beef for three weeks, before serving it as a roast fillet dipped in herbs with a Fleurie sauce. Mrs Randolph is out front, as charming as ever. The hundred-strong wine list is intelligently chosen and well introduced; the house selections offer good-value drinking for under £10. More reports, please.

CHEF: David Randolph PROPRIETORS: Mr and Mrs David Randolph
OPEN: all week, exc Sat L and Sun D MEALS: 12.30 to 2, 7 to 9.30
PRICES: Set L £11·50 (£17), Set D £19·50 (£26) CARDS: Access, Amex, Visa
SEATS: 60. 5 tables outside. Private parties: 30 main room, 25 private room. Car-park, 40 places. Wheelchair access (1 step)
ACCOMMODATION: 8 rooms, all with bath/shower. B&B £55 to £105. Afternoon teas. Garden. TV. Phone. Scenic. Doors close at 12

HOLDENBY Northamptonshire

map 2

▲ *Lynton House* [new entry, zero rated]

The Croft, Holdenby NN6 8DJ
HOLDENBY (0604) 770777

£15–£22

Carlo and Carol Bertozzi, after ten years on the canalside at the Butty at Stoke Bruerne, have moved to this old, red-brick rectory with views across rolling countryside from both bar and dining-room. After a decade, the Italian menu shows commendable signs of life, bringing in regional dishes alongside the antipasto. Here we have much-praised brodetto, risotto, monkfish with pesto, freshly made and cooked tortelloni, and excellent crème brûlée with cherries. Of the fifty wines, thirty are Italian and – compared with the French bottles – priced to encourage drinking. House Sicilian Corvo is £7·95. CELLARMAN'S CHOICE: Aglianico del Vulture, £12·75.

CHEFS: Carol Bertozzi and Roger Jones PROPRIETORS: Carlo and Carol Bertozzi
OPEN: all week, exc Mon L, Sat L and Sun D MEALS: 12.15 to 1.45, 7.15 to 9.45
PRICES: £17 (£22), Set L £9·50 (£15), Set D £14·50 (£20). Minimum £14. Service inc
CARDS: Access, Visa
SEATS: 45. 4 tables outside. Private parties: 55 main room, 20 private room. Car-park, 30 places. Vegetarian meals. Children's helpings (L only). No children under 8. Smart dress preferred. No smoking during meals. Wheelchair access
ACCOMMODATION: 5 rooms, all with bath/shower. B&B £48 to £70. Deposit: £20. No children under 8. Afternoon teas. TV. Phone. Scenic. Doors close at 12.30. Confirm by 9

[GHG] *after the details of an entry means that the establishment is also included in* The Good Hotel Guide.

The entries are compiled from the views of readers who have eaten at the restaurants in the last year, backed up by anonymous inspections and by information supplied and facts verified by the restaurants.

HOOK Hampshire   map 2

Whitewater House   [11/20]

Hook RG27 9EH
HOOK (025 672) 2436   £24–£32
1m E of Hook on A30

The mill provides a near-perfect setting, with only its battered, irregular roof testifying to its former use; it is now gentrified with beautiful gardens and maze. Its beams and rafters are have been exposed, cleaned, and some varnished. In the dining-room, one wall is covered with a massive wall carpet, the other by a stone fireplace with a detailed, carved wooden surround. The monthly, handwritten, all French *carte* is augmented with dishes of the day; during the week there are only bar meals at lunchtime, offering the setting without the cost. The style mixes modern cooking, for instance pot-roast pheasant with calvados and apples, with more familiar, conservative choices, like avocado and prawns. Good sweets include crème brûlée and the Pavlova. House French is £7·50 and the cellar also supplies a new off-licence business.

CHEF/PROPRIETOR: Vanessa Hoare
OPEN: Tue to Sun, exc Sun D   CLOSED: 1 week at Christmas, bank hols   MEALS: 12.30 to 2.30, 7.30 to 9.30
PRICES: £23 (£32), Set L £16 (£24), Snacks from £2·90   CARDS: Access, Amex, Diners, Visa
SEATS: 40. 12 tables outside. Private parties: 50 main room, 14 private room. Car-park, 80 places. Children at Sun L only. Smart dress preferred. Wheelchair access

---

HORTON Northamptonshire   map 3

French Partridge   [13/20]

Horton NN7 2AP
NORTHAMPTON (0604) 870033   £19

After more than twenty years in the *Guide*, the Partridge remains as good value as ever. The impressive, French-style barn by the main road offers four courses of French-inspired food paired with an immaculate wine list. David Partridge combines traditional home cooking with modern inventions, without showing off. A meal in December featured smoked salmon tart, pheasant with port in pastry with fresh, lightly done vegetables, and a grand finale of a three-chocolate dessert. Other highly praised dishes have been fish sausage in chive and butter sauce; osso buco; chicken in mint sauce; and a biscuit tulip filled with fresh fruit and creme pâtissière. The splendid French wine list is good value, encouraging classy drinking at nominal prices. Many restaurants could learn a thing or two from this burgundy section, and there are inexpensive bottles from south-west France, as well as good Germans, and a brace of New Zealand Chardonnays at under £10.

CHEFS: D. C. Partridge and Justin Partridge   PROPRIETORS: D. C. Partridge and M. Partridge
OPEN: Tue to Sat, D only   CLOSED: 2 weeks at Christmas and Easter, 3 weeks July to Aug
MEALS: 7.30 to 9
PRICES: Set D £16 (£19). Service inc
SEATS: 50. Private parties: 10 main room. Car-park, 50 places. Children welcome. Wheelchair access (also WC)

HUDDERSFIELD West Yorkshire   map 5

Pisces [new entry, zero rated]

84 Fitzwilliam Street, Huddersfield HD1 5BD
HUDDERSFIELD (0484) 516773   £8–£13

The inside of this creditable fish restaurant, in the cellar of a converted
warehouse close to the station, has been given a lavish facelift: varnished pine
floors, stained-glass windows, pink marble-topped tables. France is the
inspiration: hot mousse of red mullet is a sandcastle surrounded by a pool of
creamy butter sauce speckled with dill; poached monkfish is dressed with thin
slices of Parma ham; paupiettes of sole in pastry come with crab sauce. Meat
eaters are offered steak or lamb cutlets with sorrel sauce. To finish there are fruity
tarts or orange mousse decorated with kumquats. Ingredients are good, fish is
from the market, and the owners say that everything is home made – apart from
the bread, which comes from the local bakers. Cheaper meals and snacks at
lunchtime. The short well-described wine list has plenty of whites. CELLARMAN'S
CHOICE: Sancerre, Les Paradis '85, £11·95. More reports, please.

CHEF: Serge Nollent PROPRIETORS: T. Y. and S. J. Wormald
OPEN: Mon to Sat MEALS: 12 to 2, 7 to 9.30 PRICES: Set L from £3·95 (£8),
Set D £8·95 (£13), Snacks from 85p CARDS: Access, Amex, Visa
SEATS: 50. Private parties: 50 main room. Car-park, 10 places. Children welcome. Smart
dress preferred. Wheelchair access. Music. Air-conditioned

HURSTBOURNE TARRANT Hampshire   map 2

▲ *Esseborne Manor* [12/20]

Hurstbourne Tarrant SP11 0ER
HURSTBOURNE TARRANT (026 476) 444
on A343,'1½m N of Hurstbourne Tarrant   £24

The setting, the service and the décor are all first class. The menu is surprisingly
strident and inclined to take risks, but at the best has a strong vein of tradition
running through it, as in rabbit and apricot pie or jugged hare. Game features
strongly: partridge with its gravy flavoured with orange; pheasant with calvados
and apples. The English cheeses are outstanding. The wine list strives valiantly to
find good-value wines across France and focuses strongly on the £10 mark.
House vin de pays des Pyrénées is £6·65. CELLARMAN'S CHOICE: Savennières,
Clos du Papillon '85, £8·85.

CHEFS: Peter Birnie and Belinda Watson PROPRIETORS: Peter Birnie and Philip Harris
OPEN: Mon to Sat, exc Sat L CLOSED: 2 weeks at Christmas MEALS: 12 to 2, 7.30 to 9.30
PRICES: £15 (£24) CARDS: Access, Amex, Diners, Visa
SEATS: 30. 3 tables outside. Private parties: 34 main room. Car-park, 20 places. Children's
helpings. Smart dress preferred. Wheelchair access (also WC). Music
ACCOMMODATION: 12 rooms, all with bath/shower. Rooms for disabled. B&B £45 to £65.
No children under 10. Afternoon teas. Garden. Tennis. TV. Phone. Scenic. Doors close
at 12 [GHG]

It is helpful if restaurateurs keep the office up to date with any changes.

ILFORD Essex map 3

Da Umberto [11/20]

361 Ley Street, Ilford IG1 4AA
01-553 5763 £18

A quiet, family-run trattoria with a good line in fish: mussels, sea bass, John
Dory, poached skate with butter and capers. Pasta and puddings are carefully
done, and there are blackboard additions to the regular run of steak, veal and
chicken. There is a lot of garlic. Good Italian wines, including Masi and Bersano,
are kept precariously above the door. CELLARMAN'S CHOICE: Chardonnay,
Buchholz '86, £6·40.

CHEF: Umberto Medaglia PROPRIETORS: Umberto and J. A. Medaglia
OPEN: Mon to Sat, exc Sat L CLOSED: Aug MEALS: 12 to 2.30, 6.30 to 11.30
PRICES: £11 (£18). Cover 50p. Service 12% CARDS: Access, Visa
SEATS: 38. Vegetarian meals. Children's helpings. Wheelchair access (1 step). Music.
Air-conditioned

ILKLEY West Yorkshire map 5

Box Tree [15/20]

29 Church Street, Ilkley LS29 9DR
ILKLEY (0943) 608484 £17–£34

A change of ownership does not appear to have interrupted the Box Tree's
sonata. Here is still Yorkshire's finest dining-room – cluttered with frames and
fine Wedgwood – and boasting a menu that ought to be across the Channel. A
hint of self-mockery creeps into the atmosphere, though not Edward Denny's
cooking, which is exact. Fish is outstanding: a gratin of langoustines comes just
sharpened with a little Stilton in the cream and wine sauce. A second course
takes the shape of a hot goats' cheese salad or a wild mushroom soup before, in
May, milk-fed lamb noisettes with rosemary, or poached halibut served with a
wine and cream sauce and oysters. Twenty regular dishes offer a genuine choice
that also extends into the desserts. The Box Tree strawberry tuile with its
rosewater sorbet remains a classic restaurant dish, but also there can be hot
strawberry tart with a champagne sabayon. Sunday lunch is a new feature.
Alcohols match the menu. The house cocktail is champagne, eau de vie and
raspberry purée, and the house burgundy is £8·95; from there the list soars into
goodish wines from most areas at goodish prices.

CHEF: Edward Denny PROPRIETOR: Eric Kyte
OPEN: Tue to Sat D, and Sun L CLOSED: 25 and 26 Dec, 1 Jan MEALS: 12.30 to 2,
7.30 to 9.45
PRICES: £24 (£34), Set Sun L £11·75 (£17), Set D £14·95 (£26) CARDS: Access, Amex,
Diners, Visa
SEATS: 50. Private parties: 30 main room, 16 private room. Children welcome. Smart dress
preferred. No cigars/pipes in dining-room. Wheelchair access

Restaurants change owners and chefs constantly. Please help keep the Guide *informed
of any changes you find.*

Olive Tree [11/20]

31 Church Street, Ilkley LS29 9DR
ILKLEY (0943) 601481   £14–£16

After a shaky patch at the end of 1986, due to the setting up of a new branch (see Leeds), this convivial Greek restaurant appears to be back on form. The kebabs, in particular, are excellent; lamb is charcoal-grilled and laid on pitta bread; the seafood selection of a huge king prawn, a fresh sardine and pieces of swordfish is skewered with bay leaves, courgette and lemon slices. Good savoury rice accompanies. Psarosouppa is a peasant-style fish broth. The quality of the meze – much better value than the *carte* – shows in the creamy melintzanosalata, the hummus, and the crispy triangles of Feta cheese and mint in pastry. Pastries and potent Greek coffee to finish. Tuesday evenings take in singing and dancing. Inexpensive Greek wines start at £5·95.

CHEF: George Psarias PROPRIETORS: George and Vasoulla Psarias
OPEN: all week, D only MEALS: 6.30 to 12
PRICES: £11 (£16), Set D £9·50 (£14). Service 10% CARDS: Access, Visa
SEATS: 90. Private parties: 90 main room, 20 and 35 private rooms. Vegetarian meals. Children's helpings. No-smoking area. Wheelchair access. Music. Air-conditioned

---

IPSWICH Suffolk   map 3

Kwok's Rendezvous [10/20] ✗

23 St Nicholas Street, Ipswich IP1 1TW
IPSWICH (0473) 56833   £11–£14

Still the most reliable Chinese restaurant in the area. The cooking centres on Peking with, fashionably, some Hunan and Szechuan dishes for good measure. Fish from the East Anglia coast features strongly: prawns with crispy rice; drunken fish. Ever popular are deep-fried shredded beef with chilli, diced chicken in yellow-bean sauce, and General Tseng's chicken. Décor is smart and service agreeable. House wine £5·50.

CHEF: Thomas Kwok PROPRIETORS: Lucia and Thomas Kwok
OPEN: Mon to Sat MEALS: 12 to 2, 7 to 10.45
PRICES: £7 (£14), Set L from £6·50 (£11), Set D from £9·50 (£13). Minimum £7·50 at D. Service 10% CARDS: Amex, Diners
SEATS: 50. Private parties: 30 main room. Car-park, 50 places. Vegetarian meals. Children welcome. Smart dress preferred. Wheelchair access (also WC). Music

---

Singing Chef [11/20]

200 St Helens Street, Ipswich IP4 2RH
IPSWICH (0473) 55236   £14–£19

Kenneth Toyé matches regional French food with French wines in his long-serving restaurant. From Provence comes soupe de poisson; from Normandy poulet vallée d'Auge and stuffed shoulder of lamb braised in cider; from the Loire pork with prunes and real mutton persillé with caper sauce. Cheeses are French and sweets take in chocolate pots and pears in red wine. Set bistro-style lunches can be booked. The wine list has twenty-six champagnes from single-vineyard owners. CELLARMAN'S CHOICE: Reuilly vin gris '85 at £9·85; there is also Normandy cider.

CHEFS: Kenneth and Jeannine Toyé PROPRIETORS: Cynthia and Kenneth Toyé
OPEN: Tue to Sat D MEALS: 7 to 11
PRICES: £13 (£19), Set D £9 (£14) CARDS: Access, Diners, Visa
SEATS: 35. 4 tables outside. Private parties: 20 main room, 15 and 20 private rooms.
Vegetarian meals. Children's helpings. No-smoking area. Wheelchair access
(also WC). Music

ISLE OF WIGHT ⠀⠀⠀⠀⠀⠀⠀⠀⠀⠀⠀⠀⠀⠀⠀⠀⠀⠀⠀⠀⠀⠀ map 2

▲ *Seaview Hotel* [new entry, zero rated]

High Street, Seaview, Isle of Wight PO34 5EX
ISLE OF WIGHT (0983) 612711 ⠀⠀⠀⠀⠀⠀⠀⠀⠀⠀⠀⠀⠀⠀⠀⠀ £12–£18

This rambling, narrow-fronted, family-run hotel is full of winding corridors and creaking floorboards. A secluded beach is close by and the lounge looks out to sea. 'An excellent place to flop in and eat well.' The cooking is homely, from thick celery soup and rough pork terrine with sharp redcurrant sauce, through to meringue and bread-and-butter pudding. Local plaice is plainly cooked in butter, and fish puff is a pastry parcel filled with chopped scallops and mushrooms, with a crab and cheese sauce. Fifty wines include Latour burgundy, Australian Chardonnay, and the island's Adgestone. House French is £5·20 a bottle. More reports, please.

CHEFS: Nicola Hayward and Stephen King PROPRIETORS: Mr and Mrs Hayward
OPEN: all week, exc Sun D MEALS: 1 to 1.45, 7.30 to 9.30
PRICES: £13 (£18), Set L £7·50 (£12), Set D £9·50 (£14), Snacks from £1 CARDS: Access,
Amex, Visa
SEATS: 30. 10 tables outside. Private parties: 30 main room, 50 private room. Car-park,
12 places. Vegetarian meals. Children's helpings. No children under 3. Smart dress
preferred. No pipes in dining-room. Wheelchair access (also WC)
ACCOMMODATION: 14 rooms, 12 with bath/shower. B&B £25 to £42. Children welcome.
Baby facilities. Pets welcome. Afternoon teas. TV. Scenic [GHG]

IXWORTH Suffolk ⠀⠀⠀⠀⠀⠀⠀⠀⠀⠀⠀⠀⠀⠀⠀⠀⠀⠀⠀⠀⠀⠀⠀ map 6

Theobalds [12/20]

68 High Street, Ixworth IP31 2HJ
PAKENHAM (0359) 31707 ⠀⠀⠀⠀⠀⠀⠀⠀⠀⠀⠀⠀⠀⠀⠀⠀⠀⠀ £13–£23

Simon Theobald's style of cooking in the converted shop on the high street is beginning to crystallise. Rumours of a sale have been put aside, and the restaurant is now open for lunch. The menu is in English and though the regional French inspiration that drew him into cooking thirteen years ago is apparent, this is another example of a kitchen moving headily into modern British. The spring menu has leek and cockerel soup; mussels have been poached

---

Please keep the Guide informed of any changes to the restaurants listed. Report forms are at the back of the book.

and served on pasta tossed in tomato, garlic and basil. What could be more English than baked wing of skate on a bed of shallots, in a butter sauce flavoured with anchovies and English mustard? Or the excellent fillet of hare in a red wine and blackcurrant sauce, in February? The pointing up of flavours and three dimensional seasoning is typical; venison, for instance, served with redcurrant jelly in a port and cinnamon sauce, brings together centuries of non-Gallic tastes. There are good cheeses, both French and English, and cosmopolitan sweets: French apple flan; New York cheesecake. Respectable wines start with house Rhône at £6·75. CELLARMAN'S CHOICE: Graves, Ch. Respide Médeville '83, £14·90.

CHEF: Simon Theobald PROPRIETORS: Simon and Geraldine Theobald
OPEN: all week, exc Mon and Sat L, and Sun D MEALS: 12.15 to 2, 7.30 to 10
PRICES: Set L from £8·50 (£13), Set D £13·50 (£19) to £17·50 (£23) CARDS: Access, Visa
SEATS: 36. 2 tables outside. Private parties: 36 main room. Children's helpings (Sun L only). No children under 8. No-smoking area. Music

---

JEVINGTON East Sussex   map 3

▲ *Hungry Monk* [10/20]

Jevington BM26 5QF
POLEGATE (032 12) 2178
on B2105, between Polegate and Friston   ▮ £18–£19

1987 marked the Monk's twentieth year under Nigel and Sue Mackenzie, still with the same chef, Ian Dowding. During that time it has been known as one of the best restaurants in Sussex. The team's five cookery books have sold over a quarter of a million copies and spawned twice-weekly cookery demonstrations. The warm salad of quail and quail eggs shows that time has not stood still, but the menu relies equally on beef Wellington, and rack of English lamb with cream and garlic sauce. Ideas are assimilated gradually, resulting in hot crab tart with pimento sauce; or breast of chicken stuffed with scallops, with a Choron sauce. Banoffi pie heads the puddings. The cellar keeps up to date with vintages – Beaujolais, and Old Triangle Riesling from Australia, are both 1986 – but still stocks mature claret, as well as lesser-known, but affordable, bottles: Ch. Méaume '82; local Berwick Glebe '85 (one of half a dozen English wines); Chardonnay di Appiano from northern Italy, all under £10. There are nearly thirty half-bottles. CELLARMAN'S CHOICE: Quincy, Domaine de la Maison Blanche '86, £9·02.

CHEFS: Ian Dowding and Kent Austin PROPRIETORS: Nigel and Susan Mackenzie
OPEN: all week, D only, and Sun L MEALS: 12.15 to 2.30, 7.15 to 10.30
PRICES: Set L from £12 (£18), Set D from £13 (£19)
SEATS: 36. 2 tables outside. Private parties: 36 main room, 16 private room. Car-park, 17 places. Vegetarian meals. Children's helpings. No children under 3. Smart dress preferred. No cigars in dining-room. Music
ACCOMMODATION: 1 room, with bath/shower. B&B £30 to £40. No children under 3. TV. Scenic. Doors close at 1

All details are as accurate as possible at the time of going to press. Please notify the Guide office of any changes.

KENDAL Cumbria
map 7

The Moon [10/20]

129 Highgate, Kendal LA9 4EN
KENDAL (0539) 29254
£12

Val Macconnell's slightly cramped, 1950s-style bistro is a former greengrocer's
shop, now done out in eye-catching shades of deep red. The cooking has a
vegetarian bias, but there are meat and fish dishes as well. Everything is home
made, from the garlicky hummus, and asparagus mousse, to rich lamb and
aubergine curry, or beef braised in brandy with walnuts. Vegetables are good
and fresh. The place has a buzzy, informal atmosphere. No bookings are
accepted, but the turnover is fast. Wines are basic, and there's usually a slightly
better wine of the week, for instance, Shiraz, Hill Smith '84, at £5·75.

CHEFS: Dianne Kinsey, Sharon Moreton and Val Macconnell PROPRIETOR: Val Macconnell
OPEN: all week, D only MEALS: 6 to 10 (11 Fri and Sat)
PRICES: £6 (£12) CARDS: Access, Visa
SEATS: 40. Vegetarian meals. Children's helpings. Music

KENILWORTH Warwickshire
map 2

Portofino [10/20]

14 Talisman Square, Kenilworth CV8 1JB
KENILWORTH (0926) 57186
£10–£18

The most useful trattoria in Kenilworth is handily situated in the modern
shopping centre. The menu makes familiar reading, from minestrone, home-
made cannelloni and osso buco, to bistecca pizzaiola and sogliola alla mugnaia.
Other good dishes are aubergine parmigiano and trout with lemon sauce and
capers, plus daily specials. House red and white – Sangiovese and Trebbiano –
£5·95.

CHEFS: Vito Ferro and Maurizio Torckia PROPRIETORS: Michele and Vito Ferro
OPEN: Mon to Sat, exc Mon L MEALS: 12.15 to 2, 6.30 to 11
PRICES: £12 (£18), Set L £5·75 (£10). Service 10% CARDS: Access, Amex, Diners, Visa
SEATS: 60. Private parties: 90 main room. Children's helpings. Smart dress preferred.
Wheelchair access. Music

Restaurant Bosquet [14/20]

97A Warwick Road, Kenilworth CV8 1HP
KENILWORTH (0926) 52463
£20–£26

The elegance of Bernard Lignier's modern French cooking is matched by Jane
Lignier's natural sense of hospitality. The menu is limited – ingredients are
supplied by van from France – but the style is exact. Desserts are pictures: of three
small tarts, one is filled with strawberries, one with wild strawberries, the last
with raspberries, served on a blackcurrant and raspberry sauce. Pastry work and

Reports on shops, cafes and farms are useful, as well as reports on restaurants.

sorbets are notable. Elsewhere there are vivid contrasts of taste: halibut with lobster and langoustine sauce; duck breast with peach; scallops with garlic. The set menus offer good value. The list of a hundred wines is a judicious selection from across France, as strong in the country as in Bordeaux. Especially interesting are the bottles from the south-west, M. Lignier's home region.

CHEF: Bernard Lignier PROPRIETORS: Bernard and Jane Lignier
OPEN: Mon to Sat, exc Sat L CLOSED: 3 weeks July MEALS: 12 to 2, 7 to 10
PRICES: £17 (£24), Set L £13 (£20), Set D £13 (£20) to £18 (£26) CARDS: Amex, Visa
SEATS: 28. Private parties: 30 main room. Vegetarian meals. Children welcome

---

KINGHAM Oxfordshire

map 2

▲ Mill Hotel [12/20]

Kingham OX7 6UH
KINGHAM (060 871) 8188

£15–£25

Extensive renovation has gone on at this country hotel on the edge of the village, but its origins still show in the flagstone floors, the baker's oven and the millstream running through the grounds. The kitchen is mostly embedded in the butter and cream style of French cooking, with dishes such as guinea-fowl with brandy sauce, pithivier of chicken, and noisettes of lamb with red wine sauce. To start there have been stuffed cabbage leaves, and soups ranging from spinach and almond to velouté of avocado and shrimp. Sweets get plenty of votes: chocolate mousse, diplomat pudding, fresh fruit in raspberry sauce. A decent spread of burgundies, and mature clarets at reasonable prices, form the backbone of the wine list, which has house French at £6·50.
CELLARMAN'S CHOICE: Gewürztraminer, Réserve Spéciale '83, from Dopff 'Au Moulin', at £13·50.

CHEF: Pascal Pommier PROPRIETORS: Mr and Mrs John Barnett
OPEN: all week MEALS: 12.30 to 2, 7 to 10
PRICES: £18 (£25), Set L from £8·95 (£15), Set D £14·50 (£21), Snacks from £1·20
CARDS: Access, Amex, Diners, Visa
SEATS: 60. 4 tables outside. Private parties: 12 main room, 12, 16 and 20 private rooms.
Car-park, 40 places. Vegetarian meals. Children's helpings. Jacket and tie. Wheelchair
access. Music
ACCOMMODATION: 20 rooms, all with bath/shower. Rooms for disabled. B&B £20 to £40.
Deposit: £10 per person. No children under 5. Afternoon teas. Garden. Fishing. TV. Phone.
Scenic. Doors close at 11.30. Confirm by 2 [GHG]

KINGSBRIDGE Devon

map 1

▲ Queen Anne Restaurant, Buckland-Tout-Saints Hotel [new entry, zero rated]

Kingsbridge TQ7 2DS
KINGSBRIDGE (0548) 3055
2½m NE of Kingsbridge

£20–£23

The hotel is one of the old school, a classical, eighteenth-century country house with fine gardens, run by two generations of the Shephard family. The arrival of chef Alastair Carter has injected some young blood. He trained with John Webber at Gidleigh Park, and with George Perry-Smith. His style is more of the former than the latter, being modern franglais with a commendable absence of French on the menu. Dinners are a fixed price for three or four courses, with suppliers listed in the menu notes. Starters might range from curried parsnip soup with almonds, to ceviche of lemon sole with tomato, chilli and avocado, before superb sirloin steak (from Russells of Exeter), fanned out, and served on an intensely reduced red-wine sauce, with peperonata. Cheeses celebrate the West Country revival, with Devon Garland, Harbourne Blue, Exmoor and Creedy Farm Cheddar alongside a French country goats' cheese in olive oil and herbs. Sweets, such as pear frangipane with clotted cream, are offered with dessert wines by the glass. The full wine list runs up to almost two hundred bottles, mostly supplied by Pipers of Ottery St Mary, and mark-ups are reasonable.

CHEF: Alastair Carter PROPRIETORS: Mr and Mrs Victor Shephard
OPEN: all week CLOSED: 2 weeks from 1 Jan MEALS: 12.30 to 1.15, 7.30 to 9
PRICES: Set L from £14 (£20), Set D from £16 (£23) CARDS: Access, Amex, Carte Blanche, Diners, Visa
SEATS: 26. Private parties: 20 main room, 12 private room. Car-park, 20 places. No children under 9. Smart dress preferred. No smoking. Music
ACCOMMODATION: 12 rooms, all with bath/shower. B&B £50 to £70. Deposit: one night's stay. No children under 9. Pets welcome. Afternoon teas. Garden. TV. Phone. Scenic. Doors close at 11.30. Confirm by 6

KING'S LYNN Norfolk

map 6

Riverside Rooms [10/20] ✗

The Fermoy Centre, 27 King Street, King's Lynn PE30 1HA
KING'S LYNN (0553) 773134

£7–£19

The old warehouse by the Ouse, converted to a brick-and-beam restaurant, is part of the Fermoy Centre and caters for a variety of needs. Lunches are fixed price and quick, with pork fillet medallions a centrepiece. Dinner offers either a set menu with some choice, or a *carte*. Hot profiteroles are filled with chicken-liver pâté and served with a green peppercorn sauce; roast rack of English lamb comes with a mint and lemon sauce. Fish is a feature: Cromer crab, monk, salmon, sole, seafood pasta. There are pre-theatre meals. House wine £5·95 a litre.

CHEF: Dennis Taylor PROPRIETORS: Michael and Sylvia Savage
OPEN: Mon to Sat MEALS: 12 to 2, 7 to 10
PRICES: £13 (£19), Set L from £2·50 (£7), Set D £8·95 (£13) CARDS: Access, Visa
SEATS: 65. 24 tables outside. Private parties: 75 main room. Car-park, 10 places. Vegetarian meals. Children's helpings. Music

---

KINGSTON UPON THAMES Surrey

map 3

Ayudhya [11/20]

14 Kingston Hill, Kingston upon Thames KT2 7NH
01-549 5984

£17

Among the first of the Thai restaurants to open in the outer London orbit. The new dining-room has an open fire upstairs, and the small basement hums. The well-described menu of more than fifty dishes includes specialities such as steamed fish curry, stir-fried mixed seafood, and chicken with coconut milk, lemon grass and laos, with occasional extras, for instance papaya and shrimp salad. Recommended dishes have included satays; chicken with cashews and chillies; and stir-fried chilli beef. South-east asian fruits feature on a regular basis. Gewürztraminer '85, at £6·95, is an appropriate wine.

CHEF/PROPRIETOR: Somjai Feehan
OPEN: all week CLOSED: 25 and 26 Dec, 1 Jan and Easter
MEALS: 12 to 2.30 (3 Sun), 6.30 to 11 (11.30 Fri and Sat)
PRICES: £9 (£17). Service 12.5% CARDS: Access, Amex, Diners, Visa
SEATS: 86. Private parties: 22 main room, 26 private room. Children welcome. Wheelchair access. Music

---

KINTBURY Berkshire

map 2

▲ *Dundas Arms* [10/20]

Station Road, Kintbury RG15 0UT
KINTBURY (0488) 58263   £15–£21

The old pub on the Kennet and Avon Canal is becoming increasingly schizophrenic. The bar is getting younger and more exuberant, which seems to make the elegant corridor of a dining-room more grown-up. The young waitresses look like refugees. But it is a sound, comfortable dining-room and the sense of well-being is reinforced by the line of digestifs displayed on the dresser and the rack of dusty clarets in the coffee-room. The menu is more conservative than it seems at first glance, and is held up by good trimmings, such as the butter and the bread rolls. The seasoning is vivid; rosemary almost overpowers the rack of lamb, as does the garlic butter the squid. The chocolate pavé is excellent, likewise the wine list, strong in both claret and burgundy. Bordeaux spans two decades, with too many amazing bargains even to start listing here. Burgundies are, correctly, more youthful, with a spattering of top names from Bize to Suremain, Roulot to Drouhin. CELLARMAN'S CHOICE: Chablis, Durup '85, £14.

CHEF/PROPRIETOR: David A. Dalzell-Piper
OPEN: Tue to Sat CLOSED: Christmas to New Year MEALS: 12.30 to 1.45, 7.30 to 9.30
PRICES: Set L from £9·50 (£15), Set D from £15 (£21), Snacks from £1 CARDS: Access, Amex, Diners, Visa
SEATS: 36. Private parties: 22 main room. Car-park, 40 places. Children's helpings. Smart dress preferred. No cigars/pipes in dining-room. Wheelchair access (also WC)
ACCOMMODATION: 5 rooms, all with bath/shower. Rooms for disabled. B&B £39 to £45. TV. Phone. Scenic. Doors close at 11.30. Confirm by 6

KIRKBY FLEETHAM North Yorkshire

map 7

▲ *Kirkby Fleetham Hall* [13/20]

Kirkby Fleetham DL7 0SU
NORTHALLERTON (0609) 748226
1m N of village   £13–£20

Only the British can make décor more important than people. Kirkby Fleetham is awesome in its grounds and architecture. The dining-room is the jewel in an already lavish crown. Double doors open on to a long oval room that looks out on to a lake and rose-beds bordered by an immaculate line of mature trees. For all this grandeur, service is pleasantly down to earth, and at least the Hall is run and managed by just the Grants. The set menu offers remarkable value. Chris Grant's style is modern British: accomplished, with a minimum of choice. Soups and sauces are carefully composed and seasoned. Presentation is artistic, without being mere titillation. Five-course dinners gear up to fine dishes like salmon poached in white wine and served with an orange butter sauce garnished with orange, or grapefruit soufflé served in scooped-out grapefruit. Fruit was evident again at the end of a June meal, with lemon mousse set in a macaroon with a raspberry coulis. This is busy cooking, perhaps not best suited to the phenomenal wine list, assembled as if for a museum: there are runs of fine claret, strong in first growths, and Ch. Margaux alone is represented in sixteen vintages, spanning '25 to '78, £125 to £27. The English and the rosé sections are extensive, but some regions and vintages seem to be token offerings.

CHEF: Chris Grant PROPRIETORS: David and Chris Grant
OPEN: all week D, and Sun L MEALS: 12.30 to 1.30, 7 to 9
PRICES: Set L £9·50 (£13), Set D £16 (£20). Service inc CARDS: Amex, Visa
SEATS: 45. Private parties: 20 private room. Car-park, 30 places. Children's helpings.
ACCOMMODATION: 15 rooms, all with bath/shower. B&B £49 to £65. Children welcome.
Garden. TV. Phone. Doors close at 11 [GHG]

KIRKHAM Lancashire   map 5

Cromwellian [10/20]

16 Poulton Street, Kirkham PR4 2AD
KIRKHAM (0772) 685680   £11–£16

Folies-Bergère posters liven up the spartan décor of Peter and José Fawcett's bistro. The menu is heroically French, mostly from Normandy and Alsace: crêpe fermière filled with ham and mushrooms; pigeon à la cocotte; tarte Normandie. Everything is done with gusto. If the sauces lack intensity, the bread is fresh and the vegetables cooked crisply. White wines on a list of twenty-six bottles are classified on a scale of one to eight for dryness.

CHEF: José Fawcett PROPRIETOR: Peter Fawcett
OPEN: Tue to Sun D, and Sun L MEALS: 12.30 to 3, 7 to 10.30
PRICES: Set Sun L £6·60 (£11), Set D £10·50 (£16)
SEATS: 30. Private parties: 17 main room, 12 private room. Vegetarian meals. Children's helpings by arrangement. Wheelchair access. Music

---

KNUTSFORD Cheshire   map 5

▲ *La Belle Epoque* [12/20]

60 King Street, Knutsford WA16 6DT
KNUTSFORD (0565) 3060   £25

The Mooneys' remarkable-looking restaurant is well supported by Manchester's business community. The luxuriously art nouveau décor has mosaic floors, frilled curtains, and bronze statues, including Guadez' impressive *La Faucheur*. Yvonne Holt's cooking is French and her alcoholic sauces shine: Marsala with lamb's kidneys in crisp wholemeal pastry; madeira for breast fillets and boned leg of guinea-fowl; calvados with stuffed pork fillets. Fish shows up well in seafood sausage with herb sauce, and in daily specials from the market, such as poached halibut in herb mayonnaise. Sweets are in the mould of seasonal fruits with sabayon or strong bitter chocolate with praline and brandy. Cheeses on the trolley look unusual and large cups of coffee come with top-drawer, home-made petits fours. The long wine list is strong on claret and champagne, well supported by burgundy. Regional French wines offer inexpensive drinking.

CHEF: Yvonne Holt PROPRIETORS: Keith and Nerys Mooney
OPEN: Mon to Sat, D only CLOSED: first week Jan MEALS: 7.30 to 10
PRICES: £15 (£25). Service 10% CARDS: Access, Amex, Diners, Visa
SEATS: 70. Private parties: 60 main room, 20, 60 and 80 private rooms. Vegetarian meals.
No children under 10. No pipes in dining-room. Music
ACCOMMODATION: 5 rooms, all with bath/shower. B&B £25 to £40. No children under 10.
Garden. TV. Doors close at 1. Confirm by 2

LACOCK Wiltshire   map 2

▲ At The Sign of the Angel [12/20]

Church Street, Lacock SN15 2LA
LACOCK (024 973) 230
on A350, outside Chippenham   £19–£24

The Angel is run, without gimmicks, just as any hostelry in an English village might have been fifty, or even a hundred years ago. The dining-room is lit by candles and a large log fire; wooden tables are old and varnished, and the glasses are large. The menu, which can be ordered only between 7.30 and 8pm, revolves round a no-choice main course, as often as not roast beef. Most of the produce is the Levis's own – the vegetable plot and chickens and ducks are at the foot of the garden. The cooking is plain and accurate: grilled lemon sole, given just a taste of cheese and shellfish in the breadcrumbs; an intense leek and potato soup; crisp meringues. The beef is sliced thickly, and one slice fills most of the old floral plate, rimmed by Yorkshire pudding. Wines are stored over the fire and are chosen to match the beef. CELLARMAN'S CHOICE: Les Forts de Latour (the second wine of Ch. Latour) '80, at £20.

CHEF: L. M. Levis PROPRIETOR: J. S. Levis
OPEN: Mon to Sat D, and Sun L; weekday L by arrangement CLOSED: 22 Dec to 4 Jan
MEALS: 1 to 1.30, 7.30 to 8
PRICES: Set L from £13.50 (£19), Set D £17.50 (£24)
SEATS: 40. Private parties: 20 main room, 20 private room. No children under 12. Smart
dress preferred
ACCOMMODATION: 8 rooms, all with bath/shower. B&B £35 to £60. No children under 12.
Pets welcome. Garden. Phone. Scenic. Confirm by 5.30 [GHG]

Many of the more expensive restaurants offer bargain lunches for half the price of a meal in the evening. Details are given in the text.

All details are as accurate as possible at the time of going to press. Please notify the Guide office of any changes.

LANGHO Lancashire   map 5

▲ *Northcote Manor* [13/20] ✕

Northcote Road, Langho BB6 9BB
BLACKBURN (0254) 40555
7m E of M6 exit 31, on A59   £10–£26

This large, elegant Victorian house on the A59 near the Langho roundabout is
filled with crystal chandeliers and Spy cartoons. Nigel Haworth trained at
Accrington, Switzerland and Gleneagles and every month produces a
gastronomic menu. His style is modern English but draws on French and even
Chinese cuisine, and responds to the seasons. A January meal consisted of
venison pâté spiked with foie gras and served with figs and cranberries; crab and
spring onion consommé; a mousse of aubergines and courgettes garnished with
asparagus and tomatoes; then a lattice of beef and veal on a typically intense
shallot sauce; and finally a compote of strawberries and lychees with a chocolate
and coconut bombe. There is obvious care and striving for impact, as in Tay
salmon with hollandaise and a garnish of courgette flower filled with scallop
mousse. The short wine list is largely French, with house wine at £6·15.

CHEF: Nigel Haworth PROPRIETORS: Craig J. Bancroft and W. Kelly
OPEN: all week, exc Sat L MEALS: 12 to 1.30, 7 to 9 (10 Sat)
PRICES: £19 (£26), Set L from £6·20 (£10), Set D from £15 (£20) CARDS: Access, Amex,
Diners, Visa
SEATS: 70. Private parties: 60 main room, 20 private room. Car-park, 50 places. Children's
helpings. Smart dress preferred. Music
ACCOMMODATION: 6 rooms, all with bath/shower. B&B £34 to £43. Afternoon teas. TV.
Phone. Scenic [GHG]

LANGLEY MARSH Somerset   map 1

▲ *Langley House Hotel* [12/20]

Langley Marsh TA4 2UF
WIVELISCOMBE (0984) 23318   £21

The romantic, rural setting inspires much comment. The mood is peaceful, and
the country-house drawing-room looks out on to the garden. The dining-room
feels more cottagey, with its wild flowers and antique salt and pepper sets. Peter
Wilson cooks a fixed-price daily menu. He is a bit swashbuckling with the black
pepper, but has a canny eye for visuals: avocado and orange salad with walnut
dressing; medallions of monkfish with two sauces of red and green peppers; and
fillet of Aberdeen Angus beef with rosemary, lemon and English mustard were
offered at one April meal. The kitchen's loyalty to modern British cooking also
shows in the soups – spiced apple; broad bean and hazelnut; pea, pear and
watercress – and in the sweets – home-made gooseberry and elderflower ice-
cream; rhubarb fool; Atholl brose; Elizabeth Moxon's lemon posset. Wines are

---

*'The nice thing, as with most Chinese places, is that they don't suddenly go off you if
you don't order wine.'* (On eating in London)

---

modest because of lack of storage space. Fifty bottles centre on France and include nearly fifteen useful half-bottles. House French £5·75.
CELLARMAN'S CHOICE: Pouilly-Vinzelles '86, £14·50.

CHEF: Peter Wilson PROPRIETORS: Peter and Anne Wilson
OPEN: all week, D only MEALS: 7.30 to 9
PRICES: Set D from £14·75 (£21) Service 10%
SEATS: 18. Private parties: 35 main room, 18 private room. Car-park, 10 places. Vegetarian meals. Children's helpings. No children under 7. No smoking in dining-room. Wheelchair access (also WC)
ACCOMMODATION: 9 rooms, all with bath/shower. B&B £33 to £59. No children under 7. Pets welcome. Afternoon teas. Garden. Fishing. TV. Phone. Scenic. Doors close at 12.30. Confirm by 6

LEDBURY Hereford & Worcester   map 2

▲ *Hope End Country House Hotel* [13/20]

Hope End, Ledbury HR8 1JQ
LEDBURY (0531) 3613
¾m N of Ledbury, just beyond
Wellington Heath   £20

The sepulchrally calm Hope End is about good food and wine, scenery and modest walking. Patricia Hegarty's menus are modern British, healthy, balanced, varied and pure: yoghurts and curds are used instead of cream, for example. The set dinner is now five courses that take in soups of wild duck and pumpkin or tomato and cardomom, spiced beetroot soufflé, and roast fillet of Ledbury lamb with apricot and walnut sauce. Salad comes instead of a sorbet – cucumber and orange, or lettuce and grapefruit – and meals end in triplicate with three farmhouse cheeses in splendid condition and old-fashioned puddings: chestnut and prune, walnut and honey tart, and maids of honour. The wine list is a long one, with conventional strengths from mature claret to domaine-bottled burgundies, and a generous supply of half-bottles. The token New World wines include Rothbury Estate Chardonnay '85 at £9.

CHEF: Patricia Hegarty PROPRIETORS: John and Patricia Hegarty
OPEN: Wed to Sun, D only CLOSED: Dec to Feb MEALS: 7.30 to 8.30
PRICES: Set D £18 (£20). Service inc CARDS: Access, Visa
SEATS: 24. Private parties: 6 main room. Car-park, 10 places. No children under 14. Smart dress preferred. No smoking in dining-room. Wheelchair access (2 steps)
ACCOMMODATION: 9 rooms, all with bath/shower. B&B £58 to £92. Deposit: £30. No children under 14. Garden. Phone. Scenic. Doors close at 11. Confirm by 6 [GHG]

LEEDS West Yorkshire   map 5

Bryan's [9/20]

9 Weetwood Lane, Headingley, Leeds LS16 5LT
LEEDS (0532) 785679   £6

There are many fine fish and chip shops in the Leeds/Bradford area. Bryan's is one of the oldest (started in 1934), least pretentious, and best. Halibut and sole, haddock and plaice are cooked in beef dripping. The freshness is obvious; the batter recipe is secret. The dining area is institutional but overwhelmingly friendly, and service is adept. Senoir citizens pay £2·56 between 2.30 and 4.30pm for three courses with tea, bread and butter.

CHEFS: David Mitchell and Alan Germain PROPRIETOR: Jan Fletcher
OPEN: Mon to Sat MEALS: 11.30am to 11.30pm
PRICES: £4 (£6). Minimum £2·43
SEATS: 140. Private parties: 100 main room. Car-park, 50 places. Vegetarian meals.
Children's helpings. Wheelchair access. Music. Air-conditioned

La Grillade [10/20]

Wellington Street, Leeds LS1 4HJ
LEEDS (0532) 459707 and 459952   £11–£15

An authentic slice of France is found in this basement – posters, bric à brac, blackboard – though the atmosphere can sag when the restaurant is not full. The small dining areas are amply heated in winter by the open kitchen, where the chefs lay out the steaks on glowing ranges. La Grillade excels at grilled fresh meats and simple details, for instance salads and breads. House French £4·50.

CHEF: Orenzo Padolino PROPRIETORS: Meritlight Ltd
OPEN: Mon to Sat, exc Sat L CLOSED: 1 week at Christmas, bank hols
MEALS: 12 to 2.30, 7.30 to 11
PRICES: £11 (£15), Set L and D £7·50 (£11) CARDS: Access, Visa
SEATS: 62. Private parties: 16 main room. Children's helpings. Music

Jumbo Chinese [11/20]

120 Vicar Lane, Leeds LS2 7NL
LEEDS (0532) 458324   £11

Fifteen years after opening, this resilient Cantonese restaurant still bubbles with enthusiasm. The menu is more limited than the nearby Sang Sang (see entry), but the quality seems to be approaching its rival's once more. The dim-sum are excellent and, like everything else in the green basement, quickly served. Good dishes worth keeping an eye out for are chicken in a paper bag, spare ribs, and fillet steak with OK sauce. The chow-mein is copious and draws large crowds after the pubs close. Stir-fry dishes can outshine those prepared in advance.

CHEFS: Yat Sun Lo and Lin Dai Lai PROPRIETORS: Lin Dai Lai, Tony Kwan and Yat Sun Lo
OPEN: all week CLOSED: 25 to 27 Dec MEALS: noon to 11.45pm
PRICES: £6 (£11) CARDS: Access, Amex
SEATS: 120. Private parties: 180 main room. Children welcome. Music. Air-conditioned

Olive Tree [new entry, zero rated]

Oaklands, Rodley Lane, Leeds LS13 1NG
LEEDS (0532) 569283   £13–£16

Related to the Ilkley taverna of the same name, though the Greekness is less obvious and further diluted by the setting – a Victorian house with matching furniture. Daily dishes on the blackboard back up the long-winded menu. What makes the place stand out is the absolute freshness of the ingredients and the accurate grilling. Fish is usually a strength; the meze arrives in three stages;

the pastry sweets are well prepared. House wine is £5·25 a carafe. More reports, please.

CHEF: Vasoulla Psarias PROPRIETORS: George and Vasoulla Psarias
OPEN: all week CLOSED: 25 and 26 Dec, 1 Jan MEALS: 12 to 2, 6.30 to 12
PRICES: £11 (£16), Set D from £6·25 (£13). Service 10% CARDS: Access, Diners, Visa
SEATS: 120. Private parties: 50 main room, 25 private room. Car-park, 25 places. Vegetarian meals. Children's helpings. Wheelchair access (also WC). Music

Salvo's [9/20]

115 Otley Road, Headingley, Leeds LS6 3PQ
LEEDS (0532) 755017   £16

Even on dark, windy Wednesday evenings the queue here threatens to snake outside along the shopping terrace. Inside is a hot and hearty haven for an inexpensive plate of pasta or a pizza, including an unlikely pizza Kiev. Blackboard specials might include bouillabaisse, stir-fried pork with noodles, or a tandoori. The staff cope, with endless good humour. House Italian is £5·15 a litre.

CHEF: Geppino Dammone PROPRIETORS: Salvo and Geppino Dammone
OPEN: Mon to Sat CLOSED: 25 and 26 Dec MEALS: 12 to 2, 6 to 11.30
PRICES: £9 (£16)
SEATS: 52. Private parties: 22 main room. Vegetarian meals. Children's helpings. Wheelchair access. Music. Air-conditioned

Sang Sang [12/20]

7 The Headrow, Leeds LS1 6PN
LEEDS (0532) 468664   £9–£18

'Then we walked into Sang Sang and one bite later, yes, that was what we had been looking for all along.' The welcome seems to get friendlier as the décor gets shabbier – always a sign of a well-patronised Chinese restaurant. The Sang Sang earns its extra mark above its old rival Jumbo for the quality of its strictly Cantonese dishes: the depths of flavours in the casseroles; the quality of the roast meats and the bean curd. The more popular western dishes, for instance sizzling fillet steak with spring onions and ginger, and the various prawn dishes, are as good. Rainbow ground duck – a mix of chopped meats and vegetables with hoisin sauce and iceberg lettuce to wrap up into a parcel – is ever popular. Fish dishes are impeccable. Dim-sum are served from noon to 6pm.

CHEFS: F. C. Cheung and Chuen Ng PROPRIETORS: Yeung Ma, F. C. Cheung, P. S. Chow and C. Ng
OPEN: all week MEALS: noon to 11.30pm
PRICES: £10 (£18), Set L and D from £5·50 (£9). Service 10% CARDS: Access, Amex, Diners, Visa
SEATS: 120. Private parties: 90 main room, 30 private room. Vegetarian meals. Children welcome. Wheelchair access (1 step). Music. Air-conditioned

'One of the things that excites me about growing our own vegetables is that we will be able to get the small sizes that are so difficult to find in the markets here.' (Essex restaurateur)

LEICESTER Leicestershire   map 6

Water Margin [10/20]

76–78 High Street, Leicester LE1 5YP
LEICESTER (0533) 516422 and 24937   £6–£15

This Chinese restaurant, not far from the market, stays open throughout the day
and serves dim-sum, a big point in its favour. The menu is quite short and
appeals to Westerners without losing sight of its Cantonese origins. One-plate rice
and noodle dishes are authentic, and the tender, fragrant barbecued pork is
highly rated. There are also a few Peking and Szechuan specialities, such as
chicken with cashews, and deep-fried beef with chilli and carrots.Well-reported
dishes have included the hot-and-sour soup, chicken dishes as various as
Szechuan or black bean, and Chinese vegetables in oyster sauce. Cakes and buns
are sometimes available; orange segments come before the bill. In Eastern style,
diners are not expected to linger.

CHEF: Tony Au PROPRIETOR: Mr Chan
OPEN: all week MEALS: noon to 11.30
PRICES: £11 (£15), Set L £2·60 (£6), Set D £7 (£11). Service 10% CARDS: Access, Amex,
Diners, Visa
SEATS: 170. Private parties: 100 main room, 100 private room. Vegetarian meals. Children
welcome. Wheelchair access. Music

LEIGHTON BUZZARD Bedfordshire   map 3

▲ *Swan Hotel* [10/20]

High Street, Leighton Buzzard LU7 7EA
LEIGHTON BUZZARD (0525) 372148   £14–£22

Once a run-down pub, now an impressively refurbished hotel with a smart
dining-room. Fish shows up well on a widely spread menu, with consistent good
reports of the poached scallops in crayfish sauce, monkfish with ginger, and fresh
salmon mayonnaise. Vegetarian main dishes sit side by side steaks. Meals end
with raspberry crème brûlée, trifle or hazelnut ice-cream. A standard list of
wines. CELLARMAN'S CHOICE: Côtes du Rhône, Pascal '80, £6·25.

CHEF: Gregor Nicholl PROPRIETORS: Eric and Felicity Stephens
OPEN: all week MEALS: 12 to 2, 7 (7.30 Fri) to 9.30 (10 Fri, 9 Sat)
PRICES: £16 (£22), Set L £9·75 (£14), Set D £14·50 (£19), Snacks from £1
CARDS: Access, Amex, Diners, Visa
SEATS: 80. 3 tables outside. Private parties: 80 main room, 40 private room. Car-park, 10
places. Vegetarian meals. Children's helpings. Wheelchair access. Music
ACCOMMODATION: 38 rooms, all with bath/shower. B&B £50 to £60. Children welcome.
Baby facilities. Pets welcome. Afternoon teas. Air-conditioning. TV. Phone. Doors close at
12. Confirm by 1

▲ *This restaurant has rooms.*

*'The human intellect owes it superiority over that of the lower animals in great
measure to the stimulus that wine has given to the imagination.'* (Samuel Butler,
Notebooks, 1902)

map 3

La Cucina [10/20]

13 Station Street, Lewes BN7 2DA
LEWES (0273) 476707   £15

Refugees from the generally appalling food in Brighton obviously come to Lewes,
which has become quite a little centre of recommendation, all of a sudden. Mr
Vilas' trattoria is among the longest established. The menu deals competently
with the usual veal and chicken dishes; portions are generous and prices
reasonable. The fish is really what sets the place apart, also some well-chosen
Italian wines, starting at £4·50.

CHEFS: P. Hicks and Jose Vilas PROPRIETOR: Jose Vilas
OPEN: Mon to Sat CLOSED: 24 Dec for 2 weeks MEALS: 12 to 2, 6.30 to 10.30
PRICES: £10 (£15) CARDS: Access, Visa
SEATS: 47. Private parties: 30 main room, 20 private room. Vegetarian meals. Children's
helpings. Music

Kenwards [14/20]

Pipe Passage, 151A High Street, Lewes BN7 1XV
LEWES (0273) 472343   £15–£21

The strength here lies in a resolute use of the fresh: if John Kenward can't find it
in the neighbourhood, he doesn't serve it. This is not uncommon on the
Continent. What is rare is the absence of pretensions. This is modern British
cooking at its starkest and often most potent: mallard with cider and apples,
salmon with lime, hare with prunes. Vegetables go to make good soups and
decorate main dishes. The sweets bring in plum and almond pudding, ginger and
lemon cake. The setting is equally forthright, but despite the lack of luxury the
gastronomy is exemplary: mutton hung for two weeks, superb British cheeses,
and a wine list as good as anywhere – essentially French, but homing in on
exceptional vineyards, concentrating on the £7 to £20 range, not the ridiculous,
overpraised territories of classical growths and famous names.

CHEF: John Kenward PROPRIETORS: John and Caroline Kenward
OPEN: Tue to Sat, D only. L by arrangement MEALS: 7.30 to 9.30
PRICES: £16 (£21), Set D (Tue to Fri only) £10.50 (£15). Service inc CARDS: Access, Amex,
Diners, Visa
SEATS: 25. Private parties: 10 main room. Vegetarian meals. Children welcome

Pattissons [10/20]

199 High Street, Lewes BN7 2NS
LEWES (0273) 472727 and 473364   £13–£16

This part of the high street is known locally as School Hill. The ground-floor
coffee-shop sells snacks and light lunches; the apricot-walled restaurant is down
some steps. The Pattissons cook an unpretentious menu using a fair amount of

If you cannot honour a restaurant booking, always phone to cancel.

cream, whether in Jerusalem artichoke soup or home-made meringue with strawberries. For the most part, good fish and meats are judiciously offset by their sauces: enormous salmon steaks arrive, in good, lemony hollandaise; sauté pork steaks are given a cream and orange sauce. Game is slow-roasted and there is normally a casserole or two. The home-made blood-orange sorbet and brown-bread ice-cream laced with brandy are good finishes. Locally produced Breaky Bottom at £7 stands out on a basic wine list.

CHEFS/PROPRIETORS: Mr and Mrs Pattisson
OPEN: Mon to Sat, exc Mon D CLOSED: 10 days at Christmas; bank hol Mons MEALS: 12 to 2.15, 7.30 to 9.15
PRICES: L £9 (£13), Set D £12·50 (£16), Snacks at L £1·50. Minimum charge at L £1·50
CARD: Visa
SEATS: 24. Vegetarian meals. Children's helpings. Music

LEWTRENCHARD Devon   map 1

▲ *Fox's Earth, Lewtrenchard Manor*   [new entry, zero rated]

Lewtrenchard
LEWDOWN (056 683) 256   £18–£22

The late 1980s will be remembered for how old rural houses were saved from ruin by becoming luxurious hotels aimed primarily at international travellers. This isolated manor dates from 1620 and was home to the Baring-Goulds; the Revd Sabine Baring-Gould composed *Onward Christian Soldiers*. It follows the pattern of having expensive rooms and extensive wines but relatively good-value food. The owners are American and, after one false start in the kitchen (a pity, as Peter Hayes, by all accounts, cooked some fine meals), David Shepherd took over in late summer 1987. The style is the same – home-made breads and chocolates; chocolates; plenty of attention paid to presentation; everything plated. Shepherd's menu – a set six or four courses, with at least two choices at each stage – has included textured pea and pear soup; excellent scallops hollandaise; the usual dull duck breast dish. Service and trimmings are of a very high level. More reports, please.

CHEF: David Shepherd PROPRIETORS: Mary Ellen Keys and Greg Shriver
OPEN: all week D and Sun L MEALS: 1 to 3, 7.30 to 9.30
PRICES: Set L £13·50 (£18), Set D from £17 (£22) CARDS: Access, Amex, Visa
SEATS: 35. Private parties: 20 main room, 50 private room. Car-park, 35 places. Children's helpings. Smart dress preferred. Wheelchair access (1 step)
ACCOMMODATION: 10 rooms, all with bath/shower. B&B £45·50 to £61. Deposit: £25. No children under 12. Pets welcome. Garden. Fishing. TV. Phone. Scenic. Doors close at 1. Confirm by 6

LIFTON Devon   map 1

▲ *Arundell Arms* [11/20]

Lifton PL16 0AA
LIFTON (0566) 84666   £13–£25

The fishing, the shooting and the food are what this comfortable but spartan country house is known for. The menu takes in hearty roasts and traditional pies, as well as elegant modern dishes along the lines of croustade of calf's sweetbreads or pot-roast chicken with mussels. Tamar salmon is served with hollandaise; with a saffron sauce; or in pastry with a mousse and a rich butter sauce. Eighty wines begin with house Rioja at £6·50. CELLARMAN'S CHOICE: Ch. Cissac '73, at £38 a magnum.

CHEF: Philip Burgess PROPRIETOR: Anne Voss-Bark
OPEN: all week CLOSED: 5 days at Christmas MEALS: 12.30 to 2, 7.30 to 9
PRICES: £18 (£25), Set L from £8·75 (£13), Set D £14 (£19), Snacks from £1·25
CARDS: Access, Amex, Diners, Visa
SEATS: 70. Private parties: 80 main room, 30 private room. Car-park, 80 places. Vegetarian meals. Children's helpings
ACCOMMODATION: 29 rooms, all with bath/shower. B&B £37 to £62. Pets welcome. Afternoon teas. Garden. Fishing. Golf. TV. Phone. Scenic. Doors close at 11.30 [GHG]

LIMPSFIELD Surrey   map 3

Old Lodge [13/20] ✈

High Street, Limpsfield RH8 0DR
OXTED (0883) 712996   £13–£22

The Lodge now splits its efforts, with a less expensive brasserie partnering the accomplished, vaulted French restaurant. In the former there are steaks, quiches, and curries; in the latter John Mann's set menus are decorated with fine sauces: saffron for a pastry case of vegetables; Swiss chard for a salmon terrine; wild mushroom for fillets of beef and veal. The operation finds its true expression with sweets such as praline-filled pancakes, or dark chocolate cup filled with Grand Marnier cream. Service is young, smart and deferential. The concise wine list picks bottles from most major French regions and adds some Australian whites. House Cabernet, Riesling and Sauvignon at £7·50.

CHEF: John Mann PROPRIETORS: The Clivaz family
OPEN: Tue to Sun, exc Sat L and Sun D CLOSED: First 2 weeks Jan, Good Friday
MEALS: 12 to 2.15, 7 to 9
PRICES: £9 (£13), Set L £14·50 (£18), Set D £18·50 (£22). Service inc CARDS: Access, Amex, Diners, Visa
SEATS: 60. 5 tables outside. Private parties: 61 main room. Car-park, 30 places. Vegetarian meals. Children's helpings. Smart dress preferred. No cigars/pipes in dining-room. Wheelchair access (also WC). Music

LINCOLN Lincolnshire   map 6

Harvey's Cathedral Restaurant [10/20]

1 Exchequer Gate, Castle Square, Lincoln LN2 1LU
LINCOLN (0522) 21886   £10–£19

The corner dining-room at the top of Steep Hill, by the cathedral, has a smart *carte* that can roam gypsy-like all over the globe for inspiration and deliver a

Restaurants change owners and chefs constantly. Please help keep the Guide *informed of any changes you find.*

good-value lunch. Steaks and cheeses are the best foils to a continually changing wine list, but white burgundies continue to be the house pride and joy, from a humble Bourgogne Chardonnay to a quartet of *premier cru* Puligny-Montrachets and a Corton-Charlemagne '83. Cape wines feature; there are a dozen half-bottles; and the fifteen house wines are served on a pay-for-what-you-drink basis.

CHEFS: Linda Pares, Bob Harvey and Andy Gibson PROPRIETORS: Adrianne and Bob Harvey
OPEN: all week CLOSED: 1 Jan MEALS: 11.45 to 2, 7 to 9.30
PRICES: £10 (£16), Set L from £4·95 (£10), Set D from £13·50 (£19) CARDS: Access, Visa
SEATS: 55. Private parties: 36 main room, 36 private room. Vegetarian meals. Children's helpings. Music

---

LISKEARD Cornwall
map 1

▲ *Well House* [new entry, zero rated]

St Keyne, Liskeard PL14 4RN
LISKEARD (0579) 42001
£19–£23

This small, isolated country-house hotel opened in the spring of 1987. Already it is shaping into one of the most interesting venues in the country. The furnishings are lavishly feminine and the menu of fifteen seasonal dishes is similarly elaborate. Chef David Pope cooks in the modern British style – in July, a salad of sweetbreads dressed in walnut oil was followed by fillet of beef cooked in a consommé with madeira, with a sauce of horseradish. The class extends to the details: granary and sesame-seed rolls served hot; good butter; rosemary and walnut bread for the farmhouse cheese. Seasoning is vivid: sage and pine kernels in a brioche with diced chicken; lemon and garlic dressing for pigeon breasts on fresh pasta. Sweets are fashionable and familiar: two chocolate marquises, bavarois, gratins, exotic fruits and ices. Cafetière coffee is served with rich chocolate truffles. Owner Nick Wainford surprises skilfully and nurtures a list of eighty wines. Like dinner, prices are relatively good value, opening at under £6, with lowish mark-ups in white burgundy and Alsace as well as a run of escalating clarets. CELLARMAN'S CHOICE: Pouilly-Vinzelles '79, £13·75.

CHEF: David Pope PROPRIETOR: Nicholas Wainford
OPEN: all week; residents only, Mon MEALS: 12.30 to 2.30, 7 to 9.30
PRICES: Set L £13·50 (£19), Set D £17·50 (£23) CARDS: Access, Amex, Visa
SEATS: 36. 5 tables outside. Private parties: 40 main room. Car-park, 32 places. Vegetarian meals. Children welcome. Smart dress preferred. Wheelchair access (1 step)
ACCOMMODATION: 7 rooms, all with bath/shower. B&B £36 to £49. Deposit: £25. Children by arrangement. Baby facilities. Pets welcome. Afternoon teas. Garden. Swimming-pool. Tennis. Snooker. TV. Phone. Scenic

---

LITTLE WALSINGHAM Norfolk
map 6

▲ *Old Bakehouse* [10/20]

33 High Street, Little Walsingham NR22 6BZ
WALSINGHAM (032 872) 454
£11–£16

The converted village bakery offers accommodation, creditable food and a bar in the cellar. The cooking has its moments: sauté calf's liver on a bed of pasta; veal

Wellington; chicken and smoked salmon pie. Hot dishes of vegetables are left on the table. Good sweets have included banoffi pie and marmalade and Cointreau ice-cream. House wine is good value at £4·95, on a forty-plus list.

CELLARMAN'S CHOICE: Côtes du Rhône, Parallèle 45 '85, £8·75.

CHEFS/PROPRIETORS: Chris and Helen Padley
OPEN: Tue to Sat D, and Sun L Apr to Oct CLOSED: 3 weeks Jan, 2 weeks Sept to Oct; Sun to Thur Jan, Feb; Tue and Wed Mar; Tue Nov, Dec MEALS: 12.30 to 2, 7 to 9.30
PRICES: £11 (£16), Set D and Sun L £7 (£11) CARDS: Access, Visa
SEATS: 36. Private parties: 40 main room. Vegetarian meals. Children's helpings (Sun L only). Smart dress preferred. Wheelchair access (1 step; also WC). Music
ACCOMMODATION: 3 rooms, all with bath/shower. B&B £11·25. Deposit: £5. Pets welcome. Scenic. Confirm by 7

LIVERPOOL Merseyside   map 5

Armadillo [11/20]

20–22 Matthew Street, L2 6RE
051-236 4123   £19

On warm summer days the front of Martin Cooper's converted warehouse is kept open. The Armadillo offers good value and is nearly always busy. The menu outside lists around twenty dishes, and wholemeal bread, salads and copious soups are supplemented by some fine fish cookery. The chocolate mousse is invariably mentioned in reports. House wine is £6·40.

CHEF: John Scotland PROPRIETOR: Martin Cooper
OPEN: all week, exc Sun D and Mon D CLOSED: 1 week at Christmas MEALS: 11 to 3, 5 to 10.30
PRICES: £13 (£19) CARD: Access
SEATS: 65. Private parties: 50 main room. Vegetarian meals. Children's helpings (L only). Music. Self-service at L

Elham [10/20]

95 Renshaw Street, L1 2SP
051-709 1589   £16–£19

There's not much décor but plenty of atmosphere in Mr Safar's converted shop. He stays open late and goes to the market in the early hours for fresh fish. The quality shows in the whole steamed sea bass, served on a bed of bulgur and rice. The menu is largely Middle Eastern – the charcoal grill delivers enormous kebabs, lamb's liver and steaks – bolstered by a few Indian dishes. Home-made Armenian sausage is lamb, spices and garlic; Turkish coffee is strong. The restaurant is licensed, but wine is not one of the specialities of the house.

CHEF/PROPRIETOR: H. M. Safar
OPEN: all week, D only MEALS: 7 to 2.30am (3.30 Fri and Sat)
PRICES: £11 (£19), Set L and D £10·50 (£16). Service 10% CARDS: Access, Amex, Diners, Visa
SEATS: 65. Private parties: 70 main room, 20 private room. Vegetarian meals. Children's helpings. Wheelchair access. Music

---

▲ *This restaurant has rooms.*

Far East [12/20]

27–35 Berry Street, L1 9DF
051-709 3141   £6–£12

Nelson Street was the traditional location of Chinatown, and very few Chinese ventured beyond it. The arrival of the Shun On supermarket at the beginning of the 1980s marked the start of the expansion into Berry Street. The Far East is part of Shun On. It opened in 1984 and must now rank among the best Cantonese restaurants in the country. Certainly it leaves other restaurant competition in Liverpool way behind for value and quality, and even atmosphere on a Sunday, when the excellent dim-sum draw crowds of Chinese families. The dining-area is large and low-ceilinged. The walls are inlaid with silk-effect panels, and there are some garish back-lit panels portraying very out-of-date scenes from London, Hong Kong, Sydney and Peking. At the back are two large gold-painted wooden carvings, one of a phoenix and one of a dragon, with the classic Chinese statues of the three men who represent wisdom, wealth/power and longevity. All this is in contrast to the urban devastation outside. The set meals rely on Anglo-Chinese clichés, but beyond there are over two hundred items of Cantonese cooking. The spring rolls, crab-meat balls, sui-mai, and beef with ginger have all been as good as anywhere, even in the early days of Manchester's Chinatown. Likewise, the roast meats stand out, which is not to deny a repertoire that takes in the sweet-and-sours; the birds' nests filled with a choice of meats and vegetables; numerous king-prawn dishes (including spectacular giant prawns, split along the body, laid flat, steamed, and then cooked in smoking hot oil scented with garlic and freshly cut chillies); the casseroled hot-pots; the fish fillets and whole fish; the classics like broccoli stems stir-fried with fillet steak in oyster sauce, or the more homely green pepper slices stuffed with minced pork and Chinese mushroom; steamed slices of belly-pork interleaved with sliced mustard greens, or braised belly-pork casseroled with yams in a sauce of soy and oysters. Not content with the above – and how many European restaurants would compete with this variety – there are daily dishes and inexpensive one-plate meals of rice and noodles.

CHEFS: Kai Wah Chan and C. L. Tse PROPRIETOR: Tsun Loi Cheung
OPEN: all week MEALS: noon to 11.30pm (11.45 Fri and Sat)
PRICES: £6 (£12), Set L £2·80 (£6), Set D from £8 (£12), Snacks from £1. Service 10%
CARDS: Access, Amex, Diners, Visa
SEATS: 250. Private parties: 300 main room, 250 private room. Vegetarian meals. Children welcome. Wheelchair access (also WC). Music. Air-conditioned

La Grande Bouffe [11/20]

48A Castle Street, L2 7LQ
051-236 3375   £11–£17

The legal fraternity supports this Habitat-style bistro with church pews and tables ranging from converted Singer sewing-machine bases to pine. Lunch is notably good value for three courses, and less formal in the brasserie than the restaurant. Daily specials are chalked on the blackboard. The eclectic evening menu changes regularly, and takes in Japanese stir-fried beef, pork fillets with prunes, and a mould of aubergine filled with lamb ragout. There are fresh sardines with aïoli, and flambé lambs' kidneys, to start. The take-away counter dispenses arguably the best sandwiches in the city. The good-value, largely French wine list has a generous range of house wines and some interesting half-bottles. CELLARMAN'S CHOICE: from the southern Rhône, Château de Ruth, Cuvée Nicholas de Beaumarnais '84, from Meffre, at £7·25.

CHEF: Jean Kassim, Terence Lewis and Mark Preston PROPRIETOR: Juliet Shield
OPEN: Mon to Sat, exc Mon D and Sat L MEALS: 12 to 2.30, 6 to 10 (10.30 Sat)
PRICES: £12 (£17), Set L £6·95 (£11), Set D from £10·95 (£16). Service 10%
CARDS: Access, Amex, Visa
SEATS: 90. Private parties: 12 main room, 20 private room. Vegetarian meals. Children's helpings. Music

Mayflower [new entry, zero rated]

48 Duke Street, L1 5AS
051-709 6339   £7–£26

This pretty, bright restaurant on the edge of Liverpool's Chinatown ranks perhaps second to the Far East (see entry) for Cantonese food in the city. Outside it has varnished pine and red plastic canopies; inside there are fresh flowers on the table and a well-stocked aquarium by the bar-lounge. The menu generally stays with Cantonese specialities, such as steamed sea bass with spring onion and ginger, but adds a few Pekinese dishes and one or two fashionable items, such as sizzling fillet steak. Some favourites, such as soya chicken, and fish head with bean curd hot-pot, are missing, although the Mayflower's version of ma-po bean curd is rated as one of the best in Liverpool. Other good dishes have included deep-fried crab claw stuffed with minced prawns; a dozen massive, skewered king prawns with satay sauce; and steamed scallops with ginger and spring onion. Boiled rice is up to the mark, and there are orange segments and grapes to finish.

CHEF: H. P. Fu PROPRIETOR: K. H. Sim
OPEN: all week, exc Sat L and Sun L MEALS: noon (6 Sat and Sun) to 4am
PRICES: £17 (£26), Set L from £3 (£7), Set D from £4 (£9). Service 10% CARDS: Access, Amex, Diners
SEATS: 80. Private parties: 100 main room. Vegetarian meals. Children welcome. Wheelchair access (1 step; also WC). Music. Air-conditioned

Orient [new entry, zero rated]

54–54A Berry Street, L1 4JQ
051-709 2555   £6–£16

Berry Street has eclipsed Nelson Street as the centre of Liverpool's Chinatown, with Chinese newsagents and video shops as well as restaurants. Mr Liu's Orient is the latest incarnation of a long-established Peking and Shanghai restaurant, opened fourteen years ago and renowned for serving many regional dishes seldom found in British Chinese restaurants. Under new owners and revamped into something of hotch-potch, it offers genuine Peking cooking, including duck (with a version marinated in scented tea), traditional, crescent-shaped meat dumplings, and dum dum noodles in a thick peanut soup flavoured with chilli

[GHG] *after the details of an entry means that the establishment is also included in* The Good Hotel Guide.

and preserved mustard greens. Noodles are made daily on the premises. For a larger outlay, there are special set banquets that can take in crispy seaweed with cold meats, fish and pickled vegetables, crispy duck, fried three delicacies (pork, chicken and king prawns), and chicken with water-chestnuts in chilli satay sauce. The tofu dishes should appeal to vegetarians. A dim-sum chef has just been appointed. House Hirondelle £4·40. By the start of 1988 the restaurant plans to open from noon to midnight, all week. More reports, please.

CHEFS: M. Yau and Y. Ho PROPRIETORS: Kenneth and Diana Liu
OPEN: Tue to Sun MEALS: 12 to 2.30, 6 to 11.30
PRICES: £9 (£16), Set L from £2·80 (£6), Set D from £8·50 (£12), Snacks from £1. Service 10%
CARDS: Access, Visa
SEATS: 210. Private parties: 100 main room, 40,70 and 100 private rooms. Vegetarian meals. Children's helpings. Wheelchair access. Music. Air-conditioned

Peking Duck [new entry, zero rated]

471 Smithdown Road, Wavertree, L15 5AE
051-733 0723   £9–£12

Smithdown Road is cosmopolitan: the Peking Duck is sandwiched between an American-style diner and a steakhouse, opposite an Indian take-away. Inside, the mock-Tudor beams are unexpected. The cooking may not be Peking-style state-of-the-art, but set dinners in particular are good value, portions are big and the mood is friendly. Typically, a banquet might take in sesame prawn toast, soup, meaty spare ribs, sweet-and-sour pork, chicken and cashews in yellow-bean sauce, plus vegetables, rice and toffee apples. The high point is very fresh crispy duck served with pancakes, spring onion, cucumber and a healthy portion of hoisin sauce. Hopefully Mr Keung will continue to promote his Peking dishes alongside the more westernised dishes. House wine £4·10. More reports, please.

CHEF/PROPRIETOR: Tsang Hong Keung
OPEN: all week, D only MEALS: 5.30pm to 1am
PRICES: £7 (£12), Set D from £5·60 (£9). Service 10% CARDS: Access, Visa
SEATS: 63. Vegetarian meals. Children's helpings. Wheelchair access (1 step). Music. Air-conditioned

---

LODDISWELL Devon   map 1

Lavinia's [10/20]

Loddiswell TQ7 4ED
LODDISWELL (054 855) 0306
First L heading N out of Loddiswell   £26

Out of the way, at the end of a long drive. Lavinia Davies cooks an imaginative, twenty-dish country menu, which might include a hot soufflé of spinach, smoked ham and salted almonds, or monkfish with rhubarb, for instance. Fish is a strong point; two can share an enormous platter of shellfish on a dumb waiter. On

'Unfortunately, vegetable supplies seem to be the problem. Sadly, Kent being the garden of England doesn't mean a plentiful supply of small, succulent vegetables. I have to go to London.' (Kent restaurateur)

Wednesdays there is a £12 set dinner. Jeremy Davies serves. House claret is £7.
CELLARMAN'S CHOICE: Mâcon-Lugny '85, £9·60.

CHEF: Lavinia Davies PROPRIETORS: Jeremy and Lavinia Davies
OPEN: Tue to Sat, D only CLOSED: Nov to Easter MEALS: 7.30 to 10
PRICES: Set D £19·50 (£26) CARDS: Access, Visa
SEATS: 30. Private parties: 36 main room. Car-park, 15 places. Children's helpings. No pipes
in dining-room. Music

LONG MELFORD Suffolk ✔   map 3

▲ *Black Lion Hotel* [new entry, zero rated]

Long Melford CO10 9DN
SUDBURY (0787) 312356   £11–£19

Dramatically transformed from a rather down-at-heel pub into a hotel and
restaurant with a country-house atmosphere. It feels comfortable rather than
grand, with fresh flowers, family portraits and pastel colour schemes, and has
drawn many keen reports over the year. Chef Ian Stanley produces good soups,
such as asparagus and watercress, and main dishes have featured well-made
sauces: brandy with poached chicken breast; cider and cream with pork cutlet;
cucumber with fillet of salmon. There is praise for sweets, such as roast bananas
in Grand Marnier sauce, dark chocolate terrine with coffee-bean sauce, Suffolk
coffee fudge almond tart. The wine list has some regional French varieties, as well
as a few from the New World. More reports, please.

CHEF: Ian Stanley PROPRIETORS: Luke and Amelia Brady
OPEN: all week (Sun D residents only) MEALS: 12.15 to 2.30, 7 to 9
PRICES: £13 (£19), Set L from £6 (£11), Set D from £13 (£18) CARDS: Access, Amex,
Diners, Visa
SEATS: 55. Private parties: 60 main room, 18 and 30 private rooms. Car-park, 8 places.
Vegetarian meals. Children's helpings. Smart dress preferred. Music
ACCOMMODATION: 10 rooms, all with bath/shower. B&B £29 to £37. Children welcome.
Baby facilities. Pets welcome. Garden. TV. Phone. Scenic [GHG]

LOUGHBOROUGH Leicestershire ✗   map 5

Angelo's [10/20]

65 Woodgate, Loughborough LE11 2TZ
LOUGHBOROUGH (0509) 266704   £13

A family-run trattoria in a bright, modern brick building, serving honest Italian
regional dishes, plus a few concessions to the prawn cocktail and chicken Kiev
brigade. Fresh crab comes from the market round the corner on Thursdays,
Parma ham is freshly sliced in thin sheets from a whole leg, and vegetables are
plentiful. Special dishes of the day are recommended: half a spatchcocked guinea-
fowl in brandy sauce; chicken cacciatore flavoured with rosemary. Sweets have

---

The Guide *recruits new inspectors from readers who write in regularly. If you would
like to apply, write to the editor with (a) a detailed report on a restaurant where you
have eaten and (b) a comparative study of restaurants known to you.*

been weak, but the coffee is good. Check the special selection of 'one-off' wines, not on the printed list. House wine £4·90.

CHEF: Pramrod Patel PROPRIETORS: Ann and Angelo Marcelli
OPEN: Mon to Sat MEALS: 12 to 2, 7 to 10 (10.45 Fri and Sat)
PRICES: £9 (£13). Service 10%
SEATS: 50. Private parties: 30 main room. Car-park, 12 places. Vegetarian meals. Children's helpings. Wheelchair access (1 step; also WC). Music

Restaurant Roger Burdell [12/20] ✗

11–12 Sparrow Hill, Loughborough LE11 1BT
LOUGHBOROUGH (0509) 231813   £14–£25

The old manor-house dates from 1410 and looks like an enormous tea-shop, with half-timbered walls and curtains billowing at the windows. It has been tastefully brought up to date in greys and pinks, and pot-plants and candles lighten a room inclined to gloom. The five-course menu is compositional – there are large arrays of salads, such as smoked chicken, mango and avocado, picturesque terrines, and brandy-snap baskets filled with sorbets and surrounded by garnished coulis. Main courses swing from stuffed squid ragout to calf's liver with apple, each with no fewer than nine types of vegetable on the plate. This bittiness can lead to meals lacking cohesion, particularly when the sauces are not sufficiently potent to provide unity. Mr Burdell reports an increasing drift in his cooking to the traditional style, which must be welcome. The wine list is unusually strong on claret, burgundy and Rhône. CELLARMAN'S CHOICE: Puligny-Montrachet '80, £21·50.

CHEF/PROPRIETOR: Roger Burdell
OPEN: all week, exc Mon L and Sun D MEALS: 12.30 to 2, 7.30 to 9.15
PRICES: Set L from £8·50 (£14), Set D £21 (£25). Service inc CARDS: Access, Amex, Diners, Visa
SEATS: 60. Private parties: 40 main room, 20 private room. Vegetarian meals. Children's helpings (Sun L only). No cigars/pipes in dining-room. Wheelchair access

---

LOUTH Lincolnshire   map 6

Alfred's [11/20] ✗

Upgate, Louth, LN11 9EY
LOUTH (0507) 607431   £11–£20

The Grant family provide some of the best food on the flatlands of Humberside and North Lincolnshire. There is a real attempt to use fresh ingredients, notably fish from local boats. Sauces tend to be dominated by indulgent, distracting quantities of cream; nevertheless, fillets of sole with white wine, monkfish with green peppercorn and Pernod, and salmon and monkfish with vermouth, have all been good. For the more carnivorous there are steaks, and dishes such as calf's liver with sage butter, or medallions of pork with brandy and grain mustard

---

Please keep the Guide *informed of any changes to the restaurants listed. Report forms are at the back of the book.*

sauce. Sweets also get their share of cream. Around 70 carefully chosen, reasonably priced wines, plus sixty or so malt whiskies, and all kinds of liqueurs.

CHEF: Iain Grant PROPRIETOR: Alistair Grant
OPEN: Mon to Sat D, and Sun L CLOSED: bank hols, exc 25 and 26 Dec MEALS: 12 to 2, 7 to 10
PRICES: £12 (£18), Set L £7·50 (£11) to £14·50 (£20) CARDS: Access, Visa
SEATS: 60. Vegetarian meals. Children's helpings. Wheelchair access (3 steps). Music

---

LOWER BEEDING West Sussex   map 3

▲ *South Lodge* [12/20]

Brighton Road, Lower Beeding RH13 6PS
LOWER BEEDING (040 376) 711   £17–£32

The Lodge, built in 1883, is a spectacular Victorian mansion set in ninety acres of parkland, with a particularly fine rhododendron garden. The style incorporates log fires, polished floors and a panelled dining-room with views across the grounds. James Hayward cooks an over-complex, but nonetheless interesting, modern menu with a complete five courses for vegetarians. Soufflés of Cheddar or mushroom are typical. At Sunday lunch, roast beef appears under a silver dome on a large mahogany trolley, otherwise there might be pan-fried salmon with fresh lime or excellent spatchcocked baby chicken on a bed of shallots and sage. Sweets are laid out on the sideboard along with the Jersey cream. A further twenty bedrooms are being added; the atmosphere of the hotel to date has been more business than personal. The wine cellar is adequate but highly priced, starting with vin de table at £7·50. CELLARMAN'S CHOICE: St Emilion, Ch. Tertre Roteboeuf '84, £20·60.

CHEF: James Hayward PROPRIETORS: Laura Hotels Ltd
OPEN: all week MEALS: 12.30 to 2.30, 7.30 to 10.30
PRICES: £24 (£32), Set L from £11·50 (£17), Set D from £23·50 (£27). Snacks from £2·50
CARDS: Access, Amex, Diners, Visa
SEATS: 65. Private parties: 8 main room, 6, 10 and 16 private rooms. Car-park, 50 places. Vegetarian meals. Children's helpings. Smart dress preferred. No cigars/pipes in dining-room. Wheelchair access
ACCOMMODATION: 26 rooms, all with bath/shower. Rooms for disabled. B&B £60·50 to £85. Children welcome. Baby facilities. Pets welcome. Afternoon teas. Garden. Tennis. Fishing. TV. Phone. Scenic. Confirm by 12

LOWER BRAILES Warwickshire   map 2

▲ *Feldon House* [10/20]

Lower Brailes OX15 5HW
BRAILES (060 885) 580   £12–£16

There is no choice on the Withericks' menu, which is agreed on booking. Nor may there be a choice of who to sit next to, unless you arrive in numbers, as there are only two tables, one for twelve, one for four. The style is English. There is always a soup – cream of carrot, or parsnip with coriander – before generous grilled salmon with hollandaise and mange tout, or large, poached chicken breasts with a delicate mango cream sauce. Vegetables are plain and first class; to finish there might be chocolate hazelnut meringue with chocolate sauce. Allan Witherick does all the cooking himself and his wife Margaret serves in the red dining-room, which is full of comfortable old furniture. Ground coffee comes in a pot. Take your own wine.

CHEF: Allan Witherick PROPRIETORS: Allan and Maggie Witherick
OPEN: all week MEALS: 12.30 to 2, 7.30 to 9
PRICES: Set L £12 (£13), Set D £15 (£17). Unlicensed, but bring your own: no corkage
SEATS: 16. Private parties:12 main room, 4 private room. Car-park, 9 places. Vegetarian meals. Children's helpings (L only). Wheelchair access
ACCOMMODATION: 3 rooms. B&B £15. Baby facilities. Pets welcome. Garden. Scenic. Confirm by 4 [GHG]

LYMINGTON Hampshire

▲ Railings, Stanwell House Hotel

High Street, Lymington SO4 9AA
LYMINGTON (0590) 77123

This restaurant was sold as the Guide *went to press.*

LYMPSTONE Devon

map 1

▲ River House [11/20]

The Strand, Lympstone EX8 5EY
EXMOUTH (0395) 265147

£10–£22

The sunsets are spectacular, seen from the dining-room of these cottages on the Exe estuary. This fishing village is built around four pubs, and fish is the pride of a menu of superior British home cooking: king prawns, halibut and lemon sole are usually plainly grilled and flavoured with herbs from the garden. No fewer than seven vegetables accompany. Elsewhere, there can be good use of local produce, such as pheasant with elderberry wine and juniper berries, alongside plainer dishes and gooey sweets, though standards are erratic, for these prices.

Personable service is from Mr Wilkes, while his wife Shirley cooks. Bedrooms opened late last year. A respectable wine list opens at £5·30 and stays mostly in France. CELLARMAN'S CHOICE: Australian dry Muscat, from Brown Bros, £8·55.

CHEF: Shirley Wilkes PROPRIETORS: Mr and Mrs J. F. M. Wilkes
OPEN: Tue to Sun, exc Sun D MEALS: 12 to 1.45, 7 to 9.30 (10.30 Sat)
PRICES: Set L from £5·75 (£10), Set D from £16·75 (£22) CARDS: Access, Amex, Visa
SEATS: 35. Private parties: 25 main room, 14 private room. Vegetarian meals. Children's helpings. No children under 5. Smart dress preferred. No cigars/pipes in dining-room
ACCOMMODATION: 2 rooms, both with bath/shower. Rooms for disabled. B&B £39 to £58. TV. Phone. Scenic

---

LYNTON Devon   map 1

▲ *Hewitt's* [12/20] ✗

North Walk, Lynton EX35 6HJ
LYNTON (0598) 52293   £10–£22

A late-Victorian country house, looking like a cross between a Swiss chalet and a church. It is in walking country, beside the Devon coastal paths, with splendid views across Lynmouth Bay to Foreland Point. The weighty feel of the dark, carved wood contrasts with a modern menu that takes fresh local ingredients as its starting-point. Dishes are original rather than fashionable. Devon beef is served with mustard and spinach, English lamb with Dorset blue cheese, and Somerset duck marries well with its pink and green peppercorn sauce. The results, even with classic dishes, such as salmon in puff pastry with sorrel and cream sauce, are light and fresh. There are English cheeses, a vegetarian menu, and a simple and reasonably priced list of over fifty wines, with a good number of half-bottles. House Provence is £5·50 a bottle.

CHEF: David Lamprell PROPRIETORS: David Holmes and Marion Wyncoll
OPEN: all week D, and Sun L MEALS: 12.30 to 2.30, 7 to 9.30
PRICES: £16 (£22), Set Sun L £6·50 (£10), Set D £13·50 (£18) CARDS: Access, Amex, Diners, Visa
SEATS: 30. 6 tables outside. Private parties: 30 main room, 8 private room. Car-park, 10 places. Vegetarian meals. Children's helpings. No smoking in dining-room. Wheelchair access (also WC). Music
ACCOMMODATION: 12 rooms, 10 with bath/shower. B&B £23 to £42. Deposit: £10. Children welcome. Baby facilities. Afternoon teas. Garden. Fishing. TV. Phone. Scenic. Doors close at 12. Confirm by 7

LYTHAM ST ANNE'S Lancashire   map 5

▲ *C'est la Vie, Dalmeny Hotel* [12/20]

South Promenade, St Anne's-on-Sea,
Lytham St Annes FY8 1LX
ST ANNE'S (0253) 725871   £13–£19

Still a cut above most hotel cooking in the area. The Webb family are at the helm after forty-three years and Paul Caddy still leads the kitchen. These are two restaurants: one is a carvery, the other – C'est la Vie – operates as a barbecue/grill at lunchtime and has an à la carte evening menu. Local produce is well supported: Paul Caddy buys fruit and vegetables from Preston market; Lancashire cheese is from Pickles Farm, Kirkham; fish and game are from Lytham; pork and lamb from James Stage of Wigan. The results can feature black pudding with Dijon cream sauce; salmon with béarnaise sauce; stuffed quail with sage sauce; rack of lamb with redcurrant and red-wine sauce. Sweets are the likes of banana and caramel flan, and chocolate velvet torte. The fifty-strong wine list has house wine at £5 a bottle.

CHEFS: Keith Davies and Paul Caddy PROPRIETORS: The Webb family
OPEN: all week, exc Sun D MEALS: 12.15 to 2 (3 Sun), 7.30 to 9.30
PRICES: L £8 (£13), D £13 (£19)
SEATS: 48. 6 tables outside. Private parties: 48 main room. Car-park, 30 places. Children's helpings. Smart dress preferred. Wheelchair access (also WC). Music. Air-conditioned
ACCOMMODATION: 85 rooms, 83 with bath/shower. Rooms for disabled. Lift. B&B £29 to £58. Deposit: £10. Children welcome. Baby facilities. Afternoon teas. Swimming-pool. Sauna. Golf. Snooker. TV. Phone. Scenic [GHG]

MALDON Essex map 3

Wheelers [9/20] ✕

13 High Street, Maldon CM9 8TB
MALDON (0621) 53647 £9

A good fish and chip restaurant, with a take-away attached. Soups, such as minestrone, and fish, are home made. Fish is served in generous portions, and on occasions has even included Dover sole. The sweets trolley shames many a more expensive restaurant.

CHEF: Ross Wheeler PROPRIETORS: The Wheeler family
OPEN: Tue to Sat CLOSED: 2 weeks Sept MEALS: 11.30 to 1.45, 6 to 9.30
PRICES: £4 (£9)
SEATS: 52. Private parties: 52 main room: Children's helpings. Wheelchair access (1 step; also WC)

MALVERN WELLS Hereford & Worcester map 2

Course [11/20]

191–193 Wells Road, Malvern WR14 4HE
MALVERN (068 45) 5065 £19

The Edneys have filled this private house, a mile from the town centre, with racing memorabilia and pine. He cooks a set-price menu and she is a good hostess. Dishes are prettily presented, if conservative – salad of avocado, shrimp and prawn with Marie Rose sauce; stuffed chicken breast; ice-cream pancake – but everything is made with good ingredients and carefully prepared. Twenty-five affordable wines are augmented by wines of the week written on the blackboard. House Bulgarian Cabernet Sauvignon '81, from Suhindol, is £4·95.
CELLARMAN'S CHOICE: Côtes du Ventoux '85, from Jaboulet, at £6·90.

The Guide is independent, accepts no advertising and survives solely on the number of copies sold.

CHEF: David Edney PROPRIETORS: David and Pippa Edney
OPEN: all week, D only CLOSED: Mon Jan to May; bank hol Mons MEALS: 7
PRICES: Set D £14·50 (£19) CARDS: Access, Visa
SEATS: 26. Private parties: 26 main room. Vegetarian meals. Children's helpings.
Wheelchair access (1 step). Air-conditioned. One sitting

Croque-en-Bouche [16/20]

221 Wells Road, Malvern Wells WR14 4HF
MALVERN (068 45) 65612 £24

The dining-room used to be a bakery and retains polished woodwork with ovens
underneath, though the chimneys have been dismantled. Robin Jones officiates
between customers and kitchen, where Marion Jones single-handedly marries
good bourgeois principles to the best local produce. The menu is French, but here
too is ample evidence of the resurgent modern British cooking: vegetable soup is
left in a tureen on the table, for you to help yourself; seasoning can include
nutmeg with Jerusalem artichoke, or garlic and ground almonds with maize-fed
chicken. The menu has its own energy – lamb is roasted with soy and spring
onion in December, and stuffed with marjoram, rosemary and ginger in
February. Salads are brilliantly crisp, colourful mixtures of frisée and radicchio
and may be flavoured with coriander and walnut oil. English regional cheeses,
such as Allendale, Shropshire Blue and Single Gloucester, vie with French for
prime position on the cheeseboard, all in perfect condition. Finish with the
compilation of blood-orange sorbet and mango and wild strawberry ice-creams
in a fragrant strawberry sauce. The wine list is legendary, featuring well over
four hundred wines from a stock of around nine hundred from seventeen
countries, representing every vintage since 1944, plus sixteen other years back
to the start of the century. It is also a very modern list, elevating areas of the Loire
and Rhône to the same stature as clarets. But even in this context, Robin Jones
singles out not a French Chardonnay but an Australian, for CELLARMAN'S
CHOICE: Rosemount, Show Reserve '85, £9·80.

CHEF: Marion Jones PROPRIETORS: Robin and Marion Jones
OPEN: Wed to Sat, D only CLOSED: Christmas MEALS: 7.30 to 9.15
PRICES: Set D £19·70 (£24). Service inc
SEATS: 22. Private parties: 10 private room. No cigars/pipes in dining-room.
Wheelchair access

MANACCAN Cornwall map 1

New Inn [9/20]

Manaccan TR12 6HA
MANACCAN (032 623) 323 £5–£10

Not new at all, but dating from the turn of the seventeenth century, and
thatched. Local boats provide fresh fish to augment a home-cooked menu of
sausage and mash, chilli, and treacle tart, for a genuine, no-frills pub. Moules

---

Reports on shops, cafes and farms are useful, as well as reports on restaurants.

---

marinière come with a big hunk of brown bread. Devenish beers and drinkable wine in the bar, children's playthings in the small garden.

CHEFS/PROPRIETORS: Mr and Mrs P. J. F. Cullinan
OPEN: all week, exc Tue D MEALS: 11 to 2, 6.30 to 9.30 (Sun 12 to 1.30, 7 to 10)
PRICES: £7 (£10), Set L from £2 (£5), Set D from £4 (£7), Snacks from 85p
SEATS: 30. 12 tables outside. Private parties: 10 main room. Car-park, 10 places. Vegetarian meals. Children's helpings. Jacket and tie. Wheelchair access

---

MANCHESTER Greater Manchester

map 5

Assam Gourmet [10/20]

17A Bloom Street, M1 3HZ
061-236 6836   £6–£15

The sparse, plain décor is a welcome change from the clutter of many Indian restaurants. The long menu offers dishes far-removed from the Madras/tandoori norm in the city. Assam is close to the Chinese border, and the influence shows in dhosai stuffed with beansprouts and vegetables, and in the deep-fried prawns with banana. Roast chicken is pointed up with ginger, coriander and garlic, and served in an envelope of nan bread. Excellent budhuk roosha is duck cooked in a clay pot with cardamom and cinnamon sauce. On more familiar ground, the kitchen also delivers good pakoras, shami gosht and prawn puri. Avoid the trolleyful of puddings, but ask for home-made pistachio kulfi. Meals end with orange segments and hot towels. Drink Kingfisher beer, or exotic fruit juice.

CHEFS: B. P. Deb and K. Bhattacharsee PROPRIETORS: Assam Gourmet Ltd
OPEN: all week CLOSED: 25 and 26 Dec, Good Friday, L bank hols MEALS: 12 to 2.15, 6 to 11.15 (12 Fri and Sat)
PRICES: £7 (£15), Set L £2.95 (£6), Set D from £6·50 (£10). Service 10% CARDS: Access, Amex, Diners
SEATS: 80. Private parties: 100 main room, 30 and 40 private rooms. Vegetarian meals. Children's helpings. Wheelchair access. Music. Air-conditioned

---

Blinkers [12/20]

16 Princess Street, M1 4NB
061-228 2503   £13–£26

This long-established European restaurant is beginning to live down a reputation for expense-account business eating and little else. The downstairs dining-room, in a terrace of Victorian commercial buildings near Chinatown, has a 1960s feel, with colourful prints on the rough plastered walls, a florid red carpet, and plastic flowers in the windows. Ian Cheetham's kitchen delivers sound, modern French cooking: lattice of salmon on a herb and red-pepper sauce; baked loin of pork with a mousse of garlic. Sauces are light, and made from stock reductions. The menu offers a broad sweep of nearly thirty dishes, opening with smoked fillet of

---

The entries are compiled from the views of readers who have eaten at the restaurants in the last year, backed up by anonymous inspections and by information supplied and facts verified by the restaurants.

---

beef salad dressed in walnut oil and ending, perhaps, with a cold passion-fruit soufflé with coconut tuiles. There is some unnecessary garnishing – the quality is there and does not need underlining. But there seems to be a palpable desire to make a success . The sixty wines carry some heavy mark-ups, beyond the house burgundy at £6·95. CELLARMAN'S CHOICE: Pouilly-Fumé '85, from Chabanne, £12·95.

CHEF: Ian Cheetham PROPRIETORS: Lewis and Christine Gerezdi
OPEN: Mon to Sat, exc Sat L MEALS: 12 to 2.30, 7.15 to 10.30
PRICES: £17 (£26), Set L £6·95 (£13), Set D £14·95 (£22). Service 10% CARDS: Access, Amex, Visa
SEATS: 45. Private parties: 70 main room. Vegetarian meals. Children's helpings. Music

Brasserie St Pierre [10/20]

57 – 63 Princess Street, M2 4EQ
061-228 0231   £18

The outside has the look of an authentic brasserie, with large plate-glass windows, but the inside is more of a hybrid. John Nelson of The High Moor at Wrightington has set up this less expensive operation. The mainly French menu moves from crisp goujons of sole with home-made mayonnaise and a wholegrain mustard sauce, to green and white tagliatelle in a cream sauce with bacon. Stalwarts, such as duck with orange and carré d'agneau, are well handled. House Gamay is £5·70.

CHEFS: David P. Bolan and David Dillon PROPRIETORS: John Nelson and James Sines
OPEN: Mon to Sat, exc Sat L MEALS: 12 to 2, 6 to 11
PRICES: £11 (£18) CARDS: Access, Amex, Carte Blanche, Diners, Visa
SEATS: 75. Private parties: 75 main room. Wheelchair access. Music. Air-conditioned

Gaylord [11/20]

Amethyst House, Spring Gardens, M2 1EA
061-832 6037 and 4866   £8 – £16

The North Indian menu holds few surprises and the style of cooking is a little dated, but the quality is consistent. The décor is a clutter of brass, beaded curtains and bells. Good dishes include chicken tikka, korma badami, mixed bhajis, kulcha bread and pilau rice. Service is brisk. Clumsy tea and coffee.

CHEF: W. Ram PROPRIETORS: Tandoori Catering Consultants Ltd
OPEN: all week MEALS: 12 to 3, 6 to 11.30 (11 Sun)
PRICES: £8 (£16), Set L £4·95 (£8), Set D from £6·75 (£11). Cover 25p. Service 12.5%
CARDS: Access, Amex, Diners, Visa
SEATS: 90. Private parties: 90 main room. Vegetarian meals. Children welcome. No-smoking area. Music

'Our duck is very popular – often 40 per cent of customers ask for duck.' (North-eastern restaurateur)

'I used to feel that long-tried and tested recipes were best and that one sent out a new idea with trepidation. Now, constantly thinking up new ideas keeps one's enthusiasm at such a high level one is bound to cook better.' (Cornish restaurateur)

Giulio's Terrazza [11/20]

14 Nicholas Street, M1 4FE
061-236 4033 and 0250   £11–£16

The Terrazza, surrounded by Chinatown, used to be known as a good, if pricey,
Italian restaurant. Lately it has seemed to be better value. The tiled, whitewashed
dining-room has an air of calm competence. The menu breaks away from the
usual trattoria dishes into stuffed zucchini, swordfish, and prawn kebabs. There
are even – cheekily for these parts – spare ribs baked in aniseed and tomatoes.
Pasta is fresh and dressed in good oils with fresh herbs. The sweets trolley is
unusually impressive and the wine, like everything else, is professionally tended.
House Tocai is £5·90. CELLARMAN'S CHOICE: Campo Fiorin at £9·85.

CHEF: Adrian Kirsten PROPRIETOR: Giulio Nobillo
OPEN: Mon to Sat MEALS: 12 to 2.30, 6.30 to 11.30
PRICES: £10 (£16), Set L £6·75 (£11), Set D from £9·50 (£14). Service 10% CARDS: Access,
Amex, Diners, Visa
SEATS: 110. Private parties: 16 main room. Vegetarian meals. Children's helpings. Smart
dress preferred. Music. Air-conditioned

Happy Garden [10/20]

753 Wilmslow Road, Didsbury M20 0DW
061-445 6979 and 8945   £5–£15

'We serve typical Hong-Kong style Cantonese foods.' The menu falls somewhere
between Chinatown eating-houses and suburban Chinese, with no one-plate
meals or roasts, but a good list of specials. Unusual dishes – fish in lemon sauce,
fried seaweed with prawn toasts, sweet-and-sour fish – are handled with aplomb.
Also there are dim-sum, and pork chop, baked with salt and pepper. The décor
remains rather like that of a tea-shop, but we have not seen the newly opened
upstairs. House wine is 70p a glass.

CHEF: Shun Loy Tang PROPRIETORS: Shun Loy Tang and Yuet Mui Tang
OPEN: all week, exc Sat L and Sun L MEALS: 12 to 2, 6 to 11.45 (12 Fri and Sat)
PRICES: £9 (£15), Set L £2·30 (£5), Set D £7·50 (£11). Service 10% CARDS: Access, Amex,
Diners, Visa
SEATS: 50. Private parties: 70 main room. Vegetarian meals. Children welcome. Wheelchair
access. Music. Air-conditioned

Hong Kong [11/20]

47 Faulkner Street, M1 4EE
061-236 0565   £12–£18

On the first floor, in a mirrored room, is found an old-style Cantonese menu.
Cheap lunches and dim-sum jostle with grander specialities, like Hong Kong
roast duck. Meals can be colourful: vivid green pak choi, yellow noodles, almost
black lacquered duck. Paper cloths and stainless steel teapots reinforce the feeling

*The entries are compiled from the views of readers who have eaten at the restaurants in
the last year, backed up by anonymous inspections and by information supplied and
facts verified by the restaurants.*

that value comes first. But look also for rarely found specialities, such as chicken-blood casserole, ducks' tongues and grilled eel. Chopsticks on request.

CHEF: Chan Ling Kung PROPRIETOR: Dai Lee
OPEN: all week CLOSED: 25 and 26 Dec MEALS: noon to midnight
PRICES: £7 (£12), Set L and D from £10·50 (£16). Service 10% CARDS: Access, Amex, Diners, Visa
SEATS: 350. Private parties: 200 main room. Children welcome. Music. Air-conditioned

Hopewell City [11/20]

45–47 Faulkner Street, M1 4EE
061-236 0091 and 0581   £7–£13

This is the rising star in Chinatown, with a three hundred-dish-strong Cantonese menu that features casseroles, roasts and one-plate dishes. Brisket chow mein has plenty of meat and greens with a rich ginger and aniseed sauce; cold roast duck gets a covering of plum sauce. There's a good range of dim-sum, including excellent kin do ribs, spring rolls and lotus paste buns. Good value. Tea is free.

CHEF: Kam Hung Yung PROPRIETORS: Tony S. K. Ng and Henry C. Y. Yu
OPEN: all week MEALS: noon to 11.45
PRICES: £8 (£13), Set L from £2·80 (£7), Set D from £4 (£8). Service 10% CARDS: Access, Amex, Diners, Visa
SEATS: 100. Private parties: 140 main room. Vegetarian meals. Children welcome. Music. Air-conditioned

Indian Cottage [10/20]

501 Claremont Road, Rusholme, M14 5WV
061-224 0376   £11–£14

In the heart of Manchester's Asian community, this first-floor restaurant is plushly done out in shades of pink and grey, with bentwood chairs and Art Deco-style lamps. The menu is North Indian, with sizzling tikkas and tandoori dishes as well as a full range of curries. There are good reports of the creamy lamb pasanda, makhani chicken, and aloo ghobi masala. Paneer (Indian curd cheese) is served six ways and Basmati rice is well handled. The sweets trolley is a let-down, considering the number of excellent sweet centres in the neighbourhood. To drink there's Kingfisher beer or masala tea flavoured with cardamom and cinnamon.

CHEFS: K. K. Rajput and J. Mall PROPRIETORS: Mr and Mrs Mehta
OPEN: all week MEALS: 12 to 2.30, 6 to 11.30
PRICES: £7 (£14), Set D £6·95 (£11). Service 10% CARDS: Access, Visa
SEATS: 200. Private parties: 250 main room. Vegetarian meals. Children welcome. Music. Air-conditioned

Kathmandu Tandoori [10/20]

42–44 Sackville Street, M1 3WE
061-236 4684   £7–£13

The inside has been refurbished, but the menu remains unchanged, offering a splendid selection of tandoori dishes, from cod to kidney, and good-value set meals, as well as chicken jalfrezi, shahi pasanda, and lobster masala. Barfi and kulfi malai are highly praised.

CHEFS: Ram Das and Bhudi Ram PROPRIETOR: Gopal Mohan Dangol
OPEN: all week CLOSED: bank hols MEALS: 12 to 2.30, 6 to 12
PRICES: £6 (£13), Set L from £3·75 (£7), Set D from £4·75 (£9). Service 10%
CARDS: Access, Amex, Diners, Visa
SEATS: 250. Private parties: 120 main room, 120 private room. Vegetarian meals. Children welcome. Smart dress preferred. Wheelchair access. Music. Air-conditioned

Koreana [10/20]

Kings House, 40 King Street West, M3 2WY
061-832 4330   £7–£16

The most northerly of the Korean restaurants stands out in the context of Manchester for its service and also for the cooking, most of which is done to order, even when quiet, which it often is. The compass points of the cooking, like kim-chee and bulgogi, are well done. Soups are spicy, and sauté squid has been good, too. House wine is £5·50.

CHEF: Hyun K. Kim PROPRIETORS: Koreana Restaurant Ltd
OPEN: Mon to Sat, exc Sat L MEALS: 12 to 2.30, 6.30 to 11.30
PRICES: £10 (£16), Set L from £2·90 (£7), Set D from £8·50 (£13). Service 10%
CARDS: Access, Amex, Diners, Visa
SEATS: 56. Private parties: 60 main room. Vegetarian meals. Children welcome. Smart dress preferred. Music

Kosmos Taverna [11/20]

248 Wilmslow Road, M14 6LD
061-225 9106   £12–£14

This long, narrow, noisy, whitewashed taverna offers good value. The meze at £7·50 is notable, mostly because the starters are the best of the cooking: aubergine purée, hummus, fried squid, chickpeas in tomato sauce flavoured with cumin. Meats tend to be of less good quality and are better in the slow-cooked casseroles than kebabs or steak Diane (a needless touch). Salads are poor, sweets are sticky. The waiters even know the history of some of the traditional dishes. House wine is Italian, at £5·50 a litre; Retsina is £6·50.

CHEF: Loulla Astin PROPRIETORS: Stewart and Loulla Astin
OPEN: all week, D only CLOSED: 25 and 26 Dec MEALS: 6.30 to 11.30 (12.30 Fri and Sat)
PRICES: £9 (£14), Set D £7·50 (£12) CARDS: Access, Visa
SEATS: 70. Private parties: 40 main room. Vegetarian meals. Children's helpings. Wheelchair access. Music. Air-conditioned

Lime Tree [new entry, zero rated]

8 Lapwing Lane, West Didsbury, M20 8WS
061-445 1217
2 miles from M56 exit 10   £11–£15

These premises in an unfashionable part of Didsbury have seen restaurants come and go. Now bright and bistro-like with spider plants, wooden floors and sewing-

machine tables, it combines bistro stalwarts with more modern dishes on a short
and seasonally changing menu. Rack of spring lamb is served with a garlic,
rosemary and redcurrant gravy; monkfish comes in a sauce with honey, ginger
and spring onions. There are black puddings too, and a dark brown one (steamed
chocolate) flanked by a bitter chocolate and butterscotch sauce. House French
£5·50. More reports, please.

CHEF: Patrick Hannity PROPRIETORS: Patrick Hannity and Robert Williams
OPEN: Tue to Sat D, and Sun L MEALS: 12 to 2.30, 6.30 to 11
PRICES: £10 (£15), Set L £6·50 (£11) CARDS: Access, Visa
SEATS: 50. 4 tables outside. Private parties: 50 main room. Vegetarian meals. Children's
helpings (Sun L only). Wheelchair access. Music. Air-conditioned

Market Restaurant [12/20]

Edge Street, M4 1HQ
061-834 3743   £15

The comment in last year's *Guide* about the dining-room being a black hole (in
the sense that it sucked in all kinds of décor) proved all too prophetic. No sooner
was it published than the discovery of an empty cellar beneath the dining-room
led to the closure of the restaurant as possibly unsafe. Now it has re-opened, on
the same principles, thirty yards across the street, but with a slightly expanded
menu of up to twenty dishes a night. Lin Scrannage takes much of the
cosmopolitan influence of Manchester markets and reworks this in modern
British style. Tabbouleh and souvlakia appear beside Stilton mousse with celery
sorbet, smoked mackerel with gooseberry sauce, and spiced beef in almond sauce
with rice. To finish there are tarts and farmhouse cheeses served with home-
made biscuits. Thirty wines keep the accent on value.

CHEF: Lin Scrannage PROPRIETORS: Peter O'Grady, Anne O'Grady and Lin Scrannage
OPEN: Tue to Sat, D only CLOSED: 1 week in spring, 1 week at Christmas, Aug
MEALS: 5 (7 Sat) to 9.30
PRICES: £10 (£15)
SEATS: 34. Private parties: 34 main room. Vegetarian meals. Children welcome. Music

Moss Nook [13/20]

Ringway Road, M22 5NA
061-437 4778
on B5166, 1m from Manchester
airport, M56 exit 5   £25–£29

After fifteen years here, close to the airport, the Nook is a commercial success and
demonstrates that Manchester can support an expensive, high-quality French
restaurant. The atmosphere – red velvet walls and Tiffany lamps – feels like New
York. The cooking represents the professional approach to good food, rather than
that of the gifted amateur: dishes are technically demanding, as is the scope of the
menu, taking in excellent canapés, walnut breads, and elegant pastry work. To
their credit, the Harrisons keep the menu interesting: smooth, rich mousse de foie
gras de canard is served in a filo pastry cup with Cumberland sauce. The black
pudding is given a touch of quality with date-sized smoked French boudins
alongside slices of the best that Bury can make, served with apple. Intriguing

salads of fruits and multifarious leaves, accompany. Duck breast is roasted pink, with matching apricot-stuffed thigh sliced alongside, or there is a generous dish of 'les trois gibiers du chef' – sliced widgeon, pheasant and venison medallions, each in a different sauce. Vegetables are inventive: deep-fried avocado balls, parsnips with honey, and celeriac and carrot mousse. The nouvelle dessert of exotic fruits with fragrant elderflower ice-cream in a brandy-snap basket is excellent. The wines are classically European and would be helped by an injection from the New World. Champagnes and burgundies keep the prices well up. House wine opens at £8.

CHEFS: Robert Thornton and Pauline Harrison PROPRIETORS: Pauline and Derek Harrison
OPEN: Tue to Sat, exc Sat L CLOSED: 24 Dec for 2 weeks MEALS: 12 to 2, 7 to 9.30 (10 Sat)
PRICES: £24 (£29), Set L and D £21 (£25). Service inc CARDS: Access, Amex, Diners, Visa
SEATS: 50. 8 tables outside. Private parties: 10 main room. Car-park, 30 places. Vegetarian
meals. No children under 12. Smart dress preferred. No cigars/pipes in dining-room. Music.
Air-conditioned

Mr Kuks [12/20]

55A Mosley Street, M2 3HY
061-236 0659   £14–£17

The powerful, vinegar-sharpened, bullying tastes of good Peking food are marked in this institutional basement. The varnished panels and the globular paper lanterns, the functional tables and chairs might place this restaurant anywhere from Peking itself to Bromley and back. But chef Mr Lau's use of garlic, chilli oil and vinegar, and his pursuit of contrasts of textures as well as of tastes pinpoint the menu's home as Shantung. Like Mr Bin at Sichuen (formerly at the Dragon Gate) in London (see entry), Chef Lau has become a lone apostle in the city, content to let fashions roll by and rest on his imperial repertoire. This is Peking food with no quarter spared – a vivid edge to the hot-and-sour soup; elegantly sliced breast of chicken and roast pork for the mixed hors d'oeuvre, pungent, tantalising ma-po bean curd, crunchy, twice-fried duck with sweet-and-sour sauce, more sour than sweet, complete with marrow-fat peas in a separate bowl. As in southern French cooking, the flavours are loud, and overshadow any lack of sophistication. Lager is brought by the pint.

CHEF: Mr Lau PROPRIETORS: Stephen Kuk and Geoffrey Cohen
OPEN: all week MEALS: noon to midnight
PRICES: £12 (£17), Set D from £8·50 (£14). Service 10% CARDS: Access, Amex,
Diners, Visa
SEATS: 95. Private parties: 95 main room. Vegetarian meals. Children's helpings. Music.
Air-conditioned

On the Eighth Day [9/20]

109 Oxford Road, All Saints, M1 7DU
061-273 1850   £4

A long-established vegetarian enterprise close to the university, the polytechnic and the BBC, to which it provides an invaluable service. Décor is basic, service matter of fact, and the menu is categorised under soup, stew, and bake, with gaps filled in from day to day. What it does it does extremely well. Two can eat for less than £5 on pea and mint soup, huge pans of salads, Mediterranean stew with brown rice, and old-fashioned puddings. Various teas are supplemented with barley cup and hot spiced apple drink.

CHEF/PROPRIETOR: Co-operative
OPEN: Mon to Sat, exc Sat D MEALS: 11.30 to 7 (4.30 Sat)
PRICES: £3 (£4). Unlicensed, bring your own: no corkage
SEATS: 42. Vegetarian meals. Children's helpings. No smoking. Wheelchair access (also WC). Music. Self-service

Pearl City [12/20]

33 George Street, M1 4PH
061-228 7683   £7 – £20

The décor amounts to some steep stairs, a few tropical fish, a view out from the first floor on to a pair of car parks, and suffers from a through-put of good people aware that this kitchen operates on a level to compete with the best French restaurants. No tricks are pulled and the menu is biased towards the fatty, bony, and textural dishes favoured by Chinese, but here are flavours of great precision, for instance spare ribs of the knobbly, knuckly, stewed kind, with black beans and ginger; tissue-thin rice-flour curves filled with diced meat and vegetables subtly flavoured with garlic; white-dough dumplings filled with intensely reduced chicken stew; neat char siu with fresh pasta. Flavours reach a depth and dimension rarely found, and reflect truly authentic Cantonese cooking in their subtle permutations of five-spice, garlic, ginger and black bean. Cold roast duck has sumptuous flesh and well-lacquered skin, though the fat may be too much for non-Chinese tastes. The 'beef brisket casserole' is pungent and aromatic with five-spice, a textural and again very Chinese dish, served in its wooden-handled, metal cooking-pan. Swift, knowledgeable staff in black uniforms serve with maximum efficiency and minimum fuss, coping well with a rapid turnover.

CHEF: Mr Kan PROPRIETOR: Mr Chan
OPEN: all week MEALS: noon to 4 am (midnight Sun)
PRICES: £12 (£20), Set L from £2.50 (£7). Service 10%
CARDS: Access, Amex, Diners, Visa
SEATS: 400. Private parties: 150 main room, 250 private room. Vegetarian meals. Children's helpings. Music. Air-conditioned

Sanam [9/20]

145 – 151 Wilmslow Road, Rusholme M14 5AW
061-224 1008   £9

One of the more ambitious Indian cafés on the Wilmslow Road in Rusholme. The atmosphere is bright and gaudy: huge, modern chandeliers hang from the varnished pine ceiling; the table-tops are plastic and so are the plants. The food is above average for the area. The kitchen turns out plump quails with butter and herbs, highly spiced kebabs, tikkas, and tandoori dishes. Lambs' brains are a

If, in your opinion, a restaurant is not maintaining the standard of its ratings please inform the Guide *office. Report forms are at the back of the book.*

speciality. Nan or rice are included in the price of main dishes. Cheerful and cheap; unlicensed.

CHEFS: Mr Jabbar and Gulzar Ahmed PROPRIETOR: Abdul Ghafoor Akhtar
OPEN: all week MEALS: noon to midnight
PRICES: £6 (£9). Unlicensed CARDS: Access, Visa
SEATS: 120. Private parties: 100 main room, 50 private room. Vegetarian meals. Children's helpings. Wheelchair access (also WC). Music. Air-conditioned

Siam Orchid [10/20]

Portland Street, M1 4QU
061-236 1388   £6–£16

Manchester's first Thai restaurant shares its entrance with a Japanese/Korean eating place. Orchids are on the tables, portraits of Thai boxing champions on the walls. The sixty-dish menu relies heavily on stir frying. There is a wide range of accessible dishes, including five satays with peanut dip and a sharply dressed salad; fried transparent noodles; steamed fish; and a good version of sweet-and-sour pork with the thinnest coating of egg. Sweets are the likes of bananas in coconut cream or mango with sticky rice. Drink Thai beer. Cheap lunches are a good introduction to the cuisine.

CHEFS: C. Sirisompan, Doy Parry and P. Prince PROPRIETORS: C. Sirisompan and K. Sirisambhand
OPEN: all week, exc Sat L and Sun L MEALS: 11.30 to 2.30, 6.30 to 11.30
PRICES: £9 (£16), Set L £3·50 (£6), Set D from £10 (£14). Service inc at L, 10% at D. Licensed, also bring your own: corkage £2 CARDS: Access, Diners, Visa
SEATS: 55. Private parties: 55 main room. Children's helpings. Music. Air-conditioned

That Café [11/20]

1031 Stockport Road, Levenshulme, M19 2TB
061-432 4672   £12–£15

The clutter of plates, ornaments and old advertising in Joe Quinn's little English bistro tells its own story of Denton's history. The teapots, fancy plates and labels of the Felt Hatters and Trimmers Association all evoke a passing era. The menu of five starters, main courses and a few more sweets is rooted – and at its best – in the tradition of leek and potato soup, Cumberland lamb pie, and rabbit in cider. It also strongly favours vegetarianism: chestnut and vegetable bake; broccoli and Brie pancakes; filo cheese pie. All come surrounded by vegetables and salads. Sweets are crumbles, creams and sundaes. Unlimited coffee, basic wines.
CELLARMAN'S CHOICE: Chablis '85, from Moreau, £8·95.

CHEF/PROPRIETOR: Joe Quinn
OPEN: Tue to Sat D, and Sun L MEALS: 12.30 to 2.30, 7.30 to 11
PRICES: £10 (£15), Set D £7·95 (£12) CARDS: Access, Amex, Visa
SEATS: 50. Private parties: 50 main room, 25 private room. Vegetarian meals. Children's helpings. Music

If, in your opinion, a restaurant is not maintaining the standard of its ratings please inform the Guide office. Report forms are at the back of the book.

Woodlands [new entry, zero rated]

33 Shepley Road, Audenshaw, M34 5DJ
061-336 4241
5m E of Manchester   £14–£25

This double-fronted house fills a gap in the bleak suburbs of east Manchester. The high-ceilinged dining-room looks shiny and polished, with stripped walls, festoon blinds and fabrics in pastel shades; there are starched linen cloths and fresh flowers on the tables. The menu has high aspirations, culling many dishes from famous restaurants. Chef Mark Jackson learned at the Savoy and Claridges in London, and specialised in fish. He follows a French-inspired menu, although the results can be patchy. To start, mille-feuille of salmon has been more successful than a version of the Roux brothers' oeuf froid Carême. Cream of broccoli soup; fillet of beef with port and Stilton sauce with wild rice; or lamb with tarragon sauce have all been creditably handled. All the sweets are home made. The short list of thirty-two wines is cleverly chosen and encourages the belief that this could develop into a serious restaurant. More reports, please.

CHEF: Mark Jackson PROPRIETORS: Rhoda and Dennis Crank
OPEN: Tue to Sun, exc Sat L and Sun D CLOSED: First week Jan, 1 week after Easter,
last 2 weeks Aug MEALS: 12 to 2, 7 to 9.30 (10 Sat)
PRICES: £19 (£25), Set L £9 (£14) CARDS: Access, Visa
SEATS: 36. Private parties: 22 main room, 14 private room. Car-park, 12 places. Children's
helpings. Smart dress preferred. No cigars/pipes in dining-room. Wheelchair access. Music.
Air-conditioned

Woo Sang [11/20]

19–21 George Street, M1 4AG
061-236 3697   £7–£19

The Woo Sang was one of the first Chinese restaurants to forge a reputation among Mancunians. Like seemingly all the restaurants in Chinatown, it is reached along a scruffy, unkempt corridor of stairs. The décor is functional, the restaurant is on two floors, over its own supermarket, and the menu is rooted in the heartland of Canton. The inexpensive meals are the soups, the dim-sum and the one-plate rice and noodle dishes. Some of the snack dishes show the depth of the cooking – wind-dried sausages wrapped in white bread dough; prawn-meat in the wun-tun; paper-wrapped prawns; stuffed bean curd. Other good dishes have included excellent duck with prawn-meat stuffing, and pork chop Shanghai-style (an unusual one-plate meal with large pieces of chop baked with curry seasoning and served on rice). The cold roast duck is one of the best in Manchester's Chinatown. The service has blunted its edge on too many uncritical English diners, but the bill is not aggressive.

Places rating 9 may not be restaurants at all, but still serve good food: expect to find pubs, cafes, small hotels and wine bars.

Restaurants are graded on a scale of 1–20. In the category of 10–11 expect to find the best food in the locality. Ratings of 12 and more are given to restaurants we regard as serving the best food in the region.

CHEF: Kwai Wah Chan PROPRIETORS: Woo Sang Ltd
OPEN: all week MEALS: noon to 11.45pm
PRICES: £11 (£19), Set L from £2·60 (£7), Set D from £15 (£26) for 2. Service 10%
CARDS: Access, Amex, Diners, Visa
SEATS: 210. Private parties: 110 main room, 100 private room. Vegetarian meals. Children's
helpings. Music. Air-conditioned

Yang Sing [15/20]

34 Princess Street, M1 4JY
061-236 2200   £12–£13

Now comfortably established in the basement of this handsome building that is a
reminder of Manchester's former industrial might, with only a red pennant flying
to mark it, the Yang Sing re-emerges as one of the major places to eat in the
north. If restaurant eating is to be both affordable and of high quality, turnover,
as here, must be fast. The décor itself is hectic, even edible. Teams of hanging
ducks line the kitchen window, cakes on shelves run along one wall, fish swim in
the tanks, and the dim-sum trolleys move around the low-ceilinged basement.
The blue fug is from sizzling dishes and is recharged every now and then by a
fresh infusion of smells as another dish is delivered across the room. There is no
finer café in the UK. The menu, in fierce Cantonese tradition, extends to three
hundred dishes, undaunted by the challenge it sets. It has been adjusted to
accommodate the customers – sizzling fillet steak outsells bean curd – but quality
remains paramount, seemingly, throughout. The dim-sum are regarded as the
best in Chinatown, where competition is high. Other highlights include steamed
sea bass, duck with orange, chicken in black-bean sauce, crispy roast chicken,
and prawns fried with salt and chilli. For Chinophiles there are ducks' tongues,
chicken feet, pigs' trotters, jellyfish and sea slug, or try braised carp with dry bean
curd skin or the casserole supreme of dry oysters, pigs' tendons, dried waterweed,
sea slug, dried scallops, squid and prawns. The service can be brusque, as there is
real pressure on tables and diners are not expected to linger in western style,
which is how the prices are kept down.

CHEF: Harry Yeung PROPRIETORS: Yang Sing Restaurant Ltd
OPEN: all week CLOSED: 25 Dec MEALS: noon to 11
PRICES: £7 (£12), Set L and D £9 (£13). Service 10% CARDS: Access, Amex
SEATS: 140. Private parties: 200 private room. Children welcome. Wheelchair access. Music.
Air-conditioned

MARCH Cambridgeshire   map 6

Acre [9/20]

March PE15 9JD
MARCH (0354) 57116   £5

Formerly the Rose and Crown, but Mrs Charnock is now so well established in
the area that regulars telephone in their orders for roast beef or chicken pie ahead
of time, before the food runs out, as it often does. Market days are particularly

---

Report forms are at the back of the book.

busy. The pattern is of good-value home cooking: sausage plait, good brown bread, steak and kidney pie. Greene King beers.

CHEF: Mrs Charnock PROPRIETOR: Mr Charnock
OPEN: Mon to Sat, L only MEALS: 12.30 to 2.30
PRICES: Set L £2·50 (£5). Service inc
SEATS: 50. 5 tables outside. Children's helpings. Wheelchair access. Music

---

MAWGAN Cornwall

map 1

Yard Bistro [10/20]

Trelowarren, Mawgan TR12 6AF
MAWGAN (032 622) 595
£15

The bistro is part of an old carriage-house facing a courtyard on the Vyvyan family estate. Trevor Bayfield's regularly changing dinner menu features the likes of grilled sardines, sirloin steak with Stilton and red-wine sauce, and guinea-fowl with black pepper. The home-pickled salmon is excellent, as are the home-baked rolls. About a dozen wines; house wine is £5·25 a litre. Soups and salads at lunchtime.

CHEF: Trevor Bayfield PROPRIETOR: Sir John Vyvyan
OPEN: all week, exc Sun L CLOSED: Jan and Feb, Mon in winter MEALS: 12 to 2, 7 to 9
PRICES: £10 (£15)
SEATS: 50. 6 tables outside. Private parties: 50 main room. Car-park, 30 places. Children welcome. Wheelchair access (also WC). Music

---

MELMERBY Cumbria

map 7

Village Bakery [11/20] ✦

Melmerby CA10 1HE
LANGWATHBY (076 881) 515
£9

This remarkable bakery uses flour ground at a local watermill, and traditional, wood-fired brick ovens. In tune with its ecological grounding, not only the vegetables are local, but also the staff. Beyond the fine bread, tarts and pies, Cumberland sausages are a fixture on a menu that might also take in pizzas. Breakfasts include Loch Fyne kippers; other fish are cooked in the ashes of the oven. Even the wine is organic: vin du pays du Gard, at £4·75.

CHEF: Diane Richter PROPRIETORS: Lis and Andrew Whitley
OPEN: Tue to Sun breakfast and L only, and bank hol Mons L CLOSED: Christmas to Easter
MEALS: 8.30 to 11.30, 12 to 2.30
PRICES: £7 (£9), Set L £6·50 (£9), Snacks from 30p. Service inc CARDS: Access, Visa
SEATS: 40. Private parties: 25 main room. Car-park, 8 places. Vegetarian meals. Children's helpings. No smoking in dining-room. Wheelchair access

---

The 1989 Guide will appear before Christmas 1988. Reports are particularly helpful in the spring. Report forms are at the back of this book, but just write a letter if you prefer. Address it to The Good Food Guide, FREEPOST, 14 Buckingham Street, London WC2N 6BR. *No stamp is necessary if you post it in the UK.*

MEVAGISSEY Cornwall   map 1

Mr Bistro [9/20] ✗

East Quay, Mevagissey PL26 6QH
MEVAGISSEY (0726) 842432/1   £8–£14

This converted pilchard store by the quay is still the only local restaurant trying
to serve fresh fish. Romer Robins is back in the kitchen and the cooking holds up
well when she is on the scene. The menu moves from specialities, such as hot
devilled crab and John Dory with prawn sauce, to deep-fried queenies and grilled
lemon sole; the choice depends on the boats. Puddings are bolstered with plenty
of Cornish cream. Coffee comes in mugs. Best value is at lunchtime. The wine list
centres on Spain. CELLARMAN'S CHOICE: Rioja, Viña Ramona, Gran Reserva '78,
at £9·25.

CHEFS: Romer Robins and Yvonne Kent PROPRIETORS: Chris and Romer Robins
OPEN: all week CLOSED: Oct to Easter, exc Sat during Feb and Mar MEALS: 12 to 2, 7 to 10
PRICES: L£5 (£8), D£14 (£19) CARDS: Access, Amex, Diners, Visa
SEATS: 32. Private parties: 20 main room. Vegetarian meals. Children's helpings.
Wheelchair access (1 step)

MIDDLE WALLOP Hampshire   map 2

▲ Fifehead Manor [12/20] ✗

Middle Wallop SO20 8EG
ANDOVER (0264) 781565   £13–£26

The red-brick Hampshire manor house is surrounded by tall trees and pleasant
gardens, on a hill set back from the main road through the village. Nicholas
Ruthven-Stuart is a serious cook. Colourful, inventive ideas span both sides of the
Channel. Starters show the style: choux pastry cases filled with cheese on a vivid
red tomato sauce; gravlax; sweetbreads in pastry with a superb meaty sauce.
Fillets of salmon and turbot are cooked together wrapped in green leaves, so the
result looks like a section of Battenburg cake. Good dishes have included veal in
orange sauce and casserole of guinea-fowl with lime and cranberries. Vegetables
vary with main courses. Well-made sweets are mainly ice-creams and sorbets.
Good value bar lunches. Fifty wines centre on France, including
CELLARMAN'S CHOICE: Montagny *premier cru*, Caves de Buxy '85, at £12·30.

CHEF: Nicholas Ruthven-Stuart PROPRIETOR: Margaret van Veelen
OPEN: all week CLOSED: 1 week at Christmas MEALS: 12 to 2.30, 7.30 to 9.30
PRICES: £21 (£26), Set L from £7·50 (£13), Set D £16 (£20), Snacks from £1·50. Service inc
CARDS: Access, Amex, Diners, Visa
SEATS: 40. Private parties: 16 main room, 14 private room. Car-park, 50 places. Children's
helpings. Wheelchair access (also WC)
ACCOMMODATION: 16 rooms, all with bath/shower. Rooms for disabled. B&B £40 to £58.
Children welcome. Baby facilities. Pets welcome. Afternoon teas. Garden. TV. Phone. Scenic.
Doors close at 12. Confirm by 6

---

*The average price quoted in brackets is for an average three-course meal including
service, VAT, coffee and half a bottle of house wine or the equivalent in an ethnic
restaurant.*

MIDHURST West Sussex

Maxine's [11/20] 🍴

map 3

Red Lion Street, Midhurst GU29 9PB
MIDHURST (073 081) 6271   £11–£18

Robert and Marti de Jager's very popular local restaurant is prominently set in a
classic half-timbered Tudor building opposite the parish church. Set lunches are
good value for tomatoes in blue-cheese dressing, fennel soup, chicken in curry
and banana sauce, and vanilla ice-cream with sticky coffee syrup. There are also
votes for the moules marinière, pasta with seafood Mornay, and honey-roast
ham. Vegetables are fresh and perfectly cooked. Service is friendly and attentive.
House wines are £5 a bottle.

CHEF: Robert de Jager PROPRIETORS: Robert and Marti de Jager
OPEN: all week, exc Mon L, and Tue MEALS: 12 to 2, 7 to 10
PRICES: £14 (£18), Set L £7·25 (£11). Service inc CARDS: Access, Amex, Diners, Visa
SEATS: 27. Private parties: 30 main room. Vegetarian meals. Children's helpings

MOLLINGTON Cheshire

map 4

▲ *Crabwall Manor* [new entry, zero rated]

Mollington CH1 6NE
GREAT MOLLINGTON (0244) 851666   £16–£35

This is an out-and-out attempt to set up a leading country-house hotel. A Grade
II Gothick, castellated manor has been refurbished into 'informal elegance'. A
proven team has been put in to make it work: David Brockett, formerly general
manager at Chewton Glen, New Milton, with Michael Truelove, formerly at the
Box Tree, Ilkley, in the kitchen. The menu reads much like the Box Tree's, and
relies heavily on saucing. First meals have been notable for the quality of the raw
materials and the cleverness of the conception: a mousse of scallops filled with
the white flesh of a crab and served with a crab sauce; fish terrine served with
warm butter sauce; loin of veal with its own sweetbreads and a sauce flavoured
by sherry. The Box Tree trademark of a tuile with rose ice-cream and
strawberries is here, too. The green and white dining-room is run by staff in
matching waistcoats who are anxiously attentive. The wine list runs to nearly
two hundred bottles, heavily weighted to burgundy and claret, with a starting
price of £7·50. CELLARMAN'S CHOICE: La Rioja Alta '73, £18·50.
More reports, please.

CHEF: Michael Truelove PROPRIETORS: Tudor Heritage Inns plc
OPEN: all week MEALS: 12.30 to 2, 7 to 9.30
PRICES: £27 (£35), Set L £12 (£16), Set D £21 (£25). Service inc CARDS: Access, Amex,
Diners, Visa
SEATS: 80. Private parties: 16 main room, 50 and 100 private rooms. Car-park, 60 places.
Children's helpings. No children under 5. Jacket and tie. No cigars/pipes in dining-room.
Wheelchair access (3 steps; also WC). Air-conditioned
ACCOMMODATION: 32 rooms, all with bath/shower. Rooms for disabled. B&B £60 to £80.
No children under 5. Afternoon teas. Garden. TV. Phone. Scenic. Confirm by 6

It is helpful if restaurateurs keep the office up to date with any changes.

MORETON-IN-MARSH Gloucestershire   map 2

Lambs [10/20]

High Street, Moreton-in-Marsh GL56 0AX
MORETON-IN-MARSH (0608) 50251   £16

The yellow stone building in the centre of the village, originally stabling, has had
a number of owners in recent years. Judy Moore has found a sensible formula to
make it work as a wine bar-cum-restaurant, making much use of organic and
local produce and serving everything with freshly baked wholemeal rolls.
Conventional centrepieces are often overshadowed by some enterprising dishes,
for instance pancakes filled with asparagus and Cheddar; smoked pork sausage in
brioche; dim-sum-style dumplings. The quality of the ingredients lifts salads. Fish
can be as daring as sole with coconut and ginger; there has been goose with a
sauce of gooseberries and elderflowers. The choices of forty wines shows similar
enterprise. House French is £6·30.

CHEF/PROPRIETOR: Judy Moore
OPEN: Mon to Sat, exc Tue L MEALS: 12 to 2, 7 to 10
PRICES: £11 (£16) CARDS: Access, Amex, Diners, Visa
SEATS: 30. Private parties: 20 main room, 20 and 12 private rooms. Vegetarian meals.
Children's helpings. No-smoking area. Wheelchair access

MORPETH Northumberland   map 7

La Brasserie [10/20]

---

59 Bridge Street, Morpeth NE61 1PQ
MORPETH (0670) 516200 and 516205   £12–£16

Mr Wilkinson changed the name of the Ponte Gourmet last year, when he
became the sole proprietor, but since he was and still is the chef, changes are
negligible and the food has remained of a standard. Home-made pasta dishes –
noodles, carbonara, cannelloni in cheese sauce – are supplemented by fish,
steaks and other items, such as game pie or chicken tempura, with crêpes Suzette
to finish. The daily changing bar meals are less expensive, there is a vegetarian
menu, and the ninety wines are reasonably priced, with a spread of Italian bottles
to match the food. CELLARMAN'S CHOICE: Vino Nobile di Montepulciano Riserva
'81, from Fognono, £7·95.

CHEF/PROPRIETOR: R. H. Wilkinson
OPEN: Tue to Sun, exc Sun D MEALS: 11.30 to 2, 6.30 to 11
PRICES: £11 (£16), Set L and D £7·25 (£12), Snacks from £1·75 CARDS: Access, Amex,
Diners, Visa
SEATS: 50. Private parties: 30 main room, 50 private room. Car-park, 6 places. Vegetarian
meals. Children's helpings

If you cannot honour a restaurant booking, always phone to cancel.

*The entries are compiled from the views of readers who have eaten at the restaurants in
the last year, backed up by anonymous inspections and by information supplied and
facts verified by the restaurants.*

MOULTON North Yorkshire

map 7

Black Bull [12/20] ✗

Moulton DL10 6QJ
BARTON (032 577) 289
1½m off A1, SE of Scotch Corner

£12–£24

The Bull charges on, and many faces are still the same after a number of years. It is to the Pagendams' credit that the separate dining-rooms, each with its own style, are integrated. The pub lounge, where orders are taken, is a country pub: wooden settles with red velour seating, lots of brass, and an inglenook. Then there is a split-level fisherman's bar, all mock-Victorian, complete with wood panelling, stuffed fish, and a portrait of Queen Victoria herself. The conservatory is airy and plant-filled, and boasts a poster of Georges Duboeuf and Paul Bocuse. Off here, opposite the kitchen, is the rabbit warren of private rooms, again mock-Victorian. Then, at the back, spoiled only because you look out on to the car park, is the Pullman carriage, fifty-three years old and lovingly restored, with all the ambience that cream lace curtains, wing chairs covered in green velvet and piped in green and cream, filigree luggage racks, and gleaming brass hangers on the doors, can muster. It is quieter here. An air of civility and propriety hovers. Fish is the main business. Stuart Birkett has taken over the range after four years as sous chef, but the style is the same, often quite 1960s: good lobsters are drowned in white gratiné sauces; dishes are let down by inexpensive butters and oils; cheeses are served out of condition. The hard core of the menu, though, is exact: fine fish and fine vegetables, both of irreproachable quality, cooked à point. Steaks also draw recommendations. The wine list has been compiled by the same sure hand, being extensive, strong in fine whites, but equally good under £10. Relative bargains last year included Côtes Rôtie '80, from Guigal, at £12·95, and Ch. Montrose '70, at £27·50. CELLARMAN'S CHOICE: Pouilly-Fumé, Château de Tracy '85, at £9·95.

CHEF: Stuart Birkett PROPRIETORS: Mr and Mrs G. H. Pagendam
OPEN: Mon to Sat CLOSED: 24 to 31 Dec MEALS: 12 to 2.30, 6 to 10.30 (11 Fri and Sat)
PRICES: £17 (£24), Set L £7 (£12), Snacks from £1 CARDS: Access, Amex, Visa
SEATS: 120. 4 tables outside. Private parties: 30 main room, 10 and 30 private rooms.
Car-park, 80 places. No children under 7

NAILSWORTH Gloucestershire

map 2

William's Kitchen [12/20] ✝

3 Fountain Street, Nailsworth GL6 0BL
NAILSWORTH (045 383) 2240

£14–£19

The restaurant is an extension of the delicatessen of the same name, and looks very new and light. Garry Flynn cooks modern, generous dishes that make the best of daily produce without resorting to precious ideas. The style is flexible: choose one course or three from a menu of fifteen dishes that might include quail eggs with courgette and a watercress mayonnaise; excellent warm

---

▮ *This symbol is awarded only to restaurants with outstanding wine cellars.*

salad of monkfish, with avocado and raspberry vinegar; feuilleté of pigeon breast with oyster mushrooms and cream, intensified with sherry vinegar. Fresh fish is a strength, since the place is also a fishmonger's: sea bass on a bed of pulses; paupiettes of lemon sole on creamed leek tartlets with langoustine sauce. Excellent, rough, moist wholemeal bread is baked on the premises. Sweets are made outside, however, and fall down badly. The wine list centres on France, with burgundy well represented. House red Ventoux, and white Lubéron, are £5.

CHEF: Garry Flynn PROPRIETOR: William Beeston
OPEN: Tue to Sat, D only MEALS: 7.30 to 10
PRICES: £14 (£19), Set D from £10 (£14) CARDS: Access, Visa
SEATS: 40. Children's helpings

NANTWICH Cheshire   map 5

▲ *Rookery Hall* [14/20]

Worleston, nr Nantwich, CW5 6DQ
NANTWICH (0270) 626866
on B5074, off A51   £24–£37

The Hall was rebuilt in 1867 in the style of a French château. It is grandly impressive as one comes up the drive past the lake, the gardens, the fountains and the cows. Inside is country-house comfort with real fires, sofas, good pictures and a magnificent panelled dining-room that shines with polished woodwork and crystal glassware. This is now one of Britain's most likeable country-house hotels, even if it's not the cheapest. Clive Howe's cooking is careful and exact. The French influence is evident, mostly in an array of sauces, but there are more British touches, from the seasonal vegetables (roots and all) to the fine selection of indigenous unpasteurised cheeses. Cheshire sausages, a variation on Glamorgan, are made with local cheese and served on leeks with beurre blanc. An authoritative menu lists no fewer than twenty-nine dishes before sweets, breaking in the middle for a Lamberhurst wine water ice or a glass of apple brandy. Centrepieces feature roast angler-fish with lemon and thyme butter; veal topped with Stilton soufflé and creamed forest mushrooms; loin of Welsh lamb with roast garlic and tarragon noodles. To finish, there is bread-and-butter pudding with honey ice-cream. Set lunches are relatively good value, although extras can put the bill up. The long wine list has some unusual bottles from France, but prices do not encourage experimentation. The house wines are unusually good burgundies and not really overpriced at £12·50; alas, there is little cheaper. CELLARMAN'S CHOICE: St Emilion, Ch. Garaud '78 at £17·50.

CHEF: Clive Howe PROPRIETORS: Audrey and Peter Marks
OPEN: all week MEALS: 12.15 to 1.45, 7 to 9.15 (9.45 Sat)
PRICES: Set L from £12·95 (£24), Set D from £25 (£37) CARDS: Access, Amex, Diners, Visa
SEATS: 55. Private parties: 12 main room, 8, 22 and 40 private rooms. Car-park, 30 places.
Vegetarian meals. No children under 10. Jacket and tie. Wheelchair access (also WC)
ACCOMMODATION: 11 rooms, all with bath/shower. Rooms for disabled. B&B £60 to £90.
Deposit: 50%: No children under 10. No pets. Garden. Tennis. Fishing. TV. Phone. Scenic.
Doors close at 12

Reports on good shops, hotels and cafes in your area are welcome.

Fisherman's Lodge [11/20]

Jesmond Dene, NE7 7BQ
091-281 3281 £15–£29

The Lodge is the most likely restaurant for a special occasion or a meal on
Tyneside expenses. The quality of the fish, much of it out of North Shields,
upholds a conservative menu strong on sauces. Service is by candlelight and the
house wines at £6·80 are served in goblets: CELLARMAN'S CHOICE: Sauvignon de
Touraine '85, at £9·40.

CHEF: Terence Laybourne PROPRIETORS: Franco and Pamela Cetoloni
OPEN: Mon to Sat, exc Sat L CLOSED: 25 Dec to 2 Jan MEALS: 12 to 2, 7 to 11
PRICES: £21 (£29), Set L from £9·80 (£15) CARDS: Access, Amex, Diners, Visa
SEATS: 70. 3 tables outside. private parties: 14 main room, 14 and 40 private rooms.
Car-park, 45 places. Children's helpings. No children under 6. Smart dress preferred.
Wheelchair access

Great Wall [10/20]

35–39 Bath Lane, Newcastle NE4 5SP
091-232 0517 and 7616 £7–£21

The smart, relaxed décor makes a comfortable setting for a mid-price Chinese
meal. The cooking has Cantonese leanings, although the kitchen seems to work
best with westernised dishes and ingredients, and sweet-and-sour is handled
better than bean curd. Starters and snacks, such as squid and crab dumplings,
seaweed, or crisp, deep-fried wun-tun, have been good, likewise noodle dishes.
There's an interesting choice for vegetarians. House wine is £6 a bottle.

CHEF: Peter Ma PROPRIETOR: Wah Fuk Ma
OPEN: all week MEALS: 12 to 1.45, 6 to 11.15 (12 Fri and Sat)
PRICES: £12 (£21), Set L £2·80 (£7), Set D £9 (£13) CARDS: Access, Amex, Diners, Visa
SEATS: 100. Private parties: 100 main room. Vegetarian meals. Children welcome.
Wheelchair access. Music. Air-conditioned

Jade Garden [10/20]

53 Stowell Street, Newcastle NE1 4YB
091-261 5889 £7–£15

While other Chinese restaurants in a bullish new Chinatown have moved flashily
upmarket, the Jade Garden has consolidated its reputation for old-style, good-
value Cantonese cooking. The kitchen still puts its faith in chicken feet and pigs'
intestines, and offers the city's best selection of roast and barbecued meats, ho fun
and noodle dishes. Roast duck and pork with noodles in soup has huge quantities
of moist meat fanned across the top, and is a bargain at £3·20. Deep-fried bean
curd with vegetables; crisp wun-tun; mushrooms in soy sauce and ginger; and
king prawns fried with ginger, have all impressed. Some reports suggest that

CELLARMAN'S CHOICE: *This is a wine recommended by the restaurateur which is more
expensive than the house wine but is good value and fitting for the kind of food served.*

performance is patchy; it may just be that some people do not find the style to their taste, and prefer the popular Peking dishes over the road. House wine is £6.

CHEF: Chuen Fai Liu PROPRIETORS: Alex Chung and Chuen Fai Liu
OPEN: all week MEALS: noon to 11.15pm (12 Fri and Sat)
PRICES: £8 (£15), Set L £3 (£7), Set D from £4·20 (£9) CARDS: Access, Amex, Diners, Visa
SEATS: 120. Private parties: 120 main room. Vegetarian meals. Children welcome.
Wheelchair access (also WC). Music. Air-conditioned

King Neptune [new entry, zero rated]

34–36 Stowell Street, NE1 4XB
091-261 6657   £7–£15

The city's Chinese restaurants tend to start with a bang and fizzle out after a few months. This smart, upstairs dining-room promises good things since opening at Christmas 1986. Despite the fashionable billing as a Peking and Seafood restaurant, the kitchen also delivers fine vegetarian dishes, such as excellent ma po bean curd, green beans with a dry dressing of black beans and roasted chillies, and an imitation of sweet-and-sour pork made with buttered Brazil nuts. Hand-made noodles are standard and little parcels of fish, wrapped in strands of beaten egg before steaming, show the skill of the kitchen. Pleasant, knowlegeable service. More reports, please.

CHEF: Edward Au PROPRIETOR: Andrew and Yen Mack
OPEN: all week MEALS: 12 to 2.15, 6.30 to 11.15 (6 to 12 Sat)
PRICES: £9 (£14), Set L £3·80 (£7), Set D £10·50 (£15) CARDS: Access, Amex, Diners, Visa
SEATS: 125. Private parties: 80 main room, 60 private room. Vegetarian meals. Children
welcome. Smart dress preferred. Wheelchair access (also WC). Music

Madeleine's [9/20]

134 Heaton Road, NE6 5HN
091-276 5277   £9

An honest, plain, vegetarian restaurant with inventive cooking and no pretensions. The menu is eclectically international, taking in tandoori Brazil nut roast and apricot soya ice, as well as more familiar Indian and Mexican dishes. The music matches: jazz, blues, African, South American. House wine is £2·50 for half a litre.

CHEF: Kate Locke PROPRIETORS: Kate and Tony Locke
OPEN: all week MEALS: 12 to 2. 7 to 10
PRICES: £5 (£9), Snacks from £1·20 CARDS: Access, Visa
SEATS: 40. Private parties: 10 main room. Vegetarian meals. Children's helpings.
No smoking. Wheelchair access (1 step). Music

Michael's Brasserie [11/20]

2 High Bridge Court, High Bridge, NE1 1EN
091-232 0056   £12–£21

Michael and Kim Powney used to run a well-thought of greengrocer's in Gosforth. Now their small restaurant – 'small enough not to make concessions to prawn cocktails' – not far from the theatre, provides a refreshing mix of modern

British and French cooking. The set lunch is excellent value, with a gist of leek and potato soup, and pork cutlets with cream sauce. The *carte* is more artful: pastry cases are filled with wild mushrooms or asparagus with an orange hollandaise. Pigeon and wild salmon feature, as do steaks, for which reports are positive. A speciality is breast of pheasant with a mushroom duxelles, wrapped in a cabbage leaf and braised over root vegetables. A stylish plate of miniature sweets consisted of passion-fruit sorbet, raspberry mousse, rhubarb parfait, chocolate marquise, and strawberry torte. Coffee comes with fudge; mineral water comes from Abbey Well at Morpeth. Fifty wines are not greedily marked up.

CHEF: Clive Imber PROPRIETORS: Michael Powney and Kim Powney
OPEN: Mon to Sat, exc Sat L MEALS: 12 to 2, 7 to 10.45
PRICES: £14 (£21), Set L £6·95 (£12). Service 10% CARDS: Access, Visa
SEATS: 32. Private parties: 18 main room. Children's helpings. Music

New Emperor [11/20]

Forth House, Berwick Street, NE1 5EF
091-232 8856   £7–£17

The place that set the trend for genuine Chinese restaurants in Newcastle has been refurbished by new owners in the Sino-Geordie style – cool blues and expensive carpets. The menu is aimed mainly at Westerners, although there are some more interesting chef's specials. The strength is in the noodles, the Singapore rice stick vermicelli and the succulent roast pork and duck. Vegetable hot-and-sour soup is strong on flavour, and spring rolls are crisply fried. Service is more willing than polished. House wine is £6·50 a litre.

CHEF: Mr Yau PROPRIETOR: Peter Wu
OPEN: all week MEALS: noon to 3.30am
PRICES: £10 (£17), Set L from £2·70 (£7), Set D £9 (£14) CARDS: Access, Amex, Diners, Visa
SEATS: 200. Private parties: 150 main room, 100 private room. Vegetarian meals. Children's helpings. Wheelchair access. Music

Rupali [10/20]

6 Bigg Market, NE1 1UW
091-232 8629   £15

Still reckoned to be the best 'bread-and-butter' curry-house in town, offering reliable North Indian curries and tandoori dishes and good value. Vegetable dishes are well reported. There are plenty of bargains, including cheap lunches and meals for early-evening eaters, plus a four-course dinner with a glass of wine for under £6 on Thursdays.

CHEF: Abdul Khalick PROPRIETOR: Abdul Latif
OPEN: all week, exc Sun L MEALS: 12 to 2.30, 7 to 11.30
PRICES: £9 (£15) CARDS: Access, Amex, Diners, Visa
SEATS: 54. Private parties: 50 main room. Vegetarian meals. Children's helpings. Smart dress preferred. Music

It is always advisable to book a restaurant in advance.

Sachins [11/20]

Forth Banks, NE1 3SG
091-261 9035   £12–£18

Once a pub, now Punjabi. Eggs and nuts supplement cream and butter for a range of dishes such as butter chicken and murgh jalfrezi. Hasina kebab (marinated lamb cooked in the tandoor) is a good starter, and vegetables include a dish of lotus roots with potatoes. Good value. To drink there's real ale from Theakston's, as well as house wine at £5·95 a bottle.

CHEF: Dinesh Rawlley PROPRIETOR: L. G. Cunningham
OPEN: Mon to Sat CLOSED: Easter and Christmas MEALS: 12 to 2.15, 6 to 11.15
PRICES: £11 (£18), Set L from £7·95 (£12) CARDS: Access, Amex, Diners, Visa
SEATS: 100. 4 tables outside. Private parties: 60 main room, 30 private room. Car-park, 6 places. Vegetarian meals. Wheelchair access. Music

---

NEW MILTON Hampshire   map 2

▲ *Marryat Room, Chewton Glen Hotel* [12/20]

Christchurch Road, New Milton BH25 6QS
HIGHCLIFFE (0425) 25341   £16–£36

Martin Skan's converted guest-house, which he took on as a decayed ruin in 1966, last year became the first hotel outside London to pick up the English Tourist Board's Five Gold Crowns award, a non-qualitative award, admittedly, but a tribute to the quantity of amenities. The transformation of Chewton Glen into a luxurious, international cocoon, has been extraordinary. Everything seems to have been swept, dusted and plumped up. The restaurant is just part of the equation, necessarily (in the marketing concept) French and modern, and necessarily (in the financial concept) expensive. The cooking, though, appears to have lost its way. Much of it is over-elaborate, overdressed, unnecessarily rich and stuffed, garnished and dolled up. It may be that the basis for this contention comes from evenings when M. Chevillard was not there – one inspection meal was a Sunday – but there is no commensurate cut in the bill on those nights. Some dishes are just plain dreary – a thick heavy ballotine of quail, for instance – and others are out of balance, like a fine chicken overpowered by a Stilton stuffing. Les deux mille-feuilles actually comprise eight different flavours all trying to shout across each other. This is a prime example of a kitchen saddled with a redundant cuisine from another country. The lengthy wine list has a few bargains, however, for the discerning eye; it is not as expensive as rooms at £116 a night might have you to expect. House wine, at lunch only, is £6.
CELLARMAN'S CHOICE: Saint Amour '85, from Sarrau, £12·25.

If you cannot honour a restaurant booking, always phone to cancel.

The 1989 Guide *will appear before Christmas 1988. Reports are particularly helpful in the spring. Report forms are at the back of this book, but just write a letter if you prefer. Address it to* The Good Food Guide, FREEPOST, *14 Buckingham Street, London WC2N 6BR. No stamp is necessary if you post it in the UK.*

CHEF: Pierre Chevillard PROPRIETOR: Martin Skan
OPEN: all week MEALS: 12.30 to 2, 7.30 to 9.30
PRICES: £28 (£36), Set L from £12·50 (£16), Set D £29·50 (£36). Service inc
CARDS: Access, Amex, Diners, Visa
SEATS: 120. 6 tables outside. Private parties: 20 main room, 6 and 80 private rooms.
Car-park, 100 places. Children's helpings. No children under 7. Jacket and tie.
No cigars/pipes in dining-room
ACCOMMODATION: 44 rooms, all with bath/shower. Rooms for disabled. B&B £106 to
£116. No children under 7. Afternoon teas. Garden. Swimming-pool. Tennis. Golf. Snooker.
TV. Phone. Scenic. Doors close at 12 [GHG]

NEWTOWN IN ST MARTIN Cornwall — map 1
Anthea's [11/20] ✘

Newtown in St Martin
MANACCAN (032 623) 352
8m SE of Helston — £12

Next to the pub, with the name on the gate. The living-room is the bistro, with
wooden tables and benches, red checked cloths and candles in bottles, and
Anthea France's daughter is the waitress. The blackboard offers mid-Channel
cooking: rough-textured pork terrine with green peppercorns; shoulder of lamb
with garlic and rosemary. But simple things are done well and monkfish with
hollandaise and rare fillet of beef with sour cream sauce are outstanding main
courses. Chocolate fudge cake, brown-bread ice-cream or Stilton to follow. No
licence, but bring your own or buy from the pub next door.

CHEF/PROPRIETOR: Anthea France
OPEN: Wed to Sat, D only MEALS: 7.30 to 10
PRICES: Set D £11 (£12). Unlicensed, bring your own: no corkage
SEATS: 26. 1 table outside. Private parties: 26 main room, 6 private room. Car-park, 8 places.
Vegetarian meals. Children's helpings. Wheelchair access (also WC). Music

---

NORTHAMPTON Northamptonshire — map 3
Sun Rise [10/20] ✝

18 Kingsley Park Terrace, Northampton NN2 7HG
NORTHAMPTON (0604) 711228 — £7–£17

The most creditable Chinese restaurant in the Northampton area is a mile from
the city centre in a parade of shops. The décor is smart, service is on the ball and
the menu has some good Cantonese and Pekinese dishes. Paper-wrapped chicken
is the best starter and there is worthwhile Peking duck with all the proper
trimmings. Sizzling king prawns come with spring onions and black-bean sauce.
The wine list has a couple from China – Dynasty is £10 – and house red and
white are £5 a bottle.

PROPRIETORS: K. F. Wan, C. Y. Wan and C. K. Wan
OPEN: all week MEALS: 12 to 2, 5.30 to 11.30 (12 Fri and Sat)
PRICES: £10 (£17), Set L £3 (£7), Set D from £8 (£12). Service 10% CARDS: Access, Amex,
Diners, Visa
SEATS: 50. Private parties: 50 main room. Vegetarian meals. Children welcome. Wheelchair
access. Music. Air-conditioned

NORTH HUISH Devon
map 1

▲ *Brookdale House* [13/20]

North Huish TQ10 9NR
GARA BRIDGE (054 882) 402 and 415
£22–£30

The Trevor-Ropers, formerly at Burghfield, have moved to this secluded
Victorian Gothic house built by a rector, which explains many of the church-like
effects. The dining-room has an exceptional ceiling, garlanded with a moulding
of flowers and fruits. It is a small room with a green view through tall windows.
The menu is short, attractively presented and makes a virtue of its supplies.
Scallops appear in a pastry case with a garlic cream sauce notable for the quality
of its butter; chicken is boned and served with Roquefort. A typically successful
main dish has been fillet of well-hung, almost gamey beef offset by a gathered,
Dick Whittington-style bag of well-browned, light filo filled with fresh spinach
and sorrel purée, both in the best type of modern red wine and stock sauce,
slightly caramelised. The wrapping up of things continues into the sweets, for
instance meringue vol-au-vent shapes filled with mango sorbet and fruits, or
pastry case filled with honey and brandy ice-cream. The wine list bears clear
signs of Mr Trevor-Roper's views – plenty of New World for value and directness;
some quality French. Though the emphasis is on the £15 to £20 bracket, ten
wines are singled out for recommendation, are not overpriced and are offered by
the glass. Bottle prices start at £7·65.

CHEF: Carol Trevor-Roper PROPRIETORS: Charles and Carol Trevor-Roper
OPEN: all week, D only MEALS: 7.30 to 9
PRICES: £22 (£30), Set D £16 (£22) CARDS: Access, Visa
SEATS: 24. Private parties: 8 main room. Car-park, 15 places. No children under 10. No
smoking in dining-room
ACCOMMODATION: 8 rooms, all with bath/shower. B&B £45 to £60. No children under 10.
Afternoon teas. Garden. TV. Phone. Scenic. Doors close at 12. Confirm by 7

NORTHLEACH Gloucestershire
map 2

▲ *Fossebridge Inn* [12/20]

Fossebridge, Northleach GL54 3JS
FOSSEBRIDGE (028 572) 721
on A429, 3m from Northleach
£19–£27

The Gloucestershire restaurant scene has suddenly come to life, and the county
now has more than its share of serious new eating places. This old, creeper-
covered inn, with its own lake and urns on the lawn, is part of the revival. The
new owners, Hugh and Suzanne Roberts (ex-White Bear, Shipston on Stour)
have brought in Bruce Buchan from The Bear Hotel at Hungerford. The menu
keeps up fashions with roulade of monkfish and spinach, on a dark meaty sauce,
with Pinot Noir; or fillet of English lamb with a blob of sliced, sauté shallots and a
powerfully reduced sauce flavoured with Wiltshire wholegrain mustard. The
cheeseboard is British, and there is grilled goats' cheese with salad before sweets,
which have more French artifice than is the English tradition. A short wine list
opens with claret at £6·50, but look for the Portuguese Dão at £7.
CELLARMAN'S CHOICE: Gigondas '85, from Jaboulet, £14.

CHEF: Bruce Buchan PROPRIETORS: Hugh and Suzanne Roberts, Janis and Andy Rork
OPEN: all week MEALS: 12.30 to 2, 7.30 to 9.30 (10 Fri and Sat)
PRICES: £20 (£27), Set L and D from £13·50 (£19) CARDS: Access, Amex, Diners, Visa
SEATS: 50. 4 tables outside. Private parties: 20 main room. Car-park, 50 places. Vegetarian
meals. Children's helpings by arrangement. Smart dress preferred
ACCOMMODATION: 13 rooms, all with bath/shower. Rooms for disabled. B&B £35 to £65.
Deposit: one night's stay. Children are restricted. Baby facilities. Pets welcome. Garden.
Fishing. TV. Phone. Scenic. Doors close at 11. Confirm by 4

Old Woolhouse [14/20]

The Square, Northleach GL54 3EE
COTSWOLD (0451) 60366   £22

Since 1974 Jacques and Jenny Astic have run this small, personalised restaurant
to their own rules – doors open at 8, dinner is at 8.15, and the small menu is
recited. The dining-room seats only eighteen, but tables are immaculately set and
spaced. Monsieur Astic is a gifted chef. He cooks in the old northern French sytle
of cream and butter relieved only by a salad course. Monkfish in a red wine
sauce, beef with mustard, and chicken in champagne sauce are frequent
landmarks. Sweets, such as fruit tarts, are displayed on a table. The quality of the
burgundies underlines the all-round pedigree.

CHEF: Mr Astic PROPRIETORS: Mr and Mrs Astic
OPEN: Tue to Sat, D only CLOSED: Christmas MEALS: 8.15
PRICES: Set D £19 (£22). Service inc
SEATS: 18. Children welcome. One sitting

NORTH WEALD BASSET   map 3

Wo Ping [10/20]

60 – 62 High Road, North Weald Basset CM16 6BY
NORTH WEALD (037 882) 3815   £12–£16

In a terraced row of shops next to a chippie; outside is a red awning, inside there's
a fish tank and Chinese pictures on the walls. The cooking, carefully tailored to
local tastes, lacks a cutting edge, but it is still a long way from the average sweet-
and-sour pork establishment. The 79-dish menu has full-bodied wun-tun soup,
crispy duck, fried rice and excellent toffee apples as well as creditable deep-fried
seaweed, sesame prawn toasts and squid with chilli and black-bean sauce.

CHEF/PROPRIETOR Alan Man
OPEN: all week D, and Thur to Sun L MEALS: 12 to 2, 5.30 to 11.30 (12 Thur, Fri and Sat)
PRICES: £9 (£16), Set L and D from £8·50 (£12), Service 10% CARDS: Access, Amex,
Diners, Visa
SEATS: 80. Car-park, 20 places. Vegetarian meals. Music. Air-conditioned

It is helpful if restaurateurs keep the office up to date with any changes.

*The average price quoted in brackets is for an average three-course meal including
service, VAT, coffee and half a bottle of house wine or the equivalent in an ethnic
restaurant.*

NORWICH Norfolk

map 6

Greens Seafood Restaurant [11/20]

82 Upper St Giles Street, Norwich NR3 1AQ
NORWICH (0603) 623733   £20

The dining-room is long and narrow with pine tables and nets hanging from the ceiling to emphasise that this is a good provincial fish restaurant. Dennis Crompton goes to Lowestoft for most of his fish, though Norwich market is useful for Cromer crabs. His purchases show up well in crisp whitebait; poached halibut with prawns and cheese sauce; and monkfish with red wine and green peppercorn sauce. Vegetables are well chosen. Good coffee and petits fours. The wine list is not well described; house wine £5·50 a bottle.

CHEF/PROPRIETOR: Dennis W. Crompton
OPEN: Mon to Sat, exc Sat L CLOSED: bank hols, 1 week at Christmas MEALS: 12.15 to 2.15, 7 to 10.45
PRICES: £14 (£20) CARDS: Access, Visa
SEATS: 54. Private parties: 30 main room. No children under 10. Smart dress preferred. No cigars in dining-room. Music. Air-conditioned

NOTTINGHAM Nottinghamshire

map 5

Les Artistes Gourmands [11/20] ✗

61 Wollaton Road, Beeston, Nottingham NG9 2NG
NOTTINGHAM (0602) 228288   £12–£15

One of the most creditable European eating places in the Nottingham area. The restaurant and the kitchen have been extended, the vegetable garden is improving, and cookery courses are now held. The regularly changing menu brings together classic French onion soup, pheasant terrine and civet of duck with Beaujolais, with more modern-sounding ideas, such as lambs' sweetbreads with hazelnut sauce, or chicken stuffed with watercress mousse. Fish and vegetables are usually steamed. Desserts are now a feature – praline vacherin with hot chocolate sauce, pear tart with almond cream, semolina pudding with caramel sauce. Good French cheeseboard, with up to a dozen varieties. Plenty of well chosen wines for around £10. CELLARMAN'S CHOICE: Côtes du Rhône, Domaine Maby'78, at £9·80.

CHEF: J. L. David PROPRIETOR: Eddy Keon
OPEN: Mon to Sat, exc Sat L CLOSED: 1 week Jan, 1 week Aug MEALS: 12 to 1.30, 7 to 10.30
PRICES: Set L from £8·30 (£12), Set D from £10·90 (£15). Service inc CARDS: Access, Amex, Diners, Visa
SEATS: 65. Private parties: 35 main room. Vegetarian meals. Children's helpings. Wheelchair access. Music

Chand [10/20]

26 Mansfield Road, Nottingham NG1 3GX
NOTTINGHAM (0602) 474103   £6–£13

An unobtrusive curry-house next to the massive Victoria shopping centre, with a ground-floor dining-room and a few tables upstairs. Nottingham's Indian restaurants are generally anglicised but this is a step nearer the real thing, with a few Persian-style and Kashmiri dishes (the chicken is pungent with garlic) among the tandooris, bhunas, jalfrezis and vindaloos. Good chapatis.

CHEF/PROPRIETOR: M. Ayub
OPEN: all week CLOSED: 25 Dec MEALS: 12 to 2.30, 5.30 to 12.30
PRICES: £7 (£13), Set L £3 (£6). Minimum £6·50 at D CARDS: Access, Amex, Diners, Visa
SEATS: 75. Private parties: 45 main room, 45 private room. Vegetarian meals. Children's helpings. Wheelchair access. Music. Air-conditioned

Mr Shing's [10/20]

148A Mansfield Road, Nottingham NG1 2HW
NOTTINGHAM (0602) 587209   £12–£17

One of the new breed of Nottingham Chinese restaurants (see also Ocean City). Mr Shing's is on the first floor above the Inkap Chinese supermarket, and judging by the exterior paintwork, they could be part of the same enterprise. The menu is more traditional than most, and still shows its Cantonese roots. The list of around a hundred and fifty dishes includes the best range of one-plate rice and noodle dishes in the city, with a good showing of roast and barbecued meats. Also there are half a dozen ways with bean curd, plus steamed seafood. Sizzling dishes make a brief appearance and include monkfish, which appears to be Nottingham flavour of the year.

CHEF: K. S. Cheng PROPRIETOR: Michael Shing
OPEN: all week CLOSED: 25 Dec MEALS: 12 to 2, 5.30 to 11.30
PRICES: £9 (£17), Set D from £8 (£12). Service 10% CARDS: Access, Amex, Diners, Visa
SEATS: 100. Private parties: 65 main room, 40 private room. Vegetarian meals. Music

Ocean City [11/20]

100–104 Derby Road, Nottingham, NG1 5FB
NOTTINGHAM (0602) 475095   £14–£16

Nottingham is seeing a minor Chinese uprising. Half a dozen significant restaurants – and at least three supermarkets – have opened in the last eighteen months. The old guard, represented by the Pagoda in Greyfriar Gate, is under threat. The best of the new bunch is this leisurely, deceptively large restaurant out on the Derby Road. It is very much a restaurant for Chinese, although it isn't stuck in the mould. It shows that Cantonese food can move into the new world without toning down its flavours or dressing up dishes with carved turnips; the essentials of the cooking haven't been sacrificed. The menu moves confidently between the classic roast meats, noodles, hot-pot and dishes such as steamed eel with crispy pork, and the fashionable eclectic style of sizzling monkfish with chilli and black-bean sauce. The cliche DIY dish of minced quail with iceberg lettuce here is boldly boosted by slivers of Chinese sausage and a hefty injection of coriander and green spring onion. Service is young and keen. Dim-sum lunches are popular with Chinese students from the nearby university.

All letters to the Guide *are acknowledged.*

CHEF: Mr Leung PROPRIETORS: Mr and Mrs Cheung, Mr Kong and Mr Leung
OPEN: all week MEALS: noon to 11.30pm
PRICES: £7 (£16), Set D £8·50 (£14). Minimum £7·50 at D. Service 10% CARDS: Access,
Amex, Diners, Visa
SEATS: 300. Private parties: 200 main room, 80 and 120 private rooms. Vegetarian meals.
Children welcome. Wheelchair access (also WC). Music. Air-conditioned

Shogun [10/20]

95 Talbot Street, Nottingham NG1 5GN
NOTTINGHAM (0602) 475611   £9–£13

As you drive into Nottingham from the west, the restaurant appears monolithic.
The building – a converted warehouse – stands in the fork of two roads. The sides
are bare, untouched brick; only the frontage suggests it is a restaurant at all,
with brown wooden pillars, a blue pennant across the doorway and the word
'Shogun' in black and gold across the entrance. Inside is another world: bright,
attractive, airy, with mock 'paper' windows, framed woodblock prints and lights
set into the ceiling. The food here compares favourably with many Japanese
restaurants in London: the freshness of the ingredients, the pure accuracy of the
cooking and the effortless artistry of the presentation suggest that this is a
kitchen with serious ambitions. Details, such as the thoughtfully chosen,
beautiful crockery, help to enhance every dish. Set dinners introduce the
subtleties of the cuisine to newcomers, and the accessible menu has
representatives of sashimi, grilled yakimono specialities, tempura, sukiyaki and
shabu-shabu. Highlights have included agedashi-dofu (cubes of deep-fried tofu in
a soy/mirin sauce), chawan-mushi (chilled savoury egg custard with seafood),
fish teriyaki and, to finish, ice-cream topped with aduki beans and a thin red
sauce. Good value set lunches are based on a single dish on rice, with salad, soup
and a dessert – all for £5.

CHEFS: Keiji Tomiyama and Makoto Kato PROPRIETORS: Keiji and Sally Tomiyama
OPEN: Mon to Sat, exc Mon L MEALS: 12 to 1.45, 7 to 11.15
PRICES: £7 (£13), Set L £5 (£9), Set D from £8 (£12) CARDS: Access, Amex, Diners, Visa
SEATS: 53. Private parties: 48 main room. Vegetarian meals. Music

---

OAKHILL Somerset   map 2

▲ *Oakhill House* [13/20]

Bath Road, Oakhill BA3 5AQ
OAKHILL (0749) 840180   £12–£20

This is a handsome, eighteenth-century house with its own drive. The high-
ceilinged dining-room, with its bare wooden floors and large fireplaces, sets the
mood for Ann Long's cooking, which is modern British. The fifteen-dish menu
changes from day to day, reflecting supplies. Main-course meat dishes are a high
point: new season's lamb cooked in pastry and served on a yellow-pepper pureé;
perfectly cooked marinated steak with a sauce of meat juices, sherry from the
marinade and a little cream; duck breast wrapped in bacon garnished with a
rhubarb purée. Vegetables follow the seasons, which means Jersey Royals at the
end of April and runner beans in August (though they carry an extra charge).
Puddings tend to be traditional, with one or two individual ideas, such as

oatmeal meringue filled with banana and spiced apple (sweets were always good at the Longs' previous restaurant, The Count House at Botallack). Bedrooms are pleasant and draw positive endorsements. The short wine list keeps its prices commendably low. CELLARMAN'S CHOICE: Fleurie, Paquet '85, £9·20.

CHEF: Ann Long PROPRIETORS: Ian, Ann and Suzanne Long
OPEN: Tue to Sun, exc Sat L and Sun D CLOSED: four weeks in winter MEALS: 12.30 to 1.45, 7.30 to 9.30
PRICES: £13 (£20), Set L £8·25 (£12) CARDS: Access, Amex, Diners, Visa
SEATS: 45. Private parties: 12 main room, 20 private room. Car-park, 30 places. No children under 12. Wheelchair access (also WC)
ACCOMMODATION: 3 rooms, all with bath/shower. B&B £28 to £40. Deposit: £10. No children under 12. Garden TV. Scenic. Confirm by 5 [GHG]

ORFORD Suffolk   map 3

Butley-Orford Oysterage [9/20] ✔

Market Hill, Orford IP12 2PQ
ORFORD (0394) 450277   £11

The Pinney family did not invent the idea of the 'local food café', but were among the first to make a success of this sort of enterprise after the Second World War. The black-and-white-fronted oysterage buzzes with life. The simplest foods are conspicuously the best – oysters grown in Butley Creek, Irish salmon specially cured over oak – and the smoked foods are the focal point – eel, sprats and cod roe. Short, interesting wine list.

CHEF: Mathilde Pinney PROPRIETORS: Mathilde, Richard and William Pinney
OPEN: all week CLOSED: Jan, first 2 weeks Feb MEALS: 12 to 2.15, 6 to 8.30
PRICES: £7 (£11)
SEATS: 50. Private parties: 25 main room. Car-park, 20 places. Children welcome. Wheelchair access (also WC)

OTTERY ST MARY Devon   map 1

The Lodge [12/20]

17 Silver Street, Ottery St Mary EX11 1DB
OTTERY ST MARY (040 481) 2356   £23

Diane Shenton runs this eighteenth-century town-house almost single-handed. She cooks in the best tradition of the English amateur, choosing her ingredients wisely (the small local firm of Pinhill supplies smoked fish, poultry, game and veal). The results show in hot salad of smoked pigeon with walnut oil or champagne vinegar dressing, and veal sweetbreads cooked in an old-fashioned cream sauce pointed up with tarragon, chervil, sorrel and parsley. Other main dishes may be duck roasted with a fruit sauce; a Devon dish of pork with orange and brandy; or lamb with laver-bread and port. Vegetables are ample and English. Ideas can at times be wayward, but any shortcomings are countered by the quality of the ingredients and the sheer enthusiasm of the place. Over seventy wines are arranged both by style and by region; there are plenty of half-bottles and mark-ups are kind. CELLARMAN'S CHOICE: Sancerre '85, from Delaporte, £10·35.

CHEF/PROPRIETOR: Diane Shenton
OPEN: Tue to Sun, exc Sun D MEALS: 12 to 2, 7 to 9.30
PRICES: Set L and D £18·50 (£23) CARDS: Amex, Diners, Visa
SEATS: 25. Private parties: 28 main room. Vegetarian meals. Children's helpings.
Wheelchair access (also WC). Music

OXFORD Oxfordshire   map 2

Browns [10/20]

5–9 Woodstock Road, Oxford OX2 6HA
OXFORD (0865) 511995   £14

Imitation is the sincerest form of flattery, and Browns has more than its share of imitators. But its style is unique, and it seems certain to outlive and outshine most of its rivals. The potted palms, mirrors, hanging plants under the skylight, even the wooden tubs with bay trees outside, have all been copied. But nowhere else can quite capture the extraordinary buzz of the place, the Tower of Babel of all ages and nationalities, the ever-observant 'seaters', and even the old porter in his braided uniform. The food is casual, and undergraduate: pasta; all kinds of salads; grills and pies; hot sandwiches and pub-style specials such as beef Stroganoff; a whole fried herring and a whole plaice; and chilli con carne. Strawberry cheesecake is made with fresh fruit, or there are ice-creams and sorbets to finish. Portions are enormous, and so are the queues. A new branch opened in Cambridge in the summer, an interesting act of colonial expansion. A pianist has been brought in to attract afternoon trade, and the wine list has been re-worked to mark the change in the licensing laws. Look for the New Zealand Cabernet Sauvignon or Chardonnay. House French is £4·65.

CHEF: Eamonn Hunter PROPRIETORS: J. L. Mogford and J. P. Mayhew
OPEN: all week CLOSED: 24 to 28 Dec MEALS: 11 (12 Sun) to 11.30
PRICES: £9 (£14). Service 10% for parties over 4
SEATS: 220. 4 tables outside. Vegetarian meals. Children's helpings. No-smoking area.
Wheelchair access (also WC). Music. Air-conditioned

15 North Parade [11/20]

15 North Parade, Oxford OX2 6LX
OXFORD (0865) 513773   £13–£23

Up the road from Le Petit Blanc (see entry), and though the cool décor of cane and plants suggest it may be an equal, this is much more a neighbourhood bistro. Michael Yeadon's wholefood background shows in the healthy style of dishes such as a tartlet of cottage cheese with quail eggs and smoked chicken, or sweet-and-sour ragout of mushrooms on a bed of spinach with cashews and Basmati rice. The menu reads well, with innovative touches, and everything looks beautiful on the plate. Vegetables are excellent. The intelligently described list of about forty wines opens with Berry Bros claret at £5·75.

The Guide *recruits new inspectors from readers who write in regularly. If you would like to apply, write to the editor with (a) a detailed report on a restaurant where you have eaten and (b) a comparative study of restaurants known to you.*

CHEFS: Michael Yeadon and Ross Boffin PROPRIETOR: Michael Yeadon
OPEN: Tue to Sun MEALS: 12 to 2, 7 to 10.30
PRICES: £17 (£23), Set L £7·50 (£13). Minimum £7·50 at L, £10 at D CARDS: Access,
Amex, Diners, Visa
SEATS: 50. 4 tables outside. Private parties: 50 main room. Vegetarian meals. Children's
helpings. Wheelchair access (also WC). Air-conditioned

Munchy Munchy [12/20]

6 Park End Street, Oxford OX1 1HH
OXFORD (0865) 245710   £8

Offers the best value in Oxford and some of the finest fast food in Britain – indeed
perhaps the best Malaysian-inspired food. The half-dozen daily dishes in Ethel
Ow's little café change daily. They rarely fail to amaze. Her cooking is
spontaneous, and the flair for spicing and subtle combinations of ingredients can
produce extraordinary results: king prawns with mango, and beef satay and stir-
fried spinach are comparatively simple, compared to the heady complexity of
sliced lamb with coriander leaves and roots in redcurrant sauce or asparagus
with crab, ground macadamia nuts and lemon grass, in Asian fashion. Plates are
piled high with rice, and dishes come in separate bowls. To finish there are
cooling fresh fruits and ice-creams. Juices or teas to drink, otherwise bring your
own wine (corkage 40p per person). Queues form at the locked front door on
busy nights, so lingering is not encouraged. Plans are afoot to revamp the whole
restaurant in late summer, which may involve a three-month closure.

CHEF: Ethel Ow PROPRIETORS: Tony and Ethel Ow
OPEN: Tue to Sat MEALS: 12 to 2.10, 5.30 to 9.40
PRICES: £7 (£8). Unlicensed: bring your own, corkage 40p
SEATS: 42. Private parties: 7 main room. No children under 6 Fri and Sat D. No cigars/pipes
in dining-room.

Le Petit Blanc [16/20] ✗

61A Banbury Road, Summertown, Oxford OX2 7DY
OXFORD (0865) 53540   £14–£26

For a short period in the summer of 1986, under the Burton-Races, Raymond
Blanc's second restaurant threatened to outshine the manor. Within a year, now
under Bruno Loubet, it has altered, declined, regenerated and is once again a
sensational restaurant in its own right. The conservatory provides a charmed
setting for unfussy modern French cooking of extraordinary potency. Classic
dishes are reworked, for instance in crème brûlée au citron, or else there are
modern versions of country dishes, like long-simmered rabbit in white wine.
Presentation can be unsophisticated and may not prepare diners for the impact –
witness an innocent wedge of chocolate and hazelnut dessert with vanilla sauce.
There is a fragrance to the cooking which takes it into a special dimension. Squid
and scallops are sauté in nut oil, laid on saffron noodles and sauced with fresh
tomatoes; roast wild pigeon is given a honeyed sauce garnished with braised
chicory and deep-fried grapes; leek terrine is with monkfish; confit of duck is with
duck liver and its ham. These are modern dishes executed with élan and courage.
The staff are formally dressed and exclusively young and French; the latter goes
for the wine list, which rises steeply from house wine at £6·50.

CHEF: Bruno Loubet PROPRIETOR: Raymond Blanc
OPEN: all week, exc Tue CLOSED: 2 weeks Jan MEALS: 12.15 to 2.15, 7.15 to 10.30
PRICES: £18 (£26), Set L £12·50 (£14). Licensed, also bring your own: corkage £5
CARDS: Access, Visa
SEATS: 70. 3 tables outside. Private parties: 76 main room. Car-park. Vegetarian meals.
Children's helpings. Wheelchair access. Air-conditioned

OXTED Surrey   map 3

Coltsford Mill [9/20]

Mill Lane, Hurst Green, Oxted RH8 9DG
OXTED (0883) 713962   £14

'I can get into Le Gavroche within a week. I got in at Paul Bocuse the same day.
But at Coltsford Mill there's a five-week waiting list.' After twenty-one years the
mill is well known locally, and Saturdays are impossible. It is rather easier on
Thursdays and Fridays, though booking is said to be essential. The décor is like
the menu – solid and traditional. Six dishes are offered at each course. Home-
made soups, chicken-liver pâté, steak and kidney pudding, roast duck with apple
sauce, and chocolate cheesecake are typical. 'Very good, unadorned English
cooking at its best.' Service is affable and maternal. In terms of value in Surrey, it
is excellent. Unlicensed and no corkage charged.

CHEFS: W. Dewson and G. Heasman PROPRIETOR: G. B. Heasman
OPEN: Thur to Sat D CLOSED: Jan, 2 weeks Oct MEALS: 7.30 to 8.30
PRICES: Set D £12·50 (£14). Minimum £12·50. Unlicensed, but bring your own: no corkage
SEATS: 60. Private parties: 55 main room, 16 private room. Car-park, 30 places. Children
welcome. Wheelchair access

PADSTOW Cornwall   map 1

▲ *Seafood Restaurant* [14/20]

Riverside, Padstow PL28 8BY
PADSTOW (0841) 532485   £20–£30

This is one of the great fish restaurants, right on the quay, in case anyone should
doubt the freshness of the produce. Padstow is in an area of outstanding natural
beauty, reached via some outstandingly steep and twisted narrow streets, and its
fleet still puts out. The atmosphere is relaxed and unpretentious, almost like the
Walnut Tree Inn at Llandewi Skirrid, but spacious, white, full of healthy plants
and invariably busy with variously dressed customers. What the long menu
does, it does brilliantly, because fish dishes are best when they are simple and
Rick Stein's genius is to keep them that way, which is not to say plain. Porbeagle
shark is cut as a steak, grilled, topped with a vinaigrette containing finely
chopped shallots (blanched, to moderate their strength) and finished with lots of
fresh fennel leaves. Red mullet is baked with diced red peppers and aubergines.
John Dory is wrapped in a leaf of spinach, steamed, and served with a mustard
and yellow cream sauce flavoured with coriander seeds. Those three come as one
main course. Of course there is also a more European-flavoured theme in fish
soup, bouillabaisse, seafood platter and standard dishes that might be expected,
for instance roast lobster with herb butter. Starters are biased away from fish,

with warm salads and charcuterie, but sweets overshadow them: chocolate marquise; hot apple tart; hazelnut meringue. The menu changes daily, which Mr Stein says has completely galvanised the kitchen. Service remains a weak spot; the front-of-house needs a firmer grip. There are good waitresses, but there are also ones who prefer to chat to each other, which can make sitting by the staff gangway both illuminating and frustrating. Of the hundred wines, 80 per cent are French and nearly half are under £10, with 22 half-bottles. House Beaujolais and Sauvignon du Haut Poitou are £6·60. CELLARMAN'S CHOICE: Meursault, Château de Blagny '83, from Latour, £25.

CHEF: Richard Stein PROPRIETORS: Richard and Jill Stein
OPEN: Mon to Sat, D only MEALS: 7.30 to 9.30 (10 Sat)
PRICES: £21 (£30), Set D £14·95 (£20) CARDS: Access, Amex, Diners, Visa
SEATS: 75. 2 tables outside. Private parties: 16 main room. Children's helpings.
Air-conditioned
ACCOMMODATION: 8 rooms, all with bath/shower. B&B £24 to £36. Deposit: £15. Baby facilities. pets welcome. TV. Scenic. Confirm by 12

PANGBOURNE Berkshire   map 2

▲ *Copper Inn* [12/20]

Church Road, Pangbourne RG8 7AR
PANGBOURNE (073 57) 2244   🍾 £17–£27

The front-runner of the Fine Inns group, whose policy is to provide English food using English ingredients, and to write menus in English. In practice, Paul Gilmore's cooking veers towards an elaborate, refined version of modern French, with some unusual touches, such as parsnip mousse with a pile of three different coloured pastas, surrounded by a cream sauce. Pasta appears again with fine-flavoured rabbit pâté and mustard sauce. Sometimes the ideas and presentation seem over-complicated, although the round of bread-and-butter pudding served with two spoonfuls of exquisite syllabub is beyond reproach. English farmhouse cheeses are a feature, and coffee is elegantly served with home-made petits fours. The atmosphere is of a dining-room in southern France, with Provençal furniture, fresh flowers, and pine screens separating serving tables. Some of the better Provençal wines help with the illusion, but the bulk of the list is classic French, topped up by a few local English bottles.

CHEF: Paul Gilmore PROPRIETORS: Fine Inns plc
OPEN: all week MEALS: 12.30 to 2, 7.30 to 9.30 (10 Fri and Sat, 9 Sun)
PRICES: £20 (£27), Set L £10·75 (£17), Snacks from £1·20 CARDS: Access, Amex, Diners, Visa
SEATS: 50. 6 tables outside. Private parties: 12 main room, 10 and 30 private rooms.
Car-park, 30 places. Vegetarian meals. Children's helpings. Wheelchair access
ACCOMMODATION: 21 rooms, all with bath/shower. Rooms for disabled. B&B £48·50 to £64.
Baby facilities. Garden. TV. Doors close at 12. Confirm by 6

All inspections are carried out anonymously.

Files are kept on every restaurant, so reports of poor meals are just as valuable as reports of good meals because they save unnecessary inspections.

PENZANCE Cornwall map 1

Harris's [10/20]

---

46 New Street, Penzance TR18 2LZ
PENZANCE (0736) 64408 £23

The Harrises run the small, flower-filled restaurant between them, for the most part. The short, conservative menu stays with the confines of pâté and steak with sauce, with the addition of some good fish, for instance John Dory, lobster and turbot. House wine from Duboeuf is £5·35.

CHEF: Roger Harris PROPRIETORS: Anne and Roger Harris
OPEN: Mon to Sat, exc Mon L CLOSED: Mon D Nov to May MEALS: 12 to 2, 7 to 10
PRICES: £15 (£23). Service 10% CARDS: Access, Amex, Diners, Visa
SEATS: 30. Private parties: 20 main room. Vegetarian meals

PETERBOROUGH Cambridgeshire map 6

Grain Barge [10/20]

The Quayside, Embankment Road, Peterborough
PETERBOROUGH (0733) 311967 £14–£18

A restored sailing barge moored on a quiet stretch of the River Nene hosts one of the better Peking/Szechuan restaurants in the region. Inside is comfortable, without being overly plush, and unhurried. The familiarity of the menu does not detract from the freshness of the food and variety of the set meals. Staples – spare ribs, sesame prawn toasts, crispy duck, toffee bananas – are all done well. Look also for the occasional prawns royal in a mildly hot sauce. Limited wines, though they take in Lebanon and California.

CHEF: Denny Cheng and C. H. Wong PROPRIETORS: Denny Cheng and Derek Greenwood
OPEN: all week MEALS: 12 to 2, 6 to 11.15
PRICES: £10 (£18), Set D £9·50 (£14). Service 10% CARDS: Access, Amex, Diners, Visa
SEATS: 100. Private parties: 70 main room. Vegetarian meals. Children welcome. Music

---

PINNER Greater London map 3

La Giralda [10/20] ✕

---

66 Pinner Green, Pinner HA5 2AB
01-868 3429 £8–£11

The emphasis on Spanish food is less pronounced these days. Gazpacho and paella are still on the menu, but as well as chicken in red wine and steak there is now a move to fish, with fresh supplies daily and a blackboard to announce them. The cellar, by contrast, is uncompromisingly Spanish, running from Rioja to Navarra, from Valdepeñas to Penedés. Mark-ups are on a fixed, rather than percentage, basis, making the higher-priced bottles particularly good value. Riojas span five decades; there are half-bottles and Cava wines; and no shortage of whites for the fish.

All letters to the Guide *are acknowledged.*

CHEFS: David Brown and Derek Knight PROPRIETOR: David Brown
OPEN: Tue to Sat CLOSED: 3 weeks Aug MEALS: 12 to 2.30, 6.30 to 10.30
PRICES: Set L from £4 (£8), Set D from £6.50 (£11) CARDS: Access, Amex, Diners, Visa
SEATS: 120. Private parties: 50 main room, 16 and 35 private rooms. Vegetarian meals.
Children's helpings. Wheelchair access (also WC). Air-conditioned

---

PLUMTREE Nottinghamshire   map 5

Perkins Bar Bistro [10/20]

Old Railway Station, Plumtree NG12 5NA
PLUMTREE (060 77) 3695   £14

Some of the best railway food in the country is served at this station, although
the trains no longer run. On summer evenings, sit outside on the platform and
wait for the meal. The cooking revolves round a short, bistro-style blackboard
menu, taking in sauté chicken livers with mushrooms and madeira, mutton and
mint sausage, casseroled wood pigeon or poached salmon dieppoise with plenty
of fresh vegetables. Hazelnut meringue gateau is a good sweet. The return to the
listings is by readers' demand. Drinkable house wine at £4·40 a bottle.

CHEF: Tony Perkins PROPRIETORS: Tony and Wendy Perkins
OPEN: Mon to Sat CLOSED: 1 week at Christmas MEALS: 12 to 2, 7 to 9.45
PRICES: £9 (£14), Snacks from £1·10 CARDS: Access, Amex
SEATS: 65. 6 tables outside. Private parties: 24 main room. Car-park, 60 places. Children
welcome. Wheelchair access (1 step). Music

PLYMOUTH Devon   map 1

Chez Nous [14/20]

13 Frankfort Gate, Plymouth PL1 1QA
PLYMOUTH (0752) 266793   £23–£31

After struggling in obscurity for seven years, Jacques Marchal's unpretentious
little French restaurant in the shopping precinct has suddenly been recognised.
Last year he earned his first entry in the *Guide*, then he got a Michelin rosette. The
stimulus can only do him good. The dining-room is small and informal, with
French posters and a blackboard menu that offers dishes of the day. Fish is
exceptional: brill, scallops, whatever is fresh from the market. Salmon is
marinated and served in fennel oil, or turned into a mousse with prawns. A
single flavour throws the fish into relief: sweet pepper with the monk, ginger with
the scallops. The French heritage comes through loud and strong with onion
soup, tongue périgourdine, pork with prunes, and the wines. The wine list is
exclusively French and largely classic, with a spread of prices and vintages,
a good selection of half-bottles, and a few old and rare wines, though why they
should be selling 1983 vendange tardive Alsace wines so young is a mystery.
CELLARMAN'S CHOICE: Savennières, Clos du Papillon, Domaine des Baumard '85,
at £9·50; and Ch. Lanessan '79, at £14·50.

---

*Good vintages for drinking in 1988: Alsace '85, Beaujolais '86, Germany '85, petits
chateaux clarets '81, lesser clarets '83.*

CHEF: Jacques Marchal PROPRIETORS: Suzanne and Jacques Marchal
OPEN: Tue to Sat CLOSED: first 3 weeks Feb and Sept, bank hols MEALS: 12.30 to 2,
7 to 10.30
PRICES: £21 (£31), Set L and D £16 (£23) CARDS: Access, Amex, Diners, Visa
SEATS: 30. Private parties: 30 main room. Children welcome. Wheelchair access. Music.
Air-conditioned

Mister Barrett's [10/20]

36 Admiralty Street, Stonehouse, Plymouth PL1 3RU
PLYMOUTH (0752) 221177   £16

Amid an alarmingly red décor, the hospitable Stephen Barrett cooks, enthuses,
serves, and books tables. The chief interest, apart from fine local fish, is historic
recipes: Lezant birds, a casserole of duck, gleanie (a west-country name for
guinea-fowl) and chicken, with lentils, celery and shallots; or eleventh century
fudge pudding. Wild boar and Dorset Blue Vinney keep, as Mr Barrett puts it, 'the
old-fashioned flavours rolling on'. Steaks with bacon and Beaujolais are also
recommended. A dozen interesting wines.

CHEF/PROPRIETOR: Stephen Barrett
OPEN: Mon to Sat, exc Sat L MEALS: 12 to 2.30, 7 to 11
PRICES: £11 (£16) CARDS: Access, Visa
SEATS: 28. 6 tables outside. Private parties: 32 main room. Vegetarian meals. Children's
helpings. Music

PONTELAND Tyne & Wear   map 7

Rendezvous [new entry, zero rated]

3 Broadway, Darras Hall, Ponteland NE20 9PW
PONTELAND (0661) 21775   £8–£18

Hits new heights in terms of comfort for Chinese restaurants in the north-east. A
whole shop-sized bar area is filled with low armchairs and coffee-tables. The
dining-room is in pastels with large, round, well-spaced tables and upholstered,
high-backed chairs. Service checks quite a lot to see if everything is OK. The menu
runs a familiar gauntlet of 160 mainly Cantonese dishes, but is speckled with
Peking and satay items because this is not a Chinatown restaurant. Nevertheless
the bean curd dishes have been excellent, which is always a good marker. Sea
bass with ginger and spring onions has been good, so too the spare ribs and the
noodle and rice dishes, though there are few one-plate meals. Three dozen
unvintaged wines start at £5·95. More reports, please.

CHEF: W. F. Ai PROPRIETORS: K. F. Liu and W. F. Ai
OPEN: Mon to Sat D, and Fri and Sat L MEALS: 12 to 2, 6.30 to 10.30
PRICES: £10 (£18), Set L £4·50 (£8), Set D £9·50 (£14). Minimum £4·50 at L, £10 at D
CARDS: Access, Amex, Diners, Visa
SEATS: 100. 1 table outside. Private parties: 100 main room. Vegetarian meals. Children's
helpings. Smart dress preferred. Music. Air-conditioned

Restaurants change owners and chefs constantly. Please help keep the Guide *informed
of any changes you find.*

POOL IN WHARFEDALE West Yorkshire

map 5

▲ *Pool Court* [13/20]

Pool Bank, Pool in Wharfedale LS21 1EH
ARTHINGTON (0532) 842288/9 £18–£32

The Gills' classily run restaurant has edged into modern British cooking. 'More taste, less show', declares Mr Gill. Amid starters can be found sweetbreads with onion Yorkshire pudding; pot roast pigeon and garlic; or – how about this – parcels of Cheddar, Stilton and Wensleydale wrapped in spinach, served warm with tomato provençale, apple chutney and marinated onion. This is a kitchen that has arrived from what might loosely have been termed nouvelle cuisine, and the presentation does not lack, even on salmon fishcakes with parsley sauce as an intermediary. Lancashire duck is served two ways on the same menu: the breast roasted, the leg braised with pulses and spinach dumplings, and pot roasted with the leg as a galantine with an orange and ginger marmalade. The rose petals for the ice-cream come from the walled garden. Service is attentive and efficient, possibly among the best in the north. There are good breakfasts. Rooms have been fitted out with thought, including copies of the 180-strong wine list. It is classically inclined: twenty white burgundies, from £9·15 to £65·25; nine superb Alsace wines; plus the sort of clarets you might expect in this setting. Look for New World Chardonnay and reds, too, for value. House claret is £11·75. CELLARMAN'S CHOICE: Montepulciano d'Abruzzo '81, £11·75.

CHEF: Melvin Jordan   PROPRIETOR: Michael W. K. Gill
OPEN: Tue to Sat, D only   CLOSED: 2 weeks July to Aug, 2 weeks Christmas   MEALS: 7 to 10
PRICES: Set D £10 (£18) to £23 (£32)   CARDS: Access, Amex, Diners, Visa
SEATS: 65. Private parties: 32 main room, 24 private room. Car-park, 65 places. Vegetarian meals. Children's helpings. Smart dress preferred. No cigars/pipes in dining-room. Wheelchair access. Air-conditioned
ACCOMMODATION: 4 rooms, all with bath/shower. B&B £55 to £79. Garden. TV. Phone. Scenic. Confirm by 6 [GHG]

POUGHILL Cornwall

map 1

▲ *Reeds* [12/20]

Poughill EX23 9EL
BUDE (0288) 2841
1m NE of Bude £21

Mrs Jackson runs her hotel thoughtfully, cooking only for overnight guests. The flourishing garden supplies vegetables, fruit and flowers, and napkins are so well starched that they crackle when opened. The three-course, no-choice menu shows similar attention to detail, both in the cookery and in finding supplies. Fish is out of Bideford; meat is from the excellent Russell's of Exeter. The style is of steak béarnaise; lemon sole stuffed with smoked salmon in white sauce; an unusual ice-cream of avocado served with prawns; marinated and roasted rack

Many of the more expensive restaurants offer bargain lunches for half the price of a meal in the evening. Details are given in the text.

of lamb; loganberry tart. The short, inexpensive wine list is supplemented by a small selection of vintage claret and burgundy. House Georges Duboeuf is £6.

CHEF/PROPRIETOR: Margaret Jackson
OPEN: Fri to Mon, D only CLOSED: 25 Dec MEALS: 8
PRICES: Set D £17·50 (£20·50). Service inc
SEATS: 10. Private parties: 10 main room. Car-park, 10 places. No children under 16. Smart dress preferred. One sitting
ACCOMMODATION: 3 rooms, all with bath/shower. B&B £30 to £60. Deposit: £10. No children under 16. Garden. Scenic. Doors close at 12. Confirm by 1 [GHG]

POWBURN Northumberland   map 7

▲ *Breamish House Hotel* [12/20]

Powburn NE66 4LL
POWBURN (066 578) 266   £11–£19

You could arrive at Graham Taylor's hotel at the end of a winding drive, with no luggage, and still find virtually everything you need in your room. The dining-room, though, is the focal point. Set menus emphasise local produce, and provide a good example of modern British cooking. A typical, abundant meal featured delicate watercress soup; pink roast loin of lamb with lemon and thyme stuffing, served with plainly cooked vegetables; followed by lemon cream meringue. Stilton stars on the well-tended cheeseboard. Sweets tend to be traditional – Bakewell tart, bread-and-butter pudding – and Sunday lunch is heroically so: thick slices of fine roast beef, with Yorkshire pud made by an expert. The wine list is succinct: Loire from Saget, Alsace from Gisselbrecht, claret from '79 and '81 at bargain prices. There is even a Portuguese Reserva '75 at under £5. Additions are tacked on frequently.

CHEFS: Patricia Portus and Graham Taylor PROPRIETOR: Graham Taylor
OPEN: all week, D only, and Sun L CLOSED: Jan MEALS: 1, 7.30 to 8.30
PRICES: Set Sun L from £8 (£11), Set D from £14 (£19)
SEATS: 30. Private parties: 8 main room. Car-park, 30 places. Vegetarian meals. Children's helpings (Sun L only). No children under 12. Smart dress preferred. No smoking. Wheelchair access (also WC). One sitting
ACCOMMODATION: 10 rooms, all with bath/shower. B&B £28 to £46. Deposit: £20. No children under 12. Afternoon teas. Garden. TV. Phone. Scenic. Doors close at 12 [GHG]

POWERSTOCK Dorset ✈   map 2

▲ *Three Horseshoes* [11/20]

Powerstock DT6 3TF
POWERSTOCK (030 885) 328 and 229
4m NE of Bridport   £12–£17

The setting is pure Thomas Hardy: rough grey stone cottages, ancient hill forts, and a beautiful church with gargoyles and angels, although the pub looks more like a Victorian railway station. The food is as straightforward and ungarnished as the décor, with a strong emphasis on first-rate ingredients: fresh fish from West Bay (only fifteen minutes away), good meat, game, and seasonal vegetables. There are no fussy or complicated sauces, just traditional British and

French provincial dishes cooked with enthusiasm. Monkfish provençale has a
fragrant sauce of tomatoes, onions, and white wine; noisettes of lamb are cooked
pink; and venison is casseroled with red wine, mushrooms and baby onions.
Vegetables are served at their peak – which means baked parsnip wedges and
leeks in a strong cheese sauce in February. Sweets are in the same homely vein.
No nibbles, no petits fours, but excellent garlic bread and strong cafetière coffee.
Exceptionally pleasant service. The conventional wine list has five house wines at
£4·75 a bottle.

CHEF: Pat Ferguson PROPRIETORS: Pat and Diana Ferguson
OPEN: Tue to Sun, exc Sun D MEALS: 12 to 2 (3 Sun) 7 to 11
PRICES: £14 (£17), Set Sun L £6·95 (£12). Service inc alc CARDS: Access, Visa
SEATS: 60. 12 tables outside. Private parties: 28 main room, 16 private room. Car-park, 30
places. Vegetarian meals. Children's helpings L and early evening only). Wheelchair access
(also WC). Music
ACCOMMODATION: 3 rooms, 2 with bath/shower. B&B £20 to £37·50. Deposit: £10. Children
welcome. Baby facilities. Pets welcome. Garden. Scenic. Doors close at 12. Confirm by 7

PRESTON Lancashire   map 5

Auctioneer [10/20]

B.C.A. Centre, Walton Summit, Bamber Bridge, Preston PR5 8AA
PRESTON (0772) 324870   £10–£17

In the last three years Nigel Brookes' team has served a thousand different dishes
at this out-of-the-way restaurant in the unlikely setting of a second-hand car lot.
The menu pursues the car-auction connection, but for all the inventions (1,069
and rising, as we went to press), steaks, roast beef, pork and fresh fruit salads are
the main points, with scallops and strawberries as a sideline. It is easily reached
from the M6, junction 29. House wine £5·95.

CHEF: Ian Jolly PROPRIETOR: Nigel Brookes
OPEN: Mon L, and Wed to Sun, exc Sat L MEALS: 12 to 2.30, 7 to 9.30 (10 Fri and Sat)
PRICES: £11 (£17), set L £5 (£10) CARDS: Access, Visa
SEATS: 100. Private parties: 100 main room. Car-park, 500 places. Vegetarian meals.
Children's helpings. Music. Air-conditioned

PUDSEY West Yorkshire   map 5

Aagrah [10/20]

483 Bradford Road, Pudsey LS28 8ED
BRADFORD (0274) 668818   £13

The new branch of the long-established Aagrah in Shipley (see entry). It has
quickly proved itself as a useful Indian restaurant on the eastern fringes of
Bradford. The menu is the same as at Shipley, with good reports of generous
tandoori mixed grill, shah jahem and rogan josh. As one of the chefs alternates
between the two restaurants, the style and spicing is typical of both places. Drink
lassi, Kingfisher beer or Indian Veena wine.

Restaurants rating 12 or more serve the best food in the region.

CHEFS: M. Aslam and M. Sabir PROPRIETORS: Mr and Mrs M. Sabir, Mr and Mrs M. Aslam
and Z. Iqual
OPEN: all week D, and Sun L MEALS: 6 (noon Sun) to 11.30 (12 Fri and Sat)
PRICES: £7 (£13) CARDS: Access, Amex, Diners, Visa
SEATS: 60. Private parties: 65 main room. Car-park, 35 places. Vegetarian meals. Children's
helpings. Wheelchair access (also WC). Music

PULBOROUGH West Sussex map 3

Stane Street Hollow [12/20] ✗

Codmore Hill, Pulborough RH20, 1BG
PULBOROUGH (079 82) 2819 £10–£18

The Swiss flag usually flies by the duck-pond and the willow tree outside René
Kaiser's restaurant in two sixteenth-century cottages squeezed together. For
many years it has been one of the best-value places to eat in the area, especially
at lunchtime. Vegetables and poultry are likely to be the Kaisers' own. The menu
encompasses a broad European sweep, from Stroganoff to home-smoked roast leg
of duckling with a piquant sauce. Fish, including salmon, is also home smoked.
The quality of the pancakes and the petits fours with coffee testify to a Swiss
upbringing. Wines are chosen with care and marked up modestly. Even the
burgundies are within reach. House wine is £3·50 for half a litre, and a brace of
Swiss wines comes in at under £10 a bottle: a red Pinot Noir and white Fendant.
CELLARMAN'S CHOICE is Riesling, Cuvée Frédéric Emile '81, from Trimbach,
at £9·85.

CHEF: René Kaiser PROPRIETORS: René and Ann Kaiser
OPEN: Tue to Sat, exc Tue L and Sat L CLOSED: 3 weeks May, 24 Dec to 5 Jan MEALS: 12.30
to 1.15, 7.30 to 9.15
PRICES: £12 (£18), Set L £4·95 (£10)
SEATS: 35. Private parties: 24 main room, 16 private room. Car-park, 14 places.
Children's helpings

RAMSBOTTOM Greater Manchester map 5

Village Restaurant [14/20]

18 Market Place, Ramsbottom BL0 9HT
RAMSBOTTOM (070 682) 5070 ▲ £24

Chris Johnson and Ros Hunter share a glorious, eccentric, intense obsession for
food and drink in their small restaurant beside the pork butcher. The menu is a
prime example of modern British cooking, offers no choice, begins at 8 for 8.30
and goes on past midnight (hardly surprising, given the number of courses). A
loaf of warm bread is put on the table first, along with a bowl of vegetables,
followed by the first starter: leek wrapped in air-dried ham with pear sauce,
perhaps, or smoked venison pâté. A soup comes next, usually vegetable –
broccoli, cock-a-leekie, fennel – and then fish, from halibut with walnuts and

---

*All details are as accurate as possible at the time of going to press. Please notify the
Guide office of any changes.*

---

orange to locally.caught pike with dill and lemon butter. The main course, simply roasted fillet of beef, or lamb brought down from Scotland, is carved, and a sauce added: mustard mousseline for the beef, minted damson for the lamb. An embarrassment of vegetables arrives: buttered carrots with herbs; kale with raisins; curried parsnips; purple broccoli with toasted almonds; creamed swede with pine kernels; parsley potatoes, all on the same evening. Then to the farmhouse Lancashire, or Tottington goats' cheese; then on to chocolate angel cake, hot apple and mincemeat pie, crème brûlée, or choux ring with lime cream. But that is not all. There is a monster wine list, organised by grape variety. Chardonnays alone are a dream, but there is also Chablis from Fèvre, Tiefenbrunner's South Tyrol from Italy, Jean León from Spain, Clos du Bois from California, Rosemont's Roxburgh from Australia. Too many, of course, to appreciate in one evening, which is why Mr Johnson makes a small selection available to partner the food by the glass, for around £8 – an excellent move.

CHEF: Ros Hunter PROPRIETORS: Ros Hunter and Chris Johnson
OPEN: Wed to Sat, D only MEALS: 8
PRICES: Set D £18·50 (£24) CARDS: Access, Visa
SEATS: 18. Private parties: 12 main room. Children welcome. Smart dress preferred. Music.
One sitting

RAVENSTONEDALE Cumbria   map 7

▲ *Black Swan* [11/20]

Ravenstonedale CA17 4NG
NEWBIGGIN-ON-LUNE (058 73) 204   £12–£17

The backdrop could hardly be more idyllic: the Howgills and Wild Boar Fell. Ravenstonedale is a doll's house village with large squat doors and chimneys; the Black Swan, a solid comfortable hotel of no particular architectural style, straddles one corner. The Davys are accommodating hosts. Alison cooks a solid menu, relying on butter and cream for both bar and dining-room: local smoked macon (lamb) with Cumberland sauce; cauliflower soup; pan-fried steak; fillets of lemon sole with a mild, mustard-grain sauce. Sweets, for instance butterscotch and shortbread tart, are rich and good. Sixty wines are classified by style – 'aromatic' and 'full bodied' are two headings – instead of region and are, like the business as a whole, workmanlike.

CHEFS/PROPRIETORS: Christopher and Alison Davy
OPEN: Mon to Sat D, and Sun L CLOSED: First week Nov, and Jan, Feb MEALS: 12.30 to
1.15, 7.30 to 8.30
PRICES: Set Sun L £8·50 (£12), Set D £14 (£17). Service inc
SEATS: 30. 4 tables outside. Private parties: 30 main room. Car-park, 20 places. Children's
helpings (L only). No children under 10. Smart dress preferred. Wheelchair access (also WC)
ACCOMMODATION: 9 rooms, 6 with bath/shower. B&B £24 to £38. Deposit: £30. Pets
welcome. Garden. Tennis. Fishing. Golf. Scenic. Doors close at 11. Confirm by 4 [GHG]

'People should be warned about partaking of the sort of meal I had unless their digestive systems can take such an onslaught. Although I try to have a healthy, nutritious, high-fibre diet, I was quite unprepared for the after-effects of lunch.' (On eating in Wiltshire)

REDCAR Cleveland   map 7

▲ *Mercury Restaurant, Newbigging Hotel* [10/20]

Queen Street, Redcar TS10 1BE
MIDDLESBROUGH (0642) 482059   £12–£20

Away from the beach and seaside boarding-houses is this unlikely family hotel,
with a restaurant that is open only to residents. The outside gives no hint of the
drama of the dining-room, cluttered as it is with antiques, nor even of the
friendliness of all concerned. Fish and burgundies are the real highlights. Coral-
red fish soup; pan-fried plaice, hanging over the plate; monkfish with cream and
ginger, all dominate an otherwise conservatively inclined menu. All main dishes
come with plentiful fresh vegetables. The wine list, which runs beyond 180 bins
before reaching champagne, is an enthusiast's list and holds much interest. The
house red, bottled by the Haiths themselves, is a Coteaux du Tricastin; house
white is English Lamberhurst at £6.

CHEF: Karen Haith PROPRIETORS: The Haith family
OPEN: all week MEALS: 12 to 1.45, 7 to 8.30
PRICES: £14 (£20), Set L £7·50 (£12), Set D £10·50 (£16), Snacks from £1 CARDS: Access,
Amex, Diners, Visa
SEATS: 60. Private parties: 30 main room, 60 private room. Vegetarian meals. Children's
helpings. Smart dress preferred. Wheelchair access. Music
ACCOMMODATION: 25 rooms, all with bath/shower. B&B £19 to £28. Deposit: 10%. Children
welcome. Baby facilities. Pets welcome. Sauna. TV. Doors close at 1. Confirm by 6.30

REDLYNCH Wiltshire   map 2

▲ *Langley Wood* [11/20] ✈

Hamptworth Road, Redlynch SP5 2PB
ROMSEY (0794) 390348   £13–£18

The Rosens' small country house is set in five acres of woodlands on the edge of
the New Forest. The style is homely: log fires, high-backed chairs and polished,
candlelit tables. Sylvia Rosen cooks fresh ingredients and presents them
unfussily. Roast fillet of beef and roast devilled duck follow interesting savoury
bread pudding with onion marmalade as a starter. Sauces and vegetables are
good, and bread is home baked. Sweets straddle mocha meringue and old English
trifle. A modest wine list has prices to match.

CHEF: Sylvia Rosen PROPRIETORS: David and Sylvia Rosen
OPEN: Wed to Sat D, and Sun L MEALS: 12.45 to 2, 7.30 to 11
PRICES: £12 (£18), Set Sun L £9·50 (£13) CARDS: Access, Amex, Diners, Visa
SEATS: 30. Private parties: 65 main room. Car-park, 25 places. Vegetarian meals. Children's
helpings. No cigars/pipes in dining-room. Wheelchair access (also WC). Music
ACCOMMODATION: 3 rooms. B&B £12. Children welcome. Baby facilities. Pets welcome.
Afternoon teas. Garden

---

*The 1989 Guide will appear before Christmas 1988. Reports are particularly helpful
in the spring. Report forms are at the back of this book, but just write a letter if you
prefer. Address it to* The Good Food Guide, FREEPOST, *14 Buckingham Street, London
WC2N 6BR. No stamp is necessary if you post it in the UK.*

RICHMOND North Yorkshire   map 7

▲ *Howe Villa* [9/20]

Whitcliffe Mill, Richmond DL10 4TJ
RICHMOND (0748) 2559   £8

This is a splendid, modest bed-and-breakfast half a mile from the town centre, by
the River Swale. Anita Berry is a fine hostess, and cooks a short Cordon Bleu
dinner. Main course might be local lamb with orange, mint and redcurrant; or
plaice Dugléré. Cheeses include Swaledale and Blue Wensleydale. No licence;
no corkage.

CHEF: Anita Berry PROPRIETORS: Tom and Anita Berry
OPEN: all week, D only CLOSED: Nov to end Mar MEALS: 7 to 7.30
PRICES: Set D from £8 (£8). Service inc. Unlicensed, but bring your own: no corkage
SEATS: 10. Private parties: 10 main room. Car-park. Children's helpings by arrangement.
No children under 8. No smoking. Music
ACCOMMODATION: 4 rooms, all with bath/shower. D, B&B £48. Deposit: £10.
No children under 8. Garden. TV. Scenic. Doors close at 11 [GHG]

RICHMOND Surrey   map 3

Kim's [10/20]

12 Red Lion Street, Richmond TW9 1RW
01-948 5777 and 5779   £8–£15

A colourful Singaporean eating place on two floors, with golden yellow cloths,
red chopsticks and exotic orchids on the table. The menu has a substantial
showing of Chinese dishes, including popular crab with ginger, but the
Malaysian dishes are the main attraction. Favourites such as satay, laksa and
mee goreng are supplemented by sizzling dishes, for instance inchi kabin –
chicken, chillies and cashew nuts with spices, served on a hot plate. Good-value
set meals. Drink Chinese tea or Tiger beer.

CHEF: Susie Wong PROPRIETORS: Mr and Mrs Karam-Singh
OPEN: all week MEALS: 12 to 2.15, 6 to 11
PRICES: £8 (£15). Set L from £4·50 (£8). Set D from £9 (£13). Service 10% CARDS: Access,
Amex, Diners, Visa
SEATS: 60. Private parties: 40 main room, 25 private room. Children welcome. Music.
Air-conditioned

RIDGEWAY Derbyshire   map 5

Old Vicarage [new entry, zero rated]

Ridgeway Moor, Ridgeway S12 3XW
SHEFFIELD (0742) 475 814   £16–£22

The Bramleys, formerly at Toffs in Sheffield, have moved up a gear into this 1849
vicarage in two acres. The grounds are mature and full of tall conifers, hedges,
holly, rose beds and almond blossom trees. There is a clematis and an outside
lamp on the house wall. The waitresses are in long dresses with cream pinnies to

match the décor. The menu reads straight out of the top drawer of modern cooking. Portions are small, nouvelle style, but the interaction of ingredients provides much interest. A free-range poussin, stuffed with tarragon, is served with the breast skinned, the legs crisped, on a saffron sauce with a lemon compote and a trio of vegetables at the top of the plate. Other flavours can be remarkable, as in apple and geranium conserve with a terrine of chicken, foie gras and pistachio. 'The menu changes frequently and we do not believe in tying ourselves down to specialities.' Most nights there will be a dozen dishes spread through three courses up to the sweets; a second vegetable course is a fixture. Everything is decorative, but in an English way, using perhaps pansy heads as garnish, or an array of different herbs. 'Eating here was an adventure', comments an inspector. The wine list is a treat: a run of seventeen Alsace wines from Gassman, Hugel, Trimbach and Gisselbrecht; all the Beaujolais from the better vintages of '83 and '85; fourteen dessert wines. Bottles from the less exploited regions help keep a check on the bill. Six en suite bedrooms are being planned. More reports, please.

CHEF: Tessa Bramley PROPRIETORS: Tessa, Andrew and Peter Bramley
OPEN: Tue to Sat D, and Sun L MEALS: 12.15 to 2.30, 7 to 9.30
PRICES: Set Sun L £10 (£16), Set D from £15·50 (£22)
SEATS: 50. Private parties: 30 main room, 30 private room. Car-park, 25 places. Vegetarian meals. No children under 12. Smart dress preferred. No smoking in dining-room

---

RIPLEY Surrey map 3

Michels' [13/20]

13 High Street, Ripley GU23 6AQ
GUILDFORD (0483) 224777 £17–£24

For many years the Clock House, as this was previously called, had a poor reputation, so much so that the Michels changed the name six months after opening. They used to have a solid following at Barford St Martin. She is a gifted hostess, he an accomplished cook with plenty of ideas: blinis are made with marinated salmon and the salmon roe; lamb is encased in vegetables for a spring terrine served with a salad of new potatoes, dill-flavoured scallops are served with salmon, potted with orange sharpened with green peppercorns, with a cream and armagnac quenelle and lobster caviare. The complexity is matched by colourful presentation. The cooking methods vary from course to course: cooked in hay (lamb, for instance); baked in a salt crust; steamed over seaweed; barbecued over wood; poached in meat stocks; wrapped in paper. For the most part, meats are served simply, their juices finished with cream, butter or maybe a vegetable purée. The menu only changes every six to eight weeks, which allows for greater artifice, for better or worse, than at equivalent establishments – one vegetable in summer was a pasta shell filled with spinach, mushroom and bacon. The heart of the cooking is modern British, for instance marinated mallard in red-wine syrup flavoured with cinnamon, a poivrade sauce and fried spätzli – the potato dish varies with each course. Equally, roast beef and Yorkshire pudding is

---

Places rating 9 may not be restaurants at all, but still serve good food: expect to find pubs, cafes, small hotels and wine bars.

praised. Sweets favour the stickiness of banana quenelles, Chartreuse soufflé or compote of prickly pear and armagnac. The fifty wines are carefully chosen with some attractive mature bottles – Rioja Gran Reserva, Berberana '73, for example – and an eye to lesser vintages – Ch. Lynch-Bages '77, Alsace '82 and '84. CELLARMAN'S CHOICE: Chardonnay, Rosemount '85, £11·80.

CHEF: Erik Michel PROPRIETORS: Erik and Karen Michel
OPEN: Tue to Sun, exc Sat L and Sun D MEALS: 12.30 to 2, 7.30 to 9.15 (7 to 9.45 Sat)
PRICES: £17 (£24), Set L and D £12 (£17) CARDS: Access, Amex, Diners, Visa
SEATS: 50. Private parties: 60 main room. Children welcome. No-smoking area. Music

---

RIPON North Yorkshire   map 7

▲ Old Deanery [11/20]

Minster Road, Ripon HG4 1QS
RIPON (0765) 3518   £15–£18

Much commends the Old Deanery: the magnificent building, cheek by jowl with the cathedral; the informal way of doing business without bookings, without hassle; the dog-eared quality of the furniture; the comfortable old sofas; the monstrous Victorian sideboard. The high, yellow-ochre ceiling is dark with age. The Bleikers have been here for twenty-one years, and although the menu stays with the seasons it has not veered away dramatically from delice Helvetia (deep-fried balls of spaghetti bound with cream and onion, 'odd but good'), or steaks with spätzli. Forty dishes populate the menu, and though fish is generally weak, salads are generous and sweets good, especially brown-bread ice-cream. The wine list matches the menu almost perfectly – fifty bottles, mostly European, mostly under £20. House Merlot is £6 per carafe. CELLARMAN'S CHOICE: Chardonnay, Vin de Pays de l'Aude, £5·95.

CHEF: Jurg Bleiker PROPRIETORS: Jurg and Jane Bleiker
OPEN: Mon to Sat, exc Sat L CLOSED: 25 and 26 Dec MEALS: 12 to 2, 7 to 10
PRICES: £11 (£18), Set L and D £10·95 (£15), Snacks from 95p
SEATS: 70. 6 tables outside. Private parties: 30 main room. Car-park, 30 places, Vegetarian meals. Children's helpings. Smart dress preferred. Wheelchair access. Music
ACCOMMODATION: 2 rooms, both with bath/shower. B&B £35 to £47·50. Garden. Scenic. Doors close at 12. Confirm by 10

ROADE Northamptonshire   map 3

Roadhouse Restaurant [13/20] ✈

16–18 High Street, Roade NN7 2NW
ROADE (0604) 863372   £15–£18

The front door leads straight into the dining-room of the Kewleys' small, relaxed restaurant. A bar is on the far side. There is a country feel, but the seriousness of intent and easy accomplishment of the twenty-dish menu are apparent in salmon mousse wrapped in sole with a beurre blanc, or lightly sauté pigeon breast fanned on the plate, with a sauce of stock, port, red wine vinaigrette and

---

Report forms are at the back of the book.

---

chocolate. Kewley is economical with themes: port sauce recurs now with duck, now with beef; watercress sauce may be with salmon or with chicken breast stuffed with Stilton. As with musical motifs, the combinations make for variety rather than monotony. Simplicity is a virtue too, with exotic flavours eschewed in favour of apples (for duck), herbs (for lamb), mushroom (for calf's liver). Fish is a strength, and lunchtime closure promises closer links with Birmingham market and a chance to expand the repertoire. A largely French list of three dozen wines includes CELLARMAN'S CHOICE: Sauvignon de St Bris '85, £9·80.

CHEF: Christopher Kewley PROPRIETORS: Christopher and Susan Kewley
OPEN: Mon to Sat, D only CLOSED: bank hol Mons MEALS: 7 to 10
PRICES: £12 (£18), Set D £13 (£15). Service 10% CARDS: Access, Amex, Visa
SEATS: 32. Private parties: 40 main room. Car-park, 15 places. Children's helpings. Smart dress preferred. Wheelchair access

---

ROBERTSBRIDGE East Sussex

map 3

Trompe l'Oeil [new entry, zero rated]

13 High Street, Robertsbridge TN32 5AE
TUNBRIDGE WELLS (0580) 880362   £16–£26

The black and white timber-framed cottage is very different inside, with pastel shades of grey and green, white bamboo chairs and silk flowers on the tables. The menu is elaborate and in French; dishes arrive under huge silver cloches. The kitchen shows its hand from the start, with an appetiser of a tiny slice of carrot and celeriac mousse layered with seaweed, sitting on a raspberry vinegar and chive sauce. The flavour contrasts are vivid: chicken livers in pastry with orange sauce; turkey with a sauce of pink and green peppercorns; poached chicken with limes in a Pineau des Charentes and vermouth sauce. Desserts are flamboyant, for instance dark and light chocolate mousse shaped like a heart, in a pool of chocolate sauce. The wine list is out to impress and has good choices in the Rhône, Alsace and Loire. House Syrah is £7·95. More reports, please.

CHEF: Graeme Meek PROPRIETOR: Nancy Pidgeon
OPEN: Tue to Sat, D only MEALS: 12 to 2.30, 7 to 10.30
PRICES: £18 (£26), Set L and D £9·75 (£16). Licensed, also bring your own: corkage £7
CARDS: Access, Amex, Diners, Visa
SEATS: 30. Private parties: 30 main room, 16 private room. Car-park, 58 places. Vegetarian meals. Children's helpings. Smart dress preferred. Wheelchair access (1 step; also WC). Music

---

ROCHDALE Greater Manchester

map 5

One Eleven [10/20]

111 Yorkshire Street, Rochdale OL16 1YJ
ROCHDALE (0706) 344901   £13–£16

A small, neat restaurant not far from the town hall, decorated with photographs of old Rochdale. Melon with ginger wine, seafood Mornay, and noisettes of lamb

---

[GHG] *after the details of an entry means that the establishment is also included in* The Good Hotel Guide.

---

with cranberry and redcurrant sauce are supplemented with casseroles mid-week. Salmon and steak are well reported. House wine £5·95 per litre.

CHEF/PROPRIETOR: Catherine Drewery
OPEN: Mon to Sat, D only CLOSED: last week June, first week July MEALS: 7.30 to 9.30
PRICES: Weekday D £8 (£13), Fri and Sat D £11 (£16) CARDS: Access, Amex, Diners, Visa
SEATS: 30. Private parties: 30 main room. Smart dress preferred. Music. Air-conditioned

---

ROCHFORD Essex map 3

▲ *Renoufs* [10/20]

1 South Street, Rochford SS4 1BL
SOUTHEND (0702) 544393 £19

Derek Renouf's flamboyant restaurant has a long menu, rich in cream. Standards have yo-yoed with the opening of his new hotel nearby but there remains a skilled professional approach behind the daft ambition to offer nearly a hundred dishes a night. Duck is done seven ways, including pressed, and langoustines and other crustacea are prominent, but the set meal is the best value. Good claret, some quite mature, dominates the cellar and there is ample choice of burgundy. CELLARMAN'S CHOICE: Graves, Ch. Respide Médeville '83, £14·95.

CHEF/PROPRIETOR: Derek Renouf
OPEN: Tue to Sat, exc Sat L CLOSED: First 3 weeks Jan MEALS: 12.15 to 1.45, 7.15 to 9.45
PRICES: £13 (£19) CARDS: Access, Amex, Diners, Visa
SEATS: 70. Private parties: 70 main room. Vegetarian meals. Children welcome. Wheelchair access (also WC). Music. Air-conditioned
ACCOMMODATION: 24 rooms, all with bath/shower. Rooms for disabled. B&B £48 to £65. Children welcome. Baby facilities. Pets welcome. Afternoon teas. Garden. Fishing. Golf. Air-conditioning. TV. Phone. Doors close at 11

ROCKLEY Wiltshire map 2

Loaves and Fishes [11/20]

Rockley Chapel, Rockley SN8 1RT
MARLBOROUGH (0672) 53737 £15–£16

Three miles outside Marlborough in old rural England, Morris Minor country. The chapel is not as historic as it looks, and for the last six years has served as a restaurant. The kitchen goes down one aisle, tables down another and up to the altar. The wood and cloth partitions lend a Nativity play feeling. Other curios abound, from the practical wood-burning stove to the gastronomic menu from Chez Panisse (see International), the different plates, each beautifully patterned, and the cut-glass butter dish. Only the food and classical music convey the present tense. Angela Rawson cooks a set menu, with no choice of main course, on an Aga. The style is seaside boarding-house, but properly done. Superb bowls of fresh vegetables accompany main-course roasts. The nutty brown bread is

---

Many of the more expensive restaurants offer bargain lunches for half the price of a meal in the evening. Details are given in the text.

served hot, and the menu does not fear to wander into avenues such as pumpkin and curry soup, Cordon Bleu meringues, and cold, creamy tangerine soufflé to finish. The coffee and the chocolate fudge disappoint. Take your own wine.

CHEF: Angela Rawson PROPRIETORS: Angela F. Rawson and Nikki R. Kedge
OPEN: Tue to Sat, D only, and Sun L MEALS: 12.30 to 1, 7.30 to 8.30
PRICES: Set L £14 (£15), Set D £15 (£16). Service inc. Unlicensed, but bring your own: corkage 5% for parties over 6
SEATS: 28. Private parties: 10 main room. Car-park, 10 places. Vegetarian meals. Children's helpings. Wheelchair access (also WC). Music

---

ROMSEY Hampshire   map 2

Old Manor House [12/20] ✗

21 Palmerston Street, Romsey SO5 8GF
ROMSEY (0794) 517353   £12–£22

An old favourite, Mauro Bregoli's traditionally furnished converted cottage with log fires continues to serve good-value lunches and, at night, a persuasive, imposing menu based largely on local ingredients. Game, sometimes even shot or caught by himself, features strongly. There is an impression that more artistry is creeping into the menu, in the form of salmon brioche or lobster and sweetbreads terrine, but the instincts are strong for more bourgeois steak au poivre; sea bass with herbs; fillet of beef with truffles. The cheese savouries, home-made rolls and plentiful coffee with Belgian chocolates emphasises that it is a serious, all-round restaurant. The strength of the wine list is in the claret.
CELLARMAN'S CHOICE: Ch. Coutet '84, £10·50.

CHEF/PROPRIETOR: Mauro Bregoli
OPEN: Tue to Sun, exc Sun D CLOSED: 25 to 30 Dec, last 2 weeks Aug, first week Sept
MEALS: 12 to 2, 7 to 9.30
PRICES: Set L £7·95 (£12), Set D £18 (£22). Service inc CARDS: Access, Visa
SEATS: 52. 5 tables outside. Private parties: 14 main room, 25 private room. Car-park, 12 places. Children welcome. Smart dress preferred. No cigars/pipes in dining-room

---

ROSS-ON-WYE Hereford & Worcester   map 2

▲ *Walford House Hotel* [11/20]

Walford Road, Ross-on-Wye HR9 5RY
ROSS-ON-WYE (0989) 63829
4m SW of Ross-on-Wye, on B4228   £20–£24

Raymond Postgate and André Simon both admired Raymond Zarb's cooking. Fifteen years ago he had a pestle and mortar in the *Guide*, though it was a controversial distinction, even then. Mr Zarb has always runs a very personal restaurant. 'I am a restorer. People come here to be restored and then go away again.' Solid local support keeps this fine old Georgian building, with its three magnificent cedars, in business. The hotel, like the menu, is decorated in conservative French style, though following its omission from last year's *Guide*, it seems to have perked up. Here is the old school: vivid, rust-coloured fish soup; duck with pickled peach; piles of prawns over little fillets of sole. The excellent cheeseboard, combined with the array of petits fours with proper coffee, make up for weak desserts. The extensive wine list moves upwards rapidly from £8·50. House white is served in gold-rimmed glasses with flower patterns, to reinforce the idea that this is what happens in Continental cuisine.

CHEF: Raymond Zarb PROPRIETORS: Joyce and Raymond Zarb
OPEN: all week MEALS: 12 to 1.45, 7.30 to 9.30
PRICES: £19 (£24), Set D from £16·50 (£20). Service inc CARDS: Access, Amex, Diners, Visa
SEATS: 35. Private parties: 50 main'room, 20 private room. Car-park, 20 places. Children's helpings. Jacket and tie. No-smoking area. Wheelchair access (also WC). Music
ACCOMMODATION: 10 rooms, all with bath/shower. Rooms for disabled. B&B £38 to £50. Children welcome. Baby facilities. Afternoon teas. Garden. TV. Phone. Scenic. Doors close at 12. Confirm by 5

ROXWELL Essex   map 3

Farmhouse Feast [11/20]

The Street, Roxwell CM1 4PB
ROXWELL (024 548) 583   £18

Rosemary and Juliet Upson's simply decorated period house stands in the shadow of the larger village pub. The formula is friendly and homely: the set menu takes in five courses, and you help yourself to starters and sweets from a side-table. Bowls filled with simple salads of the bean, rice, wholemeal pasta and couscous variety are complemented by excellent home-made pasta and quiche. Wholesome soup, such as potato and onion, is served from a plain brown tureen. Main courses are recited: stuffed trout with sesame seeds; steak and kidney pie with red wine; pork with beer and mushroom sauce; honey-roast chicken; plus even better vegetarian dishes, such as cashew-nut and rice loaf; and stuffed aubergine with spicy beans and lentils. Sweet raspberry sorbet makes a lighter finish than creamy banana Pavlova. The wine list has grown to twenty-four bottles, but they are rather puritanically described. House Italian is £4.50.

CHEFS: Juliet Upson, John Wealleans, Allan Greene and Peter Spence
PROPRIETORS: Rosemary and Juliet Upson
OPEN: Tue to Sat D, and Wed to Fri L CLOSED: 2 weeks June, 1 week Jan MEALS: 12 to 1.30, 7.30 to 9.30
PRICES: Set L and D £13·95 (£18)
SEATS: 60. Private parties: 24 main room (12, 16 and 24) private rooms. Vegetarian meals. Children's helpings. Wheelchair access. Music. Air-conditioned. Partly self service

---

RYE East Sussex   map 3

Landgate Bistro [13/20] ✈

5–6 Landgate, Rye TN31 7LH
RYE (0797) 222829   £13

Calls itself a bistro, but the cooking is more serious. The décor is mellowing, there are more pictures on the walls and the atmosphere is friendlier. Toni Ferguson-Lees' cooking goes from strength to strength and is moving towards modern British. There's more emphasis on game and fish from the Rye boats, sauces are pointed up with fresh herbs from the garden, and the cream and alcohol have been reduced. Vegetables follow the seasons – extraordinary salad leaves from Appledore, in summer, English roots in winter. This translates into a menu that takes in scallop mousse, noisettes of lamb with tomatoes and mint, and summer pudding. Squid is braised with white wine, tomatoes and garlic; wild rabbit is cooked with whisky, mustard and tarragon; there is jugged hare in season. The cheeseboard favours unpasteurised English farmhouse cheeses rather than Stilton and Brie. The short wine list has a good showing of bourgeois clarets, and there is a wine of the month promotion. CELLARMAN'S CHOICE: Montagny *premier cru*, Les Chagniots '83, from Delaunay, at £9·60.

CHEF: Toni Ferguson-Lees PROPRIETORS: Nick Parkin and Toni Ferguson-Lees
OPEN: Tue to Sat, D only MEALS: 7 to 9.30
PRICES: £9 (£13). Service 10% CARDS: Access, Amex, Diners, Visa
SEATS: 34. Private parties: 34 main room. Vegetarian meals. Children's helpings. Music

---

SAFFRON WALDEN Essex   map 3

Old Hoops [10/20]

15 King Street, Saffron Walden CB10 1HE
SAFFRON WALDEN (0799) 22813   £21

Don Irwin and Ray Morrison cook and their wives serve in the upstairs of this three-hundred-year-old pub. The mood is that of a casual bistro and it is possible to eat one course or a full meal. The cooking has ambitions, but simple dishes are often the most successful. Roast lamb with mint and tarragon gravy has been better than fillet of lamb wrapped in spinach and served with mustard sauce. Some of the flights of fancy – breast of chicken with Bayonne ham and bananas – may not live up to their promise. On the wine list, most bottles are under £10.

CHEFS: Don Irwin and Ray Morrison PROPRIETORS: Chris and Don Irwin, Sue and Ray Morrison
OPEN: Tue to Sat MEALS: 12 to 2.30, 7 to 10
PRICES: £14 (£21) CARDS: Access, Amex, Diners, Visa
SEATS: 44. Private parties: 40 main room. Vegetarian meals. Children's helpings. Music

---

ST ALBANS Hertfordshire   map 3

Langtrys [11/20]

1 Approach Road, St Albans AL1 1SP
ST ALBANS (0727) 61848   £27

The building is like a private house in the French countryside: imposing, three storeys high, with pink wooden shutters, dormer windows, and an angular slate roof. Inside, a big photograph of Lillie Langtry looks down from one wall of the dining-room. Paul Shepherd's main courses are exclusively fish, apart from a single steak dish, and the menu centres on old-style English and French dishes with a few additions, such as the Spanish stew, zarzuela. There is a lot of butter and cream about, but the excellent quality of the fish shines through. Scallops are cooked with garlic, butter and parsley; skate with black butter and capers; monkfish with curry sauce. Salmon with ginger and currants in pastry on a tarragon sauce is a good, workman-like version of the George Perry-Smith classic. Oysters come from Loch Fyne, and there are also lobsters, langoustines, crabs and soles, depending on the market. Sweets are mostly hot English favourites: spotted dick, apple crumble and excellent treacle tart with properly made custard. The consistency that was lacking in the food a couple of years ago, is now present. A simple 'starters and sweets' menu is also available at lunchtime. The fifty-strong wine list has some good-value French and German whites to suit the food. House French is £6·50 a bottle.

CHEF: Paul Shepherd PROPRIETORS: Paul Shepherd and Susan de Faye
OPEN: Mon to Sat, exc Sat L MEALS: 12 to 2, 7 to 10
PRICES: £18 (£27) CARDS: Access, Amex, Diners, Visa
SEATS: 50. Private parties: 50 main room. Children welcome. Music

---

ST MARGARET'S AT CLIFFE Kent   map 3

▲ *Wallett's Court* [11/20]

West Cliffe, St Margaret's at Cliffe CT15 6EW
DOVER (0304) 852424   £22

The Oakleys run this historic Elizabethan brick house essentially as a B&B, but will cater for private parties by arrangement, and open as a restaurant on Fridays and Saturdays. The dining-room of the much-restored house is delightful, and Chris Oakley is a polished chef. Four-course meals run through the evening, almost to midnight. Starters range from chicken and avocado salad to creamy mussel soup. The fish is good, from crab in sweet sherry sauce to wild salmon with tomatoes and basil. Beef is robustly cooked in claret, and served with baby vegetables: thick green beans, crinkled carrots, baby broccoli and dauphinois potatoes. A tray of pretty, but not bland, desserts includes even-textured iced raspberry mousse, or Bavarian cream with blackcurrant sauce. The wine list is truncated, but well picked. House claret is £6. CELLARMAN'S CHOICE: Sancerre, Clos du Chêne Marchand '85, £12·50.

CHEF: Chris Oakley PROPRIETORS: Chris and Lea Oakley
OPEN: Fri and Sat, D only MEALS: 8 to 11.30
PRICES: Set D £17 (£22). Cheaper meals for residents. Licensed, but bring your own
SEATS: 30. Private parties: 30 main room. Car-park, 16 places. Vegetarian meals.
Children's helpings
ACCOMMODATION: 7 rooms, all with bath/shower. Rooms for disabled. B&B £22 to £38.
Children welcome. Baby facilities. Garden. Tennis. Golf. Scenic. Doors close at 12.
Confirm by 4

SALISBURY Wiltshire   map 2

Crustaceans [new entry, zero rated]

2–4 Ivy Street, Salisbury SP1 2AY
SALISBURY (0722) 333948   £22

This fashionably pink and grey fish restaurant in a pair of blue and white cottages in the centre of town was opened in April 1987 by Roy Thwaites, a licensed netsman for the River Dart in Devon. Some of the catch – especially salmon and sea-trout – finds its way on to a long and varied menu with a few steaks to offset the theme. Specialities include roast lobsters (£8) and crawfish

(£20 for two) and a substantial bouillabaisse made of seasonal fish and shellfish, complete with aïoli and more garlic on the bread. The cooking relies on the freshness of its produce and some Villeroy and Bosch plates for its impact, but extends beyond the platters of prawns or oak-smoked fish into dishes such as John Dory with a vividly coloured lemon and chervil sauce. The use of fruit and herbs in combinations re-appears in orange and tarragon with grilled bass. Good cheeses are served, alas ready sliced; summer pudding has been fruity; coffee is a bit thin and served with commercial mints. The wine list is eighty-strong and spread through the major regions, opening at £7·50. More reports, please.

CHEF: Roy Thwaites PROPRIETORS: Roy and Lois Thwaites
OPEN: Mon to Sat, D only MEALS: 7 to 10.30
PRICES: £15 (£22). Service 10% CARDS: Access, Amex, Visa
SEATS: 48. Private parties: 12 main room. No children under 8. Music. Air-conditioned

---

SALISBURY Wiltshire

map 2

Harper's [10/20]

7 Ox Row, The Market Square, Salisbury SP1 1EU
SALISBURY (0722) 333118 £14–£16

Several fine restaurants have failed to establish themselves in Salisbury over the last decade, but the Harpers' family-orientated establishment, overlooking the vast market square, survives. The lunch menu is as good as a bargain as any to be had nearby. Natural tastes abound, and the food has a typical Wiltshire robustness in the thick soups and gravies. Cod with parsley, haddock with cream and coriander, roast lamb, steak-and-kidney pie are the measure, with meringues, and treacle tart and cream to finish. Dinners are more expensive but still good value, and might include a revived Cumbrian sweet, fig Sue: dried figs, stewed in brown ale, rum and orange, blended with double cream. Service is amiable. House claret is £7 a litre. CELLARMAN'S CHOICE: Médoc, Ch. La Lagune '76, £17·95, or Côte Rôtie '70, £17·50.

CHEFS: Adrian Harper, Mo Parker and Julie West PROPRIETOR: Adrian Harper
OPEN: all week, exc Sun L CLOSED: 25 and 26 Dec MEALS: 12 to 2, 6.30 to 10 (10.30 Sat)
PRICES: L £9 (£15), D £10 (16), Set D £8·95 (£14), Snacks from £1
CARDS: Access, Diners, Visa
SEATS: 60. Private parties: 60 main room. Car-park. Vegetarian meals. Children's helpings. Music. Air-conditioned

---

SCARBOROUGH North Yorkshire

map 6

Lanterna [10/20]

33 Queen Street, Scarborough YO11 1HQ
SCARBOROUGH (0723) 363616 £17

The Arecco family's dark, solid, bourgeois trattoria has been trading for sixteen years, and the sense of continuity extends to the menu, which is cooked to order.

▲ *This restaurant has rooms.*

Fish is notable. Steaks are 'cooked on the lamp' Fine meringues. House Barbera is £5·50.

CHEF: G. Arecco PROPRIETORS: Mr and Mrs G. Arecco
OPEN: Tue to Sat, D only MEALS: 7 to 9.30
PRICES: £11 (£17) CARD: Visa
SEATS: 36. Private parties: 36 main room. Vegetarian meals. No children under 5. Wheelchair access. Music

---

SEVENOAKS Kent   map 3

▲ *Royal Oak Hotel* [10/20]

Upper High Street, Sevenoaks TN14 5PG
SEVENOAKS (0732) 451109   £13–£16

The hotel is in brick, next to the pub of the same name, opposite Sevenoaks school (in the evening use the prefects' car park). The bar has a conservatory, while the more modest dining-room is done out in shades of green. Three fixed-priced dinner menus offer much fish, perhaps fillets of brill with a sauce made from vinegar, cream, red peppers and cayenne, or suprême of salmon with a strawberry coulis. Otherwise the menu runs to kidneys with capers and Pommery mustard or lamb cooked pink, with madeira. Austrian coffee cake is a good, rich sweet. Service seems to have a high turnover. Three dozen wines start at £4·50. CELLARMAN'S CHOICE: white Rully, La Bergerie '85, at £11·25, or red Ch. La Tour Bicheau '82, at £10·25.

CHEF: Raymond Patterson PROPRIETORS: Mr and Mrs M. R. Nix
OPEN: all week, exc Sat L and Sun D MEALS: 12.30 to 2, 7.30 to 9.30
PRICES: Set L £9·75 (£13), Set D from £12·50 (£16) CARDS: Access, Diners, Visa
SEATS: 40. Private parties: 12 main room, 26 private room. Car-park, 21 places. Children's helpings (L only). Smart dress preferred. No pipes in dining-room. Wheelchair access. Air-conditioned
ACCOMMODATION: 21 rooms, all with bath/shower. B&B £40 to £45. Children welcome. Baby facilities. Pets welcome. Air-conditioning. TV. Phone. Confirm by 6

SHARPTHORNE West Sussex   map 3

▲ *Gravetye Manor* [15/20]

Vowels Lane, Sharpthorne RH19 4LJ
SHARPTHORNE (0342) 810567   ▮ £31–£38

Gravetye is like the Connaught in an English country setting. The Elizabethan stone manor-house is surrounded by wonderful gardens, laid out and landscaped by the Victorian gardener and horticulturist William Robinson, while inside, the panelled dining-room is run with impressive attention to detail and smoothness. Leigh Stone-Herbert, after a seven-year absence, has returned from Australia to take over the kitchen. He has sharpened up technique, and begun to use combinations such as venison with a nut pancake and wine sauce, or chicken breast with Sauternes, while keeping within a modern British framework. Dishes

---

An index of restaurants by name appears at the back of the Guide.

can read like family Sunday lunch affairs – grilled sirloin steak with a layer of breadcrumbs, herbs and bone marrow – and there is a fondness for wrapping and layering fish and meat: salmon, for instance, is coated with its own mousse and wrapped in a spinach leaf before a champagne and mushroom sauce is added; saddle of lamb is rolled round asparagus and sliced, each piece overlaid with a spoonful of hollandaise with shredded mint leaves. The six vegetables are a course in themselves. For pudding, carrot and hazelnut cake with apricot sauce stands beside chocolate marquise with coffee sauce. Wines owe their principal allegiance to France. White burgundy relies heavily on Louis Latour, Alsace goes back to 1967, and white Bordeaux to 1919, and they are not given away. Water from the Gravetye spring is free, or there is CELLARMAN'S CHOICE: Pouilly-Fumé, Les Loges '81, from Pabiot, £14.

CHEF: Leigh Stone-Herbert PROPRIETOR: Peter Herbert
OPEN: all week CLOSED: 25 Dec D to non-residents MEALS: 12.30 to 2, 7.30 to 9.30 (10 Sat)
PRICES: £24 (£38), Set L £15 (£26), Set D £19 (£31). Service inc
SEATS: 50. Private parties: 10 main room, 20 private room. Car-park, 30 places. No children under 7. Smart dress preferred. No smoking in dining-room
ACCOMMODATION: 14 rooms, all with bath/shower. B&B £55 to £120. No children under 7. Garden. Fishing. TV. Phone. Scenic. Doors close at 12

SHEFFIELD South Yorkshire

map 5

Nirmal's Tandoori [11/20]

193 Glossop Road, Sheffield S10 2GW
SHEFFIELD (0742) 24054   £14–£16

Nirmal Gupta is one of very few Asian women restaurateurs. She also does the cooking, or at least some of it. Her busy, cramped, but now established restaurant can be a culture shock to those used to plush Manchester or London places but there is a genuine air of hospitality and culinary confidence: the bias is towards fresh ingredients and fresh ideas, emphasised by the daily blackboard menu of specialities. Punjabi dishes are cooked in ghee, not oil. Rogan josh and chicken jalfrezi are subtly spiced; nan and rice are impeccable. Start with sour almond and yoghurt soup, and finish with excellent kulfi. The wine list is better than in the average Indian restaurant.

CHEF: Nirmal Gupta PROPRIETORS: Mr and Mrs P. L. Gupta
OPEN: all week, exc Sun L MEALS: 12 to 2.30, 6 to 12 (1 Fri and Sat)
PRICES: £8 (£16), Set L and D from £8·50 (£14). Service 10% CARDS: Access, Amex, Visa
SEATS: 80. Private parties: 30 main room. Vegetarian meals. Children welcome. Wheelchair access (also WC). Music

---

SHEPTON MALLET Somerset

map 2

Blostin's [10/20]

29 Waterloo Road, Shepton Mallet BA4 5HH
SHEPTON MALLET (0749) 3648   £14–£17

Off the tourist track near a disused viaduct of the old Somerset and Dorset Railway, this brown-walled, brown-cloth'd bistro puts the emphasis on fresh, locally bought produce: vegetables and fruit from a smallholding, organic herbs, and fish from Cornwall. Good dishes have included Stilton soup, pork with four peppers, and brown-bread ice-cream. Vegetables are abundant and cheeses from a local shop have featured Shropshire Blue and Cornish Yarg as well as some from Somerset. There is a magnum of Beaujolais '85 on the largely French wine list (Brouilly, Château des Tours, £17·25), and most bottles are modestly priced. House French is £4·95. CELLARMAN'S CHOICE: Cabernet-Shiraz, McWilliams '84, £5·95.

CHEF: Nick Reed PROPRIETORS: Nick and Lynne Reed
OPEN: Tue to Sat, D only. L by arrangement MEALS: 7 to 9.30 (10 Sat)
PRICES: £12 (£17), Set D from £8·95 (£14) CARDS: Access, Diners, Visa
SEATS: 32. Private parties: 30 main room. Vegetarian meals. Children's helpings.
Wheelchair access. Music

▲ *Bowlish House* [11/20]

Wells Road, Shepton Mallet BA4 5JD
SHEPTON MALLET (0749) 2022   £18

Brian Jordan's spacious Georgian house complete with conservatory and walled garden, on the outskirts of Shepton Mallet, provides a comfortable overnight stop. It has outlasted most of its local rivals on the strength of its honest cooking and splendid wines from an encyclopaedic list. Typical of the kitchen's work are wholewheat pasta flavoured with saffron with a sauce of mussels, spinach and sorrel, and breast of duck fried in walnut oil and served with a walnut and cream sauce. The chocolate marquise tastes like the inside of a chocolate truffle – all chocolate and butter. But while the food is admirable, the serious business of this house is downstairs in the cellar. Altering the layout of the list to group wines by style and grape variety has had the effect, so Mr Jordan informs us, of reducing consumption of French wines to a mere five per cent of total sales. His splendid assembly of wines from around the world provides an opportunity to experiment, without just taking a blind stab at something unknown. Full dry whites include not just Chardonnay but also Malvasia (Frascati) and Australian Semillon; light-bodied reds include Valpolicella and Gamza from Sukhindol in Bulgaria, as well as Beaujolais. CELLARMAN'S CHOICE: Australian Chardonnay, Rosemount '85, at £6·80.

CHEF: Adrian Johnson PROPRIETORS: Brian and Julia Jordan
OPEN: all week, D only CLOSED: 4 days at Christmas MEALS: 7 to 10
PRICES: Set D from £14 (£18) SEATS: 26. 3 tables outside. Private parties: 36 main room, 12 private room. Car-park, 20 places. Vegetarian meals. Children's helpings. Smart dress preferred. No smoking in dining-room. Wheelchair access (also WC)
ACCOMMODATION: 4 rooms, all with bath/shower. Rooms for disabled. B&B £32. Children welcome. Baby facilities. Pets welcome. Afternoon teas. Garden. TV. Doors close at 1 [GHG]

All inspections are carried out anonymously.

The 1989 Guide will appear before Christmas 1988. Reports are particularly helpful in the spring. Report forms are at the back of this book, but just write a letter if you prefer. Address it to The Good Food Guide, FREEPOST, *14 Buckingham Street, London WC2N 6BR. No stamp is necessary if you post it in the UK.*

SHINFIELD Berkshire   map 3

L'Ortolan [16/20]

The Old Vicarage, Church Lane, Shinfield RG2 9BY
READING (0734) 883783   £24–£34

The Old Vicarage is set in three acres of quince, apple, and pear trees. Inside, peachy-apricot is the dominating colour, with pleasing pictures in all rooms, antique mirrors, good furniture, and masses of fresh flowers and plants. Tables are large and well spaced, with beige and apricot linen. On a golden autumnal day, eating lunch in the conservatory is a delight. Hardly anything has changed since the Ladenis's left a year ago for London (see London entry, Simply Nico). Throughout the county it is still known as, 'that place where the chef throws you out'. The Burton-Races have worked hard to bring about a good ambience. He is technically one of the best of the young chefs, exploding with ideas, easily reworking well-known modern dishes, for instance foie gras parfait, combining it with leeks, soaking it in jelly, and serving it with a glass of Pineau des Charentes. The menu, which is enormous by modern standards, with eleven starters and as many main dishes, overflows with flavour speculations and combinations, demonstrating a passionate affair with gastronomy. It reflects his previous employer, Raymond Blanc, but is richly coloured, and so obviously in tune with modern British cooking that it is his own style, even though that style – 'I like to call it contemporary classic cuisine' – has still to clarify. The cooking is almost classically complicated: squid stuffed with scallop mousse, with a basil sauce; the leg of a poussin, stuffed with snails, with a Beaujolais sauce; ox-tail, boned, filled with a quenelle of wild mushrooms, simmered in Chablis, enriched with a confit of grapes, and topped with a ravioli of sweetbreads. Somehow, a clear theme is sustained; in many cases the elaboration is simply a question of seasoning, balancing, and re-aligning, although on occasions it becomes self-defeating. Sometimes it acts as a prelude to something plainer, like a glorious lemon soufflé. The wine list matches the culinary aspirations: 159 bottles, strong in burgundy and claret, but also including regional French wines under £10. House Bergerac is £8·45. CELLARMAN'S CHOICE: Ch. d'Issan '78, £39·80.

CHEF: John Burton-Race PROPRIETORS: Mr and Mrs Burton-Race
OPEN: Tue to Sun, exc Sun D MEALS: 12.15 to 2.15, 7.15 to 10.30
PRICES: Set L £15·50 (£24), Set D £25 (£34) CARDS: Access, Amex, Visa
SEATS: 70. Private parties: 40 main room, 32 private room. Car-park, 15 places. Vegetarian meals. Children's helpings. Wheelchair access (2 steps; also WC)

SHIPLEY West Yorkshire   map 5

Aagrah [11/20] 🍴

27 Westgate, Shipley BD18 3QX
BRADFORD (0274) 594660   £8–£14

The colourful basement has had a facelift and the menu has been expanded, but Mr Sabir and his brother continue to serve some of the most creditable North Indian restaurant food in an area dominated by cafés and sweet-centres. Best bets are the selection of specialities, such as shah jajam – meat, chicken and prawns with fresh ginger, green chillies and coriander – and balti chicken (familiar in the Midlands, but rare in the North of England). The restaurant caters well for vegetarians, although the results can sometimes be disappointing. Spicing is moderate and subtle, though the menu promises 'any strength on request'. Drink lassi or Kingfisher beer.

CHEFS: M. Sabir and M. Aslam PROPRIETORS: Mr and Mrs M. Sabir, Mr and Mrs M. Aslam
OPEN: all week, D only MEALS: 6pm to 12.45am (1.30am Thur to Sat)
PRICES: £7 (£14), Set D from £4·60 (£8) CARDS: Access, Amex, Diners, Visa
SEATS: 40. Private parties: 40 main room. Vegetarian meals. Children's helpings. Smart dress preferred. Wheelchair access. Music

---

SHIPSTON ON STOUR Warwickshire   map 2

▲ *White Bear* [10/20]

High Street, Shipston on Stour CV36 4AJ
SHIPSTON ON STOUR (0608) 61558   £17

The Roberts have taken on a new venture in the Fossebridge Inn at Northleach (see entry), but keep this old pub, which is very much part of the village, as a second string. The bar snacks are well above average and the credit spills over into the small restaurant dining-room. The style is no-frills English and seasonal: pigeon and bacon pâté, tomato and fennel soup, pan-fried breast of duck cooked pink with rosemary and green grapes. Fish is from the West Country, and cheeses are British. Beers are draught Bass or Springfield, house Rhône is £4·95.

CHEF: Andrew Purdy PROPRIETORS: Hugh and Suzanne Roberts
OPEN: all week MEALS: 12 to 1.45, 7.30 to 9.30
PRICES: £11 (£17), Snacks from £1·45 CARDS: Access, Amex, Diners, Visa
SEATS: 35. 4 tables outside. Private parties: 24 main room. Car-park, 20 places. Vegetarian meals. Children's helpings. Smart dress preferred. Wheelchair access (also WC)
ACCOMMODATION: 10 rooms, all with bath/shower. B&B £25 to £40. Deposit: £20. Children welcome. Baby facilities. Pets welcome. TV. Doors close at 11.30. Confirm by 6

SHIPTON GORGE Dorset   map 2

▲ *Innsacre Farmhouse Hotel* [11/20] ✆

Shipton Gorge DT6 4LJ
BRIDPORT (0308) 56137   £13–£19

Hotel is the wrong word: the long, low tunnel of a building, set between two hillocks off the main road, still has signs of the farm it was – straw, pigs, dogs. Rooms are functional but the cooking, without being gastronomic, fussy or pretentious, makes skilful use of unusual combinations. It is eclectic in the best sense. In March, kebabs of monkfish, scallops and bacon dressed with lime and dill vied as a starter with hot quail salad with grapes and toasted hazelnuts dressed with sherry vinegar and walnut oil. But there are curries, roasts and sound country notions, like braised ox-tail, plus a formal, catering-school-style

---

Good vintages for drinking in 1988: Alsace '85, Beaujolais '86, Germany '85, petits chateaux clarets '81, lesser clarets '83.

---

sweets trolley. The inglenook, the exposed brickwork and the Wedgwood add to the charm and character rather more than does the wine list, which has some odd mark-ups. House wine is £6.

CHEFS: H. M. Smith, Amanda Buttle and Susan Bowditch
PROPRIETORS: J. H. and H. M. Smith
OPEN: all week MEALS: 12 to 2, 7.15 to 10.30
PRICES: Set L from £9·25 (£13), Set D from £14·25 (£19), Snacks from £1·25
CARDS: Access, Amex, Diners, Visa
SEATS: 42. 4 tables outside. Private parties: 60 main room. Car-park, 40 places. Vegetarian meals. Children's helpings. No cigars/pipes in dining-room. Wheelchair access (also WC). Music
ACCOMMODATION: 8 rooms, 4 with bath/shower. B&B £16 to £40. Children welcome. Baby facilities. Pets welcome. Afternoon teas. Garden. TV. Scenic

---

SHIPTON-UNDER-WYCHWOOD Oxfordshire map 2

▲ *Lamb Inn* [10/20]

Shipton-under-Wychwood OX7 6DQ
SHIPTON-UNDER-WYCHWOOD (0993) 830465   £12–£17

The stone pub set back from the main road is well supported for its blackboard menu of hearty, home-cooked dishes, for instance roast garlic lamb, Cotswold pie, seafood pancake, and treacle tart. A beamed dining-room at the back lets the kitchen show off more – fine roast Sunday lunches and notable jugged hare on occasion. Buffet lunches are held in summer. The atmosphere is unrushed. Hook Norton and Wadworth real ales. House French is £5·25.

CHEF: George Benham PROPRIETORS: Hugh and Lynne Wainwright
OPEN: Mon to Sat D, and Sun L MEALS: 12.30 to 1.45, 7.30 to 9.15
PRICES: Set L £7·50 (£12), Set D £11·75 (£17) CARDS: Access, Amex, Diners, Visa
SEATS: 26. 8 tables outside. Private parties: 26 main room. Car-park, 30 places. Vegetarian meals. No children under 14. Wheelchair access
ACCOMMODATION: 5 rooms, all with bath/shower. B&B £25 to £38. Deposit: £10.
No children under 14. Garden. TV. Scenic. Confirm by 6

SHREWSBURY Shropshire map 5

Delanys [9/20] ✝

St Julians Craft Centre, St Alkmonds Square, Shrewsbury SY1 1UH
SHREWSBURY (0743) 60602   £5

Outside there is historic medieval and Tudor architecture. Inside, this church vestry has been turned into a jazzy vegetarian restaurant with brilliant green tablecloths and blue chairs. The food is freshly prepared and takes in anything from curried lentil soup to cauliflower paprika, or vegan chickpea and vegetable casserole. Burgers are celery and lentil. Stilton and walnut pâté is first rate and sweets are wholefood. There are even organic wines.

Restaurants are checked every year and their entries rewritten. The restaurant scene changes very rapidly. Don't trust an out-of-date Guide.

CHEFS/PROPRIETORS: Peter Gwynne and Gary Kirkman
OPEN: Mon to Sat L, and Sat D MEALS: 10.30 to 4.30 (L 11.30 to 2.30), 8 to 8.30
PRICES: £2 (£5)
SEATS: 32. Private parties: 32 main room. Vegetarian meals. Children welcome. No smoking. Music. Self-service

Old Police House [10/20]

Castle Court, off Castle Street, Shrewsbury SY1 2BG
SHREWSBURY (0743) 60668   £9–£16

The old police station – and one-time county jail – has been given the Victorian treatment and gains lots of popular support. David Campbell's menu takes few risks, relying on good soups, solid main courses and home-made sweets. Cheeses include Shropshire Blue, Cornish Yarg, and locally made ewes' and goats' milk, served with home-made soda bread. The wine list is kind under £10 – Rioja, Viña Real Gran Reserva '75 is £9·90. CELLARMAN'S CHOICE: Montepulciano d'Abruzzo, at £6·80.

CHEF: David Campbell PROPRIETORS: Simon and Alison Rudd-Clarke
OPEN: Tue to Sat MEALS: 12 to 1.45, 7 to 9.45
PRICES: Set L from £4·95 (£9), Set D £11·20 (£16), Snacks from 40p
CARDS: Access, Visa
SEATS: 36. Private parties: 34 main room, 10 private room. Car-park, 2 places. Vegetarian meals. Children's helpings. No-smoking area. Music

---

SHURDINGTON Gloucestershire   map 2

▲ *Greenway*

Shurdington GL51 5UG
CHELTENHAM (0242) 862352

As the Guide *went to press there was a change of chef at this restaurant.*

Restaurants are graded on a scale of 1–20. In the category of 10–11 expect to find the best food in the locality. Ratings of 12 and more are given to restaurants we regard as serving the best food in the region.

SLAIDBURN Lancashire   map 5

▲ *Parrock Head Farm* [10/20]

Slaidburn BB7 3AH
SLAIDBURN (020 06) 614
1m NW of Slaidburn   £16

The Holts have sold up and are now at the Hark to Bounty in the village, but the
Umbers have carried on in much the same style at this favourite hill-farm, well
used by walkers. The cooking is more ambitious – tomato rose garnishes and
petits fours appear. But dishes like tomato and basil soup; salmon trout with a
cucumber and dill sauce; roasts, such as duck, which form the centre of meals;
and apple pie, are of a standard. The tradition of hearty breakfasts continues.
House wine £5·50 a litre.

CHEFS: Stephen Kerfoot and Deborah Wareing PROPRIETOR: Richard Umbers
OPEN: all week, D only CLOSED: Dec to Jan MEALS: 6.45 to 8.45
PRICES: £11 (£16) CARD: Amex
SEATS: 25. Private parties: 16 main room. Car-park, 20 places. Children's helpings.
Wheelchair access (also WC)
ACCOMMODATION: 9 rooms, all with bath/shower. Rooms for disabled. B&B £18·50 to £37.
Pets welcome. Afternoon teas. Garden. Fishing. Golf. Snooker. TV. Scenic.
Doors close at 12 [GHG]

SOLIHULL West Midlands   map 5

Liaison [13/20]

761 Old Lode lane, Solihull B92 8JE
021–743 3993   £21–£27

Still one of Birmingham's better-kept secrets, but still one of the best restaurants
in the West Midlands. Patricia Plunkett's cooking is modern, drawing its
inspiration from further south in England and France. Tradition is seen in classic
onion soup, and lamb with rosemary; the modern style in, say, an asparagus
gateau with chervil butter and smoked salmon. The décor is spick and eclectic,
and service from partner Ank Van Der Tuin is studious. The main surprise is
often on the plate, as the rarely changing menu does not reveal all in its

CELLARMAN'S CHOICE: *This is a wine recommended by the restaurateur which is more
expensive than the house wine but is good value and fitting for the kind of food served.*

323

descriptions: sweets, like the brochette of hot fruits or the four chocolate desserts, can be visually spectacular. Eighty wines are fittingly chosen and start at £6·25. CELLARMAN'S CHOICE: Chiroubles, Château de Javernand '85, £11·75.

CHEF: Patricia Plunkett PROPRIETORS: Patricia Plunkett and Ank Van Der Tuin
OPEN: Tue to Sat, D only CLOSED: 2 weeks at Christmas, Aug MEALS: 7 to 10
PRICES: £20 (£27), Set D £15·95 (£21) CARDS: Access, Amex, Diners, Visa
SEATS: 34. Private parties: 40 main room. Car-park, 15 places. Vegetarian meals. Children welcome. No pipes in dining-room. Wheelchair access. Music

---

SOUTHALL Greater London   map 3

Brilliant [9/20]

72–74 Western Road, Southall UB2 5DZ
01-574 1928   £11–£18

When the Prince and Princess of Wales went to Southall, Mr Anand supplied a buffet, which was delivered to the local community centre. This café is still the pride of the neighbourhood and has lost none of its cutting edge. It is smarter and less of a canteen than it used to be, but the kitchen hasn't sold out to the biriani brigade. Butter chicken and jeera chicken are perennial snacks, as are the incomparable keema peas. Breads and rice are well up to standard. To drink there's Kenyan or Kingfisher beer, plus lassi.

CHEF: D. K. Anand PROPRIETORS: K. K. and D. K. Anand
OPEN: Tue to Sun D, and Tue to Fri L CLOSED: Aug MEALS: 12 to 3, 6 to 11.30 (12 Fri and Sat)
PRICES: £11 (£18), Set L from £7 (£11), Set D from £8 (£12). Service 10% CARDS: Access, Amex, Diners, Visa
SEATS: 120. Private parties: 80 main room, 40 private room. Vegetarian meals. Children's helpings. Wheelchair access (also WC). Music. Air-conditioned

---

SOUTHAMPTON Hampshire   map 2

Geddes [new entry, zero rated]

Town Quay, Southampton SO1 0AR
SOUTHAMPTON (0703) 221159   £17–£38

A converted warehouse with cellars in the medieval town walls, facing the old pier and landing-stage for the Isle of Wight ferry. The restaurant is on the ground floor, but its pretensions are rather higher, as are its prices. No expense has been spared on the décor: woven carpets, low-voltage lamps on movable copper wires, mirrors in frames, and the latest Habitat-style chairs. The menu is in the butter-and-cream mould of showy French cooking: pretty omelette 'arlequin'; pavé of fresh turbot wrapped in a cabbage leaf; sliced duck with raspberries; monkfish with green peppercorns. This is a kitchen struggling to assert itself, through an over-rigid formula. Meals finish on a high note, with fruit tart and charlottes. Good cheeses come on a trolley the size of a small greenhouse. The set menu

---

Restaurants change owners and chefs constantly. Please help keep the Guide *informed of any changes you find.*

offers better value than the *carte*. Wines follow suit, with some reasonably priced bottles alongside some unaffordable museum pieces. More reports, please.

CHEF: Christophe Novelli   PROPRIETORS: A. R. and S. R. Grimble-Harper
OPEN: Mon to Sat   MEALS: 12 to 2.30, 7 to 10.30
PRICES: £29 (£38), Set L £7·90 (£17), Set D £14·80 (£22). Service 10%   CARDS: Access, Amex, Diners, Visa
SEATS: 56. Private parties: 56 main room. Vegetarian meals. Children welcome. Wheelchair access (also WC). Music. Air-conditioned

---

SOUTHEND-ON-SEA Essex map 3

Alvaro's [10/20]

32 – 34 St Helens Road, Westcliff-on-Sea, Southend SSO 7LB
SOUTHEND (0702) 335840 £11 – £24

For a decade this double-fronted terraced house next to an old-fashioned tailor's has been serving fine steak and chips, as well as a handful of unpretentious Portuguese dishes. Meat is good quality, and fish is often fresh. Soup is made from rich stock packed with cabbage, potato and onion; sardines are cooked with red and green peppers; and there's plenty of juicy halibut, potatoes and oil in the fish casserole. When fresh clams are available, Jose Rodrigues served traditional cataplana, baked in a copper dish. The atmosphere is sedate and the service polite. It is popularly used for celebrations. Good-value Portuguese wines include Periquita '78, at £6·95.

CHEF: Jose Rodrigues   PROPRIETORS: Alvaro and Joyce Rodrigues and Jose Rodrigues
OPEN: Tue to Sun, exc Sat L   MEALS: 12 to 2 (2.30 Sun), 7 to 10 (11 Fri and Sat)
PRICES: £16 (£24), Set Sun L £7·25 (£11). Service 10%   CARDS: Access, Visa
SEATS: 60. Vegetarian meals. Children's helpings. Smart dress preferred. Wheelchair access. Music

Slassor's [11/20]

145 Eastern Esplanade, Southend-on-Sea SS1 2YD
SOUTHEND (0702) 614880 £15

A modest place, on the seafront, with bowls of olives set out on the gingham table- cloths. It is unlicensed, and the menu is written on the blackboard. Nevertheless, Leslie Slassor is a skilful cook, and makes good use of fish: salmon mousse, grilled Dover sole, fish soup with scallops and prawns. More prawns are used as a stuffing for chicken legs, and there are steaks, too. Bread is baked on the premises.

CHEF: Leslie Slassor   PROPRIETORS: Margaret and Leslie Slassor
OPEN: Mon to Sat, exc Mon L   MEALS: 12 to 2, 7 to 9.30
PRICES: £12 (£15). Unlicensed, but bring your own: corkage 75p.   CARDS: Access, Visa
SEATS: 22. Private parties: 30 main room. Children's helpings. Music

---

Restaurants are graded on a scale of 1–20. In the category of 10–11 expect to find the best food in the locality. Ratings of 12 and more are given to restaurants we regard as serving the best food in the region.

SOUTH GODSTONE Surrey   map 3

La Bonne Auberge [12/20]

Tilburstow Hill, South Godstone RH9 8JY
SOUTH GODSTONE (0342) 893184   £18–£28

Jean-Pierre Bonnet's cooking stands out from the run of expensive Surrey
restaurants, as does the exceptional wine cellar. The menu is French, and
especially good in the more provincial dishes, such as fish soup, calf's liver with a
sauce of veal stock flavoured with orange, or apple tart with armagnac. Service is
too often rushed. The wine list extends to a hundred bottles, mostly French, well
spread in price and value, from house wine at £6·20 onwards, and a monthly
selection of their own CELLARMAN'S CHOICE.

CHEF: Jean-Pierre Bonnet PROPRIETOR: Antoine L. S. Jalley
OPEN: Tue to Sun, exc Sun D MEALS: 12 to 2, 7 to 10
PRICES: £23 (£28), Set L from £13·50 (£18), Set D from £18 (£23). Service inc
CARDS: Access, Amex, Visa
SEATS: 48. 4 tables outside. Private parties: 80 main room, 3 private room. Car-park,
70 places. Vegetarian meals. Children's helpings. Smart dress preferred. Wheelchair
access. Music

SOUTH MOLTON Devon   map 1

▲ *Stumbles* [11/20]

131–134 East Street, South Molton EX36 3BU
SOUTH MOLTON (076 95) 4145   £18

The large, Mediterranean-style patio at the back of this wine bar-cum-
restaurant, is a summer attraction. The full menu ranges far and wide for
Scottish pancake (with smoked haddock), prawns with aïoli, and lamb shashlik.
There are also snacks at lunchtime: pizzas, ham salad, apricot and hazelnut
meringue with real cream. Sausages are from the excellent Heal Farm, King's
Nympton. The wine list is strong in conventional areas of France, but, like the
menu, roams abroad to Spain, Portugal, Italy, Lebanon, California, Australia and
New Zealand. CELLARMAN'S CHOICE: Australian Cabernet Sauvignon, Wynns
Coonawarra '80, at £12.

CHEF: Colette Potter PROPRIETORS: Mr and Mrs M. J. Potter
OPEN: Mon to Sat MEALS: 12.30 to 2.30, 7.30 to 10
PRICES: £12 (£18) CARDS: Access, Amex, Diners, Visa
SEATS: 50. 10 tables outside. Private parties: 50 main room. Car-park, 30 places. Vegetarian
meals. Children's helpings. Music
ACCOMMODATION: 7 rooms, all with bath/shower. Rooms for disabled. B&B £17·50 to £50.
Pets welcome. TV. Phone

All inspections are carried out anonymously.

*The average price quoted in brackets is for an average three-course meal including
service, VAT, coffee and half a bottle of house wine or the equivalent in an ethnic
restaurant.*

SOUTHWELL Nottinghamshire · map 5

Leo's [10/20]

12 King Street, Southwell NG25 0EN
SOUTHWELL (0636) 812119 · £24

Heather Hodgkinson cooks an eclectic, modern menu in this good-humoured little restaurant. She terms it 'international', meaning timbale of sweet peppers with green peppercorns; créole salad; and lamb kofta. The experimentation rarely overshadows what is good cooking of good ingredients. The desserts are noticeably British: rhubarb tart flavoured with cinnamon; Hampton Court tart. The ninety wines are more conventionally anchored in classical regions, though the mark-ups, on the Beaujolais in particular, are very steep. House Ropiteau is £6·50. CELLARMAN'S CHOICE: Vacqueyras '81, from Pascal, £10·45.

CHEF: Heather Hodgkinson PROPRIETORS: Heather and Tony Hodgkinson
OPEN: Tue to Sat, D only MEALS: 7 to 10
PRICES: Set D £17·50 (£24) CARDS: Access, Amex, Diners, Visa
SEATS: 26. Private parties: 30 main room. Children's helpings. No children under 5. Music. Air-conditioned

SOUTHWOLD Suffolk · map 6

▲ Crown [12/20]

90 High Street, Southwold IP18 6DP
SOUTHWOLD (0502) 722275 · £12–£15

The popularity of the re-born Crown has led to the opening of a second dining-room, 'the parlour', in what was the hotel lounge. Tim Reeson's set lunch and dinner menus are still extremely good value, and the prospect of three glasses of classy wine from the Cruover machine for £6, is an offer few can refuse. The cooking is modern British, taking full advantage of excellent local ingredients and seasonality. Every chef needs a good fishmonger, and John Huggins regularly obtains the very best from Lowestoft market and the local boats. The fish – often steamed – is paired with vivid sauces: orange and tarragon for lemon sole; citronella and basil for a duo of brill and monkfish. There is good poultry and game, too: breast of duck is cooked pink and served with plums and mirabelle; pigeon appears with chicken as a terrine, or cooked medium-rare with red wine and juniper berries. In line with current trends, the menu always includes simple vegetarian dishes, such as pear with Stilton dressing or broccoli and tomato flan. Cheeses come from the excellent Oulton Broad cheese shop and sweets are fruity fools, sorbets and crumbles. Similar dishes can be eaten in the bar as well as the restaurant, and there is a fine Sunday brunch for £5. Wines are from the parent company, Adnams, and are available by the case. The full list is recognised as one of the finest merchant lists for European wines outside claret and burgundy – notably for Italy, Rhône and Loire – and with twenty-four hours' notice, any bottle on the list can be ready for a meal. That is in addition to the

Files are kept on every restaurant, so reports of poor meals are just as valuable as reports of good meals because they save unnecessary inspections.

twenty-page list operating for the restaurant, and the selection from the Crouver machine. In restaurant terms, that is outstanding service.

CHEF: Tim Reeson PROPRIETORS: Adnams plc
OPEN: all week MEALS: 12.30 to 2, 7.30 to 9.45
PRICES: £7 (£12), Set L from £9 (£13), Set D from £11 (£15) CARDS: Access, Amex, Visa
SEATS: 26. 4 tables outside. Private parties: 40 private room. Car-park, 18 places. Children's helpings
ACCOMMODATION: 12 rooms, all with bath/shower. B&B £22 to £35. Pets welcome. Afternoon teas. TV. Phone. Scenic. Doors close at 11. Confirm by 6

SPARK BRIDGE Cumbria   map 7

▲ *Bridgefield House* [13/20] ✗

Spark Bridge LA12 8DA
LOWICK BRIDGE (022 985) 239
4m N of Ulverston, off A5084 on back
road from Spark Bridge to Coniston   £22

The shy, retiring violet of Lakeland blooms. The Glisters have, over the last few years, quietly modernised their secluded Victorian house, and the expanded garden now contributes vegetables, herbs and fruit. The place is without frills or trimmings, like TVs, but Rosemary's cooking would not be out of place in a house with more presence. Dish for dish, on the set meals, she holds her own with the best. Take these, from a meal in March: yellow plums in tarragon cream, or hot Morecambe shrimps in butter; then a warm salad of smoked trout with pasta; pheasant with a sauce of redcurrant, red wine and pan juices; five vegetables; sorbet of elderflower and blood orange; flummery of loganberry and Drambuie; and finally, either a savoury of sauté lamb's kidneys, or cheese, served with a Chinese pear. It is in the Lakes that traditional cooking seems to fuse most successfully with the modern style. There is a strong showing of '78 claret, plenty of Louis Latour burgundy, and good support from the Loire, Rhône and Alsace. The stock of half-bottles is particularly impressive. CELLARMAN'S CHOICE: Australian Chardonnay, Hill Smith Estate '85, £8·45.

CHEF: Rosemary Glister PROPRIETORS: David and Rosemary Glister
OPEN: all week, D only MEALS: 7.30
PRICES: Set D £16 (£22)
SEATS: 20. Private parties: 24 main room. Car-park, 10 places. Vegetarian meals. Children's helpings. Smart dress preferred. No smoking in dining-room. Wheelchair access (also WC). One sitting
ACCOMMODATION: 5 rooms, 3 with bath/shower. B&B £18·50 to £50. Children welcome. Baby facilities. Pets welcome. Garden. Fishing. Scenic. Confirm by 3

'Restaurants could make more effort to put half-bottles on their wine lists. I do not drink alcohol, my husband has to choose from halves and often has very little choice.'
(On eating in Hereford)

The entries are compiled from the views of readers who have eaten at the restaurants in the last year, backed up by anonymous inspections and by information supplied and facts verified by the restaurants.

SPARSHOLT Hampshire   map 2

▲ *Lainston House*   [new entry, zero rated]

Sparsholt SO21 2LT
WINCHESTER   (0962) 63588   £14–£32

The house presents itself dramatically through an avenue of limes; it is a
rambling, red-brick manor claiming to date from William and Mary. Everything
has been done in the grand manner. The modern menu is a great sweep of
luxuries, not so much cooked, as arranged into graphic, tasteful designs: duck
breast on a light garlic sauce is served with apple and celeriac layers and a mixed
salad with a truffle dressing and the crisped leg. One opinion is that the
complexities tend to overshadow the cooking, which can have a second-hand
feel – an increasingly common view on hotel food these days – but others
enthuse, quoting ginger bavarois in a light caramel sauce as just one of many
good examples. The trimmings are luxuriant, as are the *carte* prices, and the wine
list of nearly two hundred bottles is in keeping. CELLARMAN'S CHOICE:
Ch. La Tour de Bessan '79, £25·50. More reports, please.

CHEF: Friedrich Litty PROPRIETORS: Pennylain Hotels Ltd
OPEN: all week MEALS: 12 to 2.30, 7 to 10.30
PRICES: £21 (£32), Set L from £12·80 (£14) CARDS: Access, Amex, Carte Blanche,
Diners, Visa
SEATS: 129. Private parties: 33 main room, 16 and 80 private rooms. Car-park, 150 places.
Vegetarian meals. Children's helpings (Sun L only). Jacket and tie. No cigars/pipes in
dining-room. Wheelchair access (also WC)
ACCOMMODATION: 32 rooms, all with bath/shower. Rooms for disabled. B&B £57 to £81.
Children welcome. Baby facilities. Pets welcome. Afternoon teas. Garden. Tennis. TV.
Phone. Scenic

SPEEN Buckinghamshire   map 2

▲ *Atkins, The Old Plow Inn*   [14/20]

Flower Bottom, Speen HP17 OP7
HAMPDEN ROW (024 028) 300
3½m NW of High Wycombe
up the Hughenden Valley   £24

It's a jack-knife of a drive through a deep-rooted neck of the woods with tracts of
ancient common land and the heavy greenness of Chiltern beeches. This used to
be 'bodger' country – the working landscape of the wood-turners, who were in
the front line of the Buckinghamshire chair industry before the days of self-
assembly furniture. Gerald and Frances Atkins moved here from their tiny tea-
shop of a restaurant in Great Missenden and have rapidly established this classic
roadside inn as one of the finest eating places in the Home Counties. The setting is
of low-beamed ceilings, dim candlelight and Victorian cook-book illustrations
mounted on the walls; drinkers are to one side, diners to the other. Gerald Atkins

---

*If you suspect that a restaurant is using processed food, always ask. It would be a
contravention of the Trade Descriptions Act for the restaurant to lie.*

---

leads out front. Frances Atkins learned her trade at the Box Tree, Ilkley, but has moved into a style she calls 'English provincial': it is meticulous without being effete. A static menu always has plates of smoked salmon and steaks on offer, but the interest is in the daily changing list of specials. Mousses and terrines are outstanding: watercress mousse with pears; terrine of grapefruit and salmon; mousseline of artichoke and parsley, which comes as a warm, two-layered slab bound with fresh pancake. Otherwise the specials are confidently eclectic, taking in ragout of veal and pears in pastry; poached turbot with julienne of vegetables; and the architectural precision of saddle of lamb with asparagus, spinach and tomato. Breast of duck and quail are cooked together with plums; duck on its own is served on a perfumed, naturelle-style sauce of fresh apricots. The power is in the use of stocks for sauces. There is also a sense of humour: mignon of beef on foie gras and mushrooms is tournedos Rossini turned on its head. The personal touch extends to the sweets: more mousses, pure fruit coulis, wine jellies and even a version of Bakewell tart that includes apples. Bar lunches show the same sense of direction. Bedrooms are clean and functional. The forty wines are adequate, though the list does not show the same acumen as the choice of beers in the bar. CELLARMAN'S CHOICE: Chablis *premier cru*, Fourchaume '83, £18.

CHEF: Frances Atkins PROPRIETORS: Mr and Mrs G. Atkins
OPEN: all week, exc Sun D and Mon D MEALS: 12 to 2, 7.30 to 10
PRICES: £18 (£24). Snacks from £1·50 CARDS: Access, Amex, Diners, Visa
SEATS: 30. Private parties: 30 main room. Car-park, 40 places. Vegetarian meals.
No children under 10. Smart dress preferred. Music
ACCOMMODATION: 3 rooms, 2 with bath/shower. B&B £35 to £55. Deposit: 20%. Garden.
Scenic. Doors close at 12

STADDLEBRIDGE North Yorkshire   map 7

▲ *McCoy's* [13/20]

The Tontine, Staddlebridge DL6 3JB
EAST HARSLEY (060 982) 671   £32

McCoy's is an eccentric muddle of exposed wires, huge parasols, palm trees and mirrors. The décor takes very much a backward glance. But the food looks forward, with its own flamboyant, unlikely style, well proven over many years: parcels of smoked salmon mousse with truffles; scallops and langoustines with lemon sauce; partridge with Sauternes sauce; stuffed cabbage and apples. Chocolate gateau has Tia Maria poured over it. House wine is £9·50, or £6·50 in the attached basement bistro, where the menu is cheaper: full-flavoured celery and red pepper soup; game pie with salad; and good-looking crêpes.

CHEFS: Thomas and Eugene McCoy PROPRIETORS: Peter, Thomas and Eugene McCoy
OPEN: all week, D only MEALS: 7 to 10.30
PRICES: £23 (£32) CARDS: Access, Amex, Diners, Visa
SEATS: 40. Private parties: 40 main room. Car-park, 100 places. Children welcome. Music.
Air-conditioned
ACCOMMODATION: 6 rooms, all with bath/shower. B&B £55 to £70. Baby facilities. Pets
welcome. Afternoon teas. Garden. Air-conditioning. TV. Phone. Scenic

---

All letters to the Guide *are acknowledged.*

STAMFORD Lincolnshire

map 6

▲ *The George* [10/20]

71 St Martin's, Stamford PE9 2LB
STAMFORD (0780) 55171

£21

One of the most historic coaching-inns in England is still a hostelry for everyman.
The garden lounge is laid out with a huge buffet of cold joints and salads, there's
a formal panelled dining-room, and plenty of space for those who simply want a
pint of beer. The roast sirloin of Scotch beef from the silver carving wagons serves
half the trade. House Italian red and white are £6·25 and £5·65 respectively.
CELLARMAN'S CHOICE is Mâcon rouge '83 at £9·25.

CHEF: Chris Pitman PROPRÌETORS: Poste Hotels Ltd
OPEN: all week MEALS: 12.30 to 2.30, 7.30 to 10.30
PRICES: £14 (£21), Snacks from £2·25. Cover 60p. Service inc CARDS: Access, Amex,
Diners, Visa
SEATS: 85. 20 tables outside. Private parties: 90 main room, 16, 22 and 30 and private
rooms. Car-park, 150 places. Vegetarian meals. Children's helpings. Jacket and tie.
Wheelchair access (also WC)
ACCOMMODATION 47 rooms, all with bath/shower. B&B £45 to £68. Children welcome. Baby
facilities. Pets welcome. Afternoon teas. Garden. TV. Phone [GHG]

STANDISH Greater Manchester

map 5

▲ *Beeches* [11/20]

School Lane, Standish WN6 0TD
STANDISH (0257) 426432

£24

The Victorian red-brick mansion has been knocked about and extended to
provide a rather soulless lounge bar and a smart dining-room, which has ladder-
back chairs, standard lamps and fresh flowers. The extensive, rather dull menu
comes into its own with top-quality fresh fish and shellfish cooked with reduced
sauces: salmon with lime hollandaise; fillets of sea bass topped with turned
cucumber on a cream sauce. Vegetables are cooked al dente if requested, and
soups are based on stocks made in the kitchen. Sweets include home-produced
ice-creams, and the profiteroles have good choux pastry. Reasonably priced
wines, as well as Tetley beers.

CHEFS: B. Higginbotham and A. Bullen PROPRIETORS: James and Peter Moore
OPEN: all week, exc Sat L MEALS: 11.45 to 1.45, 6.45 to 9.45
PRICES: £16 (£24), Snacks from £1·95 CARDS: Access, Amex, Diners, Visa
SEATS: 60. Private parties: 70 main room. Car-park, 70 places. Children's helpings. Smart
dress preferred. Wheelchair access (3 steps). Music
ACCOMMODATION: 7 rooms, all with bath/shower. B&B £29 to £35. Baby facilities.
Afternoon teas. Garden. TV. Phone. Scenic. Doors close at 1. Confirm by 5

*Good vintages for drinking in 1988: Alsace '85, Beaujolais '86, Germany '85, petits
chateaux clarets '81, lesser clarets '83.*

*If you suspect that a restaurant is using processed food, always ask. It would be a
contravention of the Trade Descriptions Act for the restaurant to lie.*

STANTON HARCOURT Oxfordshire

map 2

▲ *Harcourt Arms* [10/20]

Stanton Harcourt OX8 1RJ
OXFORD (0865) 882192 and 881931

£19–£20

Stanton Harcourt is tiny, made up of a church, chapel and a pope's tower, and
can almost appear medieval. George Dailey has finally bought his creeper-
covered stone inn from the brewery. The excellent quality fish and seafood are
what to go for, from seafood pie, through haddock and chips, to exotic grilled
king prawns. The rest of the long menu is less exciting, and desserts fade badly.
A good family place: Wadworth's 6x and guest beers, or house wine at £5.50
a bottle.

CHEF: Gerard Crowley PROPRIETOR: G. Dailey
OPEN: all week MEALS: 12 to 2, 7 to 10
PRICES: £11 (£19), Set L and D £13·75 (£20), Snacks from £1·50
CARDS: Access, Amex, Diners, Visa
SEATS: 90. 6 tables outside. Private parties: 90 main room. Car-park, 30 places. Children's
helpings
ACCOMMODATION: 10 rooms, all with bath/shower. B&B £24·50 to £44·50. No children
under 8. Afternoon teas. Fishing. TV. Phone. Scenic. Doors close at 11.30. Confirm by 6

STAPLETON North Yorkshire

map 7

Bridge Inn [11/20] ✗

Stapleton DL2 2QQ
DARLINGTON (0325) 50106

£12–£19

This village pub serves bar food but the Youngs also run a Victorian-look dining-
room. The cooking is enterprising: scallops with ginger and cream sauce; quail
breasts stuffed with quail mousse. The style ranges from delicate prawn
mousseline with avocado sauce, through rack of lamb with port and peppercorn
sauce, to rich toffee and banana flan. House French is £4·95 a bottle.

CHEF: Nicholas Young PROPRIETORS: Nicholas and Catherine Young
OPEN: Tue to Sun, exc Sat L and Sun D MEALS: 12 to 2, 7 to 9.30 (10 Sat)
PRICES: £12 (£19), Set L £7·25 (£12), Snacks from £1 CARDS: Access, Amex, Diners, Visa
SEATS: 30. 4 tables outside. Private parties: 30 main room. Car-park, 30 places. Vegetarian
meals. Children's helpings. Wheelchair access (also WC)

STEEPLE ASTON Oxfordshire

map 2

Red Lion [10/20]

South Street, Steeple Aston OX5 3RY
STEEPLE ASTON (0869) 40225

£17

There are two lions in Steeple Aston, a red and a white. The red is the white-
plastered old pub on the hillside. Margaret Mead runs a short menu relying

It is helpful if restaurateurs keep the office up to date with any changes.

strongly on grills but with some fine dishes, for instance guinea-fowl with juniper. Sweets tend to be British, and include syllabubs. The wine list is unusually informative and lists over a hundred bottles, mostly French, starting at £5·25.

CHEF: Margaret Mead PROPRIETORS: Colin and Margaret Mead
OPEN: Tue to Sat, D only CLOSED: 2 weeks Oct MEALS: 7.30 to 11.30
PRICES: Set D from £12·50 (£17) CARDS: Access, Visa
SEATS: 20. Private parties: 12 main room, 20 private room. Car-park, 16 places. Vegetarian meals. Children's helpings. No children under 3. No smoking in dining-room. Wheelchair access (2 steps; also WC)

STOCKBRIDGE Hampshire

map 2

Game Larder [12/20]

New Street, Stockbridge SO20 6HG
ANDOVER (0264) 810414

£20

Stockbridge, being on the Test, holds interest for fishermen. The eighteenth-century brewery and malthouse retain many old features. The Donovans run a short, French-inspired menu using the best local produce, in particular good quality meats: lamb with a rosemary and redcurrant sauce; pheasant with mushrooms, brandy and wine. Trout, served grilled with almonds, is not, alas, out of the Test. Monkfish is served provençale. Lemon tart or cold almond soufflé are good sweets. The wine list is especially good on lesser known claret. Pudding wines are offered by the glass. CELLARMAN'S CHOICE: Médoc, Ch. Latour St Bonnet '82, £11. The long-standing Sheriff House – the other place to eat in Stockbridge – only accepts bookings from existing customers.

CHEF: Charles Donovan PROPRIETORS: Charles and Joan Donovan
OPEN: Tue to Sat MEALS: 12 to 2, 7 to 10
PRICES: £15 (£20). Service inc CARDS: Access, Amex, Diners, Visa
SEATS: 60. 2 tables outside. Private parties: 70 main room, 20 private room. Car-park 6 places. Children's helpings. Wheelchair access (also WC). Music

---

STON EASTON Somerset

map 2

▲ *Ston Easton Park* [13/20]

Ston Easton BA3 4DF
CHEWTON MENDIP (076 121) 631

 £22–£34

The imposing Palladian mansion has all the trappings of high class, country-house elegance, from the magnificent ceiling plasterwork and the *trompe l'oeil* panels on the walls to the enormous flower arrangements. Compared with all this, the dining-room is light and informal. The waitresses are effortlessly efficient, and do not miss much. In the last six years the Smedleys have developed every aspect. Mark Harrington was promoted from number two in spring 1986. His style is modern, with expensive trimmings, all revealed from under silver

---

Places rating 9 may not be restaurants at all, but still serve good food: expect to find pubs, cafes, small hotels and wine bars.

---

salvers: sauté scallops with fresh herbs and champagne; smoked haddock and spinach roulade, garnished with quails' eggs and caviare; chicken-liver parfait with truffles and morels. Four-course dinners feature no fewer than thirty dishes. Centrepieces impress, always a sign of a good chef: roast fillet of lamb, cooked pink and served with a delicate sauce of tarragon and meat juices; or breast of duckling with a caramelised peach sauce or, on another night, with fresh, not preserved, ginger. Tulip Ston Eaton is still the most remarkable of the sweets, but there's excellent coffee sauce with the almond and chestnut parfait. Cheeses include some fine Somerset examples. The peripherals could benefit from attention – better bread; less clichéd petits fours and sorbets – but there are characterful signs starting to appear on what might otherwise look like an anonymously international nouvelle *carte*. Although the wine list has its museum pieces – claret from the 1920s and 1940s – there is continuity right up to the present, with good, but less expensive, bottles to balance the big names. Mark-ups and half-bottles are generous. CELLARMAN'S CHOICE: Chardonnay, Clos du Val '83, £13·50.

CHEF: Mark Harrington PROPRIETORS: Peter and Christine Smedley
OPEN: all week MEALS: 12.30 to 2, 7.30 to 9.30 (10 Fri and Sat)
PRICES: Set L £15 (£22), Set D £26 (£34) CARDS: Access, Amex, Diners, Visa
SEATS: 40. 8 tables outside. Private parties: 40 main room, 14 and private rooms. Car-park, 40 places. Vegetarian meals. Children's helpings. No children under 12. Jacket and tie. No cigars/pipes in dining-room. Wheelchair access
ACCOMMODATION: 20 rooms, all with bath/shower. B&B £60 to £190. No children under 12. Afternoon teas. Garden. Tennis. Golf. Snooker. TV. Phone. Scenic. Doors close at 12. Confirm by 6 [GHG]

STONHAM Suffolk   map 3

▲ *Mr Underhill's* [13/20]

Stonham IP14 5DW
STOWMARKET (0449) 711206
on A140, 300 yds S of junction with A1120   £23

After seven years, the Bradleys' small, no-choice menu is probably the most reliable and adventurous of its kind in the county. The style is modern, with shades of Senderens at Lucas-Carton, moving comfortably with the seasons. For spring: asparagus beurre blanc; lamb with parsley sauce and garlic mushrooms; salmon as a mille-feuille with sorrel or red-wine sauce. Veal dishes have been remarkable for their flavour, sauced either with red pepper, or with tarragon, served with sweetcorn and pancakes. Cheeses are from Androuët in Paris. To finish: poached pear with blackcurrant; tarte Tatin. Judy Bradley controls the front of house with care. The wines draw most of their inspiration from France, but Spain and California are equally interesting, and Australia stays helpfully under £10. CELLARMAN'S CHOICE: Chardonnay, Hill-Smith '84, £9·50.

CHEF: Christopher Bradley PROPRIETORS: Christopher and Judy Bradley
OPEN: Tue to Sat, D only MEALS: 7.30 to 8.45
PRICES: Set D £16·95 (£23) CARDS: Access, Amex, Visa
SEATS: 30. Private parties: 30 main room, 16 private room. Car-park, 12 places. Vegetarian meals. Children's helpings by arrangement. No-smoking area. Wheelchair access (also WC)
ACCOMMODATION: 1 room, with bath. B&B £38. Garden. TV. Scenic. Confirm by 12

STONY STRATFORD Buckinghamshire

map 2

Stratfords [11/20]

7 St Paul's Court, 118 High Street, Stony Stratford MK1 1LA
MILTON KEYNES (0908) 566577   £15–£20

There are signs that the kitchen in this Victorian chapel is moving towards more home production: meat and fish are smoked on the premises, bread and biscuits are baked in-house, and the emphasis is on local supplies. Fixed-price menus change every few weeks, and have featured some very good dishes, such as leek and potato soup, fennel and mustard pâté, and monkfish cooked in the style of osso buco. Otherwise, there are plenty of adventurous ideas – cold mange-tout soufflé; layered fish mousse wrapped in an almond pancake with Seville orange sauce; chicken stuffed with curried crab-meat on a lemon butter and mint sauce. To finish, there might be meringues with butterscotch sauce, or English cheeses with home-made celery relish. The strong wine list has a balanced spread, taking in the Loire, Beaujolais and Alsace, plus representatives from the New World.
CELLARMAN'S CHOICE: Fleurie, La Madone '85, from Georges Duboeuf, at £11·50.

CHEFS/PROPRIETORS: Michael Roberts and Linda Membride
OPEN: Tue to Sun, exc Sat L and Sun D CLOSED: First week Jan, 2 weeks July
MEALS: 12 to 2, 7.30 to 9.30 (10 Fri and Sat)
PRICES: Set L £9·50 (£15), Set D from £13·95 (£20)
SEATS: 70. Private parties: 70 main room. Car-park, 20 places. No children under 6.
Wheelchair access. Music

STORRINGTON West Sussex

map 3

▲ Manleys [15/20]

Manleys Hill, Storrington RH20 4BT
STORRINGTON (090 66) 2331   £24–£33

Just off the main village road in an old-world building, Karl and Margaret Löderer continue to run one of the most correct restaurants in the south. Tables are immaculately laid, service is unobstrusive, and some of the cooking is excellent. The style is formal French: lamb is roasted pink and its sauce flavoured with tarragon. Fish is first class: salmon is coated with trout mousse and horseradish, steamed over star anise, and served in a champagne sauce; Dover sole and crab are made into a soufflé and given a ginger-flavoured butter sauce. The technique of the kitchen is seen again in desserts like the parfait au nougat. Prices reflect the quality of the operation, which means it is not cheap. The single room to let is a luxurious £65. Respectable house wines come from Jaboulet (Côtes du Ventoux) and the co-operative at Oisly-et-Thésée (Sauvignon), both at £8·80.
CELLARMAN'S CHOICE: Chassagne-Montrachet '82, from Ramonet-Prudhon, at £18·90.

Restaurants rating 12 or more serve the best food in the region.

Restaurants are checked every year and their entries rewritten. The restaurant scene changes very rapidly. Don't trust an out-of-date Guide.

CHEF; Karl Löderer PROPRIETORS: Karl and Margaret Löderer
OPEN: Tue to Sat, exc Sun D CLOSED: 2 weeks Jan, 1 week Aug, 1 week Sept
MEALS: 12 to 2, 7 to 9.15
PRICES: £19 (£29), Set Sun L £15 (£24), Set Fri D £23 (£33). Service inc
CARDS: Access, Amex, Diners, Visa
SEATS: 46. Private parties: 10 main room, 24 private room. Car-park, 22 places. Vegetarian
meals. Children's helpings. No cigars/pipes in dining-room. Air-conditioned
ACCOMMODATION: 1 double room, with bath/shower. B&B £65. No children. No pets. TV.
Phone. Scenic

STOURPORT-ON-SEVERN Hereford & Worcester   map 5

Severn Tandoori [10/20]

11 Bridge Street, Stourport-on-Severn DY13 8UX
STOURPORT (029 93) 3090   £14–£17

A smart, comfortable Indian restaurant. Courteous, well-dressed waiters guide
customers through a familiar menu of North Indian specialities. Tandoori
chicken is the highlight; other good dishes have included vegetable biriani and
chicken jhal fry, and there are decent breads and kulfi. Drink lassi or lager.

CHEF: A. Audud PROPRIETORS: S. A. Quayum, M. Miah, A. Audud, Z. Ali and M. Meah
OPEN: all week MEALS: 12 to 2.30, 6 to 11.30
PRICES: £8 (£14), Set D from £12·50 (£17) CARDS: Access, Amex, Diners, Visa
SEATS: 70. Private parties: 70 mainroom, 70 private room. Car-park, 70 places. Vegetarian
meals. Children's helpings (weekend D only). No children under 4. Smart dress preferred.
Wheelchair access (also WC). Music

STRATFORD UPON AVON Warwickshire   map 2

Shepherd's, Stratford House Hotel [10/20]

Sheep Street, Stratford upon Avon CV37 6EF
STRATFORD UPON AVON (0789) 68233   £21

Since Shaun Hill left two years ago for Gidleigh Park (see Chagford), Stratford has
been an uncomfortable place to find anything good to eat. It is to our national
shame that our greatest theatre company can play surrounded by an
accompanying catering cast of third-rate eating places. The main exception is the
commendable Rumours, which as the *Guide* goes to press is to move to the
Charlcote Pheasant Hotel; Shepherd's is now a lone star. The dining-room is in a
semi-circular conservatory looking on to a floodlit courtyard. The menu is
English, running to twenty dishes and changing weekly. The raw materials are
good, as in mussel soup; veal with noodles; fillet steak with peppercorn sauce.
More virility would help the saucery. Twenty well-spread wines start with
Bocuse's selection at £6.

---

*If, in your opinion, a restaurant is not maintaining the standard of its ratings please
inform the* Guide *office. Report forms are at the back of the book.*

All details are as accurate as possible at the time of going to press. Please notify the
Guide *office of any changes.*

CHEF: Nigel Lambert PROPRIETOR: Sylvia Adcock
OPEN: Tue to Sat MEALS: 12 to 2, 5.30 to 11
PRICES: £15 (£21) CARDS: Access, Amex, Diners, Visa
SEATS: 40. 3 tables outside. Private parties: 40 main room, 10 private room. Vegetarian
meals. Children welcome. No-smoking area. Wheelchair access (3 steps)
ACCOMMODATION: 10 rooms, all with bath/shower. B&B £40 to £54. Deposit: £10. No
children under 7. Afternoon teas. Garden. TV. Phone. Doors close at 12. Confirm by 4

STREATLEY Berkshire — map 2

▲ *Swan Hotel* [13/20]

Streatley RG8 9HR
GORING-ON-THAMES (0491) 873737 £15–£35

The hotel stands on the Thames, looking on to the river, the weir and the lock.
The trees on the far bank are spotlit at night, and the dining-room feels like a
conservatory. Richard Sparrow's classical French training shows in the sole with
a beurre blanc, and the fricassee of chicken with lobster sauce. Other dishes have
a more modern touch, which really brings the menu into the province of modern
British cooking: fillet steak garnished with little gnocchi and tiny vegetables;
calf's liver and sweetbreads in pastry; rabbit with its own liver; and bavarois of
passion-fruit. The giant cheeseboard has up to thirty British specimens from
Patrick Rance's shop up the road, served with biscuits, walnut bread, radishes,
and celery threaded through cucumber rings. The wines are classic too, with
good showings among Bordeaux communes and burgundy producers, but Spain,
Italy and the New World are perfectly sound. CELLARMAN'S CHOICE: Chardonnay,
Hunter Valley '85, from Pokolbin, £13.

CHEF: Richard Sparrow PROPRIETORS: Gulliver Hotels Ltd
OPEN: all week MEALS: 12.30 to 2, 7.30 to 9.30
PRICES: £26 (£35), Set L from £10 (£15), Set D from £16·50 (£22), Snacks from £1·95
CARDS: Access, Amex, Diners, Visa
SEATS: 100. 20 tables outside. Private parties: 8 main room, 12, 24 and 100 private rooms.
Car-park, 125 places. Children's helpings. Smart dress preferred. No cigars/pipes in dining-
room. Wheelchair access
ACCOMMODATION: 46 rooms, all with bath/shower. Rooms for disabled. B&B £47·50 to
£62·50. Baby facilities. Pets welcome. Afternoon teas. Garden. Swimming-pool. Sauna. Golf.
TV. Phone. Scenic. Confirm by 6

STRETTON Leicestershire — map 6

▲ *Ram Jam Inn* [9/20]

Great North Road, Stretton LE15 7QX
CASTLE BYTHAM (078 081) 776 £15

Tim Hart of Hambleton Hall has gone down-market with this 1988 version of a
coaching-inn, bang on the left-hand side of the A1, travelling north, by Stretton
service station. The open-plan lounge-bar runs into the dining-room. Although

---

*Places rating 9 may not be restaurants at all, but still serve good food: expect to find
pubs, cafes, small hotels and wine bars.*

the menu is sealed into plastic permanence, the dishes are to be applauded. The range is short, careful to offer the traditional travel fodder of banger, burger and steak with chips or jacket potatoes, but also has a crack at brioche (only partially successful), kebabs and a few puddings. Stocks, sauces and meats seem to come from Hambleton, even if the execution does not always match. Service is relaxed. The short wine list raises questions: who would drink vintage Bollinger with a banger, or blow £17·50 on Gevrey-Chambertin (which the list says is, 'supposed to remind you of a farmyard muck heap') with a £3·50, half-pound, real steak burger? Interesting beers; fresh orange juice. All in all, about twenty per cent more expensive than the chain stopping-places, and about fifty per cent better.

CHEF: Chris Ansell-Green PROPRIETORS: Hart Hambleton plc
OPEN: all week MEALS: 11am to 11pm
PRICES: £10 (£15), Snacks from £2 CARDS: Access, Amex, Visa
SEATS: 200. Private parties: 100 main room, 40 private room. Car-park, 60 places.
Vegetarian meals. Children's helpings. No cigars/pipes in dining-room. Wheelchair access (also WC)
ACCOMMODATION: 10 rooms, all with bath/shower. B&B £35 to £45. Garden. TV. Phone.
Doors close at 12 [GHG]

STROUD Gloucestershire — map 2

Oakes [16/20]

169 Slad Road, Stroud GL5 1RG
STROUD (045 36) 79950
on B4070 ½m from Stroud centre

GLOUCESTERSHIRE
OF THE YEAR
RESTAURANT

£12–£23

Chris and Caroline Oakes, who did much to establish the reputation of the Castle Hotel at Taunton, re-emerge in their own, barn-like restaurant. The atmosphere has something of a monks' refectory, with bare, varnished oak floorboards, large, varnished tables, a huge log fire in the enormous chimney, and open curtains. Suppliers are listed on the menu, as an indication of quality. There are three set menus at different prices, all modern and exciting. Home-made noodles, chutney (with a chicken-liver parfait), and milk cheese feature on the menu, which has a strong *nouvelle* element – pigeon breasts with salade tiède – but also takes in modern and traditional British cooking: soup of smoked haddock, or leek and prune; steak, kidney and Guinness pie; bread-and-butter pudding. Chris Oakes is perhaps the most controlled of the modern British chefs, reworking lamb so that in January the rack is spiced with mustard, and served with a reduced stock, rosemary and a side pastry containing its offal, but in February it is braised with shallots and carrots. The cinnamon soufflé served hot with Drambuie cream is admirable. Wines are reasonably priced – rarely do they creep above £10; rarely do they stray outside France. CELLARMAN'S CHOICE: Gewürztraminer, Cuvée Particulière '83/'85, Baron de Hoen, £8·30.

CHEF: Chris Oakes PROPRIETORS: Chris and Caroline Oakes, Nowell and Jean Scott
OPEN: Tue to Sun, exc Sun D CLOSED: late Dec to late Jan MEALS: 12.30 to 2, 7.30 to 10
PRICES: Set L from £7·50 (£12), Set D £14 (£19) to £18 (£23) CARDS: Access, Visa
SEATS: 30. Private parties: 30 main room. Car-park, 12 places. Children's helpings by arrangement. Wheelchair access

---

The Guide does not accept free meals.

STUCKTON Hampshire   map 2

Three Lions [11/20]

Stuckton Road, Stuckton SP6 2HF
FORDINGBRIDGE (0425) 52489
½m off A338 at Fordingbridge   £25

The Wadsacks' former village pub has found its new persona as a serious
restaurant, with a free-house bar as an afterthought. The place is high on
atmosphere, low on décor: nothing distracts from the food on the plate. Karl
Wadsack's long menu goes to the heart of Europe for its inspiration. The style is
rich and generous, with touches of nouvelle delicacy. Thick slices of calves'
brains, on a slice of buttery brioche with caper sauce, bundles of spinach and
Edam cheese in home-made filo pastry, and fillet of venison in a juniper sauce
with gin-soaked prunes, are the style. Fish gets a good showing, with home-
cured Swedish herrings, and paupiettes of plaice stuffed with salmon mousse, on
a delicate cucumber sauce tinged with fennel. The rich vein picks up again in the
sweets: chocolate roulade, chocolate marquise, île flottante on raspberry coulis;
although there is light relief in the lime sorbet garnished with vodka-soaked kiwi-
fruit. The long list of fine wines ranges far and wide, but appropriately centres
on Alsace and Germany. CELLARMAN'S CHOICE: Riesling, Schloss Vollrads '85,
at £10·95.

CHEF: K. H. Wadsack PROPRIETORS: Mr K. H. and Mrs J. Wadsack
OPEN: Tue to Sun, exc Sun D CLOSED: 24, 26 Dec, 1 Jan MEALS: 12.15 to 1.30, 7.15 to 9
PRICES: £17 (£25), Snacks from £2·85. Service 10%
SEATS: 55. Private parties: 14 main room. Car-park, 40 places. No children under 14.
Wheelchair access (also WC). Air-conditioned

STURMINSTER NEWTON Dorset   map 2

▲ *Plumber Manor* [11/20] ✗

Sturminster Newton DT10 2AF
STURMINSTER NEWTON (0258) 72507
2m SW of Sturminster Newton off
A357 on Hazelbury Bryan road   £20

The Jacobean mansion has been in the Prideaux-Brune family for four hundred
years and as an up-market restaurant with fine rooms for the last fifteen. Brian
Prideaux-Brune cooks a country menu: courgette or cream of artichoke soup;
seasonal game, such as pheasant, in wine sauce garnished with flaked almonds;
and excellent old-fashioned sweets, such as home-made mousses, fools, pineapple
macaroons, and strawberry mille-feuille. The sixty-odd wines try to keep
everyone happy. CELLARMAN'S CHOICE is Bourgogne Aligoté '85 at £9·50 and
Côtes de Duras Sauvignon at £6·50.

Reports on good shops, hotels and cafes in your area are welcome.

Please keep the Guide *informed of any changes to the restaurants listed. Report forms
are at the back of the book.*

339

CHEFS: Brian Prideaux-Brune, Mrs Baker and Robert Doble
PROPRIETORS: The Prideaux-Brune family
OPEN: Tue to Sun, D only MEALS: 7.30 to 9.30
PRICES: Set D from £15 (£20)
SEATS:60. Private parties: 40 main room, 12 and 22 private rooms. Car-park, 20 places.
Vegetarian meals. No children under 12. Smart dress preferred. No cigars/pipes in dining-
room. Wheelchair access
ACCOMMODATION: 12 rooms, all with bath/shower. Rooms for disabled. B&B £40 to £65.
No children under 12. Garden. Tennis. TV. Phone. Scenic [GHG]

SURBITON Surrey   map 3

Chez Max [13/20]

85 Maple Road, Surbiton KT6 4AW
01-399 2365   £25

Max Markarian's small, elegant restaurant has built up a solid local following
since 1982. The dining-room is neatly laid with pale linen and carnations. There
is a richness about the cooking – calf's kidneys in pastry with madeira sauce;
venison with juniper and pear sauce – that is occasionally relieved by some
sharpness: duck liver mousse, for instance, comes with lime sauce; salmon
quenelles with lemon sauce. But puddings are kept simple, so the total effect is of
balance: fruit salad, sorbet, chocolate mousse. A largely French wine list favours
good vintages of claret and burgundy. House wine is £7·50 a bottle.

CHEF: Max Markarian PROPRIETORS: Mr and Mrs Markarian
OPEN: Tue to Sat, exc Sat L MEALS: 12.30 to 2, 7.30 to 10.30
PRICES: £17 (£25). Service 12.5%. Cover 75p CARDS: Access, Amex, Diners, Visa
SEATS: 32. Private parties: 32 main room. No children under 7. No pipes in dining-room.
Wheelchair access (also WC)

SUTTON Surrey   map 3

Partners 23 [14/20]

23 Stonecot Hill, Sutton SM3 9HB
01-644 7743
on A24 near Woodstock pub   £16–£26

The ornate interior reassures that this suburban shopping arcade really does
contain a serious restaurant. Like the fine cheeseboard, the menu takes equal
measure of French and English inspiration. Nouvelle English is one description.
Presentation matches. Sauces, made mainly from butter and cream, run liberally
and colourfully through the dishes, and are usually offset by a third element, for
instance two butters with the lamb. On another night, the lamb comes with its
own mousse and a tarragon jus for variety. Service has improved and, once
again, sweets – lemon tart, bread-and-butter pudding, hazelnut parfait with a
chocolate sauce – draw most praise, perhaps for their simplicity, after a menu

---

[GHG] *after the details of an entry means that the establishment is also included in*
The Good Hotel Guide.

---

increasingly inclined to complexity. The hundred wines include some choices for house wine at £7·95, plus pedigree vintages from the secondary, good-value regions, such as Alsace, Loire and Rhône. CELLARMAN'S CHOICE: Chinon rouge, Madeleine Baronnie '78, from Couly-Dutheil.

CHEFS: P. T. McEntire, Maxine Redford and Karen MacDonald
PROPRIETORS: A. W. Thomason and P. T. McEntire
OPEN: Tue to Sat, exc Sat L CLOSED: Christmas to New Year, 2 weeks Aug
MEALS: 12.30 to 2, 7.30 to 9.30
PRICES: Set L from £10·75 (£16), Set D £19·95 (£26) CARDS: Access, Amex, Diners, Visa
SEATS: 34. Private parties: 36 main room. No children under 10. Wheelchair access.
Air-conditioned

SWAY Hampshire map 2

▲ *Pine Trees* [11/20] ✗

Mead End Road, Sway SO41 6EE
LYMINGTON (0590) 682288 £12–£19

The Davids' modest Victorian house ticks over at a calm, leisurely pace. Guests are as well tended as the indoor plants. The cooking is honest, simple and English, moving from watercress and tomato salad, or lemon sole, as a starter, to home-made tangerine ice-cream, and a huge selection of cheeses. In between there has been good fillet steak, poached salmon, and roast sirloin of beef with all the trimmings. Good meats are usually roasted, and vegetables seasonal. There is no choice, and booking is essential. Fine breakfasts have included croissants with home-made marmalade. Twenty wines, without detail, from £5.

CHEFS/PROPRIETORS: Mr and Mrs David
OPEN: all week, D only, and Sun L MEALS: 12.45 to 1.15, 8 to 8.45
PRICES: Set L £9 (£12), Set D £16 (£19). Service inc CARDS: Access, Amex,
Diners, Visa
SEATS: 18. Private parties: 24 main room, 6 private room. Car-park, 12 places. Children's helpings. Wheelchair access (also WC)
ACCOMMODATION: 6 rooms, 5 with bath/shower. B&B £24 to £44. No children under 12.
Afternoon teas. Garden. Scenic. Doors close at 12. Confirm by 6

▲ *Provence* [15/20] ✗

Gordleton Mill, Silver Street, Sway SO41 6DJ
LYMINGTON (0590) 682219 £14–£25

Jean-Pierre and Claire Novi moved to this idyllic old Hampshire mill from Southbourne. He remains the most likely chef in the *Guide* to produce a typical one-star Michelin meal, as might be found in France. In French style, also, he employs older, professional waiters. The rural mill is the sort of setting that chefs dream about. The menu has half a dozen choices at each stage, with fish optional as either starter or main. This is top stuff: raw beef marinated with olive oil, black olives and anchovies; duck foie gras on a celeriac pancake; sweetbreads galette

---

Please keep the Guide *informed of any changes to the restaurants listed. Report forms are at the back of the book.*

on a bed of spinach. Fresh ravioli are filled with morels, or scattered with diced buttered scallop, with a lobster claw to ignite the dish. The saddle of hare is remarkable: roasted on the bone, it is then laid across the plate, the fillets carved off in medallions to either side, all sitting in a treacle-black sauce garnished with prunes filled with foie gras. The fire carries through to the end: mango gratin in a tea sabayon, or a shortbread basket of caramelised pear, figs and strawberries under a spun-sugar dome. There are still hiccups – dry meats, slow service – but these will be ironed out as the kitchen beds in. The French wine list embraces classics and bargains alike. CELLARMAN'S CHOICE: Château Fonsalette '85, red and white, £13.

CHEF: Jean-Pierre Novi PROPRIETOR: William F. Stone
OPEN: Tue to Sun, exc Sun D MEALS: 12 to 2, 7.30 to 10
PRICES: £21 (£25), Set L from £10·50 (£14). Service inc CARDS: Access, Diners, Visa
SEATS: 30. Private parties: 30 main room, 12 and 14 private rooms. Children's helpings. Music
ACCOMMODATION: 8 rooms, 5 with bath/shower. B&B £25 to £49. Garden. TV. Phone. Scenic

---

TAPLOW Buckinghamshire	map 2

▲ *Cliveden* [14/20]

Taplow SL6 0JF
BURNHAM (062 86) 64246   £24–£40

Cliveden is among the finest of all the National Trust assets. John Webber has marshalled the kitchen into a team capable of producing food to match the grandiose setting. The emphasis is on exceptional, costly raw materials, but used skilfully, not decadently. The menu is sophisticated, balanced and characterised by fragrant subtle sauces. Four steaks of monkfish, sauté to brownness in nut oil, served on a pool of cream-coloured sauce flavoured with mustard, and given texture with some shards of blanched cucumber, is a typical second of five courses. A *carte* has been added and features fine dishes, such as sweetbreads with spinach and madeira sauce. Meals seem to get more anglicised as they go on, ending with good examples of modern English cheeses, as well as French, and perhaps a Queen of Puddings. Details, for instance the bresaola on toast with drinks, and the butter are, for the most part, immaculate (although, oddly, not the peanuts or the biscuits with cheese). The wine list is expensive and extensive. House wine is £3 a glass.

CHEF: John Webber PROPRIETORS: Blakeney Hotels Ltd
OPEN: all week MEALS: 12.30 to 2, 7.30 to 9.30
PRICES: £28 (£33), Set L from £18·60 (£24), Set D £35 (£40). Service inc CARDS: Access, Amex, Diners, Visa
SEATS: 49. Private parties: 100 main room, 50 private room. Car-park, 100 places. Children's helpings. Jacket and tie. Wheelchair access (also WC)
ACCOMMODATION: 25 rooms, all with bath/shower. Rooms for disabled. Lift. B&B £120 to £300. Deposit: £100. Baby facilities. Pets welcome. Garden. Swimming-pool. Sauna. Tennis. Fishing. Golf. Snooker. TV. Phone. Scenic

---

If you cannot honour a restaurant booking, always phone to cancel.

TAUNTON Somerset   map 2

▲ *Castle Hotel* [15/20]

Castle Green, Taunton TA1 1NF
TAUNTON (0823) 272671   £13–£32

The hotel looms out on a frosty winter's night, half monstrous, half magnificent.
towers and battlements grandly turn their back on the High Street multiples – an
appropriate gesture for a place that so clearly rejects the concept of product
standardisation. The 1930s baronial dining-room, with its half-panelled walls,
golden velvet drapes and blue portcullis-patterned carpet, is being re-decorated
as the *Guide* goes to press; the new look may lend it an allure it lacked before.
Gary Rhodes's cooking is sharply modern and heroically supportive of local
supplies. The set menus are augmented by a dozen starters and main courses on
the *carte*, which has an infinite variety of textures, with sauces made from butter,
oils and stocks. On its night the restaurant is very fine. The smells of a warm
pigeon salad with a garlic confit and a dressing of vinaigrette mixed with the
meat juices, rise up across the table. Look also for fish: black bream on a green
purée with a tomato vinaigrette (a great summer dish, although served here in
January); red mullet with olive and coriander dressing; sea bass braised with
cabbage; cream of mussel soup. There are roasts too, at lunch, and fine lamb with
a rosemary tartlet and a stock reduction. As with many hotels, standards are
frustratingly erratic – a Sunday night inspection found a kitchen struggling with
the more complex dishes, like rabbit pithivier. Surely it would be better to take
the *carte* off when the number one is not on, than risk losing a good reputation.
The cheeseboard is magnificent, essentially English, and served with walnut
bread. Sweets, like the spirit of the place, straddle the artifice of French nouvelle –
prune and rum ice-cream in a brandysnap basket with sauce anglaise – and the
power of modern British – there is a traditional hot pudding of the day. The tarts
are the thing, though: apple on the thinnest of pastries is served hot with its own
apple sorbet, for instance. The wine list is like a Jackie Collins novel – it goes on
for pages – with claret in profusion scattered across the decades, pedigree
burgundy, a thorough treatment of Germany, wines from Somerset, and
Chardonnay from the New World. CELLARMAN'S CHOICE: Cabernet Sauvignon
'80, from Robert Mondavi, £15·25.

CHEF: Gary Rhodes PROPRIETORS: The Chapman family
OPEN: all week MEALS: 12.30 to 2, 7.30 to 9
PRICES: £26 (£32), Set L from £8·50 (£13), Set D £18·50 (£24) CARDS: Access, Amex,
Diners, Visa
SEATS: 110. Private parties: 65 main room, 50 and 110 private rooms. Car-park, 40 places.
Vegetarian meals. Children's helpings. Smart dress preferred. Wheelchair access (also WC)
ACCOMMODATION: 35 rooms, all with bath/shower. Rooms for disabled. Lift. B&B £51 to
£86. Children welcome. Baby facilities. Afternoon teas. Garden. TV. Phone. Doors close
at 12. Confirm by 6

Reports on shops, cafes and farms are useful, as well as reports on restaurants.

*Many of the more expensive restaurants offer bargain lunches for half the price of a
meal in the evening. Details are given in the text.*

TETBURY Gloucestershire

map 2

▲ *Calcot Manor* [14/20] ✗

Beverston, Tetbury GL8 8YJ
LEIGHTERTON (066 689) 355 and 227
3m W of Tetbury, on A4135   £15–£27

The manor is an isolated group of ancient buildings, including a medieval tithe
barn, and stables. Only the hotel part has been completely restored, and its pale
interior gives an air of spaciousness. The short menu is modern, with brilliant
sauces, lots of herbs, alcohol and mousses. Ramon Farthing combines the
sophistication and mastery of technique of Chris Oakes, with whom he worked at
the Castle Hotel at Taunton, with the daring and distinctive, clear tastes of his
predecessor, Redmond Hayward (now at Cheltenham). His skill lies in taking
classic dishes and giving them a new twist. Tournedos Rossini is a modern
version: Scotch beef fillet with baked garlic and goose-liver sausage, in a sauce
flavoured with cèpe mushrooms. The soft liver sausage surrounds a rare fillet
topped by a sharp concasse of tomatoes with onion, parsley and cassis. Two
sauces form the backdrop, unevenly dividing the plate, and *nouvelle* vegetables
complete the picture. Starters are similarly picturesque, and include a hot
mousse of pigeon, with braised red cabbage and light apple sauce; or slices of
fresh salmon with baby leeks and puff pastry, served with a champagne and
butter sauce. Cheese are British, ranging from Shropshire Blue and Stilton to
Cotherstone, with Cerney or Capricorn goats', all served with home-made
caraway biscuits. For dessert, the high-sided, flat-topped, tart-tasting hot
rhubarb soufflé is softened with cream and vanilla sauce, and the home-made
banana ice-cream, with cinnamon and praline roulade, is yet another example of
sophisticated balancing of tastes and contrasts. The mainly French wine list
includes three choices from Gloucestershire, and a trio from Provence, including
CELLARMAN'S CHOICE: Bandol, Mas de La Rouvière '82, £13·40.

CHEF: Ramon Farthing PROPRIETORS: Brian and Barbara Ball and family
OPEN: all week, exc Sun D MEALS: 12.15 to 1.45, 7.30 to 9.30
PRICES: Set L from £10·50 (£15), Set D from £21 (£27), Snacks from £2·50. Service inc
CARDS: Access, Amex, Diners, Visa
SEATS: 45. 6 tables outside. Private parties: 40 main room, 12 private room. Car-park,
75 places. Vegetarian meals. Children's helpings (L only). Jacket and tie. Wheelchair
access (also WC)
ACCOMMODATION: 13 rooms, all with bath/shower. Rooms for disabled. B&B £45 to £110.
No children under 12. Afternoon teas. Garden. Swimming-pool. Fishing. Golf. TV. Phone.
Doors close at 12

THAXTED Essex

map 3

Lee Kiang House [9/20]

25 Mill End, Thaxted CM6 2LT
THAXTED (0371) 830101   £15–£17

Despite their restaurant being open for only three nights a week, Bob Firmin and
Lee Yong are extending into a new kitchen, and converting the old one into a
dining-room for small parties. In a scaled-down Chinese menu fish, crab, beef,

pork and chicken come with ginger and spring onion; or chilli and black-bean sauce; there are set meals, too. Special requests are catered for, or the choice can be left to the house. Monosodium glutamate and other preservatives and enhancers are not used. There is a short list of inexpensive white wines.

CHEF: Lee Yong PROPRIETORS: R. W. Firmin and Lee Yong
OPEN: Thur to Sat, D only MEALS: 7.30 to 10.30
PRICES: £9 (£17), Set D from £11 (£15) CARDS: Access, Visa
SEATS: 28. Private parties: 12 main room, 12 private room. Vegetarian meals. Children welcome. Smart dress preferred. Wheelchair access (also WC). Music

Recorder's [11/20]

17 Town Street, CM6 2LD
THAXTED (0371) 830438   £16–£19·75

The Recorder's House was built for Samuel Benelowes, Recorder of Thaxted in the fifteenth century. The heavily beamed and finely panelled rooms are complemented by floral wallpaper and reproduction Audubon bird prints. The cooking also combines traditional and nouvelle, English and French. Set meals which include a half-bottle of house wine and coffee, keep the costs in check. Textures are nicely varied, with chopped walnuts in the Dijon mustard sauce with lamb; and there's a kick of garlic and tarragon butter with snails. Other frequent successes have been chicken or salmon timbales; local pike with sorrel; pork with pink peppercorns; though the saucing could pack a little more elbow. The sweets trolley is laden with creamy confections, and some fruitier puddings or sorbets would be another good addition. A largely French wine list, with house red and white at £5·50 a bottle.

CHEF: Roy Hawkins PROPRIETORS: Roy Hawkins and Michael Rubal
OPEN: Tue to Sat, D only, and Sun L CLOSED: 26 Dec to third week Jan MEALS: 12.15 to 2, 7 to 10
PRICES: Set L £11·50 (£16), Set D £19·75 (£19·75). Service inc D only, 10% at L
CARDS: Access, Amex, Diners, Visa
SEATS: 50. 4 tables outside. Private parties: 50 main room, 12 private room. Vegetarian meals. No children under 5. Smart dress preferred. Music

THORNBURY Avon   map 2

▲ Thornbury Castle [12/20]

Castle Street, Thornbury BS12 1HH
THORNBURY (0454) 418511   ▮ £19–£26

Kenneth Bell gave up his long reign at this sixteenth-century castle in 1986, and the kitchen is now powered by Colin Hingston, one of his pupils. The grandeur remains – the imposing battlements, the high baronial dining-room with arrow slits in the deeply recessed walls, the wooden panels depicting angels. Some new old masters have appeared on the walls of the drawing-room and the Liberty prints that once adorned the great heights of the public rooms have gone.

▮ This symbol is awarded only to restaurants with outstanding wine cellars.

Kenneth Bell's spirit still lingers in the kitchen, and the short, weekly menu has many of his trademarks – a fondness for fish and cream sauces, a loyalty to British dishes and traditions – though there are innovative ideas, too. The quality of the ingredients shows, not only in the poached scallops with white wine and basil, or fillet of monkfish sauté with dill and ginger, but also in the breast of free-range chicken stuffed with avocado and smoked bacon, or the venison and port pie. There's also a regular vegetarian dish, such as wholemeal pancakes filled with ratatouille. Cheeses are from the farm, and sweets are traditional: Hannah Glasse's syllabub, treacle tart, hot butterscotch pudding. New owner Maurice Taylor has inherited the bulk of the wine cellar, and retains the emphasis on classical French wines, with English bottlings of older vintages and plentiful halves of claret. Spain and California stand out, too, including a trio of Chardonnays. CELLARMAN'S CHOICE: Coteaux de l'Ardèche '84, from Louis Latour, £9·40.

CHEF: Colin Hingston PROPRIETOR: Maurice Taylor
OPEN: all week MEALS: 12.15 to 2, 7 to 9.30 (9 Sun)
PRICES: Set L from £12·50 (£19), Set D from £19·50 (£26). Service inc CARDS: Access, Amex, Carte Blanche, Diners, Visa
SEATS: 60. Private parties: 30 main room. Car-park, 30 places. Vegetarian meals. No children under 12. Smart dress preferred. No smoking in dining-room. Wheelchair access
ACCOMMODATION: 14 rooms, all with bath/shower. Rooms for disabled. B&B £64 to £98. No children under 12. Garden. TV. Phone. Scenic. Doors close at 12

THORNTON HEATH Greater London   map 3

Ming Garden [10/20]

850 London Road, Thornton Heath CR4 7PA
01-684 0991   £10–£15

A marble and bamboo Peking restaurant, evolved from a take-away, now with a westernised menu incorporating Peking duck at £18, popular satay dishes and calm, solicitous service. The premier dishes in particular – hot-and-sour soup, chilli prawns, Manchurian lamb – draw positive reports. Set meals start at £6. House French £5.

CHEF: For Tai To PROPRIETOR: Sau Chuen To
OPEN: all week CLOSED: 25 and 26 Dec MEALS: 12 to 2.30, 5.30 (6 Sun) to 12
PRICES: £9 (£15), Set L and D £6 (£10). Minimum £5. Service 10% CARDS: Access, Amex, Diners, Visa
SEATS: 44. Private parties: 40 main room. Vegetarian meals. Children's helpings. Wheelchair access. Music. Air-conditioned

---

The Guide recruits new inspectors from readers who write in regularly. If you would like to apply, write to the editor with (a) a detailed report on a restaurant where you have eaten and (b) a comparative study of restaurants known to you.

'Can you do anything to stop chefs putting huge pats of butter on so many dishes? I don't like a plate swimming in butter anyway, and at present I've been stopped using much of it, so it does revolt me. (On eating in London)

THORNTON-LE-FYLDE Lancashire   map 5

▲ *River House* [11/20]

Skippool Creek, Thornton-le-Fylde FY5 5LF
POULTON-LE-FYLDE (0253) 883497   £15–£36

Go inland at Victoria Square, Cleveleys; turn left at the sign for Skippool Creek.
The Scott family has run this small, Victorian house for almost thirty years, and
the mood is as convivial as ever. Furnishings and trappings are luxurious, and so
are some of the ingredients: snail caviare with scrambled quails' eggs is £23;
salmon is served as sashimi or gravlax; fillet of beef is stuffed with steak tartare,
and served with tomato and brandy sauce. The style is essentially English, if
inclining to the old-fashioned, which means traditional roast sirloin with good
Yorkshire pudding and home-made horseradish, as well as guinea-fowl with
blackcurrants, chicken fillets with garlic and chive sauce, and stuffed loin of lamb
in pastry. Good home-made ice-creams, or hot walnut and date sponge to finish.
Standards seem to be back to where they were in the 1970s. The two hundred-
strong wine list has French regional varieties, and plenty of bin-ends.
CELLARMAN'S CHOICE: Mâcon-Lugny, Les Genièvres '85, £10.

CHEFS/PROPRIETORS: Bill and Carole Scott
OPEN: all week MEALS: 12 to 2, 7.30 to 9.30
PRICES: £28 (£36), Set L from £10 (£15) CARDS: Access, Amex
SEATS: 45. Private parties: 100 main room. Car-park, 20 places. Vegetarian meals.
Children's helpings. Wheelchair access. Music
ACCOMMODATION: 4 rooms, 1 with bath/shower. B&B £34 to £49. Baby facilities. Pets
welcome. Garden. Fishing. TV. Phone. Scenic. Confirm by 6

TICKHILL South Yorkshire   map 5

Forge [new entry, zero rated]

1 Sunderland Street, Tickhill DN11 9PT
DONCASTER (0302) 744122   £21

This is perhaps the most booked-ahead restaurant in the north of England. Its
friendliness and value are overwhelming factors that draw a committed local
following to the old building with 'mind your head' signs over nearly every door.
The generosity extends through the service into a menu that has picked up the
modern virtues of brevity and use of fresh produce, and put them to use in some
interesting, sometimes over-complex combinations. The fondness of cream runs
through the sauces, such as ginger and pineapple for pork, and it is served
separately in a jug to add to a stoneware bowl of mushroom and fennel soup.
Main dishes are exuberant, for instance breast and thigh of guinea-fowl stuffed
with chestnut and apple, or a pancake with a cider sauce and innumerable
garnishes and vegetables covering the plate. Poacher's pie in December has been
splendid. The sweets trolley is a local legend for its flans, trifles, brûlées, gateaux,
Pavlovas, mousses and meringues, all of which are offered as seconds or more.

*All details are as accurate as possible at the time of going to press. Please notify the
Guide office of any changes.*

Truffles and peppermints appear with the coffee. The wine list is more modest, with the emphasis strongly under £7. More reports, please.

CHEF: Helen Taylor PROPRIETORS: Helen and Howard Taylor
OPEN*:Tue to Sat, D only MEALS: 7.15 to 9.30
PRICES: Set D £16·75 (£21)
SEATS: 36. Private parties: 36 main room. Vegetarian meals. Children's helpings. No cigars/pipes in dining-room. Wheelchair access (also WC). Music. Air-conditioned

---

TIDEFORD Cornwall map 1

Heskyn Mill [11/20]

Tideford PL12 5JS
LANDRAKE (075 538) 481 £19

It is several years since this was a working mill, but the guts of the machinery is still intact. The Edens have converted the low-beamed rooms into a dining-area, and added comfortable fireside sofas in the downstairs bar. The strength of the cooking is the imaginative use of first-class ingredients, especially fish, seasonal vegetables and game. Quality shows in the roast rack of lamb, or pan-fried fillets of chicken, pork and beef with a cream and white wine sauce. Home-made ice-creams are the best of the sweets. A modest pricing policy runs through the wine list, and the variety extends to Spain and the New World, whence come CELLARMAN'S CHOICE: Valdepeñas, Senorio de Los Llanos Gran Reserva '75, at £8·50, and Semillon, Rothbury Estate '85, at £9·95.

CHEFS: K. Williams and F. A. Eden PROPRIETORS: F. and S. M. Eden
OPEN: Tue to Sat MEALS: 12 to 1.45, 7 to 10
PRICES: £14 (£19), Snacks from £1·25 CARDS: Amex, Visa
SEATS: 60. 6 tables outside. Private parties: 50 main room. Car-park, 25 places. Vegetarian meals. Children's helpings. Music

---

TISBURY Wiltshire map 2

The Garden Room [12/20]

2 High Street, Tisbury SP3 6PS
TISBURY (0747) 870907 £12–£19

The garden notion extends to the décor – which is of garden murals and flowers – and, to some extent, to the menu. Chef Paul Firmin cooks an inventive, modern set menu with a choice of six dishes at each course, changed regularly to keep pace with fresh ingredients. Main courses, such as loin of veal with lemon and sorrel, or duck with kumquats and honey, impress, and there are some make or bust dishes, like pigeon breast in pastry with a sauce of coriander. A little artifice could be traded for more concentration on details; despite this, and despite some of the sweets, for instance, lacking character, all round this is an increasingly

---

'We arrived at 8.45 and concluded dinner at midnight. However interesting our conversation, no meal can stand such a strain. My sleep was disturbed by a waitress continually bringing clean knives and forks for each of six courses.' (On eating in the Home Counties)

---

accomplished operation. The wine list is fittingly short, and mainly French, with house wine at £6. CELLARMAN'S CHOICE: Canon Fronsac, Ch. Bodet la Justice '79, at £13·50.

CHEF: Paul Firmin PROPRIETORS: Paul Firmin and Jonathan Ford
OPEN: Tue to Sun, exc Sat L and Sun D MEALS: 12.30 to 2, 7.30 to 10
PRICES: Set L £7·95 (£12), Set D £14·50 (£19) CARDS: Access, Amex, Visa
SEATS: 32. Private parties: 22 main room, 12 private room. Car-park, 12 places. Vegetarian meals. Children's helpings. Wheelchair access (also WC). Music

---

TIVERTON Devon   map 1

Hendersons

18 Newport Street, Tiverton EX16 6NL
TIVERTON (0884) 254256

As the Guide *went to press there was a change of chef at this restaurant.*

TORQUAY Devon   map 1

▲ *Mulberry Room* [9/20]

1 Scarborough Road, Torquay TQ2 5UJ
TORQUAY (0803) 213639   £8

A rare find – a genuine tea-room-cum-restaurant-cum B&B, serving cheap, real food with no fancy touches. Lesley Cooper runs her corner terrace almost single-handed, but keeps up her standards. A sideboard of cakes and tarts stands invitingly, strategically, at the entrance. Roast chicken is a farmyard bird, soups are honestly home made, and the menu also takes in beef and carrot suet pudding, as well as pork and apple pie. The wholefood tendency waits in the wings, with peanut rissole accompanied by tomato and chilli pickle. Sunday

349

lunchtime roasts feature superb meat, rounded off with riotous creamy sweets. Dinners by arrangement. House Côtes du Rhône is £3 for a half-litre.

CHEF/PROPRIETOR: Lesley Cooper
OPEN: Tue to Sun MEALS: 10 to 5
PRICES: £5 (£8), Snacks from £1·50
SEATS: 30. 2 tables outside. Private parties: 40 main room. Vegetarian meals. Children's helpings. Wheelchair access (also WC). Music
✗ACCOMMODATION: 3 rooms. B&B £8·50 to £21. Deposit: 10%. Afternoon teas. TV. Doors close at 9. Confirm by 7

Remy's [10/20]

3 Croft Road, Torquay TQ2 5VN
TORQUAY (0803) 22359   £15

The family atmosphere in Rémy Bopp's converted Victorian guest-house is one of its attractions. The cooking is Gallic: herby pork pâté; onion soup made with French cider, topped with cheese croûtons. Fish comes fresh each day from Brixham and shows well. Sole, monkfish and sea bass share a sauce of cream, shallots and fish stock. Vegetables are lightly done, prettily presented, and generous. The ice-cream-based sweets are similarly attractive. The fixed-price menus are good value, while the wine list, with a good showing in Alsace, has plenty under £10.

CHEF/PROPRIETOR: Rémy Bopp
OPEN: Tue to Sat, D only CLOSED: 2 weeks at Christmas, 2 weeks Aug MEALS: 7.15 to 9.30
PRICES: Set D from £10·85 (£15). Service inc CARDS: Amex, Visa
SEATS: 40. Private parties: 26 main room, 20 private room. Children's helpings. Smart dress preferred. Music

TREWELLARD Cornwall   map 1

Trotters [11/20]

The Barn, Trewellard Hill, Trewellard TR19 7TD
PENZANCE (0736) 787108 and 731072
2m N of St Just   £11–£20

The Hubands' converted granite barn is in a rural, Atlantic-swept corner, but they have given it a homely atmosphere with Victorian furniture, fresh flowers and pink tablecloths. There's a strong French flavour to Jacqueline-Blanche's cooking; many dishes receive their quota of cream. Fresh fish dominates the menu: Newlyn crab with chicory, cucumber and tarragon cream; scampi provençale on a bed of spinach; poached salmon steak. Tournedos and veal escalopes are offered for meat eaters. Generous helpings of vegetables come on a separate plate. To finish there is a rich chocolate marquise. The wine list has about two dozen bottles, mostly French, and mostly well under £10. There is

---

Restaurants are graded on a scale of 1–20. In the category of 10–11 expect to find the best food in the locality. Ratings of 12 and more are given to restaurants we regard as serving the best food in the region.

Muscadet and Chablis for the fish, but CELLARMAN'S CHOICE is Morgon '83, from Patriarche, at £7·50.

CHEF: Jacqueline-Blanche Huband PROPRIETORS: Jacqueline-Blanche and Geoffrey Huband
OPEN: Wed to Sat D and Sun L MEALS: 12.30, 7.30
PRICES: £11 (£20), Set L from £6 (£11) CARDS: Access, Visa
SEATS: 20. Private parties: 20 main room. Car-park, 10 places. Children welcome. Music. One sitting

---

TUNBRIDGE WELLS Kent   map 3

Cheevers [13/20]

56 High Street, Tunbridge Wells TN1 1XF
TUNBRIDGE WELLS (0892) 45524   £14–£18

Halfway up the hilly High Street is this stylish restaurant. Pale grey and custard-yellow walls are offset by black shiny woodwork, pure white table linen and plain Royal Doulton crockery. Martin Miles runs the front of the house while Tim Cheevers cooks in the modern British style. Herbs figure prominently in the seasoning: tarragon with the lemon-baked guinea-fowl; dill with the mousseline of salmon; mint with the breast of chicken grilled with yoghurt and cardamom. This is also the post-nouvelle world of walnut oil, fennel, saffron and wild mushrooms. A slice of toasted home-made brioche is served with terrine of sweetbreads and duck livers, while roast saddle of hare with baby leeks and button mushrooms is enhanced by its concentrated sauce of red wine and stock. To finish there are English cheeses or traditional sweets, such as brown-bread ice-cream, hot walnut and ginger pudding, and rhubarb fool. The lemon tart has been first rate. The short, modern wine list keeps to a respectable price range and crams in a variety of styles. CELLARMAN'S CHOICE: Vouvray, Domaine de L'Epinay '85, from Felicien Brou, at £9·50, and Bourgogne, Passetoutgrain '83, from Lamblin, at £8·85.

CHEF: T.J. Cheevers PROPRIETORS: T. J Cheevers, M. J. Miles and P. D. Tambini
OPEN: Tue to Sat MEALS: 12 to 2.30, 7 to 10.30
PRICES: £9 (£14), Set D £13·95 (£18) CARDS: Access, Visa
SEATS: 36. Private parties: 36 main room. Children's helpings. No cigars/pipes in dining-room. Wheelchair access. Music. Air-conditioned

---

Thackeray's House [14/20]

85 London Road, Tunbridge Wells TN1 1EA
TUNBRIDGE WELLS (0892) 37558   £16–£29

William Makepeace Thackeray lived here, but the house pre-dates him. As a restaurant it has an air of sophistication, with lots of gilt-framed mirrors, candlesticks, old paintings and upright chairs with carved backs. Bruce Wass matches this with some inspired cosmopolitan cooking, very modern and very classy. Dishes are impeccably executed, perfectly timed and delightful to look at. His capabilities show in the brilliant quails' eggs in miniature brioches filled with an earthy mixture of mushrooms and chopped spinach, all covered in a classic frothy hollandaise. Ingredients are outstanding, as in the croustade of mackerel, scallops, smoked salmon, and chives. As well as a healthy fondness for fish, the menu exploits the possibilities of fruit and vegetables: noisettes of venison come with wild cherries; new season's lamb is paired with glazed turnips and radishes. Sweets also rely heavily on fruit. All the details are of a very serious restaurant, from the little pieces of French stick with grilled cheese and capers served as canapés, to the home-made bread and excellent unsalted butter, to the British farm cheeses from James Aldridge of Beckenham and the exquisite petits fours. Cheaper meals are served downstairs. Good burgundies and Bordeaux are the mainstays of the wine list, although there is good drinking under £10 and a generous selection of half-bottles. CELLARMAN'S CHOICE: Mercurey blanc, Michel Juillot '85, £17·85.

CHEFS: Bruce Wass, Gordon Malcolm and Nigel Ramsbottom PROPRIETOR: Bruce Wass
OPEN: Tue to Sat CLOSED: 1 week at Christmas MEALS: 12.30 to 2.30, 7 to 10
PRICES: £21 (£29), Set L from £9·45 (£16), Set D from £18·50 (£26). Service 10%
CARDS: Access, Visa
SEATS: 35. 8 tables outside. Private parties: 16 main room. Children's helpings

---

TWICKENHAM Greater London   map 3

Cézanne [13/20] ✈

68 Richmond Road, Twickenham TW1 3BE
01-892 3526   £12–£17

Cézanne might have baulked at the eclectic décor, but the rich palette of foods has, in the last few years, established the Jeffersons' restaurant as *the* place to eat in Twickenham. The mood remains unpatronising and relaxed, but the cooking has pace – timbale of wild mushrooms; scallop terrine in orange sauce; red mullet with Beaujolais. The sweets course draws universal praise for dishes such as apple tart with calvados cream, and crêpes filled with fruit. The concise wine list is sensibly priced and mostly French, but includes a California Chardonnay, from Wente Brothers. CELLARMAN'S CHOICE: Savennières, Château de Chamboureau '84, £9·50.

CHEFS: Tim Jefferson and Keith Saxon PROPRIETORS: Tim and Philippa Jefferson
OPEN: Mon to Sat, exc Sat L CLOSED: bank hols MEALS: 12.30 to 2.30, 7 to 10.30
(11 Fri and Sat)
PRICES: £13 (£17), Set L £8·25 (£12) CARDS: Access, Amex, Visa
SEATS: 38. Private parties: 40 main room. Vegetarian meals. Children's helpings.
Wheelchair access. Music

McClements [new entry, zero rated]

12 The Green, Twickenham TW2 5AA
01-755 0176   £14–£22

This is a tiny, personal restaurant in one of the terraced houses overlooking the Green. John McClements cooks everything himself, a mite needlessly, ambitiously perhaps, and even serves the main dishes himself. Of perhaps fourteen dishes an evening, there has been fine crab gateau wrapped in spinach, lamb with couscous, guinea-fowl with pistachio, and some luscious sweets. The short wine list tries to be all things to all people. House claret is £7. More reports, please.

CHEF/PROPRIETOR: John McClements
OPEN: Mon to Sat, exc Mon D and Sat L MEALS: noon to 11pm (5pm Mon, 7 to 11pm Sat)
PRICES: £16 (£22), Set L £9·50 (£14), Set D £15·50 (£21). Service 10% CARDS: Access,
Amex, Diners, Visa
SEATS: 25. Private parties: 25 main room, 15 private room. Car-park, 20 places. Vegetarian
meals. Children welcome. Smart dress preferred. No-smoking area. Music

---

ULLSWATER Cumbria   map 7

▲ *Sharrow Bay* [14/20] ✗

Howtown Road, Ullswater CA10 2LZ
POOLEY BRIDGE (085 36) 301 and 483
2m from Pooley Bridge on E side of
lake, signposted Howton and
Martindale   £22–£32

Forty years ago Francis Coulson founded the first and, arguably, the seminal,
country-house hotel on £500 and an overdraft of £2000. The cooking, without
being modern, has moved with the times. It is English, using traditional roasts,
game in season, and making much of English puddings. Baking is done in-house,
including five kinds of breads. Dinner is an event, with twenty-plus starters to
choose from; then a fish course; perhaps a sorbet; and a range of main dishes,
featuring meat. Sweets are shown, and ordered, at the beginning. The menu style
is chicken terrine with Cumberland sauce; salmon with sorrel; fried calf's liver
with a Dubonnet sauce; rhubarb tart. The view on to Ullswater eases the
busyness of the décor, which extends to the rooms. The cellar benefits from
longevity. Claret relies heavily on '75 and '78, Louis Latour dominates the
burgundies, and double-figure prices abound, except in the Loire, Italy and
England. Half-bottles are in plentiful supply.

CHEFS: Johnnie Martin, Colin Akrigg, Philip Wilson, Alison Kennedy, Paul Brodie and
Tim Ford PROPRIETORS: Francis Coulson and Brian Sack
OPEN: all week CLOSED: Dec to Feb MEALS: 1 to 1.45, 8 to 8.45
PRICES: Set L from £18·50 (£22), Set D from £28·50 (£32). Service inc
SEATS: 65. Private parties: 10 main room. Car-park, 30 places. Vegetarian meals.
No children under 13. Jacket and tie. No smoking during meals. Wheelchair access
ACCOMMODATION: 30 rooms, 26 with bath/shower. Rooms for disabled. D, B&B £61 to
£114. No children under 13. Afternoon teas. Garden. TV. Phone. Scenic. Doors close at 12.
Confirm by 10 [GHG]

UPPINGHAM Leicestershire ✗   map 6

▲ *Lake Isle* [11/20]

16 High Street East, Uppingham LE15 9PL
UPPINGHAM (0572) 822951   £12–£17

Across the road a note on a hotel menu says, 'if you believe you have received
exceptional service please feel free to reward the staff accordingly'. Such
unctuous solicitude could not be further removed from the atmosphere in the
Whitfields' converted butcher's, essentially now a restaurant with rooms,
concentrating on fine wines and essentially French country cooking. The décor
amounts to a pine dresser at one end, assorted chairs and tables, and prints and

plates on the walls. A short, weekly dinner menu runs to five courses, and pricing is flexible. Typically there might be tomato and fennel soup, then smoked fish and avocado salad before lambs' kidneys en croûte or duck breast with orange and green peppercorn sauce. Fine cheeses come mainly from Paxton and Whitfield, though a Sunday lunch inspection disappointed. The wine list has been pruned but is more manageable at around three hundred bottles. It is long on half-bottles and fits the more peasant dishes on the menu, which allow it to be used for tasting.

CHEF: David Whitfield PROPRIETORS: David and Claire Whitfield
OPEN: Tue to Sun, exc Sun D MEALS: 12 to 2, 7 to 10
PRICES: Set L from £8·45 (£12), Set D from £12·75 (£17) CARDS: Access, Amex, Diners, Visa
SEATS: 35. Private parties: 40 main room. Vegetarian meals. Children's helpings. Wheelchair access
ACCOMMODATION: 8 rooms, all with bath/shower. B&B £26 to £36. Pets welcome. TV. Doors close at 12

VERYAN Cornwall map 1

▲ *Treverbyn House* [10/20]

Pendower Road, Veryan TR2 5QL
TRURO (0872) 501201 £14

The Gardners let four rooms near the centre of this sprawling, pretty village. They are amenable hosts. John cooks a menu written in French, but reliant on fresh Cornish produce. Meals revolve round roasts with wine gravies, sandwiched by mushrooms in garlic butter, and meringues. 'We find people now prefer more simple dishes.' Forty French wines. House wines £4·20.
CELLARMAN'S CHOICE: St Emilion, Ch. d'Armens '81, £12·90.

CHEF: John Gardner PROPRIETOR: Josephine Gardner
OPEN: all week, D only CLOSED: Nov to Easter, exc by arrangement MEALS: 7.30 to 8.30
PRICES: Set D £11 (£14)
SEATS: 18. Private parties: 14 main room. Car-park, 10 places. Children's helpings. No children under 7. Jacket and tie. Wheelchair access
ACCOMMODATION: 4 rooms. B&B £17 to £34. Deposit: £10. No children under 7. Afternoon teas. Garden. Fishing. Golf. Scenic

---

WADHURST East Sussex map 3

▲ *Spindlewood Hotel* [10/20]

Wallcrouch, Wadhurst TN5 7JG
TICEHURST (0580) 200430
on B2099, between Wadhurst and
Ticehurst £14–£20

The gloom of the entrance hall is relieved by the oak panels of the dining-room. The cooking is modern and full of good intentions, though on some nights it has more presence than on others. Successes include skilfully made tarts with spinach and poached egg, and home-made seafood ravioli, with chive sauce. Vegetables are crisp and seasonal. Good crème brûlée to finish. The wine list of fifty bottles includes half a dozen from England. CELLARMAN'S CHOICE: from just down the road, Lamberhurst Priory '85, £8·95.

CHEF: Paul Clayton PROPRIETOR: R. V. Fitzsimmons
OPEN: all week CLOSED: 4 days at Christmas MEALS: 12.15 to 1.30, 7.15 to 9 (9.15 Sat, 8.30 Sun)
PRICES: £12 (£17), Set L from £10·25 (£14), Set D £15·45 (£20) CARDS: Access, Amex, Diners, Visa
SEATS: 40. Private parties: 50 main room, 18 private room. Car-park, 60 places. Vegetarian meals. Children's helpings. No cigars/pipes in dining-room. Music
ACCOMMODATION: 9 rooms, all with bath/shower. B&B £25 to £50. Deposit: £25. Baby facilities. Garden. Tennis. TV. Phone. Doors close at 12. Confirm by 6

WALLINGFORD Oxfordshire map 2

Brown & Boswell [12/20] ✕

28 High Street, Wallingford OX10 0BU
WALLINGFORD (0491) 34078 £7–£20

The Browns and the Boswells are partners in this striking Victorian building with wall-to-ceiling stripped pine and half-curtains at the bay windows. The menu is modern British and attractive, changing monthly: smoked fish pâté; lemon sole with pesto sauce; grilled loin of veal in hazel-nut butter; and pigeon breasts with a Cabernet Sauvignon glaze. Vegetables are innovative without being outlandish: earthy potatoes cooked in milk with horseradish, smooth beetroot and apple purée, and there's also a vegetarian dish such as quiche with wild and button mushrooms. The cooking may have ups and downs, but there is always compensation in a short, modern list of wines with low mark-ups arranged by style rather than by country: dry, fruity, rich, robust or sweet. It is also very young, with little before '80, but none the worse for that. Jaboulet's Cornas '80 and an '83 Australian Cabernet Sauvignon, Balgownie, from Stuart Anderson, share the rich red grouping. CELLARMAN'S CHOICE is for a dry and a fruity white respectively: Quincy '85, from Pierre Mardon, at £8·95, and Torre di Gianno '84, from Lungarotti, at £7·50.

CHEFS: Robert Boswell and Paul Bridgewood PROPRIETORS: Bryan and Buzz Brown, Robert and Patricia Boswell
OPEN: Tue to Sun, exc Tue L and Sun D CLOSED: 2 weeks Mar, 1 week Oct MEALS: 12.30 to 1.30, 7 to 10
PRICES: £13 (£20), Set L from £3 (£7), Set D £15 (£16·50). CARDS: Access, Amex, Diners, Visa
SEATS: 36. Private parties: 24 main room, 12 and 24 private rooms. Vegetarian meals. Children's helpings. Wheelchair access, Music

---

WARSOP Nottinghamshire ✈ map 5

Goff's [new entry, zero rated]

4 Burn Lane, Warsop NG20 0PB
MANSFIELD (0623) 844137 £7–£20

Such has been the force for change in catering that classical cooking has been almost totally eclipsed, but Lin and Graham Goff's tightly run restaurant continues to produce fine versions of consommé célestine, boeuf bourguignonne, and poularde Princesse, sauce allemande. The Goffs, who also own the butcher's shop four doors away, are a hard-working presence in the dining-room, and spent many years renovating the building itself. Lunch is a bargain. The wine list is well spread and, as in other areas, there is a feeling of constant up-dating and improvement going on. More reports, please.

CHEF: Rex W. Howell   PROPRIETORS: Lin and Graham Goff
OPEN: Tue to Sun, exc Sat L and Sun D   MEALS: 12 to 2, 7 to 9.45
PRICES: £16 (£20), Set L £4·50 (£7), Snacks from 95p. Service inc   CARDS: Access, Amex, Carte Blanche, Diners, Visa
SEATS: 50. Private parties: 60 main room. Car-park, 20 places. Vegetarian meals. Children's helpings. Music. Air-conditioned

---

WATERHOUSES Staffordshire   map 5

▲ *Old Beams* [12/20]

Waterhouses ST10 3HW
WATERHOUSES (053 86) 254   £15–£27

Built in 1746, and an inn for many years, this roadside building now has a sophisticated atmosphere, enhanced by the glass-roofed conservatory overlooking the garden. Well-spaced tables are laid with huge plates and fine glassware. Ann Wallis attends to every detail out front, while husband Nigel cooks. The style is mid-Channel: cucumber and coriander soup, duck terrine, lamb en croûte, game pie. Sorbets are offered between courses, and sweets have included chocolate mousse. There are plenty of good touches, such as the home-made walnut and sultana bread to start, and the home-made chocolates served with coffee. House Rhône, red and white, is £7·25.

CHEF: Nigel Wallis   PROPRIETORS: Nigel and Ann Wallis
OPEN: Tue to Sat   MEALS: 12 to 2 (1.45 Sat), 7 to 10
PRICES: £19 (£27), Set L £8·95 (£15)   CARDS: Amex, Diners, Visa
SEATS: 50. 3 tables outside. Car-park, 18 places. No children under 4. Wheelchair access (also WC). Music
ACCOMMODATION: 2 rooms, both with bath/shower. B&B £43 to £58. Garden. TV. Scenic

---

WATH-IN-NIDDERDALE North Yorkshire   map 7

▲ *Sportsman's Arms* [12/20]

Wath-in-Nidderdale HG3 5PP
HARROGATE (0423) 711306
1½m NW of Pateley Bridge   £12–£20

The valley is known for its bird-life, the Sportsman for its coal fires, spaced tables, pot-plants and lack of formality. Orders are taken at the bar. Fish is out of Whitby, game off the nearby moors. The cooking is confident: quail and pigeon with garlic; lamb with fresh herbs, or rack with beetroot. Steaks are excellent, and sweets show the same exactness, though the service can be haphazard. The list of 130 wines has great range, a good eye in lesser regions, as well as vintages in the clarets from £5·95. CELLARMAN'S CHOICE: Pouilly Fumé, La Loges aux Moires '85, £11·50.

CHEF/PROPRIETOR: J. R. Carter
OPEN: all week, exc Sun D MEALS: 12 to 1.45, 7 to 10
PRICES: £14 (£20), Set L from £6·80 (£12), Set D from £7·50 (£13) CARDS: Access, Amex, Diners, Visa
SEATS: 45. 6 tables outside. Private parties: 60 main room. Car-park, 50 places. Vegetarian meals. Children's helpings. Wheelchair access (also WC)
ACCOMMODATION: 6 rooms, 2 with bath/shower. B&B £27 to £40. Baby facilities. Pets welcome. Garden. Fishing. TV. Scenic

---

WATLINGTON Oxfordshire   map 2

▲ Well House [10/20]

High Street, Watlington OX9 5PZ
WATLINGTON (049 161) 3333   £20

The open archway of this neat town house of red and silver bricks leads through to the car-park. The dining-room, a converted tea-room, is full of fat beams and bright carpets. The menu is in keeping – old fashioned and unpretentious – and chiefly notable for its range. At one end is calf's liver with gin and lime and at the other is prawn cocktail. The plainer dishes, such as the fine Sunday roasts, are the best. House wine is from the Midi (£5·50). CELLARMAN'S CHOICE: Ch. Léoville-Barton '76 at £31·30.

CHEFS: Patricia Crawford, Debbie Nun and Sharon Harrington PROPRIETORS: Patricia and Alan Crawford
OPEN: Tue to Sun, exc Sat L and Sun D MEALS: 12.30 to 2.15, 7.30 to 9.30 (10 Sat)
PRICES: £13 (£20), Snacks from £3·50 CARDS: Access, Amex, Diners, Visa
SEATS: 40. Private parties: 50 main room, 10 private room. Car-park, 15 places. Vegetarian meals. Children's helpings (Sun L only). Smart dress preferred. Wheelchair access
ACCOMMODATION: 8 rooms, all with bath/shower. Rooms for disabled. B&B £28·80 to £42·80. Children welcome. No pets. Afternoon teas. TV. Phone. Doors close at 11. Confirm by 8.30

WELLS-NEXT-THE-SEA Norfolk   map 6

Moorings [11/20] ✈

6 Freeman Street, Wells-next-the-Sea NR23 1BA
FAKENHAM (0328) 710949   £13–£15

Carla Phillips, an amateur cook who won a *Sunday Times* cook of the year contest, and her husband Bernard, who left King Edward VII school, King's Lynn, where he was head of English, have restored the hundred and fifty-year-old building beside the harbour into a small, open-plan restaurant, the kitchen being visible to all. A deliberate attempt to use local produce appears through the menu of three starters, main courses and puddings. In modern British style, it changes for every meal. Home-made chicken-liver pâté, hot crab, and crudités are followed by: local clams dipped in maize-meal and sauté; a cassoulet made with black-eyed beans; Norfolk garlic sausage and lamb served in a piquant sauce; and a vegetarian dish, such as Mexican pepper, cheese and egg casserole. The style is

---

Many of the more expensive restaurants offer bargain lunches for half the price of a meal in the evening. Details are given in the text.

---

eclectic and experimental and stretches from a ragout of wild mushrooms – including saffron milk caps, parasols and ceps – to fish pie. The technique to handle such a menu is developing. Finish with unpasteurised cheese, or trifle. House wine is £4·75, on an interesting list of sixty bottles that inspires occasional special wine and food evenings. CELLARMAN'S CHOICE: Château Vignelaure '80, from Provence, £11·20.

CHEFS/PROPRIETORS: Bernard and Carla Phillips
OPEN: Thur D to Tue L CLOSED: 3 weeks June, 2 weeks Nov, 22 to 27 Dec MEALS: 12.30 to 2, 7.30 to 9
PRICES: £9 (£13), Set L from £8 (£13), Set D from £10·50 (£15)
SEATS: 44. Private parties: 44 main room. Vegetarian meals. Children's helpings. Wheelchair access (also WC)

WENTBRIDGE West Yorkshire

map 5

▲ *Wentbridge House* [10/20]

Wentbridge WE8 3JJ
PONTEFRACT (0977) 620444   £15–£28

The building is of good old Yorkshire stone, blackened by decades of smoke. There is plenty of lobster, prawn and steak about the menu which might be a defence of catering college manuals. Sauces are made with a barful of alcohol – vermouth, Pernod, brandy, madeira, Beaujolais – thickened with cream and butter. The major asset is the imposing wine list, which runs through the best claret vintages back to '55, some at very imposing prices; burgundies add their weight, too. Nevertheless there are interesting bottles under £10, and some from the New World, including Chardonnays from Rosemount, Jordan and Mondavi. CELLARMAN'S CHOICE: Côtes du Ventoux, La Vieille Ferme '85, £7·50.

CHEF: David Siddall PROPRIETORS: M. M. and K. C. Dupuy
OPEN: all week CLOSED: D 25 Dec MEALS: 12.30 to 2, 7.30 to 9.30
PRICES: £18 (£28), Set L from £10 (£15) CARDS: Access, Amex, Diners, Visa
SEATS: 55. Private parties: 140 main room, 25 private room. Car-park, 100 places. Children's helpings. Smart dress preferred. Wheelchair access (also WC)
ACCOMMODATION: 20 rooms, 17 with bath/shower. B&B £34 to £48. Garden. TV. Phone. Scenic. Doors close at 12.30

WEOBLEY Hereford & Worcester

map 2

▲ *Jule's Café* [11/20]

Broad Street, Weobley HR4 8SB
WEOBLEY (0544) 318206   £15–£17

Julian and Juliet Whitmarsh moved from the Radnor Arms at Llowes to this fine, timbered building, formerly a bakery, in an impressive black and white square. During the day it operates as a modest café/bar/restaurant, serving home-made cakes and pies as well as lunch and afternoon tea. The fixed-price, four-course dinner menu adapts to the market and tends to be hearty: chicken-liver pâté

Report forms are at the back of the book.

---

followed by smoked haddock lasagne, sweet-and-sour pork with oranges and honey, and chocolate roulade. Vegetarian dishes jostle with beef, mussel and Guinness pie, and local game features in season, but there is only house wine to drink, at £4·95 a bottle.

CHEFS/PROPRIETORS: Julian and Juliet Whitmarsh
OPEN: all week MEALS: 12 to 2, 7.15 to 9.30
PRICES: £10 (£15), Set D £12·95 (£17), Snacks from 95p CARD: Visa
SEATS: 36. Private parties: 30 main room. Vegetarian meals. Children's helpings. Wheelchair access (also WC)
ACCOMMODATION: 5 rooms. B&B £13 to £22. Pets welcome. Afternoon teas. Phone. Doors close at 1. Confirm by 6

WEST BEXINGTON Dorset   map 2

▲ *Manor Hotel* [10/20]

Beach Road, West Bexington DT2 9DF
BURTON BRADSTOCK (0308) 897616   £14–£17

The manor overlooks the anglers' favoured stretch of Chesil Bank. It is without pretensions, and the food is honest, fresh, and plentiful. The menu rotates every three days and its apparent conservatism is countered by splendid local fish. The bar is well patronised for its good ales and snacks. Seventy wines, from £5·25.
CELLARMAN'S CHOICE: Ch. Cissac '81, £12·95.

CHEF: Clive Jobson PROPRIETORS: Richard and Jayne Childs
OPEN: all week MEALS: 12 to 2, 7 to 10 (10.30 Sat)
PRICES: Set L £9·65 (£14), Set D £11·95 (£17), Snacks from £1·10 CARDS: Access, Amex, Visa
SEATS: 65. 18 tables outside. Private parties: 65 main room, 20 private room. Car-park, 80 places. Vegetarian meals. Children's helpings. Music
ACCOMMODATION: 10 rooms, all with bath/shower. B&B £23 to £32. Deposit: £10. Children welcome. Baby facilities. Afternoon teas. Garden. Fishing. Golf. TV. Scenic. Confirm by 6

WEST MERSEA Essex   map 3

▲ *Le Champenois, Blackwater Hotel* [11/20] ✗

20–22 Church Street, West Mersea CO5 8QH
COLCHESTER (0206) 383338   £12–£19

The Frenchness is spread as thickly as Normandy butter in this coastal hotel dining-room with its red checked tablecloths, strings of onions, 'hommes' and 'dames' toilets and cries of 'Voilà!' as each dish appears. The Gallic mood is bolstered with French oysters (Natives have to be ordered twenty-four hours in advance); mushrooms dosed strongly with onions, white wine and cream; authentic-looking tarte aux pommes; and good cheeses. Main courses can be conventional: duck with port and cherries; steak au poivre; guinea-fowl with cream and marsala; lemon sole gratin. Vegetables are variable, but steamed new potatoes are excellent. Service is professional. The small but well-chosen wine list has a few examples of the major French regions, but also some high mark-ups. House champagne from Armand Perron is £15; house wine from Georges Duboeuf £5·55.

CHEF: R. Roudesli·PROPRIETOR: Mrs M. Chapleo
OPEN: all week, exc Tue L and Sun D CLOSED: 2 weeks Jan MEALS: 12 to 2, 7 to 10
PRICES: £13 (£19), Set L from £7·30 (£12) CARDS: Access, Amex
SEATS: 46. 3 tables outside. Private parties: 55 main room, 25 private room. Car-park, 20
places. Vegetarian meals. Children's helpings. Smart dress preferred. Wheelchair access (also
WC). Music
ACCOMMODATION: 7 rooms, 4 with bath/shower. B&B £19 to £40. Deposit: £10. Children
welcome. Baby facilities. Pets welcome. Afternoon teas. Garden. TV. Scenic. Doors close at 1.
Confirm by 9

WESTON-SUPER-MARE Avon   map 2

▲ *La Petite Auberge* [10/20]

37 Upper Church Road, Weston-Super-Mare BS23 2DX
WESTON-SUPER-MARE (0934) 22351   £11–£22

Ian and Margaret Williams' split-level bistro is a glass-fronted building in a dull,
dark street full of bed-and-breakfasts. Inside are rough timbers, and carnations
on the tables. The mood is easy-going. Fish is a major attraction, and the dishes
of the day on the blackboard can score over more complex items. Prawns in
garlic butter, roast pheasant with red wine, and venison chasseur, all come with
plentiful vegetables. The wine list has been expanded with fizz and some country
wines from France. House Rhône is £5·50. CELLARMAN'S CHOICE: Chardonnay
du Haut Poitou '86, £7.

CHEF: Margaret Williams PROPRIETORS: Ian and Margaret Williams
OPEN: Mon to Sat, exc Mon L; Sun L in summer CLOSED: 3 weeks a year MEALS: 12 to 2,
7 to 10.30
PRICES: £17 (£22), set L from £6·25 (£11) CARDS: Access, Amex, Visa
SEATS: 32. Private parties: 32 main room. Children's helpings (L only). No children
under 7. Music
ACCOMMODATION: 2 rooms. B&B £14 to £24. TV

WETHERAL Cumbria   map 7

Fantails [10/20]

The Green, Wetheral CA4 8ET
WETHERAL (0228) 60239   £18

The Ferguson family runs these converted cottages, drawing on old British
recipes to give breadth to an otherwise conservative menu. Salmon grilled with
butter and honey and topped with sage is credited to the local, twelfth-century
Constantine monks. As well as steaks and stuffed tomatoes there are subtle
puddings, such as chocolate terrine with pistachios. Fifty wines take in some
interesting drinking, much of it under £10. House Chardonnay is £5·85.
CELLARMAN'S CHOICE: Castello de Tiebas '76, £6·75.

CHEFS: G. S. Ferguson and D. Todhunter PROPRIETORS: P. M. Ferguson, G. S. Ferguson,
L. A. Norman, Les Ferguson and Isabel Ferguson.
OPEN: Tue to Sat CLOSED: Feb MEALS: 12 to 2, 6 to 9.30
PRICES: £11 (£18) CARDS: Access, Amex, Diners, Visa
SEATS: 75. Private parties: 50 main room, 25 private room. Car-park, 16 places. Vegetarian
meals. Children's helpings

WETHERBY Yorkshire

map 5

L'Escale [12/20]

16 Bank Street, Wetherby LS22 4NQ
WETHERBY (0937) 63613

£12–£20

These two three-hundred-year-old stone cottages have been a restaurant for
more than twenty years. The small, L-shaped dining-room is not cramped and
there is plenty of space in the lounge bar for drinks. Fish broth with saffron and
vegetables suggests that this is a serious French restaurant, and there is praise for
the monkfish and trout mousse, as well as quenelles of sole, salmon pie, first-class
venison cooked pink, and roast duck with red wine and pears; chocolate pot is a
favourite sweet. Ingredients come from some of the best-known names in the
north: Ramus Seafoods, Ingles of Harrogate, Alan Porter Provisions. House wine
is £6.95 a bottle.

CHEF: Paul Bidgood PROPRIETORS: Mr and Mrs Paul Bidgood
OPEN: Tue to Sun, exc Sun D MEALS: 12 to 2, 7 to 11
PRICES: £16 (£20), Set L £7.95 (£12), Set D £10 (£13). Service inc
CARDS: Access, Amex, Diners, Visa
SEATS: 65. Private parties: 35 main room, 35 private room. Car-park, 7 places. Children's
helpings (L only). Smart dress preferred. No pipes in dining-room. Wheelchair access (1 step;
also Gents' WC). Music. Air-conditioned

WEYBRIDGE Surrey

map 3

Colony [11/20]

3 Balfour Road, Weybridge KT13 8HE
WEYBRIDGE (0932) 842766

£18–£20

Great emphasis is placed on the serving of ceremonial dishes, such as Peking
duck, the dramatic sizzling dishes and tureens of fragrant fish soup at this smart,
relatively expensive Chinese restaurant. The cooking is from North China and
dishes like aromatic duck, with which other Peking restaurants seem to have
grown increasingly cynical, have been properly executed. Fried lemon sole in
sauce provides a good contrast to the spiciness of other dishes – deep-fried beef
with chilli or Singapore noodles, for instance. Portions are small. The value for
money goes up according to the number of people eating together. House French
is £6.

CHEF: Kam Yau Pang PROPRIETOR: Michael Tse
OPEN: all week MEALS: 12 to 2.30, 6 to 11 (11.30 Fri and Sat)
PRICES: £11 (£20), Set L and D from £12·50 (£18·23). Minimum £12·50. Service 12.5%
CARDS: Access, Amex, Diners, Visa
SEATS: 80. Private parties: 70 main room, 20 private room. Children welcome. Music.
Air-conditioned

*Restaurants are not expected to solicit customers to send in reports. Please let us know
if this happens to you.*

*If, in your opinion, a restaurant is not maintaining the standard of its ratings please
inform the Guide office. Report forms are at the back of the book.*

WHALLEY Lancashire

map 5

Foxfields [12/20]

Whalley Road, Billington, Whalley BB6 9HY
WHALLEY (025 482) 2556
M6 exit 31. Take A59 to Langho
roundabout, follow signs for Billington
and Whalley   £14–£24

A dormer bungalow in pretty countryside. Inside the décor is in pink and Dralon,
and the well-spaced, polished tables are set neatly. The cooking is solid, treating
irreproachable ingredients with care; for instance, guinea-fowl, sweetbread and
morel pâté comes with a compote of white grapes in a sloe-gin jelly to start.
Sauces provide much of the impact for main courses, as in marchand de vin, or
noisettes of veal topped with a langoustine apiece. It is the sweets, though, that
stand out. Wondrous concoctions include frangipane of black cherries and
almonds, and luxurious chocolate marquise spiked with brandy and coffee.
House claret and burgundy are £7 and £7·25 respectively. CELLARMAN'S CHOICE:
Rioja Reserva 904, La Rioja Alta '73, at £14·25.

CHEF: Henk Van Heumen PROPRIETORS: T. H. Parkinson, K. W. Bradshaw and
C. Parkinson
OPEN: Tue to Sun, exc Sat L CLOSED: bank hols MEALS: 12 to 1.30, 7 to 9.30 (9 Sun)
PRICES: £17 (£24), Set L £9 (£14) CARDS: Access, Amex, Diners, Visa
SEATS: 60. Private parties: 20 main room, 140 private room. Car-park, 65 places. Vegetarian
meals. Children's helpings (L only). No children under 4. Smart dress preferred. Music

WHEATON ASTON Staffordshire ✈

map 5

La Calvados [new entry, zero rated]

29 High Street, Wheaton Aston ST19 9NP
STAFFORD (0785) 840707   £9–£15

After running restaurants in Paris and Blackpool, Didier Guerin and his wife
have set up in this small, currently thriving town. The cooking has its heart in
the bourgeois French style, and set dinners are good value. Salads feature among
the starters: cold wing of skate with Meaux mustard vinaigrette; chicory, celery
and apple. Main courses might include duck with raspberry vinegar, chicken in
ginger and soya sauce, and paupiettes of sole in cider sauce. Chocolate mousse on
a sponge base with crème anglaise is a good sweet. Appropriately, the house
aperitif is a blend of calvados with raspberry liqueur and sparkling white wine.
The wine list is well spread. CELLARMAN'S CHOICE: Jurançon, Ch. Jolly's '85, at
£5·80. More reports, please.

All inspections are carried out anonymously.

*The 1989 Guide will appear before Christmas 1988. Reports are particularly helpful
in the spring. Report forms are at the back of this book, but just write a letter if you
prefer. Address it to* The Good Food Guide, FREEPOST, 14 Buckingham Street, London
WC2N 6BR. *No stamp is necessary if you post it in the UK.*

CHEFS: Didier Guerin PROPRIETORS: Mr and Mrs D. P. Guerin
OPEN: Tue to Sun D and Sun L CLOSED: last week Jan, first week Feb MEALS: 12.30 to 2, 7
to 9.30
PRICES: Set L £6·50 (£9), Set D £11 (£15). Service inc CARDS: Access, Amex, Diners, Visa
SEATS: 36. Private parties: 36 main room. Car-park, 11 places. Vegetarian meals. Children's
helpings. Music

WHITBY North Yorkshire map 6A

Magpie Cafe [9/20]

14 Pier Road, Whitby YO21 3JN
WHITBY (0947) 602058 £8–£14

Whitby is famed for the quality of its fish and for the skills of its fryers. This
Georgian café overlooking the harbour has in recent years been regarded as the
pick. Fish is from the local boats, of course. The menu has everything from grills
and salads to a choice of some thirty home-made sweets. Pots of tea come
automatically. House wine is £5.50.

CHEFS/PROPRIETORS: Sheila and Ian McKenzie
OPEN: all week CLOSED: Nov to week before Easter MEALS: 11.30am to 6.30pm
PRICES: £10 (£14), Set L from £4·95 (£8)
SEATS: 95. Private parties: 47 main room. Vegetarian meals. Children's helpings.
No-smoking area

WHITLEY BAY Tyne and Wear map 7

Le Provencale [10/20]

183 Park View, Whitley Bay NE26 3RE
091-251 3567 £9–£23

If you are in Whitley Bay, this is where to eat. The Guijarros' small French
restaurant is almost Regency in style, with floral curtains and cloths. Lunches
are especially good value, with main courses from £2·35. The cooking is old-
school French: scallops Mornay; braised venison; salmon hollandaise.
Understandably, standards fluctuate with such a long menu, but service is
cheerful and the place is usually busy. House wine is £5·80.

CHEF: Michel Guijarro PROPRIETORS: Mr and Mrs M. Guijarro
OPEN: Mon to Sat, exc Mon L and Wed L CLOSED: 2 weeks in summer MEALS: 12 to 2, 7.30
to 9.45 (10.15 Sat)
PRICES: L £4 (£9), D £18 (£23), Set Mon D £9·95 (£15) CARDS: Access, Amex, Diners, Visa
SEATS: 26. Private parties: 26 main room. Children's helpings (L only). No children under 7.
Music

WICKHAM Hampshire map 2

▲ *The Old House* [12/20]

The Square, Wickham PO17 5JG
WICKHAM (0329) 833049 £22

Good, unpretentious French restaurants are rare enough, but for nearly two
decades the Skipwiths have kept up their standards in this Georgian house. The

atmosphere can be rather starched, but the menu is a relaxed, well-balanced collection of four dishes at each stage, and is neither over-fashionable nor over-dependent on cream or butter. Fish soup, cheese soufflé, roast quail, navarin of lamb, are typical. Skate is poached, flaked, tossed in a mustard and caper vinaigrette, and served as a salad. The wine list is similarly restrained, French and sensible. House Côtes du Rhône at £7·25 is also the CELLARMAN'S CHOICE.

CHEF: Nicholas Harman PROPRIETORS: Richard and Annie Skipwith
OPEN: Mon to Sat, exc Mon L and Sat L CLOSED: 2 weeks July to Aug, 1 week at Christmas, 2 weeks at Easter MEALS: 12 to 1.45, 7 to 9.30
PRICES: £16 (£22). Service inc CARDS: Access, Amex, Diners, Visa
SEATS: 35. Private parties: 35 main room, 14 private room. Car-park, 12 places. Children's helpings. No cigars/pipes in dining-room. Wheelchair access (also WC)
ACCOMMODATION: 10 rooms, all with bath/shower. B&B £45 to £70. Children welcome. Baby facilities. No pets. Garden. TV. Phone. Scenic. Doors close at 12

WILLERBY Humberside map 6

▲ Le Restaurant Français, Willerby Manor Hotel [13/20]

Well Lane, Willerby HU10 6ER
HULL (0482) 652616 £12–£22

In recent years Derek Baugh has dramatically lifted the cooking at this essentially business-oriented hotel. He trained at the Dorchester, and this shows in some elaborate dishes: a trio of mousses – chicken, pigeon and guinea-fowl – on a truffle and wild mushroom sauce, or a smoked salmon roulade filled with a prawn mousse and set on a sorrel sauce. Plates are octagonal, to show off the presentation. Lamb is impressive, and is sometimes served with its kidney and sweetbread. Norwegian lobsters also feature. Sweets are picturesque. Service, especially for Sunday lunch, can be rushed, but the set meals are especially good value. The wine list has a good breadth in 150 bins, launching off with Bocuse's choice of Loire wines at £6·50. CELLARMAN'S CHOICE: Mâcon-Villages '85, from Bocuse, £8·50.

CHEF: Derek Baugh PROPRIETORS: Willerby Manor Hotels Ltd and J. Townend and Sons Ltd
OPEN: all week, exc Sat L and Sun D MEALS: 12.30 to 1.45, 7 to 9.45
PRICES: £17 (£22), Set L £7·50 (£12), Set D £9 (£13) Snacks from £1·50 CARDS: Access, Amex, Visa
SEATS: 75. Private parties: 70 main room, 45 and 300 private rooms. Car-park, 250 places. Children's helpings. Smart dress preferred. Music. Air-conditioned
ACCOMMODATION: 41 rooms, all with bath/shower. B&B £49 to £60. Pets welcome. Garden. TV. Phone. Doors close at 1. Confirm by 10

WILLINGTON Durham map 7

Stile [new entry, zero rated]

97 High Street, Willington DL15 0PE
BISHOP AUCKLAND (0388) 746615 £9–£14

A dilapidated roadside cottage between Willington and Crook has been transformed into a country restaurant with an airy, Victorian-style conservatory and a sober dining-room. It seems quite a boon to the area. The kitchen can handle the old favourites convincingly: pâté-stuffed mushrooms; well-hung sirloin steak stuffed with Stilton; steak pie laced with red wine ('boeuf bourguignonne under a crust'). The menu also offers jugged hare, monkfish with bacon and tomatoes, and guinea-fowl. Vegetables are fresh; sweets include home-made sorbets and ice-creams. The short wine list doesn't stray much above £10. More reports, please.

CHEF: Jenny James PROPRIETORS: Mike Boustred and Jenny James
OPEN: Tue to Sun D, and Sun L CLOSED: first 2 weeks Sept MEALS: 12 to 2.15, 7 to 10.15
PRICES: £10 (£14), Set L £5·75 (£9) CARDS: Access, Visa
SEATS: 50. Private parties: 40 main room. Car-park, 14 places. Vegetarian meals. Children's helpings. No cigars/pipes in dining-room. Music

---

WILLITON Somerset   map 1

▲ *White House Hotel* [14/20]

Williton TA4 4QW
WILLITON (0984) 32306   £22

The Georgian house is rather more imposing than the unpretentious dining-room, but the cooking is resolutely provincial, in the French sense, and makes use of some fine local produce. The menu has even changed to offer specialities, augmented by dishes of the day, a sign of increasing emphasis on the restaurant, rather than the hotel, side and also, now, of the Smiths' twenty-one years' experience in building up a repertoire. Typically, food has been Provençal tarts; soufflé suissesse, using Gruyère, Parmesan and cream; wild salmon with sorrel; roast quail with grapes; venison with spiced plums. The cheeseboard includes many examples of the farmhouse revival. Sweets change daily, and favour the French style of short, dramatic tastes: ices, crème brûlée, fruits. The wine list is magnificent, with much pedigree drinking at affordable prices. Averys' champagne is sold by the glass; Gould-Campbell crusted port is passed after dinner. Among the greatest assets are those Dick Smith picks out, as house wines, from all the illustrious bottles: Jean Teiller's Ménétou-Salon '84 (a Pinot) or more traditionally, Fronsac, Château La Valade '80, in reds, and Armand Maby's La Fermade '85.

CHEFS/PROPRIETORS: Dick and Kay Smith
OPEN: all week, D only CLOSED: Nov to 17 May, exc weekends MEALS: 7.30 to 8.30
PRICES: Set D £16·60 (£22)
SEATS: 30. Private parties: 20 main room. Car-park, 20 places. Children's helpings. Wheelchair access
ACCOMMODATION: 13 rooms, 7 with bath/shower. Rooms for disabled. D, B&B £34 to £41. Deposit: £20. Pets welcome. TV [GHG]

WILMSLOW Cheshire   map 5

Yang Sing Bistro [new entry, zero rated]

70 Grove Street, Wilmslow SK9 1DS
WILMSLOW (0625) 528799   £16

This branch of the magnificent Yang Sing restaurant in Manchester is a garish clutter of mirrors and colourful Chinese prints. The menu here shows a much greater element of east meets west: coconut cream balls; lightly battered, fried crab-meat balls; jumbo prawns with a Szechuan sauce; steamed scallops on the shell, with garlic and black-bean sauce. Drama is the keynote. The sizzling fillet of steak with black pepper, which is, in essence, just steak au poivre, requires diners to take refuge behind the tablecloth to avoid the spitting. Dim-sum are reportedly good, too. Drink jasmine tea or Grolsch lager. The wine list is uninspired. More reports, please.

CHEF: Harry Yeung PROPRIETORS: Pemberange Ltd
OPEN: Tue to Sun, D only, and Sun L MEALS: 12 to 2.30, 6 to 11
PRICES: £10 (£16). Service 10%
SEATS: 80. Private parties: 80 main room. Vegetarian meals. Children welcome.
Music. Air-conditioned

WINCHCOMBE Gloucestershire   map 2

Corner Cupboard Dining Room [13/20]

Gloucester Street, Winchcombe GL54 5LX
WINCHCOMBE (0242) 602303   £18

The name is fairly apt. Christopher Wickens' tiny dining-room, part of the pub but not connected, is dominated by an enormous old stone fireplace, and characterised by dripping red candles and snapshots of wine-makers. The menu could hardly be shorter. It is decidedly British, more modern than traditional, with a superfluity of greens throughout, and excellent traditional puddings (his grapefruit cheesecake, which he used to make at Food For Thought at Cheltenham, is one of the best recipes in *The Good Food Guide Second Dinner Party Book*). The clash of differing thoughts is seen in a superb starter of cold asparagus on a salad of coloured lettuces, with home-made puff pastry (how rare these days), a silky smoked trout, and a sauce of yoghurt, dill and mustard. A casserole always features among main courses, which can be strikingly plain: roasts with thin sauces and unadorned vegetables; or perhaps a baked chicken breast, glazed with honey and mustard. The cheeses, by contrast, provide a high point – a pick of three of the best unpasteurised British farmhouse cheeses, perhaps Sharpham, Cerney, and Belstone, depending on the season. Sweets excel: sticky toffee pudding; walnut roulade; and what are essentially cake variations, served either with cream or yoghurt. The wine list is a scrapbook with labels pasted in and extensive handwritten information, with plenty of exclamation marks. All fifteen are under £10. House French is £5·25.

CHEF/PROPRIETOR: Christopher Wickens
OPEN: Tue to Sat, D only MEALS: 7.15 to 8.30
PRICES: Set D £12·95 (£18). Service 10%
SEATS: 16. Private parties: 16 main room. Children welcome. No smoking. Wheelchair access. Music

---

▮ *This symbol is awarded only to restaurants with outstanding wine cellars.*

The average price quoted in brackets is for an average three-course meal including service, VAT, coffee and half a bottle of house wine or the equivalent in an ethnic restaurant.

WINDERMERE Cumbria   map 7

▲ *Miller Howe* [15/20]

Rayrigg Road, Windermere LA23 1EY
WINDERMERE (096 62) 2536
on A592 between Windermere and Bowness   £29

John Tovey takes an increasingly executive role, but Robert Lyons runs the
kitchen (and Miller Howe Kaff, see below), with such energy and verve that
Miller Howe remains one of the great restaurants of the north. If the English have
a need to formalise dining out, then Miller Howe caters to this decadent tradition.
There is nothing man-made about the setting, overlooking Windermere, with
views of the central fells. There is a depth of scenery, just as there is a depth to the
extraordinary, ever-evolving, no-choice menus. In midstream, after a fruit salad
and a vegetable soup, meals can change tone for a third course of, say, salmon
with hollandaise, accompanied by a pastry boat of cream cheese and salmon roe.
The menu descriptions understate the vividness of the flavours. Roast breasts of
duck on a red pepper cream sauce, with a sage and onion stuffing, is no mound of
tiny pink slivers but a substantial, traditionally roasted portion, on a smooth
sauce, dressed with the traditionally flavoured stuffing and wonderfully arrayed
with the seven famous vegetables. Tovey says himself that the mood is away
from cream, and into old-fashioned stock sauces and gravies. 'Buying is still the
most important aspect of the kitchen.' At the end of the meal there is a choice of
sweets, although with a little cajoling, it is possible to taste a number:
sumptuous, sticky-toffee pudding with butterscotch sauce, or Nan's typsy trifle.
Saturday night has two sittings, alas, and the formula feels like a production
line. The wine list has moved away from South Africa to Australia and New
Zealand, with nightly choices matched to the food. Given the variety of flavours
involved, the recommendations can be followed with confidence.

CHEF: Robert Lyons PROPRIETOR: John J. Tovey
OPEN: all week, D only CLOSED: Dec to Feb MEALS: 8.30 (7 and 9.30 Sat)
PRICES: Set D £22 (£29). Service 12.5% CARDS: Access, Amex, Diners, Visa
SEATS: 70. Private parties: 30 main room. Car-park, 40 places. Vegetarian meals by
arrangement. No children under 12. Smart dress preferred. No smoking in dining-room.
Wheelchair access limited. Music. Air-conditioned
ACCOMMODATION: 13 rooms, all with bath/shower. D, B&B £55 to £190. No children under
12. Pets welcome. Afternoon teas. Garden. Scenic. Doors close at 11. Confirm by 10 [GHG]

Miller Howe Kaff [9/20] ✈

Lakeland Plastics, Station Precinct, Windermere LA23 1BQ
WINDERMERE (096 62) 2255   £8

Robert Lyons takes time off from Miller Howe (see above) to oversee this little café
in a corner of Lakeland Plastics, just behind the old Windermere railway station.
The up-market snacks offer glimpses of the Miller Howe menu from the night
before, at a fraction of the price. Salads come with home-made mayonnaise or
superb oily dressings, and there are fine pâtés, subtly flavoured soups, and a
couple of hot dishes, such as bobotie, or fresh sea trout on a provençale sauce.
Sweets are Tovey classics, such as sticky-toffee pudding, or Nan's typsy trifle.
Excellent value. Wines are from New Zealand, and £1·50 a glass.

CHEFS: Robert Lyons and Miller Howe kitchen PROPRIETORS: John J. Tovey and
Robert Lyons
OPEN: Mon to Sat, L only MEALS: 10 to 4
PRICES: £5 (£8)
SEATS: 28. Private parties: 28 main room. Car-park, 60 places. Vegetarian meals. Children
welcome. No smoking. Wheelchair access. Self-service

Roger's [13/20]

4 High Street, Windermere LA23 1AF
WINDERMERE (096 62) 4954   £19

Roger Pergl-Wilson's passion for fish and fondness for local produce come
together in fine dishes, such as salmon with ginger en croûte, Windermere char
with fresh herb sauce, and mousseline of plaice with spiced mussel cream sauce.
The style is French, with English overtones: there is a good showing of game, for
example, from venison with port and cranberries to roast pigeon breast with
mushrooms. The menu has also featured good starters, such as avocado with
Roquefort sauce and fresh orange, as well as impressive hot almond and apricot
pudding with butterscotch sauce. Careful choice of top ingredients is backed by
caring, serious cooking and beautiful presentation. The small dining-room has
been augmented by a room upstairs. Seventy-five wines include interesting
choices from small French vineyards. House Cordier is £5·90. CELLARMAN'S
CHOICE: white St-Joseph '83, from Grippat, £9·50.

CHEF: Roger Pergl-Wilson PROPRIETORS: Roger and Alena Pergl-Wilson
OPEN: Mon to Sat D, Mon to Sat L by arrangement MEALS: 7 to 10
PRICES: £12 (£19) CARDS: Access, Amex, Diners, Visa
SEATS: 24. Private parties: 28 main room. Children's helpings, Wheelchair access. Music

---

WISBECH Cambridgeshire   map 6

▲ Rose and Crown [13/20]

Market Place, Wisbech PE13 1DG
WISBECH (0945) 583187   £17–£22

London readers enthusiastically supported John Martin and Christopher Lennox-
Bland at Tourment d'Amour in Covent Garden; now they have taken over this
established roast and two veg. hotel that is at the heart of Wisbech. The contrast
in styles could not be greater, yet this could be the best hotel restaurant in East
Anglia. The building is old and black, the first-floor restaurant sleek and filled
with flowers. The menu is modern, with a little needless French artifice, but a lot
of modern British gusto: roast pigeon with rhubarb compote; salmon wrapped in
spinach; wonderful cheeses. The sweets platter brings five miniatures: brandy-
snap, lemon mousse with its sauce, strawberry mille-feuille, kiwi and pineapple
sablé, ice-cream with raspberry coulis. The 140 wines concentrate almost
exclusively on France, being long on familiar names in claret and burgundy.
House wine is from £6·50 a bottle.

---

*Files are kept on every restaurant, so reports of poor meals are just as valuable as
reports of good meals because they save unnecessary inspections.*

CHEF: Christopher Lennox-Bland PROPRIETORS: John Martin and David Owens
OPEN: all week MEALS: 12.30 to 2, 7.30 to 10
PRICES: £16 (£22), Set D £12 (£17), Snacks from £2 CARDS: Access, Amex, Diners, Visa
SEATS: 60. Private parties: 14 main room, 20, 60 and 100 private rooms. Car-park,
10 places. Vegetarian meals. Children's helpings. Smart dress preferred. Wheelchair access
(also WC). Music
ACCOMMODATION: 21 rooms, 18 with bath/shower. B&B £22 to £34. Children welcome.
Baby facilities. Pets welcome. Afternoon teas. TV. Phone. Doors close at 12

WITHERSLACK Cumbria   map 7

▲ *Old Vicarage* [14/20]

Witherslack LA11 6RS
WITHERSLACK (044 852) 381
off A590; follow signs to Witherslack
church   £22

A mile and a half off the Kendal to Barrow road, this small, secluded, comfortable,
country house now aspires to compete with the élite of the Lakes. The
Burrington-Browns and the Reeves run it in tandem. The no-choice menu is a
remarkable example of modern British cooking. Excellent home-made bread
comes with the vegetable soups, perhaps cauliflower flavoured with turmeric
and aniseed, or tomato and basil. Centrepiece meats are usually roasted but
offered with vigorous relishes – duck with curaçoa; guinea-fowl with redcurrant
and a bread sauce; chicken with ginger and lime – and fine vegetables. Tumbet,
which often features, is a Majorcan dish of baked onions, aubergines, tomatoes,
potatoes and red peppers. The only choice is at the end of the meal, between a hot
and a cold pudding; plum pudding with Cumberland butter, apricot and pecan-
nut pudding, as well as the Pavlovas and cream. English cheese follows and
Kendal mints come with the coffee and teas. The style is almost homely, but not
quite. Similarly the wine list is deep and characterful, representing a huge
investment – a complete run of '85 Beaujolais, a choice of four Chablis, and so
on. Wines of the month are picked out to complement the food. Look also for the
Hugel Alsace wines. CELLARMAN'S CHOICE: Médoc, Ch. La Lagune '78,
£29·90; St Estèphe, Ch. Cos d'Estournel '78, £25·75; Torres, Gran Coronas,
Reserva '81, £10.

CHEFS/PROPRIETORS: Roger and Jill Burrington-Brown, Irene and Stanley Reeve
OPEN: all week, D only CLOSED: 1 week at Christmas MEALS: 7.30
PRICES: Set D £16·50 (£22) CARDS: Access, Amex, Diners, Visa
SEATS: 40. Private parties: 25 main room, 12 private room. Car-park, 18 places. Vegetarian
meals. No smoking in dining-room. Music. One sitting
ACCOMMODATION: 7 rooms, all with bath/shower. B&B £35 to £50. Pets by arrangement.
Afternoon teas. Garden. TV. Phone. Scenic

Restaurants rating 12 or more serve the best food in the region.

*The entries are compiled from the views of readers who have eaten at the restaurants in
the last year, backed up by anonymous inspections and by information supplied and
facts verified by the restaurants.*

WOBURN Bedfordshire	map 3

Crispins [10/20]

22–23 Market Place, Woburn MK17 9PZ	
WOBURN (052 525) 516	£13–£20

The Manns' converted butcher's shop has a strong local following for its long menu with a vegetarian bias. The cooking is English, old and new. Pies, stews and game feature in winter. More complex are smoked chicken mousse, chicken breast en croûte, or rich rum and chocolate mousse to finish. The beams and the log fire add atmosphere. Twenty-five wines, from £5·95.

CHEF: David Mann PROPRIETORS: David and Gina Mann
OPEN: all week MEALS: 12.15 to 2, 7.30 to 9.30 (7 to 10 Sat)
PRICES: Set L from £9 (£13), Set D £14·75 (£20), Snacks from £2·75 CARDS: Access, Amex, Diners, Visa
SEATS: 56. 3 tables outside. Private parties: 28 main room, 14 private room. Vegetarian meals. Children's helpings. No cigars/pipes in dining-room. Wheelchair access. Music

Paris House [14/20]

Woburn MK17 9QP	
WOBURN (052 525) 692	
1½m E of Woburn in Abbey grounds	£19–£26

The black and white timber folly, built originally for the 1878 Paris Exhibition, then dismantled piece by piece and placed in a field near the abbey, has its own entrance on the east side of the town. Peter Chandler's cooking might also have been picked up and transported from the kitchens of his mentors, the Roux brothers. Set dinners stroll through the evening at about the same speed as the Père David deer in the grounds adopt to graze from one tree to the next. A Sunday lunch can run on until five. The sauces are signature Roux brothers: almost metallic for crustacea; a sticky glaze for beef and lamb. Chandler's own special skill is in decorative sweets, notably his tulipe en fantaisie – spun sugar over a tuile filled with ice-cream and fruit with another feathered fruit coulis – and the waves of petits fours. Before these come salmon, still his main choice of fish, as a salad, as a mousse, as a hure, with fennel, with lobster sauce. Much of the art of the menu is surprisingly and happily angled towards the bourgeois: duck rillettes; poulet à la Basquaise; rabbit in cider. Ingredients are impeccable and the service professional, if lacking personality. The house Duboeuf is £8 on a pricey list. CELLARMAN'S CHOICE: Cabernet d'Anjou '85, £11; Madiran, Château Montus '79, £13.

CHEF/PROPRIETOR: Peter Chandler
OPEN: Tue to Sun, exc Sun D CLOSED: Feb MEALS: 12.30 to 2.30 (12 to 2 Sun), 7 to 10
PRICES: Set L £13·50 (£19), Set D £19·50 (£26) CARDS: Access, Amex, Diners, Visa
SEATS:40. 3 tables outside. Private parties: 40 main room, 16 private room. Car-park, 20 places. Vegetarian meals. Children welcome. Smart dress preferred

All inspections are carried out anonymously.

Report forms are at the back of the book.

WOODBRIDGE Suffolk map 3

Wine Bar [10/20]

17 Thoroughfare, Woodbridge IP12 1AA
WOODBRIDGE (039 43) 2557 £12

Above Suffolk Larder, an excellent provisions shop. The wine bar is colourfully done out, with a yellow ceiling, emerald green walls and dark blue chairs contrasting with the old wooden beams and pillars. Sally O'Gorman changes her menu every week, cooking to order, and offers exceptional value. Dishes are enterprising and look good: walnut roulade is filled with mustard hollandaise; a timbale of minced lamb with aubergine purée comes with a red-pepper sauce; plaice is cooked with basil and tomato. Fruit tarts and unusual ice-creams, such as toffee or lavender, to finish. The handwritten list of around forty wines is developing, with the accent strongly on the £6 area.

CHEF: Sally O'Gorman PROPRIETORS: Sally O'Gorman and Richard Lane
OPEN: Tue to Sat CLOSED: 25 and 26 Dec MEALS: 12 to 2, 7 to 10
PRICES: £8 (£12)
SEATS: 50. Vegetarian meals. No children under 14. Music

WOODSTOCK Oxfordshire map 2

▲ *Feathers Hotel* [12/20]

Market Street, Woodstock OX7 1SX
WOODSTOCK (0993) 812291 £16–£27

The hotel is a fine old building with low beams and a rabbit warren of rooms filled with interesting furniture. There is a lot of praise for imaginative modern cooking, which is in tune with the British revival: home-made soups; fresh vegetables (including, perhaps, roast parsnips, and broccoli with pine nuts); the roast beef; chicken with orange and basil, or with leeks in madeira sauce; duck with a redcurrant and green peppercorn sauce. Sweets reinforce the British theme, with rhubarb mousse, treacle tart with lemon cream, and pear and walnut crumble. The thick, creamy chocolate mousse has been good, too. The real value of the wine list is at the expensive end, but watch for wines such as Rioja, Cerro Añon Reserva '78, from Olarra, at £9·25. CELLARMAN'S CHOICE: Ch. Coufran '79, £14·75.

CHEF: Sonya Kidney PROPRIETOR: Gordon Campbell-Gray
OPEN: all week MEALS: 12.15 to 2.15, 7.15 to 9.45 (10.15 Sat)
PRICES: £20 (£27), Set L from £10·50 (£16), Set D £15·50 (£21), Snacks from £1·45
CARDS: Access, Amex, Diners, Visa
SEATS: 35. 6 tables outside. Private parties: 10 main room, 40 private room. Vegetarian meals. Children's helpings. Wheelchair access
ACCOMMODATION: 16 rooms, all with bath/shower. B&B £40 to £68. Children welcome. Baby facilities. Pets welcome. Afternoon teas. Garden. TV. Phone. Scenic. Doors close at 12. Confirm by 4 [GHG]

CELLARMAN'S CHOICE: *This is a wine recommended by the restaurateur which is more expensive than the house wine but is good value and fitting for the kind of food served.*

WOOLER Northumberland

map 7

▲ *Ryecroft Hotel* [10/20]

Wooler NE71 6AB
WOOLER (0668) 81459 £8–£15

This small hotel with eleven bedrooms does good-value set meals. The menu changes daily but stays with the style of game pie and chicken Maryland. Sweets are a feature. House Bulgarian is £4·50. CELLARMAN'S CHOICE: Sancerre, Domaine des Cotelins '85, £6·95.

CHEFS: Pat McKechnie and Michael Ord PROPRIETORS: Pat and David McKechnie
OPEN: Wed to Sat, D only, and Sun L CLOSED: first 2 weeks Nov, 24 Dec to 1 Jan
MEALS: 12.30 to 1.30, 7 to 8.30
PRICES: Set L £5 (£8), Set D £12 (£15) CARDS: Access, Visa
SEATS: 50. Private parties: 30 main room, 20 private room. Car-park, 20 places. Vegetarian meals. Children's helpings. No smoking in dining-room
ACCOMMODATION: 11 rooms. B&B £25 to £40. Deposit: £5. Children welcome. Baby facilities. Pets welcome. Afternoon teas. Garden. Scenic. Doors close at 12. Confirm by 6

WOOLHOPE Hereford & Worcester

map 2

▲ *Butchers Arms* [10/20]

Woolhope HR1 4RF
FOWNHOPE (043 277) 281
off B4224, 7m SE of Hereford £15

An ancient half-timbered inn that has moved on from pub clichés by offering good English cooking. Woolhope pie – rabbit and bacon cooked in local cider – is the house speciality, but the kitchen can also deliver good mushroom soup, Mediterranean king prawns with garlic, and pork tenderloin in cream and brandy sauce. To finish, there's a stunning meringue dessert. Drink Hook Norton or Marston's.

CHEF: Mary Bailey PROPRIETORS: Mary Bailey and Bill Griffiths
OPEN: Wed to Sat, D only MEALS: 7 to 9
PRICES: £11 (£15), Snacks from £1·95
SEATS: 70. 7 tables outside. Private parties: 26 main room. Car-park, 80 places. Vegetarian meals. No cigars/pipes in dining-room. Music
ACCOMMODATION: 3 rooms. B&B £17·50 to £29. TV. Scenic. Doors close at 11.30 [GHG]

WORCESTER Hereford & Worcester

map 2

Brown's [12/20]

24 Quay Street, Worcester WR1 2JN
WORCESTER (0905) 26263 £19–£25

This romantic, spacious old corn-mill overlooks the river. The menu of twenty dishes is modern, using many herbs, organic salads, reduction sauces, and has a refreshing combustion about it. Typical dishes might be a warm duck salad; crab with radicchio, endive, and oak-leaf lettuce; salmon with tarragon sauce. But the plainer items, like smoked salmon, grilled fillet of beef, cheeses, are equally attractive. A serious list of wines starts at £6·95. CELLARMAN'S CHOICE: Riesling, Cuvée des Seigneurs '83, £11·50.

CHEFS: W. R. Tansley and S. Meredith PROPRIETORS: W. R. and P. M. Tansley
OPEN: all week, exc Sat L and Sun D CLOSED: 1 week at Christmas, bank hols
MEALS: 12.30 to 1.45 (2 Sun), 7.30 to 9.30
PRICES: Set L £13·95 (£19), Set D £18·95 (£25). Service 10% CARDS: Access, Amex, Visa
SEATS: 80. Private parties: 80 main room. Vegetarian meals. No children under 5.
Wheelchair access (also WC)

WORFIELD Shropshire

map 5

▲ *Old Vicarage Hotel* [new entry, zero rated]

Worfield WV15 5TZ
WORFIELD (074 64) 497 and 498   £16–£23

When Peter Iles was made redundant, he turned his spacious Edwardian house into a hotel. There is a small dining-room filled with twentieth-century dark oak. Five-course dinners reflect the thoughtfulness of the hotel-keeping. The menu is English: veal terrine with pickled damsons; poached turbot rolled in crushed hazelnuts; lamb with onion sauce; trifle. Meats tend to be well cooked; cheeses are English. Mr Iles serves and his wife, Christine, cooks alongside chef Raymond Williamson. Plenty of half-bottles help the wine list. House burgundy is £7·25. More reports, please.

CHEF: Raymond Williamson PROPRIETORS: Peter and Christine Iles
OPEN: all week CLOSED: 2 weeks at Christmas MEALS: 12.30 to 2, 7 to 9
PRICES: Set L £10·95 (£16), Set D £17·50 (£23), Snacks from £1·25 CARDS: Access, Amex, Diners, Visa
SEATS: 36. Private parties: 50 main room, 15 private room. Car-park, 30 places. Vegetarian meals. No children under 10. No smoking in dining-room. Wheelchair access (1 step; also WC). Music
ACCOMMODATION: 10 rooms, all with bath/shower. B&B £40 to £60. Deposit: £30. Children welcome. Baby facilities. Afternoon teas. Garden. TV. Phone. Scenic

---

WRIGHTINGTON Lancashire

map 5

The High Moor [12/20]

High Moor Lane, Wrightington WN6 9PS
APPLEY BRIDGE (025 75) 2364   £12–24

John Nelson's restaurant looks over the moors to Wigan. The building dates from 1642, and the dining-room is respectful to the history – tables are laid out with standard napkins and money has gone into the appointments. The menu is ambitiously modern – lamb with kidneys in a brioche, fillet of beef with garlic – although the service and execution may not always keep pace. There are good reports of salmon roulade with crab and avocado mousse, and dark chocolate cake with rum truffle. Wine mark-ups can be as Gothic as the script on the

---

All letters to the Guide *are acknowledged.*

---

menu: £49 for Ch. Gruaud-Larose '73! Even CELLARMAN'S CHOICE, a Vin de Pays des Côtes de Gascogne '85, is £7·50.

CHEF: James Sines PROPRIETOR: John Nelson
OPEN: Tue to Sun, exc Sat L and Sun D MEALS: 12 to 2, 7 to 10
PRICES: £17 (£24), Set Sun L £7·50 (£12) CARDS: Access, Amex, Diners, Visa
SETA: 65. Private parties: 52 main room. Car-park, 35 places. Vegetarian meals. Children welcome. Wheelchair access. Music. Air-conditioned

---

WYMONDHAM Norfolk
map 6

Adlard's [16/20]

16 Damgate Street, Wymondham NR18 0BQ
WYMONDHAM (0953) 603533
 £20

The Adlards' small, cluttered cottage restaurant is now recognised as one of the finest in East Anglia. The décor is grandmotherly and informal, but Mary Adlard manages to squeeze most people into the rickety chairs. David Adlard is an exceptional cook. His repertoire is based on a classical French training, allied to what might be called country cooking. Quail eggs on pastry with hollandaise; veal with ginger and lime; excellent poultry, and caramelised apple tart all stand out. The menu is short, offering three dishes at three courses, plus optional cheese or salad, but there is genuine choice. The wine list is equally remarkable, grouped by style, kind on prices, and brimming with goodies from Tiefenbrunner, Coste, Duboeuf, Jaboulet, Chapoutier, Bize. From the New World come Australian Semillon, Moss Wood '85, and Californian Chardonnay, Trefethen '81. CELLARMAN'S CHOICE: Mâcon-Villages, Domaine de la Bon Gran '84, at £12 (£6·10 per half-bottle).

CHEF: David Adlard PROPRIETORS: David and Mary Adlard
OPEN: Tue to Sat, D only MEALS: 7.30 to 9
PRICES: Set D from £16 (£20). Service inc
SEATS: 25. Private parties: 22 main room. Children welcome. Air-conditioned

---

YARM Cleveland
map 7

Santoro [new entry, zero rated]

47 High Street, Yarm TS15 9BH
EAGLESCLIFFE (0642) 781305
£11–£19

A well-heeled international restaurant with a strong Italian flavour and a dining-area on a raised dais. Pasta is good: try tortellini in a Pecorino cheese sauce. The sweets trolley is heavy with home-made Italian confections: orange cream cheese soufflé; black cherries in cherry brandy topped with whipped cream and grated walnuts. In between, main courses rely on heavy sauces bolstered with cream, alcohol and black pepper. Meals begin with a pile of garlic bread and end with plenty of good strong coffee. House burgundy is £6·30 a bottle. More reports, please.

Restaurants that we have not been able to assess as fully as we would like are given a zero rating this year. We are particularly keen to have reports on these places.

CHEF: David Brownless PROPRIETOR: Vince Serino
OPEN: Mon to Sat, exc Sat L MEALS: 12 to 2, 7 to 10
PRICES: L £6 (£11), D £13 (£19), Set D £9·50 (£14). Service 10% CARDS: Access, Amex,
Diners, Visa
SEATS: 65. Private parties: 60 main room. Vegetarian meals. Children's helpings. Music

---

YATTENDON Berkshire   map 2

▲ *Royal Oak* [15/20]

The Square, Yattendon RG16 0UF
HERMITAGE (0635) 201325   £23–£30

The Smiths have turned this local pub on the village square into one of the finest
venues in the Home Counties. It is all things to all people, and all the better for it;
it still retains its pub status, but is also like a compact country-house hotel. There
is a small, formal dining-room, a lounge, a bar, and tables outside. The kitchen
cooks the same menu for each. The cooking is sharp, and essentially modern
British with a few French frills: soufflés – spinach with crab sauce, or plain with a
wild mushroom sauce – before sole and monk, seared and served in a saffron
sauce with asparagus, or venison with confit of shallots and chestnuts. Huge
trays of vegetables accompany main courses. To finish there is rice pudding or
lemon pudding with custard. The subtlety of the cooking is seen in dishes like
warm pancakes, with spiced plums and a scoop of ice-cream. It is possible to eat
crab salad or fish soup in the bar. Pedigree wines at pedigree prices have the
saving grace that, with certain bottles, you can drink just half, and be charged
half the price, plus 75p. Glasses of bin-ends are £2.

CHEF: Richard Smith PROPRIETORS: Richard and Kate Smith
OPEN: all week (bar menu only, Sun D) MEALS: 12 to 2, 7.30 to 10
PRICES: £20 (£30), Set L and D from £17·50 (£23) CARDS: Access, Amex, Visa
SEATS: 36. 10 tables outside. Private parties: 30 main room, 8 and 14 private rooms. Car-
park, 35 places. Children's helpings. No cigars/pipes in dining-room. Wheelchair access
ACCOMMODATION: 5 rooms, all with bath/shower. B&B £40 to £60. Baby facilities. Pets
welcome. Afternoon teas. Garden. TV. Phone. Scenic. Confirm by 6.30

YORK North Yorkshire   map 5

▲ *Middlethorpe Hall* [12/20]

Bishopthorpe Road, York YO2 1QP
YORK (0904) 641241
1½m outside city, by racecourse   £12–£32

The mansion dates from 1699 and has been superbly restored to a state of
elegant grandeur (like Bodysgallen Hall at Llandudno, owned by the same
group). A haughty stone eagle looks down from the roof; inside are exquisite
flower arrangements, oversized oil paintings, and classy antiques. The beautiful,
panelled dining-room is on a small scale, with a large marble fireplace and silver

---

*All details are as accurate as possible at the time of going to press. Please notify the
Guide office of any changes.*

---

candlesticks. The grill has opened again, with a set menu and simpler dishes. This may prove to be a good bet, as the cooking is excellent when it steers clear of too many fancy ideas: smoked duck with beetroot mousse is simple and full of flavour; collops of beef with shallots comes with a fine reduced sauce of juices; medallions of veal are successfully married to raspberries. Puddings can be less impressive when, in common with other hotels, all the effort put into the visuals overtakes the tastes, and flavours can verge on the genteel. Not so the wine list, which is massive, and contains an assemblage of famous vintages and champagnes – almost mandatory now, with country-house hotels. House Merlot and Chardonnay are, at £8·50, at the foot of a very fast, steep climb, financially. Service is from well-disciplined Yorkshire lads and lasses.

CHEF: Aidan McCormack PROPRIETORS: Historic House Hotels Ltd
OPEN: all week MEALS: 12.30 to 1.45, 7.30 to 9.45
PRICES: £26 (£32), Set L from £13 (£13), Set D from £19·50 (£24). Service inc
CARDS: Access, Amex, Diners, Visa
SEATS: 60. Private parties: 40 main room, 14, 20 and 40 private rooms. Car-park, 70 places. Vegetarian meals. No children under 8. Jacket and tie
ACCOMMODATION: 31 rooms, all with bath/shower. Lift. B&B £72 to £99. No children under 8. Afternoon teas. Garden. TV. Phone. Scenic

---

Oat Cuisine [new entry, zero rated]

13A High Ousegate, York YO1 2RZ
YORK (0904) 27929   £11–£14

Louisa Farino and David Harley's menus may look like American Express brochures, but they point up just how far wholefood cookery has come from brown rice and bare floorboards. This is a serious restaurant that happens to cook without meat. The décor carries on the sleek profile: plain black floor-tiles and matt black metal chairs contrast with the all-white walls, with a slight softening produced by tiny pink flowers in white vases, each lit by a miniature pink spotlight shining down from the ceiling. There is no shortage of imagination on the menu – asparagus flummery in filo; vegetable fondue – and the thoughtfulness runs to still warm wholemeal cheese scones with celeriac soup, and courgette and mushroom lasagne. Mexican dishes also figure, and to finish there have been fine strudels and cheesecakes. Fourteen interesting wines, mostly between £5 and £7. More reports, please.

CHEF: Neil David Harley PROPRIETOR: Louisa Farino
OPEN: Mon to Sat CLOSED: first week Jan MEALS: 12 to 3, 7 to 10.30
PRICES: £9 (£14), Set L £7·25 (£11). Minimum £2·50 at L, £4·50 at D. Service 10%
CARDS: Access, Amex, Visa
SEATS: 56. Private parties: 25 main room. Vegetarian meals. Children's helpings. No-smoking area. Wheelchair access (1 step). Music

Scotland

Atlantis [new entry, zero rated]

16 Bonaccord Crescent,
Aberdeen AB1 2HR
ABERDEEN (0224) 591403   £22

In a basement not far from the fish market, Ian Wilson takes full advantage of the location to serve a handsome fish menu. Staff are friendly and the service polished. The strengths are fine basic ingredients – lobsters are kept in an aquarium – and the kind of dexterous technique that wins catering prizes evident in mousselines and roulades. Moneybags of seafood set on a light curry sauce work well as does turbot stuffed with creamed leeks, poached and served with a rich saffron butter sauce, or scallops and monk-fish together in a vermouth cream sauce sharpened with fennel. The expertise extends to beautiful-looking sweets such as raspberry and pear parfait, or brandy baskets filled with fresh strawberries on a raspberry coulis. The wine list by comparison is basic, with only a dozen bottles. House Muscadet is £6 a litre.
CELLARMAN'S CHOICE: Riesling Réserve '85, £11·50. More reports, please.

CHEF: Ian Wilson PROPRIETOR: David Edwards
OPEN: Mon to Sat CLOSED: Christmas and New Year MEALS: 12 to 2, 6 to 10
PRICES: £16 (£22) CARDS: Access, Amex, Diners, Visa
SEATS: 34. Private parties: 34 main room. Car-park, 12 places. Vegetarian meals. Children's helpings

---

Braeval Old Mill [new entry, zero rated]

By Aberfoyle FK8 3UY
ABERFOYLE (087 72) 711
on A81, Callander road, 1m from
Aberfoyle   £16

Made from local stone, this old mill still has the wheel on the side of the building. A large wood-burning stove divides the dining-room, which has a stone floor and interesting wall hangings made by Mrs Nairn's mother. Nick Nairn cooks a wide-ranging, home-produced menu from falafel with a sesame, garlic and yoghurt dip to a little casserole of mussels in a mushroom and white wine sauce and terrine of wood-pigeon and chicken, all served with wholewheat bread. Main dishes are hearty; vegetables fresh, if well cooked and swimming in butter. To finish, there may be fresh fruit Pavlova, Cranachan, and profiteroles with caramel and chocolate sauce. Coffee comes with a slab of Scottish fudge. The fifty wines don't stretch the pocket but do run to Australia for CELLARMAN'S CHOICE: Seppelt Shiraz Black Label '82, £8·25. More reports, please.

CHEF: Nick Nairn PROPRIETORS: Nick and Fiona Nairn
OPEN: Tue to Sun, D only CLOSED: 4 Jan to Feb, 1 to 12 Nov MEALS: 7 to 9.30
PRICES: £13 (£16). Service inc CARDS: Access, Amex, Visa
SEATS: 34. Private parties: 34 main room. Car-park, 16 places. Smart dress preferred.
Wheelchair access (also WC). Music

ACHILTIBUIE Highland   map 8

▲ *Summer Isles Hotel* [11/20]

Achiltibuie IV26 2YG
ACHILTIBUIE (085 482) 282
26m N of Ullapool   £24

The smokehouse has moved around the bay. Father Robert Irvine is immersed in his hydroponicum supplying vegetables, fruit and flowers, but the style at the restaurant remains much the same though run now by Mark and Geraldine. The menu is modern British. Five courses can include chilled avocado and grapefruit soup with hot onion loaf; Stilton soufflé; scallops with asparagus in vermouth sauce; a choice of puddings; then cheese. A variety of breads is baked in-house, and fish from the bay opposite is lightly handled. Wine is opened to match the food and served by the glass. Otherwise there are bargains among the claret, which is the mainstay of the cellar, and good support from the major French regions. CELLARMAN'S CHOICE: Sancerre, Clos du Chêne Marchand, Crochet '85, £11·50.

CHEF: Chris Firth-Bernard PROPRIETORS: Mark and Geraldine Irvine
OPEN: all week, D only CLOSED: mid-Oct to Easter MEALS: 7.30
PRICES: Set D £19 (£24). Service inc
SEATS: 28. Private parties: 8 main room. Car-park, 24 places. Vegetarian meals. No children
under 8. No smoking in dining-room. One sitting
ACCOMMODATION: 13 rooms, 11 with bath/shower. B&B £17 to £56. Deposit: £30. No
children under 8. Pets welcome. Afternoon teas. Fishing. Scenic. Doors close at 10.30.
Confirm by 6 [GHG]

ANSTRUTHER Fife   map 8

The Cellar [13/20]

24 East Green, Anstruther KY10 3AA
ANSTRUTHER (0333) 310378   £13–£31

Peter and Vivien Jukes' low-ceilinged, narrow restaurant in the old part of town is filled with old sewing-machines for tables. Fine use is made of local and other Scottish fish in the form of crab, turbot, scallops, lobster, and so on – usually handled simply, the best way. The choice of fine wines is as extensive as the catch – especially so in Alsace and Burgundy.

CHEF: Peter Jukes PROPRIETORS: Peter and Vivien Jukes
OPEN: Mon to Sat, exc Mon L CLOSED: Christmas MEALS: 12.30 to 1.30, 7.30 to 9.30
PRICES: L £8 (£13), Set D £9·95 (£15) to £25 (£31) CARDS: Access, Amex, Visa
SEATS: 32. Private parties: 32 main room. Children's helpings. No cigars/pipes in dining-room. Wheelchair access (also WC). Music

---

ABROATH Tayside   map 8

Carriage Room [11/20]

Montrose Road, Arbroath DD11 5RA
ARBROATH (0241) 75755   £9–£21

The Carriage Room is part of a complex, with a transport cafe-style forecourt. It has been here in its present form since 1980, but in that time chef Stephen Collinson has been away and is now back. He is prepared to be more adventurous than most (it is still possible to get trout with gravy if you are unlucky around these parts). The room is large, broad, with tables arranged around the walls in a horseshoe. They know how to dress a table. The menu is modern, a bit of French, a bit of flair, a bit of Scottish. The bread rolls are granary and hot. The mussel soup is good, vegetable soup likewise. Chicken breast is slit in two, poached, and filled with Emmental. There are some very pretty fish – turbot garnished with three scampi, sole fillets rolled around salmon mousse. Steak au poivre is of a standard. Exotic fruits, from papaya to passion to sharon, are sliced and spread around vanilla ice-cream; soft meringue is filled with cream and, like Carmen Miranda, topped with fruit; there is banana in the bread-and-butter pudding. Wine prices stay within reason, from Portugal to New Zealand, and the notes suggest what to drink them with. CELLARMAN'S CHOICE: Pouilly-Loché '85, £11·95.

CHEF: Stephen Collinson PROPRIETOR: Ian R. Stirling
OPEN: Tue to Sat, exc Sat L CLOSED: 1 week Jan, 2 weeks in summer
MEALS: 12 to 2, 7.15 to 9.30
PRICES: £16 (£21), Set L from £5·75 (£9), Set D £13·50 (£17) CARDS: Access, Amex, Diners, Visa
SEATS: 56. Private parties: 60 main room. Car-park, 150 places. Children's helpings. Smart dress preferred. No smoking. Wheelchair access (also WC). Music

---

ARDEONAIG Central   map 8

▲ Ardeonaig Hotel [10/20]

Ardeonaig FK21 8SU
KILLIN (056 72) 400
7m NE of Killin on S of Loch Tay   £14

This remote drovers' inn on the bank of Loch Tay is looking a bit run down but provides good-value bar snacks and five-course dinners. As well as classic roast

---

Report forms are at the back of the book.

Aberdeen Angus beef, salmon with hollandaise, and haunch of venison with rowanberries, there are interesting touches like yellow pepper soup, cider sorbet, chocolate ginger gateau, and hot rolls, most of which seem to double on both menus. House wine is £4·88.

CHEF: Ellis Jones PROPRIETORS: Mr and The Hon Mrs John Russell
OPEN: all week CLOSED: Nov to Mar MEALS: 12.30 to 2, 8 to 8.45
PRICES: Set D from £11·50 (£14). Service inc
SEATS: 35. Car-park, 40 places. Vegetarian meals. Children's helpings. Jacket and tie.
One sitting
ACCOMMODATION: 14 rooms, all with bath/shower. B&B £20·50 to £41. Deposit: £20.
Children welcome. Baby facilities. Pets welcome. Afternoon teas. Garden. Fishing. Scenic.
Doors close at 11.30. Confirm by 6

ARISAIG Highland   map 8

▲ *Arisaig Hotel* [10/20]

Arisaig PH39 4NH
ARISAIG (068 75) 210 and 240   £8–£20

Local fish is the highlight of the menu at this carefully restored eighteenth-century inn by the shores of Loch Nan Ceal. The drive from Glenfinnan is spectacular. This is the more modest place in Arisaig, a comfortable hotel, but the food seems to have got an edge on its more illustrious neighbour, Arisaig House. Scallops are cooked within an hour of delivery, plaice is baked with clam sauce, halibut with lemon sauce. Otherwise there are Scottish meat and game dishes such as venison pâté, and beef olives with a whisky and haggis stuffing. Steaks and roasts are good, too. Sweets always include a traditional hot pudding. Short, adequate wine list with a few half-bottles; house French is £6·15 a carafe.

CHEFS: Janice and Gordon Stewart PROPRIETORS: Mr and Mrs George William Stewart
OPEN: all week CLOSED: Oct to Mar exc Christmas and New Year
MEALS: 12.30 to 2, 7.30 to 8.30
PRICES: L £8 (£13), Set L from £3 (£8), Set D from £14 (£20). Snacks from £1
SEATS: 50. Private parties: 12 main room. Car-park, 60 places. Vegetarian meals. Children's
helpings
ACCOMMODATION: 13 rooms, 3 with bath/shower. B&B £30 to £63·50. Children welcome.
Baby facilities. Pets welcome. Afternoon teas. Fishing. Phone. Scenic [GHG]

AUCHMITHIE Tayside   map 8

The But 'n' Ben [new entry, zero rated]

Auchmithie, by Arbroath DD11 5SQ
ARBROATH (0241) 77223
3m NE of Arbroath   £7–£13

Auchmithie was originally where Arbroath smokies started; a tiny fishing hamlet perched precariously over the cove. These would have been fishermen's

---

If, in your opinion, a restaurant is not maintaining the standard of its ratings please inform the Guide *office. Report forms are at the back of the book.*

---

cottages – a but 'n' ben is a two-roomed cottage. Margaret Horn is from the village and cooks throughout the day in proper Scottish fashion: soups of crab, of smokies; a deep broth made by boiling beef, barley and winter vegetables; cock-a-leekie are features. Baking results in an evening sweets trolley. The quality of the meat – Aberdeen Angus – and fish – from Spinks in Arbroath – is untouchable. Salmon is served with an orange sauce, smokies with butter or in a pancake, haddock in oatmeal. The cooking is generous and exact. On a night in May, fruits of the sea comprised: a fresh oyster, still closed but with a 'shucking' knife; a whole Arbroath smokie; six Dublin Bay prawns still in their shells; three prawns; a whole dressed crab; a piece of bread and butter heaped with smoked salmon; a smoked mackerel; a rollmop herring; and a small pot of Marie Rose sauce. Each item was prepared individually and was perfect – plus, the dish came with a salad, potatoes and vegetables. The basket of wholemeal bread is kept topped up through the meal. Lobsters are £10·50. There are fourteen wines from seven regions. House claret is £5·50. CELLARMAN'S CHOICE: Mâcon-Lugny, Les Charmes '84, £7·90. More reports, please.

CHEFS: Margaret and Angus Horn PROPRIETORS: Margaret, Iain and Angus Horn
OPEN: all week, exc Tue and Sun D MEALS: noon to 9.30pm
PRICES: L £4 (£7), D £10 (£13). Service inc
SEATS: 34. 2 tables outside. Private parties: 34 main room. Car-park, 10 places. Vegetarian meals. Children's helpings. Wheelchair access (also WC)

AUCHTERARDER Tayside   map 8

▲ *Auchterarder House* [10/20]

Auchterarder PH3 1DZ
AUCHTERARDER (076 46) 2939 and 3646
on B8062, NE of Auchterarder   £14–£18

A winding drive through rhododendrons and big beech and fir trees leads to Ian and Audrey Brown's red sandstone mansion designed in the Scottish-Jacobean style. Fires are kept burning, and the décor impresses with its panelling and carved door surrounds. The menu plays to the Scottish Tourist Board, opening with no fewer than five soups, including Hebridean broth with plenty of fish; then baked Tay salmon in a well-reduced buttery sauce, collops of beef, and saddle of hare with black grapes. The menu suggests a wine for each dish. Sweets include home-made ice-cream, deep fried and served with a butterscotch sauce. The wine list has a few petit château clarets and house wine at £6·95; there's also a large selection of malt whiskies.

Restaurants are graded on a scale of 1–20. In the category of 10–11 expect to find the best food in the locality. Ratings of 12 and more are given to restaurants we regard as serving the best food in the region.

Good vintages for drinking in 1988: Alsace '85, Beaujolais '86, Germany '85, petits chateaux clarets '81, lesser clarets '83.

Restaurants are not expected to solicit customers to send in reports. Please let us know if this happens to you.

CHEF: Paul Brown PROPRIETORS: Mr and Mrs Ian Brown
OPEN: all week MEALS: times by arrangement
PRICES: Set L from £9·50 (£14), Set D from £12·50 (£18) CARDS: Access, Amex, Carte Blanche, Diners, Visa
SEATS: 25. Private parties: 60 main room. Car-park, 40 places. Vegetarian meals. No children under 12. Jacket and tie. Wheelchair access
ACCOMMODATION: 11 rooms, all with bath/shower. Rooms for disabled. B&B £39 to £65. Deposit 25%. Afternoon teas. Garden. Fishing. TV. Phone. Scenic. Doors close at 11. Confirm by 5

BALLATER Grampian   map 8

▲ *The Green Inn* [12/20]

9 Victoria Road, Ballater AB3 5QQ
BALLATER (0338) 55701   £16

The simply decorated house on the square is hung with local artists' pictures and dried flowers. Salad vegetables and herbs come out of the Hamiltons' garden; salmon out of the Dee is smoked by a gillie. The menu is unfussy, with good-quality main pieces set off by singular, definite sauces – the salmon with a mildly piquant one of chives, cream and wine, pork with a light cider and apple, venison with port and redcurrant. Other touches are country: terrines, smoked haddock pâté, overcooked vegetables. Sweets are homely: chocolate layer-cake, bread-and-butter pudding, apple crumble. Two dozen inexpensive wines manage to roam the world. CELLARMAN'S CHOICE: Dalwood Shiraz-Cabernet, Penfolds '83, £6·25.

CHEF: A. C. S. Hamilton PROPRIETORS: Mr and Mrs A. C. S. Hamilton
OPEN: all week `CLOSED: end Oct to mid-Mar MEALS: 12.30 to 2, 7 to 9.30
PRICES: £11 (£16), L Snacks from 75p
SEATS: 30. 2 tables outside. Private parties: 28 main room. Vegetarian meals. Children's helpings. Wheelchair access. Music. Air-conditioned
ACCOMMODATION: 3 rooms, all with bath/shower. B&B £17·50 to £30. Deposit: £10. Children welcome. Baby facilities. Pets welcome. Air-conditioning. TV. Scenic. Doors close at 11.30

▲ *The Oaks, Craigendarroch Hotel and Country Club*
[new entry, zero rated]

Braemar Road, Ballater AB3 5XA
BALLATER (0338) 55858
on A93, 1m W of Ballater   £17–£30

A leisure complex and time-share lodges have been grafted on to the main building of this pink stone mansion. Bill Gibb runs the kitchen and cooks impressively. Sauces are his forte, and presentation is thoughtfully artistic. Slices of free-range chicken are arranged on a bed of spinach with a champagne sauce; pink fillet of lamb gets two sauces – one cream and fennel, the other dark truffle. Sweets are the likes of orange bavarin cream and Drambuie beignet soufflé. Good cafetière coffee comes with home-made petits fours. The wine list helpfully explains pairings with food but is mainly over £10 a bottle. More reports, please.

CHEF: Bill Gibb PROPRIETORS: Intertown Leisure (Deeside) Ltd
OPEN: all week CLOSED: L 1 Nov to 31 Mar MEALS: 12.30 to 2, 7.30 to 10
PRICES: £24 (£30), Set L £12·50 (£17), Set D from £18·95 (£24). Minimum £18·95 at D.
Service inc CARDS: Access, Amex, Diners, Visa
SEATS: 54. Private parties: 12 main room, 120 private room. Car-park, 100 places. No
children under 8. Jacket and tie. No smoking in dining-room. Wheelchair access (also WC)
ACCOMMODATION: 29 rooms, all with bath/shower. Rooms for disabled. Lift. B&B £55 to
£69·50. Deposit: 50%. Children welcome. Baby facilities. No pets. Afternoon teas. Garden.
Swimming-pool. Sauna. Golf. Snooker. TV. Phone. Scenic. Confirm by 6 [GHG]

▲ Tullich Lodge [11/20]

Ballater AB3 5SB
BALLATER (0338) 55406
on A93, 1½m E of Ballater   £18–£19

The sea view is from the bedrooms rather than from the bar or dining-room. The
garden is natural but overgrown, which might be a comment on this solid
baronial fixture of the *Guide* for many years. Neil Bannister's cooking of four-
course dinners was an early example of modern British cookery: terrine of
sweetbreads with sweet-pickled gherkin, spring cabbage with fresh ginger and
smoked goose breasts, wild duck on brown lentils. Fish varies from haddock in a
seaweed parcel to baked bream in a red wine sauce. A good selection of British
cheeses – Barac, Lanark blue, Bonchester, for instance – vies for attention with
old-fashioned puddings of gooseberry dumpling with custard, or Brown Betty.
Service, as indeed everything else about the Lodge, gets more personalised. Forty
wines from £6 for the house wine.

CHEF: Neil Bannister PROPRIETORS: Hector MacDonald and Neil Bannister
OPEN: all week CLOSED: mid-Dec to mid-Mar MEALS: 1, 7.30 to 9
PRICES: Set L £15 (£18), Set D from £16 (£19), L Snacks from £4. Service inc
CARDS: Access, Amex
SEATS: 26. Private parties: 10 main room. Car-park. Vegetarian meals. Children's helpings (L
only). Jacket and tie. No smoking in dining-room. Wheelchair access (also WC)
ACCOMMODATION: 10 rooms, all with bath/shower. D, B&B £60 to £120. Garden. TV. Phone.
Scenic. Doors close at 1. Confirm by 5

BLAIR DRUMMOND Central   map 8

Broughton's [11/20]

Blair Drummond FK9 4XE
DOUNE (0786) 841897
on A873, ¼m W of Blair Drummond   £19

This is a country restaurant. The emphasis is on fish and game. Huge West Coast
mussels are served in a beery cream and garlic sauce; pike is stuffed with
walnuts, grapes and sage. Venison is prominent sauté with chestnuts and
garnished with mangoes, made into a pie, or cooked as a carbonnade on a bed of
tagliatelle. A pond has been added to the vegetable plot and Tony and Helen
Broughton hope to raise crayfish. A vegetarian option features regularly on the

Reports on good shops, hotels and cafes in your area are welcome.

good-value set menu. Sweets are home-made. The well-spread wine list has a strong showing of vintage clarets. CELLARMAN'S CHOICE: Ch. Cambon-la-Pelouse '79, £12·40.

CHEF: Helen Broughton PROPRIETORS: Tony and Helen Broughton
OPEN: Tue to Sat, D only CLOSED: 2 to 3 weeks early spring MEALS: 7 to 10
PRICES: Set D £13·75 (£19) CARD: Access
SEATS: 40. 2 tables outside. Private parties: 28 main room. Car-park, 20 places. Vegetarian meals. Children welcome. Wheelchair access (also WC)

BLAIRGOWRIE Tayside   map 8

▲ *Kinloch House Hotel* [new entry, zero rated]

By Blairgowrie PH10 6SG
ESSENDY (025 084) 237
3m W of Blairgowrie towards Dunkeld   £12–£19

A magnificent oak bar and a dining-room overlooking the water are the focal points of this well-maintained ivy-clad house, at the end of a rhododendron-lined drive. David Shentall presides in his kilt. The menu is long and old school – sauces come over the meats and fish – but uses the finest produce. Salmon is marinated in sugar, salt, herbs, honey, and whisky, and sliced in the dining-room. There is fine grouse and excellent steaks, and a classic Scottish sweets trolley. Service is first-rate and the cellar holds 240 wines from £4·85.
CELLARMAN'S CHOICE: Ch. La Tour de By '79, £9·95. More reports, please.

CHEF: Bill McNicoll PROPRIETORS: David and Sarah Shentall
OPEN: all week MEALS: 12.30 to 2, 7 to 9.15
PRICES: £8 (£12), Set D £14·50 (£19) CARDS: Access, Amex, Diners
SEATS: 60. Private parties: 30 main room, 25 and 30 private rooms. Car-park, 40 places. No children under 5. Smart dress preferred. No cigars/pipes in dining-room. Wheelchair access (also WC)
ACCOMMODATION: 13 rooms, all with bath/shower. B&B £29·50 to £44. Children welcome. Baby facilities. Pets welcome. Garden. Fishing. Phone. Scenic. Doors close at 12 [GHG]

CALLANDER Central   map 8

▲ *Roman Camp Hotel* [10/20]

Main Street, East End, Callander FK17 8BG
CALLANDER (0877) 30003   £13–£20

The historic hunting-lodge on the banks of the River Teith fills a gaping hole in Central Scotland. Inside it is all old woodwork and antique furniture, and even when meals move into one of their increasingly frequent eccentric patches one can always admire the ceiling painted according to a sixteenth-century pattern. The kitchen has developed some wacky ideas, such as boula boula soup, but is safer with a mild gazpacho, fine meats for main courses, less fine sauces, and the presentation is at its best by the calorific sweets. The Denzlers' ambitious

---

If you suspect that a restaurant is using processed food, always ask. It would be a contravention of the Trade Descriptions Act for the restaurant to lie.

---

emigration from Edinburgh seems poised between decline and regeneration. The Swiss wines add interest to the list. House French is £6·95 a litre.

CHEFS: Sami Denzler and Keith Mitchell   PROPRIETORS: Mr and Mrs Denzler
OPEN: all week   CLOSED: mid-Nov to mid-Feb   MEALS: 12.30 to 1.30 (2 Sun), 7 to 8.55
PRICES: Set L from £8·50 (£13), Set D from £17 (£20). Service inc
SEATS: 40. Private parties: 20 main room. Car-park, 30 places. No smoking in dining-room.
Wheelchair access
ACCOMMODATION: 14 rooms, all with bath/shower. Rooms for disabled. Lift. B&B £38 to
£76. Deposit: £20. Children welcome. Baby facilities. Pets welcome. Garden. Fishing. TV.
Phone. Scenic. Doors close at 11   [GHG]

CANONBIE Dumfries & Galloway   map 8

▲ *Riverside Inn* [13/20]

Canonbie DG14 0UX
CANONBIE (054 15) 295 and 512   £19

The Phillipses have modernised and improved this turn-of-the-century house and adjoining cottage until now it is among the most pleasant places to stay in the country. The cooking is without pretence and the bar meals justifiably widely known. In the dining-room, itself an addition, the menu is set-price, leaning strongly on fish and local ingredients: smoked trout pâté; monk-fish with mussels, tomato and garlic sauce, reduced to the same colour as the shells of the langoustine garnish; or roast venison with a bacon and herb pudding. Four vegetables are served. Sweets revive the great Borders history of rhubarb tansy or fruits in a choux bun coated with butterscotch sauce, slightly browned to produce a coffee effect. There is a freshness to the cooking that stands out. House red burgundy is £8·95, and so are three Australians from Rosemount, including Chardonnay '85. CELLARMAN'S CHOICE: Morgon, Domaine de Lathevalle '85, from Mommessin, at £9·60 (£4·95 for a half).

CHEFS/PROPRIETORS: Robert and Susan Phillips
OPEN: Mon to Sat   CLOSED: 2 weeks in Feb   MEALS: 12 to 2, 7.30 to 8.30
PRICES: Set D £14·50 (£19), Bar L from £3   CARDS: Access, Visa
SEATS: 28. 4 tables outside. Private parties: 28 main room. Car-park, 25 places. Vegetarian
meals. Children's helpings. No smoking in dining-room. Wheelchair access (also WC).
One sitting
ACCOMMODATION: 6 rooms, all with bath/shower. Rooms for disabled. B&B £34 to £48.
Deposit: £15. Children welcome. No pets. Garden. Tennis. Fishing. Air-conditioning. TV.
Scenic. Doors close at 11.30   [GHG]

COLONSAY Strathclyde   map 8

▲ *Isle of Colonsay Hotel* [10/20]

Colonsay PA61 7YP
COLONSAY (095 12) 316   £14

The Byrnes' business is hotel-keeping and they do it well. Lots of hot water is provided for walkers, golfers, and swimmers. And the cooking is honest. Half the vegetables are home-grown, and they make their own bread and marmalade. Dinner is a set menu. Colonsay oysters are fine, fresh and fat, and other shellfish is unsurpassed. Three-course dinners can include dishes such as carbonnade of beef, or steak and kidney pie. The ferry goes to Colonsay three times a week; next year (1989) this may be cut to once. The wine is thus restricted, but usually there will be CELLARMAN'S CHOICE: Ch. Lynch-Bages '73 at £14·65.

CHEF: Christa Byrne PROPRIETORS: Kevin and Christa Byrne
OPEN: all week MEALS: 12 to 1.30, 7.30 to 8
PRICES: Set D £11·75 (£14), Snacks from 70p. Service inc CARDS: Access, Amex, Diners, Visa
SEATS: 30. 3 tables outside. Private parties: 30 main room. Car-park, 30 places. Vegetarian meals. Children's helpings. No cigars/pipes in dining-room. Wheelchair access (also WC). One sitting
ACCOMMODATION: 11 rooms, 8 with bath/shower. Rooms for disabled. B&B £25 to £50. Deposit: £25. Children welcome. Baby facilities. Pets welcome. Afternoon teas. Garden. Fishing. Golf. Snooker. TV. Phone. Scenic [GHG]

CRINAN Strathclyde   map 8

▲ Lock 16, Crinan Hotel [11/20]

Crinan PA31 8SR
CRINAN (054 683) 235, 243 and 207   £21–£34

Tables are angled to the sunset and to the view out to sea from this fishing village. The formula is simple, and it works: a choice of starters – maybe Loch Craignish mussels – then lightly smoked wild salmon cut too thick to see the plate through it, then a large copper pan crammed with sizzling jumbo prawns, dotted plentifully with kiwi-fruit, pineapple and chunks of papaya. Pudding, cheese and coffee follow. There are bar meals and a *carte* at lunchtime, and three dozen white wines.

CHEF: Nick Ryan PROPRIETORS: Nick and Frances Ryan
OPEN: Tue to Sun, exc Tue L CLOSED: 31 Oct to Easter MEALS: 12.30 to 2, 8
PRICES: £14 (£21), Set D £27·50 (£34) CARDS: Access, Visa
SEATS: 24. Private parties: 24 main room. Car-park, 30 places. Vegetarian meals. Children welcome. Jacket and tie. Wheelchair access (also WC). One sitting at D
ACCOMMODATION: 22 rooms, all with bath/shower. Rooms for disabled. Lift. B&B £35 to £60. Deposit: £35. Children welcome. Baby facilities. Pets welcome. Afternoon teas. Garden. Swimming-pool. Fishing. Phone. Scenic. Doors close at 12. Confirm by 6 [GHG]

CROMARTY Highland   map 8

Le Chardon [11/20]

Church Street, Cromarty IV11 8XA
CROMARTY (038 17) 471   ▮ £13–£20

The Chardon is the only proper restaurant for a few miles, though things are hotting up in Cromarty with two tea-rooms and a furniture restorer open now. Polished floorboards, traditional old rugs and a more modern menu attract, with

---

Places rating 9 may not be restaurants at all, but still serve good food: expect to find pubs, cafes, small hotels and wine bars.

---

an emphasis on fish: salmon with tarragon sauce, scallops with ginger sauce, steamed fillet of red mullet with vinaigrette. Vegetables feature widely, too, in the modern British style in avocado soup, red pepper terrine, and Gruyère roulade with a watercress and spinach filling. Classic French wines are the mainstay of the long list, with CELLARMAN'S CHOICE: Bourgogne Irancy, Luc Sorin '85, £13·70.

CHEF: Robyn Aitchison PROPRIETORS: Robyn and Mena Aitchison
OPEN: Tue to Sun, D only, and Sun L CLOSED: 1 week Jan, 1 week Oct
MEALS: 12.30 to 2, 7.30 to 9.30
PRICES: Set L £9 (£13), Set D £15·50 (£20) CARDS: Access, Amex, Visa
SEATS: 25. Private parties: 30 main room. Vegetarian meals. Children's helpings (L only). No children under 8. No smoking. Wheelchair access. Music

---

CULLIPOOL Strathclyde   map 8

Longhouse Buttery [11/20]

Cullipool, Isle of Luing PA34 4TX
LUING (085 24) 209   £12

A large bay window now offers even more spectacular views of Scarba, the Garvellachs and Mull from every table in the remote dining-room. There is no fixed lunch hour – the whole menu is available throughout the day. The last car ferry leaves at six in the evening so dinners have been abandoned. Locally caught wild salmon, lobsters, squat lobsters and large prawns are the highlights, served simply with salads or as open sandwiches. Otherwise there is soup, home-boiled gammon or venison pâté, with frozen chocolate pot or triple meringues to finish. Home-made lemonade is 48p and there is house wine by the glass.

CHEF: Audrey Stone PROPRIETORS: Audrey Stone and Edna Whyte
OPEN: Mon to Sat CLOSED: Oct to mid-May MEALS: 11 to 5
PRICES: £8 (£12)
SEATS: 24. Private parties: 12 main room. Car-park, 10 places. Vegetarian meals. Children's helpings. Wheelchair access (also WC)

CUPAR Fife   map 8

Ostlers Close [12/20]

25 Bonnygate, Cupar KY15 4BU
CUPAR (0334) 55574   £21

Amanda and James Graham's restaurant is shaped around the local foods. Fish is from Pittenweem market; a farmer supplies eggs and new season's lamb; the butcher has set up a contact for locally reared veal; a man in Cupar shoots game to order; market gardens grow many of the vegetables; the Grahams now have a kitchen garden that helps to supply the five vegetables served separately with main courses. The menu has strong modern British overtones: pot-roast pigeon

---

Restaurants are graded on a scale of 1–20. In the category of 10–11 expect to find the best food in the locality. Ratings of 12 and more are given to restaurants we regard as serving the best food in the region.

---

with rhubarb and port sauce; scallops and prawns with fresh spinach cake; guinea-fowl with gin and juniper berries. Home-made jellies are served with roast meats or used to sweeten the light, modern sauces, which are reductions of natural juices and alcohol. Sweets range from interesting home-made sorbets to hot apple strudels. Fifty wines include half a dozen from Australia.
CELLARMAN'S CHOICE: Chardonnay, Mount Pleasant '82, £10·80.

CHEF: James Graham PROPRIETORS: Amanda and James Graham
OPEN: Tue to Sat MEALS: 12.15 to 2, 7 to 9.30
PRICES: £15 (£21). Minimum £10 at D CARDS: Access, Visa
SEATS: 30. Private parties: 22 main room. Vegetarian meals. Children's helpings. No children under 6. No smoking during meals. Wheelchair access (also WC)

DRUMNADROCHIT Highland   map 8
▲ *Polmaily House Hotel* [13/20]

Drumnadrochit IV3 6XT
DRUMNADROCHIT (045 62) 343   £18

The Parsons' elegant country house is filled with classical bohemian touches in their choice of antiques. The menu of half a dozen dishes at each of the three courses evolves from day to day. It is furnished from the kitchen garden, the 54-foot polythene tunnel used for exotics, with Orkney shellfish and excellent local meats. At first glance the style seems French, but is as much modern British. Take the seasoning – melon sorbet with a tomato, orange and cucumber salad; dill pickled herrings with chive sauce; baked salmon with tomato and basil; duck with blackcurrants. Aberdeen Angus sirloin is served plain grilled; crab is cooked into profiteroles and lasagne. Cheeses are from Scottish farms, and the sweets are Delights, Cranachans, meringues and roulades. Breakfasts have all the traditional features, as well as black and white puddings, kippers, and Finnan haddock. The wine list, like the cooking, is a cut above average, with a hundred-plus bottles, strong on the classics but with plenty of interest around the world.
CELLARMAN'S CHOICE: Marqués de Griñon Cabernet-Sauvignon '83, £12.

CHEF: Alison Parsons PROPRIETORS: Alison and Nick Parsons
OPEN: all week, D only CLOSED: mid-Oct to end Mar MEALS: 7.30 to 9.30
PRICES: £14 (£18). Service inc CARDS: Access, Visa
SEATS: 30. Private parties: 12 main room. Car-park, 20 places. Vegetarian meals. Children's helpings. No smoking in dining-room. Wheelchair access
ACCOMMODATION: 9 rooms, 7 with bath/shower. B&B £28 to £62. Deposit: £25. Children welcome. Baby facilities. No pets. Garden. Swimming-pool. Tennis. Fishing. Scenic. Doors close at 12. Confirm by 4 [GHG]

DUNOON Strathclyde   map 8
▲ *Ardenslate Hotel* [10/20]

James Street, Hunter's Quay, Dunoon PA23 8JS
DUNOON (0369) 2068   £9–£15

Mary Hunter's parents ran this old-fashioned Victorian country house for almost twenty years before she took over. Very little has changed. There are fine views over Holy Loch from the colourful gardens and the dining-room, and the cooking is enthusiastic. Local ingredients and traditional touches show in the clear chicken broth with leeks, in the crisp oatmeal coating around trout and over the boiled potatoes. Smoked haddock is turned into a mousse with beaten egg whites and cream, thick slices of tongue come in a red wine sauce. Sweets are well worth a special trip: wedges of hazel-nut meringue, or rum bavarois with fresh raspberry sauce. The short wine list has half-carafes of Paul Masson at £3·10.

CHEF/PROPRIETOR: Mary Hunter
OPEN: all week, exc Sun D CLOSED: end Oct to Easter. Rest. open weekends Dec to May
MEALS: 12.15 to 1.45, 6.30 to 8.30 (9 Fri and Sat)
PRICES: £10 (£15), Set L from £5·50 (£9), Set D from £7·50 (£12), Snacks from £1·75
CARDS: Access, Visa
SEATS: 35. Private parties: 40 main room. Car-park, 6 places. Children's helpings. No smoking in dining-room. Wheelchair access (also WC)
ACCOMMODATION: 8 rooms, 6 with bath/shower. Rooms for disabled. B&B £15 to £34. Deposit: £10. Children welcome. Baby facilities. Pets welcome. Garden. Scenic. Doors close at 12. Confirm by 6.30

DUNVEGAN see SKYE

EDDLESTON see PEEBLES

EDINBURGH Lothian   map 8
Alp-Horn [11/20]

167 Rose Street, EH2 4LS
031-225 4787   £9–£17

The cowbells and alp-horns testify to the pedigree of the Swiss cooking, which is genuine and reliable. There are only a few Swiss restaurants in the country and this is arguably the best. Air-dried meats; intensely flavoured soups; rösti potatoes; fondue, of course; and combinations of cream, meringue and ice-cream are mainstays. The speciality of the house is Emince de veau à la zurichoise. The cheeseboard is a crazy EEC hybrid, ranging from Fontina to Stilton, and, apart from Gruyère, does not take advantage of the fine range of Swiss cheeses. But the well-spread wine list includes at least five Swiss wines, among them Fendant and Twanner, both at £5·50 a half-litre.

CHEFS: Miggi Meier and Kenneth Dickson PROPRIETOR: Miggi Meier
OPEN: Tue to Sat CLOSED: 2 weeks at Christmas, 3 weeks June MEALS: 12 to 2, 6.30 to 10
PRICES: £10·45 (£17), Set L from £4·20 (£9) Service 10% CARD: Access
SEATS: 66. Private parties: 44 main room. Children's helpings. No-smoking area. Wheelchair access. Music. Air-conditioned

---

▲ *Buntoms, The Linden Hotel* [new entry, zero rated]

9–13 Nelson Street, EH3 6LF
031-557 4344   £7–£15

Wonderful golden dragons adorn the walls of this light and elegant Thai restaurant inside the Georgian Linden Hotel. Since opening in March 1987 it has filled up quickly in the evenings even early in the week. The dishes on the long menu are deliberately spiced to produce that typical hot and sour of proper Thai cooking. Vegetable curries are hot to Western palates, though not to Thai. Herb and anise lift the flavours of, say, fried aubergine and green peppers, garlic those of mixed vegetables. The choice for dessert is between American dairy ice-cream (bizarrely described in Spanish) or tropical fruits served in sweetened iced water. Staff are courteous and helpful. House wine is £4·50. More reports, please.

CHEF/PROPRIETOR: Tom Dedfrudi
OPEN: Mon to Sat MEALS: 12 to 2, 7 to 11
PRICES: £9 (£15), Set L £3·50 (£7). Service 10% CARDS: Access, Amex, Diners, Visa
SEATS: 46. Private parties: 40 main room, 30 private room. Vegetarian meals. Children's helpings. Smart dress preferred. Wheelchair access. Music
ACCOMMODATION: 21 rooms, 11 with bath/shower. B&B £25 to £40. Deposit: 1 night's stay. Children welcome. Baby facilities. Pets welcome. TV. Phone

Champany Grill [11/20]

2 Bridge Road, Colinton, EH13 0LF
031-441 2587   £23

The village branch of the Davidsons' prestigious steak-house in Linlithgow (see entry) seems to have lost some of its edge. The dining-room is as comfortable and as well maintained as ever, but the cooking is not what it used to be. The menu seems to have got distracted from its main purpose of matching the well-hung steaks with the good, but shortened list of red wines, and has faltered on over-chilled marinated salmon, tired salads and greasy chips. Hopefully, these lapses are temporary, because the basic idea is solid gold. House wine is £6·50. A cocktail bar is due to open.

CHEF: Nigel Best PROPRIETORS: Clive and Anne Davidson
OPEN: Mon to Sat CLOSED: 3 weeks Jan MEALS: 12.30 to 2, 7 to 10
PRICES: £14 (£23). Minimum £5·50. Service 10% CARDS: Access, Amex, Diners, Visa
SEATS: 36. Private parties: 36 main room. Children welcome. Wheelchair access (also WC)

Cosmo's [10/20]

58A North Castle Street, EH2 3LU
031-226 6743   £22

Of all the Italian restaurants in the city, Cosmo still seems to be the most dependable, filling a much-needed void. Pasta is home made, sauces have character, salads are fresh. Fish also sets the menu apart: baked salmon, halibut, turbot. House Merlot is £6·80.

CHEF/PROPRIETOR: Cosmo Tamburro
OPEN: Tue to Sat, exc Sat L MEALS: 12.30 to 2.15, 6.30 to 10.15
PRICES: £15 (£22). Minimum £6. Service 10% CARDS: Access, Visa
SEATS: 60. Private parties: 20 main room. Children's helpings. No pipes in dining-room. Wheelchair access. Music

Restaurants are graded on a scale of 1–20. In the category of 10–11 expect to find the best food in the locality. Ratings of 12 and more are given to restaurants we regard as serving the best food in the region.

Handsel's [13/20]

22 Stafford Street, EH3 7BD
031-225 5521 £29

Handsel's has been a restaurant for years. Originally it was the first Danish restaurant in Edinburgh, but went downhill under different owners. Now sumptuously revamped, it is the kind of excellent restaurant Edinburgh has needed for a long time. Only a fairly discreet sign by the front door indicates that it is no longer a private house. The ground floor is the good-value and popular wine bar.A graceful curved staircase leads up to the first-floor dining-room in what was obviously the drawing-room. Tables are fully clothed in floor-length white and set with flowers. The surroundings are generous, intimate and artful. Young staff are well versed. Andrew Radford cooks a no-choice menu in modern British style which has had flashes of brilliance. Witness a starter of halibut and salmon in a saffron beurre blanc garnished with asparagus and an oyster; or a sweet of bitter chocolate roulade. Complexities combine to balance the flavours, just like the rich, clear, intense truffle sauce with the duck. All these dishes were from the same meal in March. Through the year there have been consistent menus of fine cooking: veal with sweetbreads, lime and tarragon; fish soup; chocolate truffle cake; almond mille-feuille. Sometimes the combinations do not work – pineapple with cheese, for instance – but there is compensation in warm oatcakes. The wine list is well balanced across Europe with a good show of half-bottles. House Beaujolais is £7·90.

CHEF: Andrew Radford PROPRIETORS: David and Tina Thomson
OPEN: Mon to Sat, D only CLOSED: 1 week Jan MEALS: 7.30 to 10
PRICES: Set D £23 (£29) CARDS: Access, Amex, Diners, Visa
SEATS: 40. Private parties: 40 main room. Vegetarian meals. Children's helpings. Music.
Air-conditioned

Helios Fountain [9/20]

7 Grassmarket, EH1 2HY
031-229 7884 £5

Part of a Rudolph Steiner book and craft shop in a Victorian Gothic tenement block at the foot of the Grassmarket. The kitchen is committed to the philosophy of vegetarian food, without any of its puritanical zeal. There are worthy soups, quiches and hot dishes such as Boston bean pie topped with light wholemeal pastry. Salads are inventive and come with the choice of a yoghurt dressing or vinaigrette made with virgin olive oil. Sweets are in the wholefood tradition: vegan carob cake; tofu, banana and apricot cheesecake. Unlicensed, but there's a good choice of fruit juices. No smoking.

CHEFS: C. Strang and J. Woodhead PROPRIETORS: C. Maclean, A. Maclean and
J. Bastiaensen
OPEN: Mon to Sat, L only MEALS: 10 to 6 (8 Aug)
PRICES: £4 (£5). Unlicensed. Service inc CARDS: Access, Amex, Visa
SEATS: 35. Private parties: 35 main room. Vegetarian meals. Children's helpings. No
smoking. Wheelchair access. Self-service

Restaurants rating 12 or more serve the best food in the region.

Indian Cavalry Club [new entry, zero rated]

3 Atholl Place, EH3 8HP
031-228 3282   £12–£17

The stylised high-ceilinged dining-room is done out like an officers' club, with cool grey-green paintwork, lances pinned to the walls and waiters in cavalry uniform. This is North Indian food dressed up for dinner. In the evening the kitchen has delivered some impressive dishes from a long, ambitious menu: four kinds of pakora with sweet-and-sour sauce; Moghlai chicken kebab, and king prawns jhal frezi cooked with green chillies and lemon juice. At lunchtime it has been more erratic, and the buffet has had overcooked curries and heavy, greasy breads. Rice is reliably good, and so is the ras malai. Kingfisher beer, sherbet, or huge glasses of house wine for £1·30. More reports, please.

CHEFS: Bilquis Chowdhury and Mohammed Abdullah PROPRIETORS: Shahid and Bilquis Chowdhury
OPEN: all week MEALS: 11.30 to 2, 5 to 11.30
PRICES: £10 (£17), Set L £7·95 (£12), Set D from £8·50 (£13) CARDS: Access, Amex, Diners, Visa
SEATS: 63. Private parties: 70 main room, 30 private room. Vegetarian meals. Children's helpings (weekend L only). Jacket and tie. No-smoking area. Wheelchair access (also WC)

Kalpna [10/20]

2–3 St Patrick Square, EH8 9ES
031-667 9890   £6–£12

Probably the first no-smoking Indian restaurant in the country. This unfussy Gujerati and South Indian vegetarian restaurant offers inexpensive lunches for students but a more wide-ranging menu in the evening. Kachori (deep-fried lentil balls) come with a sweet tamarind-based dip, and other good dishes have included mushroom bhajia in a cream and coconut sauce, and excellent carrot halva. Pilau rice is light and fragrant, and brown is offered as an alternative to Basmati. The thalis are good value. Drink lassi or Kingfisher beer. The elephant logo emphasises that it is possible to grow big and strong without eating meat.

CHEF: Ajay Bhartdwaj PROPRIETOR: M. E. Jogee, Mrs Mehta, E. Barton and A. Bhartdwaj
OPEN: Mon to Sat MEALS: 12 to 2, 5.30 to 11
PRICES: £7 (£12), Set L from £2·50 (£6), Set D from £5 (£9). Service 12.5%
CARDS: Access, Visa
SEATS: 60. Private parties: 40 main room, 30 private room. Vegetarian meals. Children's helpings. No smoking. Wheelchair access. Music

Loon Fung [10/20]

32 Grindlay Street, EH3 9AP
031-229 5757   £8–£19

Handy for Usher Hall and the Lyceum. The dining-room is big and cheerful and decorated with enormous oriental fans. Previously it was an Italian restaurant, but now it is Cantonese. Dim-sum are available throughout the day. Standard dishes like sweet-and-sour fish or squid with black beans are executed skilfully, and there are embellishments such as mango chicken served in the mango shell.

Prices are higher and standards not as sharp as they might be in a Chinatown, but nevertheless it is a valuable addition to the Edinburgh eating scene.

CHEF: Chung Lo   PROPRIETORS: Paul Tsang and Chung Lo
OPEN: all week   CLOSED: Chinese New Year   MEALS: noon to midnight (1am Fri and Sat)
PRICES: £11 (£19), Set L £3 (£8), Set D from £8·50 (£13)   CARD: Amex
SEATS: 60. Private parties: 40 main room. Vegetarian meals. Children welcome. Wheelchair access. Music. Air-conditioned

Loon Fung   [10/20]

2 Warriston Place, EH3 5LE
031-556 1781 and 557 0940   £8–£14

Behind smoked-glass windows is this offshoot of the established Loon Fung – see above – not of the supermarket opposite. The décor is brown and creams, and the staff speak unusually good English. The menus centre on Canton, and have a fine range of dim-sum. Also good have been the barbecued roast pork, steamed lemon sole with ginger, and lemon duck. Specials of the day appear on the blackboard, and seafood is reliable: lobster in ginger sauce; steamed fish in black-bean sauce; fresh scallops. The Botanic Gardens are nearby.

CHEF/PROPRIETOR: Tin Fat Siu
OPEN: all week, exc Sat L and Sun L   CLOSED: 25 Dec, Chinese New Year
MEALS: noon to midnight (1am Fri and Sat)
PRICES: £9 (£14), Set L £3·50 (£8), Set D from £8 (£13)   CARDS: Access, Amex, Visa
SEATS: 75. 14 tables outside. Private parties: 45 main room, 45 private room. Vegetarian meals. Children welcome. Music

Le Marché Noir   [12/20]

2/4 Eyre Place, EH3 5EP
031-558 1608   £10–£14

More of a restaurant than a brasserie: the small dining-room has plain floors and no fancy touches. A loaded cheese trolley is at the serving end, where salamis and sausages hang next door to the kitchen. The menu features country-style French cooking with a few Sri Lankan specialities (one of the chefs is from Sri Lanka), such as breast of duck with ginger and lemon grass. Otherwise there might be French onion soup, rillettes of pork, plump mussels in tomato and garlic sauce, and plaice meunière. To finish, the fresh mango and rum ice-cream has been more convincing than the tarte aux pommes. The wine list tops the hundred mark, and there is plenty of good, inexpensive drinking: organic wines, vin jaune from Château Chalon, Brown Brothers Orange Muscat and Flora, Rancio de Rivesaltes, an Algerian, and a Moscato Passito di Pantelleria.

CHEFS: Robin Bowie and Anil Haththotuwegama   PROPRIETORS: Robin Bowie, Anil Haththotuwegama and Stephen Catterall
OPEN: Mon to Sat   CLOSED: 3 weeks after Edinburgh Festival   MEALS: 12 to 2.30, 7 to 10.30
PRICES: Set L £6·50 (£10), Set D from £10 (£14)   CARDS: Access, Visa
SEATS: 36. Private parties: 40 main room. Children welcome. Wheelchair access. Music

Many of the more expensive restaurants offer bargain lunches for half the price of a meal in the evening. Details are given in the text.

Martins [11/20]

70 Rose Street North Lane, EH2 3DX
031-225 3106   £10–£21

The tacky alley gives no clue to the airy dining-room lit by candles and filled with
sparkling glass and flowers. Owner Martin Irons serves himself. The cooking is
French with an emphasis on sauces and also substantial fish dishes: salmon
wrapped in spinach; veal kidneys with mustard; chocolate roulade. The menu
jumps from the plainer salmon meunière to overloading halibut with smoked
salmon, avocado and hollandaise. Espresso coffee. The flat-rate mark-up brings
the more expensive domaine-bottled wines into a better financial light. The list
opens at £6·50 and stays largely under £12.

CHEFS: Michael Wildman and Forbes Stott PROPRIETORS: Martin and Gay Irons
OPEN: Tue to Sat, exc Sat L CLOSED: 2 weeks from 25 Dec
MEALS: 12 to 2, 7 to 10 (10.30 Fri and Sat)
PRICES: £14 (£21), Set L from £4·85 (£10), Set D from £13 (£19). Service 10% on parties of
6 + CARDS: Access, Amex, Diners, Visa
SEATS: 28. Private parties: 34 main room, 10 private room. Children's helpings. No-smoking
area. Wheelchair access

Raffaelli [10/20]

10 Randolph Place, EH3 7TA
031-225 6060   £20

This Italian restaurant, well used by the financiers of the West End, is like a
cappuccino – plenty of froth but a little short on substance. To the right is the
wine bar, to the left is the restaurant, with its terracotta and green colour scheme
and discreet curtains at the window. The wide-ranging menu is Italian: escalope
zingara – with chopped tongue in the sauce –and osso buco alla romana. Mussels
are good, too. Plenty of service from the waitresses. Useful range of Italian wines
from £5·20.

CHEFS: Gerry Duffy and Aldo Scanferia PROPRIETOR: Bruno Raffaelli
OPEN: Mon to Sat, exc Sat L MEALS: noon to 9.30pm (6.30pm to 10.30pm Sat)
PRICES: £14 (£20). Service 10% CARDS: Access, Amex, Diners, Visa
SEATS: 65. Private parties: 60 main room. Smart dress preferred. Wheelchair access

Shamiana [11/20]

14 Brougham Street, EH3 9JH
031-228 2265   £10–£15

What is probably the best Indian restaurant in the city has a black and white
tiled floor, mirrors on the walls and pink tablecloths. It isn't a place for those with
huge appetites or a taste for platefuls of throat-burning Madras. Portions are
manageable and dishes are to savour. The short menu is North Indian and
Kashmiri, with tandoori dishes and a range of subtly spiced curries such as
chasni tikka in hot sweet-and-sour sauce, makni choosa, and badami josh – lamb
cooked with cream, almonds, saffron and asafoetida. Some of these specialities
require two cooking processes for full effect. Vegetables are first-rate: aubergine
cooked to softness, tiny firm bhindis, cumin-flavoured koftas in a creamy sauce.

Pilau rice is fragrant and aromatic, breads are light, and to finish there's rabri – a creamy pistachio pudding. To drink, there's Kingfisher beer or spiced Indian wine.

CHEFS/PROPRIETORS: M. Jogee and R. Sehgal
OPEN: Mon to Sat, exc Sat L CLOSED: Christmas and New Year
MEALS: 12 to 1.30, 6 to 11.30
PRICES: £8 (£15), Set L from £5·50 (£10). Minimum £5. Service 12.5% CARDS: Access, Amex, Diners, Visa
SEATS: 42. Private parties: 18 main room. Vegetarian meals. Children's helpings. No pipes in dining-room. Wheelchair access. Music

Vintners Room   [new entry, zero rated]

87 Giles Street, Leith, EH6 6BZ
031-554 6767   £13 – £26

Once the centre of the Scottish claret trade, with plasterwork dating from 1632, this well-restored stone building is now the offices of the Scotch Malt Whisky Association. Downstairs is the Vintners Room, with its ornate wood carvings, antique chandeliers and bas-reliefs of nymphs and cherubs. Fish is the main feature on the French menu: red mullet and red pepper sauce; lemon sole; and a dish of mixed seafood with oysters, scallops, prawns, turbot, mussels and smoked salmon in a light tarragon sauce. There are good meat and game dishes too: duck breast with ginger and lime sauce, medallions of beef with a trio of sauces. Sweets are very much an afterthought. The wine list is monumental. House wine is £7·50. More reports, please.

CHEF: Pierre Leuicky PROPRIETOR: David Baird
OPEN: Mon to Sat MEALS: 12 to 2.30, 7 to 10.30
PRICES: £18 (£26), Set L £6·90 (£13) CARDS: Access, Amex, Diners, Visa
SEATS: 75. Private parties: 40 main room, 25 private room. Car-park, 7 places. No young children. Smart dress preferred. Wheelchair access (also WC). Air-conditioned

Waterfront Wine Bar   [9/20]

1C Dock Place, Leith EH6 6LU
031-554 7427   £11

The big pluses here are the dockside setting and the chance of eating in the open air. Barbecues are the mainstay during fine weather; otherwise the kitchen turns out good pies served in pudding basins, and bistro-style dishes such as fillet of pork with mustard sauce, or stuffed trout. A big plateful of cheese with oatcakes is enough for two. Forty or so wines from around the world.
CELLARMAN'S CHOICE: Australian Chardonnay, Wyndham Estate Bin 222 '86, £6·20.

CHEFS: Caroline Conway, Lisa Fletcher and Helen Ruthven PROPRIETORS: Helen and Ian Ruthven, Sarah Reid and Robin Bowie
OPEN: Mon to Sat MEALS: 11am to midnight
PRICES: £7 (£11)
SEATS: 180. 20 tables outside. Private parties: 26 main room, 15 private room. Vegetarian meals. No children under 5. Wheelchair access. Music

Whigham's Wine Cellars [9/20]

13 Hope Street, EH3 9JR
031-225 8674   £7

Down in the basement, with its stone walls, stone ceilings and flagstone floors, it can feel like being in a wartime pillbox. Crowds descend at lunch for Nicholas Henderson's real soups, cold roast meats and mature cheeses. Smoked salmon is good, naturally, and there is beef and oyster pie. It is quiet in the evening, when the menu is more restricted. House claret is £5·25. CELLARMAN'S CHOICE: Ch. Cantemerle '79, £14·95.

PROPRIETOR: Nicholas Henderson
OPEN: Mon to Sat, exc Fri D MEALS: 12 to 2.30, 6 to 9
PRICES: £4 (£7), Snacks from £1 CARD: Visa
SEATS: 70. Vegetarian meals. Music. Air-conditioned

ERISKA Strathclyde   map 8

▲ *Isle of Eriska Hotel* [11/20]

Eriska PA37 1SD
LEDAIG (063 172) 371
off A828, 12m N of Oban   £8–£27

The Buchanan-Smiths' Victorian baronial mansion is entrenched in the traditions of old-fashioned Scottish cooking. It stakes its reputation on superb raw materials, including eggs, cream and meat as well as home-grown vegetables. Roasts are the centrepieces for dinner and Sunday lunch, but sweets such as upside-down ginger cake and rhubarb pie are enhanced by unpasteurised Jersey cream. Buffet lunches during the week. A well-spread list of around 150 wines has some venerable vintage clarets and heavyweight burgundies at affordable prices. CELLARMAN'S CHOICE: Ch. Guionne, Côtes de Bourg '82, £8·10.

CHEF: Simon Burns PROPRIETORS: Robin and Sheena Buchanan-Smith
OPEN: all week CLOSED: Dec to Jan MEALS: 12.45 to 1.45, 7.30 to 8.30
PRICES: Set L £4 (£8), Set D £21 (£27)
SEATS: 40. Private parties: 10 main room, 12 private room. Car-park, 50 places. Children's helpings. No children under 10. Jacket and tie. Wheelchair access (also WC)
ACCOMMODATION: 16 rooms, all with bath/shower. Rooms for disabled. B&B £62 to £124. Deposit: £50. Baby facilities. Garden. Tennis. Fishing. TV. Phone. Scenic. Confirm by 4
[GHG]

FORT WILLIAM Highland   map 8

▲ *The Factor's House* [new entry, zero rated]

Torlundy, Fort William PH33 6SN
FORT WILLIAM (0397) 5767
on A82, 3m N of Fort William   £19

A sympathetically restored and extended pink-painted house, just inside the gates of the tradesmen's entrance to Inverlochy Castle (see entry; Peter Hobbs is Grete's son). But the style is different from that at the Castle – less ambitious, or

Cordon Bleu with a blackboard menu that changes daily. First courses are left on the table: tureens of soup (always a good bet in the Highlands), pork terrine still in its ceramic dish with three slices cut off and a knife and fork *in situ*. Salmon is smoked, or grilled with parsley sauce, and steaks and casseroles feature strongly. Puddings run to strawberry eclairs with butterscotch sauce. Service is excellent. Twenty wines, with vin de table £8 a litre. More reports, please.

CHEF: Sara Ross PROPRIETOR: Peter Hobbs
OPEN: Tue to Sun, D only CLOSED: mid-Dec to mid-Mar MEALS: 7.30 to 9.30
PRICES: Set D £12·75 (£19) CARDS: Access, Amex, Diners, Visa
SEATS: 24. Private parties: 24 main room. Car-park, 16 places. Vegetarian meals. Children's helpings. No children under 8. Wheelchair access (also WC)
ACCOMMODATION: 6 rooms, all with bath/shower. B&B £40·25 to £57·50. Deposit: 1 night's stay. No children under 8. Garden. Tennis. Fishing. Golf. TV. Phone. Scenic. Doors close at 12.30 [GHG]

▲ *Inverlochy Castle* [13/20]

Fort William PH33 6SN
FORT WILLIAM (0397) 2177
on A82, 3m N of Fort William   £19–£35

The castle is a vast, grand, Victorian edifice standing in five hundred acres of grounds filled with rhododendrons. The furnishings reflect thirty years of one ownership under Grete Hobbs, and this helps give Inverlochy a humanity that might otherwise be missing. Graham Newbould, formerly chef to Prince Charles, has picked up a menu that for many years has been the most northerly testament to *haute cuisine*. The style is fine soups (as elsewhere in the Highlands), such as mussel or mulligatawny, a reliance on fine fish from local Loch Linnhe prawns to poached salmon with egg and oyster sauce or turbot with a scallop mousseline; and, to finish, some showy, inventive sweets for which the liqueur bottle has been used, as in Chartreuse ice-cream with an apple galette, or Strega sorbet in melon. Teas are very proper, as is the wine list, though it is stronger over £100 than under £10. Lunch is the bargain. House burgundy is £8·70.

CHEF: Graham Newbould PROPRIETOR: Grete Hobbs
OPEN: all week CLOSED: mid-Nov to mid-Mar MEALS: 12.30 to 1.45, 7.30 to 9
PRICES: Set L £15 (£19), Set D £27·50 (£35) CARDS: Access, Visa
SEATS: 10. Private parties: 8 main room. Car-park, 10 places. No children under 10. Jacket and tie. No smoking in dining-room
ACCOMMODATION: 16 rooms, all with bath/shower. B&B £80 to £115. Baby facilities. No pets. Garden. Tennis. Fishing. Snooker. TV. Phone. Scenic [GHG]

GLASGOW Strathclyde   map 8

Buttery [12/20]

652 Argyle Street, G3 8UF
041-221 8188   £15–£25

The auction-rooms of Glasgow were raided for the Victoriana that fills this former pub with its dignified, club-like atmosphere, much favoured for business. The Svengali McCulloch and chef Richardson have moved on, leaving Alloa Brewery in charge. The service has not improved and the menu seems intent on showing its *nouvelle cuisine* credentials by providing small portions. But the presentation is well thought out, from eye-catching combinations of rakishly angled prawn shells to triangular mounds of julienne of vegetables. The visual tricks do not compensate for the fussiness or the imbalance on the menu – no hot puddings in May in Glasgow? But the centrepieces, such as venison and redcurrant sauce and the halibut with a cream sauce flavoured with grapes and walnuts, are powerfully mitigating. Brian Graham is eminently capable of producing suitably fine meals. Fifty wines are carefully chosen but are generously marked up too. House Chenin Blanc is £6·95. CELLARMAN'S CHOICE: Fleurie '83, £13·55.

CHEFS: Brian Graham and Joseph Queen PROPRIETORS: Alloa Brewery
OPEN: Mon to Sat, exc Sat L MEALS: 12 to 2, 7 to 10
PRICES: £16 (£25), Set L £11·50 (£15). Service 10% alc, inc Set CARDS: Access, Amex, Diners, Visa
SEATS: 50. Private parties: 12 main room, 8 private room. Car-park, 30 places. Smart dress preferred. Wheelchair access. Music

Colonial [13/20]

25 High Street, G1 1LX
041-552 1923   £9–£26

Peter Jackson has established this as the premier restaurant in Glasgow. The décor still lacks some presence, but not the staff, who are professional and push the ever-changing six-course *menu surprise*. Mr Jackson's cooking is confident and up to the minute – squat lobster ravioli with basil sauce; salads are warm – but he is not frightened to induce an old-fashioned impact with breast of free-range chicken in a wine and cream sauce. To finish, in May, the trademark dish has been a crystallised daffodil set on a circle of peaches with a strawberry coulis. Other interesting points are tiny home-made black pudding served with drinks, and the Irish biscuits with fine cheeses, both French and British, but there are not enough hands to produce vegetables that begin to match the main courses. The set Taste of Modern Scotland menu is just that. The wine list runs to 150 bottles, with vintage clarets of substance, some expensive, some accessible. House burgundy is £6·45. CELLARMAN'S CHOICE: Ch. Dudon '82, £9·95.

CHEF/PROPRIETOR: Peter Jackson
OPEN: Mon to Sat, exc Mon D and Sat L MEALS: 12 to 2.30, 6 to 10.30
PRICES: £19 (£26), Set L from £5·25 (£9), Set D from £15 (£20) CARDS: Access, Amex, Diners, Visa
SEATS: 40. Private parties: 40 main room. Vegetarian meals. Children welcome. Wheelchair access

Loon Fung [10/20]

417 Sauchiehall Street, G2 3LG
041-332 1240   £8–£19

The swirling patterns on the carpets and the calligraphic scrolls on the walls barely add a flourish to what is a large, spacious room. The attraction is the long Cantonese menu. Dim-sum are a major feature. So too are the kind of dishes for which the cooking is renowned, such as the bean-curd or the noodle dishes. Pork and preserved vegetable soup, and chicken with black-bean sauce also draw good reports.

CHEF: Mr Cheung PROPRIETOR: Mr Cheng
OPEN: all week CLOSED: Chinese New Year MEALS: noon to 11.30pm
PRICES: £11 (£19), Set L from £4·50 (£8), Set D £10 (£14). Service 10% CARDS: Access, Amex, Visa
SEATS: 150. Private parties: 150 main room. Vegetarian meals. Children welcome. Wheelchair access. Music. Air-conditioned

▲ *One Devonshire Gardens* [12/20]

1 Devonshire Gardens, G12 0UX
041-339 2001   £19–£25

The first impression is dramatic, an almost decadent reincarnation of Victorian nostalgia filled with heavy patterns, long sweeping drapes and thickly varnished, broodingly sober oil portraits. It is spectacularly bijou in its conception – another creation from Glasgow Svengali Ken McCulloch, following on from Rogano and The Buttery, among others. The kitchen, amid all this show, is honest, dealing in fresh produce. Chef Jim Kerr took over at Christmas after a number of changes in the early months. He cooks a modern fixed-priced menu: terrine of salmon and scallops or melon filled with citrus sorbet and champagne might precede a westernised beef teriyaki or poached chicken breast with avocado and a sauce flavoured with dill. Main courses appear under silver domes. Meals taper off, but there are exotic fruits to finish. Courteous service. There are ten half-bottles among the carefully chosen wine list of seventy, with the emphasis on France. Chardonnay has its own section of five wines from £13·50 (Australia) to £25 (Burgundy). The typography is refreshing. CELLARMAN'S CHOICE: Lalande-de-Pomerol, Ch. des Moines '83, £13.

CHEF: James Kerr PROPRIETOR: Martenby Ltd
OPEN: all week, exc Sat L MEALS: 12.30 to 2, 7 to 10
PRICES: Set L £12·50 (£19), Set D £18·50 (£25). Service 10% CARDS: Access, Amex, Diners, Visa
SEATS: 56. Private parties: 40 main room, 16 private room. Jacket and tie. Music
ACOMMODATION: 8 rooms, all with bath/shower. B&B £70 to £95. Children welcome. No pets. Afternoon teas. TV. Phone. Confirm by 6 [GHG]

Rogano [13/20]

11 Exchange Place, G1 3AN
041-248 4055   £24

For fish and for an authentic 1930s period atmosphere, Rogano is the place to eat at. It is stylish, unstuffy and its humour Glaswegian. The atmosphere extends into the cooking, which is without side or pretence, and the handling of fish has been exemplary. Salmon is cooked properly, bouillabaisse is served as a main course, sauces are light and creamy without being showy. The emphasis is on the food, and the wonderful art deco just extends its style. Unexpectedly, perhaps, the kitchen here seems to have created a more successful working of the Auld Alliance than other Glasgow French kitchens, which is why people tend to come here on their own money. Hopefully, Alloa Brewery will retain the standard – at the time of going to press this was the best 'pub-run' restaurant in the UK. House Chinon – red or white – is £6·95 from a sixty-strong list biased towards France and white wines.

CHEF: Steven Smith PROPRIETORS: Alloa Brewery
OPEN: Mon to Sat MEALS: 12 to 2.30, 7 to 10.30
PRICES: £16 (£24), Snacks from £2·50. Service 10% CARDS: Access, Amex, Diners, Visa
SEATS: 100. Private parties: 25 main room. Children welcome. Music. Air-conditioned

Ubiquitous Chip [12/20]

12 Ashton Lane, G12 8SJ
041-334 5007
 £22

The Chip, as we have said before, remains the benchmark for judging Glasgow restaurants. Painstakingly erratic, perhaps, but always at least of *Guide* standard, occasionally surprising, and with a backbone of excellent wines. The atmosphere splits between the cobbles, ivy, plants, iron and water in the conservatory to one side and the enclosed art gallery on the other. The cooking is modern British and unafraid to experiment: beetroot and white cheese roulade, Oban sole with Chinese leaves, and ox-tail ragout feature alongside more French-style main dishes like gigot of lamb or loin of pork with cream and wine sauce. A good choice of sweets includes lemon tart. It might be a bit fuller if it were a bit cheaper, but with the closure of Poachers who is to say? The wine list is as comprehensive within France as anybody is likely to need, and then some. Claret is the mainstay, with a spread of mature vintages. Burgundy names good names, and there is support from Spain, Australia, California and Germany. Single malts are taken very seriously.

CHEF: R. Clydesdale PROPRIETORS: R. Clydesdale and T. I. R. Brydon
OPEN: Mon to Sat MEALS: 12 to 2.30, 5.30 to 11
PRICES: £15 (£22) CARDS: Access, Amex, Diners, Visa
SEATS: 100. Private parties: 60 main room, 40 private room. Vegetarian meals. Children's helpings. Wheelchair access (also WC)

GULLANE Lothian
map 8

La Potinière [15/20]

Main Street, Gullane EH31 2AA
GULLANE (0620) 843214
 £15–£21

The Browns' small restaurant is without pretensions but not class and has over many years earned its reputation for consistency. The crockery is from Limoges, the paintings are contemporary originals. Flowers fill the room. The main difficulty is getting a table. There is no choice in the four courses, but the style is set in a French provincial mould and stays within a tight formula, though there are subtle evolutions – the sole mousseline as a second course flavoured one day predominantly with lemon, another with orange, another with tarragon, then in hollandaise. Breast of hen turkey has been a frequent main-course variation on chicken – served with a wine and cream sauce, prunes and cranberries; or pork cutlets with rock salt, cumin, coriander, fennel and cider; or lately fillet of beef. Potatoes dauphinoise are definitive. Salads that follow often use thick vegetables like fennel or red cabbage, or both, to bring drama. To finish, there might be a soufflé glacé with caramelised pieces of orange and ginger. David Brown moves swiftly to serve the dining-room single-handedly. The same attention to detail is found in the cellar. How far can a wine list go? There are, for example, seven vintages of Jaboulet's Hermitage La Chapelle, eight Corton Charlemagnes, a dozen Alsace Gewürztraminers, thirteen Volnays, twenty-one Chablis . . . That there is not a single bottle from outside France matters not at all in the face of such thoroughness and quality. How this vast stock is financed on such slender mark-ups is a mystery. Drink. Enjoy.

CHEF: Hilary Brown PROPRIETORS: David and Hilary Brown
OPEN: all week L, exc Wed and Sat, and Sat D CLOSED: Oct, 1 week June MEALS: 1, 8
PRICES: Set L from £10·75 (£15), Set D £16·75 (£21)
SEATS: 32. Private parties: 30 main room. Car-park, 10 places. No smoking during meals.
Wheelchair access. One sitting

HADDINGTON Lothian
map 8

▲ *Brown's Hotel* [10/20]

West Road, Haddington EH41 3RD
HADDINGTON (062 082) 2254
£19

The handsome stone house lacks organisation, but at heart Colin Brown's cooking and the wines from good years in the cellar make this still somewhere to seek out. On some nights menus seem to be dispensed with completely, but dishes rotate through smoked fish beignets, cauliflower soup, Cullen skink, pork fillet, boeuf en croûte, and decorative sweets. Meats are of good quality, sauces are cream-based, and custard is properly made. The forty wines are almost exclusively French. CELLARMAN'S CHOICE: Ch. Romefort '82, £7·90.

CHEF: Colin Brown PROPRIETORS: Margaret and Colin Brown
OPEN: Mon to Sat, D only CLOSED: 2 weeks Oct MEALS: 7.30 to 9
PRICES: Set D £14·95 (£19)
SEATS: 30. Private parties: 30 main room. Car-park, 10 places. Vegetarian meals. Children's helpings. Wheelchair access (also WC)
ACCOMMODATION: 6 rooms, 4 with bath/shower. B&B £26 to £45. Deposit: £5. Baby facilities. Garden. TV. Scenic. Doors close at 12. Confirm by 8

HARRIS Western Isles
map 8

▲ *Scarista House* [12/20]

Scarista, Isle of Harris PA85 8HX
SCARISTA (085 985) 238
on A859, 15m SW of Tarbert
£21

The Johnsons now delegate much of the cooking and day-to-day running of their remote Church of Scotland manse-style house to their long-standing assistants Morag Macleod and Lena Maclennan. Dinner comes down to three courses, but the style remains emphatically the same – a no-choice menu made up mostly of wild produce, especially fish, but with an increasingly vegetarian bias. Sweets, as ever, are traditional. The wine cellar has good, not overpriced wines.

CHEFS: Alison Johnson, Morag Macleod and Lena Maclennan PROPRIETORS: Andrew and Alison Johnson
OPEN: Mon to Sat, D only CLOSED: Nov to Mar MEALS: 8
PRICES: Set D £16 (£21)
SEATS: 20. Private parties: 8 main room. Car-park, 10 places. Vegetarian meals. Children's helpings. No children under 8. No smoking in dining-room. Wheelchair access. One sitting
ACCOMMODATION: 7 rooms, all with bath/shower. B&B £37 to £56. Deposit: £10. No children under 8. Pets welcome. Garden. Scenic [GHG]

INVERNESS Highland   map 8

▲ *Dunain Park* [new entry, zero rated]

Inverness IV3 6JN
INVERNESS (0463) 230512
on A82, 1m from Inverness   £14–£22

Yet another minor Scottish baronial building, overlooking superb lawns, trees and shrubs. The Nicolls took over in January 1986. They have made it less hotel-like than some. There is a comfortable mix of old and new and the luxury of having the central heating on full blast with the windows open. The menu changes daily and features some fine local produce: properly hung venison, roasted, sliced and served with a damson sauce; impeccable scallops hollandaise. The sweets table is a dramatic tour de force: vast feather-light profiteroles; posset; oranges drowned in Drambuie; lemon cheesecake and lemon pudding; ginger cream, etc. The hundred wines open at £5 and are well spread in quality and price. More reports, please.

CHEF: Ann Nicoll PROPRIETORS: Ann and Edward Nicoll
OPEN: all week MEALS: 12 to 2, 7 to 9
PRICES: Set L £10·50 (£14), Set D £17·50 (£22) CARDS: Access, Amex, Diners, Visa
SEATS: 32. Private parties: 20 main room, 20 private room. Car-park, 30 places. Vegetarian meals. Children's helpings. Smart dress preferred. No smoking in dining-room. Wheelchair access
ACCOMMODATION: 8 rooms, all with bath/shower. B&B £26·50 to £40. Deposit: £40. Children welcome. Baby facilities. Pets welcome. Afternoon teas. Garden. Fishing. Golf. TV. Phone. Scenic. Doors close at 12 [GHG]

KELSO Borders   map 8

▲ *Sunlaws House* [11/20]

Heiton, Kelso TD5 8JZ
ROXBURGH (0573) 5331
3m outside Kelso on A698   £13–£21

The Duke of Roxburghe's relaxed, well-staffed fishing and shooting house is three miles out of Kelso. The menu is well supplied with fine ingredients, which are mostly allowed to come through in the cooking: 'We hold true to Scottish country-house cooking.' Fish has been excellent – grilled langoustine tails from Eyeworth or halibut with a saffron-coloured sauce. Lamb has been pan-fried, its juices extended with meat stock, flavoured with rosemary and garnished with wild mushrooms. Meals end with bramble cheesecake and halves of Stilton. The 120 wines are based largely in France but contain bargains in the New World.

House claret is £6·95. CELLARMAN'S CHOICE: Selaks' Sauvignon-Semillon '86 from New Zealand, £13·10.

CHEF: Robert Grindle PROPRIETORS: The Duke and Duchess of Roxburghe
OPEN: all week MEALS: 12.30 to 2, 7.30 to 9.30
PRICES: £12 (£21), Set L £8·50 (£13) CARDS: Access, Amex, Diners, Visa
SEATS: 40. 5 tables outside. Private parties: 45 main room, 20 private room. Car-park, 30 places. Children's helpings. No pipes in dining-room. Wheelchair access (also WC)
ACCOMMODATION: 21 rooms, all with bath/shower. Rooms for disabled. B&B £39 to £59 minimum. Deposit: 20%. Children welcome. Baby facilities. Pets welcome. Afternoon teas. Garden. Tennis. Fishing. Golf. TV. Phone. Scenic. Doors close at 11.30. Confirm by 7.30

KENTALLEN Highland   map 8

▲ *Ardsheal House* [11/20]

Kentallen PA38 4BX
DUROR (063 174) 227   £10–£25

At the end of a rough, mile and a quarter drive stands this small house, a choice of green wellies and a dozen walking-sticks in the porch. The grounds overlook Loch Linnhe. The Taylors are American and encourage guests to talk to each other in this country-house atmosphere of oil paintings, grand staircase and hairy hounds lolling on comfortable, lived-in chairs. The menu changes daily, and offers a minimum of choice through five courses. The flavour combinations are vivid: mange-tout and lovage soup; sweetbreads and wild mushrooms on a salad with a sauce Vierge; pineapple sorbet with orange and mango coulis. The cooking may be plain, as in roast rack of lamb, or striking, as in turbot, monk-fish and halibut, each cooked differently – poached, steamed and grilled – and served together in a watercress sauce. John Bussey took over the kitchen last summer, but reports have not wavered. The twice-baked goats' cheese and garlic soufflé is excellent. Guests are encouraged to help themselves to fruit and cheese, but otherwise the service is in the American tradition – nothing is too much trouble. The wine list of a hundred bottles has some interesting vintages of claret and a good spread of Beaujolais. House French is £6. CELLARMAN'S CHOICE: Ch. Fourcas-Dupré '79, £11.

CHEF: Colin John Bussey PROPRIETORS: Jane and Robert Taylor
OPEN: all week CLOSED: 1 Nov to Easter MEALS: 12.30 to 2, 8.15 to 8.30
PRICES: Set L from £6 (£10), Set D £20 (£25)
SEATS: 34. Private parties: 38 main room. Car-park, 20 places. Children's helpings. Smart dress preferred. No smoking in dining-room. Wheelchair access (also WC). Music. One sitting
ACCOMMODATION: 13 rooms, all with bath/shower. D, B&B £65 to £116. Children welcome. Baby facilities. Pets welcome. Afternoon teas. Garden. Tennis. Snooker. Scenic. Doors close at 12. Confirm by 5.30 [GHG]

▲ *The Holly Tree* [11/20]

Kentallen PA38 4BY
DUROR (063 174) 292   £17–£20

This former railway station on the shore of Loch Linnhe has been enlarged and extensively renovated – the old station platform is part of the new reception area, the waiting-rooms are bedrooms – and there are photographs of royalty stepping out of the train at Kentallen. Lunch is a mixture of snacks and items off the *carte*, while dinner is a more serious modern menu of veal kidneys with poached eggs and madeira, wild mushroom and red wine soup, and breast of pigeon in a dark brown bitter chocolate sauce with barley-cakes. Fruits and herbs team up with main-course meats too: turkey with pear and mint, casserole of hare with tarragon and blackcurrants. Puddings are traditional, and there is Lanark blue cheese and a short wine list with house red and white at £5·25.

CHEF: Alasdair Robertson PROPRIETORS: Alasdair and Jane Robertson
OPEN: all week CLOSED: Mon to Wed and Sun L Oct to Easter, Fri to Mon Easter to May
MEALS: 12.30 to 2.30, 6.30 to 9.30
PRICES: £15 (£20), Set D £12·50 (£17). Minimum £6·50 CARDS: Access, Diners, Visa
SEATS: 60. Private parties: 16 main room. Car-park, 30 places. Vegetarian meals. Children's helpings. No smoking in dining-room. Wheelchair access (also WC). Music
ACCOMMODATION: 12 rooms, all with bath/shower. Rooms for disabled. B&B £16 to £68. Deposit: £20. Children welcome. Baby facilities. Pets welcome. Afternoon teas. Garden. Fishing. Snooker. TV. Phone. Scenic

---

KILCHRENAN Strathclyde   map 8

▲ *Taychreggan Hotel* [11/20]

Kilchrenan PA35 1HQ
KILCHRENAN (086 63) 211   £13–£18

The setting, beside Scotland's longest (24 miles) freshwater loch, is a draw to this family-run hotel. The menu depends on local produce, with a few eclectic ideas like Peking duck. Lunch is a buffet with giant local sausage, a variety of salads, and the Loch Awe Monster sandwich. Dinner is four courses, with fish a highlight: salmon in flaky pastry, turbot with crayfish sauce, scallop and vermouth mousse. Home-made sweets are first-class. Reasonably priced petit château clarets head up the wine list. A curiosity is a dessert wine from Scotland.
CELLARMAN'S CHOICE: Gewürztraminer Cuvée Traditionnelle, Hugel '85, £9·80.

CHEFS: Gail Struthers, Dorothy Laurie, Joyce MacDougall and Nan MacIntyre
PROPRIETORS: John and Tove Taylor
OPEN: all week MEALS: 12 to 2.15, 7.30 to 9
PRICES: Set L £8·50 (£13), Set D £13·50 (£18) CARDS: Access, Amex, Diners, Visa
SEATS: 40. 10 tables outside. Private parties: 16 main room. Car-park, 30 places. Vegetarian meals. Children's helpings. Wheelchair access
ACCOMMODATION: 16 rooms, 15 with bath/shower. B&B £28·50 to £57. Children welcome. Baby facilities. Pets welcome. Afternoon teas. Garden. Fishing. Scenic. Doors close at 12. Confirm by 6 [GHG]

KILFINAN Strathclyde   map 8

▲ *Kilfinan Hotel* [10/20]

Kilfinan PA21 2AP
KILFINAN (070 082) 201   £16–£19

An old coaching-inn next to the church houses this pub (with bar meals) and restaurant. It is remote enough to ensure that fish and shellfish have to be locally caught, as is game, and the freshness of scallops in particular is remarkable. The menu rings the changes with home-made soups, chicken with mango and papaya, salmon or mushrooms in pastry, and pork fillet with paprika. Crème brûlée stands out among puddings of butterscotch puffs with whisky cream, lemon cheesecake, and strawberry shortcake. Some fine bottles of claret constitute the pick of the wine list. CELLARMAN'S CHOICE: Ch. Moulin Haut Villars '75, £9·50 (£5 per half-bottle).

CHEF: David Kinnear PROPRIETOR: N. K. S. Wills
OPEN: all week MEALS: 12 to 2, 7.30 to 9.30
PRICES: £14 (£19), Set D from £14 (£16), Snacks from £1·50. Service inc set only
CARDS: Access, Amex, Diners, Visa
SEATS: 24. 2 tables outside. Private parties: 50 main room. Car-park, 20 places. Children's helpings. Smart dress preferred. Wheelchair access (also WC). Music
ACCOMMODATION: 11 rooms, all with bath/shower. B&B £28 to £44. Deposit: 10%. Children welcome. Baby facilities. Pets welcome. Afternoon teas. Garden. Fishing. Golf. TV. Phone. Scenic. Doors close at 11 [GHG]

KILLIECRANKIE Tayside   map 8

▲ *Killiecrankie Hotel* [10/20]

Killiecrankie PH16 5LG
PITLOCHRY (0796) 3220   £15

The former dower house has been a hotel since the 1930s. The wildlife in the oak forests around make it an attractive stopping-point. The menu is rather dated, but the kitchen has a proper brigade of four, including a pâtissier, and uses the best national produce: salmon, Angus beef, Orkney cheese. Bar meals are always popular, and there is a four-course dinner. Typical might be grilled herring with beurre noisette; poached rainbow trout with Chablis sauce; Ayrshire pork chop with cider sauce. Home-made sweets from the trolley. The majority of the two dozen wines are available as halves. House French is £5·10. CELLARMAN'S CHOICE: Mâcon Villages, La Floret '86, £7·50.

CHEF: Paul Booth and Brian Syme PROPRIETORS: Mr and Mrs D. Hattersley Smith
OPEN: all week CLOSED: mid-Oct to late Mar MEALS: 12.30 to 2, 7 to 9
PRICES: Set D from £12·50 (£15). Service inc
SEATS: 70. Private parties: 20 main room. Car-park, 30 places. Vegetarian meals. Children's helpings. No children under 5. No smoking in dining-room. Wheelchair access (also WC)
ACCOMMODATION: 12 rooms, 10 with bath/shower. Rooms for disabled. B&B £18·20 to £36·40. Baby facilities. Pets welcome. Afternoon teas. Garden. Fishing. Golf. Scenic. Doors close at 12. Confirm by 6 [GHG]

KINGUSSIE Highland   map 8

▲ *The Cross* [13/20]

25–27 High Street, Kingussie PH21 1HX
KINGUSSIE (054 02) 762   🍾 £17–£21

In the last few years the Hadleys have developed their converted shop into an increasingly serious restaurant; it might claim now to be the rising star of the Highlands. The dining-room holds just five well-spaced tables set with thick linen and white Wedgwood Etruscan china. Ruth Hadley cooks a modern British menu in a ten-feet by ten-feet kitchen at the far end. Fine produce is set off by good sauces: typically, in the venison Fracatelli, roasted, sliced, and sauced with its juices mixed with port and redcurrant, or else in the rolled saddle of lamb with a sauce of its own juices, cream and sorrel. Other good dishes have been pesto mushrooms, pheasant with green peppercorns, pigeon salad dressed in walnut oil, squash with oatmeal, lemon balm sorbet, and an unusual chocolate whisky laird cake. The wine list tops 350 bins dating back to '47 at not unreasonable prices. As well as fifty half-bottles there are a hundred wines around £7 and no fewer than thirty sweet pudding wines.

CHEF: Ruth Hadley PROPRIETORS: Tony and Ruth Hadley
OPEN: Tue to Sun, D only CLOSED: Sun winter, 2 weeks May, 3 weeks Dec
MEALS: 6.30 to 9.30
PRICES: £12 (£17), Set D £15·50 (£21)
SEATS: 24. Private parties: 18 main room. Vegetarian meals. No children under 8. No smoking in dining-room. Wheelchair access
ACCOMMODATION: 3 rooms, all with bath/shower. B&B £14·50 to £25. Deposit: £10. No pets. Fishing. Golf

---

LINLITHGOW Lothian   map 8

Champany Inn [14/20]

Champany Corner, Linlithgow EH49 7LU
PHILPSTOUN (050 683) 4532 and 4388
2m NE of Linlithgow at junction of
A904 and A803   £16–£30

The Inn, which earned its reputation as the best steak-house in Britain, has developed into a full-scale restaurant. Shellfish, salmon and fine wines have been added to the repertoire, though the philosophy remains unaffected: the finest ingredients worked in plain ways. Steaks, of which seven different cuts are offered, including the virtually extinct but highly prized Pope's Eye, are properly hung, fiercely grilled, and unmatched. Salmon Bagger is a huge sirloin with pieces of smoked salmon in a pouch. The salad afterwards can make vegetables optional. Framing these centrepieces are good soups – served in tureens ladled out at the table – and sweets such as chocolate pot or elderflower sorbet set in a meringue decorated with elderflowers. The atmosphere is thick with offerings – the basket of vegetables shown over drinks, the selection of mustards, the array of teas. Choice is not a problem. Nor with the wines: eleven Chambertins, thirteen Pommards, twenty-one Nuits-St-Georges give some idea of the size of the wine list, which must be one of the most comprehensive burgundy selections for a long way. If they don't come cheap, then sixteen Beaujolais will help, or some of the lesser clarets, or bottles from Spain and South Africa, and fine Australians and Californians. CELLARMAN'S CHOICE: Hautes Côtes de Nuits '81, £14·50.

CHEFS: David Gibson and Clive Davidson PROPRIETORS: Clive and Anne Davidson
OPEN: Mon to Sat, exc Sat L CLOSED: 3 weeks at Christmas MEALS: 12.30 to 2, 7.15 to 10
PRICES: £20 (£30), Set L from £9·50 (£16). Minimum £7·50. Service 10% CARDS: Access, Amex, Diners, Visa
SEATS: 50. 13 tables outside. Private parties: 50 main room. Car-park, 100 places. No children under 8. Smart dress preferred. Wheelchair access

LYBSTER Highland

map 8

▲ *Bayview Hotel* [10/20]

Russell Street, Lybster KW3 6AG
LYBSTER (059 32) 346   £9–£15

The Huttons' small whitewashed hotel offers excellent value – the more so in this
rapacious part of the country. It combines the atmosphere of a pub with the
formality of a restaurant. A four-course dinner might include sweet pickled
herrings, vegetable soup, sole gratin, and hazel-nut gateau. The quality of the
produce, such as the Angus steaks and venison, is high. Breakfasts are
challenging. The list of malts rather overshadows the wine list of forty bottles.
House Bulgarian Chardonnay is £4. CELLARMAN'S CHOICE: Chassagne-
Montrachet from Drouhin '84, £12·50.

CHEF: Norma Hutton PROPRIETOR: Ranald Hutton
OPEN: all week, exc Sun D MEALS: 12 to 2.30, 7.30 to 10
PRICES: Set Sun L £6·50 (£9), Set D £11·75 (£15), Snacks from 60p CARDS: Access, Amex,
Carte Blanche, Diners, Visa
SEATS: 40. Private parties: 20 main room. Car-park, 20 places. Children's helpings. Smart
dress preferred. Wheelchair access
ACCOMMODATION: 3 rooms. B&B £13·50 to £24. Children welcome. Baby facilities. Pets
welcome. Afternoon teas. Fishing. Golf. Doors close at 1.30

MELROSE Borders

map 8

Marmion's Brasserie [10/20]

Buccleuch Street, Melrose TD6 9LB
MELROSE (089 682) 2245   £14

Pretty close to a genuine brasserie: the lofty dining-room makes use of wood and
plants but avoids pretensions and the menu takes its cue from there. Two dozen
dishes are assembled with care. The earthier, like potato soup, croque-monsieur,
even pork hongroise, rate higher than the more fanciful items like scampi. But
the desserts shine, notably profiteroles. Coffee is ad lib. The fourteen wines stretch
up to Juliénas '83 at £8.

CHEF: Seoras Lindsey PROPRIETORS: Ian and Sheila Robson
OPEN: all week MEALS: 10am to 11pm (1 to 5 Sun)
PRICES: £10 (£14), Snacks from £1·75 CARD: Access
SEATS: 60. Private parties: 60 main room. Vegetarian meals. Children's helpings. Smart
dress preferred. No pipes. Wheelchair access (also WC). Music. Air-conditioned

MULL Strathclyde

map 8

▲ *Tiroran House* [11/20]

Tiroran, Mull PA69 6ES
TIRORAN (068 15) 232   £21

An immaculate house, with views of the sea, Loch Scridain and the hills, set in a
well-manicured garden through which a small river flows in a series of
waterfalls. There is a weighty feel to the converted shooting-lodge: cutlery and

cruets are cut-crystal Stuart and the tables are antique. Not only are prawns, mussels, oysters, crabs and salmon local, but the Blockeys use their own beef, venison and lamb; chicken and duck eggs; herbs, soft fruits and lettuces, which they convert into a Gallic-Gaelic menu. Fresh gulls' eggs come with a watercress mayonnaise, gravlax is homemade, steak and kidney pie is served with a fresh Mull oyster sauce. Muill Cheddar, Caboc or Orkney cheeses follow hot rhubarb crumble meringue, or Ecclefechan pie. Lesser-known clarets help to keep prices manageable, there is a single Australian Chardonnay, and ten half-bottles. CELLARMAN'S CHOICE: Ch. des Moines '83, £11.

CHEF: Sue Blockey PROPRIETORS: Wing Commander and Mrs Blockey
OPEN: all week, D only (L residents only) CLOSED: mid-Oct to 1 May MEALS: 7
PRICES: Set D £18 (£21). Service inc
SEATS: 20. Private parties: 8 main room. Car-park, 20 places. No children under 10. Jacket and tie. No smoking in dining-room. One sitting
ACCOMMODATION: 9 rooms, all with bath/shower. B&B £30 to £65. Deposit: £25. No children under 10. Garden. Fishing. Scenic. Confirm by 12 [GHG]

NAIRN Highland
map 8

▲ *Clifton Hotel* [11/20]

Viewfield Street, Nairn IV12 4HW
NAIRN (0667) 53119
£16–£21

Theatrically eclectic; every inch of wall space is covered with framed pictures and every surface with books; dinners are acted out under the direction of Mr Macintyre, who wears a kilt. The script is in French and runs to more than a dozen dishes before sweets, including, in case anyone were worried, poulet rôti à l'écossaise. Turbot is grilled with melted butter, lamb's liver served with bacon, or there's beef Stroganoff. Starters are simple: smoked salmon, melon with ginger, duck pâté with prunes. Well-kept cheeses include goats' and ewes' milk. The concertina wine list has pedigree claret from the '60s and '70s, half a dozen Gewürztraminers, and inexpensive bottles from Central and Southern France. CELLARMAN'S CHOICE: Sancerre, Clos du Chêne Marchand '84, £12·50.

CHEFS: J. Gordon Macintyre and Graeme Allan PROPRIETOR: J. Gordon Macintyre
OPEN: all week CLOSED: Nov to 1 Mar MEALS: 12 to 1.30, 7 to 9.30
PRICES: £14 (£21), Set L from £9 (£16), Set D from £10 (£17), Snacks from £2
CARDS: Access, Amex, Diners, Visa
SEATS: 55. Private parties: 80 main room, 12 private room. Car-park, 20 places. Vegetarian meals. Children's helpings. Smart dress preferred. No smoking in dining-room. Music
ACCOMMODATION: 16 rooms, all with bath/shower. B&B £43 to £62. Deposit: 10%. Children welcome. Pets welcome. Afternoon teas. Garden. Doors close at 12 [GHG]

NEWTON STEWART Dumfries & Galloway
map 8

▲ *Kirroughtree Hotel*

Newton Stewart DG8 6AN
NEWTON STEWART (0671) 2141

This restaurant was sold as the Guide *went to press.*

map 8

▲ *Ard na Coille* [10/20]

Kingussie Road, Newtonmore PH20 1AY
NEWTONMORE (054 03) 214
£16

The name means 'high in the woods', and this old-fashioned hotel is among fir trees on raised ground between Newtonmore and Kingussie. The dining-room has panelling and fine views, not to mention a stag's head on the wall. The fixed-price menu is good value for mid-Channel-style dishes such as cold watercress soup, veal and ham terrine, and mussels in white wine and cream. A thick piece of sirloin steak is cooked in crisp, buttery pastry. Well-kept cheeses include Lanark Blue and a Welsh goats'. Breakfast has featured peat-smoked haddock and home-made muesli. Plenty of wines under £10, including CELLARMAN'S CHOICE: Château du Grand Moulas, Côtes du Rhône '84, £5·80.

CHEF: Annie Murchie PROPRIETORS: Alastair and Annie Murchie
OPEN: all week, D only CLOSED: 1 Nov to 31 Mar MEALS: 7.45
PRICES: Set D £13 (£16). Service inc
SEATS: 24. Private parties: 12 main room. Car-park, 15 places. Children welcome. No smoking during meals. One sitting
ACCOMMODATION: 10 rooms, 4 with bath/shower. B&B £18 to £47. Children welcome. Pets welcome. Garden. Scenic. Doors close at 11. Confirm by 6 [GHG]

The entries are compiled from the views of readers who have eaten at the restaurants in the last year, backed up by anonymous inspections and by information supplied and facts verified by the restaurants.

OBAN Strathclyde   map 8

▲ *Knipoch Hotel* [11/20]

Oban PA34 4QT
KILNINVER (085 26) 251
on A816, 6m S of Oban   £28

'The water is coloured with peat. We looked from wine (Sauvignon) to water and
from water to wine again, but it was impossible to say which was which.' On the
frontier of the Oban desert for eating out, the former tax collector's house – the
earliest part is fifteenth century, the main part Georgian, and the Craigs have
sympathetically restored it – provides a welcome, gastronomically orientated
household. Outside, the view is to Loch Feochan. Inside is log fires. Set dinners –
'We take it as a compliment if you dress for dinner, but fully understand if you
would prefer not to' – change daily. Loch Feochan salmon is filleted, dry-salted,
and marinated in sugar, juniper, rowan, thyme and tarragon, given a tot of
whisky, and cold-smoked oven hardwood for one to four days. Gravlax is also a
feature, as Jenny and Jytte Craig are Danes. Fresh salmon from the loch and
scallops from Luing are transformed into a roulade wrapped in sea-kale leaves.
Otherwise whole fillet of Aberdeen Angus beef becomes chateaubriand with a
perfect béarnaise sauce. Wild oyster mushroom soup tastes of itself – stocks are
enforced with supplies of free-range birds – and a crisp brandy-snap basket filled
with exotic fruits comes with a bramble coulis that tastes of the hedgerows. The
list of over two hundred wines roams around the world, taking in fine selections
from Tuscany, Australasia and California, a fistful of English, some inexpensive
eastern Europeans, and does more than justice to the classic regions of France, all
at reasonable mark-ups. CELLARMAN'S CHOICE: Sauvignon du Haut Poitou '85,
£6·30.

CHEFS: Colin and Jenny Craig PROPRIETORS: The Craig family
OPEN: all week CLOSED: early Jan to mid-Feb MEALS: 12.30 to 2, 7.30 to 9
PRICES: Set D £22·50 (£28), cheaper L available CARDS: Access, Amex, Diners, Visa
SEATS: 46. Private parties: 24 main room. Car-park, 40 places. Children's helpings
ACCOMMODATION: 21 rooms, all with bath/shower. B&B £39·50 to £79. Deposit: £50.
Afternoon teas. Garden. Fishing. Golf. TV. Phone. Scenic. Doors close at 11. Confirm by 6
[GHG]

ORKNEY   map 8

Hamnavoe [10/20]

35 Graham Place, Stromness KW16 3BY
STROMNESS (0856) 850606   £21

Widely held to be the best place to eat on the island. Catriona Cussen and Denis
Moylan serve fresh food throughout the year. Many ingredients, especially fish,
are local, but the style looks towards France. A trio of salmon, haddock and king
prawn comes with saffron sauce; breast of chicken is stuffed with salmon and
served with wild thyme sauce. The vegetable soup has been good. Pork gets a
hearty stuffing of lemon, nuts and apple. Hamnavoe swan is back on the menu as
the most popular sweet – a biscuit, fruit and cream concoction – and there is also
local cheese. The name means a sheltered harbour. The short wine list opens at

£5·75. CELLARMAN'S CHOICE: Chardonnay, Hunter Valley, Rosemount Estate '85, £9·75.

CHEF: Denis Moylan PROPRIETORS: Catriona Cussen and Denis Moylan
OPEN: Wed to Mon CLOSED: Jan MEALS: 12 to 2.30, 7 to 10
PRICES: £15 (£21) CARDS: Access, Visa
SEATS: 36. Private parties: 38 main room. Children's helpings. Smart dress preferred.
Wheelchair access

PEAT INN Fife   map 8

▲ *Peat Inn* [15/20]

Peat Inn KY15 5LH
PEAT INN (033 484) 206
6m SW of St Andrews at junction of B940/B941   £17–£30

For sixteen years David Wilson has provided a level of cooking virtually unknown in Scotland at his lovely refashioned pub at a solitary crossroads. Some days the operation is slow to start – reception does not know what the menu will be before 12.30 – but the cooking speaks for itself. Here are two autumn dishes: two fillets of sole, one filled with a sole mousse sharpened with lemon, the other with a lobster mousse decorated with a basil leaf set on a few spoonfuls of intensely flavoured lobster sauce. A week before: a dozen thick slices of pigeon breast, cut across the grain, set at the hours on the face of the octagonal plate, with a mould of dark fungi and some stripes of aubergine in a pool of brandy and juniper sauce, accompanied by a side plate of broccoli, French beans, and a medallion of roast potatoes. The polish is obviously French, but a zealous hunt for Scottish raw materials and an enjoyment of vivid flavours – as in a caramelised apple tart with caramel butterscotch sauce, or wild duck with blueberries, or monk-fish with chives – is true to the wealth of the region. The set menus are good value, with lunch of four courses, dinner of six. Last year David Wilson finally received his Michelin rosette, but the cooking is not radically different from when the *Guide* discovered him. Eight rooms opened in autumn 1987. The wine list has been drawn up by a wine lover who wants to share the pleasures, and well-chosen bottles at reasonable prices ensure first-class drinking. To pursue this approach with claret is commendable – there are even classed growth '70s that would be reasonably priced if they were bought in a shop – but to succeed with burgundy as well is a rare achievement; Drouhin, Latour, Ponnelle, Tollot-Beaut, Dujac *et al* are out in force but not out of reach. The New World gets a look in, and the same attention is lavished on half-bottles.

CHEF: David Wilson PROPRIETORS: David and Patricia Wilson
OPEN: Tue to Sat CLOSED: 2 weeks Jan, 1 week Apr, 1 week Oct
MEALS: 12.30 to 1, 7 to 9.30
PRICES: £21 (£28), Set L £12·50 (£17), Set D £25 (£30). Service inc CARDS: Amex, Access, Diners, Visa
SEATS: 48. Private parties: 24 main room, 12 private room. Car-park, 24 places. Children's helpings. No smoking during meals. Wheelchair access (also WC)
ACCOMMODATION: 8 rooms, all with bath/shower. Rooms for disabled. B&B £55 to £70. Children welcome. No pets. Fishing. Golf. TV. Phone. Scenic. Confirm by 4

PEEBLES Borders map 8

▲ *Cringletie House Hotel* [10/20]

Eddleston, Peebles EH45 8PL
EDDLESTON (072 13) 233
on A703, 2m N of Peebles £13–£22

The new upholstery of this baronial hotel, a fixture of the Scottish listings since
1973 – with a garden fine enough to be opened twice a year to the public –
throws an unkind light on a menu enriched in béchamel. Straying from the fine
roasts and the good, less expensive red wines has been increasingly foolhardy in
recent years. The twin laws of Scottish eating out apply, with fine soups but poor
cheeses. There is a commendable effort to provide food throughout the day, and
there is substantial choice in the four-course dinner menu. House French is
£6·90 a litre.

CHEFS: Aileen Maguire and Sheila McKellar PROPRIETORS: Mr and Mrs Stanley Maguire
OPEN: all week CLOSED: Jan and Feb MEALS: 1 to 1.45, 7.30 to 8.30
PRICES: £8 (£13), Set D £15·50 (£22) CARDS: Access, Visa
SEATS: 56. Private parties: 30 main room. Car-park, 40 places. Vegetarian meals. Children's
helpings. No smoking in dining-room
ACCOMMODATION: 16 rooms, 11 with bath/shower. Lift. B&B £26·50 to £55. Children
welcome. Baby facilities. Pets welcome. Afternoon teas. Garden. Tennis. Scenic. Doors close
at 11. Confirm by 5 [GHG]

PERTH Tayside map 8

Coach House [13/20]

8 North Port, Perth PH1 5LU
PERTH (0738) 27950 £11–£20

Tony and Betty Heath offer a fixed-price menu for lunch and (remarkable value)
for dinner. Scottish produce mostly inspires their cooking. The style isn't overdressed and avoids unnecessary garnishes and outlandish marriages of
ingredients. Instead, there is a ragout of West Coast mussels and prawns in
saffron sauce; smoked venison and smoked duck with avocado; Arbroath smokie
and tomato mousse; fillet of lamb cooked pink with a charlotte of aubergine and
port wine sauce. Tony Heath's skills take in everything from a delightfully simple
orange and tomato soup to perfectly executed salmon coulibiac with lobster
sauce or sauté of calves' kidneys with calvados and grain mustard. A van drives
to Paris every week for vegetables, including half a dozen kinds of lettuce. Sweets
stay with the likes of honey and brandy ice-cream, Cassis mousse and chocolate
bavarois. Coffee comes with home-made truffles. A well-spread wine list of good
French pedigree has many halves. House Provence is £5.
CELLARMAN'S CHOICE: Ch. Gazin '79, £14.

CHEF: Tony Heath PROPRIETORS: Tony and Betty Heath
OPEN: Tue to Sat MEALS: 12.30 to 2, 7.15 to 10
PRICES: Set L from £7·50 (£11), Set D from £16 (£20) CARDS: Access, Visa
SEATS: 36. Private parties: 24 main room. Children's helpings. No children under 8. No pipes
in dining-room. Wheelchair access

Timothy's [11/20]

24 St John Street, Perth PH1 5SP
PERTH (0738) 26641   £11

The Laings' town-centre restaurant is as consistent as ever. Although it is best
known for its Danish snitter (snacks), smørrebrød (open sandwiches), and a beef
fondue with six sauces, Caroline Laing continues to experiment with starters and
sweets. Soups can bring together all kinds of ingredients: Brie with celery and
nutmeg; avocado and lettuce; beef with beer and bulgur wheat. Sweets vary with
the seasons, from syllabubs and mousses in summer to steamed fruit pudding in
winter, while the Danish chocolate cake has drawn good reports, as has the roast
beef platter with jacket potato and pickled onion. The emphasis is on local
ingredients supplemented by herbs, fruit and vegetables from the garden. To
drink, there is Löwenbräu on draught, and ice-cold akvavit.
CELLARMAN'S CHOICE: dry white Bergerac at £5·90.

CHEF: Mrs C. Laing PROPRIETORS: C. and A. Laing
OPEN: Tue to Sat CLOSED: 3 weeks in summer MEALS: 12 to 2.30, 7 to 10.15
PRICES: £6 (£11). Post-theatre menu. Cover 25p at D. Minimum £5 at D CARD: Access
SEATS: 54. Private parties: 20 main room. Vegetarian meals. Children's helpings.
Wheelchair access. Music. Air-conditioned

PORT APPIN Strathclyde   map 8

▲ The Airds Hotel [15/20]

Port Appin PA38 4DF
APPIN (063 173) 236   £29

The hamlet of Port Appin is quiet, uncommercialised and surrounded by echoes
of Scottish history – the Jacobite Rebellion, the Appin Murder and the Massacre
of Glencoe. The Allens' dining-room has an uninterrupted view of Loch Linnhe,
the sea and the mountains of Morvern. The Airds is characterised by the
combination of genuine personal warmth, impeccable housekeeping and
cooking of real class. Here is one of the great hotels of Scotland. Betty Allen cooks
a daily four-course menu. On paper it reads simply, but the quality of the
ingredients (obviously shellfish and meats), the lightness of touch and the sheer
honesty of style can produce dazzling results. Soups set the tone: celery and
tomato, pea and ham, courgette and rosemary, served with home-made rolls.
Centrepieces highlight the fine British tradition of tracklements – venison with
rowan berry; roast rack of lamb sliced into medallions with crabapple and mint
jelly – or else they take in influences from France, such as poached chicken with
wild mushroom sauce or turbot with creamy tarragon sauce. Vegetables can be a
revelation: tiny new potatoes, cabbage with juniper, swede purée seem to have
an extraordinary freshness. To finish, the rage of 1987 – terrine of oranges in
home-made jelly – or more traditional date sponge with butterscotch sauce is
admirable. Breakfast – a great test of hotels – never fails; guests are offered fresh
orange juice, bread with lavish amounts of butter, good porridge, generous
helpings of bacon and eggs, toast with home-made marmalade, poached prunes
and apricots with yoghurt and nuts, plus cafetière coffee. Eric Allen loves his
wines, all 320 of them, and six dozen halves. To balance first growths and

mature vintages of claret and the glittering names of burgundy, there are humbler but well-chosen bottles from around the regions; among non-French wines bringing up the rear are New World Chardonnays.

CELLARMAN'S CHOICE: white Rully, Clos St Jacques, Domaine de la Folie '83, £15·50, and red Mercurey, Clos des Barraults, Juillot '82, £15·50.

CHEF: Betty Allen PROPRIETORS: Eric and Betty Allen
OPEN: all week, D only CLOSED: mid-Nov to Mar MEALS: 8
PRICES: Set D £22 (£29)
SEATS: 50. Private parties: 40 main room. Car-park, 30 places. Children's helpings. No children under 6. No smoking in dining-room. One sitting
ACCOMMODATION: 15 rooms, all with bath/shower. B&B £50 to £80. Deposit: £50. No children under 6. No pets. Afternoon teas. Garden. Scenic. Doors close at 11.30. Confirm by 4 [GHG]

PORTPATRICK Dumfries & Galloway   map 8

▲ *Knockinaam Lodge* [new entry, zero rated]

Portpatrick DG9 9AD
PORTPATRICK (077 681) 471   £6–£22

Built as a holiday house in 1869, Knockinaam Lodge stands at the foot of a thickly wooded glen and looks to the distant Irish coastline from the grounds and the private sandy beach. The interior is beautifully judged, with heavy fabrics in natural colours and exquisite flower watercolours on the walls, echoing the real flowers in vases. The atmosphere is tranquil, and the new owners, Marcel and Corinna Frichot, with Daniel Galmiche in the kitchen, have made a big impact since opening in February 1986. Saucing is often traditional: Bordeaux with Galloway beef; honey and port with Landais duck; and medallions of veal, just pink in the middle, with a garlicky red wine sauce. But the effect can be more modern, as when fresh asparagus in season comes with a fennel mousseline. Vegetables are minuscule, but sweets are showy mousses with fruit coulis. The cheeseboard has well-kept French goats', Gorgonzola and Gruyère. Coffee is served in the lounge with tiny fragile strawberry tartlets and fudge. The French wine list has sixty bottles from Whighams of Ayr, ranging from house claret at £7·40 to £50-plus. CELLARMAN'S CHOICE: Pernand Vergelesses '82, £14·50. More reports, please.

CHEF: Daniel Galmiche PROPRIETORS: Marcel and Corinna Frichot
OPEN: all week CLOSED: Jan to Easter MEALS: 12.30 to 1.45, 7.30 to 9
PRICES: Set L from £2 (£6), Set D £18 (£22). Service inc CARDS: Access, Amex, Diners, Visa
SEATS: 28. Private parties: 40 main room. Car-park, 25 places. No children under 12 at D. Jacket and tie. Wheelchair access (also WC)
ACCOMMODATION: 10 rooms, all with bath/shower. Rooms for disabled. B&B £65 to £130. Deposit: £100. Children welcome. Baby facilities. Pets welcome. Afternoon teas. Garden. Fishing. TV. Phone. Scenic [GHG]

SCARISTA see HARRIS

If you suspect that a restaurant is using processed food, always ask. It would be a contravention of the Trade Descriptions Act for the restaurant to lie.

---

map 8

Knights of Scone   [new entry, zero rated]

80 Perth Road, Scone PH2 6JL
SCONE (0738) 52329   £9–£18

The frontage reveals that this was once a shop, but the restaurant has grander
intentions. It is a large, high-ceilinged room with a hotch-potch of furniture
divided up by screens and tables. There's a faded Edwardian charm. Helen Pirie
cooks a short, manageable menu that can take advantage of fresh market
produce, and she uses plenty of fresh herbs from a nearby grower. The style is
Scottish with a French accent: fennel sauce with a salad of marinated red mullet;
tarragon with casseroled rabbit; basil with quenelles of sea-trout. Otherwise
there is venison pudding and wild duck with rowanberries and orange. To finish
there are mounds of white chocolate mousse on a pool of strawberry sauce or a
two-inch-high toffee apple pudding with whipped cream. Sunday lunch is good
value at £6·50. Eighteen wines, with few over £6. More reports, please.

CHEF: Helen Pirie PROPRIETORS: Helen Pirie and Norman Cooper
OPEN: Tue to Sat, D only, and Sun L MEALS: 12.30 to 2, 7 to 10.30
PRICES: Set Sun L £6·50 (£9), D £14 (£18). Service inc CARDS: Access, Carte Blanche, Visa
SEATS: 25. Private parties: 28 main room. Car-park, 12 places. Children's helpings. No
smoking in dining-room. Wheelchair access (also WC)

▲ *Murrayshall Hotel*   [new entry, zero rated]

Scone PH2 7PH
SCONE (0738) 51173   £14–£23

This is a rising star: a sumptuous blue and gold dining-room, renovated at
substantial expense, cooked for by Bruce Sangster, who in a short time has made
quite a reputation for himself. His style is encouragingly concentrated on the best
of Scottish produce. Some of the artifice is striking: an open-weave pastry
fisherman's crawl floating on a bowl of mussel soup with saffron. From the same
meal, a breast of chicken came sliced on a sauce of butter, orange and lemon,
stuffed with bread and herbs and spiced with a few green peppercorns. The
chocolate sweets are rich, the petits fours home-made. The wine list was still in
embryo last summer. More reports, please.

CHEF: Bruce Sangster PROPRIETORS: Macolsen Ltd
OPEN: all week MEALS: 12 to 2.30, 7.30 to 10
PRICES: £16 (£22), Set L £10 (£14), Set D £17·50 (£23) CARDS: Access, Amex, Diners, Visa
SEATS: 40. Private parties: 20 main room, 70 private room. Car-park. Vegetarian meals.
Children welcome. Jacket and tie. No smoking in dining-room. Wheelchair access. Music
ACCOMMODATION: 20 rooms, all with bath/shower. B&B £39 to £54. Deposit: 20%. Children
welcome. Baby facilities. No pets. Afternoon teas. Garden. Tennis. Fishing. Golf. TV. Phone.
Scenic. Confirm by 7

*The 1989 Guide will appear before Christmas 1988. Reports are particularly helpful
in the spring. Report forms are at the back of this book, but just write a letter if you
prefer. Address it to* The Good Food Guide, FREEPOST, 14 Buckingham Street, London
WC2N 6BR. *No stamp is necessary if you post it in the UK.*

SHETLAND   map 8

▲ *Burrastow House* [10/20]

Burrastow, Walls, Shetland ZE2 9PD
WALLS (059 571) 307
3m W of Walls   £16

The Tuckeys are now in their sixth year as hosts at this remote, eighteenth-
century listed house. Stella Tuckey's cooking reflects what is local and
seasonal: seashore mussels appear as a starter, boned leg of Shetland lamb is
stuffed with apricots; rabbit is cooked with mustard; hares are jugged. The steak,
kidney and mushroom pie has been memorable. Vegetarian dishes now feature
strongly: brown rice risotto; aubergine and red-bean hot-pot; vegetable
croustade. Granary bread is baked each day, and vegetables are from the garden.
House wine is £5·58. CELLARMAN'S CHOICE: Pinot Noir, Charles Viénot, £8·98.

CHEF: Stella Tuckey PROPRIETORS: Stella and Harry Tuckey
OPEN: all week, D only CLOSED: 23 Dec to 10 Jan MEALS: 7 to 9.30
PRICES: Set D £13·50 (£16), Snacks from £2·50. Service inc
SEATS: 10. Private parties: 12 main room. Car-park, 8 places. Vegetarian meals. Children's
helpings. No smoking in dining-room. Music
ACCOMMODATION: 3 rooms, all with bath/shower. B&B £24·75 to £50. Baby facilities. Pets
welcome. Garden. Fishing. Golf. TV. Scenic [GHG]

SKYE Highland   map 8

▲ *Harlosh Hotel* [10/20]

Dunvegan IV51 5AB
DUNVEGAN (047 022) 367   £13–£15

Well away from the bustle of modern, everyday life, on the shores of Loch
Bracadale, the hotel looks rather austere and is plainly decorated inside. There
are few frills, but the cooking is patriotic and sound. Haggis is served in vast
quantities and is not as overly seasoned as some. Fish is excellent, from crabs
served dressed in the shell or cod with parsley sauce. The set menu changes daily.
Snacks, drawn mainly from starters off the *carte* and served throughout the day,
are very good value. Service is reserved, as is the short wine list.

CHEF: Peter Bates PROPRIETORS: Peter and Rosalyn Bates
OPEN: all week, D only CLOSED: mid-Nov to Easter MEALS: 6.30 to 9
PRICES: £11 (£15), Set D from £9 (£13), L Snacks from £1
SEATS: 20. Private parties: 30 main room. Car-park, 15 places. Vegetarian meals. Children's
helpings. Wheelchair access
ACCOMMODATION: 8 rooms, 2 with bath/shower. B&B £14 to £28. Deposit: 10%. Children
welcome. Baby facilities. Pets welcome. Afternoon teas. Garden. Fishing. Scenic. Doors close
at 12. Confirm by 6

---

*The 1989 Guide will appear before Christmas 1988. Reports are particularly helpful
in the spring. Report forms are at the back of this book, but just write a letter if you
prefer. Address it to The Good Food Guide, FREEPOST, 14 Buckingham Street, London
WC2N 6BR. No stamp is necessary if you post it in the UK.*

▲ *Kinloch Lodge* [13/20]

Isle Ornsay, Sleat IV43 8QY
ISLE ORNSAY (047 13) 214/333
1m off A851 between Broadford and Armadale   £22·50

'The best Macdonalds we have been to' is one testimony. Historically, the
hunting-lodge is where Sir Alexander Macdonald decided not to support Prince
Charles Edward at Culloden. It is a graceful white house overlooking Loch na Dal,
not large or grand but with the atmosphere of somewhere that has been lived in.
The enthusiastic Claire Macdonald cooks a brief menu of fine modern British
dishes in which the ingredients retain their individual tastes. Lord Macdonald
and two casually dressed waitresses serve in the dark green room with polished
tables and family portraits looking down. Soups are based on fine stocks; main-
course meats are usually roasted and offset by exact, imaginative vegetables – for
instance, rough-cut carrots sauté in cognac. Fish is of course a feature, and the
potency of the cooking can be seen in the mixed seafood with a devil sauce of
deep pungency or a Jerusalem artichoke timbale with a Bercy sauce. A new
supply of unpasteurised cheeses is welcome. Sweets are, as ever, a rainbow of
mousses, creams, fruits, and ices. The 130-strong wine list has good clarets,
young burgundy and a smattering from everywhere else from £5.
CELLARMAN'S CHOICE: Châteauneuf-du-Pape, Domaine du Vieux
Télégraphe '84, £13.

    Lady Macdonald adds her own postscript: 'I have always fought against
putting "wild" salmon as such on the menu, but this year we will have to refer to
it as such. I have never tasted farmed salmon that is really good. Even if there
does exist such a fish it is still farmed in cruel conditions (overcrowded) and
unnatural – no currents to swim against so their flesh is mushy, and they are fed
chemicals to make their flesh pink.

    'I do not approve of the way Scotland is being covered on its every waterway
with hideous farming contraptions. To bring it home to us we learn that an
application has been put in for a 37-acre fish farm in the sea loch outside
Kinloch! This is designated an area of specific natural interest – we have a seal
colony, otters, rare sea birds, and an old oyster bed which last year we were
intrigued to find signs that is reviving. All these natural things would be
jeopardised if not wiped out by such a huge fish farm.'

CHEFS: Lady Macdonald and Peter Macpherson PROPRIETORS: Lord and Lady Macdonald
OPEN: all week, D only CLOSED: 4 days at Christmas, 11 Jan to 28 Feb MEALS: 8
PRICES: Set D £20 (£22·50). Service inc
SEATS: 25. Private parties: 8 main room. Car-park, 25 places. Children's helpings. No
children under 10. Wheelchair access (also WC). One sitting
ACCOMMODATION: 10 rooms, 9 with bath/shower. Rooms for disabled. B&B £30 to £74.
Deposit: £40. Baby facilities. Afternoon teas. Garden. Fishing. Scenic. Confirm by 3 [GHG]

Three Chimneys [12/20]

Colbost, Dunvegan IV51 9SY
GLENDALE (047 081) 258
on B884, 4m W of Dunvegan   £14–£21

The low-beamed ceiling and thick walls give the Spears' converted cottages on
the shore of Loch Dunvegan an atmosphere of days past. Open fires in both rooms

make it warm and homely. The views and their new wine and whisky shop –
next door and overcrowded with three visitors – draw people throughout the
day. Lunch is mainly cold dishes, dinner has a steak menu as well as a *carte*.
Shellfish and salmon are the lynchpins. Hot tarts are filled with white crab
flavoured with nutmeg, or with salmon, plain *and* smoked. Skye prawns are as
large as langoustines; at night they go into pastry boxes or crêpes. These apart,
the menu has more modern British aspects, taking its inspiration from tradition –
Highland lamb hot-pot with parsley dumplings; roast pigeon with skirlie
(oatmeal, onion and butter stuffing) and raspberries; and fine puddings such as
bread flavoured with whisky; marmalade; apple and oatie nut crumble, all served
with fresh cream. Sixty wines come from all over France and are mainly under
£10, with very good '83 Alsace. House wine, chosen by Bocuse, is £5·95.
CELLARMAN'S CHOICE: Beaumes-de-Venise rouge, Domaine Les Goubert '83,
£9·50.

CHEF: Shirley Spear PROPRIETORS: Eddie and Shirley Spear
OPEN: all week, exc Sun L CLOSED: end Oct to Mar MEALS: 12.30 to 2, 7 to 9
PRICES: £14 (£21), Set D from £8·95 (£14) CARDS: Access, Visa
SEATS: 35. 2 tables outside. Private parties: 24 main room. Car-park, 30 places. Vegetarian
meals. Music

SLEAT see SKYE

ST ANDREWS Fife   map 8

▲ *West Park House* [new entry, zero rated]

St Mary's Place, St Andrews KY16 9UY
ST ANDREWS (0334) 75933   £8–£17

The cooking is surprisingly good at this rather unpromising green house at the
top end of town. Owner Brian MacLennan also runs the kitchen. Carrot and
apple soup is made from good stock, plaice fillets are sauté with fresh tarragon,
and breast of chicken is served with a delicate brandy and mushroom sauce.
More ambitious dishes include poached halibut with shrimp sauce and crayfish,
or guinea-fowl with bordelaise sauce. Vegetables are carefully undercooked, and
to finish there's splendid apple pie or extravagant gateaux. House wine, off a
largely French list, is £5·50 a litre. More reports, please.

CHEF: Brian MacLennan PROPRIETORS: Brian and Rosemary MacLennan
OPEN: Mon to Sat, exc Mon D MEALS: 12 to 1.30, 7 to 8.30
PRICES: L £4 (£8), Set D £12·75 (£17)
SEATS: 18. Private parties: 18 main room. Vegetarian meals. Children's helpings (L only). No
children under 10 at D. Smart dress preferred. Wheelchair access (also WC)
ACCOMMODATION: 5 rooms, 4 with bath/shower. Rooms for disabled. B&B from £23.
Deposit: £10. Children welcome. Baby facilities. Afternoon teas. TV. Doors close at 11

STROMNESS see ORKNEY

All inspections are carried out anonymously.

SWINTON Borders   map 8

▲ *Four Seasons, Wheatsheaf Hotel* [10/20]

Swinton TD11 3JJ
SWINTON (089 086) 257   £17

The grey stone inn overlooks the village green and provides a useful detour off
the main A627 from Newcastle to Edinburgh. The spirit is Victorian. Restaurant
meals are limited to three evenings a week, but bar meals are served earlier in the
week. Alan Reid goes to Eyemouth and Aberdeen for fish, which appear as
scallops provençale or squid stuffed with prawns. A twenty-dish menu is headed
by steaks and lobsters. Soups are well made. Sauces for the most part rely on
butter, cream or cheese. Venison Baden Baden is the real thing. Sweets range
from chocolate and rum mousse to passion-fruit sorbet. Twenty wines, and four
good house wines at £4·50. CELLARMAN'S CHOICE: Australian Cabernet-
Sauvignon, Orlando, £6·95.

CHEF: Alan Reid PROPRIETORS: Alan and Julie Reid
OPEN: Thur to Sat, D only, and Sun L CLOSED: 1 week Feb MEALS: 12.30 to 2.15, 7 to 10
PRICES: £12 (£17) CARDS: Access, Visa
SEATS: 20. Private parties: 22 main room. Vegetarian meals. Children's helpings. Smart
dress preferred. No cigars/pipes in dining-room. Wheelchair access (also WC)
ACCOMMODATION: 3 rooms. B&B £15 to £25. Children welcome. Baby facilities. Pets
welcome. Garden. TV. Scenic. Doors close at 2. Confirm by 6

TARBERT Strathclyde   map 8

▲ *West Loch Hotel* [11/20]

Tarbert PA29 6YF
TARBERT (088 02) 283
on A83, 1m S of Tarbert   £13–£19

The Thoms' attractive stone building is on the old drovers' road, overlooking
West Loch pier and the Islay ferry. Inside it feels calm, cosy and comfortable in an
old-fashioned way. Janet Thom shows off honest Scottish cooking at its best,
which means fresh ingredients cooked with care and attention. Three-course set
dinners start off with fresh home-baked bread, and there's no stinting on
helpings. One typically good meal in June featured twenty tiny queenies with a
creamy curry sauce, and a mushroom and coriander pâté, before a parcel of
halibut in lettuce leaves with smooth white wine sauce, or carbonnade of beef.
Puddings are home made: walnut meringue with strawberry cream; sherry trifle;
chocolate cheesecake. Lunchtime bar snacks are excellent. The short wine list
holds no surprises; house red and white are £5·55 a bottle.

CHEF: Janet Thom PROPRIETORS: Alistair and Janet Thom
OPEN: all week CLOSED: Nov MEALS: 12 to 2, 7 to 8.30
PRICES: £9 (£13), Set D £14·50 (£19) CARD: Access
SEATS: 30. 2 tables outside. Private parties: 30 main room. Car-park, 20 places. Children's
helpings. No smoking in dining-room. Wheelchair access (also WC). Music
ACCOMMODATION: 6 rooms. B&B £20 to £31. Children welcome. Baby facilities. Pets
welcome. Afternoon teas. Scenic

TIRORAN see MULL

TURNBERRY Strathclyde   map 8

▲ *Turnberry Hotel* [13/20]

Turnberry KA26 9LT
TURNBERRY (0655) 31000 and 31706   £18–£33

Everything about Turnberry is big. The sprawling Edwardian mansion
dominates a hill overlooking the sea towards Arran and boasts not one but two of
the finest golf courses. It would be easy for the kitchen to churn out bland,
ostentatious food for expense accounts and tourists, but not so – in fact, set meal
prices are good value compared to the South, even without the setting, and
Stewart Cameron has earned the right to have his dining-room judged with the
best. As well as well-tried classics, such as poached salmon with hollandaise,
entrecôte bordelaise, and roast best end of lamb, the kitchen tackles more
elaborate modern dishes: perfectly cooked fillets of sole coated in passion-fruit
sauce; suprême of chicken wrapped in leeks and baked in puff pastry. Vegetables
are served from copper pans, and the menu acknowledges the trend towards
vegetarian and healthy food with steamed salmon kebab and cucumber purée;
cauliflower and broccoli mousse with watercress sauce; and vegetable salad with
walnut dressing. To finish, there's a good version of English summer pudding,
but the barmy habit of writing the menu in French means it is christened
'pouding d'été'. The wine list is predictably expensive, launching off from Ch.
Puyfromage '85 at £11·25 into vintage clarets and burgundies. Even Muscadet
is £14·25, £2·25 more than lunch.

CHEF: D. S. Cameron PROPRIETORS: Orient Express Hotels
OPEN: all week MEALS: 1 to 2.30, 7.30 to 9.30
PRICES: £26 (£33), Set L £12 (£18), Set D £21 (£27), Snacks from £1·05. Service inc
CARDS: Access, Amex, Diners, Visa
SEATS: 250. Private parties: 150 main room, 20 and 40 private rooms. Car-park, 200 places.
Vegetarian meals. Children's helpings. Jacket and tie. Wheelchair access (also WC). Music
ACCOMMODATION: 130 rooms, all with bath/shower. Rooms for disabled. Lift. B&B £60 to
£95. Baby facilities. Afternoon teas. Garden. Swimming-pool. Sauna. Tennis. Fishing. Golf.
Snooker. TV. Phone. Scenic

TYNDRUM Central   map 8

Clifton Coffee House [9/20]

Tyndrum FK20 8RY
TYNDRUM (083 84) 271   £8

Homely cooking is the essence of this self-service cafe. Hearty soups include Fife
broth and cock-a-leekie. The taste of Scotland menu takes in stovies with
sausages, cold salmon, and Tipsy Laird. House Bulgarian is 75p a glass, and there
are quarter-bottles of South African wines.

Restaurants that we have not been able to assess as fully as we would like are given a
zero rating this year. We are particularly keen to have reports on these places.

CHEFS: Lesley V. Wilkie, Mary Smith and Moira Atkinson PROPRIETORS: Derek D. Wilkie,
Lesley Wilkie and Lamond P. Gosden
OPEN: all week, daytime only CLOSED: Nov to Mar MEALS: 8.30 to 5.30
PRICES: £5 (£8), Snacks from 98p CARDS: Access, Amex, Diners, Visa
SEATS: 220. Car-park, 100 places. Vegetarian meals. Children's helpings. No-smoking area.
Wheelchair access (also WC). Air-conditioned. Self-service

ULLAPOOL Highland   map 8

▲ *Altnaharrie Inn* [15/20]

Ullapool IV26 2SS
DUNDONNELL (085 483) 230   £33

A foot-track leads to Altnaharrie, but Fred Brown picks up guests from Ullapool
harbour on his boat. The hotel is at the foot of a steep hill, a small white building
with a Scandinavian feel. Gunn Brown's training as an artist dominates both the
Liberty-inspired house and also her menu. She is one of the most accomplished
modern British chefs. Something quite unusual happens here for the fourteen or
so people who reach this far outpost. Distance may make the reports wax
warmer, but what of this main dish: breast of wood-pigeon with a sauce of its
own juices, leeks, grapes and juniper, served with a cake of its liver and brown
mushrooms? Meals open with a soup, such as marrow and coriander; nettle;
cucumber and hawthorn, sorrel and watercress; fish with pieces of sole, salmon
and monk-fish. Fish is abundant, often preserved, such as gravlax or pickled
herrings, or more sophisticated, such as lobster in two sauces – one of its juices
with a Mâcon, the other from the roe and dark meat – or crab in pasta. The
quality of main-course meats is as good as in lamb with rosemary, thyme and a
leek sauce. Choice comes with the sweets: baked peaches with macaroons,
rhubarb tart, chocolate meringue. Extensive breakfasts have included venison
sausages. Claret and burgundy are plentiful, there are mature vintages, and
mark-ups are not excessive. CELLARMAN'S CHOICE: Santenay, Clos de Tavannes,
Gaguard '83, £16·50.

CHEF: Gunn Eriksen Brown PROPRIETORS: Fred and Gunn Brown
OPEN: all week, D only CLOSED: late Oct to Easter MEALS: 7.45
PRICES: Set D £27·50 (£33). Service inc
SEATS: 14. Private parties: 14 main room. Car-park, 20 places. Vegetarian meals. Children's
helpings. No children under 10. No smoking in dining-room. One sitting
ACCOMMODATION: 5 rooms, all with bath/shower. D, B&B £58 to £116. Deposit: £25. No
children under 10. Garden. Fishing. Scenic. Confirm by 4 [GHG]

▲ *Morefield Motel* [10/20]

Ullapool IV26 2TH
ULLAPOOL (0854) 2161   £19

The pick of the fish off the Ullapool boats ends up here at this modern,
unimposing low-slung building a mile out of town on the road to Achiltibuie.
David Smyrl and David Courtney Marsh started as scallop divers twelve years ago

▮ *This symbol is awarded only to restaurants with outstanding wine cellars.*

and arrived via the wholesale trade. Mussels, squid, scallops, turbot, and halibut are at their best cooked plainly with just a minimum of saucing. Lobster and langoustines are served six ways. The décor is spartan, but the hospitality is genuine. Wines are limited. House Italian is £4·95.

CHEF: Robert Giovaninni PROPRIETORS: David Smyrl and David Courtney Marsh
OPEN: all week MEALS: 12 (12.30 Sun) to 2, 6 to 9.30
PRICES: £15 (£19) Service inc CARDS: Access, Amex, Visa
SEATS: 36. Private parties: 40 main room. Car-park, 35 places. Children's helpings. No-smoking area. Wheelchair access (also WC). Music
ACCOMMODATION: 11 rooms, all with bath/shower. Rooms for disabled. B&B £15·50 to £27. Children welcome. Baby facilities. Pets welcome. Afternoon teas. Garden. Doors close at 12. Confirm by 6

WALLS see SHETLAND

WHITEBRIDGE Highland   map 8

▲ *Knockie Lodge* [10/20]

Whitebridge IV1 2UP
GORTHLECK (045 63) 276
8m N of Fort Augustus on B862   £19

'Change is not something our guests particularly look for in this timeless part of the world.' The Milwards run a personable small hotel in this 200-year-old shooting-lodge. The cooking provides fine bar lunches and four-course dinners around good soups, steaks with mustard and whisky, and salmon with sorrel hollandaise. Sweets provide the only choice at dinner: damson and port parfait, fine ginger bombe with blackcurrant coulis. 'We do not insist on jacket and tie, but most male guests do wear them.' Vegetarians are welcome. House wines are £5·50, but look to the New World, with California Cabernet-Sauvignon at £25 or CELLARMAN'S CHOICE: Shiraz, Château Tahbilk '80, from Australia, £9.

CHEF: Christopher Freeman PROPRIETORS: Brenda and Ian Milward
OPEN: all week CLOSED: Nov to Easter MEALS: 8 to 8.45
PRICES: Set D £15 (£19), Bar L from £3 CARDS: Access, Amex, Visa
SEATS: 22. Private parties: 12 main room. Car-park, 30 places. No children under 10. Smart dress preferred. One sitting
ACCOMMODATION: 10 rooms, all with bath/shower. B&B £25 to £75. Deposit: £50. No children under 10. Garden. Fishing. Scenic [GHG]

Wales

ABERDOVEY Gwynedd   map 4

▲ *Maybank Hotel* [new entry, zero rated]

Aberdovey LL35 0PT
ABERDOVEY (065 472) 500   £10–£15

Robert Hughes gave up running his family's delicatessen to open this hotel in a
granite town house. The first-floor restaurant feels like a bistro and has fine views
of the Dovey Estuary from its Queen Anne-style windows. Sally Hughes cooks
honestly, uses fresh ingredients and changes her menu every day – all features of
the modern British idiom. There are nice touches to the set menu, with four or
five dishes per course: asparagus with salmon mousse in a delicate oregano
vinaigrette; suprême of chicken in wine sauce topped with shredded fennel; and
lamb chops with a sauce of orange and fresh mint. Sweets range from bread-and-
butter pudding to home-made chocolate and rum roulade. Much of the seventy-
strong wine list is under £10 and mostly from '80s vintages.

CHEF: Sally Hughes PROPRIETORS: Robert and Sally Hughes
OPEN: all week, D only, and Sun L CLOSED: 1 week at Christmas, Jan
MEALS: 12.45 to 1.45, 7 to 9.30
PRICES: Set Sun L £5·95 (£10), Set D £10·50 (£15) CARD: Visa
SEATS: 32. Private parties: 32 main room. Children's helpings. Music
ACCOMMODATION: 6 rooms, all with bath/shower. B&B £15 to £35. Deposit: £10. Children
welcome. Baby facilities. Pets welcome. Fishing. Golf. TV. Scenic. Doors close at 12

ABERSOCH Gwynedd   map 4

▲ *Porth Tocyn Hotel* [11/20]

Abersoch LL53 7BU
ABERSOCH (075 881) 2966   £12–£15

'We managed to spend over £5000 on fish in August alone last year, more than
on wine!' After thirty years of inclusion, these converted lead-miners' cottages
overlooking Cardigan Bay are the longest-running *Guide* entry for Wales. The
Fletcher-Brewer family still ring the gong for dinner, as they have done for forty
years. The menu changes daily and has moved to some extent with the times –

Restaurants change owners and chefs constantly. Please help keep the Guide *informed
of any changes you find.*

---

courgette and basil soup, sea-bass with hazel-nuts – though it is starting to show its age with some bland edges. Fish is very good. The style of roasts and hot puddings is still commendable, and it is these dishes at which the kitchen excels. Desserts are always alcoholic, and even the bread-and-butter pudding is given a whisky sauce. House claret is £6, on a sensible, not overpriced list of seventy wines.

CHEF: E. L. Fletcher-Brewer PROPRIETORS: The Fletcher-Brewer family
OPEN: all week MEALS: 12.30 to 2, 7.30 to 9.30
PRICES: Set Sun L £8 (£12), Set D from £10·50 (£15), L Snacks from £1 CARD: Access
SEATS: 60. 12 tables outside. Private parties: 60 main room. Car-park, 60 places. Children's helpings (with prior notice). No children under 7 at D. Smart dress preferred. Wheelchair access (also WC)
ACCOMMODATION: 17 rooms, all with bath/shower. Rooms for disabled. B&B £26 to £40. Deposit: £30. Baby facilities. Pets welcome. Afternoon teas. Garden. Swimming-pool. Tennis. TV. Phone. Scenic. Doors close at 12 [GHG]

ABERYSTWYTH Dyfed
map 4

Gannets [10/20]

7 St James Square, Aberystwyth SY23 1DU
ABERYSTWYTH (0970) 617164
£5–£9

Tucked away in a back street near the old market, and not far from the sea, this colourful family-run bistro is probably the best for many miles. Local salmon and game feature on the blackboard menu along with home-made soups, hot garlic mushrooms, turkey and cranberry pie, and suprême of chicken in flaky pastry. A couple of vegetarian dishes also appear. 'No tins, no sauce mixes – stocks made from beef bones.' Desserts are from the nursery: apple pie, trifle, treacle tart, pineapple cheesecake. Italian house wine is £5 a litre.

CHEF: David Mildon PROPRIETORS: Mr and Mrs David Mildon
OPEN: Mon to Sat MEALS: 12 to 2, 6 to 9.30
PRICES: £6 (£9), Set L from £2 (£5), Set D from £4 (£7). Service inc CARDS: Access, Visa
SEATS: 40. Private parties: 40 main room. Vegetarian meals. Children's helpings. Wheelchair access. Music

---

BRECHFA Dyfed
map 4

▲ *Ty Mawr* [new entry, zero rated]

Brechfa SA32 7RA
BRECHFA (026 789) 332
on B4310, 10m NE of Carmarthen
£10–£15

The Flaherty family have a bakery in the outbuildings which supplies local shops. The attractive farmhouse, which has been in the *Guide* before under different owners, is plainly decorated but has beautiful stone fireplaces. Dinner is priced according to the main course – turkey escalope with a green peppercorn sauce,

---

It is always advisable to book a restaurant in advance.

---

or guinea-fowl in a wine sauce. Carrots, cauliflower and new potatoes are simply cooked without butter. House wine is £5·75. More reports, please.

CHEFS: Alan and Timothy Flaherty PROPRIETORS: The Flaherty family
OPEN: all week, D only, and Sun L MEALS: 12 to 2, 7 to 9.30
PRICES: Set L £6·50 (£10), Set D from £10·95 (£15) CARDS: Access, Visa
SEATS: 60. Private parties: 40 main room. Car-park, 60 places. Vegetarian meals. Children's helpings. Smart dress preferred. Wheelchair access (also WC). Music
ACCOMMODATION: 5 rooms, all with bath/shower. B&B £35 to £45. Children welcome. Baby facilities. Pets welcome. Afternoon teas. Garden. Scenic. Doors close at 11.30. Confirm by 2

BROAD HAVEN Dyfed   map 4

▲ *Druidstone Hotel* [11/20]

Broad Haven SA62 3NE
BROAD HAVEN (043 783) 221   £13

The view over St Bride's Bay is as spectacular as the décor is worn at the Bells' hospitable hotel, which is really their home. It is that rarity – a family hotel run for families. The bar lunches are good value, and the multi-national dinners are at their best with the tried and tested – devilled crab, pepper steak, fresh salmon, alcoholic ice-creams, and home-made puddings. 'We still have no microwave.' Good English breakfasts. Plenty of malt whiskies. House wine is £5·50 a litre.

CHEFS: Rod and Jane Bell, Anna Pugh PROPRIETORS: Rod and Jane Bell
OPEN: Mon to Sat, D only, and Sun L CLOSED: Nov MEALS: 1 to 2, 7 to 10
PRICES: £8 (£13). Snacks from £1·10 CARDS: Amex, Visa
SEATS: 40. 8 tables outside. Private parties: 36 main room, 12 private room. car-park, 40 places. Children's helpings. Wheelchair access (also WC)
ACCOMMODATION: 8 rooms. Rooms for disabled. B&B £16·50 to £33. Deposit: £10. Children welcome. Baby facilities. Pets welcome. Afternoon teas. Garden. Scenic. Doors close at 12

CAERNARFON Gwynedd   map 4

Bakestone [new entry, zero rated]

26 Hole in the Wall Street, Caernarfon LL55 1RF
CAERNARFON (0286) 5846   £14

This small, neat French bistro by the castle, complete with red check tablecloths, has drawn uncommon enthusiasm for Yves Monin's cooking. Lunch brings enterprising dishes, such as fresh gull's egg, grilled Conwy sparling and monk-fish baked with rosemary and bacon. For meat-eaters there might be baked saucisson with spiced red cabbage, or beef carbonnade. These supplement daily offerings of crêpes. Good-looking Gallic sweets. Afternoon teas are also available. House wine is £5·80. More reports, please.

'The presentation of a credit card slip with the total left blank when the service has already been added to the bill is undignified and very irritating. If the service had been so outstanding, I, and I imagine others, would leave an additional amount in cash. Please could we outlaw restaurants that do this?' (On eating in London)

CHEF: Yves Monin PROPRIETORS: Guy Cutler and Yves Monin
OPEN: L Tue to Sun, exc Thur, D Mon to Sat MEALS: 12.30 to 2.30, 6.45 to 8.45
PRICES: £9 (£14), Snacks from £3·50. Minimum £3·50
SEATS: 32. 2 tables outside. Private parties: 16 main room. No children under 8.
No pipes. Music

CARDIFF South Glamorgan
map 4

Armless Dragon [11/20]

97 Wyvern Road, Cathays, Cardiff CF2 4BG
CARDIFF (0222) 382357
£17

'In a small kitchen, freshness forces simplicity on us.' The variety of Cardiff
market produces a vividly international menu with wholefood, fish and
European strains. Stir-fried samphire with seafood or laver balls with mushrooms
are typical, as are sesame toasts; hake baked with onions, garlic and tomatoes;
and fillet of beef in a red wine sauce with kidneys and mushrooms. Vegetables are
British. Hunza apricots and chocolate liqueur gateau is a favourite sweet. The
short, practical wine list has two from Wales. House French is £4·90 a bottle.

CHEF: D. Coleman PROPRIETORS: M. Sharples and D. Richards
OPEN: Mon to Sat, exc Sat L CLOSED: bank hols, Christmas to New Year
MEALS: 12.30 to 2.30, 7.30 to 10.30
PRICES: £12 (£17) CARDS: Access, Amex, Diners, Visa
SEATS: 50. Private parties: 45 main room. Vegetarian meals. Children welcome. Wheelchair
access (also WC). Music

Blas Ar Cymru/A Taste of Wales [10/20]

48 Crwys Road, Cardiff CF2 4NN
CARDIFF (0222) 382132
£12–£17

A laudable attempt to provide traditional Welsh cooking in the heart of urban
Cardiff. The mood is cramped and folksy, but the kitchen succeeds with trout
wrapped in smoked bacon, and no fewer than nine unpasteurised Welsh cheeses,
cockles, laver-bread, Glamorgan sausages, and salt duck are offered. The rabbit
stew has been good. A whole cottage loaf is left on the table complete with bread-
knife and butter. The limited wine list has a couple of Welsh representatives,
including Croffta.

CHEFS: Patricia Dally, Neil Baker and Robert Millard PROPRIETORS: Patricia
and Meirion Dally
OPEN: Mon to Sat, exc Sat L MEALS: 12 to 2, 7 to 10
PRICES: £12 (£17), Set L £7·95 (£12). Minimum £5·95 CARDS: Access, Amex, Diners, Visa
SEATS: 50. Private parties: 50 main room. Car-park, 30 places. Vegetarian meals. Children
welcome. Wheelchair access (also WC)

'"Good evening, you are holding the hand of X," says our host, paying particular
attention to the female diners – he had a tremendous penchant for my wife's chin.
"When I see something lovely it makes me feel like a barrel of butter on hot toast," he
told us on both occasions.' (On eating in Wales)

La Brasserie [9/20]

60 St Mary Street, Cardiff CF1 2AT
CARDIFF (0222) 372164 £12

Beams and sawdust make up the décor of this wine bar, which has proved
consistent and reliable. There are some good wines to go with good-quality
steaks and salads, which are carefully and simply presented. Fish and cheese can
also be good. House claret is £4·35.

CHEF: Mr Juan PROPRIETORS: K. Brenton and B. D. Martinez
OPEN: Mon to Sat MEALS: 12 to 2.45, 7 to 12.15
PRICES: £9 (£12). Service inc CARDS: Access, Amex, Diners, Visa
SEATS: 49. Children welcome. Smart dress preferred. Music

China City [9/20]

207 City Road, Cardiff CF2 3JD
CARDIFF (0222) 462668 £11–£16

Somewhere to eat, rather than somewhere to be seen. The plain cream walls,
worn red carpet, paper cloths, and the few lanterns barely amount to a décor, but
dishes off the long, mainly Cantonese menu, like the rice or the aubergine filled
with prawns and served with black beans, have been accomplished. The rows of
tables add to the institutional feeling, but some people hold that this may be the
best Chinese food in the city. It is certainly among the most consistent. House
Spanish is £5.

CHEF/PROPRIETOR: Mr Cheung
OPEN: all week MEALS: noon to 11.45pm
PRICES: £9 (£16), Set D from £13·50 (£22) for two. Service 10% CARDS: Access, Amex,
Diners, Visa
SEATS: 74. Private parties: 80 main room. Music. Air-conditioned

Everest Indian Cuisine [11/20]

43–45 Salisbury Road, Cathays, Cardiff CF2 4AB
CARDIFF (0222) 374881 £15

The ethnic star fades substantially this far west, but the Everest goes some way to
living up to its name. The décor is comfortable – not overly flock, rather a dusky
pink. Chicken tikka, lamb korma and other familiar staples draw warm
enthusiasm. The cooking is not greasy. Vegetarians are well catered for, though
the menu is a sensible selection of the greatest hits of India rather than
specialising in a particular region's cuisine. Some fancy cocktails supplement the
fundamental wine list.

CHEF: Mathaur Rahman PROPRIETORS: Abdul Kowsor and Abdul Miah
OPEN: all week MEALS: 12 to 2, 6 to 11.45 (12.30 Fri and Sat)
PRICES: £8 (£15). Minimum £5. Service 10% CARDS: Access, Amex, Diners, Visa
SEATS: 120. Private parties: 80 main room, 30 private room. Vegetarian meals. Children's
helpings. Wheelchair access (also WC). Music

Reports on shops, cafes and farms are useful, as well as reports on restaurants.

Gibsons [11/20]

8 Romilly Crescent, Canton, Cardiff CF1 9NR
CARDIFF (0222) 41264   £15–£22

Gibsons has regained its reputation as one of the best restaurants in Cardiff since Irene Canning's son Andrew took on the kitchen. The vein is reliable French provincial, avoiding the fashionable lure of *nouvelle*. This translates into salami with warm potato salad; chicken liver terrine with a confit of onions; strongly flavoured Mediterranean-style bouillabaisse packed with chunky seafood; and baked pike with an orange butter sauce. The speciality is stuffed chicken breast with Pernod cream. The cheeseboard has one representative from Wales, while sweets sound a distinctly English note: summer pudding, Cambridge burnt cream, charlotte, raspberry ice-cream. The wine list has a special section of champagnes and some bin-end clarets. Few bottles are under £10, but there is a good Beaujolais at £6·80. CELLARMAN'S CHOICE: Muscadet, Château de l'Oiselinière '85, £7·60.

CHEFS: Irene, Andrew and Matthew Canning PROPRIETOR: Irene Canning
OPEN: all week, exc Sun D MEALS: 12.30 to 2.30, 7.30 to 9.30
PRICES: £15 (£21), Set L £8·75 (£15), Set D £15·50 (£22) CARDS: Access, Amex, Diners, Visa
SEATS: 38. Private parties: 12 main room. Car-park, 5 places. Vegetarian meals

The Hamilton [12/20]

Tyla Morris House, Pentyrch, Cardiff CF4 8QN
CARDIFF (0222) 892232   £20–£23

The house was imported from Stockholm in kit form in 1892 for £655. It is completely wooden and was occupied by the Hamilton family until the M4 shattered their peace and quiet. It is now safely double-glazed and filled with Laura Ashley-style fabrics. The cooking is French, but promotes Welsh produce in an almost British way – a Welsh goats' cheese is grilled and served with an extraordinary salad of exotic fruits, lamb with a tomato and basil sauce. There has been deep-red fish soup, fine confit of duck, served cold, and strawberry vacherin. The eccentricity of the wooden home in a Welsh mood seems to extend to the staff, who are relaxed and friendly but professional. A short list of wines is fully detailed and has a good eye for quality in clarets (including magnums) and burgundy. House Bulgarian opens at £6·95.

CHEF: Christopher Billingley PROPRIETOR: Richard Perkins
OPEN: Mon to Sat, D only CLOSED: 2 weeks Jan MEALS: 7.30 to 10
PRICES: £18 (£23), Set D £15·95 (£20). Service inc CARDS: Access, Amex, Diners, Visa
SEATS: 34. Private parties: 45 main room, 20 private room. Car-park, 20 places. Children's helpings. Smart dress preferred. Music

All inspections are carried out anonymously.

Files are kept on every restaurant, so reports of poor meals are just as valuable as reports of good meals because they save unnecessary inspections.

Happy Gathering [9/20]

233 Cowbridge Road East, Canton, Cardiff CF1 9AL
CARDIFF (0222) 397531 £11·50–£20

The local Chinese community supports this spacious Cantonese restaurant in force. Sunday is dim-sum day and quite a crush. At other times it can be less reliable if the kitchen gets becalmed. Sizzling dishes and birds' nests are worth seeking out. House French is £4·80.

CHEF: Kin Kwun Chan PROPRIETOR: Sui Sang Chan
OPEN: all week MEALS: noon to 11.45pm
PRICES: £13 (£20) Set D from £15 (£23) for two. Service 10% CARDS: Access, Amex, Diners, Visa
SEATS: 250. Private parties: 180 main room, 40 private room. Vegetarian meals. Children welcome. Music. Air-conditioned

Riverside [10/20]

44 Tudor Street, Cardiff CF1 8RM
CARDIFF (0222) 372163 £11–£13

The decline of the Riverside has been frequently predicted but so far averted. Wendy Chan is in sole charge. Sunday is dim-sum day and requires booking. Fish is always good – spicy king prawns or stuffed crab claws. Notable also are spare ribs in a sweet-and-sour sauce; breast of duck stuffed with minced pork, spices and sweetcorn; steamed sea-bass; and crispy Cantonese chicken. Instead of rice, try vermicelli Singapore-style. Muscadet, Gewürztraminer and Chablis supplement the house white at £4·40 and provide sound accompaniments.

CHEF: K. Wong PROPRIETOR: Wendy Chan
OPEN: all week MEALS: noon to 11.45pm (12.15am Fri and Sat, 11pm Sun)
PRICES: £9 (£13), Set L from £7·50 (£11), Snacks from 95p. Service 10% CARDS: Access, Amex, Diners, Visa
SEATS: 140. Private parties: 75 main room, 65 private room. Vegetarian meals. Children welcome. Music. Air-conditioned

Salvatore's [10/20]

14 Romilly Crescent, Canton, Cardiff CF1 9NR
CARDIFF (0222) 372768 £19

Rough-plastered walls, landscape watercolours and a dimly lit bar with views of the kitchen at the back suit the trattoria menu. Most things are home-prepared: spaghetti, minestrone, saltimbocca alla romana. Daily specials often include fine fresh fish. The short international wine list ranges upwards from Merlot at £5·95. CELLARMAN'S CHOICE: Montepulciano d' Abruzzo '82 at £8·95.

CHEF: Mario Salvatore Colayera PROPRIETORS: Mario Turco and Mario Salvatore Colayera
OPEN: Mon to Sat, exc Sat L CLOSED: 2 weeks in summer MEALS: 12.30 to 2, 7.30 to 10
PRICES: £15 (£19). Service inc CARDS: Access, Amex, Diners, Visa
SEATS: 50. Private parties: 50 main room. Children's helpings. Wheelchair access. Music

It is helpful if restaurateurs keep the office up to date with any changes.

Spanghero's [new chef, zero rated]

Westgate House, Westgate Street, Cardiff CF1 1DD
CARDIFF (0222) 382423   £13–£20

Having set this up as the premier restaurant in Cardiff, David Evans has moved
into the background and let his number two, Paul Lane, take on the cooking. The
bistro and wine bar are usually lively, especially on match days (it is opposite
Cardiff Arms Park and takes its name from the French rugby player), and the
Cruover means fine wines can be drunk by the glass. The dining-room is a
serious place to eat. A range of menus contain some surprising, sometimes
elaborate combinations, such as fried langoustine with potatoes, tomatoes and
artichokes. Classic steak tartare is executed with skill. The French accent is eased
somewhat in places when the vivid flavours of modern British cooking come
through, as in a passion-fruit sauce for duck or in the basket of Welsh and
English cheeses. The strong wine list features a showy section of expensive
clarets, but also offers a good spread of better-value younger wines from the
regions, starting with house Gamay or Chardonnay at £5·75. CELLARMAN'S
CHOICE: Ch. du Clos-Renon '82, £14·25.

CHEF: Paul Lane PROPRIETORS: Vouchdawn Ltd
OPEN: Mon to Sat, exc Mon D and Sat L MEALS: 12 to 12.30, 7 to 9.30
PRICES: £16 (£20), Set L £9·95 (£13), Set D from £14·95 (£18). Service inc CARDS: Access,
Amex, Diners, Visa
SEATS: 50. Private parties: 30 main room. Children's helpings. Music. Air-conditioned

Thai House [10/20]

23 High Street, Cardiff CF1 2BX
CARDIFF (0222) 387404   £17–£18

Thai restaurants have become popular almost everywhere they have emerged in
the last three or four years. Mr Ramasut takes a personal interest in his
customers in this first- and, now, second-floor restaurant opposite the castle. The
menu features the key points like satay, stuffed chicken wings, fried fish, and
much stir-frying. The restaurant does not seem to have any difficulty in getting
herbs and seasonings like lemon grass and wood-ear mushrooms. Thai beer or
house Loire at £5·25.

CHEF: Nakorn Yimchareong PROPRIETOR: V. Ramasut
OPEN: Mon to Sat MEALS: 12 to 2.30, 6.30 to 11
PRICES: £11 (£17), Set D from £12·50 (£18). Minimum £10 at D. Service 10%
CARDS: Amex, Diners, Visa
SEATS: 64. Private parties: 22 main room, 20 private room. Vegetarian meals. Children
welcome. Music. Air-conditioned

[GHG] *after the details of an entry means that the establishment is also included in* The
Good Hotel Guide.

The Guide *recruits new inspectors from readers who write in regularly. If you would
like to apply, write to the editor with (a) a detailed report on a restaurant where you
have eaten and (b) a comparative study of restaurants known to you.*

CARDIGAN Dyfed   map 4

▲ *Rhyd-Garn-Wen* [11/20]

Cardigan SA43 3NW
CARDIGAN (0239) 612742
on A487, 2½m S of Cardigan

The Joneses' personally run, old-fashioned home is now open only to hotel
guests. They are exemplary hosts. Susan cooks a five-course menu, rather
affectedly written in French, but she does everything herself. Some of it is
complex, ambitious stuff: monk-fish and laver-bread in an orange sauce wrapped
in pancakes and baked with crème fraîche. It was not dishes like this that first
brought Mrs Jones into the *Guide* but rather the superb gooseberry pie, and
indeed the quality of the breads and the breakfasts. The opening of the doors to
suppliers from wider afield is in danger of undermining what was a very fine local
restaurant. Thirty wines are served with gusto. House Merlot is £4·50.
CELLARMAN'S CHOICE: Château du Grand Moulas '85, £6·50.

CHEF: Susan Jones PROPRIETORS: Susan and Huw Jones
OPEN: all week, D only CLOSED: Oct to Easter MEALS: 7.30 to 9.30
PRICES: See accommodation details CARD: Access
SEATS: 10. 4 tables outside. Car-park, 10 places. Vegetarian meals. Children's helpings. No
children under 12. Jacket and tie. No smoking in dining-room. Wheelchair access
ACCOMMODATION: 3 rooms, all with bath/shower. D, B&B £35 to £61. No children under 12.
No pets. Garden. Fishing. Golf. Scenic. Confirm by 6 [GHG]

CARMARTHEN Dyfed   map 4

Hoi San [10/20]

15 Queen Street, Carmarthen SA31 1JT
CARMARTHEN (0267) 231100   £7–£17

One of the most creditable restaurants in the far West of Britain. It is central,
cheerful, and family-run, with pink table linen and an elaborate oriental ceiling.
The long Cantonese menu includes good crabmeat and sweetcorn soup, soya
chicken, and duck with pineapple and ginger. There are also sizzling dishes,
Cantonese roast belly of pork, and salmon cooked like sea-bass with ginger and
spring onions. Dim-sum are also available, and children's menus at lunchtime on
Saturday and Sunday. House wine is £5·50.

CHEFS: Tommy Cheung and Tran Loc PROPRIETOR: K.C. Cheung
OPEN: all week CLOSED: 3 days at Christmas MEALS: 12 to 2.30, 7 to 10.30
PRICES: £11 (£17), Set L £3·50 (£7), Set D from £6·05 (£9), Snacks from £1·15. Minimum
£4·35 at D CARDS: Access, Amex, Diners, Visa
SEATS: 60. Private parties: 32 main room, 32 private room. Vegetarian meals. Children's
menu (weekend L only). Wheelchair access. Music

*'Back to back with my husband was a South American heiress receiving international
telephone calls. On our other side was an American literary agent talking non-stop to
her English guests about the advantages of buying real estate in Connecticut rather than
New York.'* (On eating in London)

CILGERRAN Dyfed
map 4

Castle Kitchen [10/20]

Cilgerran SA43 2SG
CARDIGAN (0239) 615055
£12

Barbara and Elizabeth Moore's cottage restaurant, at the end of a terrace close to the castle immortalised in a Turner painting, has an air of adventurous homeliness which extends to the cooking. It is unpretentious, largely British, but goes its own way with dishes such as tofu and baked chestnuts in mushroom sauce. Soups are hearty, country-style broths made with good stock, and savoury pies are models of their kind: rabbit pie is packed with meat and vegetables in a sharp mustard sauce with perfect short pastry. Lamb casserole is boosted with ginger and pine kernels, and broccoli roulade is simple but effective. Vegetables are fresh and good – even late on a Sunday night. Orange syllabub made with thick yellow Jersey double cream is a fitting finish. There are basic wines at really low prices.

CHEFS: Barbara, Elizabeth and Beryl Moore PROPRIETORS: Barbara and Elizabeth Moore
OPEN: all week CLOSED: daytime Nov to Easter MEALS: 12 to 5, 7.30 to 9.30
PRICES: £7 (£12), L Snacks from £1
SEATS: 25. Private parties: 16 main room. Vegetarian meals. Children's helpings (L only). Wheelchair access. Music

COWBRIDGE South Glamorgan
map 4

Basil's Brasserie [10/20]

2 Eastgate, Cowbridge CF7 7DG
COWBRIDGE (044 63) 3738
£15

The brasserie – actually a cross between a pub and a wine bar – is a series of connecting rooms with arches, bare boards and yellow walls. Orders are taken at the old-fashioned wooden bar counter. The long blackboard menu, quickly depleted on busy nights, offers straightforward bistro cooking with some imaginative touches – but also a few rough edges. The charcoal grill is used for steaks, Welsh lamb cutlets, and loin of pork with Stilton. Otherwise the menu roams around for fish chowder, rabbit terrine with pistachios and kumquat sauce, and Italian sausages with red cabbage. Seafood is a strong point: poached wild salmon with beurre blanc, stir-fried monk-fish with Chinese vegetables, dressed Cornish crab. Main courses come with potatoes or salad. The short wine list has one or two interesting burgundies. House Bulgarian is £4·45 a bottle.

CHEF: Giampiero Fama PROPRIETORS: Giampiero and Virginia Fama
OPEN: Tue to Sat CLOSED: Christmas, part of Jan MEALS: 12 to 2, 7 to 10
PRICES: £10 (£15), Snacks from £1·65 CARDS: Access, Visa
SEATS: 80. Private parties: 25 main room. Car-park, 10 places. Vegetarian meals. Children's helpings. No pipes in dining-room. Wheelchair access. Air-conditioned

'I was with my uncle, and the waiters made me feel I was Ms Floozy. I didn't really mind. Out of the main course the mushrooms were best, especially the one that was dropped on my skirt.' (On eating in London)

Off the Beeton Track [9/20]

1 Town Hall Square, Cowbridge CF7 7DD
COWBRIDGE (044 63) 3599 £10–£17

Jo Reardon-Smith and her team cook solid provincial British dishes at these converted stone cottages connected by a log fire. The menu takes in winter soups like ox-tail and chestnut, patriotic starters like laver-bread with smoked bacon, as well as deep-fried cheese puffs, and avocado and prawns. Main dishes vary from salmon kedgeree to fillets of beef. Sweets draw most praise, though, from treacle tart and Atholl brose to rich walnut meringue with creamy rum and chocolate and clotted cream. Three dozen wines include Welsh Croffta at £7·75 and house French at £4·75.

CHEF: R. Whitbread PROPRIETORS: Mr and Mrs J. Reardon-Smith
OPEN: Tue to Sun, exc Sun D MEALS: 12 to 2.30, 7.30 to 10
PRICES: £13 (£17), Set D from £6·50 (£10) CARDS: Access, Amex, Visa
SEATS: 36. 3 tables outside. Private parties: 36 main room. Vegetarian meals. Children's helpings (Sun L only). Wheelchair access. Music

---

CRICKHOWELL Powys map 4

▲ *Bear Hotel* [10/20]

High Street, Crickhowell NP8 1BW
CRICKHOWELL (0873) 810408 £21

Five hundred years of history behind the black and white façade of this old coaching-inn appear as beams, panelling and pewter. The kitchen makes the best of local produce, often with imaginative results: deep-fried goats' cheese comes with a strawberry sauce; salmon out of the Usk is cooked en papillote and served with a vol-au-vent of leeks; beef Wellington is prepared with fine-quality meat and garnished with a sprig of home-grown sorrel. Sometimes the garnishing and saucery detract needlessly from what are essentially first-class centrepieces. Interesting parfaits, sorbets and sherbets to finish. Real ales and snacks in the bar. House wine is £6·90 a litre.

CHEFS: J. L. Hindmarsh, Stephen Hindmarsh and Peter Adams PROPRIETOR: J. L. Hindmarsh
OPEN: all week, exc Sun D MEALS: 12 to 2, 7 to 9
PRICES: £15 (£21), Bar snacks from £1·95 CARDS: Access, Visa
SEATS: 58. 6 tables outside. Private parties: 70 main room, 30 private room. Car-park, 28 places. Children's helpings. No children under 5. Smart dress preferred. Wheelchair access (also WC). Music
ACCOMMODATION: 25 rooms, 22 with bath/shower. Rooms for disabled. B&B £29·90 to £38. Pets welcome. Afternoon teas. Garden. Fishing. TV. Phone. Scenic. Doors close at 12.30. Confirm by noon

---

If, in your opinion, a restaurant is not maintaining the standard of its ratings please inform the Guide *office. Report forms are at the back of the book.*

The price quoted in brackets is for an average three-course meal including service, VAT, coffee and half a bottle of house wine or the equivalent in an ethnic restaurant.

DOLGELLAU Gwynedd

map 4

▲ *George III Hotel* [10/20]

Penmaenpool, Dolgellau LL40 1YD
DOLGELLAU (0341) 422525
2m W of Dolgellau   £9–£19

A commanding view over the estuary is to be had from this small hotel – restaurant which has been in the Hall family for many years. It has a reputation as being good for lobsters and champagne and a cut above the local competition. The style otherwise is chicken liver pâté, smoked mackerel, blanquette de veau, and sewin steaks. More traditional are the roast beef and the trifle – and the dining-room, with its dark wooden tables set with mats and gleaming glasses. The staff are helpful. House burgundy is £5·25.

CHEF: David Collette   PROPRIETOR: Gail Hall
OPEN: Mon to Sat, D only, and Sun L   CLOSED: Christmas and New Year
MEALS: 12.30 to 2, 7.15 to 8.45
PRICES: £14 (£19), Set L £5·25 (£9), Snacks from 80p. Service 10%   CARDS: Access, Amex, Carte Blanche, Diners, Visa
SEATS: 45. 5 tables outside. Private parties: 20 main room. Car-park, 100 places. Children's helpings. Smart dress preferred. Wheelchair access (also WC)
ACCOMMODATION: 12 rooms, 7 with bath/shower. Rooms for disabled. B&B £17·50 to £50. Children welcome. Baby facilities. Pets welcome. Garden. Fishing. TV. Phone. Scenic. Doors close at 11.30. Confirm by 6

La Petite Auberge [10/20]

2 Smithfield Street, Dolgellau LL40 1BS
DOLGELLAU (0341) 422870   £13

This bistro, in a granite terrace near the centre of town, has red paper tablecloths and wild flowers on the modern pine tables. The Tonnerres are from Brittany, and there are Breton echoes in the lace curtains and in Evelyne's naïf paintings. The menu concentrates on unpretentious French country cooking: thick, garlicky fish soup; navarin of lamb; chicken provençale. Pork escalopes come with a creamy port sauce, poached fillet of lemon sole is dressed with a pink sauce tasting of prawns and salmon. To finish, there are excellent home-made sorbets. Twenty French wines with a few half-bottles.

CHEFS/PROPRIETORS: Evelyne and Yannick Tonnerre
OPEN: Mon to Sat, D only   CLOSED: 30 Sept to 1 Apr   MEALS: 7 to 9.30
PRICES: £8 (£13)
SEATS: 34. Private parties: 20 main room. Children's helpings

ERBISTOCK Clwyd

map 4

Boat Inn [10/20]

Erbistock LL13 0DL
BANGOR-ON-DEE (0978) 780143   £10–£20

In spring this genuinely old inn, where the ferry crossed the Dee, is among the most beautiful spots in North Wales, with daffodils everywhere. The field to the river is filled with wild flowers. The road does not go any further. Erbistock is only a church and a few cottages. The menu is modern – leek and onion soup, pâté with apple chutney, a vegetarian main dish of aubergine bake, or home-baked ham with orange and cress. There are more worked dishes of mousses and pastries too, and lobster down from Anglesey. Terry Lee in the kitchen has developed the cooking over the last two years, basing it on fine local produce. Service, though, can be forward. There are also good-value bar meals and cheap set lunches. House wine is £5·50.

CHEF: Terry Lee PROPRIETOR: John Chamberlain
OPEN: all week, exc Sat L CLOSED: mid-Jan to end Feb MEALS: 12 to 2, 7.30 to 9.30
PRICES: £15 (£20), Set L from £5·95 (£10), Set D £11·95 (£16) CARDS: Access, Amex, Diners, Visa
SEATS: 70. 20 tables outside. Private parties: 45 main room. Car-park, 100 places. Vegetarian meals. Children's helping (Sun L only). Wheelchair access. Music

---

GLANWYDDEN Gwynedd map 4

Queen's Head [10/20]

Glanwydden LL31 9JP
LLANDUDNO (0492) 46570 £15

A modernised village pub down a steep hill, with hunting prints on the walls and a sense of space. 'We take pride in using totally fresh local produce,' declares Robert Cureton. There is fine fish: lobster, crab, and salmon all appear with fresh salad and new potatoes, plus mayonnaise and French dressing on the side. Order at the entrance desk. Tables are quickly cleared. The varied British menu is supplemented by blackboard specials of the day. Local lamb is served with tomato and ginger. The home-made sweets are a feature, and both bread-and-butter pudding and rum and raisin flan have been good. House wine is £5·75 a carafe.

CHEFS: Robert Cureton and Bryn Powell PROPRIETOR: Robert Cureton
OPEN: all week MEALS: 12 to 2.15, 7 to 9
PRICES: £10 (£15)
SEATS: 120. 12 tables outside. Private parties: 26 main room. Car-park, 25 places. Vegetarian meals. Music

---

HARLECH Gwynedd map 4

▲ Castle Cottage [11/20]

Pen Llech, Harlech LL46 2YL
HARLECH (0766) 780479 £16

The cottage was starting to look well worn last year, which might be taken as an endorsement of Jim Yuill's cooking. The menu wanders about some, and can take in Welsh lamb Moroccan-style with lemon and spices. Laver-bread features

---

The Guide *recruits new inspectors from readers who write in regularly. If you would like to apply, write to the editor with (a) a detailed report on a restaurant where you have eaten and (b) a comparative study of restaurants known to you.*

---

with deep-fried cockles, and locally smoked goose breast is served with prune chutney as a starter. Scotland contributes Tipsy Laird and Cranachan for pudding, and the wines take in the Napa and Barossa Valleys. The fifty wines are splendid value – you can drink well for under £6 – and include CELLARMAN'S CHOICE: Coteaux du Languedoc La Clape, Château de Pech Redon, Demolombe '85, £7.

CHEF: Jim Yuill PROPRIETORS: Jim and Betty Yuill
OPEN: all week, D only; L by arrangement MEALS: 7 to 9.30
PRICES: £11 (£16), Snacks from £1·35 CARDS: Access, Visa
SEATS: 34. 4 tables outside. Private parties: 40 main room. Vegetarian meals. Children's helpings. No smoking in dining-room. Wheelchair access. Music
ACCOMMODATION: 6 rooms, 4 with bath/shower. B&B £14 to £30. Deposit: 25%. Baby facilities. Pets welcome. Scenic [GHG]]

▲ *The Cemlyn* [13/20]

High Street, Harlech LL46 2YA
HARLECH (0766) 780425   £15

Cemlyn is Welsh for frog. They are everywhere – painted, wooden, stuffed – but Ken Goody's cooking is serious enough. The menu of half a dozen starters and the same number of main dishes follows on from bowls of fine soup and wholemeal rolls. The style is modern British, absorbing home-cured bresaola served with melon, or gravlax, before three-dimensional main courses such as roast duck with sage, apple and onion purée, its crisp skin basted with honey; or grilled steaks with béarnaise and oyster mushrooms, served with four vegetables. The boozy trifle is just so, and the expanded wine list deserves serious consideration. Prices are low enough to invite a crack at most things on the list, and Italy is dealt with region by region, with not a single bottle over £10. California Chardonnay keeps under the same ceiling, and a dozen wines are picked out to offer good drinking at £6 or less, including Château de Fonscolombe from Coteaux d'Aix-en-Provence.

CHEF/PROPRIETOR: Ken Goody
OPEN: all week, D only CLOSED: Jan to Easter MEALS: 7 to 9.30
PRICES: Set D from £9·95 (£15) CARDS: Amex, Diners
SEATS: 36. 3 tables outside. Private parties: 40 main room, 10 private room. Vegetarian meals. Children's helpings. Wheelchair access (also WC)
ACCOMMODATION: 2 rooms, 1 with bath/shower. B&B £8·50 to £21. No children under 10. No pets. Golf. TV. Scenic. Doors close at 12. Confirm by 6

HAVERFORDWEST Dyfed   map 4

▲ *Jemima's* [new entry, zero rated]

Nash Grove, Freystrop, Haverfordwest SA62 4HB
JOHNSTON (0437) 891109
2m S of Haverfordwest   £15

'We are very much a family enterprise, which probably accounts for customers' comments on how French this place is.' Everything is made on the premises. In summer the herbs from the back garden abound through a menu of 21 dishes. Local sewin steaks are poached in wine and fish stock, the sauce reduced, and finished with cream and sorrel. Lovage goes into the carrot soup, blackcurrant leaves into a sorbet with melon for starters. Welsh farmhouse cheeses vie with fools, fruit and alcoholic creams to finish. Two dozen wines stay firmly around £7. House French is £5. More reports, please.

CHEF: Anne Owston PROPRIETORS: Ann Owston and Wendy Connelly
OPEN: Mon to Sat, D only, and Sun L MEALS: 12.30 to 2, 7 to 9.30
PRICES: £11 (£15) CARD: Access
SEATS: 20. Private parties: 24 main room. Car-park, 10 places. Children welcome. No smoking in dining-room
ACCOMMODATION: 2 rooms, 1 with bath/shower. B&B £12·50 to £25. Afternoon teas. Scenic. Doors close at 12. Confirm by 7

HAY-ON-WYE Powys   map 4
Lion's Corner House [10/20]

6 Market Street, Hay-on-Wye HR3 5AF
HAY-ON-WYE (0497) 820175   £6–£16

The restaurant has moved from its corner to opposite the Buttermarket. Colin Thomson continues to evolve slowly from cafe to restaurant. All the produce is local, and lunches remain exceptional value for straightforward no-nonsense dishes such as fennel soup, beef lasagne, home-baked ham with eggs, fruit salad, and ginger ice-cream. Dinners are more ambitious: roast rack of Welsh lamb studded with garlic and ginger, served with a rosemary and mint sauce; filo pastry filled with cheese and stir-fry vegetables with a mushroom and tarragon sauce. Forty inexpensive wines manage to take in California and Chile, Spain and Portugal, Bulgaria and Hungary, Australia and New Zealand. CELLARMAN'S CHOICE: Tanners' claret at £5·75 (£3 for a half).

CHEFS: Colin Thomson, Bernice Brown and Sean Ennis PROPRIETOR: Colin Thomson
OPEN: Mon to Sat CLOSED: Mon D out of season MEALS: 11 to 2.30, 7 to 9.30 (10 Sat)
PRICES: £11 (£16), Set D from £2·25 (£6), Snacks from 75p
SEATS: 60. Private parties: 30 main room. Vegetarian meals. Children's helpings. Wheelchair access. Music

---

LALESTON Mid Glamorgan   map 4
Great House [10/20]

High Street, Laleston CF32 0HP
BRIDGEND (0656) 57644
3m W of Bridgend   £6–£20

Ty-Mawr (the Great House) is a fine example of history preserved: the house was a sixteenth-century yeoman's cottage, later enlarged and now a Grade II listed building. When the Bonds took it on it was derelict. The dining-room was once a two-storey hall, with small windows high up, and exposed rafters. Since opening in May 1986 the Bonds have used the local markets, and the cooking has got its priorities right. The style is classical French from Escoffier, and main dishes are silver service. A 25-dish *carte* is supplemented in the week by a set menu. Reliable indicators have been baked eggs in pastry with a warm fennel sauce, and generous lamb à la grecque with saffron rice. Enthusiasm can overrun, as in the excellent cheese parcels with an over-the-top cream and black grape coulis. The sweets trolley is made up of gateaux, mousses, and fruit, and liqueurs are used freely. The cheeseboard claims a Welsh contingent. Snack lunches – starting at £1·95 – offer first-rate value. Sixty mainly French wines from £5. CELLARMAN'S CHOICE: Pécharmant, Château de Tiregand '82, £8·75.

CHEF: Barry Bingham PROPRIETORS: Stephen and Norma Bond
OPEN: Mon to Sat, exc Sat L MEALS: 12 to 2, 6.30 to 9.30 (9.45 Sat)
PRICES: £15 (£20), Set L from £1·95 (£6), Set D £10·95 (£16) CARDS: Access, Diners, Visa
SEATS: 120. 3 tables outside. Private parties: 80 main room, 40 private room. Car-park, 30 places. Vegetarian meals. Children's helpings. Wheelchair access (also WC). Music

LLANARTHNEY Dyfed
map 4

▲ *Golden Grove Arms* [12/20]

Llanarthney SA32 8JU
DRYSLWYN (055 84) 551 and 552
£10–£21

Not in Golden Grove itself, but on the road between Llandeilo and Carmarthen, is this large, square, painted inn. The front bar is solid and comfortable, with an open fire and a menu of soup, wholemeal bread, bacon and eggs, but the top cooking is in the formal Georgian dining-room – poached salmon or cod in a beurre blanc, fillet steak with shallots in a rich wine gravy of reduced Crozes-Hermitage. On demand, a boned whole lamb or a suckling pig can be roasted over an open fire. Local fish is treated with some skill. With 24 hours' notice a nine-course tasting menu will be arranged. The atmosphere can seem chaotic, even casual, but James Thomas seems to be deliberately setting out to make this one of the best restaurants in South Wales – and succeeding. A new wine bar, Bensons, has been added (open at weekends), served from the same kitchen and drawing on the same intelligent and varied choice of wines from £4·95. CELLARMAN'S CHOICE: Muscadet '85, £7·95.

CHEFS: James Thomas and Gerald Sandberg PROPRIETOR: James Thomas
OPEN: all week, exc Sun D MEALS: 12.15 to 2.30, 7.15 to 10.15
PRICES: £16 (£21), Set L from £5·95 (£10), Set D from £9·95 (£14), Snacks from £1·25. Service 10% alc, inc set CARDS: Access, Visa
SEATS: 30. Children welcome
ACCOMMODATION: 8 rooms, 3 with bath/shower. B&B £15 to £50. Deposit: 10%. Children welcome. Baby facilities. Pets welcome. Garden. Tennis. Fishing. Golf. Scenic [GHG]

'A rather odd-looking character wearing "trainer" footwear and an overcoat came up the stairs, ignored the waiter, crossed the room and sat at a corner table for two. He removed his coat and the waiter gave him a menu. Within minutes he replaced his coat and left, this by the time the waiter had returned. I spoke to the waiter, mentioning the man's odd behaviour and dress. He said he had queried this at reception, but they had said he was meeting someone in the restaurant. I joked and said: "Make sure he hasn't left a bomb under the table". Thankfully there was no bomb, but when our neighbours were about to leave some time later the lady found her handbag missing.'
(On eating in London)

LLANBERIS Gwynedd

map 4

Y Bistro [13/20]

53–45 High Street, Llanberis LL55 4EU
LLANBERIS (0286) 871278   £11–£18

Nerys Roberts' high-street restaurant is still one of the finest in Wales. The place
has plenty of local support, which is why the concise menu is written in Welsh
and English. A rich vein runs through the cooking, from the duck pistachio
terrine with Cumberland sauce to brown-sugar meringue filled with crushed
hazel-nuts and Jersey cream. Dishes are familiar and imaginative by turns,
taking in deep-fried choux pastry puffs filled with bacon, hazel-nuts and Gouda;
breast of chicken cooked with kumquats and Grand Marnier; stuffed fillet of brill
with cream sauce; and lamb en croûte. Other details show the dedication of the
enterprise: bread and biscuits are home baked, cheeses are from Welsh dairies,
and meals end with excellent home-made petits fours. The ninety-strong wine list
is heavy on clarets, and there's a Welsh wine for good measure.

CHEF: Nerys Roberts PROPRIETORS: Danny and Nerys Roberts
OPEN: Mon to Sat CLOSED: L Sept to Whitsun MEALS: 12 to 2, 7 to 9.30
PRICES: L £7 (£11), Set D from £13·50 (£18) CARDS: Access, Visa
SEATS: 48. Private parties: 36 main room, 20 private room. Vegetarian meals. Children
welcome. Smart dress preferred. Wheelchair access (also WC). Music. Air-conditioned

LLANDDERFEL Gwynedd

map 4

▲ *Palé Hall* [11/20]

Llandderfel LL23 7PS
LLANDDERFEL (067 83) 285   £13–£24

The cooking is almost as good as the surroundings at this remote ancient hall, set
in handsome countryside. The air of being a museum is dispelled by the staff,
who combine professionalism with friendliness. The menu is overly florid in its
descriptions and in all the mousses and stuffings employed. But ingredients are
good, as is the technique. Asparagus is served with black butter; lamb is roasted
pink; and the fish chowder, served as a second-course alternative to sorbet, is
excellent. Whiting is poached in Noilly Prat with a sauce of scallops and cream.
To finish, there have been fine sticky toffee pudding and a good range of British
cheeses. The set meals are excellent value. The wine list extends to a hundred
bottles from their own-label house wines at £6·50 to a widely roaming selection.
CELLARMAN'S CHOICE: Mâcon Villages, Château de Mirande '85, £13.

*The 1989 Guide will appear before Christmas 1988. Reports are particularly helpful
in the spring. Report forms are at the back of this book, but just write a letter if you
prefer. Address it to The Good Food Guide, FREEPOST, 14 Buckingham Street, London
WC2N 6BR. No stamp is necessary if you post it in the UK.*

*Good vintages for drinking in 1988: Alsace '85, Beaujolais '86, Germany '85, petits
chateaux clarets '81, lesser clarets '83.*

CHEF: Nicholas Walton PROPRIETORS: The Duffin family
OPEN: all week MEALS: 12 to 2, 7 to 9.30
PRICES: £16 (£24), Set L £8·50 (£13), Set D £15 (£20), Snacks from £1·25. Service 10%
CARDS: Access, Amex, Diners, Visa
SEATS: 50. Private parties: 50 main room, 24 and 45 private rooms. Car-park, 150 places.
Vegetarian meals. Children's helpings. Jacket and tie. Wheelchair access (also WC)
ACCOMMODATION: 17 rooms, all with bath/shower. Rooms for disabled.Lift. B&B £45 to £75.
Deposit: £20. Children welcome. Baby facilities. Pets welcome. Afternoon teas. Garden.
Sauna. Fishing. Golf. TV. Phone. Scenic. Doors close at 1 [GHG]

LLANDDOWROR Dyfed   map 4

▲ *Old Rectory* [10/20]

Llanddowror SA33 4HH
ST CLEARS (0994) 230030   £11–£21

This converted rectory looks out over the main road to the woods and hills, and
serves from a menu of eight to ten starters and main courses. Sewin stands out
among the fish, served with grapes and walnuts, and there are smoked trout and
duck, onion soup, and home-made pâté. Some *naturelle* dishes are scheduled.
The two dozen wines include house red and white at £5·40 a bottle.

CHEF: Michael Redvers du Mayne PROPRIETORS: Michael Redvers and Susan du Mayne
OPEN: Tue to Sun, exc Sun D MEALS: 12.30 to 2, 7 to 9.30
PRICES: £17 (£21), Set Sun L £7·50 (£11), Snacks from £1. Minimum £5. Service inc alc
CARDS: Access, Amex, Diners, Visa
SEATS: 33. 3 tables outside. Private parties: 40 main room, 12 private room. Car-park, 20
places. Children's helpings. No-smoking area. Wheelchair access (also WC). Music
ACCOMMODATION: 1 room, with bath/shower. B&B £9·50 to £19. Children welcome. Baby
facilities. No pets. Afternoon teas. Garden. Fishing. Golf. TV. Scenic. Doors close at 11.
Confirm by 6

LLANDEWI SKIRRID Gwent   map 4

Walnut Tree Inn [15/20]

Llandewi Skirrid NP7 8AW
ABERGAVENNY (0873) 2797
on B4521, 2½m NE of Abergavenny   ▮ £28

By car the journey here takes three hours from London now, but when the
Walnut Tree opened in 1964 it might have taken seven hours. In that time
Franco Taruschio has kept the kitchen of this small inn on a tight rein, producing
marvellous dishes without fuss or pomp. Forget the décor; this is a pub. The mood
is closer to big city brasseries than anything else. The breadth of the cooking is a
joy: crab pancakes; duck with strawberries; the brodetto; lobster with garlic;
trenette con pesto; mussels with mint; intoxicating peaches in brandy. The small
dining-room at the back does for formal occasions and parties, but more than
any other chef of his generation Franco Taruschio has held to his principle that
good food does not have to sell out to higher prices and pretensions. Last year the
Egon Ronay guide made this Welsh restaurant of the year, but it has been the
highest-rated Welsh restaurant in this *Guide* since the 1960s. The Taruschios'
support for Vin Sullivan in the early days helped establish the major catering

supplier to top restaurants in the West. The wine list has the scope one would expect of anywhere supplied by Reid Wines: it is no surprise to take a trip through history with claret from '59 and '24, burgundy from '49, Châteauneuf-du-Pape from '21 . . . But there are everyday bottles too: Gamay from the Ardèche, Saumur blanc, Alsace Riesling, all under £10, and an impressive collection of thirty wines from Italy. House Verdicchio and Rosso Piceno are £6·75 a bottle.

CHEF: Franco Taruschio PROPRIETORS: Franco and Ann Taruschio
OPEN: Mon to Sat, exc Mon L CLOSED: 2 weeks Feb MEALS: 12 to 2.30, 7.15 to 10
PRICES: £20 (£28). Cover 90p
SEATS: 40. 5 tables outside. Private parties: 30 main room. Car-park, 60 places. Vegetarian meals. Children's helpings. Wheelchair access (also WC). Air-conditioned

---

LLANDRILLO Clwyd map 4

▲ *Tyddyn Llan* [11/20]

Llandrillo LL21 0ST
LLANDRILLO (049 084) 264 £6–£15

This fishing, shooting, walking hotel in an eighteenth-century country house is run by the Kindreds without fuss. The set menus are augmented with baskets of freshly baked breads. The cooking is seasonal, modern British, and, if a shade overcooked in the main dishes for cosmopolitan tastes, still based on sound produce: watercress soup, avocado and orange salad, Anglesey eggs, Glamorgan sausages, sirloin steak with green peppercorns, veal with ginger, salmon hollandaise, smoked trout, and cheeses from Shropshire and Cheshire. Coffee is served in the lounge with a trio of different chocolate mints. Snack lunches are good value. There are ten house wines from which both the Syrah and the Chardonnay at £5·50 and £7·60 are worthwhile; the rest of the sixty-strong list is wide ranging geographically and stays substantially under £10.

CHEF: Bridget Kindred PROPRIETORS: Peter and Bridget Kindred
OPEN: all week, exc Mon L CLOSED: Mon and Tue Nov to Mar (exc residents)
MEALS: 12.30 to 2, 7 to 9.30
PRICES: Set L from £3 (£6), Set D from £10·50 (£15) CARDS: Access, Visa
SEATS: 35. Private parties: 45 main room. Car-park, 15 places. Vegetarian meals. Children's helpings. Wheelchair access. Music
ACCOMMODATION: 9 rooms, all with bath/shower. B&B £25 to £43. Deposit: 10%. Children welcome. Baby facilities. Pets by arrangement. Afternoon teas. Garden. Fishing. Scenic. Doors close at 12. Confirm by 6 [GHG]

LLANDUDNO Gwynedd map 4

▲ *Bodysgallen Hall* [new chef, zero rated

Deganwy, Llandudno LL30 1RS
DEGANWY (0492) 84466
from A55 join new A470 and follow
Llandudno signposts; hotel 1m on right £12–£26

This landmark of North Wales gastronomy was caught by a changeover of chefs as we went to press. David Harding is opening his own restaurant in Llandudno and his place is taken by Martin James. The style remains the same: modern country-house hotel cooking from a set menu of more than twenty starters and main dishes encompassing the conservative, especially at lunchtime, and the modern. Early meals confirm the quality of the succession. Ingredients are impeccable, using, as far as possible, local meats and fish and dairy produce augmented with a few luxuries like foie gras. The house is deep in history and has wonderful gardens with views. The 250 wines have pedigree vintages in claret, but also a good eye for the Loire and Rhône and spreads from the rest of the world. House burgundy is £7·50. CELLARMAN'S CHOICE: Rioja, Carta de Oro '84, £7·50. More reports, please.

CHEF: Martin James PROPRIETORS: Historic House Hotels
OPEN: all week MEALS: 12.30 to 2, 7.30 to 9.45
PRICES: £19 (£26), Set L from £7·50 (£12), Set D from £18·50 (£24), Snacks from £1·50. Minimum £18·50 at D. Service 10% CARDS: Access, Amex, Diners, Visa
SEATS: 62. Private parties: 48 main room. Car-park, 50 places. No children under 8. Jacket and tie at D. No cigars/pipes in dining-room. Wheelchair access. Music
ACCOMMODATION: 28 rooms, all with bath/shower. Rooms for disabled. B&B £55 to £75. No children under 8. Pets welcome. Afternoon teas. Garden. Tennis. TV. Phone. Confirm by 3 [GHG]

Floral [10/20]

Victoria Street, Craig-y-Don, Llandudno LL30 1LJ
LLANDUDNO (0492) 75735   £11–£19

The wine cellar is a big attraction here, particularly the strong showing of Australians, including a fistful of first-class Chardonnays from Brown Bros, Rosemount, Hill-Smith, Tisdall and Wynn. From outside the traditional areas of France come organic wines, even 'vegetarian' wines produced without the use of animal products. By contrast, the menu follows a well-trodden path, relying heavily on steaks and classical fish dishes with a few flourishes on occasion – celeriac and cardamom soup or pigeon with chocolate and raspberry vinegar.

CHEF: Tony Muff PROPRIETORS: Tony Muff, Bill Johnson and Michael Ratcliff
OPEN: Tue to Sun, exc Sat L CLOSED: 26 to 28 Dec MEALS: 12 to 2, 7 to 10
PRICES: £13 (£19), Set Sun L £7·50 (£11) CARDS: Access, Visa
SEATS: 60. Private parties: 24 main room, 12 and 14 private rooms. Vegetarian meals. Children's helpings. No children under 10. Wheelchair access. Music

▲ St Tudno Hotel [10/20]

North Parade, Llandudno LL30 2LP
LLANDUDNO (0492) 74411   £13–£21

The Victorian hotel is part of a sea-front terrace near the pier, and has a modern green dining-room with patterned walls echoing the basketwork on the chairs. The room rates are not excessive and it's a pleasant place to stay at, though some things can be over-done. The menu offers choices of all four courses, and through its many themes can be found starters such as smoked halibut salad, good soups as varied as consommé and tomato and apple, and big helpings of main courses like poached lemon sole, chicken with cheese and asparagus, and roast leg of Welsh lamb in pastry with minced kidneys, all served with extraordinarily over-

Restaurants rating 12 or more serve the best food in the region.

elaborate vegetables. The sweets are bombes, fruits – and rich. Welsh Croffta is one of nearly a hundred wines off a list that is sound in all the main regions, with a good spread of prices. CELLARMAN'S CHOICE: Chablis, *premier cru* Vaillons, Dauvissat '83, £16; and Château de Fonscolombe from Coteaux d'Aix en Provence, £7.

CHEFS: John Gabbatt and Steve Rawicki PROPRIETORS: Martin and Janette Bland
OPEN: all week CLOSED: Christmas and New Year
MEALS: 12.30 to 1.45, 6.45 to 9.30 (8.30 Sun)
PRICES: £14 (£19), Set L £8·75 (£13), Set D £15·50 (£21) CARDS: Access, Visa
SEATS: 60. Private parties: 25 main room. Car-park, 4 places. Vegetarian meals. Children's helpings. No children under 5. No smoking in dining-room. Wheelchair access. Air-conditioned
ACCOMMODATION: 21 rooms, all with bath/shower. Rooms for disabled. Lift. B&B £30·45 to £40·75. Deposit: £20. Children welcome. Baby facilities. Afternoon teas. Swimming-pool. TV. Phone [GHG]

LLANDYBIE Dyfed
map 4

The Cobblers [12/20]

3 Church Street, Llandybie, SA18 3HZ
LLANDYBIE (0269) 850540
£5–£17

Margaret Rees champions Welsh ingredients and uses them imaginatively in what was indeed the village cobbler's. The ground floor is for lighter lunches, the first floor for dinner. The menu is written equally in Welsh and English, but the style is really modern British. Wholemeal pastry is filled with cockles and covered in creamed laver-bread or used as a wrapping for lamb, rosemary and leeks. Boned stuffed chicken is served with a sauce of elderberry wine. Otherwise the menu can take in adventurous rhubarb and orange soup, vegetarian oriental dishes, fine farmhouse cheeses, and a table loaded with sweets. Unusual herbs feature strongly from no fewer than eighty in the garden. Twenty-one wines are under £8, with heavy house red at £6·50 a bottle. CELLARMAN'S CHOICE: Chinon '85, from Jean Maurice-Raffault, £8.

CHEF: Margaret Rees PROPRIETORS: Hywel and Margaret Rees
OPEN: Tue, Wed, Fri and Sat MEALS: 12 to 1.30, 7 to 9.30
PRICES: Set L from £1·25 (£5), Set D from £12 (£17), Snacks from £1 CARDS: Access, Visa
SEATS: 70. Private parties: 50 main room, 20 private room. Vegetarian meals. Children's helpings. Wheelchair access (also WC). Music

---

LLANGOLLEN Clwyd
map 4

Caesar's [11/20]

Castle Street, Llangollen LL20 8PN
LLANGOLLEN (0978) 860133
£15

The best restaurant for many a mile. A doll's house of a building on the edge of the Dee, within earshot of the water. The bar is made from furniture salvaged from Wrexham Courtroom. The five-course menu is priced according to the main dish, and if the cooking is rich, the ingredients are good enough to stand up to the treatment. A starter of terrine of halibut comes with two sauces before lettuce soup or a sorbet, then fillet of salmon or crispy duckling, with brandy-snap basket or peaches in red wine to finish. House wine is £4·95 from a short list.

CHEF: Richard Hendey PROPRIETORS: G. Hughes, Pat Hughes and Richard Hendey
OPEN: all week, D only MEALS: 7 (6.30 in summer) to 10
PRICES: Set D £12·95 (£15). Service inc CARDS: Access, Visa
SEATS: 30. Private parties: 28 main room. Children's helpings. Wheelchair access. Music

▲ *Gales* [9/20]

18 Bridge Street, Llangollen LL70 8PF
LLANGOLLEN (0978) 860089   £8

Old chapel pews, local artists' paintings and a blackboard menu of soups, pâtés, quiches, pancakes, smoked fish and a number of salads characterise this convivial oak-panelled wine bar. All but a dozen of the seventy wines are under £10 thanks to a few négociants. CELLARMAN'S CHOICE: João Pines Branco '85, £5·80, a dry moscato.

CHEFS: Jo Johnson, Gillie Gale and John Gosling PROPRIETORS: Richard and Gillie Gale
OPEN: all week CLOSED: Sun and Mon Sept to May MEALS: 12 to 2, 6 (7 Sun) to 10.15
PRICES: £4 (£8)
SEATS: 70. 10 tables outside. Private parties: 12 main room, 8 private room. Children's helpings. Wheelchair access. Music
ACCOMMODATION: 8 rooms, all with bath/shower. B&B £18 to £30. Deposit: £10. Children welcome. Baby facilities. Pets welcome. TV. Scenic. Doors close at 11

LLANRWST Gwynedd   map 4

▲ *Meadowsweet Hotel* [12/20]

Station Road, Llanrwst LL26 0DS
LLANRWST (0492) 640732   ▮ £20–£24

The double-fronted late Victorian house stands on the edge of Llanrwst, overlooking the Conwy Valley and the mountains beyond. Inside, the Evanses have created an atmosphere that blends Belle Epoque with Old England. Fish arrives three times a week and appears in many guises: monkfish as a terrine or with a cream and cider sauce, or, if local supplies are short, there might be sardines or swordfish. John Evans reports that the improved quality of supplies now available has galvanised his interest in cooking. There are fine sauces: tarragon for poached chicken, orange with hare, rich red wine with Welsh lamb or fillet steak. The cheeseboard has an exceptional range of mainly French ones, and sweets range from crème de menthe ice-cream to amaretto parfait with butterscotch sauce. Breakfasts are extravaganzas of bubble and squeak, black pudding, liver and bacon, Finnan haddock, ham, cheeses, figs, fruit salad and lots more besides. The Frenchness of the cooking is echoed in the wines. CELLARMAN'S CHOICE: Parallèle '45' '85, from Jaboulet, £10·50.

Restaurants are graded on a scale of 1–20. In the category of 10–11 expect to find the best food in the locality. Ratings of 12 and more are given to restaurants we regard as serving the best food in the region.

CHEF: John Evans PROPRIETORS: John and Joy Evans
OPEN: all week, D only MEALS: 6.30 to 9.30
PRICES: £18 (£24), Set D from £14·50 (£20)
CARDS: Access, Amex, Visa
SEATS: 36. Private parties: 50 main room. Car-park, 10 places. Vegetarian meals. Children's helpings. Smart dress preferred. No smoking in dining-room. Wheelchair access. Music
ACCOMMODATION: 10 rooms, all with bath/shower. B&B £24 to £40. Deposit: £3. Children welcome. Baby facilities. Pets welcome. TV. Phone. Scenic. Doors close at 12. Confirm by 6.30 [GHG]

LLANTWIT MAJOR South Glamorgan   map 4

Colhugh Villa [10/20]

Flanders Road, Llantwit Major CF6 9PR
LLANTWIT MAJOR (044 65) 2022   £12–£20

Follow the signs to the beach, as this double-fronted rose-covered house, what an estate agent might describe as a gentleman's residence, is rather hidden away. The dining-room is arranged around a large central table laden with desserts and cheeses. The menu is ambitious and the sauces are potent. Fish is a strong point: mousse of salmon and turbot baked in pastry; Pembroke smoked salmon salad with mango and avocado; poached turbot on a bed of noodles with saffron sauce. Service is uncoordinated, which is a pity. Home-made shortcake biscuits come with Cona coffee. Few wines under £8. More reports, please.

CHEF: Martin Dobson PROPRIETORS: Mr and Mrs Elward
OPEN: Tue to Sat, D only, and Sun L MEALS: 12 to 2.15, 7 to 9.30
PRICES: £14 (£20), Set L £7·50 (£12), Set D £10·95 (£16) CARDS: Access, Amex, Diners, Visa
SEATS: 86. 4 tables outside. Private parties: 86 main room. Car-park, 30 places. Vegetarian meals. Children's helpings. Smart dress preferred. Music. Air-conditioned

---

LLANWRTYD WELLS Powys   map 4

▲ *Llwynderw Hotel* [12/20]

Abergwesyn, Llanwrtyd Wells LD5 4TW
LLANWRTYD WELLS (059 13) 238   £25

As in the Lake District, it is the boarding-house principle of a minimum of choice, and everyone eating at the same time, that provides a framework for the kitchen to excel. The lack of choice is compensated for by a combination of tastes that can run from one course to the next. Michael Yates mixes English roasts and puddings with classical French soufflés and sauces. The results might be mushrooms à la grecque, cream of celery soup, roast quail on its own croûton, four vegetables, orange tart, and truckle Cheddar. The house is Georgian with

---

'Certainly the standards achieved are comparable to other restaurants in this area, and if its listing in next year's Guide *could save someone some of the bad experiences we have endured elsewhere then writing this report will have been worthwhile.'* (On eating in Lancashire)

---

the feeling of somewhere lived in and not of a museum; rather it is genuinely silent, as it always was. The only thing to spoil the after-dinner conversation is the coffee. The cellar holds some very fine wines, with clarets going back to the early '70s and before – alas, at a price mostly at £20-plus, although there are Rhônes and Loires under £10.

CHEF: Valentino Bayona PROPRIETOR: Michael Yates
OPEN: all week, D only, L by arrangement CLOSED: Nov to Mar MEALS: 7.45
PRICES: Set D from £18 (£25)
SEATS: 21. Private parties: 8 main room. Car-park, 12 places. Vegetarian meals. No children under 10. One sitting
ACCOMMODATION: 11 rooms, all with bath/shower. D, B&B £60 to £120. No children under 10. Afternoon teas. Garden. Fishing. Golf. Scenic. Doors close at 11.30

MACHYNLLETH Powys   map 4

Janie's [10/20]

57 Maengwyn Street, Machynlleth SY20 8EE
MACHYNLLETH (0654) 2126   £15

Janie Howkins' beamed bistro is committed to fresh ingredients. Home-baked rolls create a good impression before dishes such as provençale-style mushrooms, thinly sliced pork with white wine, and noisettes of lamb. Vegetables are not overcooked, sweets are calorific, the atmosphere pleasantly informal. Modest wines include house wine at £2·95 a half-litre, but CELLARMAN'S CHOICE is Ch. Cissac '80, £9·95, or Ch. Rouet '82, £8·95.

CHEF/PROPRIETOR: Jane Howkins
OPEN: Tue to Sun CLOSED: Oct to Easter MEALS: 12 to 2, 7.15 to 9
PRICES: £10 (£15), L Snacks from 95p
SEATS: 24. Private parties: 24 main room, 25 private room. Children's helpings. Wheelchair access. Music

---

MATHRY Dyfed   map 4

Ann FitzGerald's Farmhouse Kitchen [12/20]

Mawbs Fawr, Mathry SA62 5JB
CROESGOCH (034 83) 347   £8–£13

Only the absence of any machinery suggests that this substantial stone house is no longer part of a working farm. The FitzGeralds run it as a bakery. The dining-room is plainly done with a blue tiled fireplace, the table linen and candlesticks adding a touch of elegance. Fish shows strongly, from scallops in champagne sauce, to salmon in sorrel sauce, to whole langoustine cooked with shallots, tomatoes, chervil, and brandy. The quality of the meat shows in the lamb noisettes chasseur tinged with tarragon, and the venison served as a thick steak on a rich, juice-laden pepper sauce laced with armagnac. Vegetables are unfussy. Sweets seem more labour-intensive than other courses, although there are some

---

Restaurants are checked every year and their entries rewritten. The restaurant scene changes very rapidly. Don't trust an out-of-date Guide.

---

interesting ideas, such as wafer-thin rectangles of chocolate masquerading as mille-feuille. All the cream used is from a local Jersey herd. There's plenty of alcohol in the cooking, although the restaurant is unlicensed. Bread is, of course, excellent. The FitzGeralds were previously in the *Guide* in 1965 under Lerryn, Cornwall.

CHEFS: Lionel and Ann FitzGerald PROPRIETOR: Ann FitzGerald
OPEN: all week CLOSED: L Christmas to Easter MEALS: 12 to 3, 6.30 to 10
PRICES: £13, Set L £8, Set D £10, Snacks from 40p. Service inc. Unlicensed, but bring your own: no corkage
SEATS: 30. 4 tables outside. Private parties: 40 main room. Car-park, 40 places. Vegetarian meals. Children's helpings. No children under 9. Wheelchair access. Music

---

NEWPORT Dyfed   map 4

▲ *Cnapan* [10/20]

East Street, Newport SA42 0WF
NEWPORT (0239) 820575   £15

The fine, pale pink Georgian house stands in the centre of town. Lunch dishes have a wholefood start – soups, savoury flans, salads. Dinners are more ambitious: hot avocado with Stilton; grilled marinated lamb with stir-fried rice and a minty yoghurt dip; hazel-nut slice with raspberries and fresh pineapple. Twenty wines include house French at £4·25 a bottle.

CHEFS: Eluned Lloyd and Judi Cooper PROPRIETORS: Eluned and John Lloyd, Judi and Michael Cooper
OPEN: all week, exc Tue MEALS: 12.30 to 2.30, 7.30 to 9
PRICES: £11 (£15) CARDS: Access, Visa
SEATS: 34. 4 tables outside. Private parties: 36 main room. Car-park, 6 places. Vegetarian meals. Children's helpings. Wheelchair access (also WC)
ACCOMMODATION: 5 rooms, all with bath/shower. B&B £18 to £26. Deposit: 10%. Children welcome. Baby facilities. No pets. Afternoon teas. Garden. TV. Scenic [GHG]

PONTSHAEN Dyfed   map 4

▲ *Farmhouse Restaurant* [9/20]

Castell Howell, Pontshaen SA44 4UA
PONTSHAEN (054 555) 209   £14

On the upper floor of a converted farmhouse in a complex of leisure facilities. It fills a gap in the area and prices are reasonable. The menu has some dishes with Welsh names – trout with bacon, and braised beef, for instance – and Dyfed smokies are smoked mackerel in a creamy wine sauce. Good steaks, Welsh cheeses, and fresh vegetables are all pluses. Locally made cheesecake is a creditable sweet. Full-bodied, fruity house wine is £4·85 a bottle.

'In consideration of the payment of £578 for the meal, I do not expect to suffer because it was an incredibly busy evening, particularly because the maître d'hôtel was nowhere in evidence.' (On eating in Oxfordshire)

CHEF: Lisa Nunn PROPRIETORS: Andrew and Lisa Nunn
OPEN: Tue to Sat, plus bank hols, D only CLOSED: Tue to Thur in winter, 2 weeks Jan,
2 weeks Nov MEALS: 7.30 to 10
PRICES: £11 (£14). Service inc CARD: Access
SEATS: 40. Private parties: 30 main room, 15 private room. Car-park, 20 places. Vegetarian
meals. Children's helpings. Music
ACCOMMODATION: 11 rooms, all with bath/shower. Rooms for disabled. B&B £15 to £20.
Deposit: 10%. Children welcome. Baby facilities. Pets welcome. Garden. Swimming-pool.
Sauna. Fishing. TV. Scenic. Doors close at 12. Confirm by 6

PONTYPRIDD Mid Glamorgan   map 4

John & Maria's [9/20]

1/3 Broadway, Pontypridd CF37 1BA
PONTYPRIDD (0443) 402977   £6–£17

A popular Welsh-Italian restaurant, built on strong family foundations, which
straddles the two cultures. Steaks with hefty helpings of vegetables, liver with
onions and chips, and steak and kidney pie rub shoulders with vitello al limone
and pasta dishes such as tortelli di spinacci. Three dozen mostly Italian wines,
with house red and white at £3 per half-litre.

CHEF: Mrs Orsi PROPRIETORS: The Orsi family
OPEN: Mon to Sat CLOSED: bank hols MEALS: 11.30 to 3, 5.30 to 10
PRICES: £12 (£17), Set L from £2·60 (£6)
SEATS: 130. Children welcome

REYNOLDSTON West Glamorgan   map 4

▲ Fairyhill [12/20]

Reynoldston, Gower SA3 1BS
GOWER (0792) 390139
M4 junction 47 to Gorseinon, then B4295 to Fairyhill   £13–£19

The Fraynes have moved on from B&B and have turned this stone country house
into one of the best eating-places in the area. Kate Cole's cooking is fresh and
convincing, with a strong Welsh bias. Local cockles are crisply fried for nibbling
with drinks, or served as a starter with laver-bread. Lamb is roasted, guinea-fowl
is served with its own juices, and there is a fine array of vegetables including
parsnip purée with almonds, crisp leeks, and dauphinoise potatoes. Sweets, laid
out handsomely on a big table in the centre of the room, are old-fashioned
favourites, such as Queen of Puddings, hazel-nut meringue, and raspberry
Pavlova. Some rooms are larger than others, and John Frayne is still developing
what will soon be grand-scale gardens, where the wild ponies come to graze from
the estuary. House Bulgarian is £4·95.

All letters to the Guide *are acknowledged.*

*If, in your opinion, a restaurant is not maintaining the standard of its ratings please
inform the* Guide *office. Report forms are at the back of the book.*

CHEF: Kate Cole PROPRIETORS: John and Midge Frayne
OPEN: all week, D only, and Sun L CLOSED: Sun D Sept to Easter
MEALS: 12 to 1.45, 7 to 9.30
PRICES: £14 (£19), Set Sun L £8·95 (£13), Set D from £12 (£17) CARDS: Access, Amex, Diners, Visa
SEATS: 60. 4 tables outside. Private parties: 45 main room, 20 private room. Car-park, 60 places.Vegetarian meals. Children's helpings (L only). Smart dress preferred. Wheelchair access (also WC). Music
ACCOMMODATION: 12 rooms, all with bath/shower. B&B £39 to £49. Pets welcome. Garden. Sauna. Fishing. TV. Phone. Scenic. Confirm by 2 [GHG]

RHAYADER Powys map 4

▲ *Workhouse* [10/20]

South Road, Rhayader LD6 5BL
RHAYADER (0597) 810111 (restaurant), 810735 (accommodation)   £11–£17

Brynafon Country House is a self-catering and B&B accommodation complex near the River Wye. The slate-floored dining-room is rustic, with beams, chapel pews and a wood-burning stove, and the cooking relies on local produce: organic vegetables from local growers; fruit from WI markets; fish from Gardiners of Hereford; dairy produce from the Dairy House, Weobley; fresh pasta made in Abergavenny. Theresa Ledford has catholic tastes; her menu is cosmopolitan, although there's a modern British note to dishes such as a coddled free-range egg with Welsh goats' cheese; Welsh lamb cutlets with garlic and green ginger; and pigeon breasts with redcurrant and rosemary. Cheeses are hand-made in Britain. Sam Powell's Original real ale or around forty wines, including CELLARMAN'S CHOICE: Chardonnay, Montana '86, £6·90.

CHEF: Theresa Ledford PROPRIETORS: Alison and André Gallagher
OPEN: Wed to Sat, D only, and Sun L CLOSED: Christmas MEALS: 12.30 to 2, 7 to 10
PRICES: £12 (£17), Set L £6·95 (£11), Snacks from £1·50
SEATS: 28. Private parties: 35 main room, 20 private room. Car-park, 20 places. Vegetarian meals. Children's helpings (Sun L only). No children under 6. Wheelchair access (also WC). Music
ACCOMMODATION: 26 rooms, 8 with bath/shower. Rooms for disabled. B&B £15 to £24. Deposit: 33%. Children welcome. Baby facilities. Pets welcome. Garden. Swimming-pool. Fishing. Golf. TV. Scenic. Confirm by 6

ROSSETT Clwyd map 4

Churtons [10/20]

Chester Road, Rossett LL12 0HW
ROSSETT (0244) 570163   £15

The menu is chalked up daily on a slate at this emergent wine bar in an old barn. There is plenty of range. As many as a dozen dishes, mostly British, with home-made pudding, back up some good choices of less expensive wines especially from

---

Restaurants are not expected to solicit customers to send in reports. Please let us know if this happens to you.

the Alsace and the Rhône. House wine starts at £4·70. CELLARMAN'S CHOICE: Ch. La Croix de Millorit '79, £6·25.

CHEF: Susan Watson PROPRIETORS: Nicholas and James Churton, Richard Bowen-Jones
OPEN: Mon to Sat CLOSED: Christmas to New Year, bank hol Mons
MEALS: 12 to 2.15, 7 to 10
PRICES: £11 (£15) CARDS: Access, Amex, Diners, Visa
SEATS: 60. 3 tables outside. Private parties: 12 main room. Car-park, 20 places. No children under 10. Wheelchair access (also WC). Music. Air-conditioned

---

ST DOGMAELS Dyfed   map 4

▲ *Crug-y-Deri* [10/20]

High Street, St Dogmaels SA43 3EJ
CARDIGAN (0239) 613118   £8 – £13

Mrs Hoggett cooks a short menu in this little cottage. Steaks and local lamb are supplemented by free-range chicken with tarragon or poached in white wine. Proper ice-cream is made with milk from local farms. House French is £4·50.

CHEF: Mrs P. Hoggett PROPRIETORS: Mr and Mrs P. Hoggett
OPEN: Tue to Sat, D only, and Sun L CLOSED: end Oct to Easter or end Mar
MEALS: 12 to 2, 7 to 10
PRICES: £9 (£13), Set L £4·95 (£8). Service inc CARDS: Access, Amex, Diners, Visa
SEATS: 24. Private parties: 30 main room. Car-park, 5 places. Children's helpings. Wheelchair access
ACCOMMODATION: 1 room, with bath/shower. B&B £12. Garden. TV. Doors close at 12

TALSARNAU Gwynedd   map 4

▲ *Hotel Maes-y-Neuadd* [10/20]

Talsarnau LL47 6YA
HARLECH (0766) 780200
off B4573, 1m S of Talsarnau   £12 – £18

A one-in-five hill up a narrow lane leads to the Horsfalls' and Slatters' hotel in its own lovely grounds. They are tidy hoteliers and provide fresh food, much of it in modern British vein – cauliflower and almond soup, lamb with honey and cider, iced apricot cheesecake. Lamb is cooked differently every night. Fifty wines from £5·70. CELLARMAN'S CHOICE: Domaine de Gaillat, Graves '78, £15·40.

All inspections are carried out anonymously.

'I entered at 6.05pm, ordered the house speciality and a beer, but at 6.35 they continued bringing food for everyone else. The waiter smiled and said it would be coming and would I like another beer? At 6.45, with two beers completed, I looked around in a state of hunger and wondered . . . at 7, with no order in sight, I was getting upset. At 7.10 I paid for the beer and left – even though they promised that the order "was coming". I still don't know why my single order was taking so long and no reasons were volunteered.' (On eating in London)

CHEFS: Olive Horsfall and Andrew Price   PROPRIETORS: Michael and June Slatter, Malcolm and Olive Horsfall
OPEN: all week, D only, and Sun L (weekday L by arrangement)   CLOSED: 3 Jan to 5 Feb
MEALS: 12.15 to 1.45, 7.30 to 9
PRICES: Set L from £7·95 (£12), Set D from £13·75 (£18)   CARDS: Access, Visa
SEATS: 40. Private parties: 70 main room. Car-park, 50 places. Vegetarian meals. Children's helpings. No children under 7. Wheelchair access
ACCOMMODATION: 16 rooms, 14 with bath/shower. Rooms for disabled. B&B £26 to £62. Deposit: £20. No children under 7. Pets welcome. Afternoon teas. Garden. TV. Phone. Scenic. Doors close at 11. Confirm by 4   [GHG]

TALYLLYN Gwynedd   map 4

▲ *Minffordd Hotel*   [11/20]

Talyllyn LL36 9AJ
CORRIS (065 473) 665
at junction of A487 and B4405   £14·25

Minffordd, meaning 'roadside', was the original name of this former coaching-inn, although it has been the Goat and the Blue Lion as well. The small, cottagey auberge nestles under the craggy slopes of Cader Idris, not far from the upper shore of Talyllyn Lake. The Pickles family have tended the hotel for a decade and have changed none of its special old-world atmosphere: guests are still greeted by name and introduced to each other. Jonathan Pickles cooks a home-spun version of modern British food, with a few forays to foreign parts. Spinach soup is the real thing, fillet of smoked mackerel comes with fennel butter, from Hungary there might be yumunta calibir (poached egg topped with yoghurt), while from Greece comes a casserole of chicken with tomatoes. Home-made lemon meringue pie is one of the best sweets. The wines, from Tanners of Shrewsbury, are sensibly chosen.

CHEF: Jonathan Pickles   PROPRIETORS: Bernard and Jessica Pickles
OPEN: Tue to Sat, D only   CLOSED: Jan and Feb   MEALS: 7.30 to 8.30
PRICES: Set D £11·50 (£14·25). Service inc   CARDS: Access, Diners, Visa
SEATS: 28. Private parties: 28 main room. Car-park, 12 places. Vegetarian meals. Children's helpings. No children under 3. Smart dress preferred. No smoking in dining-room. Wheelchair access
ACCOMMODATION: 7 rooms, all with bath/shower. D, B&B £37 to £74. No children under 3. Garden. Phone. Scenic. Doors close at 11. Confirm by 6   [GHG]

THREE COCKS Powys   map 4

▲ *Three Cocks Hotel*   [11/20]

Three Cocks LD3 0SL
GLASBURY (049 74) 215   £18 – £20

The fifteenth-century L-shaped stone inn, with its ivy, tiled roof and cobbled forecourt, has been taken over by Michael Winstone. His arrival has been greeted with a host of recommendations. There is a large and spacious dining-room with some real cooking of a style not found elsewhere in Powys. The menu is modern, Belgian rather than French, and shows some excellent dishes – brill with a butter sauce dashed with curry; watercress soup; duck with sesame seeds; roast venison with peppercorns and apple sauce. Some of the sauces can overshadow main dishes, which come garnished with as many as seven minute vegetables. Sweets are less strong. Service is organised and charming, and the pace sufficient to convince that much cooking is done to order. Rooms are being upgraded and the hotel is well placed for the Brecon Beacons. The thirty or so wines have been carefully chosen and start at £4·75. CELLARMAN'S CHOICE: Ch. Giscours '81, £18·25.

CHEF: M. E. Winstone   PROPRIETORS: M. E. and M. J. Winstone
OPEN: all week   CLOSED: Jan   MEALS: 12 to 1.30, 7 to 9
PRICES: £17 (£20), Set L and D £15 (£18), Service inc   CARDS: Access, Visa
SEATS: 35. Car-park, 30 places. Children welcome. Music
ACCOMMODATION: 7 rooms. B&B £18 to £36. Children welcome. Baby facilities. Pets welcome. Garden. Scenic

---

WOLF'S CASTLE Dyfed   map 4

▲ *Wolfscastle Country Hotel* [11/20]

Wolf's Castle SA62 5LZ
TREFFGARNE (043 787) 225   £17

Nothing but good is said about Andrew Stirling's well-run greystone hotel. Alas, recent extensions have obliterated the views from the homely dining-room. The short menu is supplemented by daily specials. Bread and pasta are home made and complement the main thrust of the menu, which is carbonnade of beef, salmon koulibiac, haddock and sweetcorn roulade, and main-course meats offset with fruit. Desserts draw praise: strawberry Pavlova, meringue shells with ice-creams and raspberry sauce, Dutch apple pie, and lemon custard with a lemon syrup. There are good-value bar meals too. Around thirty wines, with house wine £5·50. CELLARMAN'S CHOICE: Mâcon-Lugny, Les Charmes, £7·80.

CHEFS: Michael Lewis and Alex George   PROPRIETOR: Andrew Maxwell Stirling
OPEN: all week, D only, and Sun L   MEALS: 12 to 2, 7 to 9.30
PRICES: £12 (£17)   CARDS: Access, Amex, Visa
SEATS: 60. Private parties: 160 main room. Car-park, 60 places. Vegetarian meals. Children's helpings. Smart dress preferred. No smoking in dining-room. Music. Air-conditioned
ACCOMMODATION: 15 rooms, all with bath/shower. B&B £20 to £38. Children welcome. Baby facilities. Pets welcome. Tennis. TV. Phone. Doors close at 12. Confirm by 6

Isle of Man

La Rosette [10/20]

Main Road, Ballasalla
BALLASALLA (0624) 822940 £23

Robert and Rosa Phillips have enlarged this former bakery and tea-room. Meals
are leisurely. The menu is one of those grand old-fashioned excursions written in
French of coquilles St Jacques maître d'hôtel; escalope de veau à la mode de
Mann (with white Manx whisky); pork viennoise. Fish is, naturally, excellent.
More hot puddings have been brought on. House Rhône £5·65.
CELLARMAN'S CHOICE: Bourgogne Aligoté '83, £9.

CHEF: Robert Phillips PROPRIETORS: Robert and Rosa Phillips
OPEN: Mon to Sat, exc Mon L MEALS: 12 to 2.30, 7 to 10.30
PRICES: £15 (£23). Cover 60p
SEATS: 47. Private parties: 24 main room, 8 and 15 private rooms. Children's helpings.
Music

Silverburn Lodge [10/20]

Ballasalla
BALLASALLA (0624) 822343 £12–£23

The low, white timbered building used to be called the Old Coach House; it now
has a helipad on the lawns, as well as a stream running through the grounds. It
feels old-fashioned, with beams and brasses everywhere and an exposed raftered
ceiling in the dining-room. Fish includes big dishes of mussels and local queenies.
Otherwise the menu roams from Manx lamb steak in red wine sauce, and pork
normande, to steak and kidney pie. Roasts are carved on the trolley. Vegetables
are fresh, and sweets are freshly made. Bernie Hamer supervises the front of the
house and the kitchen with equal vigilance. The mainly French wine list includes
CELLARMAN'S CHOICE: Ch. Talbot '74, £16·75.

CHEF: Eddie Murphy PROPRIETORS: Bernie and Jo Hamer
OPEN: Tue to Sun, exc Sun D CLOSED: 3 weeks Oct MEALS: 12 to 1.45, 7.30 to 9.30
PRICES: £15 (£23), Set L £7·50 (£12) CARDS: Access, Visa
SEATS: 65. Private parties: 80 main room. Car-park, 40 places. Wheelchair access (also WC).
Music

ONCHAN   map 4

Boncompte's [11/20]

King Edward Road, Onchan
DOUGLAS (0624) 75626   £13–£23

Still one of the most popular places on the island, much favoured by business people from nearby Douglas. Set lunch is one of the main attractions, with dishes such as cod in prawn sauce or shoulder of pork. The hors d'oeuvre table has about fifteen choices, and the sweets trolley is loaded with rich concoctions such as raspberry vacherin and chocolate eclairs. Vegetables are crisp. Dinners are more ambitious, taking in fillet steak with Stilton sauce, quail with grapes, and turbot Dugléré. Oysters are from Port Erin, queenies are local, and Manx lamb appears as a double Barnsley chop or as roast rack. The seventy-strong wine list is mainly French, but CELLARMAN'S CHOICE is Tinto Gran Reserva Rioja '78 at £9·50.

CHEF: Jaime Boncompte PROPRIETORS: Jaime and Jill Boncompte
OPEN: Mon to Sat, exc Sat L MEALS: 12.30 to 2, 7.30 to 10
PRICES: £16 (£23), Set L £8 (£13) CARDS: Access, Diners, Visa
SEATS: 90. Private parties: 90 main room. Car-park, 10 places. Vegetarian meals. Children's helpings. Smart dress preferred. Wheelchair access (also WC). Music

PORT ERIN   map 4

Molyneux's [10/20]

2 Spaldrick, Port Erin
PORT ERIN (0624) 833633   £18

Molyneux's restaurant in a pair of bow-windowed converted shops draws a strong local following. The set menu of five starters, main dishes and desserts uses a lot of cream and alcohol. Fish is the main feature, quite often *nouvelle* and elaborate: salmon and scallop terrine with ginger and a yoghurt and lime dressing. Monk-fish is served with cream and Stilton, beef with cream and brandy. Sweets can be excellent – witness the brandy-snap basket with banana and butterscotch sauce. Some of the details fall down, which is a pity. The wine list is suitably adjusted to white wines, with sweet wines for dessert. House French is £9 a litre.

CHEF: Stephen Molyneux PROPRIETORS: Stephen and Gillian Molyneux
OPEN: Mon to Sat, D only MEALS: 7.30 to 10
PRICES: Set D from £12·50 (£18) CARD: Visa
SEATS: 45. Private parties: 50 main room, 25 private room. Vegetarian meals. Children's helpings. Smart dress preferred. Music. Air-conditioned

Northern Ireland

The Ulster section of the *Guide* has in recent years become less and less significant, but lately there have been signs of revival in the restaurant scene. This year we canvassed Northern Ireland readers for suggestions. None of the restaurants has been inspected (hence they aren't rated), but all have received at least three nominations. We hope to set up a Northern Ireland inspectorate in time for next year's edition, and suggestions and reports are especially welcome.

BALLYNAHINCH Co. Down   map 9
Woodlands
---
29 Spa Road, Ballynahinch BT24 8PT
BALLYNAHINCH (0238) 562650   £19

This nineteenth-century farmhouse is surrounded by mature trees and gardens. David and Alison Sandford run it as their home, serving pre-dinner drinks and coffee in the lounge, which has blazing turf fires. The emphasis is on local produce: seafood comes from Strangford, game from local estates and herbs and vegetables from their own garden. Starters are particularly good – chicken livers with bacon, or pheasant mousse – and there is a dazzling variety of puddings, including pashka, a creamy cheese dessert with nuts and raisins and soaked in liqueur. The set menu changes every two weeks. House wine is £5·50.

CHEF: Alison Sandford PROPRIETORS: Alison and David Sandford
OPEN: Thur to Sat D MEALS: 7.30 to 9.45
PRICES: Set D £14·50 (£19) CARDS: Access, Diners, Visa
SEATS: 45. Private parties: 45 main room, 14 private room. Car-park, 20 places. Children's helpings. No cigars/pipes in dining-room.

BELFAST Co. Antrim   map 9
La Belle Epoque
---
103 Great Victoria Street, Belfast BT2 7AG
BELFAST (0232) 223244   £17

Right in the centre of Belfast, this French restaurant only opens in the evenings and the cooking is ambitious. Salmon comes in filo pastry with a Pernod sauce; trout terrine is served with a lemon sauce. For dessert there's crêpe Suzette or rich chocolate mousse. House wine is £3·95. There's an accordion player Monday to Thursday.

CHEFS: Alan Rousse and Chris Fitzgerald PROPRIETORS: Alan Rousse, Chris Fitzgerald, Judith and John Delbart and Gonzalez Sanchez
OPEN: Mon to Sat, D only MEALS: 6 to 12.30 (11.30 Sat)
PRICES: £11 (£17) CARDS: Access, Diners, Visa
SEATS: 80. Private parties: 40 main room. Vegetarian meals. Music

Strand

12 Stranmillis Road, Belfast BT9 5AA
BELFAST (0232) 682266   £12

In the heart of the university area, 100 yards from the Ulster Museum, this cheerful, bistro-style restaurant is part of a Victorian terrace. The menu changes monthly, offering a selection of dishes such as stuffed aubergines, Strand mushrooms and chilli con carne. Wild salmon, Dublin Bay prawns and mussels are available in season. House wine is £3·95.

CHEFS: M. Paine, M. McAuley, Stephen Galway and Marie Hickey
PROPRIETOR: Anne Turkington
OPEN: Tue to Sat MEALS: noon to 11pm
PRICES: £8 (£12) CARDS: Access, Amex, Diners, Visa
SEATS: 80. Vegetarian meals. Children welcome. Music. Air-conditioned

---

BELLANALECK Co. Fermanagh   map 9

Sheelin

Bellanaleck
FLORENCECOURT (036 582) 232
4 miles from Enniskillen   £7–£13

The quaint thatched building was originally the village post office. The Cathcart family now run it as a restaurant with a bakery and it has a high reputation for home cooking and baking. It is open all week for lunches, but the Saturday dinner menu stands out. Typical are mushrooms stuffed with Stilton, roast duck with apricot stuffing, and walnut cheesecake with a caramel sauce. House wine is £4·50.

CHEFS: The Cathcart family PROPRIETOR: Arthur Cathcart
OPEN: Mon to Sat L and Fri and Sat D; plus Sun and Tue to Thur D 20 June to 20 Sept
MEALS: 12.30 to 2.30, 7 to 9.30
PRICES: £9 (£13), Set L from £4 (£7), Set D from £10 (£13), Snacks from £1·25. Service 10%
CARDS: Access, Amex, Visa
SEATS: 30. Private parties: 30 main room. Car-park. Vegetarian meals. Children's helpings. Smart dress preferred. Wheelchair access

---

The entries are compiled from the views of readers who have eaten at the restaurants in the last year, backed up by anonymous inspections and by information supplied and facts verified by the restaurants.

COLERAINE Co. Derry　map 9

▲ *MacDuff's*

112 Killeaugue Road, Blackhill, Coleraine BT51 4HH
AGHADOWEY (026 585) 433　　　　　　　　　　　　　　　£16

The Erwins' restaurant is in the basement of their home, an old renovated farmhouse. The menu does not change; long-standing dishes that draw praise include cream cheese roulade and scampi with a chilli dip, to start, then chicken with avocado or lamb in a port and plum sauce. Goose features regularly. Meringues to finish are mentioned frequently.

CHEF: Alan Wade　PROPRIETORS: Joseph and Margaret Erwin
OPEN: Tue to Sat, D only　MEALS: 7 to 9.30
PRICES: £11 (£16)　CARD: Visa
SEATS: 34. Private parties: 34 main room, 15 private room. Car-park, 20 places. Vegetarian meals. No children under 10
ACCOMMODATION: 6 rooms, all with bath/shower. B&B £25 to £40. No children under 10. Garden. Swimming-pool. T V. Phone. Scenic

DUNADRY Co. Antrim　map 9

▲ *Dunadry Inn*

Muckamore, Dunadry BT41 2HA
TEMPLEPATRICK (084 94) 32474　　　　　　　　　　　£11–£19

Set in ten acres of maintained gardens on the site of an old linen- and paper-mill, this family-run hotel has a reputation as one of the best in Northern Ireland. Menus are changed on a regular basis, with a strong emphasis on locally caught fish; there is also a changing daily *carte*. The buffet lunch (available all week, except Sunday) has been praised. House wine is £5·40.

CHEF: Pat Kell　PROPRIETOR: C. G. Mooney
OPEN: all week　CLOSED: 24 to 27 Dec　MEALS: 12.30 to 1.45, 7.30 to 9.45 (carvery 5.30 to 8 Sun)
PRICES: £12 (£19), Set L £7·50 (£11), Set D £11·50 (£16)　CARDS: Access, Amex, Carte Blanche, Diners, Visa
SEATS: 300. Private parties: 300 main room, 12, 30, 60 and 100 private rooms. Car-park, 350 places. Children's helpings (Sun L only). Wheelchair access (also W C)
ACCOMMODATION: 64 rooms, all with bath/shower. Rooms for disabled. B&B £50 to £62. Children welcome. Baby facilities. Afternoon teas. Garden. Fishing. T V. Phone. Scenic. Confirm by 6.

HILLSBOROUGH Co. Down　map 9

Hillside

21 Main Street, Hillsborough BT26 6AE
HILLSBOROUGH (0846) 683475　　　　　　　　　　　£12–£17

The bar lunches draw much praise at this busy pub in this Georgian village a dozen miles outside Belfast. There are usually two or three hot dishes on offer, plus a good selection of cold meats and salads. Wholewheat bread is home made

457

and sweets tempt. The restaurant upstairs has a small menu that might feature goose or suckling pig. House beer is Hilden, house wine is £6·75; there are some interesting wines.

CHEFS: Noel Doran and John McAvoy PROPRIETORS: Harlequin (Hillsborough) Ltd
OPEN: Mon to Sat D, and Mon to Fri L Dec only MEALS: 12 to 3, 7 to 9.30
PRICES: £12 (£17), Set L £8·50 (£12), Set D from £8·95 (£13) CARDS: Access, Amex, Diners, Visa
SEATS: 46. 3 tables outside. Private parties: 30 main room. Vegetarian meals. No children under 18

HOLYWOOD Co. Down   map 9

Iona

Holywood BT18 9BO
HOLYWOOD (023 17) 5655   £18

Dutch-born chef/patron Bartjan Brade changes his menu every two months in this cosy little first-floor restaurant. A selection from his summer menu included home-made fresh spinach ravioli, fillets of beef in a pink peppercorn sauce, breast of pigeon cooked off the bone in a fresh cherry sauce, and passion-fruit mousse. Service is relaxed. The restaurant is not licensed, and makes no corkage charge.

CHEF/PROPRIETOR: Bartjan Brade
OPEN: Tue to Sat, D only MEALS: 6.30 to 10.30
PRICES: £14 (£18), Set D from £15·95 (£18), Snacks at L from 65p
SEATS: 28. Private parties: 32 main room. Vegetarian meals. Children welcome. Music

---

KILLINCHY Co. Down   map 9

Nick's Place

18 Kilmood Church Road, Killinchy BT23 6SB
KILLINCHY (0238) 541472   £17

This converted court-house dating from 1822 uses the stables as the bar area and the upstairs court-room as the dining-room. Nick Price changes his handwritten menu each day, offering a sensibly limited range of dishes, such as cream and spinach soup, halibut with beurre blanc, and loin of pork with port and pepper sauce. Home-made ice-cream for dessert. Service is friendly and there is a good wine cellar.

CHEFS: Nick Price and Jenny McCrea PROPRIETORS: Nick and Kathy Price
OPEN: Tue to Sat, D only CLOSED: 2 weeks Sept to Oct, one week Feb MEALS: 7.30 to 10
PRICES: £12 (£17) CARDS: Access, Diners, Visa
SEATS: 45. 3 tables outside. Private parties: 30 main room. Car-park, 60 places. Children's helpings. Music

---

▲ *This restaurant has rooms.*

'Just for interest, at all these meals our aperitifs were two campari and soda, and the prices varied from £1.70 in Avon, £1.82 in Wiltshire, £2.20 in Devon, and £3.00 in Edinburgh.' (On eating in Strathclyde)

PORTRUSH Co. Antrim	map 9

Ramore

The Harbour, Portrush BT56 8DQ
PORTRUSH (0265) 824313 £18

Overlooking the small harbour at this popular seaside resort on the northern
Antrim coast, this family-run restaurant is one of the best-known in Northern
Ireland. The Caithness's son-in-law, George McAlpin, uses local produce and
changes the menu every three months. Fish is a speciality and desserts are home
made, as is the traditional Irish soda bread. Good reports of dishes as varied as
Camembert fritters, pork with apple and plums, and salmon mousse with prawn
sauce. Booking essential.

CHEF: George McAlpin PROPRIETORS: John and Joy Caithness, George McAlpin
OPEN: Tue to Sat, D only MEALS: 7 to 10
PRICES: £11 (£18)
SEATS: 55. Private parties: 60 main room. Car-park, 8 places. Children welcome. Music

SAINTFIELD Co. Down	map 9

Barn

120 Monlough Road, Saintfield BT24 7EU
SAINTFIELD (0238) 510396 £18

This small, family-run restaurant with its own herb garden is based on a small-
holding in the countryside of Co. Down. Robbie and Jane Wright have converted
two interconnecting barns to create a cosy lounge with log fires and a separate
dining-room. The menu changes regularly, using local produce for stuffed beef
tomatoes baked with a mild mustard sauce and lamb with mint sauce. Due to
demand there are always at least three fish dishes on offer, sometimes lobster
thermidor, or salmon en croûte with a wine and cream sauce. Everything, from
the cheese straws with pre-dinner drinks to the fudge served with coffee, is home
made. Well over a hundred wines.

CHEF: Robbie Wright PROPRIETORS: Robbie and Jane Wright
OPEN: Tue to Sat D, and Tue to Fri L in Dec CLOSED: 2 weeks Jan to Feb MEALS: 12.30 to
2.30, 7.30 to 10
PRICES: Set L £8·50 (£13), Set D £13·80 (£18) CARDS: Access, Amex, Diners, Visa
SEATS: 40. Private parties: 40 main room. Car-park, 12 places. Children's helpings. Jacket
and tie. Wheelchair access (1 step). Music. Air-conditioned

Republic of Ireland

map 9

Park [12/20]

26 Main Street
DUBLIN (01) 886177 £15–£27

Colin O'Daly's cooking in this Dublin suburb is exotic and unexpected.
Medallions of monkfish are with dates, coconut, almonds and honey; pan-fried
hake gets a plum sauce. Similar treatment is given to meat and game – roast
breast of duckling is paired with fresh mussels in a red wine sauce, and loin of
lamb en croûte comes with cranberry and ginger sauce. The short menu changes
frequently to make the best use of the market. Sweets are the likes of chocolate
truffle cake and little pots of coffee custard. Lunches are more simple. Service is
courteous and table setting immaculate. The wine list has house French at
£9·25, as well as recommended wines to complement special dishes, such as
Mâcon-Lugny, Les Charmes '85, at £14.

CHEF: Colin O'Daly PROPRIETORS: Colin and Lyn O'Daly
OPEN: Tue to Sat, exc Sat D MEALS: 12.30 to 2, 7.30 to 9.45
PRICES: Set L £8·50 (£15), Set D £19·50 (£27). Service 12.5% CARDS: Access, Amex,
Diners, Visa
SEATS: 50. Private parties: 50 main room. Children welcome. Smart dress preferred.
Air-conditioned

BORRIS Co. Carlow map 9

▲ Step House [11/20]

MUINE BEAG (0503) 73209 £25

Between cream of nettle soup with choux dumplings and 'Death by Chocolate' is
a changing repertoire of dishes that takes in wild mushroom strudel, wild rabbit
in mustard sauce, and chicken with potato and walnut stuffing. Essentially Breda
Coady runs a French restaurant with Irish hospitality – the door is usually open.
Local salmon is poached with a butter sauce, or turned into gravlax or a mousse,

---

*All prices in this section are in punts. If dialling from mainland Britain prefix
Dublin numbers with '00' and other numbers with '010 353', dropping the first '0'
of the code.*

and fruit and herbs are from the garden. Sunday lunch is traditional. Nearly fifty wines, mainly French, including CELLARMAN'S CHOICE: Côtes du Rhône Villages '85, £10·40.

CHEF/PROPRIETOR: Breda Coady
OPEN: Tue to Sat D, and Sun L CLOSED: Nov to Apr MEALS: 11.30 to 2.30, 7 to 10.30
PRICES: L £8 (£14), D £14 (£25), Set D £16 (£26). Licensed, also bring your own: corkage £3
CARD: Visa
SEATS: 30. Private parties: 30 main room. Children welcome. Smart dress preferred. Music
ACCOMMODATION: 4 rooms, all with bath/shower. B&B £16 to £35. Pets welcome. Afternoon
teas. Fishing. Golf. Snooker. Scenic

BRAY Co. Wicklow   map 9

Tree of Idleness [11/20]

Seafront
DUBLIN (01) 863498 and 828183   £17–£26

A little bit of Cyprus grafted on to Ireland brings about some unusual and successful dishes; tarama, tahini, wines, nuts, herbs and fruit combine with local ingredients. Lamb is a strong point: saddle comes with feta cheese and raspberry vinegar sauce; smoked best end with blackcurrant vinegar and wine sauce. Fish is plentiful: Dover sole with tarama sauce; smoked salmon with a yoghurt and herb dip; aubergine stuffed with monkfish, smoked salmon and prawns with a cream-cheese sauce. These are backed up by more traditional dishes, from hummus to moussaka, dolmades to kleftiko. An exceptional run of claret spans nearly every post-war vintage of note, but there are relatively inexpensive petit château wines from recent years for everyday drinking. There is support from the rest of France, and from Greece and Cyprus. CELLARMAN'S CHOICE: Château Clauss '73, £13.

CHEF: Akis Courtellas PROPRIETORS: Akis and Susan Courtellas
OPEN: Tue to Sun, D only MEALS: 7.30 to 11 (10 Sun)
PRICES: £18 (£26), Set D from £11 (£17). Minimum £7·50. Service 10% CARDS: Access,
Diners, Visa
SEATS: 60. Private parties: 16 main room. Vegetarian meals. Children's helpings. No
children under 10. Smart dress preferred. Wheelchair access. Music.

CORK Co. Cork   map 9

▲ *Arbutus Lodge* [13/20]

Middle Glanmire Road, Montenotte
CORK (021) 501237   £21–£30

This great stalwart continues to impress with some inventive cooking, though the grandeur of the décor belongs to yesterday. Despite the Frenchness of salade landaise, quail with armagnac, or veal kidney with mustard sauce, the cooking is firmly rooted in Ireland. There are Galway oysters, hot with cucumber and herbs; Irish smoked salmon, sometimes served hot with horseradish; thick and creamy nettle soup; Cork crubeens (pickled pigs' trotters); and Irish farm cheeses. Fish is a delight, with sauces to match: scallops with beurre blanc; turbot with sea-urchin sauce. The tasting menu is seven courses, including a half-way sorbet. Arbutus

Lodge is famous for its wines. Among the clarets it is no surprise to see runs of vintages of Langoa-Barton and Léoville-Barton, the Bartons being an Irish family, and the balance of Bordeaux and burgundy is unashamedly aristocratic. Italy helps with wines under £12, although it too has a classy collection.

CELLARMAN'S CHOICE: Jurançon sec '85, £7·50; and St Julien '83, £13·95.

CHEFS: Michael Ryan and Tom Rowe PROPRIETOR: The Ryan family
MEALS: 1 to 2, 7 to 9.30
PRICES: £22 (£30), Set L from £14·95 (£21), Set D from £17·95 (£24). Minimum £12
CARDS: Access, Amex, Diners, Visa
SEATS: 60. 6 tables outside. Private parties: 8 main room, 20 private room. Car-park, 35 places. Children welcome. No smoking. Wheelchair access. Air-conditioned
ACCOMMODATION: 20 rooms, all with bath/shower. B&B £36·50 to £66. Children welcome. Baby facilities. Garden. TV. Phone. Scenic [GHG]

Crawford Gallery [10/20]

Emmet Place
CORK (021) 274415   £15

A gallery-cum-café next door to the Opera House, hung with contemporary paintings, which are changed monthly. It is run by Myrtle Allen from Ballymaloe House (see Shanagarry), and her daughter, Fern. Mussels are stuffed with garlic and breadcrumbs, and there are pancakes folded like a purse and stuffed with mushrooms and spinach. Irish cheeses feature. Outside meal times, home-made cakes and scones are served with tea or coffee, and pre-theatre meals or snacks are available. House Duboeuf is £8·50 a bottle.

CHEFS: Myrtle and Fern Allen, Paddy and Don Cullinane PROPRIETORS: Myrtle and Fern Allen
OPEN: Mon to Sat L and Wed to Fri D CLOSED: a few days at Christmas MEALS: 12 to 2.30, 6.30 to 9.30
PRICES: £11 (£15), Snacks from £1. Minimum £2·50 at L
SEATS: 62. Private parties: 40 main room. Vegetarian meals. Children welcome. Wheelchair access. Music

DINGLE Co. Kerry   map 9

▲ Doyle's [12/20]

4 John Street
TRALEE (066) 51174   £20

Stella Doyle works in the kitchens of the great chefs during the winter months – Raymond Blanc was planned for winter 1987. Fish is the mainstay of her menu, not fussed over and never overcooked, simplicity being the key word. Local scallops are briefly steamed and served with a leek sauce; mussels come with a light, very garlicky Provençale sauce; hen lobster is caught from the tank, poached, and presented hot at the table with garlic butter and nothing else. Stella Doyle is particularly fond of making puddings. Lemon ice-box is a kind of mousse ice-cream; orange custard tart is a small miracle of dark brown shortcrust filled with a tangy orange purée. California Chardonnays are the pride of the list, including bottles from Iron Horse, Monticello, Trefethen, Mark West and Heitz;

Australia contributes Wynns and Rosemount Chardonnays. Good Spanish wines offer a choice at £10 or under.

CHEF: Stella Doyle PROPRIETORS: John and Stella Doyle
OPEN: Mon to Sat CLOSED: mid-Nov to mid-Mar MEALS: 12.30 to 2.15, 6 to 9
PRICES: £14 (£20), Snacks from £1·65. Service 10% CARDS: Access, Amex, Diners, Visa
SEATS: 49. Children's helpings. Wheelchair access (also WC)
ACCOMMODATION: 8 rooms, all with bath/shower. Rooms for disabled. B&B £40 to £50.
Deposit: 20%. Children welcome. TV. Phone. Doors close at 12

DUBLIN Co. Dublin   map 9

▲ *Le Coq Hardi* [12/20]

35 Pembroke Road, Ballsbridge, Dublin 4
DUBLIN (01) 689070 and 684130   £19–£38

John Howard describes his style as, 'creative classic cooking with a tendency towards lightness'. In practice, this is where much of Dublin's expense-account money goes, in an atmosphere of upper-crust sobriety. Some dishes are deliberately showy: poached breast of free-range chicken with cream and truffles, for instance, is presented under a glass dome. But there are simpler, more modern overtones, particularly in the fish dishes: poached Irish wild salmon with Chablis and watercress sauce; steamed monkfish with seaweed and saffron; seafood with fresh noodles. There is also game in season. Pastry cooking has been enhanced with the arrival of a specialist chef from Cliveden (see Taplow, England). The monumental wine list spans the decades, and has some four-figure museum pieces, including 1870 Ch. Mouton-Rothschild at £4,750. At the other extreme there are house wines at £12. CELLARMAN'S CHOICE: Morgon, Jean Descombes '85, at £16·55.

CHEFS: John Howard and James O'Sullivan PROPRIETORS: John and Catherine Howard
OPEN: Mon to Sat, exc Sat L CLOSED: 2 weeks at Christmas, 2 weeks Aug MEALS: 12.30 to 2.30, 7 to 11
PRICES: £26 (£38), Set L £13·75 (£19). Service 12.5% CARDS: Amex, Diners, Visa
SEATS: 45. Private parties: 20 and 15 private rooms. Car-park, 40 places. Children welcome. Jacket and tie. Air-conditioned
ACCOMMODATION: 2 rooms, all with bath/shower. B&B £40 to £170. Deposit: £20.
Air-conditioning. TV. Phone. Doors close at 2. Confirm by 6

Ernies [13/20]

Mulberry Gardens, Dublin 4
DUBLIN (01) 693300   £35–£39

Ernie Evans' restaurant seems to live heroically in another age. His renovated cottage is hung with paintings of his beloved Kerry, and the menu is entrenched in the flavours of old-style bourgeois cooking. This translates into fine versions of salmon mousse, moules marinière, roast Wicklow lamb, grilled fillet of plaice with béarnaise sauce. Terrine of chicken and vegetables, and monkfish with ginger suggest that the kitchen isn't standing still, while details, such as the fresh

---

The Guide *does not accept free meals.*

---

vegetables, the home-made sweets and the Irish cheeses, prove that this is a restaurant with serious intentions. House wine at £12·75 a bottle gives some indication of the price of drinking here. CELLARMAN'S CHOICE: St Amour '85, from Joseph Drouhin, £18·50.

CHEF/PROPRIETOR: Ernie Evans
OPEN: Tue to Sat, D only MEALS: 7 to 10.15
PRICES: £24 (£39), Set D £25 (£35). Minimum £15. Service 12.5% CARDS: Amex, Diners, Visa
SEATS: 60. Private parties: 30 main room. No children under 12. Smart dress preferred. Wheelchair access (also WC). Air-conditioned

Mitchells [10/20]

21 Kildare Street, Dublin 2
DUBLIN (01) 680367   £13

A busy bistro-cum-wine bar in the cellars of Mitchells Wine Merchants, open at lunchtime. Have a bowl of soup or a plate of cheese or order from the menu, which features quiches, baked haddock with shrimp sauce, curry, or veal florentine with pasta. The short wine list (from Mitchells) has plenty of drinking under £10.

CHEFS: Patricia Hogan and Anne MacCarthy PROPRIETORS: Mitchells and Son
OPEN: Mon to Sat, L only CLOSED: 24 Dec to 2 Jan, bank hol weekends
MEALS: 12.15 to 2.30
PRICES: £8 (£13) CARDS: Access, Amex, Diners, Visa
SEATS: 60. Private parties: 15 main room. Children's helpings

Patrick Guilbaud [13/20]

46 James's Place, Dublin 2
DUBLIN (01) 764192   £32

Patrick Guilbaud's converted mews house has a reputation as Dublin's premier nouvelle cuisine restaurant. The style is classical, with an understated menu that has echoes of the Roux brothers and the superstar brigade of best-selling chefs/authors in France. The menu begins with terrine of leeks in vinaigrette, ravioli of langoustines with lobster, and fresh scallops with basil, before wild salmon baked in sea salt, pigeon with lime mousse and beetroot, and fillet of lamb with mint sabayon. The flamboyant artistry of the sweets shows in the peach cut to form the leaves around a 'flower' of strawberry slices, in a Sauternes sauce. The wine list is dominated by big vintage clarets and burgundies, with only a token showing of bottles and half-bottles under £10.

CHEF: Guillaume Lebrun PROPRIETOR: Patrick Guilbaud
OPEN: Mon to Sat, exc Sat L MEALS: 12.30 to 2, 7.30 to 10.15
PRICES: £22 (£32). Service 15% CARDS: Access, Amex, Diners, Visa
SEATS: 50. Private parties: 70 main room. Car-park, 20 places. Children welcome. Smart dress preferred. No pipes in dining-room

'With so many high-quality beers available, why do so few restaurants offer a real choice in this regard? Why should wine buffs monopolise the show?'
(On eating in Yorkshire)

Rajdoot [10/20]

26–28 Clarendon Street, Westbury Centre, Dublin 2
DUBLIN (01) 794274 and 794280   £11–£25

One of a reliable mini-chain, with branches in Bristol, Birmingham and
Manchester. The cooking is Punjabi, taking in specialities such as quail makani
and crab bhuna, as well as the familiar run of curries and tandoori dishes. Lassi is
£1·50; house French, from Georges Duboeuf, £9·25 a bottle.

CHEFS: Kamal Singh Bisht and Ram Narayan Poudel PROPRIETOR: D. R. Sarda
OPEN: Mon to Sat MEALS: 12 to 2.30, 6.30 to 11.30
PRICES: £13 (£25), Set L £5·95 (£11), Set D from £13 (£19). Minimum £6·50. Service
12.5%, inc for Set L CARDS: Access, Amex, Diners, Visa
SEATS: 96. Private parties: 30 main room. Vegetarian meals. Children welcome. Music.
Air-conditioned

White's on the Green [12/20]

119 St Stephen's Green
DUBLIN (01) 751975 and 751181   £19–£36

The kitchen brigade in this sophisticated, comfortable restaurant has an
interesting pedigree: Michael Clifford has been at Arbutus Lodge, Mark Gibbs
trained at the Connaught in London, and Phillippe Berthier is from a long line of
French pâtissiers. Together they produce serious food in one of the most dignified
restaurants in Dublin. Although the emphasis is still on French-style feuilleté of
chicken quenelles with walnut and apple, quail with mango, ginger, mint and
Sauternes, and lobster bavarois with champagne sauce, the menu now takes in
prawn and lentil soup, Irish stew, and grilled black sole. The dessert menu is
decorated with exotic fruits. The brilliant wine list runs to twenty-four printed
pages. Vintage clarets dominate, but there's a good spread extending from France
to the New World, including fine regional wines, and no fewer than half a dozen
Sancerres. CELLARMAN'S CHOICE: Jurançon sec, Château Jolys '85 at £11·50.

CHEFS: Michael Clifford and Mark Gibbs PROPRIETORS: Peter and Alicia White, Philip
Frederick
OPEN: Mon to Sat, exc Sat L CLOSED: bank hols MEALS: 12.30 to 2.30, 7.30 to 10.30
PRICES: £25 (£36), Set L from £10·50 (£19), Set D £18 (£26). Service 12.5%
CARDS: Access, Amex, Diners, Visa
SEATS: 60. Private parties: 60 main room. Children's helpings. Smart dress preferred

ENNIS Co. Clare   map 9

Cloister [11/20]

Abbey Street
ENNIS (065) 29521   £25

Formerly the abbey bakehouse and attached to the round, thirteenth-century
Franciscan abbey, here is somewhere to eat the fish from the Clare coast. Salmon
comes from the River Fergus, to be baked in champagne with grapes or stir-fried
with oyster sauce. Shellfish is from the shores of County Clare: mussels steamed
with garlic, herbs, wine and cream; hot crab. There is game in season, and roast
loin of Corofin lamb. Snacks, such as baked ham on French bread, come with a

selection of freshly prepared salads – green peppers, carrots, orange, red cabbage, cucumber and finely shredded lettuce. Apple pie, and hazelnut roulade on blackberry are alternatives to local cheeses. Over forty wines include a Chardonnay each from Australia and California.

CHEF: Tim Gibbons PROPRIETOR: Rosaleen Spooner
OPEN: all week MEALS: 12 to 3.30, 6 to 9.30 (12.30 to 2, 4 to 10 Sun)
PRICES: £18 (£25), Snacks from £1. Service 10% CARDS: Access, Amex, Diners, Visa
SEATS: 45. 7 tables outside. Private parties: 30 main room, 25 private room. Children's helpings. No children after 8pm. Smart dress preferred. Wheelchair access. Music

---

GOREY Co. Wexford   map 9

▲ *Marlfield House* [11/20]

Courtown Road
GOREY (055) 21124 and 21572   £24–£27

A Regency dower house, on to which has been tacked an unusually impressive Victorian cast-iron curvilinear conservatory with an ogive-shaped roof. Lunch is a la carte, dinner fixed price, and both rely on alcohol for much of the saucing; white wine and marc de Bourgogne for breast of chicken; vermouth, cream and butter for brill. But fresh herbs and some vegetables are from the garden: chervil with a pastry case of asparagus; tomatoes and chives with wild Slaney salmon. Puddings, like everything else, vary with the season and there are Irish cheeses on the board. There is an occasional '59 or '45 claret hidden among more recent vintages, and prices rarely dip below £10 anywhere on the list. But there is a handful of attractive non-French wines including a Californian Chardonnay.
CELLARMAN'S CHOICE: Muscadet, Marquis de Goulaine '86, £11·50.

CHEF: John Dunne PROPRIETORS: Ray and Mary Bowe
OPEN: all week CLOSED: 3 days at Christmas MEALS: 1 to 2.30, 7.30 to 9.30
PRICES: £16 (£24), Set D £19·50 (£27), Snacks from £2·50. Service 10%
SEATS: 80. Private parties: 40 main room. Car-park, 70 places. No children under 5. Jacket and tie. No cigars/pipes in dining-room. Wheelchair access (also WC)
ACCOMMODATION: 12 rooms, all with bath/shower. Rooms for disabled. B&B £55 to £80. Deposit: £60. No children under 5. Afternoon teas. Garden. Sauna. Tennis. Fishing. Golf. TV. Phone. Scenic. Doors close at 12. Confirm by 5 [GHG]

KILLORGLIN Co. Kerry   map 9

▲ *Bianconi Inn* [10/20]

Annandale Road
KILLORGLIN (066) 61146   £21

A comfortable, family-run bar and restaurant where the food is cooked to order. Lunches are bar meals, and include plates of Killorglin oak-smoked salmon (a good half pound for each person), with an imaginative salad, grated red cabbage, and home-made mayonnaise for £6·50. They also do vegetarian salads, pâtés, ham and salami, and a range of hot dishes. Full restaurant dinners are the likes of broccoli soup, seafood mousseline, lobster, then traditional puddings or regional cheeses. House French is £7·90 a bottle.

CHEF: Ray Sheehy PROPRIETORS: Elizabeth, Rick, and Ray Sheehy
OPEN: all week, exc Sun D MEALS: 12 to 2, 6.30 to 9.30
PRICES: £15 (£21), Set D £15 (£21). Minimum £5. CARDS: Access, Diners, Visa
SEATS: 40. Private parties: 40 main room. Vegetarian meals. Children's helpings (D only). No children under 6. Wheelchair access (1 step). Music. Air-conditioned
ACCOMMODATION: 14 rooms, 6 with bath/shower. B&B £13 to £21. Deposit: £15. Children welcome. Baby facilities. Pets welcome. Afternoon teas. Scenic. Doors close at 12.30. Confirm by 6

LEIGHLINBRIDGE Co. Carlow

map 9

Lord Bagenal Inn [10/20]

Leighlinbridge
LEIGHLINBRIDGE (0503) 21668

£8–£16

A spacious inn on the bank of the River Barrow, whence come trout and salmon, best partnered by Australian Chardonnay from Rosemount. There is Gewürztraminer for spiced seafood, Viña Sol from Torres for plainly cooked fish, and Ch. Maucaillou for game and offal. Bar meals are good value. Good cheeses. Wines start at £6·95.

CHEF: Eric Lyons PROPRIETOR: James Kehoe
OPEN: all week, exc Mon D MEALS: 12.30 to 2.30, 6.30 to 10
PRICES: £12 (£16), Set L from £4·50 (£8), Set D from £12·50 (£16). Service inc
CARDS: Diners, Visa
SEATS: 110. 7 tables outside. Private parties: 50 main room. Car-park, 80 places. Vegetarian meals. Children's helpings. Music

---

MALLOW Co. Cork

map 9

▲ Longueville House [13/20]

Mallow
MALLOW (022) 47156

£24–£28

Breakfast typifies the mood of enterprise and good living that pervades Michael and Jane O'Callaghan's Georgian mansion deep in the country. The spread might include home-made yoghurt, compotes and jams with fruit from the garden, local Blackwater trout, home-made sausages, lambs' liver from the owners' farm animals, and black and white pudding, as well as free-range eggs. Lunch is excellent soup and open sandwiches on soda bread, and afternoon tea is a vast tray laden with scones, cakes, biscuits and preserves – all from the kitchen. John Sheedy's cooking shows itself to the full at dinner. The emphasis is on high-quality home-produced dishes made with local ingredients, from a menu that takes in oak-smoked salmon with horseradish cream, noisettes of veal with celery-flavoured juices, and pan-fried salmon with herb and tomato butter sauce. In line with healthy trends, there is fish cooked in its own juices with julienne of vegetables, or breast of chicken with apricot sauce spiked with pink pepper berries. To finish there are local hand-made cheeses. Around seventy wines are dominated by Bordeaux and burgundy. CELLARMAN'S CHOICE: Bourgogne Aligoté, Mommessin '84, at £11·50.

CHEF: John Sheedy PROPRIETORS: Michael and Jane O'Callaghan
OPEN: all week, D only CLOSED: 21 Dec to 17 Mar MEALS: 7 to 9
PRICES: £16 (£24), Set D £19·50 (£28) CARDS: Amex, Diners, Visa
SEATS: 45. Car-park, 80 places. Vegetarian meals. No children under 10. Smart dress
preferred. No cigars/pipes in dining-room. Wheelchair access (also WC)
ACCOMMODATION: 18 rooms, all with bath/shower. B&B £81 (double room). Deposit £25. No
children under 10. Garden. Fishing. Golf. Snooker. Scenic. Doors close at 12. Confirm by 6

MOYCULLEN Co. Galway
map 9

Drimcong House [11/20]

Moycullen
GALWAY (091) 85115
£20

A Queen Anne house on the edge of Connemara is the setting for Gerry and
Marie Gavin's restaurant. Interest now centres on two fixed-priced menus split
by a between-course soup or sorbet. To start there might be oysters in filo pastry
or a salad of grilled goats' cheese, before roast loin of veal with white port and
rosemary, or steamed brill with a herb crust on saffron sauce. Some of the ideas
can sound fanciful: smoked salmon served warm with chive sauce; confit of duck
with pineapple and crème de cassis. Quenelles of pike have been outstanding. To
finish there might be chocolate terrine with pistachios or sweet geranium mousse
'in a strawberry pool'. The cheese trolley is one hundred per cent Irish and has
been for eleven years, proof of the resurgence of Irish farmhouse cheesemaking.
Fourteen wines under £12 are all considered house wines, and there's a good
showing of half-bottles. CELLARMAN'S CHOICE: organically grown Mas de
Daumas Gassac '79, at £17·50.

CHEF: Gerry Gavin PROPRIETORS: Gerry and Marie Gavin
OPEN: Tue to Sat, D only CLOSED: Christmas to Mar MEALS: 7 to 10
PRICES: Set D from £14·95 (£20) CARDS: Access, Amex, Diners, Visa
SEATS: 60. Private parties: 50 main room, 12 private room. Car-park, 30 places. Children's
helpings. Wheelchair access (also WC). Music

ROSSES POINT Co. Sligo
map 9

Reveries [11/20]

SLIGO (071) 77371
£20

The menu changes monthly in the Brennans' restaurant overlooking Sligo Bay.
The style is modern: filo pastry is used for wrapping Irish cheese or mousseline of
salmon and sole; monkfish gets a red pepper sauce; there's a medley of game
birds with port and orange sauce. The mood is confirmed in the desserts: rhubarb
charlotte rubs shoulders with terrine of strawberries in wine jelly. The restaurant
boasts a prize-winning Irish cheeseboard. The fifty-strong wine list has house
wines at £8, as well as representatives from Chile, Lebanon, Portugal and the
New World.

CHEF: Paula Brennan PROPRIETORS: Damien and Paula Brennan
OPEN: Mon to Sat D MEALS: 6.30 to 10
PRICES: Set D from £14·25 (£20). Service 10% CARDS: Access, Visa
SEATS: 36. Private parties: 55 main room. Car-park, 10 places. No children under 8. Music

ROSSLARE Co. Wexford   map 9

Le Gourmet [10/20]

Rosslare Strand
WEXFORD (053) 32157   £17–£33

A tank keeps the lobster fresh before they are cooked and served with butter and
coral sauce, and oysters are kept in captivity, too. Fresh fish benefits from simple
saucing: turbot with hollandaise, sole with butter, monk with saffron. Other
dishes have a wider allegiance: veal with Marsala sauce, osso buco, moussaka,
lamb shish kebab, with crêpes Suzette to finish. House French is £9·50 a bottle.

CHEF/PROPRIETOR: Claude Kelly
OPEN: all week D, and Mon to Wed L CLOSED: End Sept to Easter MEALS: 1 to 2, 7 to 10
PRICES: £24 (£33), Set L £9·50 (£17), Set D from £15·50 (£23). Service 10%
SEATS: 36. Children welcome. Wheelchair access (also WC)

SHANAGARRY Co. Cork   map 9

▲ *Ballymaloe House* [14/20]

Shanagarry
CORK (021) 652531   £15–£25

For years Myrtle Allen has proved the good sense behind the notion of 'real food'.
Her support of local producers and suppliers is as much about good cooking as
about ideology. She buys fish from small, local boats not for any sentimental
reason, but the fish suffers less bruising and doesn't require refrigeration; she
prefers beef reared on old pasture because the meat is likely to be of better quality
and more nutritious. This kind of passion for the essentials of food is a rare thing
in Irish restaurants with their tendency to ostentatious menus and exorbitant
wine lists. The style of the restaurant is homely and relaxed. The brilliance of the
cooking is its apparent simplicity – superb potato and fresh herb soup; sensuous
sea urchin with mayonnaise in the shell; monkfish sprinkled with still-crisp
peppers; a classic version of Irish stew. The flaws in the cooking appear when
Myrtle Allen is away, and more variety day to day would please long stayers. The
wine list has house wine at £9 a bottle, as well as a good showing of '70 clarets.

CHEFS: Paddy Cullinane, Rory O'Connell and Billy Motherway PROPRIETORS: Ivan and
Myrtle Allen
OPEN: all week CLOSED: 3 days at Christmas MEALS: 1 to 2, 7 to 9.30 (7.30 to 8.30 Sun)
PRICES: Set L from £9·50 (£15), Set D from £18·50 (£25). Service 10% CARDS: Access,
Amex, Diners, Visa
SEATS: 80. Private parties: 35 main room, 18 and 30 private rooms. Car-park, 100 places.
Vegetarian meals. Children's helpings (D only). Wheelchair access (also WC)
ACCOMMODATION: 30 rooms, 29 with bath/shower. Rooms for disabled. B&B £32 to £56.
Pets welcome. Garden. Swimming-pool. Tennis. Golf. Phone. Scenic [GHG]

Restaurants change owners and chefs constantly. Please help keep the Guide *informed
of any changes you find.*

*Files are kept on every restaurant, so reports of poor meals are just as valuable as
reports of good meals because they save unnecessary inspections.*

YOUGHAL Co. Cork
map 9

Aherne's [11/20]

163 North Main Street
YOUGHAL (024) 92424 and 92533
£13–£24

This long-standing family fish restaurant has picked up in the last year and it is once again somewhere to eat Ireland's pride – fish. Lobsters are out of a vivier and expensive; most other fish come from the nearby village of Helvick. Sole, turbot, brill, prawns have been exemplary. Portions are generous; in season, vegetables are out of the garden. House wine £8·60.

CHEF: David Fitzgibbon PROPRIETORS: The Fitzgibbon family
OPEN: Tue to Sun, and Mon D July and Aug MEALS: 12.30 to 2.30, 6.30 to 11.30 (10 Sun)
PRICES: £16 (£24), Set L £7·25 (£13), Set D £12·50 (£18), Snacks from £2. Service 10%
CARDS: Access, Amex, Diners, Visa
SEATS: 70. 4 tables outside. Private parties: 80 main room. Car-park, 30 places. No children under 8. Smart dress preferred. Wheelchair access (also WC). Music

Channel Islands

First and Last [10/20]

Braye Bay
ALDERNEY (048 182) 3162   £16

Near the harbour is this all-female-run, no nonsense, mainly fish restaurant,
which caters predominantly for yachtsmen. The atmosphere is friendly.
Bouillabaise is listed as a speciality; lobsters hot or cold are £13·50. Oysters,
squid and grilled sardines are worth looking for, as are the extra dishes of the day.
The wine list shows the same resolute approach, majoring in Beaujolais and the
Loire in only twenty bottles. House 'pot du patron' is £5 a litre.

CHEF: Valerie Webb PROPRIETOR: Rita L. Gillmore
OPEN: Tue to Sun MEALS: 12 to 1.45, 7 to 10.30
PRICES: £12 (£16). Service 10% CARDS: Access, Amex, Carte Blanche, Diners, Visa
SEATS: 75. Private parties: 40 main room. Vegetarian meals. Children's helpings. Music.
Air-conditioned

Apple Cottage [11/20]

Rozel Bay
JERSEY (0534) 61002   £8 – £17

Rozel amounts to one or two hotels, a few cafés along the quay and a community
of ducks and geese who live on the beach. Mr and Mrs Pozzi run this low-beamed,
shadowy cottage between them. For an island not sure of its reputation for fish
cooking, this is where to eat fish. The cooking is according to Escoffier. Fine
lobster soup is half the price of the whole beast but has all the flavour; sea bass is
is baked with garlic and fennel; turbot is grilled and served with good hollandaise
to the side in a sauceboat. Sweets also, notably apple pie, stand out as a cut above
the rest of the island. The small dining-room can get stuffy when crowded, which
is often, but the terrace outside is a wonderful site on a warm day for al fresco
eating, perhaps a lobster salad or platter of shellfish. House Italian is £3; look also
for some quality white burgundies.

Reports on shops, cafes and farms are useful, as well as reports on restaurants.

CHEF: S. C. Pozzi PROPRIETORS: Mr and Mrs S. C. Pozzi
OPEN: Tue to Sun, exc Sun D CLOSED: Jan MEALS: 12 to 2.15, 7 to 9.30
PRICES: £13 (£17), Set L £6 (£8) CARDS: Access, Visa
SEATS: 65. 12 tables outside. Private parties: 55 main room. Car-park, 15 places. Children's
helpings. Wheelchair access (1 step; also WC). Music

ST ANNE Alderney   map 1

▲ *Georgian House* [10/20]

Victoria Street, St Anne
ALDERNEY (048 182) 2471   £10–£19

One of the attractive old houses in the heart of the town. The 'Garden Beyond'
has a bar and barbecue in fine weather, otherwise the dining-room offers sound
professional cooking with a bias towards seafood. The Hopes are proud of their
fresh crab and local lobsters. Chef's specialities range from a cold soufflé of
smoked oysters to English lamb with creamy redcurrant and mint sauce. Melons
are grown on the island. House wine is £3·75 a bottle.

CHEFS: John Renshaw and Richard Cousins PROPRIETORS: Stephen and Elizabeth Hope
OPEN: all week MEALS: 12 to 2.15, 7.30 to 9.30
PRICES: £15 (£19), Set L from £6·50 (£10), Set D £6·50 (£10). Service 10% CARDS: Access,
Diners, Visa
SEATS: 40. Private parties: 50 main room, 25 private room. Vegetarian meals. Children's
helpings. No children under 8 at D. Smart dress preferred. Wheelchair access. Music
ACCOMMODATION: 5 rooms, all with bath/shower. B&B £19·50 to £39. Deposit: £10. No
children under 8. Afternoon teas. TV. Scenic. Doors close at 12.30. Confirm by 6

Nellie Gray's [10/20]

Victoria Street, St Anne
ALDERNEY (048 182) 3333   £15

Named after Nellie Gray, a famous gypsy beauty, who was the proprietor's great-
aunt. It is at its best in summer, when meals are served in the garden. The
emphasis is on straightforward cooking with a bias towards fresh fish: turbot
with hollandaise is a favourite. Portions are generous. House wine £4·50 a litre.

CHEF: Piel Hein PROPRIETOR: Raymond Parkin
OPEN: Mon to Sat CLOSED: Jan to Easter MEALS: 12 to 2, 7.15 to 9.30
PRICES: £12 (£15). Service inc CARDS: Access, Amex, Diners, Visa
SEATS: 50. Private parties: 50 private room. Car-park, 6 places. Vegetarian meals. Children's
helpings. Smart dress preferred. Music. Air-conditioned

ST BRELADE'S BAY Jersey   map 1

Sabrina [10/20]

St Brelade's Bay
JERSEY (0534) 41081   £7–£16

This small, quite smart seaside restaurant has a stunning view over sands and
sea and a good local reputation for value, especially for the set lunch (served

Tuesday to Saturday). A conventional avocado and steak menu is supplemented by a blackboard of fish dishes of the day, which are what to have. Fine turbot has been sauced with mushrooms, fennel and asparagus. Lobsters are direct from the pots. House wine £3·75.

CHEF: Mr Burridge PROPRIETORS: Mr and Mrs Bannon
OPEN: Tue to Sun CLOSED: Sun D in winter MEALS: 12.15 to 2, 7.15 to 10
PRICES: £11 (£16), Set L £4·90 (£7), Set D £9·50 (£13). Service 10%
CARDS: Access, Amex, Diners, Visa
SEATS: 65. Private parties: 70 main room. Car-park, 30 places. Children's helpings.
Wheelchair access. Music

ST HELIER Jersey — map 1

▲ *Chico's* [10/20]

Kensington Place, St Helier
JERSEY (0534) 58196 — £13

An interesting phenomenon seems to have occurred in Jersey, which has escaped the attention of both residents and tourists. The island depends heavily on guest workers to staff the hotel and restaurant industries and also to pick the famous potatoes. Most of these tend to be Portuguese, a lot of them coming from Madeira in particular. A number of restaurants have opened to cater for them and to act as social centres; in the summer Chico's gets packed as the night goes on, with waiters or barmen on their night off, taking out the English chambermaids. The food is Portuguese and excels in seafood. It is simple, fresh and ethnic; where some of the other restaurants have adapted their food to local tastes, Chico's more than most has an authentic whiff of vinho verde. Typically fine are the green vegetable soup; king prawns with a piri-piri-style sauce; char-grilled black bream; pork with clams; three ways with salt fish. Fried baby hake is served, tail in mouth, with round-grain rice and black olives. The national flair for sweets is found also. House Portuguese is £4. Look for the fine Dão, too.

CHEFS: George Juakuin and F. Presume PROPRIETORS: Repose Hotels Ltd
OPEN: all week MEALS: 12 to 2, 7 to 12
PRICES: £10 (£13) CARDS: Access, Visa
SEATS: 30. Private parties: 20 main room. Car-park, 12 places. Children's helpings.
Wheelchair access (2 steps). Music
ACCOMMODATION: 75 rooms, all with bath/shower. Rooms for disabled. Lift. B&B £15 to £30. Deposit: £20. Baby facilities. Confirm by 6

ST PETER PORT Guernsey — map 1

La Piazza [10/20]

Under the Arch, Trinity Square, St Peter Port
GUERNSEY (0481) 25085 — £16

A thoroughly Italian restaurant in a converted stable with local paintings and local pottery for plates. The menu takes advantage of the supply of fish and shellfish to supplement steaks and pasta dishes such as tortellini stuffed with spinach and ricotta. Forty wines include a dozen Italian, but house wine is French and £4·50 a litre.

CHEF: Olivier Diverio PROPRIETORS: G. Bianco, O. Diverio and N. Bonanni
OPEN: Mon to Sat CLOSED: 20 Dec to 20 Jan MEALS: 12 to 2, 7 to 10
PRICES: £11 (£16) CARDS: Access, Amex, Visa
SEATS: 54. 4 tables outside. No children under 6. Smart dress preferred. Wheelchair access
(also WC). Music

Le Nautique [10/20]

Quay Steps, St Peter Port
GUERNSEY (0481) 21714   £15

This eighteenth-century warehouse on the front, facing the marina, is well
regarded on the island. Mr Graziani is always on hand, backed by an anarchic
but professionally efficient crew. The menu is French but, like many other menus
on Guernsey, has at its heart avocado vinaigrette, sole Walewska and ice-cream.
The famous luxuries of the island, like lobster, sole and turbot, are expensive. But
the signatures of the genre are well handled: escargots Bourgogne; champignons
frits; the plate of cold hors d'oeuvre; noisettes de porc au Gruyère. Vegetarians
are catered for with fish-shaped pastry coffins filled with vegetables and white
sauce cut with nutmeg. Sweets are a weak point. Coffee comes with Dorchester
chocolates. House Gamay at £4·80 opens a conservative list with only a few
bargains. CELLARMAN'S CHOICE: Quincy, Domaine Maison Blanche '85, £6·30.

CHEF: V. Garau PROPRIETOR: C. Graziani
OPEN: Mon to Sat CLOSED: First 2 weeks June MEALS: 12 to 2, 7 to 10
PRICES: £12 (£15). Service inc CARDS: Access, Amex, Diners, Visa
SEATS: 70. Private parties: 14 main room. 30 private room. No children under 6. No pipes in
dining-room. Music

ST SAVIOUR Jersey   map 1

▲ St Saviour [13/20]

St Saviour
JERSEY (0534) 25501   £16 – £26

The old ivy-clad stone manor in its own twenty-two acres is a model of older
fashions. The ticking of old clocks and the flicker of candles fills the oak-panelled,
flower-filled rooms. Service is of the Grand Hotel school. Barry Forster impressed
at Ettington Park at Alderminster and has taken a similar approach here,
providing a trio of limited set menus, including vegetarian and dégustation
versions, as well as an eighteen-dish *carte*. Some of the raw materials, for
instance fillet of beef, are not as good as at Ettington Park, but some of the dishes
that the kitchen has worked at, are impressive: terrine of duck with peppered
madeira jelly served with real brioche; fish soup, really a bisque with rouille and
Gruyère; deeply rich chocolate cake. Warm gratin of poached pears in a vanilla
sabayon, flashed under the grill, served alongside a gingerbread pouch
containing a scoop of caramel ice-cream covered in spun sugar, provides a
contrast of warm and cool, smooth and crunchy. The cheese trolley imports
some fine English farmhouse rounds. The wine list offers a good slice of most
French regions – a good conservative choice, but with drinking under £10.
House wine is £4. CELLARMAN'S CHOICE: Ch. Laroque '83, £22.

CHEF: Barry Forster PROPRIETORS: The Lewis family and the Dufty family
OPEN: all week MEALS: 12.30 to 2, 7.30 to 9.30
PRICES: £21 (£26), Set L £12·50 (£16), Set D £16 (£20). Snacks from £1·90. Service 10%.
Licensed, also bring your own: corkage £4 CARDS: Access, Amex, Carte Blanche,
Diners, Visa
SEATS: 65. 8 tables outside. Private parties: 75 main room, 16 private room. Car-park, 30
places. Vegetarian meals. Children welcome. Smart dress preferred. Wheelchair access (also
WC). Air-conditioned
ACCOMMODATION: 35 rooms, all with bath/shower. Rooms for disabled. Lift. B&B £46 to
£105. Deposit: £40. No children under 7. Pets welcome. Afternoon teas. Garden.
Swimming-pool. TV. Phone. Scenic [GHG]

France: Channel ports

Edited by Patricia Fenn

CALAIS

Shopping

The new Mammouth, three kilometres to the west, clearly marked from both the N1 and the coast road, is brighter, fresher and better than its tired predecessor, with an excellent cheese counter, fresh local fish, good charcuterie and an outstanding drinks section. In town there's usually easy parking in the place d'Armes. Most of the interesting food shops are in the rue Royale, which leads off it, and in its continuation, the bvd Jacquard and a left turn into the bvd Lafayette.

MARKETS Thursday and Saturday at place Crêvecoeur. Wednesday and Saturday at place d'Armes.

CHARCUTERIES **Bellynck**, rue Royale; **Davélu**, rue Royale; **Patrick et Stéphanie**, bvd Lafayette; **Gastronomie du Sud-Ouest**, bvd Lafayette.

PÂTISSERIES/CHOCOLATIERS **Ducard**, bvd Lafayette; **La Fraîche Saveur** (a salon de thé with garden), off place d'Armes; **Outhiers**, rue Royale; **Léonidas**, rue Royale.

FROMAGERIES **Maison du Fromage**, with at least 200 cheeses, place d'Armes; **Le Fin Bec**, bvd Lafayette.

BOULANGERIE **J. C. Delahaye**, rue des Thermes.

POISSONNERIES **Blondel**, bvd Lafayette, and stalls on the quays.

COFFEE **Cafféa**, rue Royale.

WINE **Caves St Pierre**, place Crêvecoeur.

MARCHAND DES LÉGUMES **Pierre-et-Béatrice**, bvd des Alliés.

HYPERMARKETS **Mammouth**, three kilometres west, open every day, 9am to 9pm; **Continent**, open Monday to Saturday, 9am to 10pm.

Restaurants

Le Channel

3 bvd de la Résistance
Tel 21.32.42.30

A French and English favourite for the ten years since M. and Mme Créspo took over. The décor has changed – the high-backed tapestry chairs, standard fittings for solidly respectable French restaurants, have given way to lighter rose-

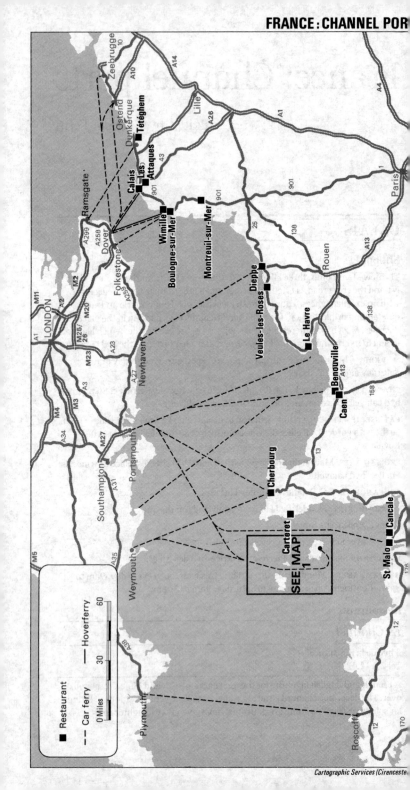

FRANCE : CHANNEL POR

Cartographic Services (Cirenceste

coloured velvet versions. The comfort and service are as welcoming as ever.

The 62fr menu (not Sundays) is remarkable for both quality and quantity: a salad of smoked haddock; cod served with a spicy coral sauce and a timbale of rice; regional cheeses in due season; and a choice of desserts, usually including six or seven tarts – strawberry, bilberry, almond . . . At the other end of the price range (with a *menu périgourdine* at 92fr in between), the *menu gourmet* at 110fr is equally good value: grilled scallops with a wine-based cream sauce and a lattice of fresh vegetables; turbot mousseline, duck pot au feu. Fine wines.

CLOSED: Sun D, Tue; Christmas to mid-Jan, 1 week in June

George V

36 rue Royale
Tel 21.97.68.00

Under new management, and making a strong bid to be Calais' second 'restaurant gastronomique'. For serious eaters the 130fr menu offers a dozen oysters or a terrine of scallops, then a panaché of fish with mushrooms or stuffed quails; a good cheeseboard with local cheeses such as Mont des Cats. The ambitious *carte* includes langoustines and duck foie gras salad; veal kidneys and sweetbreads on a bed of fresh noodles; turbot and monk-fish feuilleté with a langoustine sauce. Outstandingly efficient, helpful service and a good wine list.

CLOSED: Sat L, Sun D; 2 weeks at Christmas

Other restaurants

L'Assiette (2 place des Suèdes) near the ferry port, scores for cheap food (allow 70fr). The patron recites what's cooking. **Le Coq d'Or** (place d'Armes), prettier inside than out, has a good-value simple 55fr menu, but you are unlikely to hear a French voice. **Fouquets** (rue Royale) includes a quarter-bottle of wine on the 44fr menu, which includes moules/fish/omelette/cheese/fruit, etc.

In striking distance

TÉTÉGHEM 43km NE

La Meunerie

Tel 28.26.01.80.

Jean-Pierre Delbé relies strongly on the Dunkerque fishing fleet and local market gardeners for his ingredients. He cooks unfussily and with imagination. The 260fr *retour de pêche* has three fish courses before cheese and dessert, and the 330fr *composition du moulin* is seven masterly dégustations, but there is no need to spend more than 160fr. This menu might yield home-made pasta laced with shrimps, and a veal kidney, roasted, on a thin cushion of foie gras mousse. The local cheeses are served with nut and raisin bread, but the star turn is undoubtedly the sweets trolley: multiple choices from the equally commendable mousses, feuilletés and gateaux are encouraged. It is wise to book.

CLOSED: Sun D; Mon; Christmas to mid-Jan

It is always advisable to book a restaurant in advance.

LES ATTAQUES 9km SE

Restaurant de la Gare The patron is a butcher, so terrines, rillettes, sausages and galantines are specialities. The *menu conseillé* costs 38fr for three courses and the plat du jour – rabbit, veal, chicken, simply cooked – is around 41·50fr. A small pichet of house wine is 4fr. More set menus up to 100fr.

BOULOGNE-SUR-MER

Shopping

Shopping is centred on a grid of streets near the harbour. Don't miss Philippe Olivier's cheese shop, which supplies many top English restaurants, and ask to visit his cellars. The market is a good one. Park along the quays or on town meters.

MARKET Wednesday and Saturday at place Dalton.

CHARCUTERIES **Derrien**, Grande Rue (also open Sundays); **La Comtesse du Barry**, Grande Rue, for up-market preserves.

PÂTISSERIES/CHOCOLATIERS **Lugand** (a salon de thé), Grande Rue; **Géneau**, bvd Daunou; **Le Cornet d'Amour** (a salon de thé) rue Thiers; **Béthouart**, 46 rue de Lille – in the old town.

FROMAGERIE **Philippe Olivier**, rue Thiers.

PRESERVED FRUITS, SPICES, NUTS **Idriss**, Grande Rue.

COFFEE **Brûlerie Faidherbe**, bvd Faidherbe.

WINE **Le Chaïs**, rue Deux Ponts, off bvd Daunou; **Les Vins de France**, rue Nationale.

BREAKFAST **Bar Hamiot**, rue Faidherbe, is open from 5am for café bistouille, etc.

Restaurants

La Matelote

80 bvd Ste Beuve
Tel 21.30.17.97

Tony Lestienne's restaurant leans increasingly towards modern cooking, with dishes such as salad of pigeon breasts in sherry vinegar; a gateau of langoustines in a courgette cream sauce; calves' sweetbreads in a sauce flavoured with pears and cinnamon. Superb wine cellar. *Carte* only: allow 250fr.

CLOSED: Sun D; Tue; 2 weeks June, Christmas to mid-Jan

La Liègeoise

10 rue Monsigny
Tel 21.31.61.15

Alain Delpierre supplements his traditional dishes – French business lunchers go specially for his fresh foie gras de canard – with some new ideas: a magret de canard infused with truffles, chopped fresh salmon encased in a roll of smoked salmon, turbotin stuffed with nuggets of scallops, and an excellent winter dish of quails on a bed of beetroot. Set menus are 84fr, 128fr and 205fr; allow 230fr for the *carte*.

CLOSED: Fri D, Sun D

L'Huîtrière

11 place de Lorraine
Tel 21.31.35.27

Perhaps the best single-minded fish eating in Boulogne. Tiny, tucked away behind a fish shop in the corner of a square, l'Huîtrière is always full at lunchtime. Seventy-five francs buys two fish dishes – fish terrine or moules and haddock with spinach or poached turbotin – plus a fruit tart or cheese. One up-market fish, like sole or halibut, costs around 70fr, as does the Flemish mixed fish Waterzoi.

CLOSED: Sun D; Mon

Other restaurants

La Plage (124 bvd Ste Beuve) is always full – booking advisable. Prime fish, gigot and cheese appear on the 64fr menu, with excellent-value wines. **Le Petit Caporal** (rue St Leonard), one kilometre out of town on the N1, is popular with local businessmen without expense accounts. Variations on traditional cooking appear on the 65fr set menus – mussels with sorrel, chicken basquaise. **Hamiot's** is the preferred fish and chippie on the front.

In striking distance

PONT DE BRIQUES 3km SE

Hostellerie de la Rivière

17 rue de la Gare
Tel 21.32.22.81

In his sober, comfortable restaurant in a Boulogne suburb Jean Martin now has son Dominique helping, notably with the sumptuous pâtisserie. There are signs that the traditional Normandy cooking is being leavened with a subtler touch in dishes like smoked duck and pear salad, turbot braised with oyster mushrooms, foie gras de canard in a mousse balanced with a langoustine sauce. The prices on both *carte* and wine list can be alarming; better stick to the set menus, of which the 210fr is recommended.

CLOSED: Sun D; Mon; Aug

MONTREUIL-SUR-MER 38km S

Château de Montreuil

chaussée des Capucins
Tel 21.81.53.04

Christian Germain trained with the Roux brothers and married an English girl, Lindsay, who guides the predominantly English clientele through the menu with

British diplomacy and French charm. The menus are deceptively simple, and the four-course, no-choice lunch (Monday to Saturday) is a snip at 130fr. A springtime example illustrates the style: asparagus with mousseline sauce; salmon with ginger; breast of Licques chicken (the village of Licques is known locally as 'la capitale des volailles') with tarragon; and champagne sorbet.

Christian cooks a little of whatever took his fancy in the market that morning for the *Menu Surprise* (200fr) – perhaps three smoked salmon rolls per person with a different filling (cream cheese and herbs, a julienne of vegetables, mustard and dill cream), with a nasturtium flower for colour. Succeeding courses are small and delicate – a rectangle of grilled brill with a lime and vanilla sauce; a langoustine tail stuffed with a crayfish mousse; a courgette flower oozing with a purée of seafood; baby pigeon, breast in one sauce, legs in another, with a fan of courgettes. The wine list is well chosen and concise, there's little under 100fr, but the house wine is reliable.

CLOSED: Thur L (exc July and Aug); mid-Dec to early Feb

La Grenouillère

La Madelaine-sous-Montreuil (2km W)
Tel 21.06.07.22

An old whitewashed, wisteria-hung farmhouse, tucked under the ramparts of Montreuil, with the river splashing by. The décor is resolutely rustic, the service and cooking anything but. Roland Gauthier, ex-Château de Montreuil, is growing in confidence and stature. On his cheapest menu, at 160fr, are quails' eggs on a pastry base, doused in a cream sauce dotted with mussels; alternating langoustine tails and monk-fish cubes, cooked in *meat* stock, in an emulsion of garlic cloves, with home-made spinach pasta alongside. Desserts are a speciality: lime mousse set in a fragrant jasmine-tea cream; les deux chocolats – dark and white swirled together in an almond-infused sauce. There is nothing under 100fr on the wine list.

CLOSED: Sun D; Wed; Feb

WIMILLE 4km E by N1

Relais de la Brocante

Tel 21.83.19.31

In an eighteenth-century presbytery the ex-chef and ex-maître d' of the doomed Atlantique at Wimereux have been in successful partnership for three years now. The *couverts* in the arched stone dining-rooms are elegant and elaborate, the food likewise: excellent fish, a wide variety of fresh vegetables (rare in France nowadays), and original cheese dishes – goats' cheese wrapped in spinach leaves, served with an apple purée. Ice-creams are recommended. The cheapest menus, at 100fr and 140fr, are good value; others are 160fr and 200fr. Allow 300fr à la carte.

CLOSED: Sun D; Mon; Feb

All inspections are carried out anonymously.

DIEPPE

Shopping

Good and easy. The pedestrianised Grande Rue leads directly from the port, with all the food shops there or on the rue St Jacques, leading off. Parking is difficult.

MARKET Saturday at place Nationale.

CHARCUTERIES **André Eurieult, J. Bucquet** and **Rôtisserie Parisienne**, all on the Grande Rue.

PÂTISSERIES/CHOCOLATIERS **Grisch**, Grande Rue, has an upstairs balcony for tea; **Patel**, Grande Rue; **A La Duchesse du Berry**, Grande Rue, has good ices.

FROMAGERIE **Claude Olivier** (Philippe's brother), rue St Jacques.

BOULANGERIE **Ethelier**, rue St Jacques.

POISSONNERIES **La Marée du Jour**, place Nationale; off the boats at the quayside, or in the fishmarket before 10am.

HYPERMARKET **Mammouth** 3 kilometres south, on the Route de Rouen, open every day, 9am to 10pm.

Restaurants
ST AUBIN SUR SCIE 3km S

Auberge de la Bûcherie

Route de Rouen
Tel 35.84.83.10

The décor is modern, smart and slick, the food traditional and copious. Fish predominates, simply cooked, immaculately fresh. Menus at 100fr, 150fr weekdays. The *carte* is expensive, the wines likewise.

CLOSED: Sun D; Mon; 1 week July, 2 weeks Oct

La Mélie

2 Grande-Rue du Pollet
Tel 35.84.21.19

A promising newcomer. Guy Brachais has moved from Tocqueville to this modest bistro in the old fishermen's quarter. Shellfish is enterprisingly cooked, and there are good Loire wines. Set menu at 120fr.

CLOSED: Sun D; Mon; 3 weeks Feb

L'Armorique

17 quay Henri IV
Tel 35.84.28.14

The best fish restaurant in town, on the first floor, has only a *carte*, with main dishes around 70fr. Takeaway fresh fish downstairs.

CLOSED: Sun D; Mon; 2 weeks June, 2 weeks Oct

Other restaurants

There are lots of tables along the quayside, with little to choose between in the restaurants. **Le Port, Le Peskett** and **Le Sully** are all fishy. In the arcades des Poissonneries, **Le Moderne** and **Le Marine** have less good views but more interesting fish, as does **La Marmite Dieppoise** in the rue St Jacques. For cheap, acceptable three-course menus from 55fr to 75fr, the French go to **Le Jupiler** and **Le Normandie,** both in the rue Duquesne.

In striking distance

VEULES-LES-ROSES   24km W

Les Galets

Tel 35.97.61.33

Maître Cuisinier de France Gilbert Plaisance combines the bounties of sea, river and countryside in dishes like his cutlet of lobster and fillet of sole with wild mushrooms. Cucumber turns up in sauces, purée with champagne, and as an accompanying vegetable sharpened with sherry vinegar. Foie gras appears in many guises – simple, as an entrée, allied with saddle of hare and chicken breasts, or in an exotic ragout with fresh pasta. The good-value 195fr menu includes similar dishes, with admirable Normandy cheeses and a remarkable sweets trolley. Expect to pay top prices for the top wines.

CLOSED: Tue D; Wed; Feb

LE HAVRE

Shopping

Halles Centrales are the easiest (good parking, trolleys, open every day) for fish, fruit, charcuterie and the best cheese shop, **Cheinisse.**

CHARCUTERIES **Rôtisserie Gaston,** place Gambetta, is open every day except Wednesday from 11am to 10.30pm; **Lefèvre,** place Gambetta.

Restaurants

La Chaumette

17 rue Racine
Tel 35.43.66.80

Lively atmosphere, weirdly rustic décor, unusually good vegetables and desserts. The 87fr menu is a bargain; allow 180fr for the *carte.*

CLOSED: Sat, Sun; Christmas; 2 weeks Aug

The 1989 Guide will appear before Christmas 1988. Reports are particularly helpful in the spring. Report forms are at the back of this book, but just write a letter if you prefer. Address it to The Good Food Guide, FREEPOST, *14 Buckingham Street, London WC2N 6BR. No stamp is necessary if you post it in the UK.*

Le Cambridge

90 rue Voltaire
Tel 35.42.50.24

The best fish restaurant, with main dishes around 75fr, set menu at 140fr.

CLOSED: Sat L; Sun; Christmas, July

La Manche

18 bvd Albert 1er
Tel 35.41.20.13

Big windows overlook the sea, the décor is modern and elegant. The best oysters in town. The four-course 105fr menu is good value; others are 160fr and 250fr.

CLOSED: Sun D; Mon; July

Le Gascon

83 rue Dauphine
Tel 35.41.71.51

A newly opened bistro specialising in Gascony cooking (foie gras, cassoulet, etc). Set menu at 59fr, *carte* from 150fr to 180fr. Excellent wines from the same area.

CLOSED: Sun D

Other restaurants

Le Beau Séjour at Ste Adresse is useful for Sunday eating, when most other restaurants are closed, and is consequently full of Brits: best position, overlooking the sea, with set menus from around 82fr. Along the quays are a chain of modest restaurants where acceptable menus cost around 50fr. **Simon** is probably the best of these, or the **Restaurant du Roy**. Three streets back, in the rue de Bretagne, **Chez Titine** is the top budget choice, with good set menus starting at 55fr.

CAEN

Shopping

Caen is excellent for food shopping, with high-class shops throughout the city. Parking can be difficult – try the quays. The Sunday market is useful for weekenders.

CHARCUTERIES **Poupinet**, rue St Jacques, is outstanding, among many others, and noted for its foie gras; **Luet**, rue St Jean, is also good for cheese.

PÂTISSERIES **Stiffler** (a salon de thé), rue St Jean; **Charlotte Corday**, rue St Jean, is expensive but classy.

CHOCOLATIERS **Daskaladier**, rue Vaugueux; **Hôtot**, rue St Pierre; **Témoins**, rue St Pierre.

FROMAGERIES **Eustache**, rue Vaugueux; **Galérie des Fromages**, rue des Chanoînes.

BOULANGERIE **Boulangerie Normande**, rue St Pierre.

WINE **Caves Thorel**, quai Vendeuvre.

GENERAL **Heiz Legrix**, place St Pierre, for bread, cakes, ice-creams, chocolates, charcuterie. Open on Sunday.

HYPERMARKET **Carrefour**.

Restaurants

La Bourride

15 rue du Vaugueux
Tel 31.93.50.76

This tiny, beamed seventeenth-century restaurant, set in Caen's prettiest street, is probably now number one in Normandy. Michel Bruneau produces unique combinations of spices and flavouring in essentially simple but inspired cooking. Local dishes, like tripes à la mode de Caen and sorbet à la pomme et au calvados, are a revelation. Oysters are served warm with a sauce made from their own juices, apple juice and calvados. Skate is sprinkled with bacon and wrapped in spinach leaves; baby pigeon is encased in smoky salt, along with cloves and vanilla seeds, the skin of the bird, crisped in almond oil, served separately. Cheeses are personally selected from farmers in the region, each in season. Desserts are magnificent: mille-feuille is stuffed with crème fraîche and seasonal fruit; the dark chocolate griottine has cherries embedded; and sorbets are triumphs.

The 153fr lunch menu is good value; the *menu normande* – salad of offal, sole with langoustines, tripe, chicken Vallée d'Auge – requires dedication. The wine list matches the food in quality, but is proportionately much more expensive.

CLOSED: Sun, Mon; 2 weeks Jan, 1 week May, 2 weeks Aug

Le Dauphin

29 rue Gémare
Tel 31.86.22.26

Regional traditional cooking – salt-marsh lamb, foie gras with apples – is served in the mock-rustic dining-room of this little hotel. Good local cider and a well-priced wine list. Set menus at 75fr (weekdays only), 120fr, 170fr and 250fr.

CLOSED: Sat; mid-July to mid-Aug

Le Pressoir

3 avenue Henry-Chéron
Tel 31.73.32.71

Antique furniture, simple cooking, with prime grills cooked on charcoal. Try boudin noir with apples for local colour. Set menu at 63fr.

CLOSED: Sun D; 2 weeks Aug

Other restaurants

Le Boeuf Ferré (10 rue des Croisiers): book at lunchtime; it is probably the best value in town, with a 55fr set menu. **La Mandarine** (18 rue Froide) is a pretty fin-de-siècle restaurant with interesting menus from 60fr.

In striking distance

BÉNOUVILLE 10km N

Manoir d'Hastings

18 avenue de la Côte de Nacre
Tel 31.44.62.43

Claude and Aline Scaviner offer exceptional service in their elegant old stone priory. M. Scaviner's presentation of traditional Breton and Norman dishes shows no skimping of the cholesterol. The 140fr menu, with grilled mussels in chive butter, baby pigeon poached in red wine, saddle of lamb with mustard, apple and calvados sorbet, is superb value. Stick to the set menus or the bill gets out of hand (350fr to 600fr for the *carte*). Good cider and an interesting and prestigious wine list chosen by Scaviner fils.

CLOSED: Sun D; Mon

CHERBOURG

Shopping

Shopping is centred on the pedestrianised area across the bridge from the ferry port. Best leave the car on the quayside – parking in the town centre is difficult.

MARKETS Tuesday and Saturday at place Général de Gaulle. Thursday at place Divette.

CHARCUTERIES **Laulier**, place Général de Gaulle; **De Poitevin**, **Collette** and **A La Renommé**, all in the rue Grande Rue.

PÂTISSERIE **L'Huilley** (a salon de thé), rue Grande Rue.

BOULANGERIE **J. J. Fillâtre**, place Henry Greville.

COFFEE **Cafféa**, rue Grande Rue.

WINE **Caves du Roy**, rue Tour Carrée.

MARCHAND DES LÉGUMES **Bébert**, place Général de Gaulle, has good cheeses too.

HYPERMARKET **Continent**, quai de l'Entrepôt, open Monday to Saturday, 9am to 10pm

---

'The other Chinese restaurant has the following at the top of its menu: "Most Chinese dishes are cooked with onion. Please tell the chef if you would like your meal without onion."' (On eating in Nottinghamshire)

'To charge extra for vegetables or salad is akin to charging for the wheels when selling a motor car.' (On eating in Durham)

Restaurants

Le Plouc

59 rue au Blé
Tel 33.53.67.64

An old stone house in a newly restored area near the quay. Lots of fish, terrines, but indifferent desserts. Good local cider. Service is by girls in regional costume. Set menus at 100fr and 130fr; *carte* around 250fr.

CLOSED: Sat L; Sun; 2 weeks Aug

Le Grandgousier

21 rue de l'Abbaye
Tel 33.53.19.43

Vaguely art deco, back-street bistro. Reliable traditional cooking, and good plâteaux de fruits de mer on the set menus from 70fr.

CLOSED: Sat L; Sun; 2 weeks Apr, 3 weeks Sept

Other restaurants

La Pêcherie (27 rue de l'Abbaye) is an up-market fish restaurant, à la carte only. **L'Ancre Dorée** (3 rue Bonhomme) is pretty and cosy with interesting set menus at 75fr and 109fr.

In striking distance

CARTERET 37km SW

La Marine

11 rue de Paris
Tel 33.53.83.81

A long-time favourite seaside hotel with the British, now revitalised with son's cooking. Good fish, with interesting accompaniments. Both 65fr and 120fr set menus are excellent value.*Carte* around 250fr.

CLOSED: Sun D; Mon; early Nov to end Feb

ST MALO

Shopping

The 'intro-muros' area of St Malo is not large, and all the food shops are within a few minutes' walk from the harbour. It's unwise to take a car inside the walls; park along the quays.

MARKET Thursday and Friday.

CHARCUTERIE **Bosquet**, rue Porçon de la Barbinais, is outstanding, especially for quiches and feuilletés, foie gras and hams.

PÂTISSERIES/CHOCOLATIERS **Cheftel** (a salon de thé), rue Porçon de la Barbinais; **Chaumont**, rue Broussais, has good ice-creams.

FROMAGERIE **Boutique aux Fromages**, rue de l'Orme.

POISSONNERIES **Gautier**, rue des Poissonneries; **Fishmarket**, place des Poissonneries, (mornings only).

MARCHAND DES LÉGUMES **Les 4 Saisons**, rue de l'Orme.

Restaurants

La Duchesse Anne

place Guy La Chambre
Tel 99.40.85.33

The warm, cosy, old fashioned interior hasn't changed for years, and neither has the menu: fish, grills and roasts are simply cooked and served with classic sauces. A dozen oysters and turbot hollandaise would cost around 120fr. No set menus. Popular with regulars – French, Channel Islanders and British – who book weeks ahead.

CLOSED: Wed; Dec, Jan

Les Ecluses

Gare Maritime de la Bourse
Tel 99.56.81.00

Huge windows overlook the sea and ramparts – particularly spectacular at night, facing west to Dinard. Modern cooking, mostly fish. The interesting set menus are 69fr and 120fr.

CLOSED: Sun D; Mon; Jan

Other restaurants

Just inside the ramparts is a string of small restaurants, with pleasant tables outside, all offering good-value meals of the mussels/poisson du jour/tarte maison genre for around 55fr or plâteaux de fruits de mers for around 90fr. A few streets back are **Le Chalut** (8 rue Corne de Cerf), a little bistro with nautical décor whose short menu (55fr) could be six oysters, grilled red mullet and house pâtisserie. **Gilles** (2 rue Pie qui Boit) has reliable traditional cooking.

In striking distance

CANCALE 14km E

Restaurant de Bricourt

1 rue Dugesclin
Tel 99.89.64.76

The Roëllingers have kept the atmosphere of a home rather than a restaurant at their eighteenth-century manor house in the town centre. The two dining-rooms are comfortable and elegant, with six tables apiece, wide apart, always occupied. Olivier Roëllinger's *carte* is short, precise, apparently simple and changes so frequently that recommendation of any specific dish is likely to be spurious. He credits St Malo's early association with the spice trade for his use of ginger and vanilla with John Dory, coriander with langoustines, 'epîces de la Compagnie des

Indes' with sole. Turbot is cooked in a court bouillon flavoured with thyme and lemon 'comme auparavant', hollandaise alongside. Tiny Breton galettes are made from dark flour and stuffed with langoustine tails, quails' eggs and his own smoked salmon; foie gras doré is cut with the sharpness of green mangoes, accented with honey-flavoured juice. Traditional desserts are brought up to date: craquelins de Cancale – a lattice of crisp almond biscuit served with poached pears and a Poire Williams coulis – and a dish of two varieties of dessert apples, baked and served with an almond cream.

On the bargain 84fr menu, served at lunchtime and evenings except at weekends, you might eat a salad of warm calves' sweetbreads, turbot cooked with a red pepper sauce, and a praline mousse with chocolate sauce. A la carte would come to around 260fr.

CLOSED: Tue, Wed; end Nov to late Feb

International

Brussels: *Comme Chez Soi*

by Brian Macy

Away from the Grand Place, Brussels is a grey city. Like the city, the cooking lacks dynamism. The tourist-traps have vast, vulgar displays of fish and crustaceans. For a fiver, mussels can be had any which way you want and taste no better than cotton wool.

In a square distinguished by a man on horseback and a table-tennis shop, Comme Chez Soi (place Rouppe 23) is a pretty cream-coloured house with green timberwork. On entry, one is welcomed by the fixed smile of Madame Wynant in her silk dress. The dining-room is surprisingly small. At one end is a large glass partition providing a view into an immaculately scrubbed stainless-steel kitchen, worktops piled high with copper saucepans. At the other end is a bay window framing an enormous vase of spiky flowers reminiscent of a Brueghel painting in the Ancient Arts Museum down the road. In between these are rows of leather-backed benches, paintings and framed letters from the famous, including one from Winston Churchill full of praise about his visit.

Far from being stuffy and overblown, the small room provides an atmosphere of relaxed informality. On one hand it seems like an English gentleman's club, with its leather upholstery and gentle understatement. On the other it is a small family-run bustling brasserie.

There are two *menus gastronomiques* at BF1700 and BF3200, with an extensive *carte* menu averaging BF3500. (As if to compensate for the steep prices, the waiters rush around to offer generous second helpings of the main courses.) Fish is the main feature, and is described with imaginative combinations; the meat dishes seem an afterthought. The predictable long wine list concentrates on clarets and burgundies. The house champagne is Lanson, and they stock a remarkable Pouilly-Fuissé which is wonderfully perfumed, buttery and flint dry to go with the fish specialities.

Dinner starts with three appetisers: huge juicy radishes, miniature black olives, and pistachios, followed by four warm tartlettes, each the size of a pound coin, with a smear of tomato sauce and a lightly cooked basil leaf, and then roasted breast of quail wrapped in the skin of a prune. Velouté du potager au homard fin is no more than a good-quality fish stock flavoured with some lobster shell. Salade des escargots et lapereau consists of vegetables diced diagonally intermixed with crunchy bits of cauliflower and walnuts. The escargots seem superfluous, whereas the white rabbit is light, soft and delicately flavoured.

The two main courses of fish rival each other in both style and quality. Filets de sole, mousseline au Riesling et aux crevettes has a deep-yellow foamy sauce. Somehow the Riesling makes the taste seem sour, and the bubble-bath texture of the sauce mismatches the fine texture of the sole. On top, a handful of shelled prawns overpowers the dish because of heavy handedness in the seasoning. By comparison, blanc de turbot au Sauvignon concasse de tomate et crème d'herbettes is brilliant, the rectangular piece of turbot gently steamed, timed to the second, the sauce vivid reds and yellows. Technical perfection cannot be said of the vegetables. A side plate consists of five baby mange-tout and courgette discs. Reheated before serving, they are tired-tasting and oversoaked in butter. Likewise, tartlette aux pommes avec son sorbet et sauce pêche could be better: paper-thin slices of apple on a paper-thin piece of puff pastry. The problem seems to be that the apple juice has toughened the pastry, and instead of crumbling at a touch, a heavy knife is needed to cut through. Meanwhile the apple sorbet is a lovely raw green mint flavour, and the peach sauce not too sweet.

Six different petits fours accompany strong, but nondescript, coffee.

Pierre Wynant can be found at the end of dinner hovering between the kitchen and hallway. While Madame's function is to greet patrons and to prepare the bills, his role is to shake their hands and thank them afterwards. Shy and quietly spoken, he obviously prefers the safety of the kitchen on the other side of the glass partition.

In the context of Brussels and its seemingly lacklustre way of life, Comme Chez Soi is a sparkling jewel.

China: *Guilin and Canton*

by Deborah Buzan

Guilin, which lies on the Li River about 250 miles north-west of Canton, is a small town by Chinese standards, with a mere 400,000 inhabitants. The surrounding countryside has inspired Chinese artists and writers for millennia, and today it is a favourite area for Chinese as well as foreign tourists. Thin, rounded, tree-dotted peaks rise abruptly out of misty meadows; bamboo groves line the banks of wide rivers where fishermen use cormorants to catch fish. It is indeed a striking evocation of classical Chinese landscape painting.

Guilin's food is essentially Cantonese, but notable for the variety and rarity of ingredients, especially meat and seafood. You can meet your dinner in cages outside many of the small hole-in-the-wall restaurants: snakes, monkeys, racoons, lizards, soft-shell turtles, pangolins (a type of armadillo), salamanders . . . Cat is also eaten, as well as a breed of dog known as 'dish dog', but these are expensive. The largest hotels and restaurants rarely serve anything more exotic than eel to foreign tour groups.

The family-run Yulong (Jade Dragon) Restaurant on Long Yin lu, Guilin, serves the local community as well as small groups of foreign tourists. It seats around 50 on folding chairs, and is tacky; plastic flowers, a tattered lantern and a few simple brush paintings are the only decoration; chopsticks are peeling; serviettes are thin tissue. But the welcome is friendly and the food is varied and tasty.

In central and northern China meals usually begin with cold nibbles, such as pickled peanuts, dried meat slices, Pidan eggs (closer to two weeks old than a thousand years), lotus or cucumber salad. Hot dishes then arrive in quick succession. Here in the south one is generally launched straight into the hot food, and dishes tend to arrive one at a time. At the Yulong they appear as they are cooked – at five-minute intervals. First a simple dish of tender sliced beef with onions in a thin gravy, oriental only in its pronounced ginger flavouring. A local speciality follows: tomato and cucumber omelette in a very sweet and slightly sour sauce. A refreshing hot tomato and chive salad in a light broth comes next, followed by fried potatoes in a garlicky meat gravy. Another regional speciality is rice noodles. These look like fat spaghetti but are more delicate in texture and are combined with spring onions, a leafy, greeny-brown tree fungus (often mistaken for seaweed) and a few small shreds of pork. Next comes a stir-fried dish of bean sprouts, mushrooms, sliced carrots, tree fungus, plus a garnish of thinly sliced beef. Steamed rice accompanies the last dishes.

In southern China thick soup usually arrives in the midst of other courses. Thin broth almost always comes at the end, sometimes long after everything else. It helps wash down the meal but rarely tastes of much. The Yulong's soup is an unusually good, rich-flavoured but non-oily broth containing slices of liver, chicken, mushrooms, and green cabbage.

Most major restaurants serve beer, usually with 3.2 per cent alcohol content and modelled on the German style. Haphazard quality control at local Chinese breweries means it sometimes comes flat or sediment-loaded, but it's tasty and suits the food. Yulong's flowery but sturdy Osmanthus tea, which comes in tall glasses, is served on request.

Three or four dishes of the day plus soup, steamed rice and beer cost around 10 yuan per head (around £1.40). All this is in contrast to the typical tourist restaurant venues in China's major cities.

Canton, southern China's largest city, boasts one homage to twentieth-century decadence: The White Swan, China's most beautiful and luxurious hotel, which sits on a small island in the Pearl River. The lobby boasts a thirty-foot waterfall, there is an arcade of posh shops, and it is plushly furnished throughout. Unlike many of China's five-star hotels, though, the décor is Chinese.

At White Swan banquets, dishes are presented at the table for approval, then removed to a side table and placed on small plates or bowls for serving. The following twelve-course banquet was served to thirteen people. (1) suckling pig: served Beijing duck-style, a square of crispy skin atop a square 'pancake' garnished with home-made plum sauce and a splayed spring onion; (2) bird's nest shrimp: a crispy rice noodle basket filled with fresh shrimp, green and red peppers, celery and chestnut; (3) miniature red and green peppers stuffed with shrimp paste; (4) chicken, sweetcorn and egg-drop soup; (5) ling lan goose: roasted the southern way, fatty but tender, garnished with fresh pineapple and a glacé cherry; (6) broccoli-like Chinese greens with puffball mushrooms in a light soy sauce; (7) tender beef fillet kebab sticks with spring onions; (8) snakehead fish steamed with ginger and spring onions in soy sauce; (9) fried rice Cantonese-style, with fresh shrimps, peas, beef, spring onions and eggs (black tea arrives at this point to wash down the heavy courses and provide a pause); (10) tapioca soup: a thin, sweet but refreshing milky white pudding; (11) dim-sum: a plate containing a meat and shrimp spring roll and a stick of colourful layered semi-sweet rice gelatine; (12) watermelon: presented at the table with the peel decoratively cut.

The White Swan will construct a meal according to what and how much you wish to eat. Ten to twelve courses, each a few mouthfuls only, plus several glasses of beer and wine, might cost 48 yuan per person (about £8).

Kuala Lumpur: *car-park food*

by Sally Bradshaw

The Kuala Lumpur car-parks near big hotels and office blocks come alive at night with stalls on wooden trestles, and metal folding tables and chairs set up by the parking-meters. Each stall specialises in a different food – soups in clay pots, a fish stall with a charcoal fire, wok stalls, noodle stalls, speciality stalls serving superb oyster omelettes, another cooking squid with a mound of pak choy. After ordering from this real-life menu, customers sit down. From somewhere out of the smoke vaguely familiar faces loom, miraculously locating customers again among the throng bearing freshly cooked dishes. In the warm night air the service is courteous and often surprisingly elegant. Malaysians come to graze – a snack before a show, a nibble before bed, or even a full-scale dinner.

In the car-park of the Regent Hotel a fixed notice in the middle of the concrete reads in Malay, English and Chinese: 'Dear customer, kindly select your favourite food.' In Kuala Lumpur food means Malayan, Indian, Thai and Chinese. The locally adapted cuisine of Straits Chinese settlers is Nonya.

The cuisine has absorbed all the wealth of local flavours – coriander, lime leaves, lemon grass, orange Malacca ginger and banana leaf. The seafood is outstanding – prawns, langoustines, crabs, clams, oysters – and there are all kinds of colourful flat and round fish. Some stalls run a Magimix hooked up to a generator to make cocktails out of the array of superb fruits – lychees, limes, oranges, mangoes, water melon, star fruit, longan, rambutan, mangosteen and durian (with the texture of crème brûlée and the smell of coffee, bananas, Camembert and incense).

Dinner comes from all corners of the car-park. Tom yam soup (Nonya-style) with chillies is cooked and served in a lovely lidded clay pot. In the light stock float cauliflower florets, miniature sweetcorns, Chinese leaves, bean sprouts, onions, tiny tomatoes, all barely cooked, and prawns, shredded beef, chicken and squid. It is flavoured with lemon grass, a few lime leaves diffusing a delicate citrus scent, and several chillies. This costs three dollars: about 85p. Satay and its sweet peanut sauce comes with a tiny dish of lethal chilli sauce and a little cake of rice. Angel-fish is grilled in an oiled banana leaf and served on the leaf with a small dish of chopped shallot and chilli in fresh lime juice.

The traditional plate of 'Penang fries' is a selection of deep-fried nibbles such as a large langoustine in batter, stuffed squid slices in batter with garlic, spring roll with a soft exterior pancake, as for Peking duck, and nearly raw bean sprouts mingled with a sweet, aromatic, aniseed-flavoured pork sausage within. To accompany this there is beer or fruit juice blended with water.

To finish there is tea and assorted dumplings, a sweetened pork mixture, like a medieval English mince pie, a butterscotch made of egg, coconut milk and palm sugar, and a sweetened black-bean purée made from beans that were originally red. There is an amazing iced Kachang made from the snow scraped off a large, revolving ice block. In the dish are diced grass jelly (blackish), green vermicelli made from rice flower, and sweetened cooked red beans. The snow mound goes on top, followed by syrup of coconut milk, palm sugar and condensed milk, with sweetened sweetcorn purée dabbed over the middle. The result is like Titania's treacle pudding, looking like treacle suet pud but in the middle, instead of stodge, is snow.

Los Angeles: *Spago*
San Francisco: *Chez Panisse*

by Ken Jacobs

Spago

Wolfgang Puck's celebrated restaurant Spago is in a somewhat unfashionable area of West Hollywood. The entrance is just off Sunset
Boulevard on a hilly side street. Most of the exterior is in Mexican style,
but the front, which looks down on Sunset, is painted to look like a ship.
The building is just behind a small car rental lot. A number of men with
moustaches surround the cars as they pull up. Some are *paparazzi* looking for celebrities and some are valet parking attendants.

Where you are seated is important in American restaurants: the front
window overlooks Sunset Boulevard, but the main view is of the large
illuminated Budget Rent-A-Car & Truck sign below the restaurant.
There is also a view of the Old World restaurant (branches in Beverly
Hills and elsewhere) and the huge Tower Records shop. Any attempt at
stylishness in Los Angeles always scrapes up against the innate tacki-
ness of much of the city.

On the white walls in an alcove are modern paintings of large paint
tubes stuck to the canvas with their contents squeezed out. Along the
longest wall is the narrow open kitchen, separated from the diners by a
wall just too high for people to see exactly what the chefs are doing.
Built into the kitchen wall and surrounded by brickwork is an intensely
hot, wood-fired pizza oven where Puck's exotic pizza fantasies are
cooked. Diners wear anything from hot-pants to tails.

Spago's creator, Wolfgang Puck, classically trained chef, media personality and brilliant publicist, is said to have caused a minor revolution
in Californian eating-out habits in a few short years.

The restaurant is cramped for its reputation as well as noisy and
informal. The white cloth-covered tables are packed quite closely
together and the ceiling is not that high. Padded wirework and metal-
framed chairs look like up-market garden furniture from John Lewis.

The menu does not say Spago anywhere. Instead, the front is an
advertisement reproducing the eye-catching cover of Wolfgang Puck's
latest cookbook. The cover shows illustrations by Puck himself of food
served at Spago and Chinois, his other restaurant in Santa Monica
specialising in Chinese/French/Puck food. (There is also a Spago in
Japan.)

The menu offers everything from American foie gras sauté with apples and ginger to pizza with lamb sausage, cilantro and freshly cut Maui onions to sauté crab cakes with lime herb butter and 'rockette' salad. The idea is to have whatever you like in whatever combination.

Puck uses vinaigrettes, butters and mousses to flavour dishes, rather than traditional or even *nouvelle*-type sauces. This, along with extensive use of charcoal grilling, unusual local vegetables and salads and the abandonment of traditional menu composition, seem to constitute his version of Californian cuisine, which has made him almost a national celebrity since he opened Spago in 1982 with his wife, Barbara Lazaroff. It is she who designed the kitchen and dining-room.

The wine list has an extensive selection of Californian wines along with a smaller selection of French wines, including well-known '78, '75 and '70 classed-growth clarets. The eye is caught by Shafer-Spago special release – 'Andy Warhol Label' Napa '83.

Puck has appeared on nationwide breakfast television and draws Hollywood celebrities to his restaurants. Deliberately knocking the pretensions of the formal French restaurant (despite his classical training, which included a stint at the three-star L'Oustaù de Baumanière (see the entry for Auberge de Provence, London) and experience as former head chef at the classical Ma Maison in Los Angeles), he has promoted informal eating at a high, but not very high, price. Puck adopts the Stephen Spielberg philosophy of giving people what they want. Everyone likes pizza, so Puck makes spectacular gourmet pizzas. Americans like rich desserts, so he serves traditional rich American desserts despite his general policy of serving only light, simple food.

Like the archetypal Californian of today, Puck is actually from elsewhere (Austria). He has perfectly epitomised the mood of this city, however, and its penchant for media hype, even down to wrapping himself in the American flag to salute American food at the expense of French.

The cottage-style bread loaves are pre-cut into sections and have dried out at the cut edges from reheating. Lobster ravioli can be rather meanly filled, which may sound unfair because it is lobster, but there is really not enough filling-to-pasta ratio. By contrast, a generous little pile of lobster with a few julienne vegetables is placed in the centre of the plate as decoration. The orange lobster butter is nicely spiked with chillies but is adequate rather than intense in flavour.

A good simple salad of mixed leaves comes topped with sauté goats' cheese and dressed with olive oil.

Spago's pizzas are topped with exotics like Shitake mushrooms and duck sausages. They are starkly at odds with the standard-issue pizzas like Original Ray's in New York, where part of the enjoyment is the feeling of oil and tomato paste dripping down your chin. By the end of the meal at such places your paper plate is translucent and soggy with an

oily sheen. Although the flavours are good, it is the sensation of the limp
pointed end of the pizza slice (which you bite off before the cheese slides
into your lap) and the dripping grease which are important.

The good strong mushroom flavour of the chanterelles at Spago are a
plus, and the crust is crispy. Artichoke hearts are undercooked and lack
flavour. The ingredients seem to stay separate in flavour rather than
blending together, as in the familiar, harmonious Neapolitan formula of
tomatoes, oregano, olive oil and Mozzarella.

Pink Sonoma baby lamb chops carved from best end of neck are
incredibly tender and juicy (probably marinated), but with a less pronounced flavour than the best English lamb. They are served with a
thin brown gravy meant to be rosemary butter and a blob of artichoke
mousse.

The best main course is a simple charcoal-grilled tuna steak with a
slightly sweet tomato and basil vinaigrette (basically tomato concasse
with basil and vinaigrette). The fish is mostly deliciously succulent, but
unevenly cooked and one end is strangely dried out.

The desserts are mostly true blue American concoctions with a smattering of French. These include blueberry pie, apple pie with caramel
ice-cream, crème brûlée, marjolaine with raspberry sauce and a cookie
assortment. The individual hot pear tart is rather ordinary, sitting in a
nest of mediocre puff pasty and surrounded by a rum butter sauce
(meant to be a sabayon?). There is also a good chocolate cake and an
amazing concoction made from alternating layers of a kind of chocolate
sponge and banana ice-cream.

The bill comes to $42 (£26) per head, with one bottle of decent
California Chardonnay between four and without the expected 15 per
cent American tip.

The food at Spago is good because it involves the use of fresh
ingredients in which to some extent at least the combinations in each
individual dish are kept simple. In the end, though, the atmospheric formula wins out over the food. The overwhelming impression is of a
Hollywood-inspired brasserie atmosphere – a bit like a high tech and
more cramped version of Langan's in London. The food at Spago is fun
but as inconsistent as at many a brasserie.

Chez Panisse

To get from San Francisco to the fashionable suburb of Berkeley, famous
hotbed of 1960s student radicalism, you cross the split-level Bay Bridge.
Chez Panisse is located in what is known as the gourmet ghetto. On the
same street and close by is a good wine shop, cheese shop, fish shop, etc.
The wooden archway leading to one of the best-known restaurants in
California has the restaurant's name carved into the wooden panel
above the arch. The structure's weathered exterior boards would not

look inconspicuous on a building set in an American National Park.

Upstairs is a bistro, where meals of pizza, pasta, calzone, salads and the like are served.

Downstairs is for the famous no-choice five-course set menus that have scarcely ever been repeated since Alice Waters opened Chez Panisse in 1971. The entire week's daily menus are posted outside in the same manner as Clarke's in London (see entry).

By Californian standards, an establishment started 16 years ago is a traditional bastion. Alice Waters and the Chez Panisse team are probably responsible for the development of what is now termed California cuisine in its many guises.

The dining-room is small and narrow with the open kitchen along a short wall at the back. The décor is stark but smart in a clean Californian sort of way. Arts and crafts-style wall-lamps are attached to otherwise bare mottled parchment walls. There is a Japanese-style archway of redwood beams towards the street end which breaks the monotony of the room. Redwood-panelled booths and curved wooden chairs encircle white-clothed tables running down each side of the room in two lines. Plate patterns change with each course.

The dining-room is surprisingly informal and noisy since the tables are quite close together. Some people are well dressed, but there are also men wearing sweaters. The house is virtually full by 6.30. Americans still generally eat earlier than Europeans.

Service is friendly and efficient, but informal sometimes to a slightly irritating extent: everyone is not necessarily served at the same time even though everyone is having the same thing. The servers wear white shirts and black aprons. Alice Waters no longer cooks, but still serves two nights a week when possible.

Many of the team in the restaurant started in 1971. Obviously there have been changes, and Jeremiah Tower, Alice Waters' former partner, has gone on to new ventures, including opening Stars, a San Francisco restaurant serving a flamboyant version of California cuisine. The current chef at Chez Panisse is Paul Bertolli, who carries on in the original style.

Bread is put on the table in a basket: cut pieces of hot sour dough baguette and a rougher, country-style sour dough bread. The latter is good, but the reheated baguette slices soon go very dry. Butter is good quality and unsalted.

The choiceless meal can start with a salad of Chino ranch curly endive (chicory) salad with pickled anchovies, garlic croûtons and Parmesan. The chicory is very fresh and delicate – quite lacking in bitterness. The marinated anchovies are delicious and mercifully unsalty. The ingredients, which also include a few pieces of egg, red onion and shavings rather than gratings of Parmesan, are simply dressed, and make an unexceptional combination but a refreshingly clean and harmonious appetite-whetting starter.

Next comes a cannellini bean and pasta soup with grilled quail and sage. The soup is served in wide bowls and unfortunately arrives tepid, as often seems to be the case in American restaurants of all standards. Otherwise it is a hearty and well-seasoned Tuscan bean soup laced with some delicate chunks of lightly grilled quail. The pasta shells are rather too soft. The sage is nicely restrained, and there is the bonus of some fresh morels.

The main course is simply called veal escalopes with spring vegetables: two escalopes the thickness of a 10 pence piece and the size of a pocket address book. They have been momentarily cooked on a very hot grill (presumably mesquite charcoal, Chez Panisse's chosen cooking fuel and the rage from coast to coast) so that they are still pink inside and with vivid black searing marks on the surface.

A thin and slightly bland-tasting yellow cream sauce is served with the escalopes. The meat is very tender and delicious and gently perfumed with the flavour of charcoal. The instinctive reaction that the sauce, which seems to lack any alcoholic or other complicated flavouring, is a little boring soon vanishes. The quality of the meat brought out by the quick grilling is so high that a more complicated sauce would be superfluous.

Despite the small amount of meat, the presentation is in no way *nouvelle*. The sauce is poured over the small overlapping slices of veal, which sit on one half of the plate, while tiny pieces of mostly baby vegetables are piled up on the other half: Japanese turnips, red turnips, asparagus tips, young peas (not mange-tout), baby artichoke tops and carrots, both the Californian white and traditional yellow.

The next course seems just too simple to be true: three skinned slices of blood orange doused in blood orange juice. (The menu outside had promised aspic; maybe it had never set.) The slightly tart orange slices are refreshing, but perhaps not special enough to stand on their own, nor absolutely necessary as an acidic palate cleanser after the clean-tasting veal and vegetables.

Dessert is warm ricotta cheesecake, a wonderfully simple wedge of a feathery light cake studded with a few pine nuts and fat sultanas. There is the thinnest of crispy, sweet crumb coating to the outside of the cake. That is it: no puddle of cranberry coulis, no embellishment, not even a mint leaf for decoration.

There are no petits fours with coffee, just as nothing is served with drinks. This is what you get for $45 (£28) per head (without wine and service).

The meals are not very exotic or peppered with surprising combinations but are breathtakingly simple, using the finest quality ingredients. It is not just the Californian austerity of simple charcoal-grilling and few sauces that produces the simplicity. Ms Waters' philosophy of serving fresh local ingredients in a harmonious way contributes to it too.

The first line in *Chez Panisse Cookbook* is: 'My approach to food is not radical or unconventional.' This is in contrast to the flamboyant first line of Wolfgang Puck's introduction to his cookbook: 'The past few years will go down in history as the rebirth of American cooking.' This illustrates a difference in temperament and thus in style.

Though Puck knows the merit of keeping food simple, he does not have the same careful attention to uncomplicated menu planning and keeping a meal straightforward. He calls his restaurants his playgrounds. He gives his fantasies free rein. The diner decides on what combinations to choose.

With the new interest in good food in many places outside Continental Europe, it may seem a small thing for Ms Waters to produce a simple and compatible but excellent meal with all first-class fresh ingredients. Having eaten out quite often in Europe and America, I have not found it so any more – not even in France. In California, where everything is a hype, it is a big deal.

The Netherlands: *Restaurant Duurstede*

by Catherine Kroon

Wijk bij Duurstede, twenty miles south-east of Amsterdam, ten miles south-east of Utrecht, lies at the conjunction of the River Rhine and the River Lek in typical Dutch countryside: all grass and water and skies and cows and great farmhouses with green-white-red painted window shutters beside the dykes lining the rivers. At the heart of the little town there is a medieval market square and church surrounded by four-teenth-century, high narrow Dutch houses.

In a cobbled street off the market square lies Restaurant Duurstede (Maleborduurstraat 7), one of the oldest buildings in the town. It has a tall, utterly severe façade of old red bricks, which are repeated in the floor of the crypt-like, silent, mirror-lined entrance hall. Once through the doors into the restaurant, all is spacious, light and modern. The high building is open to the roof. A gallery runs at different levels along all the interior walls, creating a broad dining-area in one part, just room enough for a single table in other places. Tables are placed like little isolated islands, none of the staff-motorway effect achieved by lesser restaurants, and waiters appear at your elbow silently, out of nowhere.

All is white, immaculate and impeccable: rough whitewashed walls, white table linen, long white aprons on the waiters. The beams are painted silver. The pendant lamps of white porcelain are decorated with hand-painted posies. Fresh flowers are on the tables, and irreproachable cutlery, crockery and glassware repeat the white and silver theme. There are restaurant matches on the tables and a haze in the room: the Dutch are still heavy smokers, and for customers of this ilk a cigar is part of restaurant ritual.

Chef-proprietor Paul Fagel is one of seven brothers, each of whom has his own restaurant. The father had a hotel-restaurant-cafe of the kind patronised by travelling salesmen. Paul Fagel trained at L'Oustaù de Baumanière in Provence, where he became chef-poissonnier. He then worked as chef in his brother Ton's restaurant just outside Amsterdam (Bistro Klein Paardenburg, Amstelzijde 59, Ouderkerk aan de Amstel) for eight years before opening his own restaurant here thirteen years ago. He has been one of the country's top chefs for twenty years.

The menu bears all the trademarks of the well to do. It is in French, sub-titled in Dutch. Salmon features largely, and comes from Scotland or Ireland. Oysters are from Yerseke in the Dutch province of Zeeland. Duck is Barbary. The entrecôte double béarnaise is Scotch Angus beef. There is terrine de foie gras de canard mariné au jus de truffe; there is paillard de pigeon au jus de truffe. Scampi are grilled on a bed of wild spinach or find themselves at the centre of a roulade of turbot. Lobster and scallops are made into a galette and placed on stewed radishes. Fish and ballotines are vacuum sealed, then poached. Noodles are home made. Meals take three and a half to four hours and cost around £45 a head, main courses around £17.50.

There is a certain uniformity in Holland in the style of cooking, whatever the restaurant; and there is a certain uniformity in prices too – they are high. There are no real individuals behind Dutch restaurant stoves. The cooking is accomplished if short on fantasy. Menus are very sophisticated, very handsome and very cosmopolitan: even in small provincial towns restaurants are producing dishes that might have come out of London or Paris. But there are a few signs that this is changing. A new type of restaurant is springing up which charges much lower prices than the temples to cuisine, and bases its profits instead on a large customer turnover. This is a typically cosmopolitan phenomenon, mostly restricted to the big cities.

One such place is Brasserie in Utrecht (Zadelstraat 20). Its short, modern, interesting and innovative menu is in Dutch, not French, and prices are half those of Restaurant Duurstede prices. There is a ragout of game on the March menu, and there is wild duck from the Dutch province of Friesland, but the fish on offer are the same expensive types as at Duurstede (lemon sole with a beetroot beurre blanc, salmon with root ginger and honey, monk-fish with oregano) and beef is the same Black Angus Scotch Aberdeen, accompanied by a bordelaise sauce.

New York: '*nouvelle* Americana'

by David Dale

Ronald Reagan's New Nationalism, among other things, has inspired a generation of chefs to create a local cuisine that leaves hot dogs and hamburgers far behind. In their passion to prove their patriotism, chefs have ranged geographically (through the regional cuisines of the back-blocks) and historically (through the chronicles of the early settlers) to develop menus that persuade New Yorkers they are still part of a nation of pioneers living on what's fresh from field, forest and foam.

In the past six years New York has seen the opening of restaurants called An American Place, American Harvest, Arizona, The Cadillac Grill, Carolina, Texarkana, La Louisiana, Memphis, and Cafe Montana. The latest is Sofi, which may at first sound Italian but which stands for South of Flat Iron, a reference to the wonderful old skyscraper called the Flat Iron Building.

This self-consciousness extends to menus. Dishes feature titles like Maine mussels with light mountain Cheddar, Ozark apple cake, Virginia ham with sweet potato salad, Pennsylvania Dutch vanilla crumb pie, marinated Oregon salmon with sweet mustard sauce, fricassee of veal with Kalamazoo celery sauce, and Cajun popcorn (crawfish tails in peppery batter). Even the dreaded chicken Maryland has come back, but the chicken is free-range and the batter is light and low-calorie. For extra colour there's a side dish of corn custard.

The appeal of this food is partly nostalgia, partly the illusion of health and partly novelty, for diners have became jaded with New York's cornucopia of French and Italian restaurants.

Key features of '*nouvelle* Americana' are:

(1) Mesquite-barbecued or mesquite-smoked meat or fish. Mesquite is a fragrant wood supposed to add an exquisite flavour to raw flesh. Not all restaurants go so far as The Red Cadillac in Greenwich Village, which offers a speciality of mesquite-grilled rattlesnake (tasting like old sock).

(2) Blackened red-fish. This recipe, invented by New Orleans chef Paul Prudhomme, has become so popular in the past two years that the red-fish, which is caught in the Gulf of Mexico, is likely to become an endangered species. The fish is smeared with a paste made of peppers, herbs and spices, and briefly seared on a very hot griddle, so it ends up with a burnt crunchy crust and moist flesh.

(3) Warm goat's cheese, usually sitting on red or purple lettuce.

(4) Soft-shell crabs, often served sauté in butter with pecan-nuts. The species shed their shells at an early age and take a long time growing

new ones. They are served whole, including claws.

(5) Charcoal-grilled slices of aubergine and courgette, with noticeable burn marks.

(6) Multi-coloured mushrooms, leaves and roots with exotic names and sharp flavours, chosen to provide textural and visual balance to a plate. '*Nouvelle* Americana' is designer food as well as nationalistic food, and must look as if it were just photographed for *Gourmet* magazine.

Patriotism doesn't come cheap. The prices charged by some places seem more suited to three-star French food. In the top-class American establishments, such as Gotham or Baton's, you'll be lucky to get out for less than £70 a couple, including a bottle of Californian Chardonnay, tax of eight per cent and tip of fifteen per cent.

My favourites among the more reasonably priced are Arizona (206 East 60 Street), with amusing Painted Desert and cactus décor; Bud's (359 Columbus Avenue at 77 Street), owned by the same people who recently opened Jam's in London, with laid-back Californian-Mexican food and equally mellow service; and Miss Ruby's (135 Eighth Avenue at 17 Street), which changes the state of origin of its menu each week, so one visit might yield a burning Texas chilli con carne, the next a New England peach cobbler.

One joyful side effect of new Americana has been the rediscovery of two old American restaurants that have been plugging away unrecognised for years. Both are run by black people and both offer the gutsy food of the old south.

The classier is Jezebel's (630 Ninth Avenue at 45 Street), near Manhattan's theatre district. It's lavishly decorated with mirrors, velvet and lace 'to look like a New Orleans whorehouse', and serves classics like ham-hocks with black-eye peas, stewed okra, candied sweet potatoes with heavy beef gravy, and baked hen stuffed with fruit and pecan-nuts. The other is Silvie's (328 Lennox Avenue at 127 Street), in deepest Harlem, where you'll find the best barbecued spare ribs in New York and a warm welcome.

New York: *UN Sichuan Pavilion*

by Yan-kit So

Having been disappointed time and time again in so-called Szechuan (Sichuan) restaurants in London and its environs where the owners have not seen to it that their Cantonese chefs learn if only the basics of Szechuan cuisine, I was delighted to find the real McCoy during a recent visit to New York where I was treated to dinner at UN Sichuan Pavilion (310 East 44th Street). Strategically situated a stone's throw from the United Nations and furnished with modern décor and comfortable chairs, the proprietors, of mixed Cantonese and Shanghai background, have arranged with the Chinese government to bring male chefs from Szechuan on a three-year rotation basis.

Besides the Today's Special comprising eleven dishes, the regular menu of some seventy-five dishes, printed both in English and Chinese, carries many popular Szechuan dishes and some less-well-known ones. The menu ends with this courageous announcement in red print: 'We do not use MSG, artificial additives or food coloring.' In fact, it was for this very reason that my American hosts chose the restaurant, for Betsy White, unlike her husband, George, is so allergic to MSG that she is unable to eat in Chinese restaurants in China, where the powder is used liberally.

We started with three hot appetisers, or dim-sum: dumplings in Szechuan sauce, boiled and complete with chilli red oil; spring rolls Szechuan-style, dainty in size, with minced pork stuffing subtly tasting of aromatic Szechuan peppercorn; and small steamer buns from Today's Special, served piping-hot in a bamboo basket, though less pleasing.

Next came the pièce de résistance, the smoked duck. It is smoked with real camphor wood-chips brought from the province, the manager told me. But to my surprise the duck was served carved into thin slices in the same way as a Peking duck, and put on pancakes – oversized, but definitely made in the kitchen – with shredded spring onions and cucumbers and a sweet sauce smeared all over. As this was so radically different from the way it is served in Chengdu (the capital of Szechuan) where the duck is chopped into pieces and no sweet sauce accompanies it, I asked the manager about it. He readily admitted it was his restaurant's way to please its customers!

Three more Szechuan dishes followed, served simultaneously with rice: spicy-hot Gungpao prawns, a whole sea-bass deep-fried until the skin becomes crispy, then laced with a spicy sauce, and sauté aubergine slices with the famed fish-fragrant sauce. On the menu, all the three dishes carry a star to indicate they are 'mild hot and spicy'. I was therefore expecting a fairly intensive range of Szechuan tastes and after-tastes, especially as the dishes looked promising.

To my utter amazement, they all tasted cloyingly sweet. So overpowering was the sweetness that any suggestion of chilli-spiciness expected from the fish and the prawns, and sweet-and-sour from the fish-fragrant aubergine were lost. I asked for vinegar and added some to the aubergine to simulate the fish-fragrant flavour. One and all around the table marvelled at the instant improvement to the dish.

Fortunately, the last course, a bowl each of velvet flowery chicken soup, was a resounding triumph, one and all agreed. In the midst of the watery clear consommé in the bowl is a pale ivory mass with attractive pink specks. This mass dissolves in one's mouth as one drinks the consommé. Commending the superb quality of the soup to the manager, I guessed that the curd-like mass consisted of purée chicken, ham and egg white. He nodded, adding it was in fact the best Virginia ham.

I then asked him why the dishes were so uncharacteristically sweet, even though I could well understand why a Szechuan restaurant operating outside the province had to tone down its fiery chilli taste. The sweetness suits the American palate, was his ready answer. More true, I suspect, is that the excessive use of sugar is the chef's way of coping with the non-use of MSG which, after all, supposedly enhances the savoury-sweetness of many an ingredient. This phenomenon I have observed during the past year in London Chinese restaurants, where chefs have tried to use less if not wean themselves off using MSG. But sugar is not the answer – good and real stock is the answer.

Nice: *La Merenda*

by Ken Jacobs

This tiny, corridor-shaped restaurant near Nice's flower, fruit and vegetable markets is the place for unpretentious Niçois cooking. The minuscule open kitchen, where the chef works alone, is at the far end of the room. Madame serves and mixes salads and pastas. The restaurant seats about twenty-four, though it seems fewer, since there are just two rows of tightly spaced tables with simple stools as seats. A cross breeze makes the place feel cool, even on hot days: the door is kept open and only wooden bead curtains guard the doorway.

La Merenda (4 rue Terrasse, 06300 Nice) has no telephone, so you must book in person. This keeps the tourists down to a reasonable number and retains the flavour of the establishment; a few regulars give the appearance of having eaten here every Saturday noon for the past ten years. Even though they have probably booked, diners scurry in promptly after opening time, as if afraid of being late for school. Madame eyes your group warily upon arrival. If she takes to you, however, she may later stroke your arm consolingly if a dish has taken a little too long to be delivered. Despite the cramped seating arrangements, the unpretentiousness of the establishment (not least induced by the unaffected middle-aged couple's dress – Madame may sport a simple blouse and Bermuda shorts) induces a feeling of relaxation and warmth.

The little-changing menu is chalked on a blackboard which is brought around the room as each group arrives. A crowded bowl of short-stemmed roses in full bloom may similarly move from table to table or be put on the floor to keep the door open. Starters typically include salami, coppa (raw shoulder of ham), pizza, beignets of courgette flowers, and pasta au pistou. Main course specialities are daube, stockfish (stew of salt cod), stuffed sardines, tripe and andouillette. Madame gently turns away a number of would-be diners and early on turns the outside menu around to display the 'Complet' sign.

It is difficult to imagine food of such simplicity being so staggeringly good. The fresh sardines are filleted and stuffed with a simple but deliciously harmonious herb and breadcrumb filling before being grilled. The tiny pizzas are a perfect example of their species – supremely hot, crisp crusts topped with tomato, herbs and cheese, with perhaps some dark green olive oil offered in a neat pouring bottle containing a layer of chillies.

The pasta dish illustrates how well the couple work as a team. The moment the thin green noodles are ready, Madame instantly appears at her husband's side without a word being spoken. She studiously mixes the pasta and sauce in a plain ceramic bowl, as if performing a religious rite. Then the requisite number of portions are doled out and served to the lucky table. The smell of garlic and basil arriving at the table makes the senses reel with pleasure even before you start to eat the tender, yet delicately firm noodles with their creamy, pungent, garlicky sauce. We certainly did not eat better pasta in our foray into Italy, nor have we within recent or not-so-recent memory.

There are also succulently gelatinous pieces of beef in a daube with a thick, richly fragrant sauce scented with tomatoes, herbs and red wine; deliciously delicate courgette flowers from the market, in a light crispy batter; a near-perfect salad of mesclun; and a wonderful goat's cheese encased in herbs and preserved in the finest olive oil. The only wines are Merenda's very drinkable house red or rosé. There is no bottled mineral water. 'C'est bien,' intones Madame knowingly as she places a jug of water on the table.

For dessert there is crème caramel, a very good coffee-flavoured chocolate mousse and perhaps a salade de pêches. The 'salade' looks very scruffy – ragged pieces of fresh white and yellow peaches served in a small bowl with sugar syrup, some tiny pieces of candied angelica and lemon peel, and a few raspberries, the latter mostly squashed. The taste is heavenly – the peaches are of a ripeness and intensity of flavour rarely to be had in England.

A meal here is a bargain – probably less than 250 francs for two, including wine. You leave feeling that, had the person who invented *nouvelle cuisine* eaten lunch here on the fateful day the idea first struck them, they would have wandered listlessly the couple of hundred yards to the beach, collapsed on to the hot, smooth stones alongside the locals lying in various states of undress, soaked in the Provençal sunshine and forgotten about the whole idea in a haze of contentment and well-being.

Paris: *Robuchon*

by Drew Smith

Paris does not give her favours lightly. The exhilaration of eating at Jamin (32 rue Longchamps) is tempered by the cost: in the 16th arrondissement, home to aristocracy and new money, £100-plus a head does not seem such big money. Along avenue Victor Hugo are the most famous names of the fashion world. *Haute couture* provides the tenor for Joël Robuchon's restaurant. France's two great contributions to twentieth-century culture combine.

Robuchon received his third Michelin star in a record 27 months from opening, rates 19.5 in Gault Millau and has achieved this in arguably the most critical city in the world, Paris.

Despite the exclusivity of the area, rue Longchamps itself is a hill of bourgeois aspirations – boulangeries, poissonneries, Chinese restaurants, one Lebanese restaurant, a bank. The pistachio-coloured frontage of the restaurant has a sign saying Jamin but, following the cult of top French restaurants being called after their chef rather than by their proper name, inscribed over the door is Robuchon.

Inside, Jamin becomes a restaurant, not devoid of show by any means, but plainer in its loyalties of taste, almost Flaubertian in its values – a marble bust, thin palm fronds growing up to the low ceiling, inlaid framed mirrors, floral prints from old books, glass separating screens. The great excesses of décor which characterise the current family of Michelin three stars in France are muted here.

Immediately, you are aware that you are in premises occupied by craftsmen. With the menu comes the first taste: in March it was a tray with a baby scallop, the size of a man's thumbnail, filled with the white flesh sliced, a nick of coriander and a yellow butter sauce of immense richness. Beside it, hardly any larger, is a pastry shell, so fragile that it bends in the fingers, filled with caviare and topped with grated truffle.

Paris waiters are the custodians of French gastronomy. Jamin is a Parisian restaurant. The staff are professionals who behave as if, at long last, they have found a kitchen worth their talents. The English-speaking waiter is despatched to the table to mention the ravioli of langoustines with foie gras and truffle in the sauce.

The menu concentrates on a short, familiar repertoire that has not noticeably developed in the last few years. The set menus are offered only to the whole table. One is a truffle menu: truffles with onion galette; lobster with asparagus and truffle; lamb with a salad; cheese; mango gratin with a pineapple sauce; cold caramelised cream with brown sugar. Alas, the 150-franc menu of four years ago has vanished.

But truffles, caviare, foie gras, asparagus, lobsters are the jewellery. The point about Jamin is the cooking. Take this dish: *blanc de bar cuit en peau, sauce verjutée*. The sea-bass steak is taken from along the bone; a mix of ginger, mace, coriander, cinnamon, allspice, salt and pepper is rubbed on the skin; the steak is then cooked on a hot oiled pan so the skin becomes crisp and imbued with the spices. The sauce is red wine, verjus, stock, vegetables and fish fumet, which creates a deep purple around the fish on the plate and is then rimmed with a little cream as a border.

Visually, sauces are neatly rounded off, edged in a line of thicker cream or another emulsion and, as in the lobster salad, decorated with a rim of peas. Sauces tend to be smears, barely enough to wet the fork, not sufficient to employ the sauce spoon provided. The kitchen is precise in controlling the quantities of food and the tastes on the plate.

As to vegetables, with the sea-bass they are reduced to the ultimate role of almost utter dismissal: shards of leeks, carrots, courgettes provide the bed on which the fish sits and are completely invisible.

All great chefs develop, in time, their own recognisable style in terms of tastes and flavours. With Robuchon it is his seasoning. Salting is a deliberate action, likewise pepper and also other aromatics – like fennel seeds in a salad, like the spicing on the skin of the sea-bass, like the potatoes boiled in their skins, peeled, sliced, each slice seasoned and then the whole re-formed.

In this style there is justification for the use of so many luxuries because they appear in small explosive quantities – like the foie gras, just 12 grammes to darken a sauce of veal and vegetable stocks with butter for the five fat langoustine tails wrapped up with a little grated truffle inside a ravioli. Another example, using less lavish ingredients, is the lamb in a salted pastry case. It arrives on a carving-board. The waiter beheads the pastry roll and flips out the long carré, wipes off the outer fat and shows it to the table. The thyme, rosemary and the salt that were in the redundant pastry have given their flavour to the meat. The meat has been cooked briefly and fiercely and then left to rest in its crust. The effect is the same consistent blush of pink throughout. A small pool of reduced lamb stock with butter is served to one side, and on the other is a clump of fat yellow egg noodles garnished with a few shards of carrot and courgettes that have been cut to the same shape as the noodles.

In other details the cooking keeps surprising – the pine-nut oil dressing for the salad, the coconut in the tuiles, a pear and honey clafouti.

After the main course the deft accuracy of the plating and portioning is lifted, and, like the end of a curfew, the arrival of the trays of cheese and trolleys of sweets begins. Sweets come as two waves, first a little tray with an eclair and other titbits and then come the madeleines, the gateaux, the tarts, the sorbets in profusion.

The wine list gives the lie to the idea that the French keep all the best wines to themselves – if this is true for *vin ordinaire*, it is not true in restaurants. The names, vintages, *négociants* are the same as can be found in many a British restaurant. The prices are steeper – Sancerre at £16, Chinon at £14, clarets moving upwards through £100. The list is predictably competent, with a taste for younger, fresher wines which might raise an English eyebrow: thoroughly safe, respectable and only the slightest hint that maybe someone had thought that perhaps the wines should not outshow the food.

Much about Jamin is safe, professional, steady. However, any cuisine that demands such enormous sums of money to support itself must be questionable. Some of the high cost might be put down to the difference between the franc and the pound; to the widening cultural gap between Britain and France; to the relative amounts people are prepared to pay for the art of restaurateuring. As an answer to those who believe that French cuisine is in decline, Jamin is emphatic and triumphant.

Most of all it is reassuring about those strengths that one would like to believe the best restaurant in Paris should have: not the décor, not the service, not the level of luxury, not the wines – though it has all these – but what is on the plate.

Provence: *Bacon*

by James Ainsworth

Of all the dishes of Provence, bouillabaisse is the most evocative. Boats spill their catches of exotic fish on to market stalls; each customer claims to know the only true recipe, and they're all different; everyone can tell you the restaurant that serves the best bouillabaisse along the whole of the Côte d'Azur, and no two people will give you the same address.

From the Bacon (bvd Bacon, Cap d'Antibes) there is a splendid view across the baie des Anges; at night a thin pencil-line of lights picks out the Promenade des Anglais in distant Nice. Inside is vivid white, like a canvas on which the customers paint themselves. As each new group of people sits down, a large plate of glistening fish is whisked around to be inspected, judged, turned over, poked, selected, picked up and hurried back to the kitchen for its transformation.

Bouillabaisse doesn't need anything else before or after; it is a complete meal, sometimes with the soup drunk before the fish, but here served together. First, as a gesture to expensive *couture*, a waiter slaps a big pink bib across the chest and secures it firmly behind. Then a large copper marmite, which it takes two to lift, is brought in, steam curling around the spiny rascasse, vive, galinette, baudroie, St Pierre, and put on a burner to keep warm.

Struggling with the whole fish, it can sometimes feel as if you've spent a day at sea by the time the heads are off, backbones lifted, and bones spat out. So it is a relief to see the filleting done quietly at a side table and the result handed to you on a plate. Broth is ladled over the fish while the trimmings appear; a mound of small toasts; a bowl of rouille, bright yellow from saffron and spicy from chilli; and four large, white, juicy cloves of peeled garlic.

The only DIY bit of the exercise is to scrape the garlic on to one toast, spoon a dollop of rouille on to another, then plop them into the soup like ducks in the bath, tossing up which to eat first, and when to alternate with a piece of firm vive or soft rascasse. The texture of the broth – not too watery, not too creamy – and the concentration and balance of flavours sets this apart from run-of-the-moulin versions. It is difficult to imagine a finer bouillabaisse.

Two of us (they serve it only for a minimum of two people) found that two bowlfuls each was all we could manage, plus a bottle of local Provençal white wine.

The only trouble was, the bill came to £100.

Rio de Janeiro: *Roanne*

by Patricia Fenn

Claude Troisgros has gone from apprenticeship at father's famous restaurant opposite Roanne station to setting up in a six-table, back-street Rio bistro nostalgically named Roanne (rua Custodio Serrão 62). Rio is warmer and less constricting than Roanne, where brother Pierre is heir-presumptive to the Troisgros throne.

For an uninhibited young cook Brazil offers a cornucopia of challenging new ingredients. Another French luminary, Paul Bocuse, had already recognised the Rio potential and set up Laurent Saundeau at the St Honoré in the Meridien Hotel. Laurent and Claude enthusiastically liaise on their culinary discoveries, in the same way as do Pierre Troisgros and Bocuse on the phone back in France.

They accept the limitations imposed by the country. Local flour does not work on the pâtisserie they trained in . . . the cream curdles before it thickens sauces . . . imported ingredients, such as foie gras and truffles, carry a 300 per cent tax . . . essential herbs, unknown in Brazil, have to be grown in their own gardens. So they have improvised. They stuff chayote with shrimps, serve okra with lamb, make quenelles from green corn, sabayon from sugar cane liqueur, fly in strange fish from the Amazon, substitute mangoes for apples in tarte Tatin, experiment with spices . . . some combinations work; some refuse to meld and have been dropped.

Le tout Rio came to witness this unorthodox marriage of flavours, expertise, cultures. Newer, smarter premises could be afforded. All the other top French restaurants in Rio are based, plushily, in hotels, with the back-up of skyscraper views of Copacabana and a comforting nucleus of hotel guests. The Troisgros restaurant is comparatively modest in size and accoutrements – white linen cloths, simple fresh flowers, and ivory-coloured walls providing a background for the prestigious framed testimonials from the French giants.

The menu is a challenge. Kir royale is conjured from 'champagne' and jabuticaba – made from small black berries akin to blackcurrants. With it come appetisers of Roquefort mini-quiches. Claude, surprisingly, claims that Brazilian Camemberts, Bries, and Roqueforts are as good as the French.

Course one was a salade de crevettes, more langoustine than shrimp, on a bed of avocado, the dressing harshly vinegary, but the appearance delicious, crowned with a cage, like spun sugar, of multi-coloured vegetable threads.

This was followed by a hot mousse de cresson, served in little copper casseroles, 'cresson' being a leaf from the Amazon. A garnish of fresh baby oysters and strips of red pepper provided clever contrasts of texture and colour. But again, somewhere lurked that jarringly inharmonious vinegar. One criticism of the parent Troisgros cooking is the drowning of the subtleties by the incautious use of vinegar. Is this a family blind spot or a local problem over finding a suitably mild Brazilian variety? Perhaps they used the dregs of the disgusting red wine – a Brazilian Cabernet – we tried to drink. The white Chandon was mitigatingly delicious.

No doubt about the origins of course three. Troisgros père 'invented' escalope de saumon à l'oseille. His son cooks a facsimile with fine Brazilian fish and a sorrel clone.

The cascais sorbet was unfaultably light and punchy. The main course – aiguillettes de canard à la mangue – was the most successful dish of the meal. Claude rejects the current chic of rare duck and cooks thin strips from the breast à l'ancienne, resulting in a rich fondant tenderness, fortified with a dark caramelised jus, and sharpened with a limey mango sauce, eye-catchingly coral.

Desserts are good, too, their restraint especially appreciated in this land of the sweet tooth. An assortment of six micro-masterpieces arrived, combinations of exotic fruits, feathery pastry, delicate mousses, chocolate and coffee fantasies. The guava tart is a particular cause for pride, since its canonisation in the new Roanne cookery book *Les Petits Plats de Troisgros*.

Dinner is considered only one of many essential Brazilian evening occupations, so courses follow thick and fast. Deploy delaying tactics or be out in an hour. On the other hand – Claude's menu comes to just £15.

Strasbourg

by Vicky Hayward

It is often said that Alsace has a problem of cultural identity. Perhaps that was true in the past, when the wounds of its war-torn history were more deeply felt and the Rhine was a political barrier rather than an economic boulevard. But today Alsace wears its unique, hybrid culture with an almost boastful pride and confidence.

Garlic and horseradish, Munster and chèvre cheeses lie next to each other on the farmers' stalls in the markets; fresh foie gras is sold along-side knack sausage in the *traiteurs*; dark rye breads and baguettes, streusel cakes and *tartes aux myrtilles*, pretzels and petits fours are arranged together in the bakers' elaborate window displays.

For a long time this gastronomic wealth lay strangely neglected. Alsace was caricatured for its culinary trademarks, choucroute and beer. But as a result of the recent broader and subtler appreciation of regional cooking outside renowned gastronomic zones, the richness of the *cuisine du terroir* is now coming to be fully appreciated.

The depth and strength of the tradition is as clearly expressed in Strasbourg as in the countryside. For although the city is known inter-nationally in its role as the symbolic capital of Europe, Strasbourg's heart beats as a provincial metropolis. The Alsace dialect still dominates street conversation, even in the tourist-thronged area around the grimily magnificent cathedral, and the smell of choucroute still lingers in the air more pervasively than that of hamburgers. Cheeringly, the *maisons d'Alsace* and *winstübe*, traditional timber-framed restaurants and drinking holes famed for their boisterous camaraderie, hold their own against the mushrooming international restaurants serving every-thing from Szechuan to Swedish food. This is thanks to the region's con-servatism and to the Strasbourgeois love of eating out with friends and family.

Inevitably, visitors who ask for good regional food are pointed in the general direction of the *winstübe* in the picturesque alleys of the old town. This is a risky business. True, the food is authentically regional. There is little variety in the menus: potato salad, onion tart, noodles in creamy sauces, coq au riesling and baeckeoffe (pork, lamb and beef marinated in white wine and cooked with potatoes) as well as the ubiquitous wine choucroute cooked in every imaginable way – in goose or bacon fat, with pork or saucisses de Strasbourg or duck, even with champagne instead of wine for a choucroute royale. But the liberal helpings of grease and the enormous portions – balloon-like sausages, mounds of potatoes and small heaps of choucroute – leave the unpractised stomach churning like a cement mixer. Unless you have been in energetic training or you come from Alsace, your appetite goes dead for about twenty-four hours.

This is a waste of time in a city where you are spoiled for choice by the restaurants of a group of chefs who are developing a modern but regionally distinctive *cuisine strasbourgeoise*. The degree of finesse in execution and the spirit of invention vary considerably, but all play with regional alliance, grafting native flavours on to their own cooking styles. Common threads strand their way through the menus. Portions remain large. Freshwater fish from the River Ill and game from the Vosges mountains appear on all the menus. Choucroute, turnips and horseradish are set alongside more predictable gourmet specialities like foie gras, magrets de canard and snails. They appear sometimes in traditional dishes and sometimes in quite new contexts. Horseradish may flavour a roast saddle of hare or a beurre blanc; the snails might be used in a bouillon or kougelhopf; foie gras could be traditionally fried with cinnamon, nutmeg and ground cloves, but it may be caramelised with soya or layered with salmon in a terrine. *Winstüb* dishes appear in equally unexpected guises. A presskopf, for example, traditionally a pig's-head brawn, may turn up as a terrine of duck and sweetbreads in a gelée flavoured with Tokay, or as slivers of carp and salmon set in a court bouillon flavoured with lemon and dill.

The most notable of this small but growing group of restaurants are Crocodile and Buerehiesel, which have two Michelin rosettes apiece; L'Arsenal and Wurtzmuhle, both unstarred, are well worth a visit. Crocodile must be the first choice. Emil Jung's menu is wonderfully inventive and the quality of his cooking superb, the cellar renowned and the service immaculate, the décor elegant enough to cocoon the occasional head of state but still welcoming for more informal visitors. Nor are the prices outrageous, especially compared with London or Paris. There is a three-course menu – with canapés, cheese and a large plate of petits fours – for 220 francs. A meal à la carte, without wine, would cost about double that.

Jung's approach is classic in its technique but unconventional in its quirky and sometimes apparently mismatched elements of surprise. The canapés to start the meal, delicious with a glass of chilled Alsace Muscat, work as carefully calculated keynotes: on one small plate a straight-forward, ungarnished sandwich of thickly sliced pâté de foie gras around ham; on another a small croustillant of caraway-flavoured choucroute wrapped in wafer-thin pastry, served with a clear white wine sauce speckled with diced red pepper.

As one course follows another, the waiters bob back and forth between the tables. A terrine de lapereau, chunks of white and dark rabbit-meat in a rich parsley gelée with a casing of carrot slices, is served on a pale green avocado sauce with a surprisingly mustardy tang; the flan de cresson aux grenouilles, a delicate layered egg custard sitting on a cream sauce, is ringed by carrots scooped out as mock pedestals, each topped by a snail and a dob of watercress purée; pickerel with juniper-flavoured beurre blanc turns out to be a steamed sealed envelope filled with finely shredded choucroute. A basket tray appears, bending under the weight of cheese, then an impressive *chariot des desserts* stacked with poached loquats and fresh soft red fruits, pâtisserie and mousses, ice-creams and sorbets. For the British visitor there is a nice touch: a trifle, the memento of a recent trip to London.

L'Arsenal offers a completely different perspective on *la cuisine strasbourgeoise*. Something of the *winstübe* has rubbed off on both the atmosphere and the cooking. The décor is traditionally beamed and panelled, children and jeans present no problem, and the kitchen takes orders until midnight. The frequently changing seasonal menu is undilutedly Alsatian, and the cooking is rich with earthy flavours. It is also full of surprises, stretching from the house aperitif, dry Alsace Crémant with peach liqueur, to the apple and cinnamon or quince sorbets on the dessert menu. In between come first courses like a warm salad of duck with sharp green rhubarb and main courses such as carp mousse baked in red cabbage leaves served with spaetzle noodles fried in butter. Prices are unbeatable: 140 francs for the four-course menu or a little more for a smaller meal eaten à la carte.

Finally, there are two everyday regional specialities, tarte flambée and the luscious asparagus of Hoerdt, which are eaten in Alsace with as much relish as choucroute and deserve to be just as well known. Tarte flambée is easily found, both in Strasbourg and in the villages a short drive away. On Sunday evenings many restaurants serve nothing else to large, relaxed groups. The tartes – large oblongs of bread dough rolled out like a wafer-thin pizza crust and covered with cream, fromage blanc, lardons and onion pieces – are baked in less than a minute in wood ovens with the flames licking at the dough. They are brought to the table burning hot, to be shared around and washed down with jugs of white wine while the next batch cooks. Alcoholic sorbets, pâtisserie and the like follow. A full meal costs only £5 or £6 a head.

The famed asparagus of Hoerdt is a more tricky matter of good timing. For two months from the middle of April, *le tout* Strasbourg drives out to this small village surrounded by asparagus fields, at most half an hour from the centre of town, to eat neatly piled stacks of deliciously tender, fat green and white stalks served with vinaigrette, mayonnaise and sauce mousseline. At the Restaurant à la Charrue, which opens only for the two-month season, the menu is slightly padded out with foie gras, local poussin and Disneyland desserts. But all attention should be on the asparagus. For once, the huge plateful is easily surmountable.

Tokyo: *Nadaman*

by Lesley Downer

Finding your way into Sazanka-so is not easy. Here you are in the middle of Tokyo – a city that makes London look positively Dickensian – and all around are gleaming glass and concrete towers. Hidden behind one, well away from the traffic, is a serene Japanese garden (tenth century, apparently) of combed sand, statuesque rocks, gnarled pine trees . . . In one corner, on the other side of a small lake (with a red curving bridge and matching red carp) is a tall brushwood fence, over the top of which you can just make out the swaying tops of a thick grove of bamboo. You probably walk round it twice before you spot a small gate, at the back where casual strollers won't stumble upon it. You go through it and up some winding stone steps through the bamboo grove to a thatched front porch where a kneeling, kimono-clad lady awaits you, bowing to the ground – you are, of course, expected.

All this is as nothing to the difficulty of making a reservation in the first place. To get anywhere in Japan, you have to be somebody, or at least know somebody – and Nadaman (Hotel New Otani, 4 Kioi-cho, Chiyoda-ku) is not just anywhere. Many things come in threes in Japan: three famous beauty spots, three beautiful gardens – and three great restaurants, Nadaman, Kicho and Tsuruya. All three, significantly, have their roots in Osaka, though Nadaman has since moved its main branch into this little house, Sazanka-so, in Tokyo. It was here, you are told almost as you are stepping out of your shoes, that Prime Minister Nakasone entertained the 1986 summit leaders (including Mrs Thatcher, who apparently cleaned her plate and said it was very nice). Only top people, and their guests, dine here.

A few things go without saying. There will be no sushi or sukiyaki today, for a place with Nadaman's pedigree could serve only kaiseki, Japan's *haute cuisine*. Similarly, while you are welcome to ask the name of the chef (it is Tanaka Hirotoshi, and he has been with Nadaman for

ten years), he would not presume to serve anything other than
traditional Nadaman cuisine. Lastly, an essential piece of information: it
is early summer, 19 June to be precise. The rainy season is just beginning and the hydrangeas are blooming in the garden outside.

There are five rooms in Nadaman, which means that only five groups
can dine at any one time. Yours is called Hana-kiri-no-ma, the paulow-
nia flower room, and, in this small, apparently invisible house, somehow contrives to look out over the lake. The room contains a table,
completely empty; a cushion to sit on; an alcove with a hanging scroll
and two huge chrysanthemums in a bamboo vase; and a screen of pale
grey silk. Apart from that? Well, there are the walls, most of which are
actually sliding doors, the floor (springy rice-straw matting) and the
ceiling, of taut parchment lit from behind. The silence is awesome.

Outside, there is the whisper of stockinged feet gliding across carpeted
floors, and the waitress (hardly an adequate word for this dowager in a
multi-layered, dark pink kimono) appears, bearing a black lacquer tray
which she places on the table, pausing to adjust the positioning of the
dishes. Centre front, behind the chopsticks, is a dark blue glass bowl
holding a peeled fig coated in a dark beige cream – pure sesame seeds,
laboriously ground by hand, strained, ground, strained and ground
again, until the last trace of graininess has disappeared. Behind, to the
left, in a clear glass dish, is a cube of silken tofu, perhaps an inch square
– texture rather than flavour, a sort of dustiness on the tongue – topped
with five little tongues of uni, salty sea-urchin eggs.

This is just by way of introduction. The hors d'oeuvre, when it
appears, is on a bed of ice (it is, you will remember, summer), enclosed
by a large round lotus leaf. Inside – together providing most of the classic 'five tastes' of Japanese cooking – are a section of lotus root with a
mustard stuffing (hot); a 'mountain peach' the size of a raspberry, red
and prickly (sweet/sour); a floury white yam the size of a rosebud,
coated in another of those creamy sauces, this time orange and silky
smooth, made, apparently, of finely ground bonito intestines (salty);
and a kind of sushi of grilled eel, cupped over rice flavoured with wild
grasses. So far you have had about nine mouthfuls and there are
another nine courses still to go.

The whole business takes perhaps three hours; each dish demands
that you linger over it. First you admire the chef's artistry, the precision
with which the food is arranged, the attention to detail – a clear soup
(the menu is planned so that each dish represents a different cooking
method) containing a whole green plum (precisely in season in mid-
June) balanced on a cube of egg custard and imbuing the liquid
memorably with its tart flavour; raw turbot, cut petal-thin, arranged on
a block of ice with a minuscule cucumber the size of a matchstick, complete with yellow flower, resting in front; or a fillet of rock-trout, served
skin-side down, the flakes eased apart so that it looks like a white

chrysanthemum. The dishes themselves – some lacquerware, some porcelain – are works of art, selected for their shape and colour to contribute to the picture.

As to the flavour – Osaka cuisine is known for its lightness of touch and there is little added flavouring as such. The meal, however, is far from bland, for the ingredients themselves provide dramatic flavours. Tiny baby ayu, 'sweetfish', for example, perfectly grilled over charcoal so that the skin is charred and the flesh sweet, comes with a brilliant green sauce with a fresh sharp flavour somehow reminiscent of new-mown grass, made from tade ('smartweed, water pepper'), not reduced but, again, ground, strained and ground to produce a pure and intense flavour.

Just as your palate is becoming jaded, the waitress announces shokuji, the meal, as if you have not yet eaten. By this she means rice, to which everything else is but a prelude – two triangular cakes of rice, grilled over charcoal and served in a bamboo box. Finally comes tea ceremony tea – the lightest I've ever had – whipped to a foamy froth and served with a small pink and white cake shaped like a hydrangea.

Japanese chefs working in the West say that it is impossible to serve true kaiseki there: the ingredients themselves – let alone ingredients of sufficient freshness and quality – are simply not available. There is no doubt that all the ingredients used at Nadaman are local and almost aggressively seasonal; imported foods or styles of cooking would not be appropriate for a restaurant of this class. Added to which, there is not enough demand for kaiseki in the West to warrant the hours of preparation which each dish demands. There is no sophisticated machinery in Nadaman's kitchens, no labour-saving devices, no food processors – just an assortment of knives, mortars, pestles and sieves, and a bevy of white-clad young men endlessly chopping, grinding and straining.

The price is, of course, outrageous – upwards of £200 a head. You are paying, though, not only for the food and for all that grinding and straining, but for the service, the priceless porcelain, the history, and the privilege of eating here.

Home thoughts

Drudgery divine

George Perry-Smith, *perhaps the most important of all post-war English cooks, sold his charming restaurant, the Riverside at Helford, in the spring of 1987 after four decades of catering. He recalls how, in 1951, a collection of well-intentioned amateurs made The Hole in the Wall, Bath into one of the most famous and respected restaurants in Europe.*

> On china blue my lobster red
> Precedes my cutlet brown.
> With which my salad green is sped
> By yellow Chablis down.
>
> Lord, if good living be no sin,
> But innocent delight,
> O polarise these hues within
> To one eupeptic white!
>
> Stephen Gaselee

That life is full of contradictions is something we learn early from the pains and pleasures of growing up; recognise again at school as we pass by the mystics and poets, the comedians and the tragedians; but tend to forget in the haste and practical preoccupations of middle age. Taking stock, a little nervously, to see how many pieces are left on the board, and how much I have failed to recover or reconcile on the way, I find it difficult to remember much, except how very busy we all were.

Certainly I must have seemed a most unlikely restaurateur, a contradiction of family background and a disappointment to a great headmaster, A.B.Sackett. I suppose I was a cook/quartermaster/houseman of some kind ever since 1940, when I interrupted university to join the Friends' Ambulance Unit, and received my only culinary training from an equally unlikely fellow-member, Eric Green, during a week in a tiny nurses' kitchen off a Middlesex Hospital ward. He was old enough to talk confidently about Antoine's and Charlotte Street just around the corner, and went on to have quite a lot to do with Shepherd's Hotel, the war-time oasis in Cairo, so he must have known what he was about. Before that I was a son of the manse: Rochdale, Widnes and Silsden hardly have a gastronomic ring – well, Silsden almost does now; Brecon, where the wisdom of the 'Corona' van parking outside the door of 8 The Watton was a matter of serious family discussion, to say nothing of the medically prescribed British wine under the stairs (beta-blockers for Sunday sermons?); up-market to Melton Mowbray and Long Clawson – names to make the juices run, had I but known it; west to Padstow, still a wonderful memory of May's ice-cream, 'obby 'osses, water polo in the harbour and rowing over to Rock, revived today by Rick Stein's exciting Seafood Restaurant; and Callington, now blessed with The Horn of Plenty nearby; back to the slag-heaps of Millom, as they then were; finally to boarding-school in Bath and holidays divided between a guardian aunt and uncle, comfortably retired to ICI country in prosperous Cheshire, and cycling all over England.

The Cheshire house, well ordered, even with gardener, housekeeper and maid for a time, in my memory revolved around the kitchen and the importance of regular family meals, splendid picnics, and self-sufficiency in the garden. At least I learned to prepare grapefruit properly, after supper every evening on the well-scrubbed wooden draining-boards among the scuttling silverfish. Very few people know how to prepare grapefruit, an accomplishment of the highest importance. I thought of writing *The Great Grapefruit Book* in retirement, for I have obviously failed to spread the word. I was recently presented, at a very grand hotel, with a breakfast grapefruit just cut in half the wrong way, like an apple, no other preparation; try tackling that in bed. Another failure has been in the promotion of open kitchens. After a few brief sorties in the 1960s, most cooks have retreated or been banished again to the back and underground regions of their establishments, fearful of the public gaze. Only the raw fish and barbecue presenters, recalling the East and the Mediterranean, remain on show – and, praise be, our partner Joyce Molyneux at Dartmouth's Carved Angel, where we re-created our Hole in the Wall-style kitchen – and at last I can begin to remember those very exciting years in Bath.

My other piece of luck, besides Eric Green and my aunt, was 1951 in Paris by courtesy of the Ministry of Education. The Lycée St Louis on the Boulevard St Michel was undemanding, my own studying intermittent. Although I had no money to speak of, I did have a car, a rare asset at that time, which took me round and about France as well as Paris itself, then fizzing with Brigitte Bardot, Claudel, Anouilh, Sartre, Cocteau, the climbing of Annapurna, and Brigitte Bardot; also, I began to realise, Paris offered extremely pleasant places where one could sit down unhurried, unfussed, with a glass of wine, un sandwich jambon, on rare occasions a real meal, prix fixe, a cup of coffee and a wide variety of strangely coloured drinks in small glasses, never seen or heard of in Brecon or even Cheshire or, so far as I knew, Bath. For it was to Bath and Bristol I returned, and when, scared by the prospect of the Masters' Common Room, I wondered what else I could possibly do, it struck me that no such pleasant relaxation seemed to be available there. How could life go on without it? No wonder most people seemed unhappy, or at any rate unsmiling. An alert estate agent told me about the lease of The Hole in the Wall, then badly run down, and there we suddenly were, for the next twenty-one years.

We closed it for three months, put up an art student's posters about men working (some art student – he became the finest picture restorer in England, later the buyer of great paintings for the Paul Getty and Norton Simon Museums; we were increasingly proud to have him writing our menus right through to the early years at Helford). That the food should be the best I took for granted, and that the house should be as open, welcoming, unexpected and attractive as I should like my own home to be. It was indeed my own home, and we always felt it in that way long after we moved out to make way for more customers and different enterprises. But I was incredibly naive about the food, and needed to be saved from early disaster; our washer-up, the only experienced member of staff recruited, told me long afterwards that she gave me six months. My saviour was an ex-navy, ex-Mountie, ex-everything man who, quite late in life, remained madly enthusiastic about food, knew that Wheelbarrow butter was the best, along with Scotch beef and Blue Mountain Jamaica coffee, that you ate the parson's nose and the oysters and threw away the chicken, that you were allowed to enjoy onion soup, tripe and treacle pudding just as much as consommé, Dover sole and oeufs à la neige; and he had a slightly less hazy idea than mine that income should exceed expenditure.

Christopher Hammond-Spencer was his name, and he and his wife Kit have a very special place in my memory and in The Hole's subsequent success. They steered me through the first six months, when the strain became too great for them and they had to give in. I took over the cooking. Somehow the enthusiasm and the learning kept pace with the customers, Elizabeth David appeared by magic in the bookshops as if to say 'Carry on, you're doing the right thing, but why not try this and that as well?'

We were a motley crew: Christopher and Kit, a French student of English culled from *The Times* Personal Column, an Estonian refugee, our part-time art student, and two washers-up who soon learnt to double as assistant cooks; Dot (the experienced one) later became famous for her beef and vegetable soup; few people knew that she also made the fish soup, absolutely consistently and successfully, satisfied that if it tasted 'orrible it must be right; and atop and behind a boss with a quite unfounded assumption that we were the best. Christopher, to my shame, persuaded me to print my MA on the first menu as some sort of reassurance to the Bath ladies that the wicked old Hole in the Wall was now a safe and respectable place to be.

The menu was embarrassingly large at first – we must have decided to offer everything both Christopher and I thought we could cook, all at the same time and then some. It was soon cut down to a more manageable size, then allowed to develop naturally. We wanted to avoid doing things in large quantities, yet preferred cooking joints on the bone and slow, full-flavoured casseroles to quick fixes. Both of us were accustomed to modest numbers sitting down all at once in a disciplined manner rather than in twos and threes at times of their own choosing, yet we wanted free will and variety both for ourselves and for our guests, and for seasonal and shopping changes. We neither liked crowded tables nor could have cooked for the numbers that most restaurateurs would have packed into our large rooms, so we had a wide open space in front of a splendid log fire, and a refectory table that we dared not fill with diners. All these circumstances combined to develop an eclectic, constantly experimenting menu that soon demanded a cold table as well as the growing number of hot dishes, by now labelled 'usually' and 'sometimes' on a large Formica board which changed with the seasons. The visual surprise and pleasure which the buffet gave to the guests sold it easily, and took the increasing pressure off the kitchen; cold food proved even more exciting to cook than hot; and so the game progressed, in a combination of schoolmasterly planning and joyous risk-taking. Raymond Postgate discovered us on one of his very early forays, but it was probably just as well that we were already too busy to notice, or realise quite what an accolade this was.

The refectory table and its glowing colours became a signal and a souvenir of happy occasions. That half the food was being served away from the kitchen was worrying for a patron-chef, so we decided to put the kitchen in the middle, open to all, where the cooks could exercise more control and direct communication, and this obliged us to make the kitchen as attractive, and functional, as the restaurant. With Larkhall builders Sims and Slocombe (more Methodists), we blundered and skated through the hallowed halls of interior decoration, guarded by the same saving grace that seemed to watch over the food. The pinnacle of our career through this china shop must have been the creation in the mid-1960s of the Bath Festival restaurant across the lovely first-floor rooms of our (by now) two Georgian houses. It survived fresh and pleasing and working well, if not quite 'timeless', until this year, when I think it is being converted into bedrooms. There was always something new to risk. There must have been disasters too, now conveniently forgotten.

To my surprise, Joyce Molyneux tells me that it was 1960 before she applied for a job. How did we ever manage without her? And she adds that even then she was a waitress for six months before she was allowed into the kitchen. I think Michael Waterfield must have appeared at much the same time, before whisking away our best girl to become The Wife of Bath near Canterbury; a team to remember; and a little before that came Heather Crosbie, kindly washing up for a sick friend and never intending to stay. Elizabeth David, almost the only writer I consulted until Jane Grigson appeared on the scene, came at last to lunch; a great day; kind, but almost too tired to eat, I rather think she had a very little cold duck, and appreciated the home-grown sorrel in the salad.

None of this was a unique achievement, just a natural development paralleled by others, the best remembered being Francis Coulson and Brian Sack at Sharrow Bay, Patrick Gibbings at Monkey Island, Yattendon and Hampstead Marshall, and Kenneth Bell, first at The Elizabeth at Oxford, then in his wide-ranging activities at Thornbury Castle. Perhaps Bath was exceptional; free from London's pressures and problems, we were visited, in its resurgence as a tourist city, by the rich, the famous and the impossible, balanced by a cross-section of eager local eaters and drinkers, supported by no less a wine merchant than Ronald Avery, 'the last great eccentric' of the trade. We had a wonderful time, serving fifty for lunch and a hundred for dinner; they even sat on the stairs; but always as individuals more important than ourselves or our food, a pale foretaste of Richard Shepherd at Langan's. We knew we had arrived when *The Sunday Times* Christmas Quiz, asking what was most associated with the following cities, answered for Bath The Hole in the Wall. But we were becoming too expensive, exclusive and revered, and when I heard someone seriously inviting his guest to kiss the threshold before entering, we moved on, with the first decimalised menu on the kitchen wall and a chipped but treasured Bath Festival vase inscribed to Heather and George with Sidney Smith's opinions about foie gras and the sound of trumpets.

I wish we could have solved this last contradiction – the expense and exclusivity now too often associated with such an ordinary, natural pleasure as eating and drinking. My stepson Tom tried but gallantly failed with a sideshow at Dartmouth. Joyce, Heather and I have accepted the new expectations and joined the club in order to pay the bills, but I hope we have stuck to our own standards and ways of doing things, despite our lack of the high professional training reinstated by friends and successors at top levels, higher than I could attempt. Joyce can, still does.

So, was there anything exceptional about the 1950s and 1960s? The 1950s: yes, perhaps there was, an upsurge of confidence, boldness, foolhardiness, folly born of war-time success in unlikely fields for which few of us had ever qualified. We were lucky to be there. Dorothy Reynolds and Julian Slade, with other great names from the singing, golden days of the early Bristol Old Vic, sometimes escaped to us for lunch. I am sure they must have enjoyed themselves as much as we did, in the pumping rhythms of *Victoria* and the fleeting tenderness of *Salad Days*:

> And if I start looking behind me,
> Or begin retracing my track,
> I'll remind you to remind me
> We said we wouldn't look back.

Perhaps, after all, my father and my headmaster can get together and sound forth from the other side with George Herbert's jerky little poem,

set to *Sandys* – come along now, page 514, hymn number 597, verse 4:
please:

> A servant with this clause
> Makes drudgery divine;
> Who sweeps a room as for Thy laws
> Makes that and the action fine.

Did I take the biscuits out of the oven?

Soho

Soho is once again the undisputed gastronomic centre of London. Berwick Street market is the focal-point for high quality specialist food shops. Chinatown is an extraordinary, condensed microcosm of all things edible. And to eat out – be it for a plate of pasta in the Cafe Pollo on Old Compton Street or for jellied carp at the Gay Hussar in Greek Street or for the dynamic cooking of Alastair Little – nowhere rivals the value or the range or the quality. Don Philpot charts the culinary history of this tiny area which has kept its character against all odds and explains how finally food has replaced sex as Soho's main pleasure.

Soho is a village trapped in the heart of London. Its name has become synonymous with sleazy sex shops, strip clubs and topless bars. But all this is changing. In the last five years the clean up of Soho has gathered momentum.

Almost 350 years ago, in one of the first references to Soho, Anna Clerke, 'a lewd woman', was bound over to keep the peace after 'threteninge to burne the houses at Soho'. That was in October 1641. The houses were on land that is now the east side of Wardour Street. They were surrounded by open country used by Elizabethan mayors and aldermen for hunting foxes, hares and deer. The name 'Soho' is thought to derive from the cry used by huntsmen.

Elizabeth I had decreed that there should be no building within three miles of city gates, but by the 1670s the Crown was selling off land for housing to boost its coffers. An early developer was Dr Nicholas Bar-

These new houses, on the unfashionable side of London, became the home of refugees who had been forced out of Europe because of religious and political persecution. By 1700 two-fifths of the population of the parish of St Anne, Soho, were French. They had their own restaurants, which attracted customers from other parts of London. It was the French who, as a result of their penury, introduced ox-tail soup to England. The tradition of Soho as a fashionable eating-out area had begun.

The first known reference to Soho as a resort of gourmets occurs in 1816, when the Sablonière Hotel on the east side of Leicester Square was commended as 'a house where a table d'hôte affords the lovers of French cookery and French conversation an opportunity for gratification at a comparatively modest charge'.

Germans and Italians, many of them cooks and waiters, arrived in the 1860s and 1870s. A Swiss population grew up in the area around Cambridge Circus, where there was a pub called The Thirteen Cantons.

Although restaurants of many nationalities thrived, they were treated with suspicion. A guidebook published in 1869 warned diners to avoid Leicester Square when choosing a hotel or dining-room. In the same year, however, a reader wrote to *The Times* to say he had enjoyed a dinner 'in this forbidden area' which had been 'much better and much cheaper' than he could have got at his club. It was the turn of the century before Soho established its credentials as a gastronomic centre.

French restaurants dominated until the end of the First World War, when the cuisines of the Italians, Chinese and Indians, and of a score of other countries, could be found. Soho blossomed at this time, and by 1939 the population topped 7500. Soho was London's Left Bank. People could listen to jazz until the early hours.

In the 1950s a five-course meal cost two shillings with coffee sixpence extra. A good bottle of Barsac could be bought for half-a-crown. The finest Havana cigar cost just a shilling. Greek Street was known at this time as the Street of a Thousand Omelettes. At number 35, Au Petit Savoyard had merged with the Restaurant d'Italie, founded in 1854. Like most of the restaurants, it was a family-run establishment, with Madame Martelli at the helm.

In neighbouring Frith Street, Isola Bella's specialities were legendary: risotto alla certosina, rice cooked in broth with fresh tomatoes, new peas and several tails of crayfish or lobster, and omelette grazialla, eggs blended with ham, mushrooms and truffles, with a layer of fresh tomato cream sauce and Parmesan cheese. A bottle of Clos de Vougeot '29 was on the list at thirty-five shillings.

Dinner at Beguinot's, which opened in Old Compton Street at the turn of the century, cost three shillings and sixpence. Down the road, the finest Greek food in London could be had at Goya's. Wheeler's Oyster Bar in Old Compton Street, founded in 1856, was frequented by film

stars and Cabinet ministers. A South African walked in one day and polished off fifteen dozen oysters at one sitting.

The best Yugoslav restaurant was Josef, at 2 Greek Street. Eisenhower
and the Queen of Siam dined there. Epstein, Somerset Maugham,
Augustus John and Paul Robeson were frequent diners at Au Jardins
des Gourmets. Kettners, in Romilly Street, had once resounded to dinner
parties attended by Edward VII, Lillie Langtry and Oscar Wilde and had
been famed 'for its bohemianism and discretion'. By the early 1950s it
had seating for 140 and served 200 lunches and 300 dinners daily.

In the 1950s Chinese restaurants flourished, hampered only by the
shortage of rice and bamboo shoots. The most popular were Choy's in
Dean Stret, Ley On's in Wardour Street and the Shanghai in Greek
Street. Ley On's, which is still going strong, was named after its owner,
who was also a film actor, and the restaurant was often full of stars.
Soho clubs abounded in the 1950s, too, and varied from the select to
the sleazy. One commentator wrote of the latter: 'It is usually a one-
room affair with a radiogram and a telephone. Membership is normally
10s, but this formality is often waived, whisky and gin is 2s a nip, and
sandwiches, even staler than the railway buffet breed, are a florin each.
The fruit machine is available for those eager to make the proprietor's
old age secure, and there is a liberal supply of bleached blondes, who
usually know a house not far away where you can learn more about a
particular lady.'

A liquor licence was not needed for establishments selling beer with
an alcoholic content of less than two per cent, and this is why such
places thrived. There were also bottle party clubs, where people could
drink and dance all night, and gambling dens known as 'spielers'. The
Gargoyle in Dean Street was the most respectable of clubs, with vintage
champagne at thirteen shillings and sixpence a bottle.

Murray's in Beak Street was the oldest dance club in London, with
3000 members. It had two dance bands, a 300-seat restaurant and the
largest American bar in the capital. Theatrical clubs included The
Interval, founded in 1926, and the Theatre Girls' Club, established in
1915 to help resting actresses – a very respectable establishment and
not the haunt of the bleached blondes to be found elsewhere.

Even in the late 1960s the sex in Soho was 'discreet' and behind
closed doors. Bryan Burrough, chairman of the 1200-member Soho
Society, says: 'It was in the early 1970s that sex proliferated. The threat
of large-scale development forced many businesses to leave. No one
knew what was going to happen. Only short-term leases were available.
These were ideal for people wanting to open sex shops or strip clubs,
where they could make a lot of money quickly. Restaurants and other
businesses, however, could not take the risk of investing heavily in a
venture with the threat that the building might be pulled down within a
few months.'

He also cites police corruption as another reason why the sex problem spread so fast. A number of senior police officers were taking bribes to turn a blind eye to what was going on. The trials that followed their arrests in the mid-1970s showed that some were even involved in vice rackets.

By 1975 there were almost four hundred premises of one kind or another used for sexual titillation, apart from those used by individual prostitutes. Big businesses had moved out, including many restaurants. There were six strip clubs, eight posing clubs, forty sex supermarkets, fifty 'escort' agencies, saunas and massage parlours, a hundred cinema clubs and a hundred gambling shops. By 1978 there were twenty-eight strip clubs. Food was eclipsed.

During this period gang warfare erupted on a number of occasions. Thirty-seven people died when fire swept through a Soho drinking club in 1980. The following year seven died in a petrol bomb attack on a gambling club in Gerrard Street – the result of a feud between rival Chinese gangs. The police denied reports that the notorious Triads, the Chinese Mafia, were involved in Soho, but Maltese and Italian gangs operated many of the clubs.

Soho's 3000 or so residents asked Westminster City Council to act. Little could be done without government intervention, and the Home Office turned a deaf ear until 1981, when legislation was finally passed to allow a clean-up in Soho. Even this was not enough, and further legislation had to be pushed through in 1983.

Premises that were sex shops are now being converted back. The Alpha One fish and chip shop in Old Compton Street used to be a hostess bar. Kettners in Romilly Street and Pizza Express in Dean Street, both run by Peter Boizot, have brought live jazz back to Soho.

Some restaurants survived all the changes. Kettners opened in 1868, three years after the Cafe Royal in Regent Street, which is considered Soho's oldest dining-room. The idea for L'Escargot had been born in 1894, when Georges Gaudin visited London from his native Bourges. He was so surprised to discover that the English had not been introduced to the delights of frogs' legs and snails that he felt obliged to open a restaurant to educate them. When he first opened, snails were 10p a dozen, and 120,000 a season were imported from Bourges.

That education continues today, but now it is the Chinese supermarkets who educate by selling dried sea-horses and snakeskin.

In the early 1950s there were four hundred restaurants and cafes in the district. Many closed during the 1960s and 1970s, but new ones have taken their place. Today, the five hundred or so places to eat out in Soho have made the area, once again, the gastronomic heart of London.

The roast beef of Old England

Historian and novelist Reay Tannahill *examines the reputation of Britain's national dish*

In 1748 a Swedish traveller, Pehr Kalm, reported that 'Englishmen understand almost better than any other people the art of properly roasting a joint' – and then ruined the effect by adding that it was not to be wondered at, 'because the art of cooking as practised by most Englishmen does not extend much beyond roast beef'.

The English were perfectly accustomed to such criticism from foreigners. Indeed, since this was the eighteenth century and the heyday of roast beef, they were much inclined to discount it, putting it all down to envy. 'Oh! The roast beef of England, And old England's roast beef', warbled Henry Fielding in the *Grub Street Opera*, while James Boswell, in expansive mood, noted in his diary that he was eating 'like a very John Bull, whose supreme joy is good beef'. After five thousand years of beef-eating, it seemed as if a rib roast rampant might well have figured in the quarterings of the royal coat of arms.

But the sad truth was that, although roast beef had been as important in 1748 BC as it was in AD 1748, English beef in the centuries between had very rarely been fit to roast.

In the early days, of course, it was a case of Hobson's choice when it came to cooking techniques. Since pottery and bronze arrived late on Europe's offshore islands, cooking was still generally restricted to spit-roasting. Joints of meat impaled on a spear or a long greenwood stake were propped up over the flames; the hide may have been left on by way of protection for the first hour or so, then stripped off to allow the fat to brown.

The 'how' of cooking was one thing; the 'what' another. There was a fair variety of meat animals that could be trapped, hunted or reared, but by the fourth millennium BC the British had already established their preference. Excavations at habitation sites have turned up a huge preponderance of beef bones.

Time passed. The neolithic revolution came (and went), and so did the Roman legions. With Roman encouragement, the English began to take a more careful and better-informed look at animal husbandry, but the roast beef of Old Britanniae must still have left much to be desired. What improved feeding and management had done was produce a beef animal about the size of a large Shetland pony, with a moderate amount of meat on it, a thick hide, and an athletic disposition.

The athleticism was an important factor. What we call 'meat' is of course muscle, and each muscle consists of a bundle of fibres encased in connective tissue. When a muscle is worked consistently hard, the connective tissue (which takes the strain) eventually toughens into a rubbery sinew that squeezes, pulls, pushes and twists the fibres inside it until they lose all their resilience. Even with the highly bred beef animal of modern times – whose unexercised back provides the finest and tenderest cuts – the muscles around the neck and the outside of the thigh remain obstinately stringy. The post-Roman beef animal was probably like that all over.

In some ways this mattered less than it might have done. During the impoverished centuries after the fall of Rome, there were few people in the Western world who could afford to eat beef at all, since cattle were too valuable to slaughter. In the hilly (mainly Celtic) areas meat remained a staple food, but over most of England grain and dairy products were of greater importance. The average countryman was more likely to graze a couple of sheep than a cow, since the sheep cropped the stubble more closely and supplied not only the usual 'white meats' or dairy products – milk, butter, cheese, whey, curds and cream – but wool for clothing as well. The Domesday Book shows fourteen times as many sheep as cattle in the South-West of England.

Until 1066 the English nobility were not much more than peasants with pretensions, but things changed after the arrival of the Normans. Now, there was a great and growing divergence between the nobleman and the serf whose task it was to care for the flocks and herds – which sometimes included cattle brought in, on the hoof, from considerable distances. The English language today still marks the class divisions of the post-Conquest period, the distinction between those whose care was for the living animal and those who were more interested in the dead. Ox, sheep and swine are all Old English words; beef, mutton and pork are Norman.

In the medieval countryside (the towns were marginally better off), beef for the common people was an annual luxury, and more likely to be stewed than roasted. The difficult trick at this time was to keep animals alive during the winter on the traditional diet of beans, dried stems, chaff and straw, and it was therefore usual at the end of the year to slaughter not only the carefully fattened household pig, destined to supply the basic salt-pork and bacon of winter and spring, but any other beast whose stamina was in doubt.

Although most of the extra meat also went into the brine tub, some of it was eaten fresh, especially the beef, which was most likely to come from an elderly cow or worn-out ox and may scarcely have been worth the salting. Salt was far from cheap. But perhaps the thirteenth-century agriculturalist Walter of Henley was right when he claimed that even an old plough animal could be made fit for the larder – he did not say for roasting – if it were allowed to fatten on grass for a week or two before slaughter. (Cunning town butchers knew a quicker and cheaper way;

they simply stripped a layer of fat from a good stout carcass and sewed it on to a lean one.)

Not until the sixteenth century were these problems overcome. Then, however, it was discovered that turnips made excellent fodder on which animals could not only be kept alive from November to May, but even fattened up. It was the end of autumn slaughter for livestock, the end of salt-meat winters for people.

It was also the beginning of cattle farming in the modern sense, its aim the production of beef not from working animals but from animals specially reared to give meat and milk. These, leading a more leisured life than their predecessors and able to put on both fat and flesh, provided meat that was tenderer and of finer flavour than ever before. Modern research with pigs shows that leanness of body has a direct metabolic connection with flabby and tasteless meat, and it seems likely that the same may be true of cattle. But whether for this reason or another, English beef consumption soared.

By 1584 Thomas Cogan, doctor and schoolmaster, felt justified in claiming that beef was one of the best and healthiest foods of all. It was also 'most usual among Englishmen'. He further suggested that the great medical authorities of the past – Galen, and the School of Salerno among them – might have fallen into the error of blaming beef for 'melancholy humours' because they had never had the good fortune to eat 'of the Biefe of England . . .'.

Thirty years later Fynes Morison (or F.Morison Gent., as he appeared on his title-page) said that English tables were so well furnished with roast meats that 'other Nationes esteeme us gluttons and devourers of flesh', an opinion that was to persist for centuries. By Morison's time the French had already begun to call their old enemies across the Channel 'the beef-eaters', a sneer that was rather more loaded than it seems at first sight.

What it actually meant was 'over-fed menials'. For centuries the name of 'beef-eater' had been applied to the better class of servitor in noble households, those who were sufficiently valued to be entitled to beef in their diet – hence the popular name for the Yeomen of the Guard and the Warders of the Tower of London. Those who were not beef-eaters were mere 'loaf-eaters'. (Even so, the fundamental importance of bread is demonstrated by the fact that the title 'lord' derives from 'loaf-keeper', and 'lady' from 'kneader of dough'.)

Perhaps because the new English bourgeoisie were caught on the raw by the menial implications of their French nickname, they responded by inventing John Bull, who seems to have made his first appearance on the national scene in the 1600s, although not in print until 1712.

Despite the general improvement in beef quality, however, seven-teenth-century English roasts continued to be served with pungent sauces, which told its own tale, and indeed there was still one very important development to come, the most important of all and the one that would in the end convert the English from '*les mangeurs de boeuf*' to '*les rosbifs*'. . .

Until the early part of the eighteenth century, all beef came from dual-purpose breeds; the cows supplied milk, and the bulls and oxen meat. The agricultural improvers of Georgian times, however, when they turned their powerful minds to the question of scientific breeding, made an interesting discovery. By breeding selectively, it was possible to produce two entirely different types of cattle, dairy and beef. The dairy cow converted relatively little of her food into body weight and most of it into milk – far more than was needed to sustain her calf – while the beef cow produced only enough milk to rear her calf and turned the rest of her food into the building up of a strong skeleton able to carry large muscles and a good proportion of fat (a body type that was, of course, passed on to her offspring). Larger may not always be finer, but in the case of beef it was. The measure of the improvers' achievement was that, whereas the average weight of the beef animal sold at Smithfield in 1710 had been 370 pounds, by 1795 it was 800 pounds.

The roast beef of the latter part of the eighteenth century was probably the finest beef the world had ever tasted, and it was to become finer yet. By the mid-nineteenth century Britain's specialised beef breeds included Shorthorns, Herefords, Aberdeen Angus, Galloways, Sussex and North Devons, and pedigree animals were being sold all over the world to help upgrade local breeding stock.

The long, sad story of developments since then has no place in a *good* food guide, but they culminated in the years of rationing between 1939 and 1953 which left most housewives and many butchers ignorant of what good meat was, unable to tell beef from cow-meat, incapable of distinguishing the well hung and tender from the scarcely hung at all. And those years were followed by the campaign against saturated fats which has taken us straight back to the bad old days when tough and tasteless lean meat was all that was to be had. Many beef farmers have switched back to dual-purpose breeds, and 'fatstock prices' is a phrase that seems to have disappeared from the language. It is a sorry waste of all those centuries of endeavour.

Even so, it is still possible to eat something very like the roast beef of Old England as it must have been at its peak. Not, alas, in the majority of restaurants; and not on the basis of an ordinary joint of English beef. First you must reconcile yourself to the fact that good beef and lean beef are a contradiction in terms. Then you must check with your bank manager. Then find a butcher who buys Aberdeen Angus and hangs it for three weeks . . .

Ice-cream

Carol Duncan *spent three months on a Nuffield Farming Scholarship travelling across Europe and America studying the milk industry. She argues that restrictive practices have destroyed the quality ice-cream market in the UK*

We are masochists to put up with the lousy ice-cream sold in this country.

No, that's not quite right. We do not care what ice-cream our children eat as long as it is cheap, and they are the consumers. Most of the ice-cream in the UK is bought by mothers and consumed by children. It is the under-15s who are the consumers of the non-milk fats, whipped with air, loaded with stabiliser, artificially flavoured, coloured and packed in garishly patterned boxes. Mothers buy it for the simple reason, according to Lyons, that it is fractionally cheaper than real dairy ice-cream and there is therefore more to go round.

There are two forms of ice-cream: ice-cream and dairy ice-cream. The one is a chemical by-product and the other is the original article based on cream, butter and milk.

Nearly all the ice-cream we eat in this country today comes from Walls and Lyons. Between them, Lyons assess they have in excess of 60 per cent of the national market. Walls attribute a quarter of the market to very small regional operators.

Dairy ice-cream accounts for less than five per cent of Lyons' output, and is negligible in the total output of Walls. The only section of the market in which dairy ice-cream features is in the take-home, where it has risen lately to 13 per cent of the total take-home market.

Ice-cream as such need contain no cream at all. It is made from sugar, air, fat, flavours and colours. The fat is unlikely to be butter and can be from any source in the world. Palm-oil is common.

The manufacturing process, though, is not essentially different from that for dairy ice-cream. The ingredients – butter, milk (or powder) and cream are mixed with sugar, then pasteurised and then frozen. Three months is a widely accepted quality limit for storage.

Good ice-cream should taste fresh. It should not have been stuck in a freezer for months with its wrapper rotting. It should be smooth and, I think, have a hint of saltiness. I don't like it too sweet. When flavoured, it should be with real fruit or real chocolate rather than with artificial flavourings. It should look attractive and appetising.

The Russians and the Americans have something in common. They both make good ice-cream. Is such a fact a basis for peace? In Moscow queues stretch for hundreds of yards on a cold, bleak November day up to a solitary lady dispensing ice-cream to well-wrapped comrades. At the International Hotel a glass case is filled with models of ice-cream desserts - delicate lavender, chocolate, some almost *avant-garde* in shape and texture.

Ten thousand miles away in Los Angeles at a Haagen Daz ice-cream parlour, thirty-six different flavoured ice-creams are on display in tubs. Choose three flavours and they are dispensed into a huge wide sugar cone. The taste is amazing.

Staff at an ice-cream factory that supplies only the catering trade, situated outside Los Angeles, explain the philosophy behind American ice-cream – it is for adults, and adults are discerning. Hence they use cream and butter and make what we in this country would call dairy ice-cream. It is the same in other countries.

In Germany many hotels and restaurants have beautifully printed ice-cream menus offering half a dozen elaborate ice-cream puddings, for example a mixture of chocolate and vanilla ice-cream topped with coconut and chocolate sauce. Each hotel makes its own slightly different-ly.

In Sweden Glace-Bolaget AB – known as GB – has a booth in the main square at Malmö. The maple and walnut is scrumptious. Melin Glass in a complex with vegetarian and wholefood shops makes ice-cream on the premises – a little heavier, using less air and sugar, but still getting a delicate flavour.

In Copenhagen wide sugar cones are filled with ice-cream, fresh whipped cream and strawberry jam.

At Tonies factory in Zurich, a dozen girls work around a table packing ice-cream-layered sponge using a vacuum cleaner-style squirter. Again, this is what we would have to call dairy ice-cream.

Santa Barbara: after three weeks in Los Angeles I feel I am an ice-cream expert. I walk in confidently. 'French vanilla, please, with fresh strawberries and a heath bar.' The assistant puts all into a blender and spoons the resulting mix into a large plastic bowl.

There are good reasons why such ice-creams are rarely found in Britain. As long ago as 1972 *Which?* reported that most countries insist on a higher proportion of milk fat and milk solids than we do in Britain. In America the basic minimum was twice as much. 'The compositional standards now seem rather low. At the time they were originally introduced, milk was scarce,' the report stated. The legislation has not changed since.

The best ice-creams in the UK, to my mind, are the American-style Dayvilles. I am exceedingly fond of Loseley's acacia honey and stem ginger. It is not too sweet and the bite of ginger in the cold smoothness is delightful. Salcombe Dairies apricot ice-cream is another favourite. They make it with stewed dried apricots. Quicke's raspberry yoghurt ice-cream is a winner. Leworthy Mill's Jersey vanilla is unbelievably rich. If you happen to be passing Bideford quay I can recommend the vanilla from Hocking's ice-cream van. Mr Hocking makes his ice-cream from milk powder and butter – hence the salty flavour.

All these ice-creams are difficult to track down. Most shops and supermarkets do not sell dairy ice-cream at all. Instead, there are heavily marketed ice-creams like Walls' Magnifico or Vienetta, slivers of chocolate between layers of slimy white tasteless ice-cream. Yet they sell.

However, ice-cream has become topical again. Ice-cream falls outside milk quotas, and Ministry of Agriculture experts are advising farmers to use up surplus milk by producing dairy ice-cream. This must be a good idea – all the ingredients are to hand. What an irony that the ice-cream industry has been so usurped by chemists' inventions that it cannot manufacture dairy ice-cream, the product it started and which is recognised, in nearly every other country but here, as superior.

But small producers of dairy ice-cream have traditionally found their distribution lines blocked.

The main two manufacturers – Walls and Lyons – effectively control the market by renting out freezers to small shops such as newsagents. Eighty-six per cent of newsagents, confectioners and tobacconists sell ice-cream. The rental agreement stipulates that the cold-cabinets are not to carry rival brands. Lyons say they have around 22,000 freezers out in rental, Walls 25,000. This is substantially fewer than the 70,000 Walls had in 1979 when the Monopolies and Mergers Commission hoped it would change this style of marketing. Nevertheless, there are only 34,000 newsagents, tobacconists and confectioners in the UK, which suggests that most cold-cabinets belong either to Walls or Lyons.

The big two therefore seem to have effectively closed down the market for dairy ice-cream.

In 1984 they threatened to stop buying milk from the Milk Marketing Board if an advertising campaign for Real Dairy Ice-Cream went ahead. The MMB backed down, and the campaign for Real Dairy Ice-Cream never got off the ground.

It may now take a foreign company to break the alliance of mediocrity that Lyons and Walls have created.

Wines

The battle for burgundy

*The international reputation of white burgundy is
matched by its soaring price. Now, across the world
winemakers are producing wines also from the
Chardonnay grape. Some sell them for a fraction of the
price of vintage Meursault or Chablis.* Alan Young,
author of Chardonnay: a definitive study *(1988),
reports*

'A weed and a flower are the same – the difference is a judgement.'
Dr Wayne Nash

The New World approach to winemaking is quantitative – trying to
assign numbers to every facet of winemaking, from the maturity of
grapes to exact bottling temperatures. This is atypical of the many
traditional Burgundian methods, by which things tend to be done by
rote, whether they are good, bad or indifferent.

The opposing philosophies are apparent in practice. The French make
a *style* of wine, whether it be white burgundy, Chablis, Mâcon or
whatever, while the New World producer is making Chardonnay with
varietal influence uppermost.

Raw materials make a difference too. New World winemakers start
with good to perfect fruit due to favourable growing conditions from
vineyards in carefully selected areas. The Burgundian doesn't enjoy
these same benefits, but rather has a spectrum of poor, normal and
exceptional vintages. Most observers will tell you that the exceptional
vintages are outnumbered two or three to one.

Of course, there are other factors, but it is the weather, above all, that
dictates what flavour is all about. The soil can change the structure and
flavour of wine, but not its inherent quality. If grapes are not at optimal
ripeness, where is the flavour? You might have green apples, maybe the
sour end of the citrus flavour range, but not Chardonnay flavour in all
its seductive glory. The winemaker can smother what's there with
expensive oak – but, please hand me the fruit flavour of ripe Chardonnay, the one commodity so often lacking.

Yeast is an important part of the juvenile flavour of wine, white wine
in particular. Almost without exception the New World winemaker
uses a cultured yeast that will provide a known performance during fer-
mentation, and certain flavour benefits. Some yeast strains can be the
source of 'off' or undesirable flavours.

The almost universal European practice uses the natural yeast on the bloom of the grape which can account for very distinctive flavours, unlike anything from cultures. This practice is beginning to change, one of the first cracks in the armour of traditional methodology.

Some of the negociants/producers who are supplying the bottom to cheap end of the market with Chardonnay – as opposed to white burgundy – are taking short cuts or using New World bulk-processing techniques in an attempt to get a reliable bottle of wine on retailers' shelves at an affordable price.

What I've seen of these wines reveal that they are made from pretty ordinary grapes, vinified without oak treatment and, in this writer's opinion, are bland, flavourless, or at their best reminiscent of vegetable consommé and of little interest at any price. Notable among these are the £5–£6 offerings. It does seem worthwhile going the extra £1 or so to get something reasonable from J. Drouhin or Antonin Rodet, especially the Mercurey Château de Chamirey which repeatedly impressed in three blind tastings and during a recent visit to the winery.

Tradition and technology are nothing more than the application of philosophies. Put another way, we can see only what we *know* or what we *believe*. And here in Burgundy (where this was written) philosophies and tradition are rooted deeper than the vines that have made the region famous.

In many countries it is a sport to knock over the tall poppies and, certainly, Burgundy and its wines are tall poppies. They've had a hammering recently from all sorts of experts.

Such lofty fame as that of Burgundy must be able to deliver – and not only in the 'good' years. A flit through the region tasting a couple of hundred wines made from Chardonnay (and a lot of Pinot Noir) has left me wondering, once again, what the ballyhoo is all about. I can understand the parochialism – it's the same all over the world – but as a wine consultant I'm used to visiting wineries in the New World where people are interested in what other winemakers around the world are doing with Chardonnay, or any other aspect of winemaking. With the rarest of exceptions in the technical institutions, the average Burgundian wine industry person, not even very politely, dismisses New World efforts with Chardonnay, and even more so with Pinot Noir.

This is sad, as the general standard of Burgundian winemaking is reflected in a lot of ordinary wine, little of which can be blamed on the climate, the normal retreat. Failings in this area are covered by eloquence and clichés that have been practised for centuries. Being a pretty ordinary Chardonnay-maker myself, I speak from experience.

Nowhere was this accusation more amply demonstrated than in the April 1987 edition of *Wine* magazine, where London panels of 15 professionals and 11 consumers judged white burgundies available in the UK market priced £5–£8. And here lies their damnation:

You can buy white burgundy in Britain for less than a fiver, but since the apologists for this region always stress that you have to be ready to pay a little extra for quality, we decided to taste wines at between £5 and £8. To keep the tasting to a manageable size, we excluded Chablis, tasting Côte d'Or, Chalonnais and Mâconnais wines.

CONCLUSIONS We were astonished at the prices being asked for wines that were often from the most humble of Burgundy appellations. And price bore little relationship to quality.

Fortunately, there is a band of young Turks in the Meursault region, led by the brothers Lafon of Domaine des Comtes Lafon, most with oenological training, who *understand* the technicalities of winemaking rather than the eloquence of tradition. These producers are making truly great white burgundy, at a price, but show what skilled hands can do in almost any vintage.

If the widespread dissatisfaction with white burgundy prices and quality is getting through to consumers, little wonder that they are turning to the delights of the New World, at affordable prices and reliable quality – in fact, quality that is becoming more reliable and more affordable as the years roll on.

And, from a food-matching viewpoint, I think the New World Chardonnays, whether they are from A, B, or C – Australasia, Bulgaria or California – offer far more variety of flavours than the £5–£8 white burgundies. It's little problem to purchase a very good New World Chardonnay at under £8. (Give me £8 and I'll bring you a good Chardonnay and £2 change!)

As Chardonnay flavours can range from green apples through grapefruit, lime, citrus, pears, melon, flowers, becoming vegetal in Chablis, and through pineapple to the rich warm fruits such as peach, nectarine and apricot, then to the full-bodied buttery character, it's extremely important we know the nature of the beast before we try to match any food with our favourite tipple.

A California wine may knock you over with smoky wood/oak/vanilla flavours, while a top Meursault is likely to have a subtle lime flavour. Despite their Chardonnay background, there is no way that this pair could accompany the same food.

If anything is going to match spicy whole prawns with a strong whack of garlic, a little paprika, pepper, ginger and cumin, it would need to be big and oaky. The same wine would destroy the delicate flavour of shellfish *au naturel*. Mark Hellbach, Swiss-born and -trained executive chef of the Shangri-La Hotel in Hong Kong uses Chardonnay and Chablis in the sauces served in the Margaux restaurant (not the 1867–1902 Ch. Margaux on their list). Rolled fillets of sole with salmon mousse, red pimento and Chardonnay sauce are natural for the less oaky style. Sauté scallops with orange segments and green peppercorn is a ragout containing Noilly Pratt in the white wine sauce, and matches Chablis. Fillet of turbot with shrimp served on a ginger and sea-urchin sauce including Chablis matches a good Meursault. Star attraction was the Boston lobster sauté with lemon and butter sauce to go with a Robert Mondavi Chardonnay. Grilled prawns with tarragon-flavoured tomato coulis are recommended to match an Australian Chardonnay!

The above dishes give some idea of the spectrum of flavours and ingredients which can be used when preparing seafood to be served with white burgundy/Chablis/Chardonnay: call it what you like.

Chardonnay tasting

by James Ainsworth

Seventy wines were tasted blind by a panel of eight judges – myself, Adam Bancroft MW, Oz Clarke, Robert Joseph, Geoffrey Roberts, Stephen Spurrier, David Wolfe MW and Alan Young – who marked them out of 20. Score of 12–13 divides the average from the good; anything below 9 is considered poor or defective, above 16 is very good to excellent. Wines were arranged roughly according to price, and grouped by country or region within price bands. The aim is not to give a detailed wine-by-wine analysis, but to consider whether white burgundy is all it's cracked up to be, and to see how Chardonnays from Bulgaria, Chile, Italy, Spain, California, Australia and New Zealand fare when put up against them, to discover where the diner should look for quality and value for money.

Despite the high prices that the grape is able to command relative to humbler Sauvignons, Sémillons, Chenins and Trebbianos, it is still possible to buy an acceptable example at a reasonable price. A *vin de pays* from Loire Atlantique, Le Chouan '85 – dry, lemony and crisp – demonstrates this easily enough. Restaurateurs can buy it wholesale for £27.50 a case, add a 100 per cent mark-up if they are so minded, then VAT, and sell it for a fraction over £5. Not all *vins de pays* make the grade, however. Our judges were divided over one from the Haut-Poitou co-operative, and were less than convinced about Latour's Coteaux de l'Ardèche '85. As one of them put it: 'I have never tasted a wine that reminds me quite so strongly of a British Transport hotel's attempt at fresh Melba toast. Too much, too damp, too burnt.'

Bulgarian Chardonnays are traditionally considered to be the best of the cheap buys, but two out of our three examples barely passed muster, and only one of them, Khan Krum '83, did as well as Le Chouan for around the same price. The Chileans were even more disappointing: sweet, sulphury and not worth the candle, whatever the asking price. Two wines from Spain – Raimat '85 and Jean León '84 – failed to draw much applause.

Northern Italy is much more promising. What the wines of Alto Adige (or Sudtirol, as it is for the German-speakers of this mountainous region) may lack in out-and-out Chardonnay character they make up for in consistently decent winemaking. High altitude and high yields produce clean, light wines, with direct, simple appeal. Tiefenbrunner and Lageder are producers to look for.

The problems with Burgundy are well known; several miles long, but often only a few hundred yards wide, and subject to the vagaries of a northern climate, its best Côte d'Or wines are in extremely short supply. Being very famous, they are in demand worldwide from rich people with strong currencies and are, therefore, very expensive. The prices of Mâconnais and Chalonnais to the south (including Montagny, St Véran, Pouilly-Fuissé, Mâcon-Villages and the like) have crept steadily upwards too, while Chablis continues to yoyo. Of four plain white burgundies we tasted (including Thevenin, Jadot and a supermarket's own label) only Drouhin's Bourgogne '85 scraped an average mark, and even then some judges had reservations about oxidation and lack of flavour.

There was a notable lack of unity among the judges concerning the wines of southern Burgundy, most of which were '85s. The same bottle could score anything from below average to very good, but the few positive judgements – elegant, balanced ripe fruit – were outnumbered by unflattering descriptions: dull and cloying, cabbage-water, heavy, unpleasant, oxidised, coarse, peardrops, yeasty. Even the best of this bunch, Latour's Montagny '85, was considered 'not bad, but merely a clean, yeasty white which the maker should not allow to be sold at this price' (nearly £70 per case wholesale); or again 'not anyone's idea of a good Chardonnay at this price'.

The shame is that it is precisely these bottles, marked up to £12 and more in a restaurant, that the average drinker is likely to buy when searching for a decent and dependable white wine. At this price the wines should be good, but they simply do not deliver.

Chablis is a better bet. Just. It will generally cost a few more pounds, but our samples, all '85s from reputable sources – Geoffroy, Moreau, Durup, Fèvre and Dauvissat – were at least more consistent in quality, and the judges were able to rise to such heights of praise as 'all right, barely exciting, adequate, it's OK' and occasionally 'an elegant, fine wine with good depth of ripe fruit'. But all in all there didn't seem much to get worked up about here.

It took the top-flight wines from the Côte d'Or to raise any real enthusiasm for Burgundy. Apart from a bottle of '73 Meursault, plainly over

the hill, here were the intensely fruity and buttery flavours of aristocratic Chardonnay that we all vainly hope will emerge like a genie
when we pull the cork from the best that we can afford: a 'superb' Meursault Poruzots '84 from Jobard; the 'elegance, finesse, complexity and
length' of Drouhin's '84 Puligny-Montrachet, Clos de la Garenne, for
instance.

The only catch is the price, bad enough in a shop, but multiplied out
of all proportion by the time it has gone through some restaurants'
accounting machinery. Jadot's Meursault '84 is 'beautifully balanced,
very good indeed' and would cost over £12 per bottle to the trade.
Chandon de Briaille's '84 Corton 'will be excellent', but then it should at
a trade price of £188 a case. Louis Latour redeemed his reputation with
the highest-scoring wine of the tasting. His Bâtard-Montrachet '82
evoked the nearest the tasters came to rapture: 'deep, ripe, full, gentle,
round, very impressive, superb, classy, fleshy, farmyardy, the real biscuity, nutty, buttery Chardonnay.' But a restaurateur would have to
fork out £310 per case, then add his mark-up and VAT, so we would
have to be talking golden wedding anniversaries at least.

It was with understandable relief that the panel fell upon Australia,
New Zealand and California. 'A bit of oak and a bit of good Southern
Hemisphere fruit does concentrate the mind wonderfully, and it's so
welcome.' 'How did this get in here? It's nice.' 'Ah (*Macbeth*, Act 1,
Scene 1), class at last!' All but four of the twenty-six New World wines
scored at least as well as the Chablis, and many of the prices were considerably lower. Whereas a good bottle of white burgundy around £12–
£15 in a restaurant seems to be the exception, a poor bottle of New
World Chardonnay at that price would be a great surprise.

New Zealand is becoming increasingly established on the British
market as a producer of quality whites; restaurants usually lag behind
wine merchants in their discovery of the latest craze, but any that list
New Zealand Chardonnay (and indeed Sauvignon) clearly know what
they are doing. Cook's Hawke's Bay '86 and Montana's '85 are both
inexpensive and widely available in shops. Babich '86 'may be a little
one-dimensional, but it's a good dimension', 'nice if you like pineapple,
kiwi and persimmon wines'. Matua Valley '85 from Judd Estate scored
just as highly.

Australian Chardonnays have been around long enough to give
every restaurant a chance to list at least a couple. Ones that did well in
this tasting included Seppelt's '86, Seaview '86, Rothbury Estate (Brok-
enback Vineyard) and, distinguished by its consistent score, Houghton
'84; seven out of the eight judges agreed to within half a point about its
undoubtedly good quality. Rosemount crops up on restaurant lists
frequently, although our tasters' comments indicate that the '85 oak-
matured Show Reserve may not be quite the wine it was. Wynn's four-
square Coonawarra '85 smells of 'coconut spice and a real "carpenter's

shop"', with 'a marvellous spread of complex flavours'. Tisdall's Mount St Helen '84 Reserve has enough flavours to complement a whole menu all by itself ('lime marmalade, melon, apple, pear, a tropical conservatory, buttery, peachy, almost meaty') and Tyrrell's '85 Vat 47 is as classic, ripe, impressive and sound as ever.

There was none of the Burgundian hit and miss about California either. Acacia from Carneros, Clos du Bois from Alexander Valley, and Beringer from Napa (all '85) were solidly good, as was Trefethen '83. In the past California has leant heavily on oak, and Mondavi's '84 still has echoes of this – 'a rich, oaky, biscuity, hazel-nutty wine: is the oak too dominant?' – but Monticello's Jefferson Ranch '84 is of the new emerging style – 'lovely, peachy, concentrated, long, delicious'.

Trying to beat the French into submission with New World varietals is a popular sport outside France, and there are all sorts of reasons why it should not be done. Wines mature differently, so a young burgundy may be shy in competition with a Californian of its own age; we may be seduced by the obvious 'up-front fruit' of an Australian and miss the finesse that characterises the best French wines; we may not be comparing like with like, since regulations allow a small percentage of other grapes in most cases, and so on.

What our tasting showed was that there are holes in the French armour. Specifically, 'inexpensive burgundy' does not draw unstinting praise; straight Bourgogne blanc is not very enjoyable, and our tasters were, at best, divided in their opinions about St Véran and the various Mâcons. Chablis '85 was better, while only the finer burgundies from Meursault, Puligny and especially their *premier* and *grand cru* vineyards, were deemed first class. But at a hefty price. Chile and Bulgaria do little to plug the gap at the inexpensive end; either a good *vin de pays*, or better still a northern Italian, will give more pleasure. At most levels of price and quality, it is difficult to beat the New World: the Californian style is becoming lighter, less oaky; New Zealand is producing some fine examples; and Australia, not least because of the dollar, offers just about the best value of all.

Drinkers' dozen

The top twelve Chardonnays in the tasting all scored within two points of each other. Five of them were French, but a glance at the trade prices shows the relatively better value of wines from California, Australia and New Zealand. VAT and the restaurateurs' profit-margin have to be added to arrive at a restaurant selling-price. Those who mark up by a hundred per cent will put the French wines at an even greater disadvantage in terms of value for money.

New Zealand
Montana '85, £2·65
Cooke's Hawkes Bay '86, £3·55 (available from supermarkets, VAT-inclusive)

Australia
Wynn's Coonawarra '85, £5·15
Rouge Homme '85, £5·35
Tyrrell's 'Vat 47' '85, £6·15

California
Monticello Jefferson Ranch '84, £5
Trefethen '83, £6·95

France
Meursault, Jadot '84, £10·95
Meursault, Poruzot from Jobard '84, £14·04
Puligny-Montrachet, Clos de la Garenne '84, £14·50
Corton, Domaine Chandon de Brialles '84, £15·65
Bâtard-Montrachet, Louis Latour '82, £25·90

What to drink in 1988

by Roger Voss, editor of *Which? Wine Guide*

Double-starred (**) wines are especially good for drinking this year, though single-starred (*) bottles are good if ** wines are either too expensive or not available at all. Countries are listed alphabetically, wine-growing regions alphabetically within their countries. Vintages that are unlikely to appear on restaurant lists are not included.

Argentina

Drink **whites** as young as possible – the **1987** vintage would be ideal. Argentine being in the southern hemisphere, grapes are picked in February and March. Any whites older than 1985 will be past it. **Reds** of older vintages occasionally surface: any up to ten years old should still be enjoyable.

Australia

WHITES
Drink the youngest you can find of Rhine Riesling – *1987s are available and are often better than 1986s. Chardonnay and Sémillon are better after two or three years: *1986s and *1985s are both enjoyable now – so are 1984s and 1983s if the wines are of top quality.

REDS

**1982 and *1984 are good now, as are some 1985s. Fine *1983s are coming on. Drink Merlot and Shiraz (Syrah) younger than Cabernet Sauvignon, and drink Shiraz/ Cabernet blends at the same age as pure Cabernet.

Austria

Drink 1986, 1985 and 1984 dry whites, and start on some sweet whites from 1984. The sweet whites of *1981 are good now. Drink reds from 1985.

Bulgaria

WHITES

1986 wines are very drinkable at the moment, especially Sauvignon and Riesling. 1985 Chardonnay is the best vintage.

REDS

1985, *1983, *1981 and 1978 are the best vintages at the moment for Cabernet Sauvignon. Drink Merlot or wines made from Bulgarian grape varieties – or the blended wines – within two or three years.

Chile

Drink most **whites** as young as possible, although Chardonnay will keep for four years. Most **reds** are better after three or four years. Older vintages of Cabernet Sauvignon can be excellent, ageing with considerable grace and elegance.

England and Wales

Drink wines from the 1986, *1985 and 1984 vintages now. Most other wines are past it.

France

Alsace

1986 Only Pinot Blanc or blends should be drunk yet.

**1985 Wines of this vintage will last well – but most can be drunk now. Riesling and Gewürztraminer are the ones most likely to be immature.

1984 Good sound wines, but with few excitements. In some cases these wines go better with food than the greater vintages of 1985 and 1983. All are drinkable at the moment.

**1983 A very fine year, and Riesling, Tokay Pinot Gris and Gewürz- traminer are fine for drinking now, although they will keep. Some Vendange Tardive are ready to drink.

1982 Riesling and Tokay Pinot Gris are still attractive, and *Gewürz- traminer will still last.

1979 Occasional Riesling are still attractively mature. Vendange Tardive and top Réserves are good to drink now.

1978 A few of the best Rieslings and Gewürztraminer are good to drink. The rest are past it.

1976 **Vendange Tardive and the occasional Gewürztraminer are still superb.

Beaujolais

1986 A year that is coming into its own after poor Beaujolais Nouveau. Drink the Villages and ordinary Beaujolais now, but leave the *cru* (Chiroubles, Fleurie, Moulin-à-Vent, Brouilly, Côtes de Brouilly, St-Amour, Morgon, Chénas, Juliénas) wines until autumn 1988.

1985 A superb year. *Villages wines are still worth drinking, and the **cru* wines are superb.

1984 A few *cru* wines are still worth drinking. Forget the others.

*1983 The *cru* wines are still worth drinking for a mature taste. Don't bother with the others.

Older vintages still worth trying are 1981 and 1978 for *cru* wines only.

Bergerac

Drink dry **whites** and **rosés** as young as possible. Drink *1985 standard Bergerac reds, and **1983, 1982 and 1978 of Côtes de Bergerac and Pécharmant. Drink 1983, *1982, 1979 and *1978 sweet white Monbazillac.

Bordeaux

REDS

Red Bordeaux (claret) ranges from very simple, inexpensive wines for drinking young to some of the world's finest wines, which need keeping for many years. Clarets (most are labelled Ch. something) called Bordeaux or Bordeaux Supérieur, or those simply called house claret, fit into the first category. Look for **1986**, ****1985**, **1984** and ***1983**.

For more expensive wines labelled Cru Bourgeois, Graves, St-Emilion Grand Cru, Montagne St-Emilion, St-Georges-St-Emilion, Fronsac or Lalande de Pomerol:

1984 Light wines, with quite a lot of acidity. The best wines will be labelled Cru Bourgeois rather than St-Emilion (or villages with St-Emilion in the name) or Lalande de Pomerol.

*1983 St-Emilion, Fronsac and Lalande de Pomerol will be ready now. The Cru Bourgeois and Graves should be kept.

**1982 Some are developing well. Others need time, especially the Cru Bourgeois.

*1981 Classic wines in the Cru Bourgeois. All are worth drinking.

1980 Cru Bourgeois are still good, others are fading.

*1979 All the Cru Bourgeois are good, as are Fronsac and St-Emilion Grand Cru.

**1978 A very fine year, and many of the wines are still very drinkable. Wines from villages around St-Emilion may be fading.

Earlier vintages: **1975**, **1970**. Avoid most others.

For classed growths (including St-Emilion Grand Cru Classé and Pomerol):

*1981 St-Emilion and Pomerol wines are beginning to be attractive. Lesser-known classed growths will mature during 1988.

1980 Some wines are drying out, but they are all good value so worth trying.

*1979 A vintage that is good, firm and fruity and should last a little longer.

**1978 St-Emilion and Pomerol are very good now. Others are just beginning to lose their toughness.

1977 Occasional top wines are good value. Avoid others.

1976 Very ripe wines, some of which have faded. Seek advice.

1975 Pomerol is enjoyable, as are top St-Emilion. Médoc and Graves classed growths still haven't opened out and show no signs of doing so.

1974 Avoid.

1973 Only top classed growths.

1972 Avoid.

1971 St-Emilion and Pomerol are better than Médoc or Graves.

**1970 Superb wines, but the top classed growths are still too young. Try everything else.

Good vintages from the 1960s are ***1966** and ****1961**; from the 1950s, **1955** and **1953**. On older vintages ******(except **1945**) ask advice.

DRY WHITES

Drink most young (**1986**), unless the wine is expensive and comes from a fine red wine château (Haut-Brion, Margaux, Domaine de Chevalier, for example), when older vintages – back to 1970 – will be good. See list of red vintages for the best years.

SWEET WHITES

1985 There will be good wines from the top estates, but they aren't ready yet. Try Premières Côtes de Bordeaux, St-Croix du Mont now, leave Sauternes and Barsac.

1984 Light wines that will never amount to much.

**1983 Marvellous wines. You could drink some now, but they will get much better.

1982 Average year. Drink now.

1981 Not much honeyed sweetness, but the wines are elegant enough.

*1980 Light but very good value, with plenty of honeyed fruit. Drink now in preference to 1983.

1979 They're softening out and losing their clean dryness and acidity. Drink now.

*1976 The best Sauternes and Barsac are still good. Others are past their best.

**1975 Wines that are still worth hanging on to. But they do taste good now.

**1970 A big, fat year, and the wines are tasting very good.
Earlier vintages: *1969, **1967, 1962, *1955, **1945. On anything older, ask advice (except **1937).

Burgundy

Vintage information for Burgundy can only be approximate. The quality of the producer is almost more important than the year – always ask advice when ordering.

REDS

**1985 A fine vintage of great quality which is developing well. Most wines – except top *premier cru* – are worth drinking now.

1984 Lean, quite soft, drink now, don't keep.

*1983 Choose carefully, because some wines aren't developing well. Others, though, are very good indeed.

1982 Drink with great care. Many are past it, others never made it.

1981 Avoid.

*1980 Good value. It all depends on the grower.

1979 A few *premier cru* wines are worth pursuing.

**1978 The best wines are just coming out of their shells, the others are becoming deliciously mature. Not cheap, though.
In earlier vintages look for 1971, 1970, 1969, 1961. Côte de Nuits wines age better than Côte de Beaune or Côte Chalonnaise.

WHITES

1986 Drink Chablis and Mâcon. Keep the others.

*1985 Not quite as good as reds, but still very attractive. Chablis softening and losing its bite.

1984 Soft, but strangely under-ripe.

Choose carefully. Côte de Beaune is best.

**1983 The best recent vintage, and the prices reflect this. But quality does vary even in this year.

1982 Drink up now.

1981 Avoid.

*1979 A few top wines are still very good.

*1978 The wines, though great, are softening dangerously. Only a few will last, so drink the rest now.
Treat older vintages with caution.

Buzet, Frontonnais, Gaillac (reds)

Look for 1985, 1983 or older vintages of top wines (1982, 1978).

Cahors

1985 Lighter, fruitier wines are good now. The tougher wines are still just that.

**1983 The big wines are good now.

*1982 Most wines are very good. Drink up the lighter style.

**1978 The best year to drink now for the top wines.

Champagne (vintage)

*1982 Still a little immature, but it should develop during the year.

1981 A few producers are making this vintage, which is delicious now.

**1979 This is the vintage to drink now for the true mature champagne taste.

*1978 Another good vintage, if drier and less rich than 1979.

1976 Drink now.

*1975 Top *cuvées* are still delicious.

Loire

DRY WHITES AND ROSÉS
Drink the youngest vintage. Anybody selling Muscadet older than 1985 should be out of business. Vouvray, Savennières, Sancerre and Pouilly-Fumé of 1985 or 1983 will still be drinkable.

SWEET WHITES
1985 This was a superb vintage, but

it would be a shame to drink anything but the most ordinary *Coteaux du Layon.

1984 Medium-weight vintage, some of which will last a long time. Don't drink yet.

1983 Another vintage which shouldn't really be touched yet.

1982 Lightweight wines. Drink now.

*1978 These wines are just coming into their own – and superb they are.

**1976 Superb wines with great concentration and richness.

*1975 Will be better than 1976 – but not just yet.

Older vintages: **1969, 1964, 1961, **1959**.

REDS

Many Loire reds, especially Sancerre and Gamay-based reds, need to be drunk young. Saumur Champigny, Bourgueil and Chinon age better.

1986 Drink the lighter wines from this year with pleasure.

*1985 St-Nicholas de Bourgueil, Saumur Champigny and Sancerre are the wines to drink from this year. Keep Chinon and Bourgueil.

1984 Avoid.

**1983 Excellent year all round. Chinon and Bourgueil will keep, though.

1982 Drink up.

*1981 Good for the top producers of Chinon and Bourgueil.

1980 Avoid.

Older vintages: **1978, 1976** for Chinon and Bourgueil.

Rhône

WHITES

Recent vintages that should be enjoyable are: **1986, 1985, 1984, 1983, 1981** and **1978**. Older vintages should be approached with caution.

REDS

Northern Rhône – Crozes-Hermitage, Hermitage, Côte Rôtie, St-Joseph, Cornas:

1985 A very good year, but it's a definite case of infanticide to touch anything yet.

1984 Lightweight wines, which are maturing quite fast. St-Joseph and Crozes are right to drink now.

1983 Excellent, top-quality wines. Try **Crozes, **St-Joseph, but keep everything else for years.

*1982 Soft wines, ready for drinking, although Hermitage is still immature.

1981 Avoid.

*1980 At its peak, and very good value.

1979 Drink most wines now.

**1978 A truly great year, and many wines, especially Hermitage and Cornas, are not ready. Others are superb.

Older vintages: **1976, 1973, 1971, 1970, 1969** for Cornas, Côte-Rôtie and Hermitage. Most others will have faded.

Southern Rhône – Côtes du Rhône, Côtes du Rhône Villages, Lirac, Gigondas, Châteauneuf-du-Pape. Other wines – Côtes du Ventoux, Côtes du Luberon, Coteaux du Tricastin should be drunk as they come on to the wine list:

**1985 A great year. Côtes du Rhône and Villages are good now. Gigondas and Châteauneuf should be kept.

1984 A light year, to be drunk soon.

**1983 Another fine year. Gigondas, Lirac and Châteauneuf are just maturing. Côtes du Rhône Villages is good, ordinary Côtes du Rhône tiring.

1982 Avoid.

*1980 Drink Châteauneuf, Gigondas and Lirac. Avoid others.

**1978 Gigondas and Châteauneuf superb. Most others are fading.

Germany

1986 Ordinary QbA wines are to be drunk now. Better wines should be kept.

*1985 A good all-round vintage, to be drunk now.

1984 Avoid.

**1983 The top Rieslings are still superb. Most other wines have tired.

1982 Drink up.

1981 Ony top wines.

**1976 Still superb. Try anything you can find (apart from Liebfraumilch). Older vintages: *1975, **1971. Many of the sweet wines age seemingly for ever.

Italy

WHITES

Drink young vintages – 1986, 1985. Avoid anything older.

REDS

Most Italian reds need to be two or three years old before being drunk. 1985 is a good vintage for reds. The only exceptions are Bardolino and less expensive Valpolicella – drink 1986.

Chianti

1986 A good year, but only the cheapest wines are ready.

**1985 The best wines are slowly coming into their own. Less expensive wines are still very good.

1984 Avoid.

*1983 Riservas are showing well. Ordinary Chianti (normale) is quite mature.

**1982 This is a year for the super vini da tavola made by Chianti producers as their top wines. Also for Chianti Riserva.

1979 Some *Riservas, but most wines are past it.

Barolo and Barbaresco

Avoid anything younger than 1982.

1982 good, ripe wines, which can be drunk now but really should be kept.

1981 Dull wines.

*1980 Huge wines, which need fruit to be drinkable. Approach with caution – but the best are very good.

1979 A good, soft year, to drink now.

**1978 One of the great vintages. Only light wines are good now.

Older vintages: 1976, 1974, 1971, 1970.

Lebanon

Best vintages of Château Musar at the moment are 1982, *1980, *1978 and 1972.

New Zealand

Anything before 1985 in whites and 1984 in reds is likely to be tiring. Drink 1985 or 1986 – or even 1987 (except Chardonnay) – whites. Drink 1985, 1984 reds.

Portugal

Table wines

WHITES

Drink vinho verde as fresh as possible. The wine doesn't have a vintage, but should certainly be no older than from the 1986 harvest.

REDS

Some Portuguese reds age remarkably well.

Bairrada: 1982, 1980, 1978, 1976.

Dão: Similar vintages – but also 1974, 1975.

Other wines: 1982, 1981, 1980, 1977, 1976, 1975.

Port

All late-bottled vintage, late bottled, vintage-character and tawny ports are ready for drinking as soon as they reach the restaurant list.

Vintage and single quinta ports

Don't touch 1977, 1980, 1982 or 1983 ports. 1980 will be approaching maturity during the year.

1975 A year to drink up. Good value, though.

**1970 This is the year to drink now.

1968/67 Some single quinta wines are worth drinking. Not official port vintage years.

*1966 Good-value ports, considering their age, and worth drinking now.

**1963 One of the best post-war vintages. Drink now, but they will keep for ever.

*1960 On very good, ripe form.

**1955 Maturing well.

Older vintages: 1950, *1947, **1945, *1935, **1927.

Spain

WHITES

Most Spanish whites need to be drunk young. Buy **1986** vintage. Exceptions are some Torres wines (Gran Viña Sol) and white Rioja from Marqués de Murrieta (Ygay), Lopéz de Herédia (Tondonia) and CVNE (Monopole).

Rioja (reds)

1985 Wines without wood ageing ('sin crianza') can be drunk.
1984 Drink up.
*1983 A good year for ordinary Crianza Rioja. Reservas are too young.
1982 Another year only for ordinary Rioja.
**1981 Try the Reservas as well as ordinary Rioja.
*1980 Reasonable vintage. Look for the Reservas only.
**1978 Reservas and Gran Reservas are very good. Some ordinary Riojas, too, but most will need drinking up.

*1975 and *1973 Gran Reservas only.

United States

California

WHITES

Drink wines from **1986** (Sauvignon or Fumé Blanc, Riesling only), **1985** (all whites, including Chardonnay), **1984** (**Chardonnay are at their best, others are fading), *1982 (Chardonnay only).

REDS

1985 The youngest reds to try. Keep the Cabernet Sauvignon, but drink Zinfandel or Pinot Noir.
*1984 A good all-round, light year.
1983 Drink most reds now. Some top Cabernet Sauvignon will last longer.
1982 Drink **Cabernet Sauvignon. Other reds are fading.
1980 *Cabernet Sauvignon and some Pinot Noir only.
1978 **Cabernet Sauvignon only.

Notes on eating ethnic

Japanese

Traditional styles of Japanese cookery

Sashimi Thinly sliced raw fish served with soy sauce and grated horse-radish ('wasabi' – not related to Western horseradish, it is green, more fragrant and less sharp).

Tempura Deep-fried, thinly battered seafood or vegetables served with a sauce of Dashi (see below) lightly flavoured with soy sauce and Mirin (see below).

Sukiyaki Means grilled to your taste: thin slices of beef, transparent noodles, assorted vegetables and bean curd are fried on a hot plate at the table, seasoned with a mixture of soy, saké (see below) and sugar and dipped in raw beaten egg before eating.

Shabu-shabu The same ingredients as in sukiyaki are simmered in stock rather than fried. The vegetables usually include cabbage. The meat and vegetables are swished to and fro (Shabu-shabued) in the stock until the meat is cooked. There are two separate dipping sauces, one flavoured with lemon juice, one with sesame. When the meat and vegetables are finished the stock is sometimes served as a soup.

Teriyaki Meat or fish marinated in soy sauce, saké and ginger before being quickly sauté or grilled and served with the reduced marinade.

Yakitori Simply means grilled chicken. Usually it is grilled chicken cubes on skewers, like kebabs, with a rich, sweet glaze of basically soy sauce, Mirin and sugar.

Sunomono A salad of vegetables and seafood flavoured with a thin vinegary dressing. There are several dressings varying in sweetness, but the basic ingredients are the same: rice vinegar, sugar, soy sauce and Mirin.

Aemono Salads with thicker dressings. The dressings are thickened using sometimes bean curd, sometimes sesame seed or peanuts or sometimes egg yolk.

Sushi Cooked white rice flavoured with vinegar, sugar and a little salt: served in rectangles with slices of raw fish and a smear of wasabi press-ed on top, rolled in seaweed with raw fish and vegetables in the centre; or in a dish topped with raw fish and vegetables. Served with soy sauce.

Flavourings

Dashi A very light, delicately flavoured stock made from kelp and shav-ings of dried bonito fish. The basic stock of Japanese cooking, used for sauces, soups and as simmering stock in any other sort of dish.

Mirin A sweet gold-coloured rice wine. Used in cooking only to add a mild sweetness, for example added to the glaze for grilled foods when used in a basting sauce.

Miso A salty soya bean paste. Used in dressings and as a pickling agent, but also served at the end of every meal in miso soup (misoshiru).

Saké As a sweet rice wine, saké is served warm, in small cups, with most Japanese meals. However, it is also used in the kitchen in almost any dish, for example to enrich simmered and steamed dishes and to tenderise fish and meat.

Soy sauce Used in sauces and as a marinating agent. Japanese soy sauce, unlike Chinese, has no additives and no caramel so it is much purer. Due to its greater wheat content, Japanese soy sauces are much sweeter and less salty than Chinese and have a relatively brighter taste and aroma. They are also lighter in colour and thinner in texture.

Of the two soy sauces in Japanese cooking, the darker is used for most cooking purposes and the lighter, a little saltier than the dark, is used to preserve the natural colour of the food.

Korean

Koreans believe in the oriental rule of five flavours: salt, sweet, sour, spicy-hot and bitter. Salt is from soy sauce and bean paste; sugar from beet, honey and sweet potatoes; sour from chilli peppers; mustard provides the heat, and ginger is the bitter. Koreans also follow an arrangement of five traditional colours: red, green, yellow, white and black.

Dinner will consist of four to seven dishes served at the same time accompanied by rice (**Bap**): two main dishes, a vegetable dish, a vegetable pickle, a soup, perhaps an extra rice dish, and dessert, largely fruit.

Main dishes feature meat (usually beef), fish, shellfish or tofu, fried, stewed or grilled. Bulgogi, Korea's most well-known dish, is thinly sliced beef marinated in sauces. Menus in Britain often feature chicken and pork versions (**Dak Bulgogi** and **Dwaji Bulgogi**). Fish is often deep fried then sautéed with a combination of vegetables (Hong-Cho).

Korean pizza (**Bintakok**) is made of ground green peas fried with minced beef, spring onions, garlic and vegetables.

Vegetable dishes are side dishes. **Kim-Chee** is preserved cabbage pickle. In Korea it will accompany every meal in restaurants. **Namul** dishes are vegetable side salads mixed with sesame oil. **Kim** is salted seaweed, oiled and toasted to a crisp.

Soups are substantial and often include combinations of meat, fish, tofu and vegetables. Two are particularly worth a mention: **Shu-sol-lo** is the soup of kings, prepared in a large cooking-pot; it consists of fish and meats cooked with vegetables. **Yuk ke jang** is slices of marinated beef with eggs, spring onions, garlic, bean sprouts and mushrooms, boiled in a spicy chilli soup.

A meal could conclude with mangoes, lychees or sweet melon. To drink one should try Korean tea (**Ginseng**).

Lebanese

Middle Eastern restaurants in Britain usually have a strong Lebanese influence. Lebanese meals pivot on charcoal-grilled meat or poultry with a side salad. Besides this main dish there will be three or four other smaller dishes, or Mezes. They are either hot or cold. Spellings vary substantially.

Cold meze

Hummus Chickpeas puréed with olive oil, flavoured with cumin, crushed garlic and fresh lemon juice.

Moutabal Peeled and baked aubergines mashed into a purée with garlic, lemon juice and Tahina (sesame paste).

Tabouleh Soaked burghul (crushed wheat), chopped mint and parsley, spring onions with plenty of lemon juice.

Fabloush Grilled pitta bread, crushed, softened with lemon juice, mixed with cucumber, tomatoes and onions, and flavoured with herbs.

Loubeh Green beans fried with garlic and onions, then simmered with tomatoes and left to cool.

Bastorma Dried and cured fillet of beef in spices.

Ful Moukala Broad beans fried with garlic and coriander.

Hot meze

Ful Medames Broad beans, boiled until soft, mixed with crushed garlic and served as a soup.

Hummus Sada Chickpeas cooked until soft then mixed with crushed garlic and olive oil.

Lahma bi-ajeen Lebanese pizza: dough topped with minced meat, onions and tomato, then baked.

Manakeish Bizzaatar An alternative Lebanese pizza without meat, topped with thyme and other herbs in olive oil, then baked.

Kallaje Halumi (hard goats' cheese) grilled on Lebanese bread.

Falafel Ground chickpeas and broad beans tossed in spices and deep fried.

Sambossak A pastry case stuffed with minced meat, onions and pinenuts.

Fatayer A pastry case stuffed with spinach, onions and lemon.

Nchaat Pane Lambs' brains dipped in flour, seasoned with salt and pepper, shallow fried and tossed in eggs.

Makenek and Sojuk Spicy sausages. These can be fried with tomatoes, potatoes, garlic and eggs to a creamy consistency.

Main dishes

Lamb (Ghanum) is by far the most common meat in Lebanon. Main dishes therefore are predominantly lamb and mostly charcoal grilled.

Skewered kebabs, lamb cubes, onions and tomatoes (**Lahma Meshui**) need no explanation. Minced meat (**Kafta**), aside from its use in many Meze dishes, often makes a main dish. **Kafta Malabiyeh** is grilled on skewers with onion and parsley. **Kafta fil Sania** is kafta mixed with grated onions and spices and baked into a meat loaf. **Kafta Yoghortlech** is minced meat cooked with yoghurt served on toast and pine-nuts.

It is, however, the **Kibbeh** dishes that are fascinating. Kibbeh, a mixture of ground wheat, grated onion and minced lamb pounded into a paste, is the national dish of Lebanon. **Kebbeh Naye** is eaten raw. **Kebbeh bil Sanieh** is a layer of Kafta sandwiched between two layers of Kibbeh then baked. **Kibbeh Bisayniyeh** is a tube of Kibbeh stuffed with Kafta, pine-nuts and onion, then baked. **Kibbeh Meshwieh** is again a tube, stuffed with minced meat and walnuts, then grilled.

Desserts

Most Middle Eastern pastries are variations of baklava (baklawa) or kadayif (konafa). Baklava are made from paper-thin pastry; kadayif are made from wheat-flour shredded dough. Both can be stuffed with a nut or cheese filling, baked, and then soaked in a sweet, lemony syrup.

Milky rice or semolina puddings are served chilled in Lebanon. Semolina dusted with cinnamon powder is often eaten for breakfast, but Mihallabia, a rich rice pudding with orange blossom and chopped nuts, is common on evening menus in Britain.

The meal is often rounded off with chilled fruit salads followed by strong black coffee.

Indonesian

A typical Indonesian meal will include four or five main dishes, each served with a rice (**Nasi**) dish, not necessarily plain, and some or all of the following; a soup (**Sop/Soto**), a selection of hot sauces (**Sambal**), savoury or sweet side dishes (**Makanan Kecil** and **Cuci Mulut**), and finishing with fruit.

Rice is served in a large communal bowl. Plain boiled rice is the most common, but rices cooked in coconut milk (**Nasi Santen**) and fried rice (**Nasi Goreng**) are popular, and variants of these will be found on Indonesian/Malay menus in Britain. **Rijsttafel** literally means rice table and is basically an Indonesian banquet. One large plate of rice is served, with generous helpings of various side dishes. In Indonesia such a meal could be enormous, with up to twenty dishes. However, in restaurants here it is possible to order a smaller version of rijsttafel (**Nasi Rames**) with your own choice of dishes. Success, of course, depends on the right choice of combination.

The main dishes will be chosen from the following; meat, usually beef (**Daging**), sometimes lamb (**Kambing**) or chicken (**Ayam**), prawn

(**Udang**), vegetable (**Sayur**) or, most commonly, fish (**Ikan**). Dishes are generally fried or cooked with herbs or more often with spicy sauces. The spices are the key to Indonesian cooking: **Sambals** are hot and/or spicy sauces or relishes.

As relishes Sambals are a side dish to be added to a meal. The chief ingredient of all Sambals are chillies (**Cabe** or **Lombok**). All main ingredients, whether meat, seafood or vegetable, can be fried in Sambal, and this is a whole class of Indonesian cuisine in itself – for example, with chicken (**Sambal Goreng Ayandi**), with fish (**Sambal Goreng Ikan**), or with aubergine (**Sambal Goreng Terong**).

Other sauces for cooking or adding at the table, in everyday use in Indonesia and common to menus here, are peanut sauce (**Saos Kacang**), coconut sauce (**Sambal Kelapa**) and spicy tamarind sauce (**Asam Pedas**), as well as soy sauce (**Kecap**). **Kecap Asin** is dark and salty, but **Kecap Mainis** is very thick, black and sweet, and is distinctively Indonesian.

Soups (**Sop** and **Soto**) are part of the meal and are usually substantial. Most contain rice or noodles, or are used to accompany them.

Savoury snacks (**Makanan Kecil**) and sweets (**Cuci Mulut**) are popular on their own, but frequently served on side dishes to the main meal. Savouries chiefly centre around peanuts: fried (**Kacang Goreng**) or dry-roasted (**Kacang Goreng Kering**). Banana fritters (**Pisang Goreng**) and pancakes (**Panekuk**) are popular sweet snacks.

Another two items found on Indonesian menus are **Tahu** and **Tempe**, both developed from soya beans. Tahu is known as bean curd in the West and will be familiar to patrons of Chinese restaurants. It is made from the liquid extracted from the beans, is soft in texture and sold in small square slabs. It is used in cooked dishes in which fresh Tahu would break up; fried Tahu is often used in salads (**Gado-gado**) and mixed vegetable dishes. It is Tempe, however, that is solely originated in Indonesia. Tempe is made by combining soaked soya beans with an enzyme-producing agent like yeast. The yeast breaks down and binds the beans, rendering them more digestible. Like Tahu, it is sold in slabs. Appearing like cheese with a white skin, it varies from soft to crunchy in texture while tasting vaguely nutty. It is a superb source of protein, carbohydrates, vitamins and minerals, and forms, as a snack or in cooked dishes, an essential and beneficial part of an Indonesian diet.

Thai

In a classic Thai meal six or seven main dishes, each with rice (**Kao**), are placed in the centre of the table and shared by everyone. These are followed by anything from one to three desserts.

The Thai diet is heavily biased towards seafood and vegetables. Meat is eaten, but the Thai, being Buddhist, do not kill animals, so meat butchering is left to the Muslims and Chinese. Beef (**Neua**) is the most commonly eaten meat, and usually comes from ox or buffalo, but pork (**Moo**), chicken (**Gai**) and duck (**Bhed**) are also eaten, and are found on Thai menus here in Britain. Thailand is a fish (**Pla**)-eating nation, and a huge variety of fish and seafood in general are used in everyday meals. Pomfret (**Pla Kapong**), prawns (**Gung Naring**), shrimps (**Gung Foi**), crab (**Poo**), lobster (**Gung Talle Yai**) and shellfish (**Moi**) are common.

The Thai meal includes one or two wok-fried dishes (**Pad**), often fried in curry pastes (**Krung Gaeng**), always with chillies (**Prik**) and other herbs, ginger (**King**), garlic (**Kratiem**), cinnamon (**Ob Chuey**), coriander seeds (**Pak Chee**), etc.

One dish, usually fish, will be steamed (**Nueng**) after marination. Vegetable (**Pak**) dishes are also steamed, or sometimes quickly boiled and served with hot sauces. Each meal will include a curry (**Gaeng Ped**, which translated means 'hot liquid'). They are cooked in coconut milk and spices and are always eaten over large mounds of rice, as just a few solids suffice. [Coconut milk (**Nam Katee**) forms part of almost all Thai foods: curries, meat and fish dishes as well as desserts, sweets and beverages.] Every meal has a soup (**Gaeng Sued**). Most common are rice soups (**Kao Dom**) or noodle soups (**Gwaytio**) served for breakfast and lunch. The soup served with the evening meal comes in smaller portions and ranges in flavour from hot and spicy to subtle and delicate. Salads (**Yam**) are an essential part of a meal; they are sprinkled with spiced dressings and topped with dried chilli flakes, chopped herbs and occasionally with crushed peanuts or coconut flakes.

The final and most crucial part of any Thai meal is the sauce. The universally used sauce (**Nam Prik**) is very hot and pungent and composed of dried fish, shrimp paste (**Kapee**), garlic, chillies, with fish sauce (**Nam Pla**), sugar and lime juice used to bind.

Desserts (**Kong Wan**) divide into solid and liquid, both usually with fruit as the key ingredient. The solid sweetmeats (**Kanom**) are usually just mouthfuls made from sweetened pastes and coconut jellies. Liquid desserts are more common. These are normally fruits, raw or boiled, served in sweetened coconut milk or sugar syrups. Thai menus in Britain, however, have a narrow choice of desserts, although **Sungk-aya**, coconut milk custard, is found on most. Fruit is usually available, and the average Thai meal will conclude with a selection of fruits (**Polamai**) which in season might include mangoes (**Mamuang**) and durian (**Turian**).

The most regular accompaniment is iced tea (**Cha Yei**) or iced coffee (**Ka fe Yer**), although beer is now widely drunk in Thailand.

General lists

The Guide's *longest-serving restaurants*

Connaught Hotel, W1	35 years	Chez Moi, W11	19 years
Gay Hussar, W1	31 years	Cleeveway House, Bishops	
Porth Tocyn Hotel,		Cleeve, Gloucestershire	19 years
Abersoch, Gwynedd	31 years	Cosmo's, Edinburgh,	
Gravetye Manor,		Lothian	19 years
Sharpthorne, West Sussex	27 years	Horn of Plenty,	
Sharrow Bay, Ullswater,		Gulworthy, Devon	19 years
Cumbria	27 years	Pool Court, Pool in	
Blooms, EC1	25 years	Wharfedale, West	
Dundas Arms, Kintbury,		Yorkshire	19 years
Berkshire	25 years	Rothay Manor,	
Box Tree, Ilkley, West		Ambleside, Cumbria	19 years
Yorkshire	23 years	Sundial, Herstmonceux,	
French Partridge, Horton,		East Sussex	19 years
Northamptonshire	23 years	At the Sign of the Angel,	
Walnut Tree Inn,		Lacock, Wiltshire	17 years
Llandewi Skirrid, Gwent	23 years	Chueng Cheng Ku, W1	17 years
Butley-Orford Oysterage,		Clifton Hotel, Nairn,	
Orford, Suffolk	21 years	Highland	17 years
Highbullen Hotel,		Le Gavroche, W1	17 years
Chittlehamholt, Devon	21 years	Summer Isles Hotel,	
Splinters, Christchurch,		Achiltibuie, Highland	17 years
Dorset	21 years	Timothy's, Perth, Tayside	17 years

Longest-serving restaurant in each county

LONDON

Connaught, W1	35 years

ENGLAND

Avon Old Parsonage,	
Farrington Gurney	13 years
Bedfordshire Paris House,	
Woburn	4 years
Berkshire Dundas Arms, Kintbury	25 years
Buckinghamshire Bell,	
Aston Clinton	7 years
Cambridgeshire Old Fire	
Engine House, Ely	15 years
Cheshire La Belle Epoque,	
Knutsford	11 years

Cornwall Treverbyn	
House, Veryan	8 years
Cumbria Sharrow Bay,	
Ullswater	27 years
Derbyshire Fischer's,	
Bakewell	6 years
Devon Highbullen Hotel,	
Chittlehamholt	21 years
Dorset Splinters,	
Christchurch	21 years
Durham Market Place	
Teashop, Barnard Castle	4 years
East Sussex Sundial,	
Herstmonceux	19 years
Essex Contented Sole,	
Burnham-on-Crouch	9 years

Gloucestershire Cleeveway House, Bishop's Cleeve	19 years
Greater Manchester Woo Sang	11 years
Hampshire Pine Trees, Sway	11 years
Hereford & Worcester Hunters Lodge, Broadway	9 years
Croque-en-Bouche, Malvern Wells	9 years
Hertfordshire The Salisbury, Hatfield	2 years
Humberside Le Restaurant Français, Willerby Manor Hotel, Willerby	2 years
Kent Paul's, Folkestone	6 years
Lancashire Danish Kitchen, Blackpool	9 years
Leicestershire Hambleton Hall, Hambleton	7 years
Lincolnshire Harvey's Cathedral Restaurant, Lincoln	7 years
Merseyside La Grande Bouffe, Liverpool	6 years
Norfolk Tollbridge, Guist	9 years
North Yorkshire Black Bull, Moulton	15 years
Northamptonshire French Partridge, Horton	23 years
Northumberland Breamish House Hotel, Powburn	3 years
Nottinghamshire Chand, Nottingham	3 years
Oxfordshire Red Lion, Steeple Aston	13 years
Shropshire Country Friends, Dorrington	3 years
Delany's, Shrewsbury	3 years
Somerset Blostins, Shepton Mallet	10 years
Bowlish House, Shepton Mallet	10 years
South Yorkshire Nirmals Tandoori, Sheffield	5 years
Staffordshire Old Beams, Waterhouses	2 years
Suffolk Butley-Orford Oysterage, Orford	21 years
Surrey Lantern, East Molesey	15 years
Tyne & Wear Jade Garden, Newcastle upon Tyne	4 years

Warwickshire Mallory Court, Bishops Tachbrook	9 years
White Bear, Shipston on Stour	9 years
West Midlands Chung Ying, Birmingham	4 years
Herbs, Coventry	4 years
Liaison, Solihull	4 years
West Sussex Gravetye Manor, Sharpthorne	27 years
West Yorkshire Box Tree, Ilkley	23 years
Wiltshire At the Sign of the Angel, Lacock	17 years

SCOTLAND

Borders Cringletie House, Peebles	15 years
Central Clifton Coffee House, Tyndrum	8 years
Dumfries & Galloway Riverside Inn, Canonbie	8 years
Fife Peat Inn, Peat Inn	14 years
Grampian Green Inn, Ballater	3 years
Tullich Lodge, Ballater	3 years
Highland Summer Isles Hotel, Achiltibuie	17 years
Clifton Hotel, Nairn	17 years
Lothian Cosmo's, Edinburgh	19 years
Orkney & Shetland Burrastow House, Walls	4 years
Strathclyde Ubiquitous Chip, Glasgow	15 years
Tayside Timothy's, Perth	17 years

WALES

Clwyd Gales, Llangollen	5 years
Dyfed Druidstone Hotel, Broadhaven	14 years
Gwent Walnut Tree Inn, Llandewi Skirrid	23 years
Gwynedd Porth Tocyn Hotel, Abersoch	31 years
Glamorgan Riverside, Cardiff	9 years
Powys Janie's, Machynlleth	5 years

The most popular restaurants

Top 10, according to volume of recommendations received in the past year.

LONDON

1 Alastair Little, W1
2 Simply Nico, SW1
3 Le Mazarin, SW1
4 Gay Hussar, W1
5 La Bastide, W1
6 Clarke's, W8
   Tante Claire, SW3
7 Auberge de Provence,
   St James's Court Hotel,
   SW1
   Hilaire, SW7
   Sonny's, SW13
8 Al Hamra, W1
   Chuen Cheng Ku, W1
9 L'Herisson, SW19
   RSJ, SE1
10 Bombay Brasserie,
   Bailey's Hotel, SW7
   Greenhouse, W1
   Orso, WC2

ENGLAND

1 Old Vicarage,
   Witherslack
2 Carved Angel,
   Dartmouth
3 Corse Lawn House,
   Corse Lawn
4 Summer Lodge,
   Evershot
   Le Manoir aux Quat'
   Saisons, Great Milton

5 Langley House Hotel,
   Langley Marsh
   Bridgfield House, Spark
   Bridge
   L'Ortolan, Shinfield
   Fischer's, Bakewell
   Breamish House Hotel,
   Powburn
6 Country Friends,
   Dorrington
7 Hintlesham Hall,
   Hintlesham
   Gidleigh Park, Chagford
8 Yang Sing, Manchester
   Paris House, Woburn
9 Royal Oak, Yattendon
10 Crown, Southwold
   Morels, Haslemere

SCOTLAND

1 Handsel's, Edinburgh
2 Airds Hotel, Port Appin
3 Colonial, Glasgow
4 Arisaig House, Arisaig
   Champany Inn,
   Linlithgow
   One Devonshire
   Gardens, Glasgow
5 Vintners Room,
   Edinburgh

6 Braeval Old Mill,
   Aberfoyle
7 Polmaily House Hotel,
   Polmaily
8 Cross, Kingussie
9 Altnaharrie Inn,
   Ullapool
10 Le Marché Noir,
   Edinburgh

WALES

1 Bodysgallen Hall,
   Llandudno
2 St Tudno Hotel, St
   Tudno
3 Wolfscastle Country
   Hotel, Wolf's Castle
4 Spanghero's, Cardiff
5 Druidstone Hotel, Broad
   Haven
6 Ty Mawr, Brechfa
7 Great House, Laleston
8 Castle Cottage, Harlech
   Meadowsweet Hotel,
   Llanrwst
9 Tyddyn Llan, Llandrillo
   Y Bistro, Llanberis
10 Cemlyn, Harlech
   Fairyhill, Reynoldston

Exceptional wine cellars

These restaurants, marked with a bottle symbol in the text, have outstanding wine cellars.

LONDON

La Bastide, W1
Cork & Bottle, WC2
Corney & Barrow, EC2
Le Gavroche, W1
Inigo Jones
Magno's, WC2
Pollyanna's, SW11
RSJ, SE1
Tante Claire, SW3
Tate Gallery, SW1

ENGLAND

Afriston Moonrakers
Ambleside Rothay Manor
Aston Clinton Bell
Bath Priory Hotel
Bishops Tachbrook Mallory
Court
Bourton on the Water Rose
Tree
Evershot Summer Lodge
Evesham Cedar Restaurant,
Evesham Hotel
Faversham Read's

Grasmere White Moss
House
Great Dunmow Starr
Hambleton Hambleton Hall
Harrogate Hodgson's,
Russell Hotel
Haslemere Morels
Hintlesham Hintlesham
Hall
Hinton Charterhouse
Homewood Park
Horton French Partridge
Jevington Hungry Monk

Bowness on Windermere Porthole Eating House
Bristol Harvey's
Broadway Lygon Arms
Brockenhurst Le Poussin
Bromsgrove Grafton Manor
Campsea Ash Old Rectory
Chagford Gidleigh Park
Chedington Chedington Court
Chilgrove White Horse Inn
Christchurch Splinters
Coggeshall White Hart
Dartmouth Carved Angel
East Bergholt Fountain House
Epworth Epworth Tap
Kenilworth Restaurant Bosquet
Kintbury Dundas Arms
Kirkby Fleetham Kirkby Fleetham Hall
Ledbury Hope End
Lewes Kenwards
Lincoln Harvey's Cathedral Restaurant
Malvern Wells Croque-en-Bouche
North Huish Brookdale House
Pangbourne Copper Inn
Pinner La Giralda
Pool in Wharfedale Pool Court
Powburn Breamish House

Ramsbottom Village Restaurant
Ridgeway Old Vicarage
Ripley Michels
Sharpthorne Gravetye Manor
Shepton Mallet Bowlish House
Shinfield L'Ortolan
South Godstone La Bonne Auberge
Southwold Crown
Spark Bridge Bridgefield House
Ston Easton Ston Easton Park
Streatley Swan Hotel
Taunton Castle Hotel
Thornbury Thornbury Castle
Ullswater Sharrow Bay
Uppingham Lake Isle
Wallingford Brown & Boswell
Wentbridge Wentbridge House
Williton White House Hotel
Witherslack Old Vicarage
Wymondham Adlard's

SCOTLAND

Achiltibuie Summer Isles Hotel
Cromarty Le Chardon

Edinburgh Le Marché Noir
Glasgow Ubiquitous Chip
Gullane La Potinière
Kingussie Cross
Linlithgow Champany Inn
Oban Knipoch Hotel
Peat Inn Peat Inn
Port Appin Airds Hotel
Ullapool Altnaharrie Inn

WALES

Llandewi Skirrid Walnut Tree Inn
Llandudno Bodysgallen Hall Floral
Llanrwst Meadowsweet Hotel
Llanwrtyd Wells Llwynderw Hotel

REPUBLIC OF IRELAND

Bray Tree of Idleness
Cork Arbutus Lodge
Dublin White's on the Green

Sunday lunch within driving distance of London

DIRECTION		MAIN ROUTE OUT OF LONDON
North West	**Aston Clinton**, Buckinghamshire, Bell Inn	A41
	Bray, Berkshire, Waterside Inn	M4
	Chinnor, Oxfordshire, Sir Charles Napier Inn	M40
	Flitwick, Bedfordshire, Flitwick Manor	M1
	Hatfield, Hertfordshire, The Salisbury	A1
	Taplow, Berkshire, Cliveden	M4
	Woburn, Bedfordshire, Paris House	M1
North East	**Broxted**, Essex, Whitehall	M11
	Thaxted, Essex, Recorders	M11
South West	**East Horsley**, Surrey, Thatchers	A24
	Egham, Surrey, La Bonne Franquette	A30
	Gatwick, Surrey, Garden Restaurant, Gatwick Hilton	A23
	Ripley, Surrey, Clock House	A307
South East	**Limpsfield**, Surrey, Old Lodge	A23
	Sevenoaks, Kent, Royal Oak	A21
	Sharpthorne, West Sussex, Gravetye Manor	A23 (M23)

London restaurants with tables outside

These restaurants all have at least two tables outside in fine weather. Check the entry for details.

Al Hamra, W1
Anna's Place, N1
The Ark, W8
Auntie's, W1
L'Aventure, NW8
La Baita da Piero, E4
La Bastide, W1
Le Café du Marché, EC1
Café Flo, NW3
Café Rouge, EC1
Champagne Exchange, W1
Chanterelle, SW7
Le Chef, W2

Chez Biba, W4
Christian's, W4
La Coupée, SE24
La Croisette, SW10
Daphne, NW1
La Dordogne, W4
Hard Rock Café, W1
Jacques, N4
Kingfisher, Halcyon Hotel, W11
Korea House, W1
Lilly's, W11
Lou Pescadou, SW7

Lowiczanka, W6
Michel, W8
Mijanou, SW1
Mon Plaisir, WC2
Nontas, NW1
Pollyanna's, SW11
Le Quai St Pierre, W8
Soho Brasserie, W1
Le Suquet, SW3
Twenty Trinity Gardens, SW9
Wiltons, SW1

London restaurants open on Sunday

The following restaurants are open for both lunch and dinner on Sundays.

Al Hamra, W1
Auberge de Provence, St James's Court Hotel, SW1
L'Aventure, NW8
Bayleaf Tandoori, N6
The Bengal Lancer, NW5
Bengal Lancer Brasserie, W1
Blakes Hotel, SW7
Bloom's, E1
Blue Elephant, SW6
Bombay Bicycle Club, SW12
Bombay Brasserie, Bailey's Hotel, SW7
Café Flo, NW3
Capital Hotel, SW3
Le Caprice, SW1
Chanterelle, SW7
Chuen Cheng Ku, W1
Cork & Bottle, WC2
La Croisette, SW10
Desaru, W1
Dorchester, W1
Drakes, W1
Fleet Tandoori, NW3
Forum Court, SE25
Fung Shing, WC2

Golden Chopsticks, SW7
Good Friends, E14
Great Nepalese, NW1
Hard Rock Café, W1
Ho-Ho, E18
Hung Toa, W2
Jacques, N4
Kettners, W1
Kingfisher, Halcyon Hotel, W11
Lal Quila, W1
Lantern, NW6
Last Days of the Raj, W1
Lilly's, W11
Lindsey House, W1
London Chinatown, W1
Lou Pescadou, SW7
Lowiczanka, W6
Malabar, W8
Maroush, W2
Maroush II, SW3
Mayflower, W1
Melati, W1
Michel, W8
Ming, W1
Monkeys, SW3
Mr Ke, NW3

Mr Tang, W1
New World, W1
Orso, WC2
Phoenicia, W8
Quincy's, NW2
Ragam, W1
Rani, N3
Red Fort, W1
Shanghai, W8
Shapla, SW9
Shireen Tandoori, W12
Si Chuen, W1
Le Soufflé, Intercontinental Hotel, W1
Sree Krishna, SW17
St Quentin, SW3
Le Suquet, SW3
Suruchi, N1
Topkapi, W1
Tui, SW7
Waltons, SW3
Wong Kei, W1
Yerakina, NW1
Yung's, W1
Zen, SW3
Zen Central, W1
Zen W3, NW3

The following restaurants are open for **Sunday lunch only**

L'Auberge, SE22
Green's, SW1
Launceston Place, W8

Laurent, NW2
Molnars, NW3

Pollyanna's, SW11
Sonny's, SW13

The following restaurants are open for **Sunday dinner only**

The Ark, W8
Bambaya, N8
La Baita da Piero, E4
Ganpath, WC1

Garbo's, W1
Good Food, WC2
Ikkyu, W1

Red Sea, NW6
Santini, SW1
Tiger Lee, W1

London restaurants open after midnight

These restaurants take last orders after midnight.

The Bengal Lancer, NW5
(Fri, Sat only)
Good Food, WC2
Hard Rock Café, W1

Langan's Brasserie, W1
Maroush, W2
Maroush II, SW3
Mayflower, W1

Melati, W1 (Fri, Sat only)
L'Olivier, SW10 (à la carte only)
Yung's, W1

London restaurants by cuisine

AFRO-CARIBBEAN

Bambaya, N8
Red Sea, NW6

CHINESE

Forum Court, SE25
Fung Shing, WC2
Golden Chopsticks, SW7
Good Food, WC2
Good Friends, E14
Ho-Ho, E18
Hoizin, SW1
Hung Toa, W2
London Chinatown, W1
Mayflower, W1
Ming, W1
Mr Ke, NW3
Mr Tang, W1
Poons, WC2
Shanghai, W8
Sichuen, W1
Tiger Lee, SW5
Wong Kei, S1
Yung's, W1
Zen, SW3
Zen Central, W1
Zen W3, NW3

FAR EASTERN

Desaru, W1
Melati, W1
Phoenicia, W8
Topkapi, W1

FISH & CHIPS

Leek's Fish Bar, SW11
Seashell, E8
Upper Street Fish Shop, N1

GREEK

Beoty's, WC2
Daphne, NW1
Kalamaras, W2
Lemonia, NW1

Nontas, NW1
White Tower, W1
Yerakina, NW1

HUNGARIAN

Gay Hussar, W1
Molnars, NW3

INDIAN

Aziz, W6
Bayleaf Tandoori, N6
The Bengal Lancer, NW5
Bengal Lancer Brasserie, W1
Bombay Bicycle Club, SW12
Bombay Brasserie (Bailey's Hotel), SW7
Fleet Tandoori, NW3
Ganpath, WC1
Great Nepalese, NW1
Lal Qila, W1
Last Days Of The Raj, W1
Mandeer, W1
Malabar, W1
Ragam, W1
Rani, N3
Red Fort, W1
Sabras, NW10
Salloos, SW1
Shapla, SW9
Shireen Tandoori, W12
Sree Krishna, SW17
Suruchi, N1

JAPANESE

Ginnan, W
Ikeda, W1
Ikkyu, W1
Miyama, W1
Miyama, EC4
Nanten Yakitori Bar, W1
One Two Three, W1
Saga, W1
Suntory, SW1
Wakaba, NW3

JEWISH

Bloom's, E1
Grahame's Seafare, W1

KOREAN

La Corée, WC2
Korea House, W1

MIDDLE EASTERN

Al Hamra, W1
Efes Kebab House, W1
Maroush, W2
Maroush II, SW3

POLISH

Lowiczanka, W6

PORTUGUESE

Ports, SW3

SPANISH

Rebato's, SW8

SWEDISH

Anna's Place, N1
Garbo's, W1

THAI

Bahn Thai, W1
Bahn Thai, W8
Blue Elephant, SW6
Chiang Mai, W1
Lakorn Thai, EC1
Lena's, SW11
Oh Boy, SW17
Royal Thai Orchids, SW15
Tui, SW7

VIETNAMESE

Saigon, W1

Food finder

The following places have been nominated to the *Guide* for a particular reason. Those with a star are in the main listings.

Views

Hilton Roof, London Hilton, Park Lane, W1A 2HH (01–493 8000)

Royal Garden, 101 Liberty Shopping Hall, East Square, Basildon, Essex (0268 20543)

Buffets

Inn on the Park, Hamilton Park, Park Lane, London W1 (01–499 0888)

Hilton Roof, as above

Sushi

Matono, 25–27 Brewer Street, London W1 (01–734 1859)

*Ikeda, 30 Brook Street, London W1 (01–499 7145)

*Miyama, 17 Godliman Street, London EC4 (01–489 1937)

*Saga, 43 South Molton Street, London W1 (01–629 3931)

Mitsukoshi, 14 Regent Street, London W1 (01–930 0317)

*Wakaba, 31 College Crescent, London NW3 (01–722 3854)

Oyster bars

Sweetings, 39 Queen Victoria Street, London EC4 (01–248 3062)

Bentleys, 11–15 Swallow Street, London W1 (01–734 0431)

Afternoon tea

Ritz Hotel, Piccadilly, London W1 (01–493 8181)

Browns, 21 Dover Street, London W1 (01–493 6020)

Beef

Rib Room, Carlton Tower Hotel, 2 Cadogan Lane, Knightsbridge, London SW1 (01–235 5411)

Rules, Maiden Lane, London WC2 (01–836 5314/2559)

Simpsons in the Strand, 100 The Strand, London WC2 (01–836 9112)

Vegetarian only

Christy's, 122–126 Wardour Street, London W1 (01–434 4468)

Compton Green, 14 Old Compton Street, London W1 (01–434 3544)

Afternoon teas

These hotels serve afternoon teas to non-residents.

LONDON

Blakes Hotel, SW7

Capital Hotel, SW3

Cannaught, W1

Dorchester, W1

Halcyon Hotel (listed under Kingfisher), W11

Intercontinental (listed under Soufflé), W1

Ninety Park Lane, W1

St James's Court, (listed under Auberge de Provence), SW1

ENGLAND

Aislaby Blacksmith's Arms

Ambleside Kirkstone Foot Country House Hotel Rothay Manor

Ascot Royal Berkshire Hotel (listed under Stateroom Restaurant)

Bilbrough Bilbrough Manor

Bath Priory Hotel

Bishops Tachbrook Mallory Court

Brampton Farlam Hall

Broughton Courtyard

Bury St Edmunds Angel Hotel

Calstock Danescombe Valley Hotel

Chaddesley Corbett Brockencote Hall

Chagford Gidleigh Park Teinworthy Hotel

Chester Grosvenor

Clanfield Plough

Clun Old Post Office

Corfe Castle Mortons House Hotel

Dulverton Ashwick House

East Horsley Thatcher's

Evershot Summer Lodge

Evesham Evesham Hotel (listed under Cedar Restaurant)

Gatwick Gatwick Hilton (listed under Garden Restaurant)

Great Milton Le Manoir aux Quat'Saisons

Guildford Manor

Halifax Holdsworth House

Hambleton Hambleton Hall

Hastingleigh Woodmans Arms Auberge

Hawes Cockett's

Hinton Charterhouse Homewood Park

Hockley Heath Nuthurst Grange

Hurstbourne Tarrant Esseborne Manor

Kingham Mill Hotel

Kingsbridge Buckland-Tout-Saints Hotel (listed under Queen Anne Restaurant)

Langho Northcote Manor

Langley Marsh Langley House Hotel
Leighton Buzzard Swan Hotel
Lifton Arundell Arms
Liskeard Well House
Lower Beeding South Lodge
Lynton Hewitt's
Lytham St Anne's Dalmeny Hotel (listed under C'est la Vie)
Middle Wallop Fifehead Manor
Mollington Crabwall Manor
New Milton Chewton Glen Hotel (listed under Marryat Room)
North Huish Brookdale House
Powburn Breamish House
Redlynch Langley Wood
Rochford Renoufs
Ross-on-Wye Walford House Hotel
Seaview (listed under Isle of Wight) Seaview Hotel
Shepton Mallet Bowlish House
Shipton Gorge Innsacre Farmhouse Hotel
Slaidburn Parrock Head Farm
Southwold Crown
Sparsholt Lainston House
Staddlebridge McCoys
Stamford George
Standish Beeches
Stanton Harcourt Harcourt Arms
Ston Easton Ston Easton Park
Stratford Upon Avon Stratford House Hotel (listed under Shepherd's)

Streatley Swan Hotel
Sway Pine Trees
Taunton Castle Hotel
Tetbury Calcot Manor
Torquay Mulberry Room
Ullswater Sharrow Bay
Veryan Treverbyn House
Watlington Well House
West Bexington Manor Hotel
West Mersea Blackwater Hotel (listed under Le Champenois)
Windermere Miller Howe
Wisbech Rose and Crown
Witherslack Old Vicarage
Woodstock Feathers Hotel
Wooler Ryecroft Hotel
Worfield Old Vicarage Hotel
Yattendon Royal Oak
York Middlethorpe Hall

SCOTLAND

Achiltibuie Summer Isles Hotel
Ardeonaig Ardeonaig Hotel
Arisaig Arisaig Hotel
Auchterarder Auchterarder House
Ballater Craigendarroch
Colonsay Isle of Colonsay Hotel
Crinan Crinan Hotel
Inverness Dunain Park
Kelso Sunlaws House
Kentallen Ardsheal House Holly Tree
Kilchrenan Taychreggan Hotel
Kilfinan Kilfinan Hotel
Killiecrankie Killiecrankie Hotel
Lybster Bayview Hotel
Nairn Clifton Hotel

Newton Stewart Kirroughtree Hotel
Oban Knipoch Hotel
Pebbles Cringletie House
Port Appin Airds Hotel
Portpatrick Knockinaam Lodge
Scone Murrayshall Hotel
Skye Harlosh Hotel Kinloch Lodge
St Andrews West Park House
Tarbert West Loch Hotel
Turnberry Turnberry Hotel
Ullapool Morefield Motel

WALES

Abersoch Porth Tocyn Hotel
Brechfa Ty Mawr
Broad Haven Druidstone Hotel
Crickhowell Bear Hotel
Llandderfel Palé Hall
Llanddowror Old Rectory
Llandudno Bodysgallen Hall St Tudno Hotel
Llanwrtyd Wells Llwynderw Hotel
Newport Cnapan
Talsarnau Hotel Maes-Y-Neuadd

REPUBLIC OF IRELAND

Gorey Marlfield House

NORTHERN IRELAND

Dunadry Dunadry Inn

Cover charge blacklist

These restaurants still have a separate cover charge, which is added as an extra to the bill. Check the entry for details.

LONDON

Al Hamra, W1
L'Arlequin, SW8
L'Aventure, NW8
Bahn Tahi, W8
La Baita da Piero, E4
Bambaya, N8
Beau-Rivage, NW6
The Bengal Lancer, NW5

Bengal Lancer Brasserie, W1
Beotys, WC2
Blue Elephant, SW6
Bombay Bicycle Club, SW12
Le Caprice, SW1
Le Chef, W2
Chez Biba, W4
Desaru, W1
La Dordogne, W4
Garbo's, W1

Gay Hussar, W1
Golden Chopsticks, SW7
Grahame's Seafare, W1
Greenhouse, W1
Green's, SW1
L'Hippocampe, SW6
Ho-Ho, E18
Ikeda, W1
Inigo Jones, WC2
Kalamaras, W2

Langan's Bistro, W1
Lena's SW11
Lou Pescadou, SW7
Magno's, WC2
Malabar, W8
Maroush, W2
Maroush II, SW3
La Mascotte, NW2
Meridiana, SW3
Miyama, W1
Miyama, EC4
Molnars, NW3
Neal Street Restaurant , WC2
L'Olivier, SW10
One Two Three, W1
Il Passetto, WC2
Phoenicia, W8
Ponte Nuovo, SW3

Saga, W1
St Quentin, SW3
Salloos, SW1
San Frediano, SW3
Santini, SW1
Shanghai, W8
Soho Brasserie, W1
Suntory, SW1
Le Suquet, SW3
Tui, SW7
White Tower, W1
Wiltons, SW1
Zen Central, W1

ENGLAND

Bristol Harvey's
    Les Semailles
    Rajdoot

Cambridge Shao Tao
Canterbury Tuo e Mio
Christchurch Splinters
East Molesey Lantern
Folkestone India
Grayshott Woods
Ilford Da Umberto
Manchester Gaylord
Stamford The George

SCOTLAND

Perth Timothy's

WALES

Llandewi Skirrid Walnut
    Tree Inn

No smoking

The following restaurants all place some restriction on cigarette smoking in the
dining-room (restrictions on cigar and pipe smoking are so commonplace now
that such places are not listed here). In some, smoking is not allowed at all.
Check entry for details.

LONDON

Auntie's, W1
Beau-Rivage, NW6
Bengal Lancer, NW5
Bengal Lancer Brasserie,
    W1
Drakes, SW3
Le Gastronome, SW6
Mandeer, W1
Mijanou, SW1
Le Soufflé,
    Interncontinental Hotel,
    W1
Tate Gallery, SW1
Tiger Lee, SW5
Twenty Trinity Gardens,
    SW9

ENGLAND

Alston High Fell
Ambleside Kirkstone Food
    Country House Hotel
    Rothay Manor
Ascot Stateroom
    Restaurant, Royal
    Berkshire Hotel
Bath Priory Hotel
Belper Remy's
Berwick-upon-Tweed
    Funnywayt'mekalivin
Birmingham Los Andes
    Forbidden City

Blandford Forum La Belle
    Alliance
Brimfield Poppies
Bristol Harvey's
Brockenhurst Le Poussin
Broughton Courtyard
Buckden Low Greenfield
Bury St Edmunds Angel
    Hotel
Cambridge Free Press
    Midsummer House
Canterbury Restaurant
    Seventy Four
Cartmel Anysome Manor
    Uplands
Chagford Teignworthy
    Hotel
Chelmsford Melissa
Chester Abbey Green
Chittlehamholt Highbullen
    Hotel
Clanfield Plough
Croydon Hockneys
Dulverton Ashwick House
Eastbourne Byrons
Elland Berties Bistro
Epworth Epworth Tap
Gatwick Garden
    Restaurant,
    Gatwick Hilton
Gillingham Stock Hill
Grasmere Michael's Nook
    White Moss House

Great Milton Le Manoir
    aux Quat' Saisons
Grimston Congham Hall
Hastingleigh Woodmans
    Arms Auberge
Herstmonceux Sundial
Hinton Charterhouse
    Homewood Park
Ilkley Olive Tree
Ipswich Singing Chef
Ixworth Theobalds
Kingsbridge Queen Anne
    Restaurant, Buckland-
    Tout-Saints Hotel
Langley Marsh Langley
    House Hotel
Ledbury Hope End Country
    House Hotel
Lewes Pattissons
Lynton Hewitt's
Manchester Gaylord
    Koreana
    On the Eighth Day
Melmerby Village Bakery
Mollington Crabwall
    Manor
Moreton in Marsh Lambs
**Newcastle Upon
    Tyne** Madeleine's
North Huish Brookdale
    House
Oxford Browns
Pool in Wharfedale Pool
    Court

Powburn Breamish House
Ridgeway Old Vicarage
Sharpthorne Gravetye Manor
Shepton Mallet Bowlish House
Shrewsbury Delanys Old Police House
Spark Bridge Bridgefield House
Steeple Aston Red Lion
Stonham Mr Underhill's
Stratford Upon Avon Shepherd's, Stratford House Hotel
Tetbury Calcot Manor
Ullswater Sharrow Bay
Walford Walford House Hotel
Whitby Magpie Cafe
Winchcombe Corner Cupboard Dining Room
Windermere Miller Howe, Miller Howe Kaff
Witherslack Old Vicarage
Wooler Ryecroft Hotel
Worfield Old Vicarage Hotel

SCOTLAND

Achiltibuie Summer Isles Hotel
Arbroath Carriage Room
Ballater Craigendarroch, Tullich Lodge
Callander Roman Camp Hotel
Canonbie Riverside Inn
Cromarty Le Chardon
Cupar Ostlers Close
Drumnadrochit Polmaily House Hotel
Dunoon Ardenslate Hotel
Edinburgh Alp-Horn, Helios Fountain, Indian Cavalry Club, Kalpna, Martins
Fort William Inverlochy Castle
Gullane La Potiniere
Harris Scarista House
Inverness Dunain Park
Kentallen Ardsheal House, Holly Tree
Killiecrankie Killiecrankie Hotel
Kingussie Cross
Mull Tiroran House
Nairn Clifton Hotel
Newton Stewart Kirroughtree Hotel
Newtonmore Ard na Coille
Peat Inn Peat Inn
Peebles Cringletie House
Port Appin Airds Hotel
Scone Murrayshall Hotel
Tarbert West Loch Hotel
Tyndrum Clifton Coffee House
Ullapool Morefield Motel
Walls Burrastow House

WALES

Brechfa Ty Mawr
Cardigan Rhyd-Garn-Wen
Harlech Castle Cottage
Haverfordwest Jemima's
Llanddowror Old Rectory
Llandudno St Tudno Hotel
Llanrwst Meadowsweet Hotel
Newport Cnapan
Talyllyn Minffordd Hotel
Wolfs Castle Wolfscastle Country Hotel

REPUBLIC OF IRELAND

Cork Arbutus Lodge

The Good Food Club 1987

Many thanks to all the following people who contributed, in one way or another, to this year's *Guide* . . .

Mr M.J. Abbott
John Abel
Ms Stephanie Abraham
Dr Sidney Abrahams
Mr A.D. Abrams
Miss Suzanne Ackerman
Mr John Acland
Mr Alasdair M.M. Adam
Dr J.C.S. Adams
Robert Adams
Mrs Wendy Adams
Mr A. Addison
Mr Ian Addison
Miss Linda Addison
W. Adshead
Dr J.B. Ainscough
Dr D.M.C. Ainscow
Mr John R. Aird
Mr & Mrs J Aisher
Mr Sulayman S. Alamuddin C.B.E.
Robert S. Albert PHD
E.J.C. Album
S.T. Alderson
John W. Alderton
Mr D.D. Alexander
Mrs K.J. Alexander
Mrs Margret Alford
Mrs Mary Ali
Mr N. Ali
Mr B.F Allen
H. Allen
Miss Jackie Allen
Dr J.P. Allen
W.R. Allen Esq
Mr R.E. Allen
Mrs Allfrey-Pizer
D.J. Allison Esq
Mr Brian Allmey

Ms S.C. Allwood
Sir Anthony Allwood
Sir Anthony Alment
Mr & Mrs J.G. Alston
Ms Jane Altenhoven
Mr A. Altorfer
Mr S. Amey
Mr & Mrs G.D. Amos
Mr Chris Anderson
Mr D.M. Anderson F.R.I.C.S.
J. Anderson
J.H. Anderson
John Anderson
Ms Thelma Anderssen-Orr
Mr & Mrs Angell
Mr J. Antell
Michael and Betty Appleby
T. Appleton Esq
Mrs A Apsey
Mrs Cynthia Archer
D.S. Archer
Mr T.J. Archer
Mrs Archer
Dr J.R. Archibald
A.J. Aris
Mr J.D. Armitage
Revd M. Armitage
Mr D Armstrong
Mr S.M.L. Armstrong
G.J. Arnold
Mr Hugo Arnold
Mrs M.E. Arnold
Mrs Wendy Arnold
Mr Nigel Arnott
H.J. Ash
Mrs H.G. Ashburn
Dr Robert Asher
Mr & Mrs C. Ashton
H.W. Ashton

Kim M. Ashton
Mr D. Ashworth
Mr P.W. Askew
Mr Alan Aspda
Mrs J.M. Aston
Mrs V. Atherton
B.D. Atkin
Mr R.A.J. Atkinas
Guy and Phoebe Atkins
Ms T.J. Atkins
Mrs E. Atkinson
Mr G. Atkinson
Mr W. Atkinson
Ms S.J. Attias
Mrs D.H. Attwood
Mrs Harry Attwood
Mr James H. Auckworth
Mr Steven Auld
Mr & Mrs D.G. Austin
Mr & Mrs R. Austin
Mrs P. Avison
A Aylwin
Leonard Baart
Mr & Mrs V Bach
Mrs J.D. Back
R.C. Black
Dr J.R. Backhurst
Cynthia Bacon
Air Cmdre, G. McA. Bacon
Susan Badman
Mrs Anne Bagert
Elizabeth Bailey
Mr & Mrs Eric Bailey
Jane & Martin Bailey
Mary D. Bailey
M.H. Bailey
Mr & Mrs M.P. Bailey

Mr & Mrs Richard Bailey
Warner M. Bailey
Mr M.H. Bailey
Mrs Elizabeth Bailey
Martyn Bainbridge
R. Bairamian
Mr & Mrs Baker
A.A. Baker
Bill Baker
M.J. Baker
Brian Baker
Mr Brian Baker
Paul & Margaret Baker
Mr Richard Baker
R.B.H. Baker
R.W. Baker
Mrs M.J. Baker
Mrs J. Baker
Mrs Peggy Balaam
Livio Balbi
David & Jean Balderston
Mr D.L.S. Baldi
J.R. Baldwin
David Ball
Mr James Bamber
Mrs S Banham
Mrs J. Banister
Mrs J Bankes
P. Bann
Dr Stephen Bann
Maureen Banner
Ms Diana Bannister
Mr H.S. Bansal
Mrs P.J. Barbour
Mrs R.L. Barclay
Mr B. Barder
Nicholas Barfield
Mrs Teresa Barker
Peter Barkworth
Dr J.A. Barley

Dr E.D. Barlow
Antony Barnes Esq
Lt Col. B.A.S. Barnes
C.A. Barnes
Mrs Marie Barnes
Simon Barnes
Ms Erica Barnett
Miss Zite Barnett
Wg Cdr D.R.
　Barnicoat
Peter Barnsley
Dr P. Barnwell ME
Miss Penny Barr
Mr & Mrs R.
　Barraclough
Geoff Barrett
Joan Barrett
N.A. Barratt
Mr O.W. Barratt
Roger Q. Barrett
Mr John Andrew
　Cecil Barrington
H.C.N. Barron
Mr Phillip Barron
Mr B.J. Barry
Mr Stuart Barry
M. Bartley
K.R. Barzey
W.R. Basham
Ms Georgina L.
　Bassett
Mr M. Batchelor
Peter Bate
Mr V.R. Bateman
M. Bates
Mr Stanley Bates
Mr & Mrs A.J.
　Bateson
Mr Peter J. Batkin
Mr David Batten
John R. Batty
Mr R. Battye
A.S.J. Baughan
E. Baughan
E. Baumber
Ms Mary Baxter
Stephen Bayley
Mr and Mrs J
　Baynes
Mrs J.P. Beale
Mr Robert Beard
Dr Alan Beaton
Mr C. Beatson-Hird
Ian Beattie
R. Beattie
Mrs M.A.
　Beaverstock
Dr M.K. Beazley
R.A. Beck
Mr Beckett
J.R.E. Bedford
Mrs W. Bedford

Mr and Mrs W.E.
　Bedford
Reverend & Mrs
　John Beech
Dr S.F. Beer
Mr Brian Begg
John Behle
Mr A.A. Bell
Miss A.M.B. Bell
Mr D.G. Bell
Miss E.R. Bell
J.D.M. Bell
Mrs A. Bellerby
A. J.'Benbow
Mr M.J. Benenson
Mrs E. Benford
Mrs Barbara
　Bennett
Mr G.G. Bennett
Mrs Marjorie
　Bentham
Miss Julia Bentley
Mr J. Benton
Mr William Bentsen
Mrs D.M. Beraud
Mr and Mrs H.I.
　Berkeley
Mrs Gabriele
　Berneck
Mr Ken Berrisford
B. Berry
George Berry, Esq
Mr W.J. Best
Mr I.M. Beswick
K. Bettle
Mr G. Betts
Mr Steve Betts
Mr C.W.L. Bevan
Mrs P.C. Bevan
Dr R. Bhabutta
S.W. Bickford-Smith
Dr and Mrs Biggaur
Mr Christopher
　Biggs
Mr M.V. Bilby & Mr
　M. Spittle
J.A. Biles
Ms Rosemary Billam
C.J. Billing
Mrs V. Bingham
Mr & Mrs R.F.
　Binmore
Mr R. Birch
Mr P.M. Bisby
L. Bishop
Miss P. Bishop
Mr S.V. Bishop
Mrs T.J.H. Bishop
G.S. Bisset
John Black
Mr J.P. Black
Mrs M.A. Blackburn

Mr L. Blair
Diana Blake
Mr L.R. Blake
Mr P.A. Blake
Mr Timothy Blake
Miss C.A. Bland
L.M. Bland Esq
P.A. Bland
Mrs J. Blanks
Mr Paul F. Blomley
Derek Bloom
Jay and Fiona Bluck
Dr Kerry Bluglass
Mr R.K. Blumenau
Mr Alan Blyth
Mrs M.V. Blyth
Ms N. Blyth
S. Bobasch
Mr S.J. Boden
Miss J. Boend
K.W. Bogle
Mrs Elizabeth Bolgar
Mrs L. Bolton
Pauline Bolton
David Bond
Mr Richard Bond
J. Bonner
E. Bonner-Maurice
N. Bookbinder Esq
Dr C. Booth
T.S. Borlano
Alister Borthwick
Mrs D. Borton
C.J. Bosanquet
Mrs G. Bostock
Krimo Bouabda
Stephen Bould
C.E. Bourchier
Rev M.A.
　Bourdeaux
A.C. Bourne
Mr B.S. Bourne
R. Bourne
Ms Anne Boustred
Mr A.S. Bowell
Mr A.J. Bowen
Mr M.H.
　Bowensiepen
A.I. Bower Esq
R.L. Bowerman
Ms M.E. Bowers
Mr Edwin Ward
　Bowie
Miss Isobel Bowler
Rev & Mrs, R.
　Bowles
Eimer and John
　Bowman
P.M. Boxshall
Mr & Mrs Gordon
　Boyes
R. Boyse

Miss M.I. Brabant,
　J.P.
Dave Brabants
A.J. Brabin
Mrs G. Bradbury
Dr J.M. Bradbury
Jack Bradley
K. Bradley
Mrs M.J. Bradley
Mr G. Bradshaw
Mr M Brady
Mr E.W. Bramford
Mr P.R Brand
Nial Brannigan
Mr J.F. Branscombe
Mrs K.M. Brassey
Dr A.M. Braverman
Mr D. Bray
Mr James E. Bray
N.P. Bray
Mrs B.J. Brayshaw
I. Brecker
W.T. Brennan
Jacques Bressler
Lindy Brett
Mr Ian Brian
H. Brickwood
Dr J.N. Bridge
J.T. Bridge
C.A. Briere-Goney
J.B. Brierley
Mr T.G. Brierly
Miss Anne Briers
Major & Mrs C.F.
　Briggs
R.J. Brightwell
Clare Brigstocke
Mr J. Bristow
Mr and Mrs B.
　Bristowe
Mr M. Broady
E.M. Le Brocq
A.W. Brodrick
Mrs Vera Bromage
Roy Y. Bromell
Mr G.J. Brook
Keith R. Brook
Mr Brooke & Ms
　Shallcross
Mrs H. Brooke
Mrs H. Brooke
Mr A.B. Brooker
Mr L.W. Brooks
Dr P.W. Brooks
H. & J. Broomhead
A.H. Broughton
Mr M.H. Browell
D.H. Brown
Revd Richard
　Brown
Miss Julie Brown
Mrs Margret Brown

A.S. Brown
J.M. Brown
Robin Brown
E.A. Brown
Rev N. Brown
Mr W. Brown
Mr Percival Brown
Mrs J.A. Brown
Mr Lawrence Brown
Michael W.L. Brown
Michael Brown
Dr & Mrs D.G. Brown
Mr L.H. Brown
Mr Neville Brown
Mrs N. Brown
M. Browne
Mrs E. Browning
W.H. Bruton Esq
Mr John Bryant
Mr J.M. Bryant
Mr M. Bryant
Mr A.W.B. Buchholz
Mr Grant Buck
R.W. Buckle
Mrs Caroline Buckley
Alexander J. Buick
J. Buldt
Mr Malcolm R. Bull
Ian L. Bull
Brian Bull
Mr & Mrs R Bull
Mr J.R. Bull
Mrs Penelope Bullivant
Mr & Mrs Bullock
Mrs H.M. Bunch
Mrs S. Bunker
Herrick Bunney
Mr D.J. Bunter
Mrs H. Burgess
James P.C. Burgess
M. Burgess-Ashton
Mr E.M. Burkitt
Ms Jill E. Burlton
David M. Burns, Esq
Mr J. Burrill
David Burrows
Mr D.R.F. Burrows
Mr & Mrs R.G. Burry
Mr Anthony Burton
Mr C. Burton
E.A. Burton
Mr G.M. Burton
Revd G.R. Bush
Mrs H Bush
R.M. & V. Bushby
Barbara Bushell
Dr and Mrs T.G. Bushell

Mr J Bussey
Mr & Mrs J. Butler
Mr R.J. Butt
D. Butterfield
Mr J.A. Butterfield
Mr S. Stuart Buttle
Ms Deborah Buzan
Mr & Mrs James Byrne
Mr Peter Cackett
Prof Robert Cahn
Dr & Mrs G.R. Caird
Barbara A. Cairns
Mr Robert Caldicott
Mr T.J. Caley
Christine Calladine
D.M. Callow
Miss Lynne J. Calvert
Mrs Elizabeth Cameron
Mrs R. Cameron
Miss Sheona Cameron
Linda Camp
A.J. Campbell
Caroline Campbell
Ms Fiona Campbell
Ms Margaret Campbell
Mrs & Mrs James Campbell-Smith
Mrs Phillippa Camps
Mr James Cane
Dr & Mrs S.M. Cannicott
Mr Stephen Cannon
Captain T.J.B. Cannon R.A.
Mr N. Cant
Mrs M.J. Cantacuzene
A. Canty
Mr & Mrs D.N. Carder
Mr D. Cardy
Guy P.L. Carless
Miss C. Carlyle-Clarke
Roberta F. Carmichael
Simon Carne RIBA
Mr Carpenter
Mr P. Carpenter
Mr Patrick Carpenter
Anne Carr
Mrs J.J. Carr
Mr M.D. Carr
Mr & Mrs P. Carraro-Jost

Mr J. Carroll
Kevin Carroll
Miss Olive Carroll
Mr Dennis Carswell
Mrs L. Carter
Mr P.E. Carter
Mr Simon Carter
Ms B. Carter
Mrs Pat Carter-Jones
Kim Cartledge
Mrs Cartwright
Mrs J.A. Cartwright
Mr Robert. Cartwright
Mr G.J. Carwithen
Mr H.J. Case
Mrs Joyce Casilio
Eric V. Cass
R.E. Catlow
Ms Linsey Caton
Cathy & Giles Cattermole
Robert & Judith Catty
Mr Leslie Caul
Mrs Rachel Cave
T.A. Cave
Mary Ceryan
Mr Peter Chadwick
Mrs Susan Chait
P.A. Chalkley
C.J. Chalmers Esq
L. Chamber
Mr David Chambers
Mrs Helen Chambers
Dr Michael Chambers
Mrs R.A. Chaple
Mr A.W.T. Chapman
Mrs Clare Chapman
Mungo Chapman
Mr W.J. Chapman
Mr John Paul Chapple
Jim Charlesworth
Mrs H. Chatten
Mr G.E. Cherry Sebastian
Cheswright, Esq
Mr & Mrs T.J. Chilvers
Dr S. Chinnapha
M. Chivers
Jonathan Choat
Rupert Christiansen
George W. Christie
Mrs. M. Churchill
Mr Simon Churchill
A.V. Chute

J. Chuton
Miss Gyda Chyfarchion
Mr Norman Civval
Marjorie Clack
Nicholas Clapton
Mr B.B. Clark
Caroline Clark
Mrs .A. Clark
Mr M.D. Clark
June Clark
Ms K.L. Clark
Roy Clark
Mr Tony Clark
Ms A.G.C. Clarke
Derek & Pauline Clarke
Mr Eric Clayton
Mr & Mrs H.W. Clayton
Mr Glenn Clear
Mr Terence Clegg
Mr W.E.M. Clegg
Mr W.H. Cleghorn
Mr Kenneth Cleveland
Mr H.C. Clifford
Mr R.L. Clifford
Mr R. Cliffords
Susan P.L. Clifford Jones
Mr R. Clifton
Capt N. Clogstoun-Willmott DSO
Mr David H. Close
Miss E.K. Cloud
Mr G.A. Clough
Mrs J. Cloutt
Major General & Mrs R.L. Clutterbuck
Mr P.J. Clymer
E. Clyne
Mr R.F. Coals
Ms S.P. Coates
Mr Peter Cobrin
E.G. Coe
Sarah Coe
W.F. Coghill
Dr D.L. Cohen
G.J. & M.E. Cohen
George Cohen, Esq
Michelle Cohen
Mr Colbatch Clark
Mr & Mrs A Cole
Dr J.A. Cole
John & Moira Cole
Mr Ron Cole
Mr & Mrs G. Coleman
Mr J.M. Coleman
T.P.H. Coleman

Mrs Lisa Coleridge
Professor Leslie Collier
Mrs R.E. Collingham
Diana Collins
Mrs J Collins
Mr Gary Collins
Mr R. Collins
A.P.J. Collinson
Barbara Collinson & Neil Markham
C.R. Collinson
Mrs J.M. Colquhoun
Dr M.P. Colvin
R.T. Combe
Mr M. Comninos
Mr Graham Connolly
Dr J.J.A. Conrad
Mrs A. Conradi
Ms Phelan Consuelo
Mr Ivan Conswelow
Godfrey J. Cook, Esq., FRICS
Ms Jackie Cook
Ronald R. Cook
Susan Cook
J.P.F. Cooke
Mrs J. Cookson
Mrs Joan Coombs
Roger Coombs
Susan M. Coombs
Miss Jo-Anne Cooper
P.J. Cooper
Mr Reginald Cooper
Mr Cope
David and Jane Copeland
Mr & Mrs D. Copeland
David Coplowe
J.H. Copping
Mr A.W. Corbett
Mr J. Corbluth
K.A. Corcoran
Mr K.R. Corcoran
Brian Cornwell
Anthony Corrales
Mr B. Cossey
Mr J. Costello
Mr J.V. Couceiro
Stuart Coulthard
Lady Couper
Jonathan Courage
M.R. Court
Mr A. Coverdale
Mr L.J. Coverley
Mr G Cowell
J. Cowell
Mr & Mrs S.J. Cowherd

Ms P. Cowley
Mr C.J. Cowlin
Mr D. Cox
Miss H. Cox & Mr T. Withers
Mr H.C. Cox
Mr J. Cox
Mr J.L. Cox
Jill Cox
Mrs M.M. Cox
Mary Jane Cox
P.D. Cox
Dr R.A.F. Cox
Ms Gillian Coy
Mr & Mrs W.J. Crabb
Mr R. Crabtree
A.C. Cracknell
John Cragg
Mrs M. Craig
Dr R.C. Keith Craigowl
R.R. Craik
R.D. Cramond
Peter Crane
Mr Phillip Cranmer
Mr J.D. Cranston
Dr K.W.E. Craven
Dr & Mrs P.G. Craven
Mrs Jean Crayson
Mr Richard Creed
Mr Anderby Creek
Mrs R.M. Crichton
Mr Russell L. Crichton
Barbara Crickmore
Mr M.G. Cripps
Mr F.C. Critchley
Julian Critchely
Mrs Gloria M. Crocker
G.S. Crockett
Mr R.C. Crockford
Mr J.H. Croker
Mr T.E. Crompton
Ms J.A. Crookes
John Crosby
Mr P.R. Crosland
Mr J. Cross
Jeanne Cross
Mrs Margaret J.N. Cross
Mary Cross
Rodney Cross
V. Cross
Mr F.B. Crossley
Dr J.M. Crossley
Miss Gabriel Crow
Ms Margaret Crowther
T. Crowther QC

Mr and Mrs J. Cull
Mr & Mrs R. Cullen
Mrs J.A. Cullinane
Mr A.C. Cullum
Mr M.C. Culver
Frank Cummins
Lord Cunliffe
Mark Cunningham
Nichola Cunningham
Dr James Stevens Curl
Mr Denis Curtis
Sir John Curtiss
Mr Mike Cushman
R. Cussons
Mrs R.B. Custerson
Mr F.A. Cusworth
Mrs T.A. Cutbill
Anne Cuthill
Mr Bill Cutler
Mr and Mrs Mark Dacey
Mr Mohamed Daho
Mr K.W. Daley
Geoffrey Dalgleish-Bond
Mrs M. Dallisson
Mrs K.M. Dalton
Mr R. Dalton
M.J. Daly
T.D. Dampney
Mr Gerry A. Danby
Miss R. Dangerfield
Mrs J. Daniel
Dr V.J. Daniel
D.R. Daniels
Mr Roger P. Daniels
Mrs P. Danvers
P.M. Darby
Mrs M. Darkin
Daniel Darwood
Wg Cdr K. Dauncey
Mrs Elizabeth Davey
Dr T.J. David
Ron and Jan Davidson
Mr Ian Davie
J.B. Davies
Mrs D.M. Davies
Colin Davies
Dr R.J. and Mrs K.B. Davies
Stephen Davies
Mr G. Davies
Mr G.H. Davies
John Davies
Maria Davies
Ms Sarah Davies
Mr Christopher Talfan Davies
L.M. & A. Davis

Mr B. Davis
Mr & Mrs N. Davis
Mrs J.S. Davison
Dr William Davison
Dr G. Davison
Anna Dawson
Mr and Mrs Dawson
E.A. Dawson
Capt P.N. Daymon
Mr R. Daysh
Vicomtesse de Contades
Ms Emanuel De Kadt
Mr Michael de la Noy
C.B. De Launay Esq
Matron P.E. De Roche
Mr David A.G. Deacon
Mr Nigel Deacon
Roger H. Deal
Mr & Mrs Alan Dean
N. Dean & N. Carslaw
Mr & Mrs S.M. Dearden
Mr. K.R. Dedman
Mr N.C. Dee
Mrs G.M. Deering
Ms B. Deinhardt
D.B. Delany
Dr Mark Delargy
Mr M.C. Delazarus
Mrs Pamela Delvin
The Earl of Denbigh
Jas & Sue Denny
Mr C.A.F. Denton
Dr S. Derek & Miss E. Wilkinson
Muriel Derry
Peter Desbottes
Mrs A. Desmond
Jeremy and Janet Dewes
Mr Charles Dewhurst
Mr J.W. Dickens
Mr H.E. Dickinson
Dr J.P. Dilworth
Mr & Mrs C.P. Diver
C.E. Dix
Mr J.A. Dixon
Mrs J.A. Dixon
Mrs Joyce Dixon
Mrs J. Dixon
Mrs M.R. Dobbins
Dr and Mrs Neville Dobie
Mr Fred Dobson
Mr Anthony Docherty

A. Docherty
Mrs D. Dodds
A.H. Doran
Mr Edward Dorrell
Mr B. Dorsett
Jayme dos Santos, Esq
James & Mary Douglas
Mr K Douglas-Jones
Roger Doulton
Roger H. Down, Esq
Mr K.R. Downes
Mr Sidney Downs
Mr R.H. Downs
Mrs P. Downward
Mr R. Doyle
Mr A.I. Doyle
Dr. C. Draper
Miss Isabell Drever
B.J. Drew
Ian Driscoll
Penny Driver
Mr P. Druee
J.N. Drummond
James H. Duckworth
Mr & Mrs A. Duff
Mrs Jane A. Duffin
Mr W.E. Dully
Mrs Karine A Dummer
Mr T.M. Duncan
N.B. Duncan
The Rev James Duncan
Mrs G. Dundas
Mr Kenneth Dunjohn
David and Eileen Dunn
Miss Rosemary Dunn
Mr & Mrs L. Dunning
Mr Raymond Dunt
Mrs M. Durant
Ms Sue Durham
Denis Durno
Norman R. Dutsson
Clive L. Duval
Miss A. Duval-Smith
Mrs Duxfield
Mrs L.A. Dyson
Louise Dyson-Wingett
Mr J. Dyst
R.S. Eades
Chris & Dill Eager
The Earl of Bradford
Mr & Mrs B. Earthy

V.J. East
Dr Lindsay Easton
Mrs J.S. Eastwood
Mr J. Eastwood
Mrs V. Eastwood
Dr R. Eban
Mr J.M. Eccleson
Dr S. Eden
Mr Arthur Edge
Mr R.W. Edmonds
Judith Edmondson
Miss Elizabeth Edmondson
Kathleen L. Edwards
Mr L.W. Edwards
A.W. Edwards
A. Edwards Esq
Squadron Leader J.A.K. Edwards
K.H. Edwards
Mr & Mrs Edwards
Mr & Mrs N.J. Edwards
Mr Anton Edwards
Mr Richard Ehrlich
Myra & Ray Elderfield
Peter Elderfield
Mr R.S. Elegant
R.F. Eliot
Tim Elkington
L.C. Elliott
Ms C.J. Elliot
Mr & Mrs P. Elliott
Mr E. Ellis
Mr N.H. Ellis
R.S. Ellis Esq
Mrs Joan Ellis
Mr Ivor Neame Ellis
D.R. Ellis
A.R. Ellis
P.R. Ellison Esq
Mrs Sue Elson
Mr John Elvidge
Mrs D.M. Emanuel
Professor H.E. Emson
Mr David End
Mr Max English
Robert Entwistle
Mrs J.B. Epstein
Mr R. Erskine
Lady Erskine-Hill
M.B. Espley
Mr & Mrs J. Ette
R.C.G. Evans
Ms Angela Evans
Mr & Mrs E.P. Evans
Ms Jan Evans
Angela and Ray Evans
Mr Phillip L. Evans

Mr Robin Evans
Dr C.S. Evans
Dr & Mrs A.M. Evans
Mr & Mrs A.J. Evans
R.G. Evans
Mr & Mrs M. Evans
D.I.K. Evans
Ms C.L. Evans
Dr & Mrs M. Evans
Mrs Jean Eve
Mrs B.R. Everett
Mr A.B. Ewart
P.M. Eyre
Mr R. Fafalko
Mr M. Fagan
J. Fairbairn
Mr & Mrs R.J. Faircliff
Mr William A. Fairke
P.A. Fairley
Mr J. Fairley
Mr R.B. Fairweather
C.J. Fallows
Mr Timothy Fancourt
Miss A.D. Fanthorpe
Roger Farbey
Mr & Mrs Farnsworth
Mr Cameron Farquharson
Julian Farr
J.S. Farr-Davies
Mr R.A. Farrand
Ann Farrow
R.P. Fawcett
Cllr. Ronnie Fearn
Paul Feldwick
Mrs Christine Fenton
A.B.X. Fenwick Esq
Mr R. Fenwick
Dr W.M. Ferguson
Ms Sarah A.D. Ferguson
Mr Miguel Fernandez
Mr Peter Ferner
Mrs J. Ferrett
Mr Alan Ferry
Mrs L. Ferstendik
Jean and Sandy Fetter
George E. Fettinger
Mr W.H. Fiden
Miss Ann Field
R.S. Fieldson
Mr Peter D. Finch
Dr Paul Fincham
Mr & Mrs J. Finkel

Mr & Mrs M. Firth
Mr A. Firth
Mr Adrian Firth
Mr Martin Fisher
I.N. Fishman Esq
Ms J. Fiske
J.J. Fitz-Earle
Mr J.B. Fitzpatrick CBE
Mr A.J. Flaherty
Mrs A.L. Fleming
J.G. Fleming
R.A. Fletcher
Ron Fletcher
Dr. G.C. Fletcher
Mr P.A.L. Fletcher
G.E. Fletcher
Clare Fletcher
Mrs J.A. Fletcher
J.K. Flood
Mrs Noren Flook
Mr Bernard Florsham
Mrs G.A. Floy
Mrs Flynn
Nigel Foley
Mr Sean Foley
Mr N.L. Foot
Mr & Mrs M.R. Foottit
J.A. Ford
Miss Suan Foreman
Mr C.R. Formby
Mr P.J. Forrest
Mr M.A.L. Forrow
Mrs Christina Forster
Mr T. Foster
B.W. Forster Esq
B. Forsyth
Mr T.V.N. Fortescue
Mr Nigel Fortnam
Ms S. Foster
A. Fortheringham
Dr D.B. Fowler
Prof. H. Fox
Mrs C. Foy
Lance Foyster
Derek & Marilyn Frampton
John Francis
Ms Constantin J. Francois
Dr A. Frank
Mrs Pamela Frankel
Mr R. Frankenburg
Mr R. Frankland
M. & D. Franklin
Mrs A.C. Franks
Dr Fraser
Mr Ian Fraser
Mrs W.A. Fray

John Freebairn
C.R. Freeman Esq
Ms P.H. Freeman
Professor H.L.
	Freeman
Dr R.H. Freeman
Philip R. Freeman
Robert Freidus Esq
Mr B.M. French
Mary J.M. Frith J.P.
Mrs J. Frost
Andrew S. Frost Esq
Ms Eva Frumin
Ms C. Fry
F. Fry
Mr & Mrs A. Fuller
Mark Fuller
Mr Roy Fuller
Mr A.R. Fulton
Mr & Mrs R. & R.
	Furlong Brown
I.F. Furmage Esq
Jane Furse
Carlo Fuselli
Dr & Mrs R. Gadsby
Mr Selwyn Gale
Mr J.M. Gallagher
Mr & Mrs P. Galt
P.H. Gannaway
J.J Gardiner & S.Y.
	Dunstan
Mr R.J. Gardner
Dr J. Gardner
Stephen Garford
Mr S. Garman
Mr W. Garney
Miss Amanda
	Garrett
Mr Conrad Garrett
Captain D.J.I.
	Garstin
Miss J. Gash
Dr M.S. Gatley
Dr R.A.P. Gaubert
Mr W. Gaughan
George Gaunt
J. Gazdak
Dr and Mrs S. Gee
Alan Genders
D.C.F. Gent
Ms Anita
	Geoghagan
D.J. Gerhard
Mrs J. Gerrad
Mr Hunter M.
	Gholson
Mr & Mrs Austin
	Gibbons
Mr & Mrs R.C. Gibbs
Richard Gibson
Richard J. Gibson
Mr S.C. Gibson

Mrs G. Gibson
Kenneth Gilbert
Susan Gilbert
Ms Rosemary Giles
Ms Mary Giles
Mr Geoff Giles
J.S. Gilks
Mr D. Gill
Ms Susan Gillies
Mrs A.M. Gillitt
Peter Gillman
Mrs S.M. Gillotti
Mr Harry Gilmore
Mr G.C. Gilroy
Wg C.D.R. & Mrs J.I.
	Gilson
Mr R. Ginn
Stefan Girstun Esq
B.D. Gisbourne
K.G.T. Gladstone
Mr D.B. Gledhill
H.R. & V.A.
	Glendenning
I.T. Glendenning
Mr P.J. Glenn
B.M. Glover
Mr M.J. Glover
R.J.N. Glover
A.J. Goater
Mr R.C. Godber
M.B. Godfrey
G. Godfrey
Mrs J. Godfrey
Leslie Godwin
M. Jacques Goffeau
Ms C.J. Gold
Kathryn Golder
C. Golding
Mr Arnold Goldman
M.P. Goldwater Esq
Mr Michael
	Goldwater
Ms Theresa
	Gomersall
Tom Gondris
M.F. Good
A.J. Goodall
Shirley Goode
N.J. Goodey
J. Elizabeth
	Goodford
Mrs T.A. Goodger
Mrs N. Goodman
Mrs P. Goodson
Dr & Mrs P.D.
	Goodstein
Mrs K. Goodwill
Noel Gordon and
	Gillian Shore
R.C.J. Gordon
Mr & Mrs Jerold
	James Gordon

Douglas Gordon
Paul Gordon-Saker
Mr & Mrs G.J. Gore
Mr P.F.O. Gorman
Mrs G.A.F.
	Gorzkowska
D.M. Gostyn
Mrs Jean Gould
Mr D.I. Goulden
Ross N.S. Gow
Mr Frank C. Grace
Dennis J. Graham
Mr Hugh Graham
Mr J.W.R. Graham
Olivia Graham
Mrs O.E. Granger
Miss Rita Grant
Albert Grant
Dr J. Grant
Mr Paul Grant
W.M. Grant
Mrs Moira Grattidge
Mrs Christine
	Gratus
Mr T.G. Graveney
Mr Crawford F.
	Gray
P.S. Gray
Michael Gray
Drs Denis & Barbara
	Gray
H. Gray
Brigadier T.I.G.
	Gray
Mrs B. Green
Mrs S.R. Green
Mrs A Greenberg
Mr Francis Greene
Mr A. Greenfield
Mr J.F. Greenhough
A.E.W. Greenwall
	Esq
Mr & Mrs K.
	Greenwood
Mr A. Greenwood
Roger B. Greenwood
Mr J. Greenwood
J.C. & D. Gregory
A.H. Gregory
J.R. & J. Gregory
Mr & Mrs J.L.
	Gregory
Declan & Alicia
	Grehan
Miss Alison
	Grenville
A.K. Grice
Mr and Mrs C.H.
	Griffin
Mr E.F. Griffin
Mrs S. Griffiths
Mrs J.D. Griffiths

W.T.G. Griffiths, Esq
Mr David Griffiths
Mr Phillip Griffiths
Jane Grigson
Mark Grimwade
Mrs Shirley
	Grimwood
Mr Don Grisbrook
Mrs Rita Gromb
Mr R. Grover
F.J. & P.D. Groves
Ms A. Gruenberg
Mrs R.A.
	Grunewald
Mr & Mrs R.K.
	Guelff
Mrs S.A. Gugen
Mr & Mrs Gunter
John M. Gurr
Alison Gurr
Mr Barton Guthrie
Mrs N. Guy
Mr & Mrs A.A. Gwilt
Dr E. Anne
	Gwinnett
S.C. Hacker
Mr Christopher
	Hackett
Mrs Joan Hadfield
Mr Russell Hafter
Mrs M. Hague
Miss June Haines
Dr. C.I. Haines
Ms Jane E. Hale
Mr J.P. Hall
I. Hall
Ms Philippa Hall
Mr P.K. Hall
Mr & Mrs Hall
J.M. Hall
Mrs June Hall
Mrs R. Hall
Mr Simon Hall
Mrs H.S. Hallett
W.J. Hallett
Mr M.V. Hambling
Mr W.B. Hamilton
A.G. Hamilton
Mary Hamlyn
Mr & Mrs S.M.
	Hamm
J. Hammond
Mr H.J. Hamp
Ms Barbara
	Hampton
N.O.M. Hancock
Mr & Mrs D.R.
	Handley
Mrs Lorraine M.
	Handley
Mr R.E. Hands
F.G. Hankins

Sir Michael Hanley
Robert Hannay
Maurice Hanssen
Esq
Mr Richard Harbord
W.A. Harbottle
Mrs B.A. Harding
R. Harding
Mr & Mrs A.J.
Harding
Vanessa Harding
Mr M. Harding
Mrs Caroline
Harding
A.I. Hardman
Mrs Y. Hardwick
Ms Helene V. Hardy
Mr Mike Hardy
Mrs A. Hardy
Mr E. Hargreaves
Ms Pamela Harman
Miss Alice Harper
Mrs J. Harper
Elaine Harries
W.F. Harrigan
David K. Harris
Mr Geoffrey Harris
Mr Henry Harris
Stuart Harris Esq
J.A. Harris & A.
Fuest
N.D.B. Harris
Mr & Mrs Harris
Mr Raymond Harris
Mr W.E. Harris
Mr P.G. Harris
Mr Alan Harris
Ms Shirley Harris
C.P. Harris
Mr B. Harrison
Mr & Mrs C.
Harrison
Vanessa Harrison
Mr R.H. Harrison
Mr John Harrison
Mr R.B. Harrison
David Harrison
Mr & Mrs Blair
Harrison
P.R. Harrison
D.T. Harrison-Sleap
P.W.J. Harrod Esq
John Harrop
H.C. Hart
M.G. & V.A. Hart
Mrs J. Hartcup
J.D. Hartley
Mr Donald Hartoe
Mr D. Hartog
Mr E.H. Harvey
Dr D. Harvey & Mr
O.L. Teck

Lauren Harvey and
Roger Cohen
Dr Haslam
Dr Colin Hastings
Mr David Hawgood
Canon P.C. Hawker
Mrs P.D. Hawker
Drs A.C. & B.L.
Hawkes
Mrs A.C. Hawkins
Peter Hawkins
Mr David Hawkins
Mr R.G.P. Hawkins
Dr E.D.A. Hay
Mrs M.M. Hay
Mr & Mrs Haydon-
Jones
Stephen Hayes
Jane Hayes
Mr John Hayes
Mr & Mrs A. Hayes
Mrs K. Hayles
Suzie Hayman
Gill Haynes
Mr & Mrs Hayter
Mr Vic Hayward
David Head
Greg Heah
P.E. Healey
Reverend Bruno
Healy
Mrs Madeleine
Heaney
G. Heap
Rev N.C. Heavisides
Mrs R.V. Hebdon
Mr and Mrs Heber-
Percy
Mrs Elspeth Hedley
N.W. Heffen
Mr John Heires
Mr J. Hemming
Mr P. Hemmings
Mrs F. Henchoz
Mr D. McM
Henderson
Mr Stuart
Henderson
Ms Daphne
Henderson
Mr R. Hendey &
Miss E. Fraser
Ms Elizabeth P.
Hendley
Lt Col & Mrs J.S.
Hendry
Mr Ian F. Hendry
Mr R. Hendy
Mr Michael Herbert
Miss Barbara
Herterich
Mr Gad Heuman

Mr & Mrs C Hewitt
Mr & Mrs George
Hewitt
Mr John Hewkin
Mr & Mrs Gilbert
Heys
D.A. Hickling
John Hicks Esq
Mrs C.J. Hicks
Nici Hildebrandt
Ms Aliana Hill
Mr & Mrs Jocelyn
Hill
Mr Christopher Hill
Mr Stephen Hill
J.M.M. Hill
Mr T.H. Hill
Dave Hill
K.E. Hill
Ms Wendy Hillary
Mr & Mrs D.W. Hills
Ronald and
Maureen Hinde
John Hindle
Dr B.P. Hindle
B.K. Hinton Esq
E.J. Hiram
G.E. Hirons
Mr & Mrs Robin
Hirshman
Linda Hitchcock
Michael Hjort
Mr T.T. Ho
Mr Reg Hoare
P.A. Hobday
Mrs G. Hobson
J. Hodds
Mrs J. Hodges
T.B. Hodgkiss
Gordon and Anne
Hodson
Mr Michael Hoggett
Adrian Hohler Esq
Mr P.B. Holden
A.C. Holden
Major H.R. Holden
Lt Col C.F.C. Holder
R.H. Holland
Charles Hollander,
Esq
Mrs D. Hollick
Christoper P.
Holliday
L. Holliday
Mr Peter Hollinson
David Hollister
Mr and Hon Mrs
Holman
Mr J.F. Holman
Mr M. Holman
Ms June Holmes
Mr & Mrs Holmes

Dr R.L. Holmes
L. Holt-Kentwell
Mr Homans
Mr W.A. Honey
Dr & Mrs C. Hood
J.E. Hooker, Esq
Dr M.A. Hooker
Mr Terry Hooker
Mrs Philippa Hooper
M.L. Hooper-
Immins Esq
Mrs B.M. Hopewell
R.R. Hopkins
Lt-Col & Mrs F.T.
Hopkinson
Mr J. Hopper
Mrs Hopper
M. Hopton Esq
Miss M.H. Hopwood
Mr M.J. Horner
Ms Rita Horridge
P.G. Horrocks
P. & F. Horsburgh
T.W. Hoskins
Keith Hotten
Dr R.A. Houston
Mr R.H. Houston
Mrs J.M. How
P.W. Howard
Miss Carol Howard
Mr Peter Howard
Francis Howard
Mr Paul Howarth
Dr P. Howden
Mr C.T. Howe
Miss K. Howell
Ms Janet E. Howell
John I. Howells
Mrs G. Howey
R. Howgego
Mrs Diane Howlett
Prof W. Hryniszak
Mr Richard Hsieh
Mr D.P. Huddinott
Mr A.M. Hudson
Paul S. Hudson
Joan and Peter
Hudson
Miss Janice Hughes
J.P.V. Hughes Esq
I.W.G. Hughes
J.G. Hughes
Mrs Betty Hughes
Mr C. Hughes
Mr & Mrs Hughes
Roy A. Hughes
B.P. Hull
G.G. Hulme
Sir Alan Hume
Miss P. Humes
D.A. Hunt
Mr N.I. Hunt

Mr & Mrs Hunt
Mrs Norman
  Hunter
Hugh C. Hunter
Dr James M. Hunter
Mr D.M. Hunter
Mr P Hunter-Jones
Geoff Huntingford
Mrs Winifred B.
  Hurley
Jules Hurry & Alan
  Griffiths
Mrs S. Hurst
Marvin Hurst
Mr H.G. Hurt
Mr J.E. Hutchinson
Ms Maureen Huth
Mr Paul Hutley
Mike Hutton
Mr Peter Huxley
Mr T.M. Hyde
Ms M. Hyde
M.C. Hyde
Dr Frank Hytten
Mr John Idris Jones
A. Iglikowski Esq
Mr Fred Inglis
Miss Gillian Inglis
Mrs Brenda Innes
V.R. Ireland
Patricia O. Irwin
Mrs Brenda Ishani
Mr Martin
  Isherwood
Christopher G. Isles
Mr Henry Israel
Mr Paul Jackson
H.C. Jackson
Dr Ian J. Jackson
Mr P.M. Jackson
Mrs L.M. Jackson
Mr James McG.
  Jackson
C. Jackson
Mr Peter Jackson
Eric Jaffe
Kenneth R. Jago
C.L. James
Mr S.K. James
Mr B.G.W. Jamieson
Mr M.D. Janson
Mr David H. Jarrett
Mrs R. Jarvis
Antony Jay
Professor Barrie Jay
Mr Patrick Jefferson
Mr Ronald Jeffery
Mr Alan Jeffrey
Mr Jeffrey
Ms Debbie Jellett
Mr D.L. Jelley
D.E. Jenkins

A.B. Jenkins
Mr C.C. Jenkins
Laurence Jenkins
Mr D.M. Jenkins
Valerie Jenkins
Mr Clive Jenkinson
J.C. Jennings
David Jennins
Mr David Jervois
Stephen Jessel
Miss S.D. Jessop
Mr G.P. Jevon
D.J. Jewell
Mr Martyn John
G.L. Johns
Mr Ron Johns
Miss Elizabeth Johns
F. Johnson
Mrs A.M. Johnson
Mrs J.M. Johnson
J.E. Johnson
Mr & Mrs Johnson
Ms Susan Johnson
Ms Geraldine
  Johnson
Alison Johnson
Mrs J.K. Johnson
W.E. & G. Johnson
Dr I.H.D. Johnston
Mr S.M. Johnston
Ms Janet Johnstone
Mrs J. Jolliffe
Andrea Jolly
Mr Michael Jollye
Mr & Mrs P.A. Jones
Dr R.W. Jones
Peter Jones
Ms Helga Jones
Mrs J. Jones
Dr N.E. Jones
Colin Jones
Mr T.S. Jones
Miss P.A. Jones
T.L. Jones
Mr Russell L. Jones
Miss Paola J. Jones
S.J.G. Jones, Esq
Mr R. Jones
D.B.T. Jones
L.D. Jones Esq
Mrs H.R. Jones
Mr K.D. Jones
Mr & Mrs W. Morris
  Jones
Mr & Mrs I. Jones
M.D. Jones
Ian Jones
Miss Carol Jones
Mr & Mrs G. Jones
J.W.W. & P.R. Jones
Dr J.B. Jones
Mr Colin Jones

Graham S. Jones
R.G. Jones
Mr D. Jopson
Mrs P. Jordon
Mr D. Joseph
Nathan & Sarah
  Joseph
E.I. Jowett
Mrs M.A. Joyce
Nick and Barbara
  Joyner
M.R. Judd
Mr A.M. Judes
R.E. Judges
Mr D.J. Juniper
Mr Andre Paul
  Kadoch
Miss Myra S. Kaffel
J.H. Kane
Miss S.M.T. Kaps
Mr & Mrs Katz
Dr Leon Kaufman
Dr Dina Kaufman
J.G. Kavanagh Esq
J. Keane
Mr J.R. Kearns
Eric Keartland
Mr J.H. Keen
Sheila Keene
Mr Michael J. Keene
Ms Alice B. Kehoe
Dr B.D. Keighley
John C. Keighley
R.G. Keight
I.C. Keizner
Mr & Mrs B. Kellett
Mrs Margret Kelly
Marion E. Kelly
Mrs M. Kelly
Mrs Kathleen Kelly
Mr L.J. Kelly
Mrs K. Kelly
Mr M.J. Kelly MChir
  FRCS
Mrs Audrey Kelly
Mr Richard Kelsall
Mr Robert Kelso
Mrs A.J. Kemp
Dr C. Kennard
Ian Kennedy
Mrs Joan Kennedy
Mr T.J. Kenny
Dr J.M.T. Kenrick
Mr P.J. Kent
Mr R.B. Kenyon
Tony Keogh
Mr & Mrs Kersh
Mr & Mrs F.S.
  Kessler
Mr A. Nayllen Khan
Miss Tania Khan
Miss Sally Kibble

Ms Sheila Kidd
Alan Kilburn Esq
Dr G.H.T. Kimble
J.L. Kimble
Mrs Krystyna
  Kimbley
J. King
Derek King
Mr Charles King
Mr J.E. King
Rev A.B. King
Mr & Mrs George
  Kingbourn
Joe & Anne
  Kingham
Lady Kingman
Philip Kingsbury
Mr Charles
  Kingsley-Evans
Mrs S.M. Kinnear
Mr & Mrs W.A.
  Kinsman
Ms Jane Kirk
Mr M.A. Kirk
Mrs Jean Kirk
Heather Kirk
Ms Valerie Kirk
Mrs J. Kirk
Mrs S.P. Kirkaldy
Ms K.D. Kirkby
J.M. & S.M. Kirkham
Mr and Mrs
  Kirkman
Dr Paul A.
  Kitchener
Mr R. Knapp
Mrs Judy Knapp
Robin Knapp
Mr G.A. Knight
Mr R.F. Knight
Jayne Knight
Mr Richard Knight
Mr J. Knighton
Mr A.J. Knights
Mr R.D. Knott
Mr Peter Knott
Mr Peter Knowles
Chris Knowles and
  Wanda Rossiter
Ms Lynne Knowles
David Kolbrook
Mrs Felicity Kramer
Julia Kreitman
Anne Krish
Ms H. Kroll
Dr D.W. Kyle
Mrs W.M. Ladd
Susan R. Laithwaite
Dr P.E. Lake
Mrs B.G. Laker
Christine Lakie
Maurice Lamb

Caroline T. Lamb
Dr and Mrs J.R. Lamb
Mr J.P. Lamb-Jackson
Mr E.G. Lambert
Mrs A. Lambert
Mrs A.C. Lambirth
Mr J.W. Lambourne
Mr J. Lancaster
Guy Landau
Mrs R. Landless
A. Landsberg
Mr & Mrs A.B. Lang
Mr R.C. Lang
Mrs J. Lang
Mrs H. Langenberg
Mr Michael Langridge
A.T. Langton Esq
Mrs E.M. Larbert
Mrs L. Lascelles
Dr R.D. Last
Dr & Mrs S.L. Last
P.D.N. Laurie
Mrs M. Lavender
Mrs J. Lawrence
J. and M. Lawrence
Mrs M.E. Lawrence
Mr A.L. Laws
Mrs. Mona E. Lawson
Dr David Lawson
P.R. Lawton
Marjorie Lazard
Allan F. Lazarus
Angela and Frank Leach
Mr Richard Leader
Mrs E.L. Leader
Pauline Leadley
Mr A. Leaman
Mrs B. Learmonth
Mrs H. Leather
Mrs G.M. Leather
Mr Geoffrey Lee
Dr R.L.G. Lee
Ms B. Lee
J.H.D. Leeke
Mr V.D. Lees
Mrs R.M. Lees
David and Barbara Lefevre
Helen Legg
Lord Leigh
K.M. Leigh
Ms Kathy Leising
Mr W. Leon
Mr Hugh Leonard
Michael Leonard
P.L. Leonard
Mr B. Leonard

Mr D.N. Lermon
Mr Stuart L. Letten
Mr Arthur Letts
Mr Christopher Leuw
Miss Alison Lever
I.E. Levey
Mr Paul Levine
A.S. Levitt
Mr R. Levy
A. Lewin
Miss D. Lewis
Mr D.J.B. Lewis
Mr L. Lewis
Mrs L. Lewis
Mr S.L. Lewis
C.A. Lewis
Mr & Mrs E. Lewis
Mrs Alison Ley
Mr Duncan Liddle
Mr and Mrs Peter H. Liechti
Harold Lievesley Esq
W.I. Light
Mrs I.H. Lightman CB
David J. Lilly
Ms L. Lim
Mr Frank Lincoln
Mr M.M. Lindley
D.R. & A.J. Linnell
Ms Sheila Linsley
Miss E.A. Linton
Mrs Margaret Lipscomb
Miss H.M. Lishman
Mrs L.A. Liston-Smith
Mr J.M. Litchfield
Mr & Mrs D.J. Little
Mr G. Little
Dorothy and Malcolm Littler
Dr D.A. Littler
Mrs S.B.S. Livesey
Mr & Mrs Noel Livesey
Ms Belinda Livingstone
C.M. & D.D. Lloyd
Peter Lloyd Esq
Dr and Mrs C. Lloyd
Mrs Y. Lloyd
Mr G.R. Lloyd
Doreen & George Lockwood
Mr J. Logan
N. Logan
N. Logan-Green
Ms Victoria Logue
W.H. Long
Adrian P.B. Long

Dr Bernard W. Longley
R.L. Longman
Prof & Mrs R. Loudon
Mr G.S. Lous
Dr J.F. Loutit, CBE, DM, FROP, FRS
Mrs Sandy Love
Mrs Elizabeth Loveridge
Mr & Mrs P.J. Lovett
F.B. Lovis
Mr Colin Low
Ms Karen Low
P.A. & J.B. Lowater
P. Lowden
Mr I. Lowe
Mr Ian Lowe
Mr & Mrs A.C. Ludlam
Ms Judy Ludlow
John Luhr Esq
Mrs Anne Lunn
Mrs J. Lunn
Ian Lush
Mr D.C. Luther
Mr G. Lyall Mason
D.F. Lyle Esq
Mr John Lymbury
Rodger Lynch Esq
H. Lynn
Michael Mabbs
Mr Richard Mabey
T.C.H. Macafee
Rev Dr R.B. MacCarthy
Mr I.A.J. MacDonald
James G. MacDonald Esq
Commander R. MacDonald-Hall
Mr M.W.B. MacEacharn
Mrs S. MacFarlane
J.C. MacFarlane
J.B. MacGill
A. MacGill
Mrs Alison MacIntosh
G. MacIntyre
Ms P.L. Mack
Mr A. Graham Mackenzie
Euan and Rona Mackie
Mr Ian Mackin
Mr R.F. Mackrill
Mr & Mrs Maclean
Mr D.B. Maclean
Robert Maclennan Esq M.P.

Ms Marcia MacLeod
D.A.L. Macure
A.K.C. Macmillan
Mrs M. Macphail
William Macpherson
Mr and Mrs D.H. Macpherson
Mr N.R.J. Madeley
Eugene M. Maggi
Mr Geoff Magnay
Dr B. Mahendra
Mr G.V. Maidment
Peter Mair Esq
Mrs M. Mair
S.C. Maisey Esq
Mr L.L. Maitland
Robert Maitland
Mr G.S. Makin
Mr Paul Makings
Mrs J.W. Makinson
Miss Joy Makison
Ellen Malcolm
Lady Malcolm
Miss Farhana Malik
Keith A. Mallinson
Mr J. Malston
S.M. Malt
Mr J. Manby-Brook
Miss R. Mandell
M. Mangan
Mr Paul Manley
Ms D. Manley
Mr K. Mann
Mrs W.E. Mann
Mr K. Mann
J.G.W. Manners
Mr R. Manning
Michael Manser
Mr Rodney Mantle
Ms Helen Manvell
F.A. Le Marchant
Ms Gill Marcus
Mr & Mrs K. Marcuse
Miss Christine Marden
Mr Barnarby Marder
His Hon Judge Bernard Marder QC
Ms Anne & D.L. Mariano
A.M. Marks
C.M. Marks
Mr Darryl Marks
Mr C.J. Marlow
Susie Marriott
Mrs C.A. Marron
Robert Marsh
Nikki Marsh

R.O. Marshall
Mr A.D.R. Marshall
Mrs J.M. Marshall
Mr T.A. Marshall
R.O. Marshall
Tony & Valerie Marshall
Mrs M. Marsland
Ms R.G. Marston
Mrs Joan Martin J.P.
Graham Martin
Flying Officer J.P. Martin
Mrs J. Martin
E.A. Martin
Susan Martin
Mr R.W. Martin
Ms Penelope Martin
Debbie Martin
Captain P.N. Martin
Mr J.S. Martin
A.R. Martin
W. Marzluff
Mrs Nora Mason
Claire Mason
Ms K. Ruth Mason
Mr Hugh Massy
Mr & Mrs Masterman
Graham & Wiescka Masterton
Ms C. Mathiasen
Mrs Shirley Mathieson
R.T. Matson
C. Matthews
Mr T.P. Matthews
Mr Arnold L. Maurice-Jones
A.C. Mawson
Michael Maxwell
Mr Bob A. May
Mr & Mrs T. May
Patrick May
Kenneth and Suzanne May
Mrs Valerie May
Scott McAlear
Mrs A. McCabe
Mrs Kay McCafferty
Brenda McCall
Mr D McClan
Dr & Mrs J.W. McClenehan
Mr Alex McClure
Mrs A. McClurkin
Mr J.W. McCulloch
David William McDonald
J.M. Mcdonald
Elizabeth McDonald
P.R. McDonald

Kate McDowall
D.H. Mcdowall Wilson
Major T.B. McDowell
Mrs C. McEvoy
J.A. McFadzean, M.D.
Mr C.J. McFeeters
Mrs J McGilling
Mr R. McGowan
Ms J.M. McGrenra
Mrs Sheila McIlwrick
Ian McIntosh
George H. McIvor
Tina McKay
Annetee McKay
Clare McKean
C.G. Mckee
Mr K. Muir McKelvey
Mr B. McKenzie
Mr W. McKeown
Mr P. McKinnon
G.S. McKnight
Peter McLachlan
Mr W.J. McLaughlin
Peter McLeod
Mrs A. McLoughlin
Mrs C. McMahon
Miss M. McMorrine
Mrs D. McNeill
Ronald S. McNeill CBE
Mr S. McNulty
Mr W.R. McPhail
Mr Gordon McSweeney
S.T. McWilliams
Mrs M. Mead
Mr J. Meade
Jeremy Meadow
Ms Ann Meadowcroft
Mr R.A. Meadows
D.G. Meager
Mr Colin Mearns
H.C. Medcalf
Mr and Mrs C.D. Mee
Mrs J.M. Meech
Ms S. Melling
Mrs M. Mellish
Diana Melly
Mrs E.C. Melville
Dr D. Melzack
Mr L. Menzies
Mr M. Menzies
Major J.B. Merritt
Mr N.J. Merryweather

Hilary Meth
Monty Meth
Mr C.R. Metham
Mrs M. Metson
Mr C.G. Metters
E.F.P. Metters
Lord Mexborough
Mr J.R. Michaelis
Lisa Michaels
Mr & Mrs Michaelson
Danielle Michalitsianos
Mrs E. Middlerniss
Doreen Middleton
Mr Robin Middleton
J.C. Middleton
J. Middleton Esq
Dr T. Miklos
Dr Rosalind Miles
Doug and Susan Miles
Ms Marilla Miles
Dr & Mrs J.G.B. Millar
Mr Richard Millar
Mr D. Milledge
Mrs P. Miller
P.A. Miller
Miss J. Miller
Mr G.S. Miller
T.W. Miller-Jones Esq
Lt Col T.W. Miller-Jones
Mr G.N. Millichap
Keith Mills
A.N. Mills
Ms Jill Mills
Mr Douglas Mills
Mr H.G. Millward
Mrs F. Millward
Mrs E. Milne-Redhead
D.J. Milner
Prof R.D.G. Milner
S.F.C. Milsom
Mr J.B. Miners
Mrs R.L. Misson
Gavin Mist
R.D. Mitchell
I.W. Mitchell
Ms Ruth Mitchell
H.J. Mitchell
Dr M.J. Mitchell
Mr R.W. Mitchell
Mrs Sian Mitchell
John Mitchelmore
G. Mitcheson
George Moffat Esq
Ralph Molland
Dr J. Mollon

S. Molloy
Tona Molyneaux
Mr John Molyneux
Mrs Monk
Miss A.J. Montgomery
T.C.W. Moody
S.J. Moody
Mr A.J.R. Moon
William Moorby
Mr R.H. Moore
Mrs T.A. Moore
Mr D.S. Moore
Mr P.W. Moore
Alun Brooks Moore
D.G. Moore Esq
Mr V.F. Moore
Mr D. Moore & Miss L. Beanlands
Mr A. Moore
Mr & Mrs G. Moore
Mrs A. Moores
M. Moorhouse
Lord and Lady Moran
Mr and Mrs Patrick Morcas
Dr James More Hunter MB CHB
Mr and Mrs F. Morgan
Dr W.T.W. Morgan
R.C. Morgan
Mr D. Richard Morgan
Kay Morgan
Ms Hazel Morgan
Mrs V. Morley
G.J. Morley
P.A. Morley
Mr F. Morrell
D.J.H. Morris
A.R. Morris
Deborah Morris
Francis Morris
Miss Robin Morrison
I.M. Morrison
Mr and Mrs I. Morrison
R.N. Mortimer Esq
Mr & Mrs B. Mortimer
Mr Iain J. Mortimer
Robin Morton-Smith
Richard F. Moy
Mr Stewart Muir
Mr J.M.W. Mullens
M. Philippe Muller
Mr D.E. Mullinger
Miss S. Mullins & M. Tungey

Mr F.G. Mulvihill, M.D.
Mrs Simon Mumford
A. Mumford
Mr S.I. Mummer
Mr Anthony Mundy
D.H. Munnings
Mr P. Munnoch
Mr D.J. Munro
Mr H.D. Munro
R.J. Murphy
Miss Bernadette Murray
D.W. Murray
Mr G. Murray Corrie
Mrs M.L. Murray Smith
Stephen & Kate Murray-Sykes
P. Myers
Ms Karen Myers
T.K. Mygind
Mrs Patricia Mylan
Mr R.V. Myott
K. Nair Esq
Mr Michael Nairn
Kenneth Nairn
Miss Naney
Mr W.J. Narbett
Mr & Mrs A. Narula
Sara Nathan
Mr S.J.G. Neal
Patrick Nealon
Peter Neate
Dr & Mrs D.A.J. Neden
Alex Neilson
Mrs C. Neilson
Pat Nelson
Mrs M. Nerri
Dr Peter M. Neumann
Mr & Mrs J. Nevalainen
Mrs Patricia Neville
Col & Mrs F.A. Newall
Professor D.E. Newbold
Nancy Newbold-Brien
Lady Newborough
Dr Peter Newbould
Mrs M. Newcomb
M.L.W. Newman
Mrs S. Newton
Mrs K. Newton
Mr Jeffrey Ng
Mr G.M. Niall
Ms Penelope Nice
Mr Tom Nicholls

Mr & Mrs George Nicholls
Mr D.J.B. Nicholls
R.A. & P.N. Nicholls
Jane Nichols
Mrs T. Nichols
Mrs Imogen Nichols
Mr B.J. Nichols
Angela Nicholson
Mr I.H. Nicol
Mr & Mrs M.C.D. Niemyski
Mr F. Nightingale
Dr Angela Ning
Felicity Nixon
Mrs Georgina Nixon
F.A. Noble
Mr Robert Noquet
Susan Norburn
Mrs S. Norman
J.A. Norris
Mrs J. Norris
Mr C.L. Notton
Mr Keith C. Noutch
Mr J.L. Nowell
Mrs B. Nultell
Mr & Mrs R.P. Numan
Phillip Nunan
Mr J.G. Nutman
C.A. O'Callaghan
Mr Eugene O'Connell
T.J. O'Connor
John J. O'Connor III
W.J. O'Connor
Mr M. O'Connor
Mr P.N. O'Donoghue
D. O'Dwyer
Mr P. O'Grady
Mrs V. O'Hagan
Dr & Mrs D. O'Keeffe
P.J.R. O'Malley
Mr A.J. O'Neil
W.B. O'Neill
Mrs D. O'Reilly
Mr & Mrs K.A. Oates
Mr M.C. Oatle
Charles Oatwig-Thain
Mr Oddey
Mr Simon Offen
Mr P.A. Ogden
Gordon & Sylivia Ogilvie
R.A.L. Ogston
Dr Catherine Ogus
Ms Clare Oldridge
Mrs Simon Oliver
Rev N.A. Oliver (Miss)

J.M. Oliver
Miss M. Oliver
Mr Stuart Ord
Mr D.S. Organ
Mrs E. Orme
Ewan & Karen Ormiston
Mr & Mrs W.M. Orr
Mr & Mrs M. Orskey
Mr Jonathon F. Osborne
R.G. Osmond
Mrs W.J. Osuji
Mrs Madeleine Oswald
J.E.P. Ovenden
Mr T.D. Overton
R.K. Owen
Mr J. Oxley
Mr M. Padina
Mr L.J. Page
Simon Page Esq
J.D. Page FRICS
Mr Nigel D. Paine
Mrs Edgar Palamountain
Mrs Palethorpe
Mr J Pallot
Mrs B.M. Palmer
Mr S. Palmer
Mr & Mrs J. Paluch
Mr J.H. Pammett
Mr Allan Parfitt
Mr Richard Parish
J.J. Parker
Mr M.J.V. Parker
Mr R. Parker
Douglas Parker
Mr G. Parker
Ms S.A. Parkinson
Mr D.J. Parkman
Ms Trudi Parnell
Mr Steve Parr
Mr C.T. Parratt
Mrs Jean Parry
Miss E.J. Parry
G.M. Parry
Mr Geoffrey Parsons
S. Parsons
Christopher Parsons
Mr and Mrs Keith Pascoe
Mr & Mrs Sheldon M. Paskow
Mr George Pate
Paul and Gill Pateman
M.H.O. Paterson
Mr & Mrs M. Paterson
Mrs D.S. Paterson-Fox

Mr & Mrs John Patrick
Mrs G. Patterson
Mr A.H. Paul
Dr Anne Paulett
Mr & Mrs L. Payne
Miss C. Payne
A. & R. Peace
Mr D.J. Peace
Ms Denise Peach
J.F. Pearce
Mr Michael Pearce
Mr & Mrs Pearman
Mrs M.F. Pearse
Mr John Pearson
Dr R. Pearson
R.M. Pearson
Miss Caroline Pearson
M.J. Pearson
Mr S. Peel
Mrs Jayne Pegler
Mr G.W. Pekarek
Mr M. Pelham
Miss L.R. Pelican
Ms Janet Pell
R.J. Penney Esq
Mr A.E. Penney
Mrs Penny
Prudence J. Perry
Mrs J. Pescod
Ms Helen Peston
Mrs Caroline Peters
R. Pethybridge
Mr W.E. Petrie
Mrs E.A. Petrie
Mrs E. Petrusewicz
Mr B.W.B. Pettifer
Mr Peter Petts
Capt. R. Philippi
C.E. Phillips
Mr R.L. Phillips
R.V.C. Phillips
K. Phillips
Mr B.J.E. Phillips
John Phillips
Ms J. Phillips
A.J. Phillipson
Mrs I.L. Phillippson
A. Piasecki
Martin Pick
Mrs G.J. Pickering
Ms Caroline Picking
Dr John Pickup
A.M. Pickup
Mr & Mrs A.R. Pigden
Mrs Amanda Pilcher
Mr F.D. Pile
Mr & Mrs R.C.M. Pilgrim

Mr Nicholas Pilkington
Jacqueline Pinder
Dr and Mrs N.J. Pinfield
Mr E.A. Pinn
H.N. Piper
Mrs D. Piper
Ms L.C. Piper
Mr Michael Pitel
R.N. Pittman
Mrs E.A. Platts
Mr Norman Plough
Mrs R.G. Plowman
Nichola M.J.Y. Plummer
Miss Catherine Plummer
Dr P. Poi
Alexander Poliakoff
Charles Pollard
D.J. Poole
Dr Jill Poole
F. Pooley
S.J. Popham
David Porter
Gavin Porter
Mr J.A. Porter
Mr A.F.D. Pott
Mr G.L. Potter
Mr David Potter
Dr J.M. Potter
P.J.E. Pottinger
M.J. Potton
Mr & Mrs Ian Potts
Mr A.M. Pountney
L.S. Powell Esq OBE
Brigadier G.N. Powell
Miss Helena Powell
Grace and Jone Powell
Joan A. Powell
Mrs V.J. Power
Mr F. Power
Helen and Anthony Powers
Pat Preston
Mrs M. Prettejohns
Mr & Mrs D.G. Price
Mrs Sandra M. Price
G. Price
Pamela Vandyke Price
Mrs M.C. Price
Mrs M.C. Price
Mr G.W. Price
Miss F.C. Pringle
Peter J. Prior
Mr D. Procter
Mr & Mrs J. Procter
Julian Proudman

Mr Gordon W. Provis
Mrs E.L. Prugar
J. Pruggmayer
Dr G.P. Pullen
Dr Oscar Puls
E. Punchard
Mr Norman Punt
J.R. Purdy
Dr M. Purshouse
Mr A.J. Purvis
Mrs Y. Pusey
Mr T.J. Putnam & Judith Alfrey
Mr & Mrs Reg Pycroft
Mr Ken Pyne
Mr A. William Radcliffe
S. Radford Esq
Mr Bob Rae
Mr Christopher J. Rae
Dr Stewart Rae
S. Raggett
Mr & Mrs Ralph
Mr D.S. Rampton
Mr & Mrs Ramsden
J. Randles
Ms Pauline Randles
Mrs C.M. Ransome
Mrs H.C. Ranson
Robert N. Rapoport
A. Rathbone
Mrs Pamela Ratoff
Ruth Raunkiaer
Mr S. Raven & Ms C. Sutton
Mr B. Raven
Baron D de Meester de Ravestin
Ms J. Ray
Miss Margaret M. Ray
Mary Rayner
Mr J.D. Rayner
Mr A.P. Rayner
Mr K. Reader
Mrs Hope Readman
D.J. Reason Esq
P. Reddin
Michael L. Reddy
Christopher Redman
Dr A.R. Reece
R.T. Reed
Mr T. Reesal
Mr M. Reese
R.A. Reeve
Mrs R.I. Reeves
David Regan Esq
Mr C.E. Reiche

Mr and Mrs M. Reid
M.J. Reid
J Reid
Mr I. Reid
Mr D.R. Reid
Nancy Reisman
Mr M.I. Rennie
Mr John Rennison
Dr & Mrs J.R. Reuter
M. Revell
Clare Reynolds
W.B. Rhodes
J.O. Rhys
Jerry Richard
W. Richards
H.W. & P.T. Richards
Mrs R.B. Richards
David Richards
Mr C. Richards
Pamela Richards
Peter Richards
Ms Deborah Richardson
E. Richardson
C.J. Richardson
Mrs Sylvia Richardson
F.G. & S.B. Riches
Mrs Carol Riddick
Mrs Linda Riley
Mr Bill Riley
Mrs M. Riley
Mr S. Rimmer
Mr Gordon Ringrose
Mrs Vivien Rink
Mr John A. Riordan
Dr B. Ritson
Mr Graeme Robbie
R.M. Robbins
Ms Paula Roberts
Mr Hugh Roberts
Mr W.F. Roberts
Dr H. Roberts
Mr A.G. Roberts
Mrs A.C. Roberts
Mrs G.R. Roberts
S.B. Roberts
Mrs L.M. Roberts
Mrs P.A. Roberts
Charlie Robertson
J. Graeme Robertson
Sheelagh Robertson
Mr Colin Robey
Mrs Anne Robiette
Mrs P.N. Robinson
J.W. Robinson
D.M. Robinson
Mr & Mrs Robinson
Mr David C. Robson
Mr Ian A.N. Robson
A.C. Robson

Mr F. Rocca
J. Roche, Esq
L.A. Roche
Mr A.G. Roddis
N.E. Roe Esq
Betty B. Roe
Mr Neil Lloyd Rogall
Dr A. Roger & Mr P. Macaulay
Miss E.L. Rogers
Charles N. Rogers
Frank J. Rogers
Ms A. Rogers
Mr Frank Rogers
Wayne A. Rohlfs
P.B. Roitt Esq
Mr P.E. Roland
Mrs Fiona Rollason
Ian A.N. Rolson
Mr R.M. Romer
Diana Rookeledge
Mr David Roper
Mr D.F. Roper
Kenneth Roper
H.D. & A.L. Rose
Daniel Rose
Mr N. Rose
C.N. Rose
Ms Nicola J. Ross
Mrs M. Ross
Mrs Margaret Ross
Mr A.H. Ross
Dr H.E. Ross
F.F. Ross
Mr Robert C. Ross-Lewin
Dr D.J. Rostron
Mr J.D. Round
Mrs Virginia Routh
Mr & Mrs N. Rowan
Mr J. Rowe
Ms R.H. Rowett
Mr Michael Rowland
Mr David Rowle
Mr P.W. Rowley
Nick Rowling Esq
P. Rozee
Harvey Bernard Rubenstein
Peter Rudd
Miss M.J. Ruddick
Mr R.J. Ruffell
Major John E.M. Ruffer
Mr John Rumsey
Mr P.A. Rusby
Mr J.C. Russell
J. Russell
Mr J. Russell
Mrs Anne Russell
Mr J.S. Rutter

Mr J.M. Ryan
R.S. Ryder
Mr A.L. Sabine
Mrs Sachs
K. Sachs
Mrs T.M. Sackin
Mr Boris Sackville
Mr L. Saffron
A.H. Sagar
Thomas and
    Catherine Salas
Mrs Lyn Sales
Ron & Vera Salmon
Mrs S.M. Salter
Mr M.R. Salter
Mrs M.H. Salton
Ms Ginette Sampson
Mr N.W.H. Samuel
Mr Sydney
    Samuelson
Ms Katherine Sand
M.M. & S.J.R.
    Sanders
J.C. Sanderson
Mr John H. Sandler
Mr D. Sandler
Mr C. Sands
Mr G. Saunders
Miss Anne Savage
Mr M. Savage
Mrs A. Sawyer
David de Saxe
Dr H.M. Saxton
Mrs Malvin Sayle
J.S. Saynor
Carolyn Scanlon
Miss M.D.
    Scarborough
Mrs F. Scarr
A.A. Schiff
Mr Michael
    Schofield
Dr Roger Schofield
Mr & Mrs C.J.
    Schofield
Mr Edward
    Schofield
H. Scholes
Dr M. Schroder
Mr & Mrs J.J. Schul
Mr R. Schwarz
Mr J.E.G. Scobie
Mrs H.J. Scoffield
David Scott
Lady Scott
G.W. Scott O.B.E.
Mr D.A. & Mrs
    Gerda Scott
Mr J.G.J. Scott
The Reverend P.L.
    Scott
Mr P.D. Scott

Mr & Mrs H.R. Scott
Mr David Scott-
    Holte
C.G.P. Scott-Malden
Miss H. Scrase
Dr B.A. Scrivings
Tony Scull Esq
Mrs Linda Sealey
John S. Seaman, Esq
Richard Seaman
Peter Searle
E.J. Seddon Esq
Mr & Mrs E.P. & S.A.
    Seedhouse
Miss K. Seeds
Mr & Mrs D. Seel
Ms Gillian Seel
Mr Ottilie Sefton
Mr D.G. & E. Sefton
Mr John Sergeant
Jan Hartman Sevilla
John Seward
Rosalind Sewell
W. Sewell
Mr J. Shaffer
Mr D.B. Shakespear
Dr A.P. Shakespeare
Mrs D.M. Shalit
Mr John Shanks
Mrs E.M. Shanks
Mr John F. Shapley
Anthony Michael
    Sharkey
Mr L.R. Sharman
J.E. Sharp
Miss Wendy Sharp
P.T. Sharpe
Mrs D.M. Sharples
Dr T. Shaw
Mr Martin Shaw
Dr & Mrs S.A.G.
    Shaw
Ms R. Shaw
Ms Geraldine Shaw
J.N. Shearman
Mr Paul Shearman
Mr Edward Sheehan
Mr David Sheldon
Vivien Sheldon
Mr Norman Shelley
Mr J.L. Shennan
Mrs J.E. Sheppard
Mrs Sherrard Smith
S. Sherwood
A. Sherwood
David J. Shiel
Mrs J. Shield
Ms Carla Shimeld
Mr John Shire
Mr W.J.A.
    Shoesmith
Mr J. Shorrocks

M.H. Shotton, Esq
Mr C. Shroff
J.G. Shurgold
Mr Simon Shute
Mrs M.
    Shuttleworth
Mr John Siddall
Ian Sier
Dr O.A. Sills
Miss B.A. Silverman
Dr & Mrs Silverstone
Mr Robert C. Sim
John Simcock
Mr Hugh J.
    Simmonds
K.J. Simmons
Mr B. Simmons
Mr J.A. Simmons
Mrs A.M. Simon
Mr R. Simon
Mr J.C. Simopoulos
Mrs Diana M.
    Simpkins
T.W. Simpson
Mrs A. Simpson
Chris Simpson
Ms Audrey Simpson
H.D. Simpson
A.D. Simpson
Ralph E.R. Sims
Ms Jane Sims
Duncan Sinclair Esq
R.J. Sinclair Taylor
Mr Tony Sinnott
Mr G. Sivewright
Graham Skeats
Mr & Mrs R.J.
    Skellorn
Mr Ross Skinner
D.M. Skinner
Dr A.K.B. Slade
Mr D.A. Slade
Ms Julia Sleeper
Mr F.C. Slegg
C. Small
N.S.L. Smart
Mr John Smillie
Mr D.C. Smith
S. Smith
M.A. Smith
J.A.V. Smith
Ms Marina Smith
Mr N.L. Smith
Mrs B.F. Smith
Mr B.D. Smith
Muriel Smith
Ms F.M.K. Smith
Mr John G.S. Smith
Eric Smith L.V.O.,
    O.B.E.
Mr A.O. Smith
Ian R. Smith

Ms Pamela Smith
Mr G.W. Smith
Professor J.A.S.
    Smith
Arthur J. Smith
Mrs M. Smith
Mrs Karin Smith
Dr A.E. Smith
Mrs D. Smith
Bernard F. Smith
Mr & Mrs S. N.
    Smith
Dr Eileen Smith
Mr Malcolm Smith
Mr S.R. Smith
Mrs M. Weston
    Smith
Professor Ivor Smith
Mrs S. Smith
Maureen Smith
D.E. Smith
Mr & Mrs Neil Smith
Kenneth E. Smith
Mr Peter Smith
Mr J.H.B. Smith
Ms Alison Jane
    Smith
I. Smith
Mr B. Smith
Mr D. Smith
Mrs Ann Smith
Kenneth E. Smith
Mr B. Smith
Mrs Sarah Smith
Mrs H. Smith
Mr Smithers
M.Q. Smye
A.M. Smyth Esq
Mr John Smythe
Mr & Mrs W.J.
    Snelson
Neil Snow
Mr Johnathan Sofer
Mrs A. Solly
Mrs E. Sones
Mr J. Southern
Mr Elwyn Soutter
Mrs Stephanie
    Sowerby
Ms Alison L.
    Sparkes
Mr D.I. Sparkes
Wg Cdr R.M.
    Sparkes
Mr & Mrs Spaull
John L. Speaight
Martha Smith
    Spencer
Mr F.E.V. Spencer
N. Spencer
Mrs S.A. Spicer
Mrs A. Spier

Philip Splett Esq
Mr K.L. Spotswood
Carol Spraggs
Mrs E. Sprake
Mr B. & Mrs C.
Spratt
J. & S. Sprigg
Ms Eileen Squires
Miss Rosemary
Squires
Mr Philip Stanbury
K.J. & M. Standley
Mrs E. Stanhope
Kim and Margret
Staniforth
K.E. Stanley
David & Jacqueline
Stanley
Mrs E. Stanton
J. Staples
Mr Marc Starling
Dr B.L. Stather-
Dunn
Mr R.H. Statt
Nurse S.J. Stead
Mrs W. M.
Steavenson
Michael Steed
Mr John Steel
Mr John Derek Steel
Mr Neil D. Stein
Mr F.M.M. Steiner
Ms J.M. Steiner
C.E. Stenham
Mr F.M.A. Stephen
Mrs Ruth Stephens
Mrs J. Stephens
Mr A.P. Stephens
Mr K. Stephenson
Maxwell Stern
M.V. Sternberg
Mr P.R. Stettner
Dr Andrew & Helen
Stevens
R.W. Stevens Esq
Ms Laura Stevens
M. Stevenson
Mr Michael Stewart
Captain & Mrs J.S.
Stewart
Dr R.H.M. Stewart
Lt Cdr. A. Stewart
Morna Stewart
Mr Peter Stewart
R.H. & J.C. Stidwell
J. Stock MCFA (CG)
Dr Mark Stocker
Mr John Stocker
Ms J. Stogdon
Mr R. Stoker
J.C.M. Stoker
D.J. Stoker

E.H. Stokes Esq
Miss Pamela Stone
A.B. Stone
Malcolm Stone
Mr J.A.G.
Stonehouse
R. Stonehouse
Rod Stoneman &
Susan Clarke
J.A. Stoner Esq
David G. Stonier
Mrs M.V. Stott
Mr and Mrs D.F.
Strachan
Leonard Strange
Mrs Rosemary
Stratford
Mrs P.Y. Strickland
Hilary and Malcom
Strong
E. Strong
Dr D. Stroud
Mrs A. Strum
Mr I.M. Stuart
Ms Fiona Catherine
Stuart
H. Style
Miss C.E. Sullivan
Dr S.F. Sullman
D.J. Sumner
Mr Alistair
Sunderland
James B. Sunley
Mrs Gillian Sunter
Mr Robert Surman
Miss J. Sutcliffe & Mr
R. Asplin
T.W. Sutherland
Dr G.M. Sutherland
Graham Sutton
Mrs Margaret Swain
Ms Susan Swan
Mr Bob Swash
Mrs J. Swift
Mr & Mrs G. Sydserff
Ms Brenda Symes
Mrs Elizabeth Syrett
Mr S. Szymana
Dr A.J. Taggart
Mr Patrick Tailyour
Dr L.S. Taitz
Mrs C. Talboys
Mrs J.H. Tallentire
Mr E.E. Tallis
Vivienne Tan
G.W. Tanner
Mrs M.A. Tanner
N.M. Tapley
Mrs A. Tarlton
A. Tarnopolsky
Mr J.A. Tarrant
George & Amanda
Tarry

Mr Henry Tassell
Mr D.W. Tate
Mr Denis W. Tate
Dr D.M. Taub
Mrs J.A. Taylor
Mr Simon Taylor
Mrs Aileen Taylor
Mrs Wendy Taylor
Mr G.C. Taylor
Ms Jean Taylor
Mrs G.J. Taylor
Mr and Mrs M.P.
Taylor
George Taylor
Mrs A.C. Taylor
Mr & Mrs J.W.
Taylor
Mr John Taylor
Mr Simon Taylor
Mrs Mabel Taylor
Denzil T. Taylor
Mrs N.C.L. Taylor
R. Taylor M.B.E.
Mr T.G. Taylor
Mr D. Taylor
Cdr Patrick Taylor
M. Taylor
Mr John Parker
Teall
Mr Anthony
Teasdale
Ronald Tedstone
Mrs M.E. Telang
Mr R.K.O. Temby
Mrs J. & Mr L.
Tempest
Mr & Mrs J. Temple
Paul Temple
Mr I. Temple-Smith
Lady E. Tennant
Paul S. Terry
Mrs G. Terry
Mr Graham D.
Tetley
Mrs R.P. Tetlow
Matthew Thackray
Mr J.C. Thackray
Cdr R.J. Theobald
Mr J. Thomas
Richard and Carol
Thomas
Dr & Mrs Duncan
Thomas
P.R. & D. Thomas
Mr Sajan Thomas
Mr & Mrs David &
Barbara Thomas
Mr Frank Thomas
Mrs V. Thomas
Miss Ruth
Thompson
Ms Jacqueline
Thompson

Mrs E. Thompson
G.L. Thompson
Amanda Thompson
R. Thompson Esq
P.D.B. Thompson
Mrs C.M. Thompson
Mrs L. Thomson
Mr J.D.V. Thomson
Mr David Thomson
Mr Erik Thorbek
Mr N. Thorn
David Thornber
Mr D. Thornton
Mr & Mrs J.
Thornton
Derek Thorpe
Mark & Rosemary
Throssel
Miss Jane Elizabeth
Tiley
Mrs T.J.E. Tilley
J.R. Tillson & S.
Simmons
Miss Ruth Tilsley
Mr G.N. Tingey &
Mr R.F. Neil
Mr A.R. Tingley
Marjorie Tipton
Roberta Tish
Peter and Helen
Titchmarsh
Mr Christopher
Toates
Carol Todd
Dr John W. Todd
Dr G.B. Todd
J. Toman
Mr & Mrs G.W.O.
Tomkins
Mr Neil Tomkinson
Mr Roger Lloyd
Tomkinson
Mr J. Tomlin
Mr. M. Tomlinson
L. Tomlinson and
M.J. Jones
Barry Toner
J.M. Toner
G.L. Tong
Mr David Tooth
Mrs Jean Toper
Ms N.E. Towell
Dr M. Townend
Mrs E. Townsend
D.G. Toynbee
Mr G. Tragen
Mr Brian A.
Tremain
Mr J.J. Trevorrow
Ms Sarah Tricks
R. Trigwell
Mrs Mary Joan
Trimble

Mr Peter Tripp
P.J. Trodden
Mr Gordian Troeller
Walter Troesch
Annie Tucker
Mr Simon Tuite
Mrs May Tully
Mr & Mrs P.R. Turier
J.A. Turkson
D.H.H. Turner
Roy and Evelyn Turner
Mr D.D. Turner
Dr H. Turner
Mrs Shirley Turner
Mr & Mrs J. Turner
Mr Keith Turner
Mr & Mrs G. Turner
David Turner & Jennifer Collier
Ms E. Turner
Mrs P.J. Turner
Mr Stuart Turner
Mrs Mary Turner
Mr & Mrs M.G. Turner
Jean M. Turner
J.S. Turpin
K.C. Turpin
Mrs Elizabeth Tweddle
Mr Richard Twinch
A.P. Tye
I. Tysh
James Tysoe
Iain Tyson
Sally Ullah
D.N. Underwood
Mrs C.P.T. Van Develbe
Mr M. Van De Wiel
Mrs I.A. Van der Heijden
Emily Van Evera
D. Vardy
Mr J. Varley
Mr Mike Varmals
R.D. Vaughan
Mrs A. Venables
Dr and Mrs P. Venn
David Venney
Michel Vercambre
Lesley-Ann Vernon
Dr E. Versi
Miss S. Vickers
M.J-L. Vidalenc
Mr and Mrs Villa
Mr N.W. Vince
Mr Adrian Vincent
Mr P.J.C. Vincent
M.J. Volans Esq

Mr Rudy Vonk
C. & D. Wade
D.G. Wadsworth
Mr K. Wadsworth
Mrs M.G. Wadsworth
Mr R.N. Wailing
Mrs J. Wainwright
Mr K.S. Wainwright
Christopher H. Waite
Dr M.C. Wake
Tom and Angela Walford
Revd D.S. and Mrs Walford
F.M.F. Walker
Mrs E. Walker
Mr Harlan Walker
Mrs V. Walker
Mr & Mrs J. Walker
Mr M.F. Walker
Mr & Mrs W. Walker
Mr Richard Walker
Mr R.J. Walker
Mrs B.L. Walker
Mr R.E. Walker
Mr A.K.F. Walker
Mr & Mrs D. Walker
Mr & Mrs P Walker
Mr C.J. Walker
Mr Peter Walker
Chris Wall
Ms Lyn Wallace
Mr & Mrs N.E. Wallace
Mr & Mrs W. Waller
James A. Waller
Miss C. Waller
Mr & Mrs Wallis
Christopher Wallis
Mr J. Walmsley
Mr T. Walsh
Mr A.J. Walsh
R.C. Walsh
Mr John Walsh
P.J. Walsh
P.K. Walsh Esq
I.D. & M.F. Walsh
O. Walston
Mr & Mrs Walters
H. Walton
Mr D. Walton
Mr R.A. Ward
Dr S.C. Ward
Mr Philip Ward
J.C. Ward
Mr G.A.B. Ward
Mr & Mrs S.M.R. Ward
Mr D. Ward

Mr A.J. Wardrop
H.J.L. Ware Esq
Mr Philip Warren
Mr C.G. Warren
G.M. Warren
Mr Stephen B. Warshaw
R.J. Warwick Esq
P.S. Wass
Mr Roger Waterfall
Mrs J. Waterhouse
J. Waterhouse
Mrs R. Watherston
Roger Watkins
C.L. Watkins
M.J. Watkins
R.C. Watkins
Mrs S.C. Watkinson
Mrs Madeleine Watson
Kenneth Watson Esq
Mr David Watson
J.T. Watson
Mr Aidan Watt
Mr John G. Watt
Dr Clyde B. Webb
Ms C. Webb
Dr T. Webb
Miss P.M. Webster
Dr D.E. & Mrs E. Webster
Mr J.J. Weddell
Tony Weekes
Mr & Mrs B. Weinreb
V.F. Weinstein
Mr Stephen Wellings
Gary P. Wells
Peter Wells
Geoffrey Wells
Mrs F. Wells
R.H. Wells
I.E. West
J.N. West
Mr J.F.M. West
Mrs V. West
Mr S.A. Westbrook
Mr M. Westby
John & Anne Westcott
Mr & Mrs Westlake
Mrs M. Weston-Smith
P.H.S. Wettern
Mrs D. Whalen
Dina Wheatcroft
Mrs V. Wheeler
John Wheeler
Mr Alan Whelan
Mrs J.E. Whigham

Dr N. Perry
Whinnom
G.T. Whitaker
Ben Whitaker Esq
G.M. Whitaker
Mr E.P. Whitaker
Mr & Mrs J. Whitaker
Mr H.M. Whitcut
Mr & Mrs G. White
Mr & Mrs Colin White
Mrs Gwen White
J. White
Mr & Mrs A.C. White
N.H. White
Mr & Mrs R. White
E. Clifford White
Mr W.G. White
Bill & Barbara White
Rene Paul White
Mr P.J. White
Mr Michael Whitehall
Mr & Mrs B.P. Whitehouse
Mr B. Whitelegg
Mr E.V.M. Whiteway
Mr D.J. Whiting
Richard Whiting Esq
Mr G. Anthony Whittaker
Miss M.L. Whitton
Ms Mary Whittington
Mr & Mrs R. Whittle
Neville T. Whittle
Mr Peter Whyman
Mr D.N. Whyte
Mr G.W. Wicken
Mr C. Wigoder
Mr Alan Wilby
Peter Wild
R.C. Wiles
Ms D. Wilhams
Mr M. Wilkes
Mr & Mrs T. Wilkes
M. Wilkie
Mrs June Wilkinson
Barbara Wilkinson
Mrs A. Wilkinson
Mrs R. Wilkinson
Mrs Anne Wilks
Mr P. Willer
Mrs W.F. Willetts
Ms Annwyl Williams
J.R. Williams

Alex and Beryl
  Williams
Mr C.B.C. Williams
Mrs Ivy Williams
Dr Simon Williams
S.B. Williams
Mrs D. Williams
P.C. Williams
Mrs Lesley Williams
Miss Sandara J.
  Williams
Mr D.A. Williams
D.R. Williams
Mr T.C. Williams
P.J. & Mrs J.L.
  Williams
Mr J.S. Williams
G.B.A. Williams
Mrs M.J. Williams
Mr M.L.B. Williams
N.M. Williamson
Gillian Williamson
Mr S. Williamson
  M.A.
B.C. Williamson
J.R. Williamson
Ms Gillan
  Williamson
Mr J.M. Willoughby
Mrs Jean M. Willson
Mrs Willson
Sue Wilshere
Dr P.N. Wilson
R.S. & P. Wilson
Mr Douglas F.
  Wilson
Sheila Wilson
Mr T.M. Wilson

Mr Ralph G. Wilson
Mrs Janice Wilson
Mr Alan Wilson
Mr M.A. Wilson
Mr & Mrs E. Wilson
Mr E. Wilson
Mrs R.S. Wilson
R. Wilson Esq,
  F.C.A.
Mr Robert Wilson
Mr John S. Wilson
Mr Alan Wilson
Alan Wilson
Mr and Mrs D.S.
  Wilson
J.C. Window
Wood Winfield
A.J. Wingate Esq
J.C. Wingate
Mr F. Wingett
Mr & Mrs Jeff
  Winston
Derek J. Winston
Mrs J.
  Winterbottom
L.M. Wise Esq
I.G. Wise Esq
Mrs Dorothy Wise
Mrs W. Witham
Mr Tim Woffenden
Mr Tim Wolfenden
Mr D. Wolfgang
  Lehmann
Miss Barbara
  Wolfinger
Mr and Mrs S.C.
  Wong
P. Wong

Dr M.D. Wood
Mrs Maureen Wood
K.W. Wood
James Wood
Mr K. Wood
Mr Bruce
  Woodhead
Mr R.J. Woodley
W.C. Woodruff
A.J. Woodyatt
Barbara M.
  Wooldridge
Mrs Vera Woolf
Mr Bud Woolsey
Mrs K. Wordsworth
Mrs J. Worrall
Mr Alan Worsdale
Mr Paul Worsley
P.L. Worthington
Ms E. Wottingham
Mr A.V. Wraight
Dr D.G. Wray
Mr and Mrs Brian
  Wright
A.C.H. Wright
D.J. Wright
Alan Wright
Mr A.J Wright
G.T. Wright
Ken Wright
Paul & Anne-Marie
  Wright
Dr & Mrs D.S.
  Wright
Anna Wright
John G. Wright
G.J. Wright Esq
Peter Wright

Mr & Mrs C. Wright
Mr John C. Wright
Mr C. Wrong
Mr Richard Wybell
C. Wycliffe Noble,
  OBE
R.A. Wyld
Mr Basil
  Wynbergen
Mr & Mrs Mark
  Wyndham
Mr B.R. Wynne
Mr J. Yaffee
Mr C.R. Yarlett
Dr H. Yarrow
Mr E.J. Yates
Mr B.D. Yates
Mr Peter York
Mrs S. Young
Mr Gavin Young
Mr Patrick Young
Mrs M. Young
Mrs M. Young
P.T. Young
Mr J.C. Young
Mrs P. Young
Mrs S.C. Young
Philip Young, Esq
Ms J. Young
Paul H. Young
Mr D. Zambra
Mr Robert Zara
Dr Ronald Zeegen
Lady de Zulueta
Alyson Zuntz

Alphabetical list of entries

London restaurants are indicated by their postal district.

Lower Pitt, East Buckland, Devon

Lowiczanka, W6

Lygon Arms, Broadway, Hereford & Worcester

Lynton House, Holdenby, Northamptonshire

Lynwood House, Barnstaple, Devon

M'sieur Frog, N1

Ma Cuisine, SW3

MacDuff's, Coleraine, Co. Derry

Madeleine's, Newcastle upon Tyne, Tyne & Wear

La Madonette, Chipping Norton, Oxfordshire

Magno's Brasserie, WC2

Magpie Cafe, Whitby, North Yorkshire

Maharaja, Birmingham, West Midlands

Malabar, W8

Mallory Court, Bishops Tachbrook, Warwickshire

Mandeer, W1

Manleys, Storrington, West Sussex

Le Manoir Aux Quat'Saisons, Great Milton, Oxfordshire

Manor, Guildford, Surrey

Manor Hotel, West Bexington, Dorset

Le Marche Noir, Edinburgh, Lothian

Market Place Teashop, Barnard Castle, Co. Durham

Market Restaurant, Manchester, Greater Manchester

Marlfield House, Gorey, Co. Wexford

Marmion's Brasserie, Melrose, Borders

Maroush, W2

Maroush II, SW3

Marryat Room (Chewton Glen Hotel), New Milton, Hampshire

Martin's, NW1

Martins, Edinburgh, Lothian

La Mascotte, NW2

Masons Arms, Branscombe, Devon

Mauro's, Bollington, Cheshire

Maxine's, Midhurst, West Sussex

Maybank Hotel, Aberdovey, Gwynedd

Mayflower, W1

Mayflower, Liverpool, Merseyside

Le Mazarin, SW1

McClements, Twickenham, Greater London

McCoy's, Staddlebridge, North Yorkshire

Meadow Farm, Elsworth, Cambridgeshire

Meadowsweet Hotel, Llanrwst, Gwynedd

Melati, W1

Melissa, Chelmsford, Essex

Meridiana, SW3

Le Metro Wine Bar, SW3

Michael's Brasserie, Newcastle Upon Tyne, Tyne & Wear

Michaels Nook, Grasmere, Cumbria

Michel, W8

Michels, Ripley, Surrey

Middlethorpe Hall, York, North Yorkshire

Midsummer House, Cambridge, Cambridgeshire

Mijanou, SW1

Mill Hotel, Kingham, Oxfordshire

Miller Howe, Windermere, Cumbria

Miller Howe Kaff, Windermere, Cumbria

Minffordd Hotel, Talyllyn, Gwynedd

Ming, W1

Ming Garden, Thornton Heath, Greater London

Mister Barretts, Plymouth, Devon

Mitchells, Dublin, Co. Dublin

Miyama, W1

Miyama, EC4

Molnars, NW3

Molyneux's, Port Erin, Isle of Man

Mon Plaisir, WC2

Monkeys, SW3

The Moon, Kendal, Cumbria

Moon and Sixpence, Bath, Avon

Moonrakers, Alfriston, East Sussex

Moorings, Wells Next the Sea, Norfolk

Morefield Motel, Ullapool, Highland

Morels, Haslemere, Surrey

Mortons House Hotel, Corfe Castle, Dorset

Moss Nook, Manchester, Greater Manchester

Mr Bistro, Mevagissey, Cornwall

Mr Ke, NW3

Mr Kuks, Manchester, Greater Manchester

Mr Shing's, Nottingham, Nottinghamshire

Mr Tang, W1

Mr Underhill's, Stonham, Suffolk

Mulberry Room, Torquay, Devon

Munbhave, Croydon, Surrey

Munchy Munchy, Oxford, Oxfordshire

Murrayshall Hotel, Scone, Tayside

Muset, Bristol, Avon

Nailcote Hall, Berkswell, West Midlands

Nanten Yakitori Bar, W1

Le Nautique, St Peter Port, Guernsey

Neal Street Restaurant, WC2

Nellie Gray's, St Anne, Alderney

New Emperor, Newcastle Upon Tyne, Tyne & Wear

New Inn, Manaccan, Cornwall

New World, W1

Newbigging Hotel, Redcar, Cleveland

Nick's Place, Killinchy, Co. Down

Ninety Park Lane (Grosvenor House), W1

Nirmal's Tandoori, Sheffield, South Yorkshire

Nontas, NW1

Northcote Manor, Langho, Lancashire

Number Twelve, Cheltenham, Gloucestershire

Nuthurst Grange, Hockley Heath, West Midlands

Oakes, Stroud, Gloucestershire

Oakhill House, Oakhill, Somerset

Oat Cuisine, York, North Yorkshire

Ocean City, Nottingham, Nottinghamshire

Odettes, NW1

Off the Beeton Track, Cowbridge, South Glamorgan

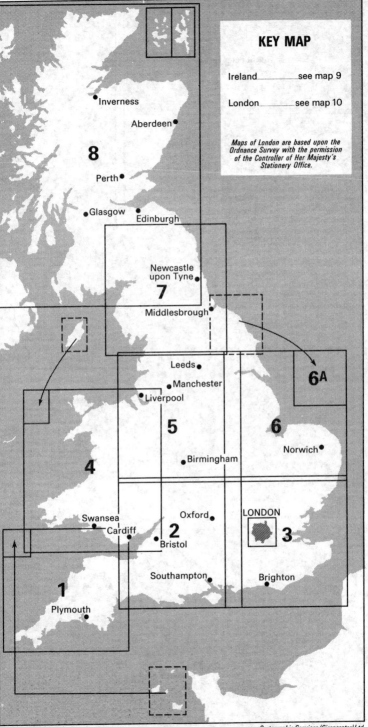

KEY MAP

Ireland................see map 9

London................see map 10

Maps of London are based upon the Ordnance Survey with the permission of the Controller of Her Majesty's Stationery Office.

Inverness

Aberdeen

8

Perth

Glasgow

Edinburgh

Newcastle upon Tyne

7

Middlesbrough

Leeds

Manchester

Liverpool

5

6A

6

Norwich

4

Birmingham

Swansea

Cardiff

Oxford

2

Bristol

LONDON

3

Southampton

Brighton

1

Plymouth

Cartographic Services (Cirencester) Ltd.

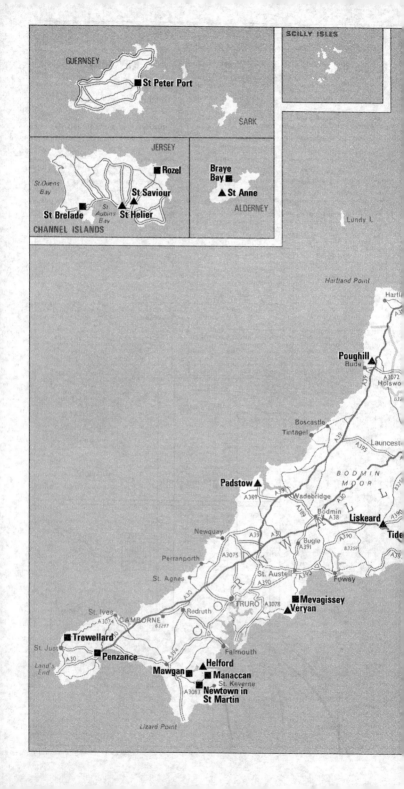

Restaurant ■

Restaurant with accommodation ▲

0 Miles　　　10　　　20

BRISTOL CHANNEL

Ilfracombe

Lynton ▲

MINEHEAD
Watchet

▲ Croyde

EXMOOR

Williton ▲

Barnstaple ■

Bideford

▲ East Buckland
South Molton

Dulverton ▲

Langley Marsh ▲

A361
Milverton

▲ Chittlehamholt

Bampton
Wellington

Great Torrington

Chulmleigh

A396

Hatherleigh

Tiverton ■
Cullompton

A3072

M5

Honiton

D E V O N

Okehampton

Drewsteignton ▲

EXETER

Ottery St Mary ■

Lewtrenchard ▲

Chagford ▲

DARTMOOR

Lympstone ▲

Budleigh Salterton
Exmouth
Dawlish

Newton Abbot

▲ Gulworthy

Buckfastleigh

Torquay ▲

Calstock

PAIGNTON

Totnes

Crown Hill

North Huish ■

Brixham

Plymouth

Modbury

Kingswear
Dartmouth ■

▲ Loddiswell

▲ Kingsbridge

Salcombe　Start Point

Cartographic Services (Cirencester) Ltd.

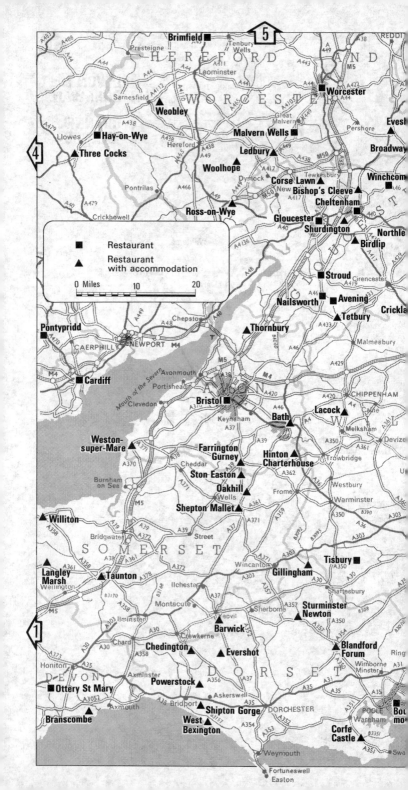

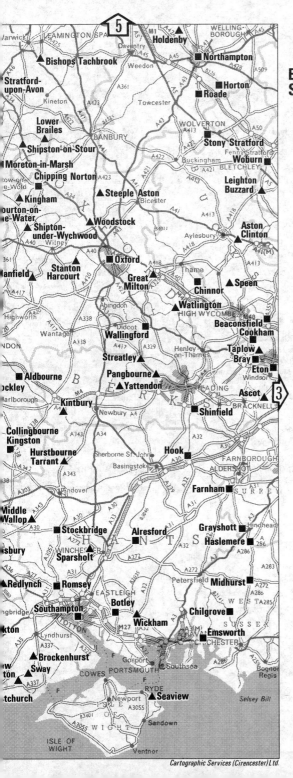

Cartographic Services (Cirencester) Ltd.

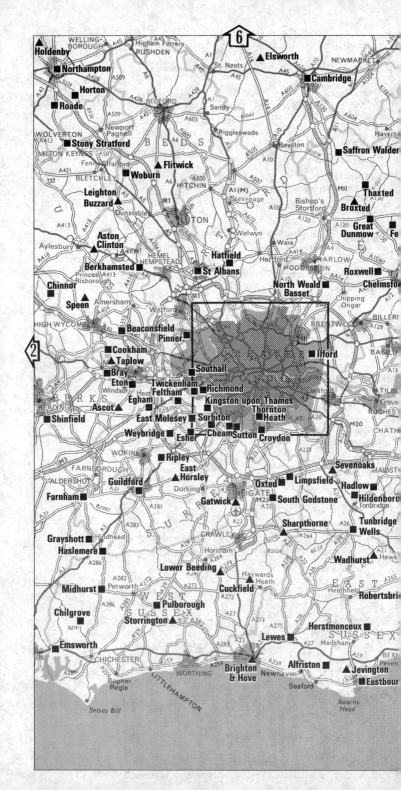

▲ Bury St Edmunds
field
bust
Stowmarket
▲ Stonham
Saxmundham
Leiston
Aldeburgh
avenham
▲ Campsea Ash
Glemsford
■ Orford
▲ Long Melford
■ Woodbridge
Orford Ness
■ Ipswich
East ▲ Hintlesham
Bergholt
FELIXSTOWE
Dedham ▲
■ Harwich
Coggeshall COLCHESTER
The Naze
Walton-on-the-Naze
Frinton
ham
CLACTON-ON-SEA
▲ West Mersea
■ Maldon

■ Burnham-on-Crouch

▲ Rochford
■ Southend-on-Sea

River Thames
SHEERNESS
Leysdown-on-Sea
MARGATE
North Foreland
Whitstable
Herne Bay
Ramsgate
SITTINGBOURNE
Sandwich
Faversham
■ Canterbury
Chilham
Deal
Welmer
▲ Hastingleigh
St. Margaret's
at Cliffe
Ashford
DOVER
Biddenden
■ Folkestone
Hythe
den
S T R A I T
■ Rye
Lydd
O F   D O V E R
Dungeness
HASTINGS

	Restaurant
■	Restaurant
▲	Restaurant with accommodation

0 Miles   10   20

Cartographic Services (Cirencester) Ltd.

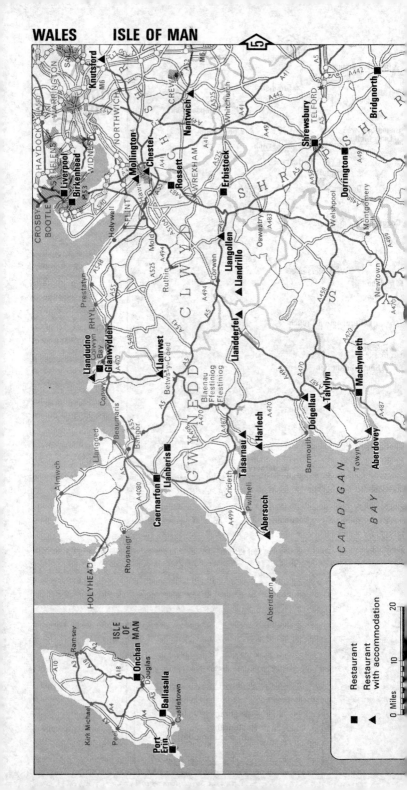

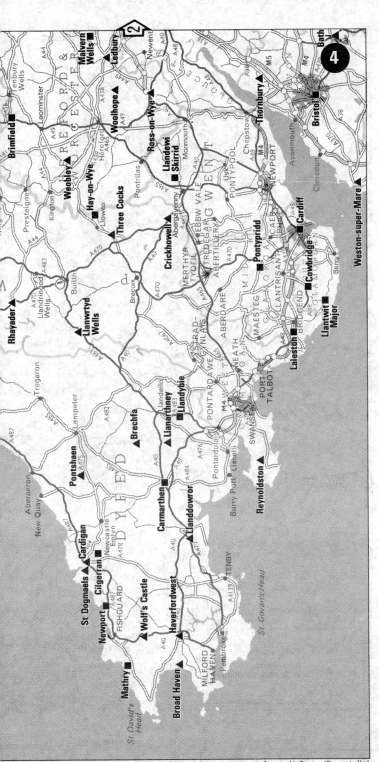

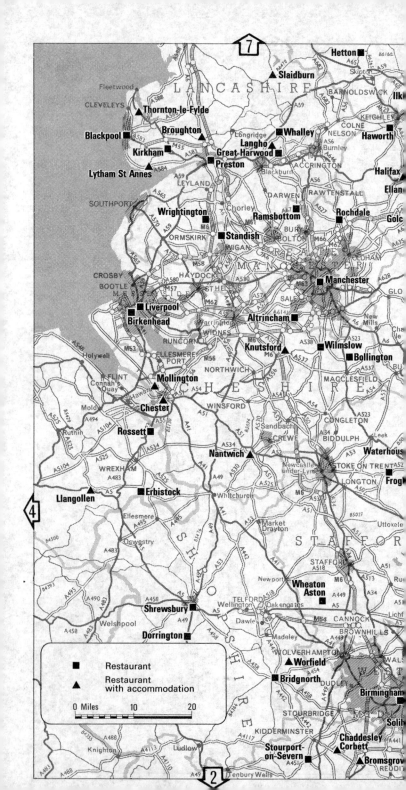

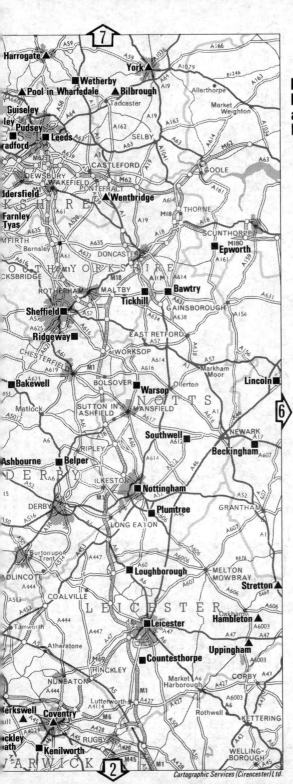

**ENGLAND:
MIDLANDS
and
NORTH WEST**

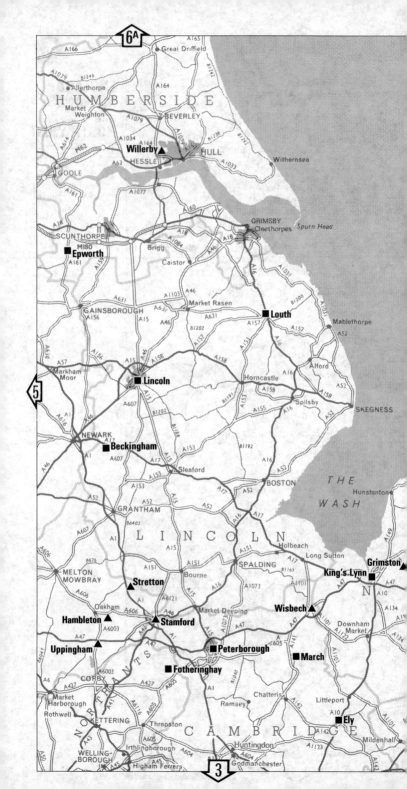

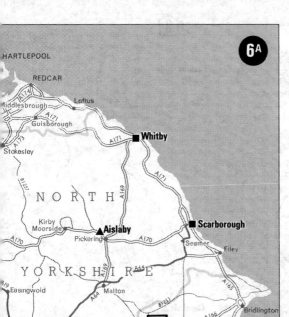

HARTLEPOOL
REDCAR
Loftus
Middlesbrough
A174
A171
Guisborough
A173
Stokesley
A171
■ **Whitby**
A171
A169
N O R T H
A170
Kirby
Moorside
▲ **Aislaby**
Pickering
■ **Scarborough**
A170
Seamer
Filey
A65
Y O R K S H I R E
A19 Easingwold
A64
Malton
B1251
A165
Bridlington
B1257
A166
A165

6

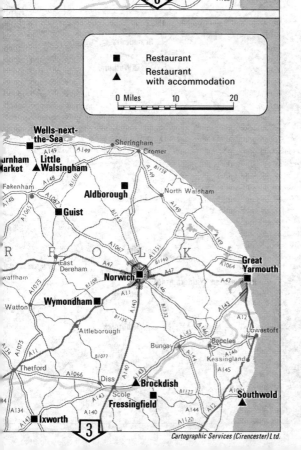

■ Restaurant

▲ Restaurant
with accommodation

0 Miles   10   20

**Wells-next-
the-Sea**
■
A149
Sheringham
Cromer
**Burnham
Market**
Little
▲ **Walsingham**
A149
A148
Fakenham
A1067
A148
North Walsham
A149
■ **Aldborough**
■ **Guist**
A1065
A1067
N O R F O L K
B1140
A47
A1064
**Great
Yarmouth** ■
East
Dereham
A47
Swaffham
A1075
■ **Norwich**
A47
A146
A143
A12
Wymondham ■
A11
A140
B1135
B1132
Watton
Attleborough
Lowestoft
A1075
B1077
A143
Bungay
Beccles
A11
A134
Thetford
A1066
Diss
B1123
Kessingland
A145
Scole
▲ **Brockdish**
Fressingfield
■
Southwold
▲
A134
■ **Ixworth**
A140
A143
A144
A12
A1120

3

Cartographic Services (Cirencester) Ltd.

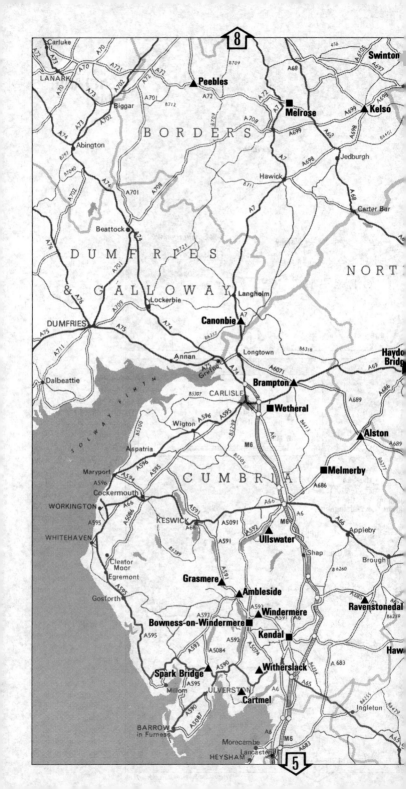

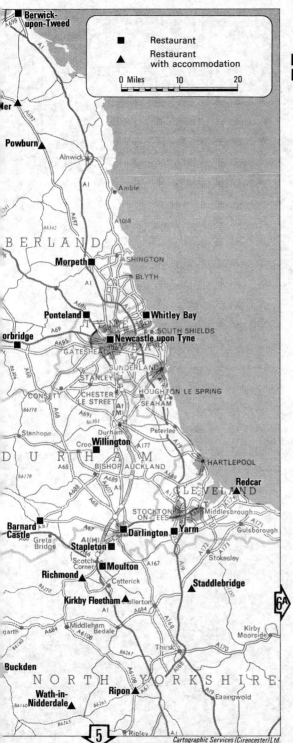

7

**ENGLAND:
NORTH**

Restaurant
Restaurant
with accommodation

0 Miles   10   20

Berwick-upon-Tweed
Powburn
Alnwick
Amble
Morpeth
ASHINGTON
BLYTH
Ponteland
Whitley Bay
SOUTH SHIELDS
Newcastle upon Tyne
GATESHEAD
orbridge
SUNDERLAND
STANLEY
HOUGHTON LE SPRING
CONSETT
CHESTER LE STREET
SEAHAM
Stanhope
Durham
Peterlee
Willington
Croo
BISHOP AUCKLAND
HARTLEPOOL
DURHAM
Redcar
CLEVELAND
STOCKTON ON TEES
Middlesbrough
Barnard Castle
Guisborough
Greta Bridge
Darlington
Yarm
Stapleton
Scotch Corner
Moulton
Stokesley
Richmond
Catterick
Staddlebridge
Kirby Fleetham
Middleham
Bedale
Kirby Moorside
garth
Thirsk
Buckden
NORTH YORKSHIRE
Wath-in-Nidderdale
Ripon
Easingwold
Ripley

Cartographic Services (Cirencester) Ltd.

SCOTLAND

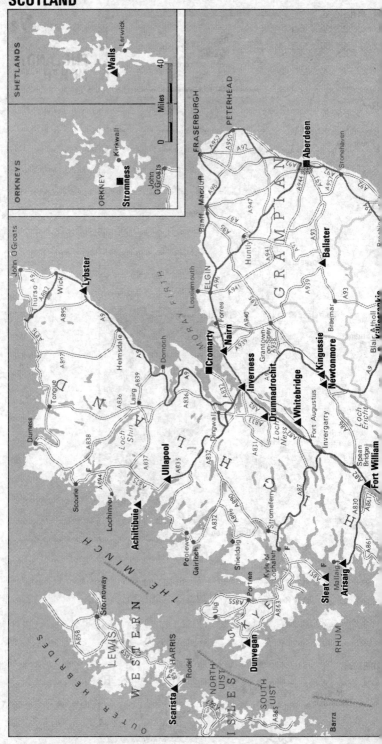

8

7

Restaurant

Restaurant with accommodation

0 Miles   20   40

Cartographic Services (Cirencester) Ltd.

IRELAND

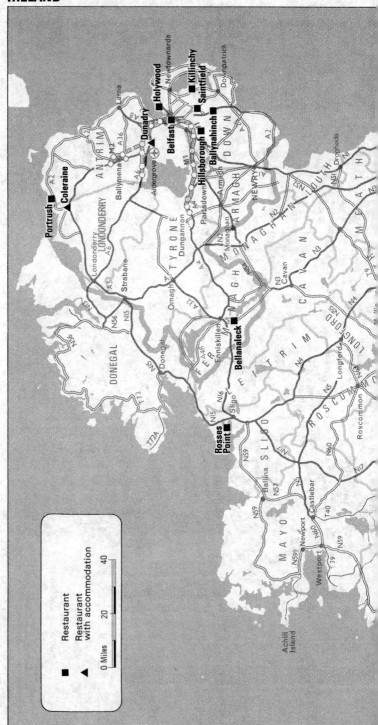

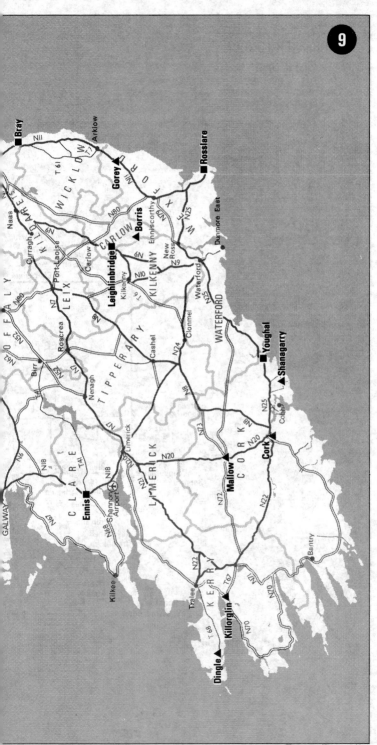

9

Bray
Rosslare
Gorey
Borris
Arklow
CARLOW
Leighlinbridge
Ennis
Shannon Airport
Youghal
Shanagarry
Cork
Mallow
Dingle
Killorglin

WICKLOW
KILDARE
LEIX
KILKENNY
WEXFORD
WATERFORD
TIPPERARY
OFFALY
CLARE
LIMERICK
CORK
KERRY
GALWAY

Naas
Curragh
Port Laoise
Carlow
Kilkenny
New Ross
Waterford
Dunmore East
Enniscorthy
Roscrea
Birr
Nenagh
Cashel
Clonmel
Limerick
Cobh
Tralee
Bantry
Kilkee
Killarney

N11
N81
T7
N80
9N
N7
N8
N10
T6
N9
N25
N24
N73
N20
N21
N72
N22
N70
T67
T68
N69
N18
N68
T41
N52
N62
N6
N25

Cartographic Services (Cirencester) Ltd.

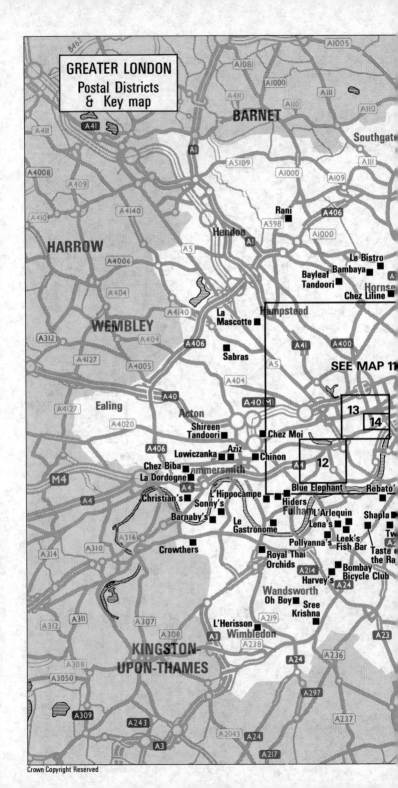

GREATER LONDON
Postal Districts
& Key map

BARNET

Southgate

HARROW

Rani

Hendon

Le Bistro
Bayleaf
Tandoori   Bambaya
             Chez Liline

Hampstead

La
Mascotte

WEMBLEY

Sabras

SEE MAP 11

Ealing

Acton

Shireen
Tandoori   Chez Moi

13

14

Lowiczanka   Aziz
Chez Biba   Chinon   12
La Dordogne ammersmith
                                  Blue Elephant   Rebato'

Christian's L'Hippocampe
             Sonny's   Hiders
Barnaby's   Fulham L'Arlequin
             Le   Lena's   Shapla
             Gastronome   Tw
                          Pollyanna's Leek's   Taste
Crowthers   Fish Bar the Ra
                         Royal Thai
                         Orchids   Bombay
                                    Harvey's Bicycle Club
                         Wandsworth
                         Oh Boy   Sree
                                  Krishna
             L'Herisson
             Wimbledon

KINGSTON-
UPON-THAMES

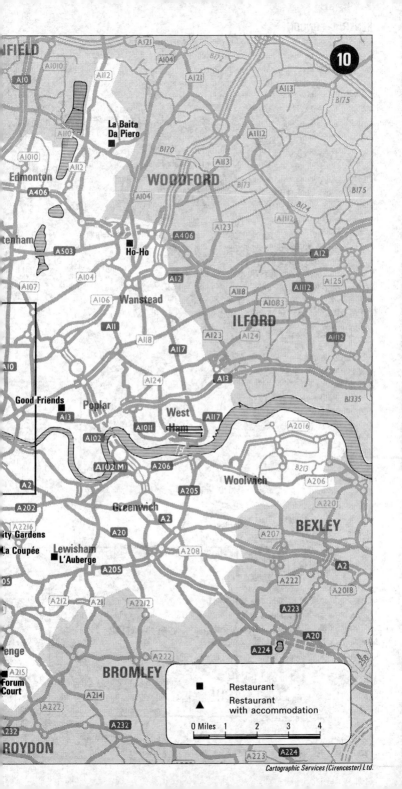

10

NFIELD
A1010
A10
A112
A121
A104
A121
A113
B172
B175

A1010
La Baita
Da Piero ■
B170
A1112
A113

Edmonton
A112
WOODFORD
A104
B173
B175
B174

A406
A123
A1112

tenham
A503
Ho-Ho ■
A406
A12
A125

A104
A12
A1112

A107
A106 Wanstead
A118
A1083
A11
A123
A124
ILFORD
A1112

A118
A117
A124
A13

A10
B1335

Good Friends
■ A13
Poplar
West
A117
A2016

A1011
Ham
A102
A102(M)
A206
B213

A2
Woolwich
A206

A202
A205
A220

A2216
Greenwich
A2
A207

ty Gardens
Lewisham
A20
BEXLEY

La Coupée
■ L'Auberge
A205
A208
A222

05
A2018

A212
A21
A2212
A223

enge
A222
A20

A215
A224
A20

Forum
Court
BROMLEY
A214

A222

232
A232

ROYDON
A223 A224

Cartographic Services (Cirencester) Ltd.

■	Restaurant
▲	Restaurant with accommodation

0 Miles 1   2   3   4

CENTRAL LONDON

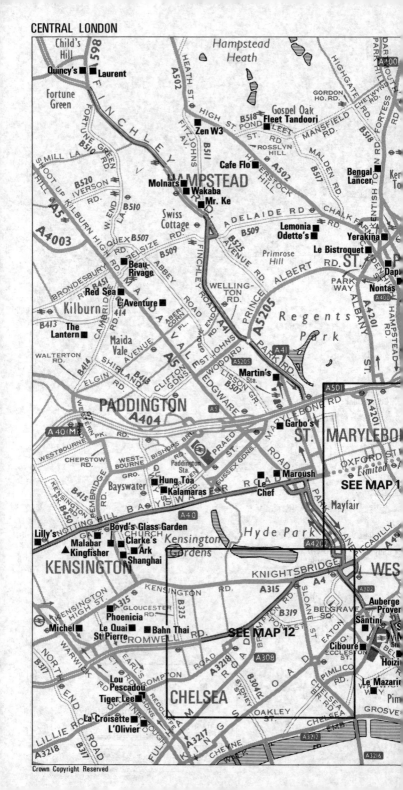

Child's Hill
Quincy's ■ ■ Laurent
Fortune Green
Hampstead Heath

A598
A502
A5
A4003
A400

Gospel Oak
B518 Fleet Tandoori
FLEET
POND
Zen W3 ■
GORDON HO. RD.
MANSFIELD RD.
ROSSLYN HILL
MALDEN RD.
B517

Cafe Flo ■
Molnars ■ ■ Wakaba
HAMPSTEAD
Mr. Ke ■
Bengal Lancer ■
Ker To

Swiss Cottage
ADELAIDE RD.
B509
Lemonia ■
Odette's ■
Yerakina ■
Le Bistroquet ■

Beau-Rivage ■
Red Sea ■
L'Aventure ■
The Lantern ■
Kilburn
Maida Vale
WALTERTON RD.
ELGIN RD.

Primrose Hill
ALBERT RD. ST.
Dap ■
Nontas ■
Regents Park

PADDINGTON
A404
Martin's Sta.
EDGWARE
B507
Garbo's ■
ST. MARYLEBO

A501
A420
OXFORD ST.
Limited
SEE MAP 1
Mayfair

Paddington Sta.
Hung Toa ■
Kalamaras ■
Bayswater
Maroush ■
Le Chef ■

Lilly's ■
Boyd's ● Glass Garden
Malabar ■
▲ Kingfisher
Clarke's ■
Ark ■
Shanghai ■
KENSINGTON
Kensington Gardens
Hyde Park
A4202
PICCADILLY
WES

KNIGHTSBRIDGE
A4
Auberge Prover ■
Santini ■
KENSINGTON HIGH ST.
Phoenicia ■
Le Quai
St Pierre ■
Michel ■
Bahn Thai ■
CROMWELL
SEE MAP 12
BELGRAVE
Ciboure ■
Hoizi ■

Lou Pescadou ■
Tiger Lee ■
La Croisette ■
L'Olivier ■
CHELSEA
Le Mazarin ■
Pim
GROSVE

Crown Copyright Reserved

CENTRAL LONDON : South-West

Legend:
- ■ Restaurant
- ▲ Restaurant with accommodation

0 Mile ¼

Kensington Gore

South Kensington Rd.

Royal College of Art

Royal Albert Hall

Imperial College

Prince Consort Road

Royal College of Music

City & Guilds College

Holy Trinity Church

Launceston Place ■

Queen's Gate Ter.

Petersham Pl.

Elvaston Place

Queen's Gate Pl.

Imperial Institute Rd.

Royal College of Science

Science Museum

Royal College of Art

Brompton Oratory

Geological Museum

Natural History Museum

Cromwell Gardens

St Quentin

C r o m w e l l   R o a d

Tui ■

Thurloe Place

French University College

Alexander Pl

South Ter.

Bombay Brasserie ■

Stanhope Gdns.

Harrington Rd.

Queensberry Way

Golden Chopsticks ■

South Kensington

Pelham Street

Thurloe Sq.

Hilaire ■

Manson Pl.

Cranley Pl.

Onslow Square

Crescent

Meridiana ■
Drakes ■

Chanterelle ■

San Frediano ■

Brompton Hospital

Royal Cancer Hospital

Blakes Hotel ▲

Roland Way

Ponte Nuovo ■

South Parade

Chelsea Hospital for Women

St. Luke's Hospital

Elm Park Gardens

Chelsea Polytechnic

Carlyle Sq.

The Boltons

Little Boltons

Gilston Road

Redcliffe Rd.

Hollywood Road

Fawcett

St. Stephen's Hospital

Crown Copyright Reserved

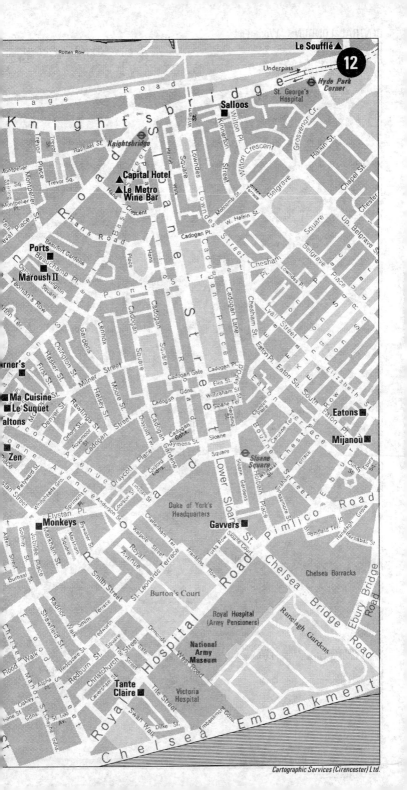

CENTRAL LONDON: West End

York Terrace
Royal Academy of Music
Madame Tussaud's Exhibition
Great Portland Street
Regent's Park
Euston Road
Lal Qila
Auntie's

Langan's Bistro

Topkapi

Nanten Yakitori Bar

Broadcasting House
All Souls Church
Post Office Tower

Ragam

Efes Kebab House

Wigmore Hall

Oxford Circus

Grahame Sea Far

Saga
Justin de Blank
Ikeda
Korea House

Bond Street

Le Gavroche

One Two Three

Connaught Hotel

Ninety Park Lane

The Greenhouse

Royal Academy of Arts
Burlington House

Jams
Wiltons

Green's

Dorchester Hotel
Champagne Exchange
Zen Central
Langan's Brasserie
Miyama
Le Caprice

Al Hamra

Suntory

Dukes Hotel

Hard Rock Cafe

GREEN PARK

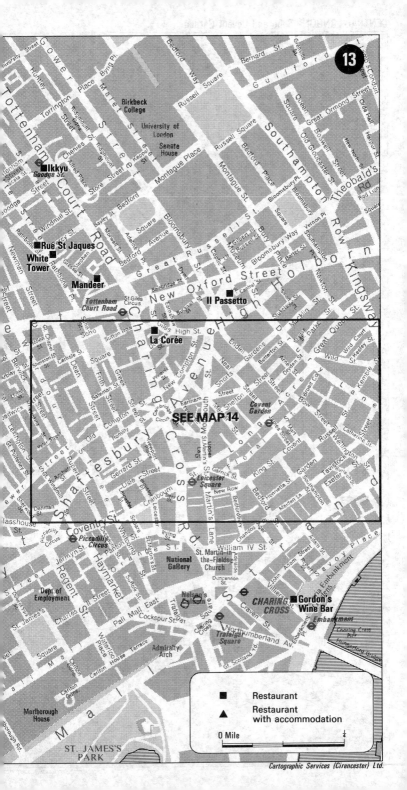

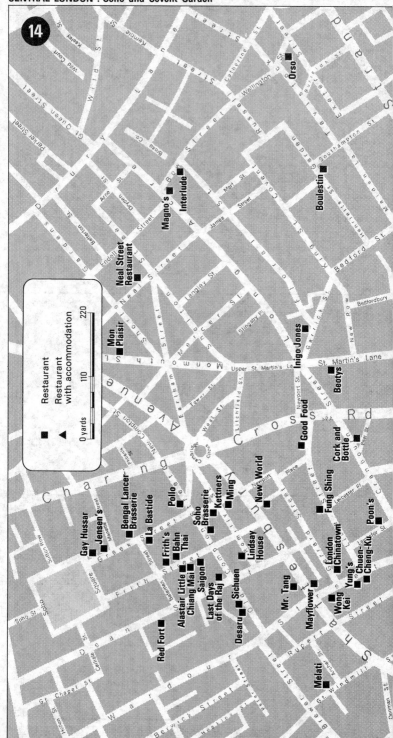

14

Orso

Interlude

Magno's

Boulestin

Neal Street Restaurant

Mon Plaisir

Inigo Jones

Restaurant ■
Restaurant with accommodation ▲

0 yards   110   220

Beotys

Good Food

Cork and Bottle

Gay Hussar

Bengal Lancer Brasserie

Jensen's

La Bastide

Pollo

Frith's

Bahn Thai

Soho Brasserie

Kettners

Ming

New World

Fung Shing

Poon's

Alastair Little

Chiang Mai

Saigon

Last Days of the Raj

Sichuen

Desaru

Lindsay House

Mr. Tang

London Chinatown

Chuen-Cheng-Ku

Yung's

Red Fort

Mayflower

Wong Kei

Melati

Report Forms

Please use a separate report form (or sheet of paper if you prefer) for each restaurant or hotel. Tell us what you ate and drank, what it cost, whether or not it was good, and why.

The 1989 *Guide* will appear before Christmas 1988 so reports are needed particularly in spring. All reports are acknowledged by letter, with information on restaurant changes since the *Guide* went to press.

Please write – and sign – as clearly as possible as we hate misprinting names.

The address to write to is *The Good Food Guide*, Freepost, 14 Buckingham Street, London WC2N 4BR (unfortunately, Freepost facilities are not available in Ireland and the Isle of Man).

To the Editor *The Good Food Guide*
FREEPOST, 14 Buckingham Street, London WC2N 6BR

From my personal experience the following establishment
should/should not be included in the *Guide*.

_____

_____

Telephone _____

I had lunch/dinner/stayed there on _____ 198___

I would rate this establishment _____ /20

please continue overleaf

My meal for _____ people cost £ _____ *attach bill where possible*

☐   Please tick if you would like more report forms

I am not connected in any way with management or proprietors.
Name and address (BLOCK CAPITALS)

_____

_____

Signed _____

To the Editor *The Good Food Guide*
FREEPOST, 14 Buckingham Street, London WC2N 6BR

From my personal experience the following establishment
should/should not be included in the *Guide*.

_____

_____

                                 Telephone _____

I had lunch/dinner/stayed there on _____ 198____

I would rate this establishment _____ /20

please continue overleaf

My meal for ____ people cost £_____ *attach bill where possible*

☐   Please tick if you would like more report forms

I am not connected in any way with management or proprietors.
Name and address (BLOCK CAPITALS)

_____

_____

Signed _____

To the Editor *The Good Food Guide*
FREEPOST, 14 Buckingham Street, London WC2N 6BR

From my personal experience the following establishment
should/should not be included in the *Guide*.

_____

_____

Telephone _____

I had lunch/dinner/stayed there on _____ 198____

I would rate this establishment _____ /20

please continue overleaf

My meal for _____ people cost £_____ *attach bill where possible*

☐   Please tick if you would like more report forms

I am not connected in any way with management or proprietors.
Name and address (BLOCK CAPITALS)

_____

_____

Signed _____

To the Editor *The Good Food Guide*
FREEPOST, 14 Buckingham Street, London WC2N 6BR

From my personal experience the following establishment
should/should not be included in the *Guide*.

_____

_____

Telephone _____

I had lunch/dinner/stayed there on _____ 198_____

I would rate this establishment _____ /20

please continue overleaf

My meal for _____ people cost £ _____ *attach bill where possible*

☐   Please tick if you would like more report forms

I am not connected in any way with management or proprietors.
Name and address (BLOCK CAPITALS)

_____

_____

Signed _____

To the Editor *The Good Food Guide*
FREEPOST, 14 Buckingham Street, London WC2N 6BR

From my personal experience the following establishment
should/should not be included in the *Guide*.

_____

_____

Telephone _____

I had lunch/dinner/stayed there on _____ 198____

I would rate this establishment _____ /20

please continue overleaf

My meal for _____ people cost £ _____ *attach bill where possible*

☐   Please tick if you would like more report forms

I am not connected in any way with management or proprietors.
Name and address (BLOCK CAPITALS)

_____

_____

Signed _____